CONCORDIA UNIVERSITY
3 4211 00132 9021
S0-BJP-215

ANNUAL REVIEW OF PHYSIOLOGY

ANNUAL REVIEW OF PHYSIOLOGY

VOLUME 61, 1999

JOSEPH F. HOFFMAN, *Editor*
Yale University School of Medicine

PAUL De WEER, *Associate Editor*
University of Pennsylvania School of Medicine

http://www.AnnualReviews.org science@annurev.org 650-493-4400

ANNUAL REVIEWS 4139 EL CAMINO WAY P.O. BOX 10139 PALO ALTO, CALIFORNIA 94303-0139

ANNUAL REVIEWS
Palo Alto, California, USA

International Standard Serial Number: 0066-4278
International Standard Book Number: 0-8243-0361-X
Library of Congress Catalog Card Number: 39-15404

∞ The paper used in this publication meets the minimum requirements of American National Standard for Information Sciences—Permanence of Paper for Printed Library Materials, ANSI Z39.48-1992.

TYPESETTING BY TECHBOOKS, FAIRFAX, VIRGINIA
PRINTED AND BOUND IN THE UNITED STATES OF AMERICA

PREFACE

Last year this space was used specifically to invite comments and suggestions from our readers with regard to our current and future performance. We were particularly interested in having feedback on our literature coverage and in our different approaches to the changing corpus of our field. The response to last year's requests was helpful, but few, and primarily directed to various topics we should consider. These suggestions will be discussed at the next (annual) meeting of our editorial board. Should we be concerned about the low number of responses? Does it represent reader contentment, apathy, or preface disregard?

The present volume continues our practice in sectionalizing the various subjects encompassed by the physiological sciences. Each section attempts to be thematic in its coverage, with the theme changing from year to year. In addition, we also include special sections: areas infrequently covered elsewhere, topics that fall on the borders of our field, or advances in related fields that our readers should be aware of. This year's special topics are Membrane Fusion and Sensory Transduction. Note should be taken of the complementary aspect that the latter special topic has with the prefatory chapter written by Carlton C. Hunt.

The publication of the *Annual Review of Physiology* is the product of the efforts of many folks in the Annual Reviews' organization. The editorial board wants to take this opportunity to particularly acknowledge the important work of our Production Editor, Sandra Cooperman, not only for her valuable involvement in the publication of each volume but also for ensuring the maintenance of the high standards of our articles. She has always served us in various capacities using her good judgment, counsel, and sense of responsibility. We are very grateful for her dedication and commitment to our efforts.

JOSEPH F. HOFFMAN
EDITOR

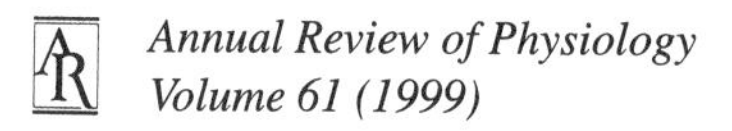
Annual Review of Physiology
Volume 61 (1999)

CONTENTS

 (*Continued*)

(*Continued*)

OTHER REVIEWS OF INTEREST TO PHYSIOLOGISTS

From the *Annual Review of Biochemistry*, Volume 67, 1998:

The Molecular Control of Circadian Behavioral Rhythms and Their Entrainment in Drosophila, Michael W. Young

Phosphoinositide Kinases, David A. Fruman, Rachel E. Meyers, and Lewis C. Cantley

The Green Fluorescent Protein, Roger Y. Tsien

Structure and Function in GroEL-Mediated Protein Folding, Paul B. Sigler, Zhaohui Xu, Hays S. Rye, Steven G. Burston, Wayne A. Fenton, and Arthur L. Horwich

G Protein—Coupled Receptor Kinases, Julie A. Pitcher, Neil J. Freedman, and Robert J. Lefkowitz

The AMP-Activated/SNF1 Protein Kinase Subfamily: Metabolic Sensors of the Eukaryotic Cell? D. Grahame Hardie, David Carling, and Marian Carlson

From the *Annual Review of Cell and Developmental Biology*, Volume 14, 1998:

The Tight Junction: Morphology and Molecules, Bruce R. Stevenson and Brigitte H. Keon

Signaling and the Actin Cytoskeleton, Anja Schmidt and Michael N. Hall

Isoform Sorting and the Creation of Intracellular Compartments, Peter Gunning, Ron Weinberger, Peter Jeffrey, and Edna Hardeman

From the *Annual Review of Medicine*, Volume 50, 1998:

Mitochondrial Disorders: Clinical and Genetic Features, D. K. Simon and D. R. Johns

Applications of NMR Spectroscopy to Study Muscle Glycogen Metabolism in Man, M. Roden and G. I. Shulman

New Transfusion Strategies: Red Cell Substitutes, Robert M. Winslow

From the *Annual Review of Neuroscience*, Volume 22, 1999:

The Cell Biology of the Blood-Brain Barrier, L. L. Rubin and J. M. Staddon

Development of the Vertebrate Neuromuscular Junction, Joshua R. Sanes and Jeff W. Lichtman

(*Continued*)

Cellular and Molecular Determinants of Sympathetic Neuron Development, Nicole J. Francis and Story C. Landis

Birdsong and Human Speech: Common Themes and Mechanisms, Allison J. Doupe and Patricia K. Kuhl

From the *Annual Review of Nutrition*, Volume 18, 1998:

Transgenic Mice in the Analysis of Metabolic Regulation, Fatima Bosch, Anna Pujol, and Alfons Valera

Cyclic AMP Signaling and Gene Regulation, Philip B. Daniel, William H. Walker, and Joel F. Habener

The Molecular Biology of Metal Ion Transport in Saccharomyces cerevisiae, David J. Eide

From the *Annual Review of Pharmacology and Toxicology*, Volume 39, 1999:

The Pineal Gland and Melatonin: Molecular and Pharmacologic Regulation, Jimo Borjigin, Xiaodong Li, and Solomon H. Snyder

New Insights into Dopaminergic Receptor Function Using Antisense and Genetically Altered Animals, David R. Sibley

Biochemical, Cellular, and Pharmacological Aspects of the Multidrug Transporter, Suresh V. Ambudkar, Saibal Dey, Christine A. Hrycyna, Muralidhara Ramachandra, Ira Pastan, and Michael M. Gottesman

Genetic Regulation of Glutamate Receptor Ion Channels, Scott J. Myers, Raymond Dingledine, and Karin Borges

ANNUAL REVIEWS is a nonprofit scientific publisher established to promote the advancement of the sciences. Beginning in 1932 with the *Annual Review of Biochemistry*, the Company has pursued as its principal function the publication of high-quality, reasonably priced *Annual Review* volumes. The volumes are organized by Editors and Editorial Committees who invite qualified authors to contribute critical articles reviewing significant developments within each major discipline. The Editor-in-Chief invites those interested in serving as future Editorial Committee members to communicate directly with him. Annual Reviews is administered by a Board of Directors, whose members serve without compensation.

ANNUAL REVIEWS OF

Anthropology
Astronomy and Astrophysics
Biochemistry
Biomedical Engineering
Biophysics and Biomolecular Structure
Cell and Developmental Biology
Computer Science
Earth and Planetary Sciences
Ecology and Systematics
Energy and the Environment
Entomology
Fluid Mechanics
Genetics
Immunology
Materials Science
Medicine
Microbiology
Neuroscience
Nuclear and Particle Science
Nutrition
Pharmacology and Toxicology
Physical Chemistry
Physiology
Phytopathology
Plant Physiology and Plant Molecular Biology
Political Science
Psychology
Public Health
Sociology

SPECIAL PUBLICATIONS

Excitement and Fascination of Science, Vols. 1, 2, 3, and 4
Intelligence and Affectivity, by Jean Piaget

For the convenience of readers, a order form/envelope is bound into the back of this volume.

Carlton C. Hunt

Annu. Rev. Physiol. 1999. 61:1–17

PULLING THE CART AND ENJOYING THE RIDE

Carlton C. Hunt
Department of Physiology, University of North Carolina, Chapel Hill, North Carolina 27599; e-mail: cmahunt@intrex.net

KEY WORDS: physiology, muscle spindles, muscle, departmental history

ABSTRACT

I was pleased to receive the invitation to write this prefatory chapter. In doing so, I join a number of physiologists whose work and writings I have often admired. There are two aspects of my experience in physiology that I discuss here. The first concerns my own research accomplishments. The second is my role in developing three departments of physiology and fostering the careers of others. While I take pleasure in the former, the overall contribution of the latter was undoubtedly greater.

Background

Looking back over the last half century since I started out in physiology, it's clear that chance and opportunity played major roles in my life. Indeed, there was little in my background to suggest that I might have an academic career. My parents separated when I was young, and I grew up as the only child of a working mother. Contact with my father was limited to annual visits. Even as a boy I wanted to become a doctor. In high school, I made friends with a local physician and enjoyed discussions with him and visits to his library. I hoped for a college education and discussed this ambition with my father, a Yale graduate. His reply was surprising and quite memorable: "I don't know why you want to do that; it never did me much good." Years later, our relationship became closer, and he was actually quite proud that I had become a professor at Yale. (Indeed, this was the only piece of personal information he listed in his 50th reunion autobiography.) My mother was always supportive, although later she had some regrets that I preferred research to clinical medicine.

0066-4278/99/0315-0001$08.00

I graduated from high school in 1935. Fortunately, Columbia College offered me a scholarship, which was essential. Our financial resources were meager and the effects of the depression were still in force. Columbia's location in New York was also an advantage, since that was where my mother worked. At 16, I became an exceedingly young college freshman. After three years, I applied to medical school at Cornell and Columbia. Cornell accepted me while Columbia wanted me to finish a fourth year of college. While this might have been a good idea, I chose to accept admission to Cornell. My paternal grandfather, whose own formal education had ended with expulsion as a teenager from a private school because of juvenile misbehavior, agreed to provide the relatively modest tuition.

Cornell University Medical College was a marvelous place for me. It was there that I began to flourish intellectually. The teaching was excellent. Although we were graded, we never knew our marks unless we were having academic trouble. As a result, there was little feeling of competition among classmates. In the first two years, preclinical subjects occupied most of the curriculum. At the time (1939), biomedical research took place largely in medical schools. Few medical students received much exposure to these subjects during their undergraduate years. As Herbert Gasser commented (1) about hearing Joseph Erlanger's lectures in Physiology as a student at the University of Wisconsin, "the subject material was a revelation."

My reaction was similar to his. I was fascinated by basic medical sciences. Of particular interest was the course in Physiology. Joseph Hinsey was the department chairman. He was a forceful, warm, and engaging person, who at another time also served as Chairman of Anatomy and later became dean at Cornell Medical College. He had done important work on the muscle spindle, which was to become my main research interest. Some 40 years later, when I was going to work in Paris, he suggested I contact his former colleague Bill Dock, who had briefly headed Pathology at Cornell. I followed his advice, and we became good friends during my four years in Paris. In large part because of the enthralling clinical stories he heard as a teenager from Dr. Dock, my son Nicholas eventually decided to become a physician.

At Cornell Medical College, laboratory experiments were a major part of the Physiology course. They were by no means trivial exercises, often lasting all day and into the evening. Each one had to be written up and submitted to the faculty. Even now, I can recall many of those experiments. Instruction in the other premedical subjects was also very good, and students did not feel, as they sometimes do today, that faculty members resented the time their teaching duties required.

Clinical Medicine and Army Service

Clinical work also interested me. I was particularly attracted by Internal Medicine and decided to seek an internship in that field. But for his untimely death, I might have worked under Soma Weiss at Harvard. Instead, David Barr, who headed Medicine at Cornell, accepted me as an intern. He was an inspiring teacher and clinician, and I thoroughly enjoyed that first year of training. The house staff had a great deal of responsibility for patient care, and we worked long, hard hours. While the experience was satisfying in some ways, it was often frustrating from a therapeutic perspective. Few antibiotics were available then, and we frequently felt helpless to intervene effectively in the course of an illness. There were a number of outstanding clinicians at Cornell who were particularly skillful at diagnosis with the simple tools and tests then available. In that era, attitudes about money and medicine were very different from what they are now. Physicians gave their time, and hospitals donated their resources to care for the indigent. The marketplace and medicine were seen as separate arenas.

I graduated from medical school in 1942, just six months after the United States entered the Second World War. This cataclysm swiftly became the central experience for my generation. Though Dr. Barr urged me to stay at The New York Hospital for residency training, I decided to join a newly formed army hospital, composed largely of doctors from Johns Hopkins and Cornell. The war gave life a transient quality. Long-term plans seemed less a concern than more immediate considerations.

Within a few months of entering the army, our group was in Britain as a general hospital. Though there was only one psychiatrist on staff, we were designated a psychiatric facility. Our first task was to care for mentally ill soldiers, who never should have been drafted, until arrangements were made to ship them back home. Later we ran a general hospital near Bristol. This period of useful work ended when we were sent to a town near Liverpool just before the invasion of Normandy. Idleness—apart from extensive marching—followed until we landed on Omaha Beach several weeks after D day. We moved inland and set up a tent hospital in fields among the surviving bovines. Several months later, after the war had moved toward Germany, we moved to Liege, in Belgium, where we ran a busy hospital until the end of the war in Europe. Shipped back to France, near Rouen, we awaited transfer to the Pacific theater. Fortunately, hostilities abruptly ended after atomic bombs were dropped on Hiroshima and Nagasaki. In later years I was uncertain that the use of those weapons was justified, but at the time I welcomed the end of the war. Army life had been an experience of a certain value, but the periods of work alternating with enforced inactivity, bizarre orders alternating with rational ones, little idea of what was happening, and only minimal control over one's work made me glad to get back to civilian life.

Return from the War and Beginnings in Research

On returning to a residency at the New York Hospital after several years in the army, I felt out of touch with the fundamentals of academic medicine. This led me to seek further experience in basic medical science. After I had spent a year as an assistant resident, my friend and medical school classmate Walter Riker helped me get an opportunity to try research in the Department of Pharmacology at Cornell Medical College, which I enjoyed. I still liked clinical medicine, and I soon became interested in diseases affecting neuromuscular transmission. At the time, the National Research Council offered a three-year fellowship in Neurology, modeled after their Welch fellowship in Internal Medicine. I applied for one to work at Johns Hopkins under AM Harvey and received the award in 1947.

Johns Hopkins University

When I arrived in Baltimore, Harvey suggested that I spend the first year of my fellowship with Stephen Kuffler, who had recently arrived from Australia, with a stopover in Chicago. Steve was just starting a lab in the basement of the Wilmer Institute. We hit it off immediately, and I spent four wonderful years in his lab. He became my mentor and friend. His influence guided me then and for years later, as it did many others who followed me as his "happy apprentices" (see 2). If anyone can be said to have founded the modern field of neurobiology, it was he. Steve was a superb experimentalist. Quick, imaginative, humorous, passionately interested in hands-on laboratory work, he had a rare talent for choosing important scientific questions and then devising elegant preparations that would yield definitive information about them.

Steve suggested that we study the function of mammalian small-diameter ventral root fibers. There had been suggestions, starting with Langley (3), that these might provide the motor innervation to muscle spindles. O'Leary, Heinbecker & Bishop (4) had found that stimulation of these fibers, in addition to the larger motor axons, produced no significant increase in muscle tension, a finding in accord with this idea. Leksell (5) found that these fibers, stimulated after block of most of the larger ventral root axons, caused an increase in firing of presumably sensory axons in muscle nerves, also supporting the idea that they were motor to spindles. But there was a contrary view, holding that these small motor axons innervated extrafusal muscle fibers producing tonic muscle contraction (6). Steve, with Laporte and Ransmeier (7), had also shown that small motor axons in the frog innervated tonic extrafusal fibers.

We developed a preparation using cat in which single sensory axons from muscle were isolated in subdivided dorsal root filaments. Those from muscle spindles could be identified by their response to stretch and to muscle contraction. Then, we isolated single axons of small diameter in subdivided ventral root filaments and tested the spindle response to their stimulation. We found six or more such small (gamma) axons that increased the discharge from single-spindle sensory axons, but they never produced any significant muscle tension. This finding opened the way to a number of studies on spindles (8–10), and the double single-fiber technique is still widely used. Many years later, I was delighted to learn from Steve's colleagues that these were among his favorite experiments.

At the beginning, our equipment was only marginally adequate, and we often borrowed a 35-mm camera from Mac Harvey to photograph our oscilloscope screen. An old continuous-feed camera that we used occasionally jammed, and we sometimes found on the day after a long and successful experiment that the data were lost. But our greatest deficiency was the lack of a mechanical puller that could provide stretch at controlled velocities. Our electronic equipment improved dramatically when Bob Bosler joined the lab as head technician. Peter Quilliam was one of the first visitors to the lab, and he worked with us on the function of the small motor axons.

After several years of exciting and productive collaboration, Steve began exploring the behavior of ganglion cells in the cat retina. Since he was, after all, in an ophthalmology institute, he felt that he should do some work on the eye. Using a so-called triple-beam ophthalmoscope, designed by Sam Talbot, he could bring a micropipette close to a ganglion cell and deliver light stimuli to its receptive field. He soon found the center-surround organization of the receptive fields of these cells, the center being excitatory and the surround inhibitory, or vice versa. This was the initial step in working out the organization of the mammalian visual system. Later the field was brilliantly explored by Hubel and Weisel, beginning in Steve's lab. This pattern became familiar in Steve's career: He would spend several years doing the pioneering experiments on some subject and then leave the problem to be pursued by younger colleagues (2). Consequently, I began to work alone on muscle spindles and described, in an early paper, the reflex activity of the gamma motor axons to spindles (11). Though I missed working with Steve, I enjoyed the independence.

The Rockefeller Institute: 1952–1955

During my fourth year in Steve's lab, I received an invitation to visit David Lloyd and Herbert Gasser at the Rockefeller Institute (now Rockefeller University). This visit eventually led to the offer of a position there. Lloyd was an important figure in spinal cord physiology. His work provided the essential bridge between Sherrington's studies on spinal reflexes and subsequent research using intracellular recording.

At the Rockefeller, apart from a study of the diameter distribution of sensory axons from muscle spindles and Golgi tendon organs (12), I worked on spinal cord physiology, using approaches that Lloyd had developed. Archie McIntyre visited from New Zealand, and he, Lloyd, and I collaborated on several studies. Wilfred Rall also visited the lab, and we worked together on the extent to which excitability fluctuations were correlated among motoneurons in the same pool. At about that time, intracellular recording from spinal neurons became popular. Lloyd thought it was a technique of doubtful value, and I avoided it while I was there. Unfortunately, Lloyd's overreliance on extracellular recording led to his making a rare mistake that competitors seized upon to attack his work. He maintained that so-called direct inhibition of antagonist motoneurons by a group I muscle nerve volley was monosynaptic. It turned out that there is an interneuron interposed in that pathway.

Gasser, who was soon to retire as director of the Institute, was a most impressive person whom I much admired. Possessed of great intelligence and high principles, at first he seemed austere. Beneath that facade he was warm and humorous. On retirement he set up a new lab and returned to problems of axonal conduction, particularly in unmyelinated axons. When he had studied these small axons earlier by light microscopy, he had been unable to measure their size accurately. With help from Keith Porter and George Palade, he studied the unmyelinated axons by electron microscopy and was able to correlate their compound action potential with the diameter distribution of the axons (13). An incidental but important finding was that these axons were suspended by infoldings of the Schwann cell membrane, structures that he called mesaxons (14). When we went to lunch, Gasser would always turn off his oscilloscope, a habit from the early days of cathode ray tubes when their life was limited.

Detlev Bronk succeeded Gasser. He chose the title of president rather than director. Very different in style and character from his predecessor, he changed the institution in many ways. The Institute became Rockefeller University and began to accept graduate students. Buildings that had been known simply by their geographic location acquired more elaborate names; for example, the New North Building became Theobald Smith Hall. There was considerable expansion in faculty and buildings and a greater dependence on external funding. During his time as director, Gasser had declined National Institutes of Health (NIH) funds that accompanied fellowship awards. He had strong reservations about the Institute taking federal funds for research, fearing that the individual investigator might lose his independence in the process (1). At the time, this position seemed overly conservative. The flow of federal funds certainly had an important and positive impact on biomedical research. Later, when funding became tighter and investigators who had become dependent on them found it difficult to obtain grants, Gasser's concerns seemed well founded.

The Albert Einstein College of Medicine: 1955–1957

In 1955, the newly established Albert Einstein College of Medicine invited me to take a position in its Physiology Department. Henry Lawson was the kind and excellent chairman. After years at well-established institutions, I felt that this was to be an exciting adventure. I can recall that when we taught the first class that winter, students wore overcoats in the still-unheated lecture rooms. We demonstrated intracellular potentials using micropipettes that had been fabricated and carried from another building some distance away.

I was appointed a full professor (although I had never been an associate professor) and invited to sit on the Executive Faculty. Among its many outstanding members were Irving London in Medicine, Al Gilman (father of AG Gilman) in Pharmacology, and Ernst Sharrer in Anatomy. In the lab I was joined by AS Paintal from New Delhi. We began a further study of the reflex activity of gamma fibers to muscle nerves (15) and coined the name fusimotor axons for them. This term was generally adopted, and the nomenclature remains better known than the reported research.

University of Utah: 1957–1964

In 1957, the University of Utah invited me to visit and consider heading the Department of Physiology. I had never given much thought to such a position. When I asked Gasser's advice, he simply said, "You know, Cuy, you are really pulling the cart in that position." Although the facilities were poor, and the school was not well supported by the state, I found the opportunity attractive and the surrounding mountains beautiful. There was a strong faculty in the medical school, including Max Wintrobe in Medicine, Louis Goodman in Pharmacology, Emil Smith in Biochemistry, and Bill Carnes in Pathology. By then, the ready availability of federal funds for research of merit made the paucity of state funds less of a problem. The challenge of recruiting able young physiologists and creating an exciting atmosphere that might lead to new directions in physiology appealed to me. Within a fairly short time the department was thriving. There was a lot of good interaction among faculty members, and the group was highly productive. AR Martin has written of that period (16, p. ix):

> The scientific activity in the Physiology Department at Utah between 1958 and 1965 was amazing. In the beginning Cuy, Ed Perl, Carlos [Eyzaguirre] and myself formed the core of the neurophysiology group. Charles Edwards and George Eisenman later joined the faculty as well. The list of visiting scientists and post-doctoral fellows included Preet Gill, Motoy Kuno, Alberto Mallart, Archie McIntyre, Autar Paintal, Guillermo Pilar, Akira and Norico Takeuchi and Koju Uchizone. During that period we contributed more than 40 papers to *J. Physiol.*, the journal of choice for cellular neurophysiology.[1]

[1] In Vol. 168, No. 2 (1963), five of the fourteen papers were from the Department of Physiology at Utah; in Vol. 175, No. 1 (1964) four out of ten.

Ed Perl subsequently made pioneering studies on nociception. Martin and Pilar began studies of the ciliary ganglion, which developed into a large field. Lynn Landmesser came as a postdoc and worked with Pilar. Arthur Hess came to do morphological studies. Dick Wylie joined me in work on reptilian spindles, and we had many visitors. One memorable symposium brought a galaxy of neural types to a lodge in the mountains for a very unstructured scientific meeting with skiing. It was an exciting place.

The course we gave in physiology was unusual. Faculty taught material they thought was especially interesting. It would hardly meet with approval today. We had limulus shipped in from Woods Hole to demonstrate photoreceptor responses and spider monkeys from Florida to show motor cortex localization and evoked cortical responses. Robert Miller, who was then a medical student, was so stimulated by the course that he became a physiologist.

By 1962, I felt the need of a sabbatical year and went to the Department of Biophysics at University College London, headed by Bernard Katz. The majority of the fellows there were other Americans. I teamed up with Phil Nelson from the NIH. We worked on the effects of axotomy on frog sympathetic ganglia, studying changes in structure by electron microscopy and in function by electrophysiology. The laboratory atmosphere was stimulating, and Katz's periodic visits were memorable. However, 1962 was one of the coldest winters ever recorded in Britain. In addition to this physical discomfort, for a good part of the year I was a single parent with three adolescent sons who found the rigorous style of British schooling both unfamiliar and uncomfortable.

Yale School of Medicine: 1964–1967

When I returned to Salt Lake City, my first marriage was coming to an end, and I wanted to make a fresh start. In 1964, I received an offer from Yale University's School of Medicine to head its Department of Physiology. The position as chairman was an open-ended appointment, and the search committee seemed to want a person who would make the department a place of excellence. The complications, not initially apparent to me, were Yale's politics and the large number of tenured faculty already located in the Department of Physiology. I was nevertheless attracted by the possibility of building a department at a major university with excellent medical and graduate students. My most significant initial appointment was a superb administrative associate, Harriet Batchelder, who was a seasoned veteran in the field. She was truly a wise woman who knew Yale well. Politically savvy, deeply loyal, and highly organized, she quickly became central to the smooth functioning of the new department.

My first and most important faculty appointment was Joe Hoffman. I thought that general (cellular) physiology, membrane transport, and cellular neurophysiology made a good combination. Joe was an outstanding person in the field of membrane transport. It took some persuasion to get him to leave the NIH for Yale, but I finally succeeded in luring him to New Haven. He was a great asset during my time there and for many years thereafter.

Yale required that new appointments be voted on by those of equivalent rank in the department. At the level of full professor, Joe and I were often faced with three negative votes to our two positive ones, but we nonetheless managed to recruit a number of outstanding people within the first two years of my arrival. These included Bob Martin, John Nicholls, Knox Chandler, Peter Curran, Carolyn and Clifford Slayman, and Denis Baylor (who was then a postdoctoral fellow in another Yale department). Peter Heistracher came from Vienna to work in my lab. We studied activation and inactivation of muscle contraction using some short extrafusal fibers in the skin of snake, and we made preliminary studies on muscle spindles in cat tail muscles that later figured importantly in my research. Bill Betz, who was then a medical student at Washington University, wanted to spend some time in the department, and I invited him to come. He never went back to medical school but instead took a doctorate in Physiology at Yale. Tony Ridge, a young scientist from Bristol, spent some time with us in New Haven and later visited my department at Washington University.

While the department looked very good to the outside academic world, the response inside Yale was less enthusiastic. There were a number of long-entrenched faculty members who were threatened by the changes I was making. Administratively, Yale was complex, with many overlapping lines of responsibility. The department chairman negotiated his budget with the provost, not with the dean. A university-wide committee oversaw appointments and promotions within the medical school. Yale had a system of obligatory periodic review for faculty promotions. On one occasion a faculty member in Physiology, with strong Yale social connections, came up for consideration. An initial round of letters from reviewers I suggested was very negative. To counter this view, the appointment and promotions committee obtained letters that were more positive. I threatened to resign if he were promoted. In the end, an unusual compromise was reached. He was transferred to another department, where he was promoted.

The department chairmen held extended discussions about how the preclinical departments should be organized. Some suggested they all be merged into a single administrative entity. The retirement of Dean Vernon Lippard, who had recruited me, was followed by his successor's first speech to the faculty, in which he stated that Yale Medical School would not become a center for what he called "subhuman biology." I felt that this negative view of basic science might bode ill for the future of the department I had gathered. (Fortunately, I was wrong about this; in ensuing years the department flourished.) I was also concerned about the introduction of rotating chairmanships in the preclinical departments. So, after a revolution lasting little more than three years, I decided it was time to move again. There was an opening for head of the Physiology Department at Washington University School of Medicine. I was invited to visit St. Louis to explore that possibility.

Washington University: 1967–1983, 1987–1994

Over the years, I had known a number of people who were working or had worked at Washington University (Herbert Gasser, George Bishop, Jim O'Leary, Joe Hinsey, Bill Landau, Henry Schwartz). In 1967, this was an institution with a great scientific tradition that had somehow managed to retain an appealing modesty. It was the reverse of Yale in the sense that the medical school had always been better known and better funded than the undergraduate campus. The Washington University School of Medicine was governed by an Executive Faculty composed of department heads whose members elected the dean every year. Its Department of Physiology, where Erlanger, Gasser, and Bishop had done their pioneering studies on nerve, had a dwindling faculty and antiquated facilities. The teaching laboratories were very much as they had been when the school was built, half a century earlier.

Despite the department's poor physical condition, the offer appealed to me. Unlike Yale, there would be fewer vested interests for me to contend with in making changes. Plans for the new McDonnell basic science building had already been finalized. Thus there was room for considerable departmental growth. My second wife, Marion, and I especially liked the people we met in St. Louis. We'd been married only a short time, and both of us found Yale's social climate chilly. Though Washington University was located in a much larger city than New Haven, the social atmosphere was far more informal and friendly. Our son's birth occurred within a few months of our arrival, and the warm welcome we received from new friends made us feel at home in St. Louis almost immediately.

The dean of the medical school, Ken King, was unusual. A highly intelligent man with a dry sense of humor and quiet integrity, he was a keen observer of the Executive Faculty, whose confidence in him was expressed in the fact that they elected him dean annually for over two decades. Because his word could be trusted absolutely, there was no need to put our negotiations in writing. Bill Danforth was then vice chancellor for medical affairs and proved very effective in bettering relationships between the medical school and related institutions. After my experience at Yale, the behavior of the Executive Faculty amazed me. They actually made me feel welcome in practical ways. One department head even suggested that since Physiology was in such need of renovation and expansion, it should receive a larger portion of certain institutional funds. In 1967, the "spirit of the school," as Carl Cori (17) once called it, was still quite exceptional. Department heads maintained an interest beyond their own immediate spheres of influence; they were concerned about the medical school's general welfare. When I arrived, the Executive Faculty was in the midst of a generational change. Several other new department heads accepted their positions at about the same time I did. Roy Vagelos had recently arrived in Biochemistry, succeeding Carl Cori, who moved to Harvard. Max Cowan took over in Anatomy just before I started to work in Physiology.

I was fortunate to find Jackie Baker to serve as my administrative associate. She was highly competent and totally trustworthy. I knew that with her help, the department would be run in a competent manner. My first academic appointment, always a critical one, was Mordy Blaustein. He was a graduate of Washington University Medical School and had worked at Cambridge with Alan Hodgkin. Mordy contributed a great deal to the department and its growth. And grow it certainly did. In spite of St. Louis's non-coastal location and its sometimes unappealing climate, once prospective faculty members visited, recruitment was not difficult. Most of the new faculty came as assistant or associate professors and stayed in the department until and after they had reached senior faculty status.

In addition to Mordy Blaustein, early recruits included Paul De Weer, Luis and Elsa Reuss, Dale Purves, Nigel Daw, Alan Pearlman, Carl Rovainen, Josh Sanes, and Phil Stahl. Usually I arranged for the medical school to guarantee new faculty the equipment they needed if federal funding was unavailable. In those golden years, getting research grants was relatively easy, and it was seldom necessary to use school funds for initial equipment. The range of departmental research interests was quite broad. Blaustein began work on synaptosomes and subsequently on Na^+/Ca^{2+} exchange, De Weer on the sodium/potassium pump, Luis Reuss on epithelial transport, Elsa Reuss on renal tubules, Daw and Pearlman on vision, Purves on neurons in the sympathetic chain, Rovainen on the lamprey nervous system, Sanes on molecules in basal lamina that determined sites of neuromuscular innervation, and Stahl on lysosomes.

In addition to administrative responsibilities, I kept my research going. Yas Fukami came with me from Yale, and we worked, sometimes together and at other times independently, on muscle receptors. I was fortunate to have Sherman Beacham, who had been a medical student at Utah, in my lab for several years. Later, Bob Wilkinson joined me. We had a highly productive and enjoyable association, working on isolated muscle spindles. Bob had been trained as a physicist at Rice and brought to our research quantitative skills and knowledge that I lacked. I spent three summers working with David Ottoson in Sweden. Not only was Stockholm a beautiful city, but we managed to make considerable progress in developing an isolated mammalian spindle preparation.

Roy Costantin was an outstanding addition to the department. He had received his MD from Columbia and then worked for some time in the Physiological Laboratory at Cambridge before joining the faculty of the College of Physicians and Surgeons in New York. He had done excellent work on muscle, some in collaboration with Richard Adrian and Lee Peachey. I made an offer, which he accepted. About a month later, I happened to be in New York and gave him a call. Roy suggested I might want to reconsider hiring him because he'd just received a diagnosis of a malignant melanoma. I assured him that this made no difference in my offer, and he and his family moved to St. Louis. For several years, until the disease recurred, he did superb work in teaching and research. His experiments on single muscle fibers, which showed that excitation spreads into skeletal muscle fibers by way of action potentials in the transverse tubules, are classics in the field. Roy was admired and respected by his colleagues, and his untimely death was a tragedy not only for his family and close friends but also for members of the department and many other colleagues who felt his loss keenly.

Some months later, we organized a symposium in his memory. Scientists who worked on basic problems of muscle physiology, many of whom had collaborated with Roy, participated; Richard Adrian and Andrew Huxley came from England for the occasion. Rather than being simply a memorial service, it was a working scientific meeting. References to Roy and his contributions were woven naturally into each speaker's talk. The bitterness of losing him far too soon was tempered by a sense of Roy's ongoing influence and the enduring affection of his friends. Because Roy had loved music, there was a chamber music recital at the meeting, which included Beethoven's *Spring* Sonata. The acoustics were so good in the medical school's then-new Carl Moore auditorium that a series of chamber music concerts was held there for several years. I always thought of Roy when I attended them.

In contrast to younger faculty members in the department who were new to St. Louis, one veteran joined our group. Albert Roos had come to Washington University in 1947 to work with the then-head of surgery, Dr. Evarts Graham, in the Division of Anesthesiology. While Albert held a joint appointment in the Department of Physiology, his laboratory had always been located near the Department of Surgery. For some years, he had helped teach respiration in the Physiology course. I found him bright, interesting, and engaging. One day we met in the elevator, and I asked if he'd consider moving across the street to join us. That turned out to be an excellent idea both for him and for the department. He moved into Physiology on a full-time basis, and the emphasis on a cellular approach among his new colleagues changed his work in that direction. Although he was over 50 at the time, Albert opened up a new line of research and became the leading authority on intracellular pH.

Another appointment at a senior level was John Heuser. Together with Reese he had done classical studies, using the technique of freeze fracturing, on the release of vesicles from presynaptic endings at the neuromuscular junction. A living nerve ending was stimulated as it fell toward a metallic block at a few degrees Kelvin. This was an important step in using electron microscopy to capture temporal events. He had a well-established laboratory at the University of California, San Francisco, with major equipment to be moved. Funds from the dean made this possible.

We were also joined by Bob Rakowski, who continued work on charge movement in skeletal muscle. In addition to new faculty, several professors who were in place on my arrival remained as members of the department. Len Banazak and Scott Matthews were doing excellent work in X-ray crystallography. Len later moved to Biochemistry, but Scott stayed in Physiology and Biophysics. Charlie Molnar and Russ Pfeiffer continued their studies on the cochlea. Charlie, one of the developers of the LINC computer, was also head of the Computer Systems Laboratory and served on the Engineering faculty.

Eventually, I was able to hire one of our own graduates. Jeff Lichtman received his MD as well as his PhD in Physiology from Washington University, completing his doctoral research in Dale Purves's laboratory. After a postdoctoral fellowship with Eric Frank, he returned to join our department. A number of our graduate students went on to have very successful careers in physiology.

In the late 1970s both Roy Vagelos and Max Cowan were considering positions elsewhere, and strenuous efforts were made to change their minds. Chief among them was the creation of a University Division of Biology and Biomedical Sciences. Roy served as its first director, and Max the second. In addition to keeping Roy and Max at Washington University a few years longer, this innovation was supposed to unite the medical school's basic science departments with related departments on the undergraduate campus. It was partially successful. Some new divisional positions were created. The Division was to provide a framework for graduate study and, to a lesser extent, undergraduate instruction. Despite this effort, both Roy and Max left St. Louis within a few years. (Later, Max returned briefly as provost.) The Division may have had some good effects, but I think it weakened or at least blurred the lines of authority within the medical school.

By the 1980s, the medical school had changed considerably. The faculty had grown substantially, as had the physical plant, and the budget had greatly increased. Most important to me, the size, composition, and character of the Executive Faculty had gradually changed from a small cohesive group with a common concern for the medical school's welfare to a larger number of disparate individuals increasingly focused on their own departmental agendas. Whereas formerly the dean controlled most institutional funds, clinical departments had begun to accumulate considerable amounts of money and power. At meetings of the Executive Faculty, I reacted negatively when some colleagues took positions that I considered self-serving or were insensitive to what I perceived as obvious conflicts of interest. My refusal to go along quietly with some decisions led to my being regarded by certain colleagues on the Executive Faculty as uncooperative and conservative.

In 1983, the National Academy of Sciences published a survey of Research Doctorate Programs in Biological Sciences, the first such assessment undertaken since the late 1960s. The only Washington University department ranked among the top ten in the country was Physiology (Yale's Department of Physiology also appeared in this group). Ironically, these findings were published just as the new Division was absorbing our graduate program. While there may have been resentment of Physiology's success in some quarters, to my surprise and delight, Carl Cori sent me the following poem from his Harvard laboratory to mark the occasion:

Chancellor, Deans, Colleagues and Students Washingtonienses
Examine important message in Science with critical lenses.*
In a contest wide, in Academia's lofty towers,
Rate programs for graduate degrees—no flowers!
Rate departments giving Ph.D. degrees in Physiologia
And be honest, this is not the casa mia.
The answer came 2000 strong
The verdict was clear as a gong.
Top rated at Washington U. is Physiologia.
Where are the Hunts—Madonna mia,
They now have a banner with which to picket,
But instead they bought to Paris a ticket.
Hurray for the Hunts.

**Science* (January 21, 1983) 219:267

Retirement: Paris: 1983–1987

As my 65th birthday approached (then the age for mandatory retirement from administrative positions at Washington University), I felt it would be less awkward for all concerned for me to be elsewhere during the search for my successor. I had headed the Physiology Department from 1967 to 1983, and in those 16 years my young recruits had become able senior faculty. An important aspect of my administrative style had been to serve as a buffer between my faculty and medical school politics. As a retiring department head, my influence was severely diminished. There seemed little point in retaining a lame-duck position. In 1983, I began an extended leave to work in Yves Laporte's laboratory at the College de France in Paris. Yves was an old friend who had worked with David Lloyd at the Rockefeller Institute. Immediately after the war, he had spent time in George Bishop's laboratory at Washington University. His research interests were close to mine. My four productive years of research at the College centered on studies of muscle spindles in vivo. I collaborated with Yves Laporte, Francoise Emonet-Denand, Lena Jami, Julien Petit, Jean Azerad, and Bernard Pollin.

On my departure from St. Louis, Nigel Daw became acting head of Physiology. The national search for a new head resulted in an internal appointment, Philip Stahl. He was a cell biologist and naturally turned the department in that direction. New faculty were recruited, and the department's name was changed to Cell Biology and Physiology. There was little interest in sustaining the strength that had been established in neurobiology. Three leading faculty members, Dale Purves, Josh Sanes, and Jeff Lichtman, moved to the Department of Anatomy and Neurobiology, then headed by Gerry Fischbach. Gradually, other senior faculty members departed for high positions at other schools. Paul de Weer left to head the Department of Physiology at the University of Pennsylvania, Dale Purves became head of the new Neurobiology Department at Duke, and Luis Reuss took the chair of physiology at the University of Texas Medical Branch in Galveston.

Although we had enjoyed our years in Paris, by 1987 our son had entered college in the United States, and we felt it was time to return. Mordy Blaustein kindly offered me space in his department at the University of Maryland, but we still had so many connections in St. Louis that it seemed easier to resettle there. Tom Woolsey and Ken King encouraged me to return. Our daughter Amanda was born in June of that year. Perhaps becoming a father again at an advanced age impaired my ability to slip gracefully into retirement. I was still interested in research, and having a vibrant young child at home made me feel that I should continue working.

Ironically, after so many years of renovating and arranging space for other people, the major political and practical problem I faced on my return to Washington University was finding laboratory space for myself. Eventually, Bill Landau gave me a lab in Neurology, which was very satisfactory until he retired. I was then able to get some space in my former department with the understanding that after a few years I would go elsewhere.

After my return to St. Louis, I was fortunate in having Michael Chua join me. He had received his PhD from the Australian National University in Canberra, Australia, and had spent a postdoctoral period with Bill Betz in Denver. Michael brought many skills to our work, and the isolated spindle research received a real boost. We used a number of fluorescent dyes to stain components within the spindle, particularly the sensory terminals. Thanks to Jeff Lichtman and Tom Woolsey, we had access to confocal microscopes. This enabled us to obtain beautiful images, free of blurring from out-of-focus information, which could then be used for three-dimensional reconstruction.

After more than 20 years, two factors caused me finally to leave St. Louis. I would soon have to give up my space in Cell Biology and Physiology. Also, our son had finished medical school at Washington University in 1994. This seemed a natural turning point. I visited Yale to explore possibilities of continuing my research there. A number of my former associates were still members of the Physiology Department (now the Department of Molecular and Cellular Physiology). Both they and the department chairman, Walter Boron (who had received both his MD and his PhD in Physiology from Washington University), seemed interested in having me come and were willing to provide space for my work. After we moved to New Haven, however, this research space failed to materialize because the then-dean refused to approve the arrangement. As one longtime Yale professor said to me with wry humor, "We don't even treat our own senior faculty very well. I don't know why you expected anything better." Since our lab at Washington University was still functioning, I commuted back to St. Louis for a year to continue research.

Our studies on spindles are unique, and there are still a number of interesting problems, approachable by new techniques, that I want to pursue. Ed Perl had suggested that he could find some space for me to continue experiments in his laboratory at the University of North Carolina, and Stan Froehner was receptive to my joining the Physiology Department. Dale Purves also encouraged us to visit Chapel Hill. We moved there in 1995, and I now hope to do some final experiments on the site of impulse initiation in somatic sensory receptors.

A Retrospective View

Looking back, was all this department building over 30 years in three different settings really worthwhile? My style was to recruit mostly young faculty, provide a stimulating setting for their activities, and enjoy watching their development as leaders in their areas of interest. For the people involved, including myself, I think it was worth the effort. While many of these individuals would have done well in any academic setting, there were many unique and productive interactions between us in the particular environments we shared. Given the fiscal constraints that exist now, it would certainly be far more difficult to build such departments today. A significant number of the young scientists I hired grew to maturity in these departments and eventually became department heads themselves in universities across this country and abroad. Today, the recruiting style in many ambitious schools is to seek instantaneous recognition by hiring world-class "stars," often requiring them to do only a minimal amount of teaching. This is often a very expensive process, and it is certainly less interesting and rewarding than nurturing the growth of outstanding younger people.

I much admire Peter Medawar's writings on science, in particular his comments about being the director of the National Institute for Medical Research. These comments reflect my feelings about the years I spent as a department head (18):

> I construe my function ... as mainly to create the kind of environment that is conducive to the advancement of learning. That sounds pompous, but this is all a director (or a chairman) can do. You cannot direct people to have ideas and no one can have a big enough grasp of the whole of biological science to be able to say which lines of research are going to be fruitful and which are certainly going to be a waste of time. So what one has to do is simply to create an environment and an atmosphere in which science flourishes ... it probably helps to create the right kind of atmosphere if people see that the director, who presumably doesn't have to do any research, actually does it and does it because he likes it."

Literature Cited

1. Chase MW, Hunt CC. 1995. Herbert Spencer Gasser 1888–1963. A Biographical Memoir. *Biogr. Mem. Natl. Acad. Sci.* 67:1–33
2. McMahon UJ. 1990. *Steve. Remembrances of Stephen W. Kuffler*. Sunderland, MA: Sinauer
3. Langley JN. 1922. The nerve fiber constitution of peripheral nerves and of nerve roots. *J. Physiol.* 56:382–96
4. O'Leary J, Heinbecker P, Bishop GH. 1935. Analysis of function of a nerve to muscle. *Am. J. Physiol.* 110:636–58
5. Leksell L. 1945. The action potential and excitatory effects of the small ventral root fibres to skeletal muscle. *Acta Physiol. Scand.* 73(Suppl. 21):1–84
6. Haggquist G. 1940. A contribution to the question of the nervous and muscular substratum of the muscle tone. *Acta Med. Scand.* 104:8–20
7. Kuffler SW, Laporte Y, Ransmeier RE. 1947. The function of the frog's small-nerve motor system. *J. Neurophysiol.* 10: 395–408
8. Kuffler SW, Hunt CC, Quilliam JP. 1951. Function of medullated small-nerve fibers in mammalian ventral roots; efferent muscle spindle innervation. *J. Neurophysiol.* 14:29–54
9. Hunt CC, Kuffler SW. 1951. Stretch receptor discharges during muscle contraction. *J. Physiol.* 113:298–315
10. Hunt CC, Kuffler SW. 1951. Further study of efferent small-nerve fibers to mammalian muscle spindles. Multiple spindle innervation and activity during contraction. *J. Physiol.* 113:283–97
11. Hunt CC. 1951. The reflex activity of mammalian small-nerve fibers. *J. Physiol.* 115: 456–69
12. Hunt CC. 1954. Relation of function to diameter in afferent fibers of muscle nerves. *J. Gen. Physiol.* 38:117–31
13. Gasser HS. 1950. Unmyelinated fibers originating in dorsal root ganglia. *J. Gen. Physiol.* 33:651–90
14. Gasser HS. 1958. Comparison of the structure, as revealed with the electron microscope, and the physiology of the unmyelinated fibers in the skin nerves and in the olfactory nerves. *Exp. Cell Res.* 5:3–17 (Suppl.)
15. Hunt CC, Paintal AS. 1958. Spinal reflex regulation of fusimotor neurons. *J. Physiol.* 143:195–212
16. Martin AR. 1995. Autobiography. In *Collected Works of A. R. Martin.* Privately printed
17. Cori C. 1969. The call of science. *Annu. Rev. Biochem.* 38:1–20
18. Medawar P. 1991. *The Threat and the Glory: Reflections on Science and Scientists*, Oxford: Oxford Univ. Press

Annu. Rev. Physiol. 1999. 61:19–43

CELLULAR AND MOLECULAR BASIS FOR ELECTRICAL RHYTHMICITY IN GASTROINTESTINAL MUSCLES

Burton Horowitz, Sean M. Ward, and Kenton M. Sanders
University of Nevada School of Medicine, Department of Physiology and Cell Biology, Reno, Nevada 89557; e-mail: burt@physio.unr.edu; sean@physio.unr.edu; kent@physio.unr.edu

KEY WORDS: gastrointestinal smooth muscle, K^+ channels, Cl^- channels, Ca^{2+} channels, enteric nervous system, interstitial cells of Cajal

ABSTRACT

Regulation of gastrointestinal (GI) motility is intimately coordinated with the modulation of ionic conductances expressed in GI smooth muscle and nonmuscle cells. Interstitial cells of Cajal (ICC) act as pacemaker cells and possess unique ionic conductances that trigger slow wave activity in these cells. The slow wave mechanism is an exclusive feature of ICC: Smooth muscle cells may lack the basic ionic mechanisms necessary to generate or regenerate slow waves. The molecular identification of the components for these conductances provides the foundation for a complete understanding of the ionic basis for GI motility. In addition, this information will provide a basis for the identification or development of therapeutics that might act on these channels. It is much easier to study these conductances and develop blocking drugs in expression systems than in native GI muscle cells. This review focuses on the relationship between ionic currents in native GI smooth muscle cells and ICC and their molecular counterparts.

INTRODUCTION

The contractile behavior of gastrointestinal (GI) smooth muscles depends to a considerable extent on the intrinsic electrical activities of the muscles. This is particularly true of the phasic portions of the GI tract where cyclic

0066-4278/99/0315-0019$08.00

depolarizations and repolarizations, referred to as slow waves, determine contractile frequency and maintain the phasic nature of contractions. The slow wave cycle insures a period of relaxation between contractions to allow mixing and movement of lumenal contents. Tonic regions of the GI tract, such as the sphincters and gastric fundus, are also regulated by electrical events but primarily by more persistent changes in membrane potential due to stimulation by neurotransmitters or hormones.

GI smooth muscles exhibit a wide range of electrical behaviors (see 1), and understanding the mechanisms of these events has been the goal of physiologists for more than half a century. Electrical activity can vary from slow changes in membrane potential, to hyperpolarization and depolarization responses to neurotransmitters, to oscillatory slow wave activity, to fast Ca^{2+} action potentials. All this behavior can be recorded during impalements of a single smooth muscle cell, which suggests that a plethora of ionic conductances and regulatory mechanisms are at play in GI muscles. Such diversity is almost unprecedented in other excitable cells. Diversity, the small size of smooth muscle cells, and the structural complexities of GI muscles have slowed progress toward understanding the ionic basis for electrical rhythmicity.

Since the mid-1980s, a considerable amount of information about the ionic mechanisms responsible for GI electrophysiology has been provided by application of the patch clamp technique (see 2, 3) and molecular techniques (e.g. 4, 5). Investigations into these areas are beginning to break apart the complexities of GI electrical rhythmicity. We can now attribute some of the events observed to specific cell types, particular ionic conductances, and specific molecular species of channels. Identification of the molecular components responsible for the ionic conductances found in GI smooth muscles is allowing studies of the biophysical and regulatory characteristics of these channels in expression systems devoid of contaminating currents. Assignment of molecular entities to the ionic events underlying GI electrical activity may allow these channels to become targets for therapeutic agents, because it is much easier to study the properties of these conductances and to test blocking drugs in expression systems than in native GI muscle cells. This review focuses on current knowledge of the cellular and molecular basis for electrical rhythmicity and the ionic species that have been identified in GI smooth muscles.

ORGANIZATION OF ELECTRICAL ACTIVITY IN GI MUSCLES

Understanding the electrical activity of the GI tract is complicated by the following. (*a*) The electrical output of GI muscles is a product of contributions from two electrically coupled cell types, smooth muscle cells and interstitial cells of

Cajal (ICC) (for review, see 6). These cells have distinct electrical missions and express different types of ionic conductances to accomplish those tasks. ICC serve as pacemaker cells and generate and propagate electrical slow waves. Smooth muscle cells respond to the depolarization/repolarization cycle imposed by ICC. The responses of smooth muscle cells are focused on the regulation of L-type Ca^{2+} current, which is the main source of Ca^{2+} for contraction. (*b*) Regulatory input from nerves, hormones, and paracrine substances are superimposed upon the ongoing myogenic activity. Responses to biologically active substances result from modulations of ionic conductances that are already active and going through dynamic changes in open probability during the slow wave cycle and from activation of new conductances that do not participate in basal electrical activity. The conductances affected by regulatory substances could be expressed in either smooth muscle cells or ICC. Finally, the conductance of both cell types mutually affects the electrical behavior of the total syncytium. Electrical responses from such a complex array of electrically coupled cells are not easily predictable from studies on isolated myocytes. Therefore, studies of GI electrophysiology must include detailed investigations of both cell types and of intact muscles to understand basic mechanisms and integrated responses.

Before we can comprehend the significance of the molecular diversity that generates the electrical behavior of GI muscles, the morphological features of GI muscles and the general organization of electrical activity must be understood. For years, smooth muscles of the GI tract were considered homogenous populations of cells within a given organ. Now we recognize that important regional differences exist: The activities of the circular and longitudinal muscle layers of a given organ can vary widely, and the activities of smooth muscle cells within a muscle layer can be profoundly different (7–10). This suggests region-by-region fine control of the development and organization of ionic conductances in GI muscles, and developmental studies have documented changes in K^+ currents as electrical activity develops (11). The developmental influences and cell biology that ultimately determine the unique characteristics of electrical activity in a given region of muscle are poorly understood. These questions are of great importance if we are to understand how electrical diversity is established and maintained in GI muscles.

Role of ICC in Electrical Rhythmicity

As stated above, a major source of regional electrical diversity arises from the contributions of ICC. These cells populate all pacemaker regions in the GI tract (see 6, 12–14), and ICC lie at the interface between varicose nerve fibers and smooth muscle cells (e.g. 15). ICC are electrically coupled to the smooth muscle syncytium via gap junctions. Therefore, expression of ionic conductances in ICC can influence the resting potential, electrical activity, and responses of the coupled smooth muscle cells. By the same reasoning, the electrical activity of smooth muscle cells may influence the output of ICC. There is not room in this review to cover the anatomy and physiology of ICC in depth. For more information the reader is directed to recent reviews (6, 16).

ICC are pacemaker cells that generate and conduct electrical slow waves to smooth muscle cells (17–20). Other types of ICC receive, transduce, and conduct neural signals to the smooth muscle (21). Therefore, the search for the ionic mechanisms that produce and regulate electrical activity in the GI tract must be expanded to include systematic investigation of ICC. We know little about the unique ionic conductances expressed by ICC.

Most investigators have envisioned ICC to be pacemaker cells like those in the heart. It has been thought that ICC generate pacemaker current that depolarizes smooth muscle cells to threshold. Slow waves were thought to be regenerated or even amplified by the smooth muscle (22). In this concept, ICC are the pacemakers because they are more excitable than smooth muscle cells. Numerous studies have shown that loss of ICC from GI muscles blocks generation of spontaneous slow waves (18–20, 23–25). If smooth muscle has the ability to regenerate and actively propagate slow waves, then in preparations lacking ICC it should be possible to evoke slow waves with an external current source. Several observations do not support this hypothesis (see Figure 1): (*a*) Slow waves passively decay as a function of distance from pacemaker areas (see 9); (*b*) removal of the pacemaker from part of a muscle strip causes slow waves to passively decay through the region lacking ICC (25, 26); (*c*) after removal of ICC, smooth muscle cells continue to be excitable, but in the absence of ICC, smooth muscles produce action potentials rather than slow wave-like activity (19, 27); and (*d*) after removing ICC, it is not possible to evoke slow waves by electrical pacing. Taken together, these observations suggest a novel hypothesis (Figure 2): The slow wave mechanism is an exclusive feature of ICC; smooth muscle cells lack the basic ionic mechanisms necessary to generate or regenerate slow waves. A corollary to this hypothesis is that active propagation of slow waves occurs through networks of ICC instead of being amplified and propagated by smooth muscle cells (e.g. 22).

Conduction of slow waves from ICC into smooth muscle cells is passive. Microelectrode impalements of smooth muscle cells record slow waves that have been conducted through gap junctions from ICC. The depolarization caused by slow waves activates different populations of ionic conductances in smooth muscle cells, most importantly L-type Ca^{2+} channels. The smooth muscle response may be manifest as a small, nonregenerative enhancement in depolarization (i.e. an apparent increase in slow wave amplitude) (see Figure 1*E*) or Ca^{2+} action potentials superimposed upon the slow waves (also see Figure 1*E*). The response of smooth muscle cells to slow wave depolarizations is determined by the magnitude of the depolarization, the passive properties of the smooth muscle syncytium, and the particular ionic conductances available. If threshold is reached, Ca^{2+} action potentials are generated. These events can propagate for short distances, but the impedance properties of smooth muscle are such that the propagation distance is limited (see 28).

This organization allows slow waves to spread actively through ICC networks within GI muscles at all times, but coupling of slow waves to contractions can be regulated by external stimuli, such as neural inputs. In regions of cells where nonselective cation channels are activated (primary electrical mechanism utilized by excitatory neurotransmitters), slow waves are superimposed upon the depolarization, and the open probability of Ca^{2+} channels is enhanced. In regions in which the open probability of K^{+} channels is enhanced (primary mechanism utilized by inhibitory transmitters), slow waves fail to produce adequate depolarization to activate sufficient numbers of Ca^{2+} channels to yield contractions. The ionic conductances activated by neurotransmitters and other agents may reside in smooth muscle cells or ICC, but activation or suppression of conductances influences the behavior of the total syncytium. This hypothesis substantially alters the old concept of the myogenic control of motility and provides a new framework for the design of studies into the molecular components of excitability. We must reduce GI muscles to smooth muscle cells and ICC and examine both for the ionic conductances that contribute to the behaviors of GI muscles.

Ionic Conductances Unique to ICC

We know little about the molecular nature of ionic conductances in ICC. ICC were first isolated in 1989 (see 17); however, work has progressed slowly on these cells because of the difficulties in isolating and identifying the cells. ICC from the canine colon pacemaker region express ionic conductances unique from smooth muscle cells isolated from the same region (29). Both cell types express 4-aminopyridine–sensitive delayed rectifier currents, but the half inactivation of the current in ICC occurred 25 mV more negative than the current found in circular smooth muscle cells from the pacemaker region. An inward current was observed in interstitial cells that had a resolution threshold of −70 mV. Activation of this current occurred at least 20 mV negative to the potential at which inward currents could be resolved in smooth muscle cells. The negatively activating inward current in ICC was carried by Ca^{2+} and had properties of a low-threshold Ca^{2+} current similar to that found in the SA node of the heart (30). Recent experiments have also detected a prominent Ba^{2+}-sensitive inward rectifier current in pacemaker ICC from the canine colon (E Flynn, SD Koh, KM Sanders, unpublished studies). This conductance may contribute to the negative resting potentials in the pacemaker area (−78 mV) (see 9).

The inward current source for pacemaker activity appears to vary in other regions of the GI tract. Recent studies on primary cultures of ICC from the

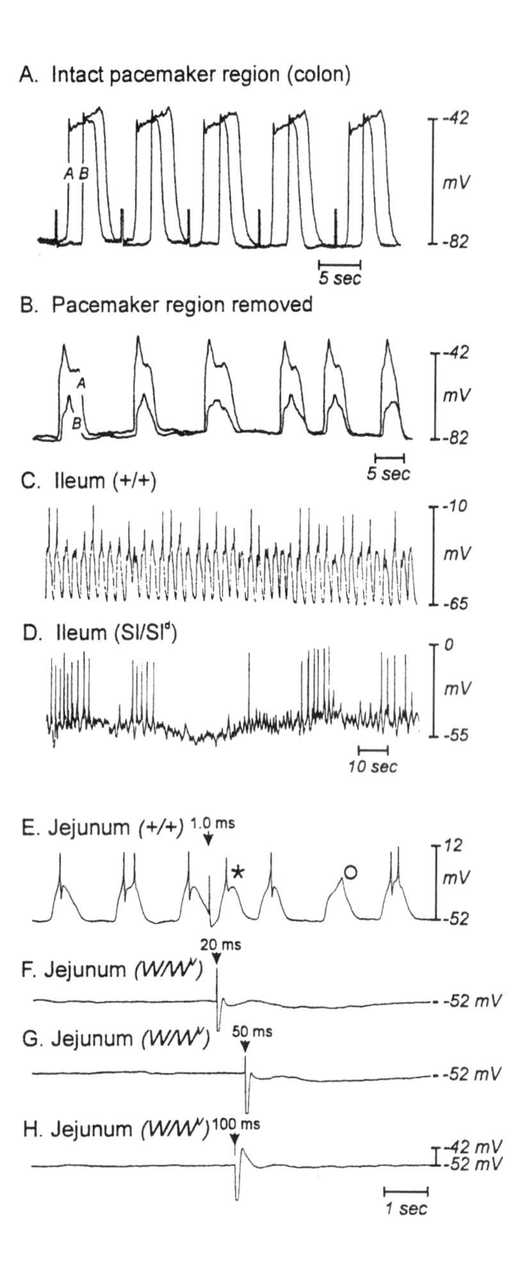
A. Intact pacemaker region (colon)
A B
-42
mV
-82
5 sec
B. Pacemaker region removed
A
B
-42
mV
-82
5 sec
C. Ileum (+/+)
-10
mV
-65
D. Ileum (Sl/Sl^d)
0
mV
-55
10 sec
E. Jejunum (+/+) 1.0 ms
12
mV
-52
F. Jejunum (W/W^v) 20 ms
-52 mV
G. Jejunum (W/W^v) 50 ms
-52 mV
H. Jejunum (W/W^v) 100 ms
-42 mV
-52 mV
1 sec

murine small bowel suggest that a Ca^{2+}-dependent Cl^- current might contribute to pacemaker activity in that region (31). Cultured small bowel ICC exhibited rhythmic inward currents that were blocked by intracellular EGTA [ethylene glycol-bis(β-aminoethyl ether)-*N,N,N′,N′*-tetraacetic acid], intracellular solutions nominally free of Ca^{2+}, and extracellular 4-acetoamido-4-isothiocyanato-stilbene-2,2′-disulphonic acid (SITS). The rhythmic currents reversed at potentials close to the equilibrium potential for Cl^-. Currently, it is difficult to reconcile these findings with the mechanism of slow wave in vivo because studies of intact murine small intestine have shown that blockers of Ca^{2+}-activated Cl^- currents, such as niflumic acid (SM Ward, unpublished observations), or replacement of most extracellular Cl^- with isethionate (32) did not inhibit slow waves. Recent voltage clamp studies of cultured ICC from murine intestine have suggested a nonselective cation conductance might participate in spontaneous rhythmicity (SD Koh, KM Sanders & SM Ward, unpublished observations). Removal of Na^+ from the extracellular solution, however, reduced, but did not

←

Figure 1 Slow waves are generated and propagate within interstitial cells of Cajal (ICC) networks in gastrointestinal muscles. *Panels A* and *B* show the need for ICC for active propagation of slow waves. *Panel A* shows records from a dual microelectrode impalement of cells along the submucosal surface of the canine colon. (*electrodes A* and *B*). Impaled cells 11 mm apart (records are denoted). A stimulator paced the muscle strip. Slow waves were evoked at a constant rate (note stimulus artifacts) and propagate with fixed conduction velocity. At all points along the submucosal surface slow waves were of approximately equal amplitude, demonstrating active propagation. *Panel B* shows a similar experiment, but a thin strip of tissue along the submucosal surface containing the pacemaker cells was removed from most of the strip. The small bit of submucosal surface remaining generated normal slow waves. These events decayed in amplitude as a function of distance from the pacemaker area. *Panel B, A* and *B* show simultaneous intracellular recordings made from cells 6 mm apart. [Data in both panels redrawn from Sanders et al (136).] *Panel C* shows normal electrical activity from the wild-type (+/+) mouse ileum. Spontaneous slow waves elicited spike potentials that were superimposed upon the slow waves. *Panel D* shows activity in a stem cell factor mutant (Sl/Sld) in which myenteric ICC (IC-MY; pacemaker cells) fail to develop. Slow waves are not generated in these tissues. However, some muscles generate spontaneous action potentials (as shown), and these events are blocked by nifedipine (1 μM) (not shown). Although the circular muscle depolarizes and produces spontaneous activity in the form of action potentials, slow wave type rhythmicity is never observed in these muscles. This suggests that the ionic mechanism responsible for slow waves is not present in ileal smooth muscle cells. [Data in *Panels C* and *D* redrawn from Ward et al (27).] *Panels E–H* show recordings from the jejunums of wild-type and a c-Kit mutant (W/WV). IC-MY also fail to develop in W/WV animals (18). In +/+ animals, spontaneous slow waves are apparent with superimposed spike activity (*Panel E*). Premature slow waves (*) can be evoked with electrical field stimulation with pulse durations as short as 1 ms (*arrow*). The slow wave (denoted by the *circle*) failed to reach threshold. Spontaneous slow waves were not recorded from muscles of W/WV animals, and electrical field stimulation (1–100 ms) was unable to elicit slow waves (*Panels F–H*) even with long-duration pulses. *Panels E–H* show experiments performed in the presence of tetrodotoxin (1 μM) to block the influence of intrinsic nerves. (*Panel H*) Time base is applicable to *Panels E–H*. These data suggest that slow waves are an exclusive property of ICC, and they are not amplified or regenerated in smooth muscle cells.

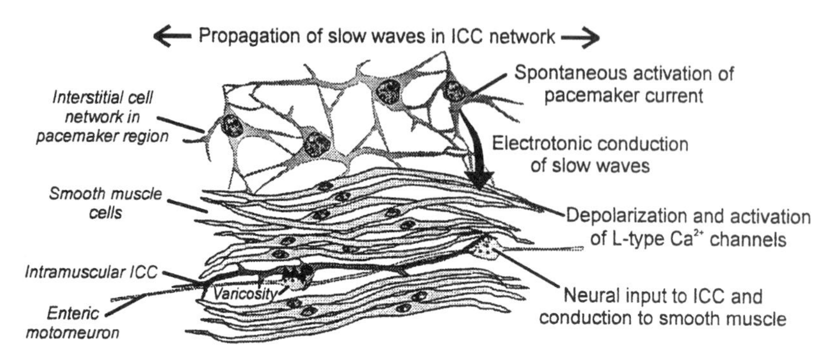

Figure 2 Model for generation and modulation of electrical activity in gastrointestinal muscles. Interstitial cell networks in pacemaker regions express the ionic mechanism to generate slow waves. These events can actively propagate through the ICC network via gap junctions connecting the ICC. Slow waves electrotonically conduct into smooth muscle cells, which are also electrically coupled to the interstitial cells of Cajal (ICC) but appear to lack the mechanism for regenerating slow waves. Slow waves depolarize the smooth muscle cells, and activate voltage-dependent (L-type) Ca^{2+} channels. If threshold depolarization is achieved, Ca^{2+} action potentials are elicited. If threshold is not achieved, the activation of inward current in smooth muscle cells is manifest as an increase in the plateau phase of slow waves. Both of these smooth muscle responses to slow wave depolarizations can be observed in the records shown in Figure 1*C* and *E*. Entry of Ca^{2+} via L-type Ca^{2+} channels in smooth muscle cells is necessary for excitation-contraction coupling. Neural inputs can condition the smooth muscle response to slow waves. Release of excitatory transmitters activates nonselective cation channels and increases the effectiveness of slow waves to bring the muscle cells to threshold. Release of inhibitory transmitters activates potassium channels, which decreases the probability of reaching threshold. Intramuscular ICC (IC-IM) are closely associated with enteric motor neurons. These cells appear to act as receivers and transducers for some of the neural inputs. Neural inputs can be transmitted through IC-IM to the smooth muscle cells because IC-IM are electrically coupled to the smooth muscle syncytium. Some neurotransmitters, particularly peptides, are likely to spill over and directly affect receptors expressed by smooth muscle cells.

completely block, rhythmicity in either intact strips of small intestinal muscle or cultured ICC. Taken together, experiments on cultured small intestinal ICC indicate that the multiple conductance pathways may be involved in the pacemaker activity of these cells.

ION CHANNEL EXPRESSION IN SMOOTH MUSCLE CELLS

Because of the relative ease in enzymatically dispersing smooth muscle cells from GI muscles, work to identify specific ionic components in these cells has progressed rapidly. Another paper in this section (32a) reviews native currents recorded from GI muscle cells. This section discusses molecular species that have been found and characterized in GI smooth muscle cells. It is important to note that while many molecular studies have been conducted on smooth muscle tissues, with a complex tissue such as GI muscle, these studies do not determine expression of specific ionic species in particular cell types. Recent studies have begun to utilize reverse transcriptase polymerase chain reaction (RT-PCR) on identified smooth muscle cells to identify cell-specific ionic species. These results are also discussed.

Voltage-Dependent K^+ Channels

The responses of smooth muscle cells to slow wave depolarizations depend to a significant extent on the types of K^+ channels expressed. The diversity of responses observed in the various organs and regions of the GI tract also appear to depend on the complement of K^+ channels present. A variety of K^+ channel blocking drugs can dramatically affect the pattern of electrical activity in GI muscles. A search for the molecular species responsible for K^+ currents has yielded evidence for a rich diversity that helps to explain the variations in the electrical patterns observed (1).

The most diverse group of conductances in GI muscles is the voltage-dependent, Ca^{2+}-insensitive K^+ (Kv) channels. These conductances have a wide variety of pharmacologies and electrical properties. For example, Kv currents of canine colonic muscles are of the delayed rectifier type and can be separated into rapidly and slowly activating components (33). In particular, I_{dkf} is a fast-activating current blocked by micromolar concentrations of 4-aminopyridine (4-AP), I_{dks} is a slowly activating current blocked by tetraethylammonium (TEA), and I_{dkn} is a TEA-sensitive current that inactivates at negative potentials.

Mammalian genes encoding Kv channels were originally identified as homologues of the *Shaker* gene in *Drosophila* (34). The predicted topological structure of these channels is depicted in Figure 3. Organizationally, Chandy & Gutman (35) proposed to group the mammalian Kv channels into families (Kv1–4) of homologous gene products. The properties of this group of channels have been reviewed (36). In the last several years, five more families have been identified (Kv5–9) that have the curious common property of not producing functional channels when expressed singly in heterologous expression systems (37–40). These "electrically silent channels," or γ subunits (37), can have subtle effects on pharmacological as well as pore-dependent properties on coexpressed Kv channels. The expression of these subunits has not been reported in GI muscles.

Gastrointestinal smooth muscles express several Kv family members. Kv1.2 was cloned from a canine colonic smooth muscle library and detected in several other GI smooth muscles, including the stomach and small bowel (4). However, expression of cKv1.2 was not detected by Northern blot analysis in other canine smooth muscles, including renal artery, uterine wall, and portal vein. cKv1.2

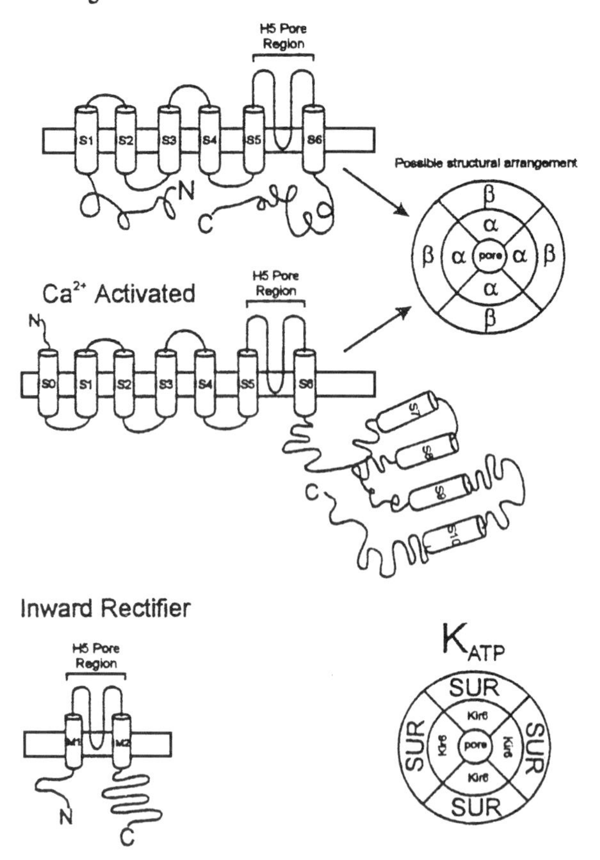

Figure 3 Predicted topological structures and hypothetical molecular arrangements of potassium channel types.

was found to be closely related to Kv1.2 genes isolated from brain libraries of other species, having only eight amino acid differences with the previously identified RCK1 from rat. (41). When expressed in *Xenopus* oocytes, cKv1.2 yielded delayed rectifier-type currents. The current activated rapidly with a half-activation time of 7.6 ± 0.2 ms and slowly inactivated. Half inactivation (V_h) occurred at −15 mV. Inactivation was incomplete (~35% of the current failed to inactivate) even with 20-s prepulses at room temperature. When the current was studied at more physiological temperatures (34°C), the activation and inactivation properties were more rapid and inactivation was more complete during a 20-s prepulse (42). cKv1.2 was found to be extremely sensitive to block by 4-AP with an IC_{50} of 74.7 μM. This sensitivity was markedly greater than for other homologues of Kv1.2 (cloned from brain) and *Drosophila Shaker* channels. Block by 4-AP was use-dependent, and 4-AP does not appear to bind to the channels in the inactivated state.

In single-channel experiments, 4-AP decreased the mean open time of cKv1.2 channels in a dose-dependent manner but did not alter the single-channel current amplitude (42). The properties and expression pattern of cKv1.2 coordinated well with the characteristics of the fast component of the native delayed rectifier current in canine colonic myocytes (I_{dkf}) (33); however, cKv1.2 was found to be sensitive to charybdotoxin (CTX) whereas the native current was unaffected by treatment with CTX (33).

Another cDNA recovered from the same cDNA library was most closely related to Kv1.5. However, unlike cKv1.2, cKv1.5 was considerably different from other Kv1.5 members isolated from brain libraries of other species. The amino acid sequence displayed a high level of identity to other K^+ channels of the Kv1.5 class in the core region between transmembrane segments S1 and S6. However, amino acid identity decreased to between 74% and 82% in the NH_2 and COOH terminal segments, which suggests that cKv1.5 was a distinct isoform of the Kv1.5 class. Functional expression of cKv1.5 in oocytes demonstrated channels highly selective for K^+ that showed voltage-dependent activation positive to −40 mV. At room temperature, the current showed fast activation (time to half of peak current, $t_{1/2} = 5.5$ ms) and slow inactivation, which was incomplete after 20-s depolarizations. Unitary current analysis displayed a linear I-V curve with a slope conductance of 9.8 ± 1.1 pS. cKv1.5 was also sensitive to block by 4-AP with an IC_{50} of 211 μM. Northern blot analysis demonstrated differential expression of cKv1.5 in smooth muscles of the GI tract and abundant expression in several vascular smooth muscles.

Except for the discrepancy in the sensitivity of cKv1.2 to CTX, both cloned Kv channels were similar to native I_{dkf} found in canine colonic myocytes. Members of the Kv1 family form heterotetramers in heterologous expression systems (43) as well as in native cells (44). Studies of the CTX pharmacology of cKv1.2 and cKv1.5 expressed in oocytes provide evidence for heterotetramer formation in colonic myocytes (45). Even a single CTX-resistant subunit rendered the heterotetrameric channel insensitive to CTX. The two K^+-channel clones differed in an amino acid at the mouth of the pore region that may be in a position to block the access of CTX to its binding site and, hence, determine CTX sensitivity of the heterotetrameric channel. These results may explain discrepancies reported between native and cloned smooth muscle K^+ channels and suggest that native I_{dkf} in canine colonic myocytes is a Kv1.2/Kv1.5 heterotetramer.

In addition to the fast, delayed rectifier component in colonic myocytes, a slowly activating component, I_{dkf}, was observed in the presence of 10 mM 4-AP. This 4-AP–insensitive component (I_{dks}), unlike I_{dkf} (33), was blocked by external tetraethylammonium (TEA). Kv2.2, homologous to the *shab* family of *Drosophila* voltage-gated K^+ channels, was isolated from human and canine colonic circular smooth muscle–derived mRNA. DNA sequence analysis detected significant homology between the human (hKv2.2), canine (cKv2.2), and rat brain (rKv2.2) clones (46). Northern hybridization analysis performed on RNA prepared from tissues and RT-PCR performed on RNA isolated from dispersed and selected smooth muscle cells demonstrates that Kv2.2 is expressed in all regions of the canine GI tract and in several vascular tissues.

Expression of Kv2.2 mRNA in *Xenopus* oocytes resulted in a slowly activating K^+ current ($t_{1/2} = 97 \pm 8.6$ ms) mediated by 15-pS (in symmetrical K^+ gradients) channels. The current was inhibited by TEA ($IC_{50} = 2.6$ mM), 4-AP ($IC_{50} = 1.5$ mM at +20 mV), and quinine ($IC_{50} = 13.7$ μM) and was insensitive to CTX. A comparison of the electrophysiological and pharmacological properties of Kv2.2 to the delayed rectifier current in native colonic smooth muscle indicates that it shares many similarities with I_{dks} and may underlie this component of the delayed rectifier K^+ current in GI smooth muscle cells. A detailed comparison of the biophysical and pharmacological characteristics of Kv clones and native currents is presented in Table 1.

An extensive analysis of the transcriptional expression of Kv channels in the canine GI tract has recently been carried out using RT-PCR performed on RNA preparations obtained from freshly dispersed and isolated smooth muscle cells (B Horowitz, unpublished observations). These experiments eliminate contamination from other cell types within GI muscles (e.g. ICC, neurons, fibroblasts, macrophages, etc) and show the presence of Kv channel types in addition to those isolated from cDNA libraries. Channels found in these studies include Kv1.4, a rapidly inactivating K^+ current (34, 47), which was found in all regions of the GI tract tested, and Kv1.6, detected in cells from the antrum, duodenum, jejunum, and colon.

Accessory subunits have been shown to associate with Kv channels to form α/β complexes (48). Three similar forms of this accessory subunit have been cloned from rat brain (β1.1, 1.2, and 2.1). These subunits affect inactivation

Table 1 Comparison of cloned Kv channels and native currents in canine colonic smooth muscle[a]

Channel	$T_{1/2}$	Activation threshold	Inactivation $V_{1/2}$	Inactivation Vs	IC_{50} 4-AP	IC_{50} Quinine	IC_{50} TEA_{out}	Channel conductance
cKv1.2	7.6 ms	−40 mV	−15 mV	7.7	75 μM	250 μM	<10 mM	14 pS
cKv1.5	5.5 ms	−40 mV	−21 mV	7.0	211 μM	365 μM	<10 mM	9.8 pS
$I_{dK(f)}$	7.8 ms	−40 mV	ND	ND	69 μM	ND	<10 mM	20 pS
cKv2.2	97 ms	−20 mV	−16.3 mV	4.8	1.5 mM	14 μM	2.6 mM	15.3 pS
$I_{dK(s)}$	31 ms	−20 mV	ND	ND	>1.5 mM	ND	2.2 mM	ND

[a]ND, Not determined. From Schmalz (46), reproduced with permission.

kinetics of Kv1.2 (49), Kv.1.4 (50), and Kv1.5 (51, 52). Kvβ1.1 and 1.2 are alternative splice products of the same gene (53) whereas Kvβ2 is the product of a separate gene. These β subunits interact only with Kv1 family members, but an additional accessory subunit (β4) associates with Kv2.2 (54). This interaction resulted in altered expression of Kv2.2 in heterologous systems but had no effect on the kinetics of Kv2.2. β1.1 as well as β4 were detected in all regions of the canine GI tract, but other β subunit isoforms have not been detected (46). It is cryptic that β1.1 as well as Kv1.4 would be expressed in canine GI smooth muscle. β1.1 has been shown to increase the inactivation kinetics of Kv1 family members. Kv1.4 is a rapidly inactivating channel, but fast inactivation has not been recorded from native canine colonic myocytes (33). However, a recent report demonstrated that Kv1.6 subunits can confer a dominant negative effect on the rapid inactivation conferred by Kvβ subunits and can decrease the inactivation kinetics of Kv1.4 (55). Expression of Kv1.6 by canine, mouse, and human GI smooth muscles may help to explain the discrepancy between cloned and native channels.

Differential expression of Kv channels has been related to electrical diversity in intact GI muscles. Kv conductances were characterized in canine colonic circular and longitudinal muscles. Longitudinal cells express a conductance that was TEA-sensitive and weakly affected by 4-AP (56). Treatment of intact muscles with TEA increased the amplitude and frequency of action potentials, but little effect was noted with 4-AP. In contrast, circular muscle cells of the same preparation express a significant 4-AP–sensitive current (see discussion above about proposed contributions of Kv1.2 and Kv1.5) and a TEA-sensitive component of delayed rectifier. Addition of 4-AP to intact muscles enhanced the amplitude and duration of slow waves (57). These experiments demonstrate the participation of specialized conductances in generating diverse electrical behaviors.

Regulation of Kv Channels

Muscarinic receptor stimulation enhances excitatory electrical and mechanical activity in GI muscles by increasing the amplitude and duration of slow waves (25, 58) and by increasing the probability of action potential generation (59). Muscarinic stimulation activates a nonselective cation current in GI muscles (e.g. 60), but suppression of delayed rectifier K^+ currents is another possible means of excitable regulation. With identification of the molecular components responsible for Kv channel expression in GI smooth muscles, analysis of the regulatory effects of neurotransmitters and hormones on these target proteins is possible without contamination from other conductances.

GI myocytes express both m2 and m3 receptor subtypes (61), and m3 receptors are coupled to phopholipase C (62). Functional coupling between m3 receptors, Kv1.2, and Kv1.5 was studied by using *Xenopus* oocytes and COS cells coinjected with cRNAs encoding human m3 receptors and Kv channel clones (63). Acetylcholine decreased whole cell Kv currents in these cells, and phorbol esters [e.g. phorbol dibutyrate (PDBu)] mimicked the action of acetylcholine (ACh). At the single-channel level, ACh and PDBu applied to the extra-patch membrane reduced the open probability of Kv channels in cell-attached patches without affecting single-channel conductance. It is difficult to extrapolate the function of this regulatory pathway to native smooth muscle cells, but the reconstitution experiments demonstrate the utility of a molecular approach in dissecting signal transduction mechanisms in GI smooth muscle cells.

Inhibitory neural regulation of GI muscles also acts via Kv-like channels, but molecular equivalents to these events have not been determined. Carbon monoxide (CO) increased whole cell outward currents, hyperpolarized membrane potential, and increased guanosine 3′,5′-cyclic monophosphate (cGMP) levels in canine jejunal smooth muscle cells (64). Heme oxygenase 2, the enzyme responsible for producing CO, has been localized to ICC cells in the murine small intestine, which suggests that CO could be an endogenous regulator of outward currents (65). Nitric oxide (NO) also has been found to activate Kv-like channels in native GI smooth muscle cells. NO and NO donors increased the open probabilities of 80-pS and 4-pS voltage-dependent K^+ channels in canine colonic myocytes (66). The molecular identification of these channels is not known. VIP (vasoactive intestinal peptide) can enhance delayed rectifier whole cell currents in native canine colon myocytes, probably via a cAMP-dependent mechanism (67). The currents activated were 4-AP sensitive and likely to be a component of I_{dk} assigned to Kv1.2/1.5; however, this type of regulation has not been examined on specific molecular targets.

Calcium-Activated K^+ Channels

The initial report of a cDNA encoding Ca^{2+}-activated K^+ channels (BK channels) was from studies of *Drosophila*, and the gene was termed *slowpoke* or *dslo* (68). Several homologues of the *Drosophila* cDNA have been isolated from mammalian brains (69, 70). A human vascular muscle homologue was also isolated (71). The topological structure of these K^+ channels is similar to Kv channels in the core domain (S1–S6) (see Figure 3) (72); however, *slo* gene products have an extensive COOH terminal tail, which possesses a "calcium bowl" domain that may impart the Ca^{2+} sensitivity to the channel (73). When injected into *Xenopus* oocytes, the *slowpoke* cRNA expressed Ca^{2+}-activated, voltage-sensitive K^+ channels with many of the electrophysiological and pharmacological properties of native channels (74). Significant differences, however, were noted between Ca^{2+} sensitivities of expressed and native channels. These differences could be due to species variability (70), diversity in alternative spice variants (75), or the presence of accessory subunits (76). A β subunit was cloned from tracheal smooth muscle (77) and shown to enhance the Ca^{2+} sensitivity of expressed channels (76). These authors observed a 10-fold increase in Ca^{2+} sensitivity when α and β subunits were coexpressed. Studies on the *dslo* channel cDNA have demonstrated that cloned channels can be modulated by protein kinase A and that phosphorylation of the *dslo* channel protein itself was responsible (78).

Both α and β subunits of Ca^{2+}-activated K^+ channels were cloned from canine colonic smooth muscle (79). This was the first report showing the cloning and expression of both subunits from the same tissue. A splice variant of the α subunit with diversity in the carboxy terminal region was also recovered. Northern analysis demonstrated expression of both α and β subunits in all canine vascular and visceral smooth muscles tested. Expression of α alone and $\alpha + \beta$ subunits in *Xenopus* oocytes resulted in Ca^{2+} and voltage-dependent conductances. The $\alpha + \beta$ channels were more sensitive to $[Ca^{2+}]$-free medium than were channels composed of α subunit alone, and the $\alpha + \beta$ channels more closely resembled the Ca^{2+} sensitivity of native BK channels in colonic smooth muscle. This suggests that native BK channels are composed of α and β subunits. Despite the enhanced Ca^{2+} sensitivity of $\alpha + \beta$ channels versus α channels, native BK channels are considerably more sensitive to Ca^{2+} than are cloned channels. For example, the voltage of half-maximal activation ($V_{0.5}$) of native BK channels at $[Ca^{2+}] = 1\ \mu M$ were approximately 0 mV (80), but for $\alpha\beta$ cloned channels $V_{0.5}$ lies in the positive range (+50 mV). The reasons for these differences between cloned and native channels is not currently understood. It should be noted, however, that cloned α channels from myometrium expressed with bovine tracheal β subunits have similar Ca^{2+} sensitivity to native myometrial channels (81).

The role of BK channels in GI electrical activity is far from clear. Although Ca^{2+} entry would tend to enhance the open probability of these channels, the negative membrane potentials at which GI muscles operate are far from optimal for channel activation. Calculations from single-channels studies in which the Ca^{2+} and voltage dependence of this conductance were characterized suggests that NP_0 was negligible at the resting potential and basal intracellular Ca^{2+} concentration of canine colonic circular smooth muscles (see 80). Application of CTX to intact colonic muscle had little or no effect on basal electrical activity (33); however, when muscles were excited with ACh, evidence was obtained for recruitment of BK channels. Thus, in some GI muscles, BK channels may be utilized as a break on excitatory stimuli. In other regions of the GI tract with more positive resting potentials and a tendency for action potential generation, BK channels may play an ongoing role in regulation of electrical activity (e.g. 33, 82).

Currents from small-conductance, Ca^{2+}-activated K^+ channels have been recorded in murine smooth muscle cells from ileum and colon, and these channels are activated by purinergic stimulation (83, 84). Apamin sensitive and insensitive components of this current were present. The molecular equivalent of these currents in GI smooth muscles have not been identified; however, currents with similar properties in mouse and human brain are encoded by members of the SK family (85). The gene products of the SK family (SK1–3) have a typical S1–S6 topological structure, including the positively charged amino acids in the S4 transmembrane segment characteristic of voltage-gated K^+ channels (85). However, the channels are not voltage dependent. Expression of SK channels resulted in Ca^{2+}-activated (0.6–0.7 μM K_d Ca^{2+}), small-conductance (9–10 pS in symetrical K^+ solutions), voltage-insensitive K^+ channels. Although SK2 was highly sensitive to apamin, SK1 showed no sensitivity. These channels can form heteromeric structures that may affect their pharmacology (86). These channels are important in GI motility because they mediate a portion of the inhibitory response to nerve stimulation.

Inward Rectifier and ATP-Sensitive K^+ Channels

Identified members of the inward rectifier gene family have expanded over the last several years, and this family now includes six subfamilies based on DNA sequence homologies (87). To date, three distinct isoforms of the Kir2 channel subfamily have been identified in the rat brain: Kir2.1 (88), Kir2.2 (89), and Kir2.3 (90). Members of the Kir2 family show strong inward rectification and possess consensus sites for phosphorylation by protein kinases A and C (PKA and PKC, respectively) (91).

Application of Ba^{2+} (1–100 μM) caused concentration-dependent depolarization of resting membrane potential in canine colon circular muscle (ERM Flynn, CA McManus, SD Koh, KM Sanders, submitted). Whole cell patch clamp studies on isolated canine colonic myocytes detected small, inwardly rectifying, Ba^{2+}-sensitive K^+ currents, indicating the presence of Kir2-like currents (SI Cho, KM Sanders, submitted). Molecular evidence demonstrated that Kir2.1 was expressed in cells from canine colon muscle as well as other canine GI smooth muscles (B Horowitz, unpublished data). Expression in oocytes and mammalian cells resulted in a strongly inwardly rectifying, Ba^{2+}-sensitive K^+ channel. Other members of the Kir2 family have not been detected in GI tissues.

Members of the Kir3 family encode G-protein–gated, inward-rectifying K^+ channels (GIRKs) (88, 94). In heart muscle, activation of a potassium current by muscarinic stimulation (I_{KACh}) mediated a slowing of heart rate (95, 96). Krapivinsky et al (97) identified the molecular components underlying this current as a combination of Kir3.1 and Kir3.4. However, other combinations of Kir3 family members can encode a similar current. In the GI tract, this type of K^+ current may act to assist repolarization between slow waves during muscarinic responses, thus preserving phasic electrical and mechanical activity. Kir3.1 expression in canine colon was found to be quantitatively similar to β-actin (i.e. high expression), and Kir3.1 can be detected in RT-PCR on RNA prepared from isolated cells (B Horowitz, unpublished data). Kir3.2 and 3.3 but not 3.4 were detectable in canine colonic myocytes, and combinations of Kir3.1 and other Kir3 family members can form heterotetrameric channels when expressed in oocytes (97).

ATP-dependent potassium channels (K_{ATP}) produce weakly inwardly rectifying K^+ selective currents that are modulated by the metabolic state of cells (98). Their physiological importance is well established in the vasculature, but less is known about the physiological significance of this conductance in GI smooth muscles. K_{ATP} channel agonists, such as cromakalim and nicorandil, have been shown to hyperpolarize and relax stomach (99), ileum (100), and colon (101, 102).

K_{ATP} channels are formed from association of a sulfonylurea receptor (SUR) and an inward-rectifier K^+ channel of the Kir6 family (103–105). Two separate genes have been identified that encode the SUR component (SUR1 and 2). Alternative splicing arrangements exist for the SUR 2 isoform that can affect the pharmacology of the resulting K_{ATP} channel. SUR2A and 2B differ in their carboxy terminal amino acid sequence. SUR2A/Kir6.2 resulted in a "cardiac-like" K_{ATP} current that is inhibited by >100 μM ATP, and the sulfonylurea glibenclamide was stimulated by pinacidil and cromakalim but not by diazoxide. SUR2B/Kir6.1 has been proposed to be the molecular equivalent of a vascular smooth muscle K_{ATP} current (105, 106). Expression of this combination in oocytes resulted in a channel that is stimulated at lower concentrations of ATP (0.1–100 μM), inhibited by higher concentrations (1–3 mM) of ATP, and activated by both pinacidil and diazoxide. These characteristics are similar to the K_{NDP} channel identified in smooth muscle (107–109). Recently, the SUR2 gene has been shown to be alternatively spliced at exon 14 and exon 17, and these variants displayed subtly altered pharmacologies (110). An analysis of mouse colon RNA using RT-PCR detected the expression of SUR2B (but not SUR1 or SUR2A) and Kir6.1 (but not 6.2) (106). However, the cellular origin of these transcripts was not made clear from this report. A recent study using RT-PCR on dispersed and isolated mouse colon smooth muscle cells (111) identified Kir6.2 (but not 6.1), in contrast to Isomoto et al (106), and SUR2B (but not SUR1 or SUR2A), confirming the report from Isomoto et al (106).

Ca^{2+} Channels

The predominant Ca^{2+} channels in smooth muscle are dihydropyridine-sensitive or L-type channels. L-type Ca^{2+} channels provide the Ca^{2+} influx that initiates contraction (e.g. 112, 113). Blockade of Ca^{2+} channels reduces the duration and amplitude of electrical slow waves in many muscles and blocks generation of action potentials. Blockade of L-type Ca^{2+} channels does not block slow waves, which suggests that other inward current sources are available in ICC and needed for these events (see discussion above).

L-type Ca^{2+} channels are composed of five subunits, $\alpha_1\beta\gamma\alpha_2\delta$, of which the α_1 subunit contains the ion perrmeation pathway (cf 114–116). The auxiliary $\beta\gamma\alpha_2\delta$ subunits modulate channel activity and channel kinetics of activation and inactivation. Several separate genes encode the conducting α_1 subunit, and there are also splice variants of these α_1 genes (117). The α_1 subtype in canine colonic smooth muscle has been identified as $\alpha_{1C\text{-}b}$ (118). However, identification of the auxiliary subunits expressed in GI smooth muscle has not been performed. In human jejunum smooth muscle, the predominant Ca^{2+} current is dihydropyridine sensitive. This current is carried by 17-pS (in 80 mM Ba^{2+}) barium-permeable channels (119). This current was found to be regulated by G-proteins (120) and has many properties in common with the $\alpha_{1C\text{-}b}$ channel identified in canine myocytes.

Cl^- Channels

The role of chloride channels in GI motility has not been studied as extensively as the functions of K^+ or Ca^{2+} channels. However, in other smooth muscles, chloride conductances are important regulators of electrical excitability (121–124). Chloride currents contribute to cell volume regulation (125), cardiac action potential modulation (126), and transepithelial transport (127). Macroscopic chloride currents recorded from native cells have either a linear or an outwardly rectifying current-voltage relationship; however, some cloned Cl^- channels show either inwardly rectifying or more complex biophysical properties when expressed in heterologous systems (128). Regulation of Cl^- currents is diverse and β adrenergic (126) and α adrenergic pathways have been shown to be involved (129). In addition, chloride channels modulated by Ca^{2+} (130), ATP (through purinergic stimulation), and cell volume or mechanical stretch (131) have been recorded. Finally, in some cells a basal chloride conductance that contributes to resting membrane potential has been reported (132).

The gene products encoding Cl^- channels include GABA receptors, the cystic fibrosis transmembrane conductance regulator (CFTR), and the ClC gene family. CFTR is likely to encode the β adrenergic–regulated Cl^- current ($I_{Cl.camp}$) and may also be responsible for Cl^- currents regulated by ATP and PKC (activated through α adrenergic stimulation). CFTR is expressed in a variety of cell types, although GI smooth muscles have yet to be examined. The molecular equivalent of a niflumic acid–sensitive, Ca^{2+}-activated Cl^- conductance ($I_{Cl.Ca}$) has not been identified, and the role of this conductance in GI smooth muscles is unclear, although evidence for $I_{Cl.Ca}$ in ICC from the murine small intestine has been reported (31). Recently, a swelling-activated Cl^- conductance ($I_{Cl.swell}$) that may also be responsible for a basal Cl^- current ($I_{Cl.b}$) in some cell types has been cloned (ClC-3) (131, 133). A swelling-activated Cl^- current with properties identical to ClC-3 has been observed in GI myocytes. This current is activated under isotonic conditions ($I_{Cl.b}$) and sensitive to PKC stimulation (134). Niflumic acid had no effect on the swelling-activated current, which suggests this current is distinct from Ca^{2+}-activated Cl^- conductance ($I_{Cl.Ca}$). ClC-3 is expressed in GI myocytes and is likely to encode the swelling-activated current. PKC activation inhibited ClC-3 and has a similar effect on $I_{Cl.swell}$ and $I_{Cl.b}$ in smooth muscle cells. Therefore, this current could be an important component of the ACh response in this tissue.

CONCLUSIONS

Electrical rhythmicity in the gut helps to organize the phasic contractions that are essential for normal GI motility. Determination of the molecular entities responsible for the ionic mechanisms of rhythmicity will provide us with a clear understanding of the basic processes underlying motility. Identification of cloned ion channel genes and association of the gene products with native currents in GI smooth muscles lies at the heart of understanding the mechanisms of rhythmicity. Molecular studies are now contributing significantly to the discovery of ionic conductances not previously described in GI muscles and providing a powerful means of studying the regulation of these channels. The precise contribution of specific molecular entities is complex and will continue to evolve. The novel suggestions in this review regarding the role of ICC in generating pacemaker activity and propagating slow waves and the distinct roles of ICC and smooth muscle cells in the electrical activity of the GI tract should alter the focus of investigations into the mechanisms of rhythmicity and emphasize the need for cell-specific identification of molecular species. As we advance with cell-specific identification of ion channels and as the molecular structures of channels are more completely understood, including the role of chaperone proteins (135) and accessory subunits, the list of molecules involved in producing, propagating, and regulating electrical activity in the gut will undoubtedly grow.

ACKNOWLEDGMENTS

Research in our laboratories was supported by a Program Project Grant (DK41315) and Research Grants (HL52803 to BH and DK 40569 to KMS). We would like to acknowledge the work of all the investigators involved in the PPG and their individual laboratories.

Literature Cited

1. Szurszewski JH. 1987. Electrical basis for gastrointestinal motility. In *Physiology of the Gastrointestinal Tract*, pp. 383–422. New York: Raven. 2nd ed.
2. Bolton TB, Lang RJ, Takewaki T, Benham CD. 1985. Patch and whole-cell voltage clamp of single mammalian visceral and vascular smooth muscle cells. *Experientia* 41:887–94
3. Mitra R, Morad M. 1985. Ca^{2+} and Ca^{2+}-activated K^+ currents in mammalian gastric smooth muscle cells. *Science* 229:269–72
4. Hart PJ, Overturf KE, Russell SN, Carl A, Hume JR, et al. 1993. Cloning and expression of a $K_v1.2$ class delayed rectifier K^+ channel from canine colonic smooth muscle. *Proc. Natl. Acad. Sci. USA* 90:9659–63
5. Overturf KE, Russell SN, Carl A, Vogalis F, Hart PJ, et al. 1994. Cloning and characterization of a $K_v1.5$ delayed rectifier K^+ channel from vascular and visceral smooth muscles. *Am. J. Physiol.* 267:C1231–38
6. Sanders KM. 1996. A case for interstitial cells of Cajal as pacemakers and mediators of neurotransmission in the gastrointestinal tract. *Gastroenterology* 111:492–515
7. Bauer AJ, Sanders KM. 1986. Passive and active membrane properties of canine gastric antral circular muscles. *Am. J. Physiol.* 251:C268–73
8. Smith TK, Reed JB, Sanders KM. 1987. Interaction of two electrical pacemakers in muscularis of canine proximal colon. *Am. J. Physiol.* 252:C290–99
9. Smith TK, Reed JB, Sanders KM. 1987. Origin and propogation of electrical slow waves in circular muscle of canine proximal colon. *Am. J. Physiol.* 252:C215–24
10. Hara Y, Kubota M, Szurszewski JH. 1986. Electrophysiology of smooth muscle of the small intestine of some mammals. *J. Physiol.* 372:501–20
11. Xiong Z, Sperelakis N, Noffsinger A, Fenoglio-Preiser C. 1993. Changes in calcium channel current densities in rat colonic smooth muscle cells during development and aging. *Am. J. Physiol.* 265:C617–25
12. Thuneberg L. 1982. Interstitial cells of Cajal: intestinal pacemaker cells. *Adv. Anat. Embryol. Cell Biol.* 71:1–130
13. Christensen JA. 1992. Commentary on the morphological identification of interstitial cells of Cajal in the gut. *J. Auton. Nerv. Syst.* 37:75–88
14. Daniel EE, Berezin I. 1992. Interstial cells of Cajal: are they major players in control of gastrointestinal motility? *J. Gastrointest. Motil.* 4:1–24
15. Daniel EE, Posey-Daniel V. 1984. Neuromuscular structures in opossum esophagus: role of interstitial cells of Cajal. *Am. J. Physiol.* 246:G305–15
16. Huizinga JD, Thuneberg L, Vanderwinden JM, Rumessen JJ. 1997. Interstitial cells of Cajal as targets for pharmacological intervention in gastrointestinal motor disorders. *Trends Pharmacol. Sci.* 18:393–403
17. Langton P, Ward SM, Carl A, Norell MA, Sanders KM. 1989. Spontaneous electrical activity of interstitial cells of Cajal isolated from canine proximal colon. *Proc. Natl. Acad. Sci. USA* 86:7280–84
18. Ward SM, Burns AJ, Torihashi S, Sanders KM. 1994. Mutation of the protooncogene c-*kit* blocks development of interstitial cells and electrical rhythmicity in murine intestine. *J. Physiol.* 480:91–97
19. Huizinga JD, Thuneberg L, Kluppel M, Malysz J, Mikkelsen HB, Bernstein A. 1995. W/kit gene required for interstitial cells of Cajal and for intestinal pacemaker activity. *Nature* 373:347–49
20. Torihashi S, Ward SM, Nishikawa S-I, Nishi K, Kobayashi S, Sanders KM. 1995. c-*kit*-dependent development of interstitial cells and electrical activity in the murine gastrointestinal tract. *Cell Tissue Res.* 280:97–111
21. Burns AJ, Lomax AEJ, Torihashi S, Sanders KM, Ward SM. 1996. Interstitial cells of Cajal mediate inhibitory neurotransmission in the stomach. *Proc. Natl. Acad. Sci. USA* 93:12008–13
22. Prosser CL. 1978. Rhythmic potentials in intestinal muscle. *Fed. Proc.* 37:2153–57
23. Suzuki N, Prosser CL, Dahms V. 1986. Boundary cells between longitudinal and circular layers: essential for electrical slow waves in cat intestine. *Am. J. Physiol.* 250:G287–94

24. Liu LW, Huizinga JD. 1994. Canine colonic circular muscle generates action potentials without the pacemaker component. *Can. J. Physiol. Pharmacol.* 72:70–81
25. Keef KD, Ward SM, Stevens RJ, Frey BW, Sanders KM. 1992. Electrical and mechanical effects of acetylcholine and substance P in subregions of canine colon. *Am. J. Physiol.* 262:G298–307
26. Sanders KM, Burke EP, Carl A, Cole WC, Langton P, Ward S. 1990. Mechanism of electrical rhythmicity in colonic smooth muscle: an hypothesis. *Prog. Clin. Biol. Res.* 327:307–22
27. Ward SM, Burns AJ, Torihashi S, Harney SC, Sanders KM. 1995. Impaired development of interstitial cells and intestinal electrical rhythmicity in *steel* mutants. *Am. J. Physiol.* 269:C1577–85
28. Sanders KM, Publicover NG. 1989. Electrophysiology of the gastric musculature. In *Handbook of Physiology: The Gastrointestinal System*, ed. S Schultz, JD Wood, pp. 187–216. Bethesda, MD: Am. Physiol. Soc.
29. Lee HK, Sanders KM. 1993. Comparison of ionic currents from interstitial cells and smooth muscle cells of canine colon. *J. Physiol.* 460:135–52
30. Hagiwara N, Irisawa H, Kameyama M. 1988. Contribution of two types of calcium currents to the pacemaker potentials of rabbit sino-atrial node cells. *J. Physiol.* 395:233–53
31. Tokutomi N, Maeda H, Tokutomi Y, Sato D, Sugita M, et al. 1995. Rhythmic Cl^- current and physiological roles of the intestinal c-kit-positive cells. *Pflügers Arch.* 431:169–77
32. Malysz J, Richardson D, Farraway L, Christen MO, Huizinga JD. 1995. Generation of slow wave type action potentials in the mouse small intestine involves a non-L-type calcium channel. *Can. J. Physiol. Pharmacol.* 73:1502–11

32a. Faruggia G. 1999. Ionic conductances in gastrointestinal smooth muscles and interstitial cells of Cajal. *Annu. Rev. Physiol.* 61:45–84

33. Carl A. 1995. Multiple components of delayed rectifier K^+ current in canine colonic myocytes. *J. Physiol.* 484:339–53
34. Stuhmer W, Ruppersberg JP, Schroter KH, Sakmann B, Stocker M, et al. 1989. Molecular basis of functional diversity of voltage-gated potassium channels in mammalian brain. *EMBO J.* 8:3235–44
35. Chandy KG, Gutman GA. 1993. Nomenclature for mammalian potassium channel genes. *Trends Pharmacol. Sci.* 14:434
36. Chandy KG, Gutman GA. 1995. Voltage-gated K^+ channel genes. In *Ligand and Voltage-Gated Ion Channels*, ed. A North, pp. 1–71. Boca Raton, FL: CRC
37. Patel AJ, Lazdunski M, Honore E. 1997. Kv2.1/Kv9.3, a novel ATP-dependent delayed-rectifier K^+ channel in oxygen-sensitive pulmonary artery myocytes. *EMBO J.* 16:6615–25
38. Hugnot JP, Salinas M, Lesage F, Guillemare E, De Weille J, et al. 1996. Kv8.1, a new neuronal potassium channel subunit with specific inhibitory properties towards Shab and Shaw channels. *EMBO J.* 15:3322–31
39. Salinas M, De Weille J, Guillemare E, Lazdunski M, Hugnot JP. 1997. Modes of regulation of shab K^+ channel activity by the Kv8.1 subunit. *J. Biol. Chem.* 272:8774–80
40. Salinas M, Duprat F, Heurteaux C, Hugnot JP, Lazdunski M. 1997. New modulatory alpha subunits for mammalian Shab K^+ channels. *J. Biol. Chem.* 272:24371–79
41. Beckh S, Pongs O. 1990. Members of the RCK potassium channel family are differentially expressed in the rat nervous system. *EMBO J.* 9:777–82
42. Russell SN, Publicover NG, Hart PJ, Carl A, Hume JR, et al. 1994. Block by 4-aminopyridine of a $K_v1.2$ delayed rectifier K^+ current expressed in *Xenopus* oocytes. *J. Physiol.* 481:571–84
43. Ruppersberg JP, Schroter KH, Sakmann B, Stocker M, Sewing S, Pongs O. 1990. Heteromultimeric channels formed by rat brain potassium-channel proteins. [see Comments] *Nature* 345:535–37
44. Wang H, Kunkel DD, Martin TM, Schwartzkroin PA, Tempel BL. 1993. Heteromultimeric K^+ channels in terminal and juxtaparanodal regions of neurons. *Nature* 365:75–79
45. Russell SN, Overturf KE, Horowitz B. 1994. Heterotetramer formation and charybdotoxin sensitivity of two K^+ channels cloned from smooth muscle. *Am. J. Physiol.* 267:C1729–33
46. Schmalz F, Kinsella JL, Koh SD, Vogalis F, Schneider A, Flynn ERM, et al. 1998. Molecular identification of a component of delayed rectifier current in gastrointestinal smooth muscles. *Am. J. Physiol.* 274:G901–11
47. Po S, Snyders DJ, Baker R, Tamkun MM, Bennett PB. 1992. Functional expression of an inactivating potassium channel

cloned from human heart. *Circ. Res.* 71:732–36
48. Scott VE, Rettig J, Parcej DN, Keen JN, Findlay JB, et al. 1994. Primary structure of a beta subunit of alpha-dendrotoxin-sensitive K^+ channels from bovine brain. *Proc. Natl. Acad. Sci. USA* 91:1637–41
49. Rettig J, Heinemann SH, Wunder F, Lorra C, Parcej DN, et al. 1994. Inactivation properties of voltage-gated K^+ channels altered by presence of beta-subunit. *Nature* 369:289–94
50. McIntosh P, Southan AP, Akhtar S, Sidera C, Ushkaryov Y, et al. 1997. Modification of rat brain Kv1.4 channel gating by association with accessory Kvβ1.1 and β2.1 subunits. *Pflügers Arch.* 435:43–54
51. England SK, Uebele VN, Shear H, Kodali J, Bennett PB, Tamkun MM. 1995. Characterization of a voltage-gated K^+ channel β subunit expressed in human heart. *Proc. Natl. Acad. Sci. USA* 92:6309–13
52. Sewing S, Roeper J, Pongs O. 1996. Kv beta 1 subunit binding specific for shaker-related potassium channel alpha subunits. *Neuron* 16:455–63
53. McCormack K, McCormack T, Tanouye M, Rudy B, Stühmer W. 1995. Alternative splicing of the human *Shaker* K^+ channel β1 gene and functional expression of the β2 gene product. *FEBS Lett.* 370:32–36
54. Fink M, Duprat F, Lesage F, Heurteaux C, Romey G, et al. 1996. A new K^+ channel β subunit to specifically enhance Kv2.2 (CDRK) expression. *J. Biol. Chem.* 271:26341–48
55. Roeper J, Sewing S, Zhang Y, Sommer T, Wanner SG, Pongs O. 1998. NIP domain prevents N-type inactivation in voltage-gated potassium channels. *Nature* 391:390–93
56. Thornbury KD, Ward SM, Sanders KM. 1992. Outward currents in longitudinal colonic muscle cells contribute to spiking electrical behavior. *Am. J. Physiol.* 263:C237–45
57. Thornbury KD, Ward SM, Sanders KM. 1992. Participation of fast-activating voltage-dependent K currents in electrical slow waves of colonic circular muscle. *Am. J. Physiol.* 263:C226–36
58. Szurszewski JH. 1975. Mechanism of action of pentagastrin and acetylcholine on the longitudinal muscle of the canine antrum. *J. Physiol.* 252:335–61
59. Sanders KM. 1983. Excitation-contraction coupling without Ca^{2+} action potentials in small intestine. *Am. J. Physiol.* 244:C356–61
60. Inoue R, Chen S. 1993. Physiology of muscarinic receptor-operated nonselective cation channels in guinea-pig ileal smooth muscle. *Experimentia* 66:261–68
61. Zhang LB, Horowitz B, Buxton IL. 1991. Muscarinic receptors in canine colonic circular smooth muscle. I. Coexistence of M2 and M3 subtypes *Mol. Pharmacology* 40:943–51
62. Lechleiter J, Hellmiss R, Duerson K, Ennulat D, David N, et al. 1990. Distinct sequence elements control the specificity of G protein activation by muscarinic acetylcholine receptor subtypes. *EMBO J.* 9:4381–90
63. Vogalis F, Ward M, Horowitz B. 1995. Suppression of two cloned smooth muscle-derived delayed rectifier potassium channels by cholinergic agonists and phorbol esters. *Mol. Pharmacol.* 48:1015–23
64. Farrugia G, Miller SM, Rich A, Liu X, Maines MD, et al. 1998. Distribution of heme oxygenase and effects of exogenous carbon monoxide in canine jejunum. *Am. J. Physiol.* 274:G350–58
65. Miller SM, Farrugia G, Schmalz PF, Ermilov LG, Maines MD, Szurszewski JH. 1998. Heme oxygenase 2 is present in interstitial cell networks of the mouse small intestine. *Gastroenterology* 114:239–44
66. Koh SD, Campbell JD, Carl A, Sanders KM. 1995. Nitric oxide activates multiple potassium channels in canine colonic smooth muscle. *J. Physiol.* 489:735–43
67. Shuttleworth CWR, Koh SD, Bayginov O, Sanders KM. 1996. Activation of delayed rectifier potassium channels in canine proximal colon by vasoactive intestinal peptide. *J. Physiol.* 493:651–63
68. Atkinson NS, Robertson GA, Ganetzky B. 1991. A component of calcium-activated potassium channels encoded by the *Drosophila slo* locus. *Science* 253:551–55
69. Pallanck L, Ganetzky B. 1994. Cloning and characterization of human and mouse homologs of the *Drosophila* calcium-activated potassium channel gene *slowpoke*. *Hum. Mol. Genet.* 3:1239–43
70. Tseng-Crank J, Foster CD, Krause JD, Mertz R, Godinot N, et al. 1994. Cloning expression and distribution of functionally distinct Ca^{2+}-activated K^+ channel isoforms from human brain. *Neuron* 13:1315–30
71. McCobb DP, Fowler NL, Featherstone T, Lingle CJ, Saito M, et al. 1995. A human calcium-activated potassium channel gene expressed in vascular smooth muscle. *Am. J. Physiol.* 269:H767–77

72. Meera P, Wallner M, Song M, Toro L. 1997. Large conductance voltage- and calcium-dependent K^+ channel a distinct member of voltage-dependent ion channels with seven N-terminal transmembrane segments (S0-S6), an extracellular N terminus and an intracellular (S9–S10) C terminus. *Proc. Natl. Acad. Sci. USA* 94:14066–71
73. Schreiber M, Salkoff L. 1997. A novel calcium-sensing domain in the BK channel. *Biophys. J.* 73:1355–63
74. Adelman JP, Shen K-Z, Kavanaugh MP, Warren RA, Wu Y-N, et al. 1992. Calcium-activated potassium channels expressed from cloned complementary DNAs. *Neuron* 9:209–16
75. Lagrutta A, Shen K-Z, North RA, Adelman JP. 1994. Functional differences among alternatively spliced variants of *Slowpoke* a *Drosophila* calcium-activated potassium channel. *J. Biol. Chem.* 269: 20347–51
76. McManus OB, Helms LMH, Pallanck L, Ganetzky B, Swanson R, Leonard RJ. 1995. Functional role of the β subunit of high conductance calcium-activated potassium channels. *Neuron* 14:645–50
77. Knaus HG, Folander K, Garcia-Calvo M, Garcia ML, Kaczorowski GJ, et al. 1994. Primary sequence and immunological characterization of beta-subunit of high conductance Ca^{2+}-activated K^+ channel from smooth muscle. *J. Biol. Chem.* 269:17274–78
78. Esguerra M, Wang J, Foster CD, Adelman JP, North RA, Levitan IB. 1994. Cloned Ca^{2+}-dependent K^+ channel modulated by a functionally associated protein kinase. *Nature* 369:563–65
79. Vogalis F, Vincent T, Qureshi I, Schmalz F, Ward MW, et al. 1996. Cloning and expression of the large-conductance Ca^{2+}-activated K^+ channel from colonic smooth muscle. *Am. J. Physiol.* 271: G629–39
80. Carl A, Sanders KM. 1989. Ca^{2+}-activated potassium channels of canine colonic myocytes. *Am. J. Physiol.* 257: C470–80
81. Wallner M, Meera P, Ottolia M, Kacsorowski GJ, Latorre R, et al. 1995. Characterization of and modulation by a beta-subunit of a human maxi KCa channel cloned from myometrium. *Recept. Channels* 3:185–99
82. Hong SJ, Roan YF, Chang CC. 1997. Spontaneous activity of guinea pig ileum longitudinal muscle regulated by Ca^{2+}-activated K^+ channel. *Am. J. Physiol.* 272: G962–71
83. Vogalis F, Goyal RK. 1997. Activation of small conductance Ca^{2+}-dependent K^+ channels by purinergic agonists in smooth muscle cells of the mouse ileum. *J. Physiol.* 502:497–508
84. Koh SD, Dick GM, Sanders KM. 1997. Small-conductance Ca^{2+}-dependent K^+ channels activated by ATP in murine colonic smooth muscle. *Am. J. Physiol.* 273:C2010–21
85. Kohler M, Hirschberg B, Bond CT, Kinzie JM, Marrion NV, et al. 1996. Small-conductance calcium-activated potassium channels from mammalian brain. [see Comments] *Science* 273:1709–14
86. Ishii TM, Maylie J, Adelman JP. 1997. Determinants of apamin and d-tubocurarine block in SK potassium channels. *J. Biol. Chem.* 272:23195–200
87. Doupnik CA, Davidson N, Lester HA. 1995. The inward rectifier potassium channel family. *Curr. Opin. Neurobiol.* 5: 268–77
88. Kubo Y, Baldwin TJ, Jan YN, Jan LY. 1993. Primary structure and functional expression of a mouse inward rectifier potassium channel. *Nature* 362:127–33
89. Koyama H, Morishige K-I, Takahashi N, Zanelli JS, Fass DN, Kurachi Y. 1994. Molecular cloning functional expression and localization of a novel inward rectifier potassium channel in the rat brain. *FEBS Lett.* 341:303–7
90. Morishige K-I, Takahashi N, Jahangir A, Yamada M, Koyama H, et al. 1994. Molecular cloning and functional expression of a novel brain-specific inward rectifier potassium channel. *FEBS Lett.* 346:251–56
91. Henry P, Pearson WL, Nichols CG. 1996. Protein kinase C inhibition of cloned inward rectifier (HRK1/KIR2.3) K^+ channels expressed in Xenopus oocytes. *J. Physiol.* 495:681–88
92. Deleted in proof
93. Deleted in proof
94. Dascal N. 1997. Signalling via the G protein-activated K^+ channels. *Cell. Signal* 9:551–73
95. Kurachi Y, Nakajima T, Sugimoto T. 1986. Acetylcholine activation of K^+ channels in cell-free membrane of atrial cells. *Am. J. Physiol.* 251:H681–84
96. Logothetis DE, Kurachi Y, Galper J, Neer EJ, Clapham DE. 1987. The beta gamma subunits of GTP-binding proteins activate the muscarinic K^+ channel in heart. *Nature* 325:321–26

97. Krapivinsky G, Gordon EA, Wickman K, Velimirovic B, Krapivinsky L, Clapham DE. 1995. The G-protein-gated atrial K^+ channel I_{KACh} is a heteromultimer of two inwardly rectifying K^+-channel proteins. *Nature* 374:135–41
98. Quayle JM, Nelson MT, Standen NB. 1997. ATP-sensitive and inwardly rectifying potassium channels in smooth muscle. *Physiol. Rev.* 77:1165–232
99. Katayama N, Huang SM, Tomita T, Brading AF. 1993. Effects of cromakalim on the electrical slow wave in the circular muscle of guinea-pig gastric antrum. *Br. J. Pharmacol.* 109:1097–100
100. Franck H, Puschmann A, Allescher HD. 1994. Functional evidence for a glibenclamide-sensitive K+ channel in rat ileal smooth muscle. *Eur. J. Pharmacol.* 271:379–86
101. Faraway L, Huizinga JD. 1991. Potassium channel activation by cromakalim affects the slow wave type action potential of colonic smooth muscle. *J. Pharmacol. Exp. Ther.* 257:35–41
102. Post JM, Stevens R, Sanders KM, Hume JR. 1991. Effect of cromakalim and lemakalim on K^+ and Ca^{2+} currents in colonic smooth muscle. *Am. J. Physiol.* 260:C375–82
103. Inagaki N, Gonoi T, Clement JP, Namba N, Inazawa J, et al. 1995. Reconstitution of I_{KATP}: an inward rectifier subunit plus the sulfonylurea receptor. [see Comments] *Science* 270:1166–70
104. Inagaki N, Gonoi T, Clement JP, Wang CZ, Aguilar-Bryan L, et al. 1996. A family of sulfonylurea receptors determines the pharmacological properties of ATP-sensitive K^+ channels. *Neuron* 16:1011–17
105. Yokoshiki H, Sunagawa M, Seki T, Sperelakis N. 1998. ATP-sensitive K^+ channels in pancreatic cardiac and vascular smooth muscle cells. *Am. J. Physiol.* 274:C25–37
106. Isomoto S, Kondo C, Yamada M, Matsumoto S, Higashiguchi O, et al. 1996. A novel sulfonylurea receptor forms with BIR (Kir6.2) a smooth muscle type ATP-sensitive K^+ channel. *J. Biol. Chem.* 271: 24321–24
107. Kajioka S, Kitamura K, Kuriyama H. 1991. Guanosine diphosphate activates an adenosine 5′-triphosphate-sensitive K^+ channel in the rabbit portal vein. *J. Physiol.* 444:397–418
108. Zhang H, Bolton TB. 1995. Activation by intracellular GDP metabolic inhibition and pinacidil of a glibenclamide-sensitive K-channel in smooth muscle cells of rat mesenteric artery. *Br. J. Pharmacol.* 114:662–72
109. Zhang HL, Bolton TB. 1996. Two types of ATP-sensitive potassium channels in rat portal vein smooth muscle cells. *Br. J. Pharmacol.* 118:105–14
110. Fan Z, Chutkow WA, McClelland DL, Burant CF, Makielski JC. 1998. Nucleotide gating of ATP-sensitive K channels formed by variants of SUR1 and SUR2 isoforms co-expressed with Kir6.2. *Biophys. J.* 74:A18 (Abstr.)
111. Koh SD, Kuenzli KA, Rae M, Keef K, Horowitz B, Sanders KM. 1998. Basal activation of ATP-sensitive potassium channels in murine colonic smooth muscle cells. *Biophys. J.* In press
112. Ozaki H, Gerthoffer WT, Publicover NG, Fusetani N, Sanders KM. 1991. Time-dependent changes in Ca^{2+} sensitivity during phasic contraction of canine antral smooth muscle. *J. Physiol.* 440:207–24
113. Vogalis F, Publicover NG, Hume JR, Sanders KM. 1991. Relationship between calcium current and cytosolic calcium in canine gastric smooth muscle cells. *Am. J. Physiol.* 260:C1012–18
114. Catterall WA. 1996. Molecular properties of sodium and calcium channels. *J. Bioenerg. Biomembr.* 28:219–30
115. Perez-Reyes E, Schneider T. 1995. Molecular biology of calcium channels. *Kidney Int.* 48:1111–24
116. Mori Y, Mikala G, Varadi G, Kobayashi T, Koch S, et al. 1996. Molecular pharmacology of voltage-dependent calcium channels. *Jpn. J. Pharmacol.* 72:83–109
117. Birnbaumer L, Campbell KP, Catterall WA, Harpold MM, Hofmann F, et al. 1994. The naming of voltage-gated calcium channels. *Neuron* 13:505–6
118. Rich A, Kenyon JL, Hume JR, Overturf K, Horowitz B, Sanders KM. 1993. Dihydropyridine-sensitive calcium channels expressed in canine colonic smooth muscle cells. *Am. J. Physiol.* 264:C745–54
119. Farrugia G, Rich A, Rae JL, Sarr MG, Szurszewski JH. 1995. Calcium currents in human and canine jejunal circular smooth muscle cells. *Gastroenterology* 109:707–17
120. Farrugia G. 1997. G-protein regulation of an L-type calcium channel current in canine jejunal circular smooth muscle. *J. Membr. Biol.* 160:39–46
121. Criddle DN, de MR, Greenwood IA, Large WA. 1997. Inhibitory action of niflumic acid on noradrenaline- and 5-hydroxytryptamine-induced pressor

responses in the isolated mesenteric vascular bed of the rat. *Br. J. Pharmacol.* 120:813–18

122. Greenwood IA, Helliwell RM, Large WA. 1997. Modulation of Ca^{2+}-activated Cl^- currents in rabbit portal vein smooth muscle by an inhibitor of mitochondrial Ca^{2+} uptake. *J Physiol.* 505:53–54
123. Criddle DN, de MR, Greenwood IA, Large WA. 1996. Effect of niflumic acid on noradrenaline-induced contractions of the rat aorta. *Br. J. Pharmacol.* 118:1065–71
124. Nelson MT, Conway MA, Knot HJ, Brayden JE. 1997. Chloride channel blockers inhibit myogenic tone in rat cerebral arteries. *J. Physiol.* 502:259–64
125. Okada Y. 1997. Volume expansion-sensing outward-rectifier Cl^- channel: fresh start to the molecular identity and volume sensor. *Am. J Physiol.* 273:C755–89
126. Harvey RD, Hume JR. 1989. Autonomic regulation of a chloride current in heart. *Science* 244:983–85
127. Carroll TP, Schwiebert EM, Guggino WB. 1993. CFTR: structure and function. *Cell. Physiol. Biochem.* 3:388–99
128. Jentsch TJ, Günther W, Pusch M, Schwappach B. 1995. Properties of voltage-gated chloride channels of the ClC gene family. *J. Physiol.* 482(Suppl. P):19–25S
129. Coca-Prados M, Anguita J, Chalfant ML, Civan MM. 1995. PKC-sensitive Cl^- channels associated with ciliary epithelial homologue of pICln. *Am. J Physiol.* 268:C572–79
130. Large WA, Wang Q. 1996. Characteristics and physiological role of the Ca^{2+}-activated Cl^- conductance in smooth muscle. *Am. J. Physiol.* 271:C435–54
131. Duan D, Winter C, Cowley S, Hume JR, Horowitz B. 1997. Molecular identification of a volume-regulated chloride channel. *Nature* 390:417–21
132. Duan D, Hume JR, Nattel S. 1997. Evidence that outwardly rectifying Cl^- channels underlie volume-regulated Cl^- currents in heart. *Circ. Res.* 80:103–13
133. Yamazaki J, Duan D, Janiak R, Kuenzli K, Horowitz B, Hume JR. 1998. Functional and molecular expression of volume-regulated chloride channels in canine vascular smooth muscle cells. *J. Physiol.* 507:729–36
134. Dick GM, Kuenzli KA, Horowitz B, Hume JR, Sanders KM. 1998. Cl^- current activated by cell swelling in visceral smooth muscle. *Biophys. J.* 74:A99 (Abstr.)
135. Xia X, Hirschberg B, Smolik S, Forte M, Adelman JP. 1998. dSLo interacting protein 1, a novel protein that interacts with large-conductance calcium-activated potassium channels. *J. Neurosci.* 18:2360–69
136. Sanders KM, Burke EP, Carl A, Cole WC, Langton P, Ward SM. 1990. *Frontiers in Smooth Muscle Research.* New York: Liss

Annu. Rev. Physiol. 1999. 61:45–84

IONIC CONDUCTANCES IN GASTROINTESTINAL SMOOTH MUSCLES AND INTERSTITIAL CELLS OF CAJAL

G. Farrugia
Division of Gastroenterology and Hepatology, Mayo Clinic and Mayo Foundation, Rochester, Minnesota 55905; e-mail: farrugia.gianrico@mayo.edu

KEY WORDS: ion channels, patch clamp, review

ABSTRACT

Ion channels are the unitary elements that underlie electrical activity of gastrointestinal smooth muscle cells and of interstitial cells of Cajal. The result of ion channel activity in the gastrointestinal smooth muscle layers is a rhythmic change in membrane potential that in turn underlies events leading to organized motility patterns. Gastrointestinal smooth muscle cells and interstitial cells of Cajal express a wide variety of ion channels that are tightly regulated. This review summarizes 20 years of data obtained from patch-clamp studies on gastrointestinal smooth muscle cells and interstitial cells, with a focus on regulation.

INTRODUCTION

The function of gastrointestinal smooth muscle is twofold: to mix intestinal content and thereby aid digestion, and to propel intestinal content. Specialized areas of the gastrointestinal tract also function as barriers (sphincters). For gastrointestinal smooth muscle to perform its function it must be able to contract and relax in synchronized patterns for the life span of the organism. Fundamental to the ability to contract is electrical excitability, with changes in smooth muscle contractile activity closely mirroring changes in smooth muscle membrane potential. The functional unit underlying the setting of the membrane potential is the ion channel. Ion channels are pores in the cell membrane

0066-4278/99/0315-0045$08.00

that allow the rapid transfer of ions across the cell membrane. Ion channels are the elemental excitable unit in all cells, including smooth muscle. Individual ion channels can respond to a specific stimulus that can be electrical, such as a membrane potential change; chemical, such as a neurotransmitter; or mechanical. The response to a stimulus is an opening or closing of the pore, altering the permeability of the ion channel and changing the flux of ions across the membrane. Most ion channels are selective; that is, they have a selective permeability to a particular ion or class of ions. The main classes of ion channels are Na^+, K^+, Ca^{2+}, nonselective cation, and anion channels. This review summarizes our knowledge of the types of ion channels found in gastrointestinal smooth muscle and interstitial cells of Cajal, describes their biophysical properties and their regulatory mechanisms, and discusses their potential role in gastrointestinal physiology. I have elected to use information only obtained by direct measurement of whole-cell or single-channel currents. I have avoided detailed kinetic analysis of each channel type, as such information is best suited for more focused reviews. On the other hand, I include, whenever possible, experimental conditions and drug doses to aid experimentalists. Finally, I only discuss the regulatory pathways and biophysical properties of gastrointestinal smooth muscle ion channels, even if substantial relevant information exists outside of the gastrointestinal tract.

CALCIUM CHANNELS

Introduction

Calcium (Ca^{2+}) plays an important role in the function of all cell types but plays an even more central role in muscle cells. Ca^{2+} triggers contraction in smooth muscle and is a ubiquitous second messenger, transducing signals from a variety of compounds including neurotransmitters, hormones, and growth factors. Opening of Ca^{2+} channels results in a rapid rise in intracellular Ca^{2+}, with an often greater than tenfold increase in cytosolic Ca^{2+} concentration.

Channel Classification

The current classification of Ca^{2+} channels includes L-type (Ca_L, high threshold) channels, T-type (Ca_T, low threshold), N-type, P-type, Q-type, and R-type. P-, Q-, and R-type Ca^{2+} channels have not been described in gastrointestinal smooth muscle, and there is only one report of N-type-like Ca^{2+} channels, from longitudinal muscle cells of the rat ileum. Therefore, this section focuses on L- and T-type Ca^{2+} channels.

Most cell types that express T-type Ca^{2+} channels also express L-type Ca^{2+} channels. In general, the maximal amplitude of current generated by T-type Ca^{2+} channels is tenfold less than the current generated by L-type Ca^{2+} channels.

It is therefore important to separate the two currents to accurately determine the channel types present in gastrointestinal smooth muscle. Maneuvers to separate the two channel types include the following (modified from 1):

1. Holding voltage. T-type Ca^{2+} channels activate at more negative potentials than L-type Ca^{2+} channels and inactivate at more negative potentials. Maximal current is also reached at more negative potentials. Therefore, at a holding voltage of −100 mV, both channel types are available for activation, whereas at −40 to −50 mV, L-type Ca^{2+} channels are still mostly available for activation, and T-type Ca^{2+} channels are mostly inactivated.

2. Permeability. The whole-cell current recorded from L-type Ca^{2+} channels with Ba^{2+} as the charge carrier is several-fold larger than with Ca^{2+} as the charge carrier. The size of T-type calcium channel current is unchanged when external Ca^{2+} is replaced with Ba^{2+}.

3. Kinetics. T-type Ca^{2+} channels inactivate faster than L-type Ca^{2+} channels and deactivate slower.

4. Blockers and activators. 1,4-Dihydropyridines such as nifedipine and related compounds are relatively specific blockers, and BayK 8644 is a relatively specific activator for L-type Ca^{2+} channels at concentrations of 10 μM or less. T-type Ca^{2+} channels tend to be more sensitive to Ni^{2+} and less sensitive to Cd^{2+} than L-type Ca^{2+} channels.

L-TYPE Ca^{2+} CHANNELS

Introduction

L-type Ca^{2+} channels are required for gastrointestinal smooth muscle contractility. Addition of nifedipine, an L-type Ca^{2+} channel blocker, to intestinal smooth muscle strips results in cessation of contractile activity. L-type Ca^{2+} channels are needed to allow Ca^{2+} entry into smooth muscle cells to sustain contractile activity. Therefore, it is not surprising that L-type Ca^{2+} channels have been found in all regions of the gastrointestinal tract.

Channel Structure

L-type Ca^{2+} channels are made up of at least five subunits, α_1, α_2, β, δ, and γ. The α_1-subunit (195 kDa) is the major transmembrane component of the L-type Ca^{2+} channel. This subunit includes the ion conductance pore, and its expression alone is enough to form a channel that conducts Ca^{2+}. The α_2-subunit is a ≈28-kDa heavily glycosylated protein and in smooth muscle is highly conserved. In cardiac Ca^{2+} channels, coexpression of the $\alpha_2\delta$-subunit with the

α_1-subunit decreased activation time (2). β- and γ-subunits have not been cloned from gastrointestinal smooth muscle. Coexpression of the cardiac α_1-subunit and the brain β-subunit resulted in a marked increase in activation rate, a negative shift in the voltage of peak inward current, and an increase in peak inward current (reviewed in 1). No non-skeletal γ-subunit has been cloned.

Single Channel Conductance

An initial study on gastrointestinal L-type single channel Ca^{2+} currents found a 30-pS Ca^{2+} channel in cell-attached patches from guinea pig taenia coli with 50-mM Ba^{2+} as the charge carrier in the bath (3). Another study found, in cell-attached patches from guinea pig taenia coli, a 25-pS channel with 50-mM Ba^{2+} as the charge carrier in the bath and 140-mM Cs^{+} in the pipette solution, as well as a 12-pS Ca^{2+} channel (4). The 25-pS channel was blocked by nifedipine (2 μM), suggesting that it was an L-type Ca^{2+} channel. In contrast, the 12-pS channel was not affected by nifedipine, was not blocked by Cd^{2+} (10 μM in pipette), and exhibited rapid inactivation. The authors suggested that the smaller conductance channel may represent a T-type Ca^{2+} channel. A 20-pS nifedipine-sensitive Ca^{2+} channel was reported from smooth muscle cells of the rabbit ileum with 50-mM Ba^{2+} as the charge carrier (5), and 2 nifedipine-sensitive Ca^{2+} channels were identified from canine colonic circular smooth muscle cells with 80-mM Ba^{2+} as the charge carrier (6). One channel had a conductance of 10 pS and was infrequently seen, whereas the dominant channel had a conductance of 21 pS. At a molecular level, only the class C α_1-subunit and only one splice variant class C α_1-subunit, rbC-II, were present. A single-channel conductance of 17 pS was reported in canine and human jejunal circular smooth muscle cells, with 80-mM Ba^{2+} as the charge carrier (7). Nifedipine (1 μM) inhibited nearly all channel activity (Figure 1).

Whole-Cell Current Kinetics and Regulation

The whole-cell current that results from the opening of any single channel conductance, including single Ca^{2+} channels in smooth muscle cells, can be modeled as:

$$I = N \cdot i \cdot P_o,$$

where I is the whole-cell current, N the number of channels in the cell membrane, i the unitary current through a single channel, and P_o the probability that a channel is open. P_o is voltage dependent and can be subdivided into the probability that a channel is available to be opened and the probability that a channel that is available to be opened is open. The relationship between steady-state activation and inactivation gives rise to the whole-cell window current, i.e. the current that would be expected to flow under steady-state conditions at a

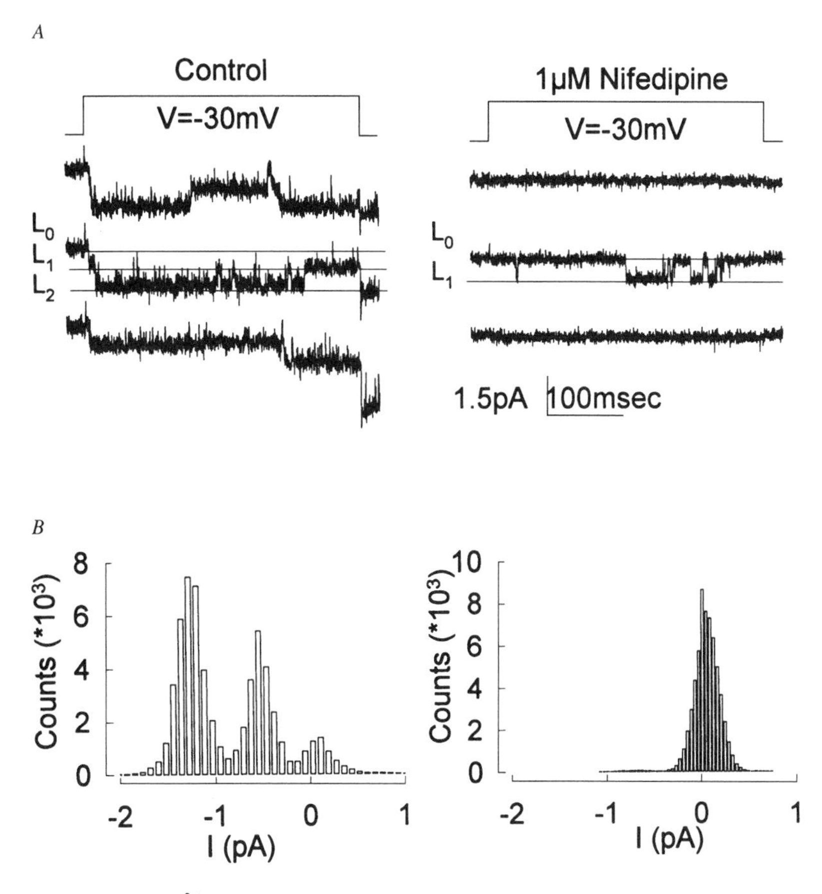

Figure 1 L-type Ca^{2+} channel activity recorded from a canine jejunal circular smooth muscle cell bathed in 150 mM KCl and 80 mM Ba^{2+} as the charge carrier. Single channel activity recorded from an on-cell patch before (*A*) and after nifedipine (*B*). At least two channels are present in this patch (L_0 = closed, L_1 = 1 channel, L_2 = 2 channels). As can be seen from the histograms, nifedipine blocked nearly all channel activity ($NP_o = 0.99$ before, $NP_o = 0.0004$ after nifedipine) (7).

particular voltage. The window current is useful as it allows assumptions to be made on the size of the steady-state Ca^{2+} current at a particular voltage, such as at the resting membrane potential of a gastrointestinal smooth muscle cell and the change that can be expected if the cell membrane potential were to change. The voltage dependence of activation and inactivation can be fit by a Boltzmann equation:

$$I/I_{max} = 1/(1 + \exp[V_h - V]/k),$$

where I is the current, I_{max} the maximal inward current, V is the test activating potential, V_h the test potential eliciting half-maximal I, and k the slope factor. The resulting curve is sigmoidal. Steady-state inactivation can also be fit by a Boltzmann equation, again resulting in a sigmoidal curve. In canine jejunal circular smooth muscle cells, steady-state activation was fit by a single Boltzmann curve with a V_h of −6 mV and a k of −5.7 mV (7). Inactivation was also fit with a V_h of −36 mV and a k of 14 mV. The two curves resulted in a peak window current at about −15 mV. The records were obtained with 80 mM Ba^{2+} as a charge carrier. The voltage sensed by L-type Ca^{2+} channels is modified by the surface charge screening effects of cations in the bath solutions. In canine and human jejunal circular smooth muscle cells, 80 mM Ba^{2+} results in a shift in the activation-voltage curve in the depolarization direction of about 25 mV.

The temperature-dependence of the L-type Ca^{2+} channel current in gastrointestinal smooth muscle appears to be similar to that reported from other smooth muscle cells. The amplitude of the inward current carried by Ba^{2+} increases by ≈3 in ventricular myocytes for a 10°C rise in temperature (Q_{10}) (8) and by 2.1–2.4 in skeletal muscle. In guinea pig taenae coli myocytes, a Q_{10} of 1.7 (9) was reported and in canine jejunal circular smooth muscle cells, the reported Q_{10} was ≈2.1 (10).

RUNDOWN L-type Ca^{2+} channel current runs down during traditional whole-cell patch-clamp recordings. Rundown may be preceded by a brief run-up period where the peak inward current increases over a short time period (≈5 min), suggesting that it is secondary to wash out of cytoplasmic contents that suppress L-type Ca^{2+} channel current. The mechanism of rundown is unclear. Contributing factors include the effects of entry of cations, such as Ca^{2+}, on intracellular phosphatases or proteases. In non-smooth muscle cells, Ca^{2+}-dependent protease inhibitors reduce rundown. Phosphatase inhibitors may also reduce rundown. Calyculin A, an inhibitor phosphatase types 1 and 2A, induces an increase in inward current recorded from canine jejunal circular smooth muscle cells (11). In a variety of cell types, including gastrointestinal smooth muscle (12), intracellular ATP reduces rundown probably by several mechanisms including favoring phosphorylation, Ca^{2+} regulation, and protecting Ca^{2+} channels from enzymatic hydrolysis (1).

In excised patches, rundown is about tenfold faster than rundown of whole-cell currents, which makes it difficult to record L-type Ca^{2+} channel current in excised patches. As in whole-cell currents, potential mechanisms include dephosphorylation, proteolysis, and change in intracellular Ca^{2+} and G-protein concentrations. There may be differences between the mechanisms of rundown in gastrointestinal smooth muscle cells and cardiac smooth muscle cells. In canine colonic smooth muscle cells, addition of BayK 8644 (1 μM) and EGTA (5 mM) to the bath enables prolonged single-channel recordings from excised patches (6), whereas a similar approach was unsuccessful in guinea pig ventricular cells (13).

CALCIUM Chelation of intracellular Ca^{2+} with EGTA or BAPTA reduces inactivation, which suggests that a rise in intracellular Ca^{2+} increases inactivation of L-type Ca^{2+} channels. More evidence for the role of intracellular Ca^{2+} in altering the behavior of L-type Ca^{2+} channels is the marked reduction in inactivation when Ba^{2+} is substituted for Ca^{2+} as the charge carrier, while peak inward current is increased. This suggests that L-type Ca^{2+} channels are more permeable to Ba^{2+} than to Ca^{2+} and that Ca^{2+} stimulates inactivation. For example, in guinea pig gastric myocytes (14) with Ca^{2+} as the charge carrier, inactivation was fitted with two exponentials of $\tau \approx 53$ and $\tau \approx 175$ ms. With Ba^{2+} as the charge carrier, inactivation was well fit with one exponential of $\tau \approx 145$ ms, suggesting that the fast inactivation time constant was Ca^{2+} dependent.

Ca^{2+}-dependent enhancement of Ca^{2+} current has been reported in gastrointestinal smooth muscle cells from the stomach of *Bufo marinus*. In these gastric myocytes, two components of the inward Ca^{2+} current were identified, a low- and a high-voltage-activated component. The high-voltage-activated component (presumably L-type) was enhanced by raising intracellular Ca^{2+}. The increase in current was maximal with an internal Ca^{2+} of $\approx$600 nM (15).

pH L-type Ca^{2+} channel activity in most cell types is inhibited by extracellular acidification and enhanced by extracellular alkalization. In guinea pig gastric myocytes (14), a change in extracellular pH from 7.2 to 8.0 increased maximal inward current by $\approx$70%, and a change in pH from 7.2 to 6.0 decreased maximal inward current by $\approx$71%. Potential mechanisms of the effects of pH include neutralization of surface charge, block by external protons, and block by internal protons.

cAMP AND PHOSPHORYLATION The effects of cAMP in gastrointestinal smooth muscle appear to be diverse. cAMP was without effect on L-type Ca^{2+} channels in guinea pig ileal smooth muscle cells (12), and phenylephrine in rat anococcygeus muscle produced a dose-dependent inhibition of L-type Ca^{2+} channel current (16). In canine colonic myocytes (17), low concentrations of cAMP activated L-type Ca^{2+} channel current and higher concentrations inhibited the current.

The effects of phosphorylation on L-type Ca^{2+} channel current have also been tested in gastrointestinal smooth muscle. Yabu et al reported that calyculin A increased inward current through L-type Ca^{2+} channels (carried by Ba^{2+}) from guinea pig taenia coli smooth muscle, which suggested that phosphorylation increased inward current in these cells (18). Ward et al studied L-type Ca^{2+} channel current recorded from colonic and gastric canine smooth muscle cells (19). In contrast to the above results, in traditional whole-cell patch-clamp experiments both okadaic acid and calyculin A reduced peak inward current. Calyculin also contracted the isolated smooth muscle cells and raised intracellular Ca^{2+} measured with indo-1. Okadaic acid did not cause gastric cell contraction or a change in intracellular Ca^{2+}, which led the authors to speculate that the apparent rise in intracellular Ca^{2+} observed with calyculin A may have been secondary to changes in cell shape. Decrease of L-type Ca^{2+} channel current with okadaic acid was also reported by Lang et al (20). A possible explanation for the apparently discordant results is that Yabu et al used Ba^{2+} as the charge carrier and Ward et al used Ca^{2+}. Ca^{2+} may have direct effects on L-type Ca^{2+} channels or modify other regulatory mechanism that control L-type Ca^{2+} channels. Another possible explanation was put forward by Obara & Yabu in 1993 (21). The authors found that low concentrations of okadaic acid (10 nM) and calyculin A (0.5 nM) decreased inward current in guinea pig taenia coli smooth muscle cells, whereas higher concentrations increased inward current. The authors suggested that the inhibitory effects were mediated through type 2A protein phosphatases and the stimulatory effects through type 1 protein phosphatases. The effects of phosphorylation on L-type Ca^{2+} current were also studied in isolated canine jejunal circular smooth muscle cells with Ba^{2+} as the charge carrier (11). G-protein stimulation via GTP-γS increased inward current, whereas G-protein inhibition via GDP-βS inhibited the inward current. The G-protein effects appeared to be mediated by a cholera toxin–sensitive, pertussis toxin–insensitive G protein. Activation of the L-type Ca^{2+} channel current by G proteins appeared to be secondary to a change in protein phosphorylation as staurosporine, a nonspecific protein kinase inhibitor, inhibited the effects of G-protein activation on inward current and calyculin A accentuated the effects of G-protein activation on inward current. Calyculin A (100 nM) had a biphasic action on L-type Ca^{2+} channel current, first activating, then inhibiting L-type Ca^{2+} channel current, which again suggested a dual effect of phosphorylation in the modulation of L-type Ca^{2+} channel current in gastrointestinal smooth muscle.

OTHER REGULATORY MECHANISMS Muscarinic receptors are found on gastrointestinal smooth muscle cells, and the receptors are coupled to a variety of G proteins. Both an inhibition of L-type Ca^{2+} channel current and an activation of L-type Ca^{2+} channel current by ACh can be predicted depending on which G-protein cascade is activated. In 1985, Sims et al (22) recorded currents from toad gastric smooth muscle and demonstrated activation of Ca^{2+} channels and inhibition of K^+ channels in response to ACh. ACh (1 μM) and erythromycin (1 μM), a promotility agent, activated L-type Ca^{2+} channel current (carried by Ba^{2+}) in canine jejunal circular smooth muscle cells (7). The increase in current was blocked by nifedipine, which suggests that it was carried by L-type Ca^{2+} channels. In contrast, ACh was found to decrease L-type Ca^{2+} current in other gastrointestinal myocytes such as guinea pig gastric myocytes (23) and canine colonic myocytes (24).

L-type Ca^{2+} channel current in human and canine jejunal circular smooth muscle cells is also modulated by the gastrointestinal hormone motilin (25). Motilin increased L-type Ca^{2+} channel current, carried by Ba^{2+}, in a dose-dependent manner. The effects of motilin appeared to be mediated through a pertussis toxin–insensitive G-protein pathway.

T-TYPE Ca^{2+} CHANNELS

Introduction

T-type Ca^{2+} channels are found in a several smooth muscle cells including vascular and cardiac smooth muscle. T-type Ca^{2+} channels have been described in gastrointestinal myocytes of the guinea pig, rat, and *Bufo marinus*. Their physiological role is not as clear as that for L-type Ca^{2+} channels. T-type Ca^{2+} channels are generally active at voltages negative to −60 mV and inactivate rapidly at more depolarized voltages. In smooth muscle cells with membrane potentials positive to −60 mV, little current is expected to flow through T-type Ca^{2+} channels. In cardiac sino-atrial cells, T-type Ca^{2+} channels have been implicated in the generation of the pacemaker current (26), and a similar role for T-type Ca^{2+} channels has been proposed in gastrointestinal smooth muscle cells and in interstitial cells of Cajal (see below).

Channel Structure

The T-type Ca^{2+} channel has not yet been cloned in gastrointestinal smooth muscle and little information is known about the channel structure. Recently, a neuronal T-type channel has been cloned and expressed. The single channel conductance in *Xenopus* oocytes was 7.5 pS (27).

Single Channel Conductance

Yoshino et al (28, 29) reported two Ca^{2+} channel types in smooth muscle cells of guinea pig taenia coli. One fulfilled the criterion for an L-type Ca^{2+}. The other had a conductance of 12 pS, inactivated rapidly, was inactivated at a holding potential of −40 mV, and was insensitive to nifedipine (2 μM). The 12-pS channel openings were mostly seen at the beginning of depolarizing pulses. The data suggest that the 12 pS channel was a T-type Ca^{2+} channel. The authors, however, also pointed out that the activation threshold for the 12-pS channel was −40 mV, a depolarized value compared with cardiac T-type Ca^{2+} channels.

Whole-Cell Current Kinetics and Regulation

Yoshino et al (28, 30) recorded whole-cell and single-channel currents from guinea pig taenia coli myocytes. Whole-cell current inactivation was best fit with two exponentials, one thought to represent the fast inactivating (T-type) Ca^{2+} channel current, insensitive to nifedipine, and one thought to represent the slow inactivating (L-type) Ca^{2+} channel current, sensitive to nifedipine. Voltage dependence of activation was similar for both components. Yamamoto et al (31) also studied inward Ca^{2+} current from guinea pig taenia coli myocytes. In their study, inactivation was best fit by three exponentials of 7, 45, and 400 msec, at 0 mV and 33°C. Activation was best fit with a single exponential. The authors suggested that the inactivation characteristics of the Ca^{2+} current reflect the presence of more than one Ca^{2+} channel type. Katzka & Morad (14) recorded whole-cell inward currents from guinea pig gastric myocytes. Inactivation was best fit with two exponentials; however, the authors found little evidence for two Ca^{2+} channel types as inward current activated at a relatively depolarized −20 mV; changing the holding voltage did not alter inactivation kinetics, as would be expected if a T-type Ca^{2+} channel was present, and nifedipine did not preferentially block a component of the Ca^{2+} current.

There also seems to be a difference in the relative expression of the putative two channel types with age (32). Two components of inward Ca^{2+} current were recorded from newborn and adult rat ileal myocytes. In newborn rat ileal myocytes (1–3 days old), two components of inward Ca^{2+} (carried by 10 mM Ca^{2+}) current were observed (apparently in all 94 cells studied). One activated at a voltage range of ≈40 mV, had a fast inactivation rate, and was completely inactivated at a holding voltage of −50 mV. The other component activated at ≈−10 to −20 mV, had a slower inactivation, and was well discernible at a holding voltage of −50 mV. Of interest, nifedipine (1 μm) had no effect on the two components of the inward current in newborn ileal myocytes. Nifedipine (30 μM) blocked ≈20% of peak inward current with no effect on the low-voltage activating component (presumably T-type) of the inward current. Cadmium (10 μM) blocked the high-voltage activating component (presumably L-type) with no effect on the low-voltage activating component. Cadmium (100 μM) blocked both components, whereas nickel (500 μM) blocked the low-voltage activating component with little effect on the high-voltage activating component. In contrast, in the adult rat (2.5–3 months), only a high-voltage activating component of the inward Ca^{2+} current was seen with a greater sensitivity to nifedipine than to the current (as in newborn rats). In several of the 16 cells studied, a fast inactivating component of the inward Ca^{2+} current was observed but was too small to study. The authors conclude that in the ileal myocytes of newborn rats a T-type Ca^{2+} channel is present, as well as another channel type suggestive of both L- and N-type Ca^{2+} channels and with a low sensitivity to nifedipine. In adult rat ileal myocytes, T-type Ca^{2+} channels are absent or present in very small numbers.

Age-dependent changes in inward current were also recorded from rat colonic myocytes from 1–820 days old (33). At a holding potential of −100 mV two components of the current were observed. The T-type component activated at about −60 mV, had a half-life of inactivation of <100 ms, was resistant to nifedipine (2–10 μM) and cadmium (20 μM), and was blocked by nickel (30 μM). The L-type component activated at about −40 mV, had a half-life of inactivation of 200 ms, was blocked by nifedipine and cadmium, but not by nickel. The L-type Ca^{2+} channel current was present in all cells of all ages studied. In contrast to the findings in the rat ileum, the T-type Ca^{2+} channel current was not present in newborn rats (1 day), was present in 50% of cells at day 30 and in 70% of cells at day 480. The current density for the T-type Ca^{2+} channel increased until day 30 where it remained stable, whereas the current density for the L-type Ca^{2+} channel increased until day 30 but declined after day 120.

In canine colon (6, 34) and in human and canine jejunum (7), only L-type Ca^{2+} channels were identified. The T-type Ca^{2+} channel current is voltage sensitive and inactivates at depolarized voltages. In the jejunum a holding voltage of −70 mV was used, whereas in the rat colon a holding voltage of −100 mV was used. In the canine colon two single channel conductances were identified; one had a conductance of ≈12 pS, which would be similar to that reported for other T-type Ca^{2+} channels. However, the channel was blocked by nifedipine (10 μM), did not exhibit rapid steady-state inactivation at depolarized voltages, and had long open times, which suggested it was not a T-type channel. The presence of T-type Ca^{2+} channels in gastrointestinal myocytes in species other than rat, *Bufo marinus*, and guinea pig therefore remains to be established. Regulatory pathways affecting T-type Ca^{2+} channels have not been studied in gastrointestinal myocytes.

Of interest, a non L-type, non T-type Ca^{2+} channel was recently identified in mouse duodenal myocytes (35). The whole-cell Ca^{2+} current was blocked by mapacalcine, a toxin derived from the marine sponge *Cliona vastifica*. Mapacalcine had no effect on T-type Ca^{2+} channels in portal vein myocytes and did not interact with the dihydropyridine receptor, suggesting a new Ca^{2+} current was identified. The occurrence of this current in other species remains to be identified.

RUNDOWN In cells where rundown of T-type Ca^{2+} channel current has been studied, little rundown has been observed (1).

CHLORIDE/ANION CHANNELS

Introduction

Anion channels are often referred to as Cl^- channels, although most are also permeable to other anions such as Br^- and I^- and often also variably permeable to larger anions. In the following section the term Cl^- channel is used interchangeably with anion channel. Under recording conditions that are close to physiological ionic conditions, opening Cl^- channels usually results in movement of Cl^- out of the cell and results in membrane depolarization toward the equilibrium potential for Cl^-. If the membrane potential is depolarized beyond Cl^- equilibrium potential, as can occur during a contraction, then opening of Cl^- channels results in Cl^- influx and membrane hyperpolarization. As the equilibrium potential for Cl^- is not far from the cell membrane potential, opening of Cl^- channels generally does not lead to large changes in membrane potential.

Channel Classification and Structure

Chloride channels can be classified, based on their mechanism of activation, into voltage-gated Cl^- channels, Ca^{2+}-activated Cl^- channels, ligand-gated Cl^- channels, mechanosensitive Cl^- channels, G protein-regulated Cl^- channels, and volume-gated Cl^- channels. Also in this classification is the cystic fibrosis transmembrane conductance regulator (CFTR) channel, which is a cyclic AMP-activated Cl^- channel. Considerable overlap exists between the groups as, for example, Ca^{2+} activated channel Cl^- channels are usually also voltage regulated, and volume-regulated Cl^- channels are often also regulated by messengers and voltage. An alternative classification is one based on structure of cloned Cl^- channels (adapted from 36). There are four broad classes of Cl^- channels: (*a*) ligand-gated anion channels, such as the glycine receptor and the $GABA_A$ receptor, which are assembled as pentamers with each monomer having 4 transmembrane spans; (*b*) CLC Cl^- channels, which include voltage-gated Cl^- channels, as well as volume-activated channel Cl^- channels such as CLC-2 and the recently cloned CLC-3, thought to represent a ubiquitous volume regulated Cl^- channel (50); channels in this family have about 12 transmembrane spans; (*c*) The CFTR channel, which is a cyclic AMP-activated channel highly selective for Cl^-, and whose mutations lead to cystic fibrosis; this channel has 12 putative transmembrane spans and may also function as an ion channel regulator; (*d*) Ca^{2+}-activated Cl^- channels, although controversy still exists on whether truly Ca^{2+}-activated Cl^- channels have been cloned. Other cloned proteins such as pl_{Cln} have been claimed to function as Cl^- channels but because controversy exists on their function and they have not been identified in gastrointestinal myocytes, they are not be dealt here.

Ca^{2+}-ACTIVATED Cl^- CHANNELS

Single Channel Conductance

Application of neurokinin (NK) agonists resulted in Ca^{2+} oscillations and activation of Cl^- channels in on-cell patches of rabbit longitudinal colonic myocytes. The Cl^- channel conductance was not stated, but based on a figure in Reference 37, it appears to be ≈20 pS.

Whole-Cell Current Kinetics and Regulation

In gastrointestinal myocytes, Ca^{2+}-activated Cl^- channels were first described by Byrne & Large in rat anococcygeus muscle (39). Application of the Ca^{2+} ionophore A23187(1 μM) or caffeine (10 mM) resulted in an increase in Cl^- whole-cell current.

Carbachol stimulates a Cl^- channel in rat small intestinal smooth muscle cells. The increase in Cl^- conductance was accompanied by a rise in intracellular Ca^{2+} and blocked by intracellular heparin but not by EGTA (2 mM), suggesting it was, in part, regulated by Ca^{2+} released from $InsP_3$-sensitive stores (40). A second Cl^- conductance was also activated by caffeine (10 mM) but was abolished by intracellular EGTA (2 mM) and extracellular ryanodine (20–50 μM), suggesting that it was regulated by ryanodine-sensitive Ca^{2+} stores (41).

A Ca^{2+}-activated Cl^- current was also described in rabbit esophageal muscularis mucosae myocytes (42). In whole-cell recordings (Cs^+ in the pipette to block K^+ currents), depolarization evoked inward Ca^{2+} currents and an outward current. The outward current was inhibited when the pipette contained EGTA or the bath contained Ba^{2+}, suggesting Ca^{2+} dependence. The reversal potential of the outward current changed in accordance to the equilibrium potential for Cl^-, and the whole-cell current was blocked by niflumic acid (10 μM), suggesting it was carried by Cl^-. Increase in intracellular Ca^{2+} activates a Cl^- conductance in opossum esophageal circular myocytes (43). Caffeine (10 mM) and carbachol (10 μM) contracted the myocytes and activated a whole-cell current that was predominantly carried by Cl^-. Ionomycin (10 μM) activated both the Cl^- current and a nonselective cation current. As the inhibitory junction potential in opossum esophageal circular smooth muscle is Cl^- dependent (44), it appears that Cl^- channels have an important role in esophageal electrophysiology of the opossum.

In canine jejunal circular smooth muscle cells (45), increases of intracellular Ca^{2+} by cyclopiazonic acid or thapsigargin activated a Cl^- conductance. Activation of the Cl^- conductance was prevented by Bapta (10 mM), suggesting the presence of a Ca^{2+}-activated Cl^- conductance.

VOLTAGE- AND SECOND MESSENGER-REGULATED Cl^- CHANNELS

Single Channel Conductance

A 300 pS Cl^- channel (140 mM Cl^- pipette, 126 mM Cl^- bath) was identified in rabbit colon longitudinal myocytes (46,47). The Cl^- channel was voltage dependent with a bell-shaped voltage activation curve. Maximal open probability was at −5 to +20 mV. Several subconductance states were observed, with a smallest subconductance state of 15 pS. The channel was not activated by Ca^{2+} (up to 1 mM) and was blocked by DIDS and NPPB. In inside-out patches, GTP-γS (nonhydrolyzable GTP analog) activated the channel within 30 sec and the inhibitor of G-protein activation, GDP-βS, reversibly inhibited channel activity. G protein-activation of the 300 pS Cl^- channel appeared to be via a pertussis toxin-sensitive G protein. The Cl^- channel was also activated by the NK-1 receptor agonist substance P methylester but not by protein kinase A or C.

Whole-Cell Current Kinetics and Regulation

The Ca^{2+}-activated Cl^- channels from rat anococcygues muscle (39) were also activated by noradrenaline (applied by ionophoresis) and by voltage. Noradrenaline activated a whole-cell current that was blocked by phentolamine.

A Ca^{2+}-activated Cl^- channel was also found in opossum esophageal circular smooth muscle cells (43). This Cl^- current was also activated by carbachol (10 μM), most likely through a rise in intracellular Ca^{2+}. Carbachol regulation of Cl^- currents may play a role in esophageal contractile activity, as explained above.

VOLUME-REGULATED Cl^- CHANNELS

Single Channel Conductance

Single channel conductances have not been reported for gastrointestinal volume-regulated (activated) Cl^- channels.

Whole-Cell Current Kinetics and Regulation

Volume-activated anion channels are found in most, if not all, mammalian and nonmammalian cell types. The channels are thought to contribute to cell-volume regulation and may also play a role in setting the membrane potential (48), as they are often active under baseline conditions. Volume-activated Cl^- channels also participate in intracellular pH regulation, epithelial Cl^- transport and fluid secretion, exocytosis, transmembrane transport of organic osmolytes (including amino acids), and cell proliferation.

In guinea pig gastric antral myocytes (49), osmotic cell swelling resulted in activation of a volume-activated anion current sensitive to DIDS (100 μM) and niflumic acid (10 μM). Arachidonic acid (25 μM) also inhibited the current. Use of indomethacin (25 μM) and chelerythrine (1 μM), cyclooxygenase, and protein kinase C (PKC) inhibitors, respectively, did not influence the volume-activated anion current or the effects of arachidonic acid. The anion permeability sequence for the anion current was $I^- > Br^- > Cl^- >$ gluconate. The current-voltage relationship showed outward rectification. The properties of this current are similar to those of a volume-regulated anion current attributable to ClC-3, a Cl^- channel recently cloned from guinea pig heart (50). However, unlike ClC-3, the volume-activated anion current in guinea pig antrum was not inhibited by PKC.

A volume-activated anion current was recently described in human and canine jejunal circular smooth muscle (51, 52). In both human and canine myocytes, the current was activated by osmotic cell swelling (212 mOSM). The volume-activated Cl^- current was not blocked by DIDS, 9-AC, ketoconazole, or tamoxifen (100 μM for all), nor was it inhibited by PKC activation (500 nM). The anion selectivity of the volume-activated current was I > Br > Cl > F. The data suggest the presence of a volume-activated Cl^- current in human and canine jejunal circular smooth muscle cells with properties different from those of CLC-3 and the guinea pig gastric myocyte volume-activated anion current, suggesting that these currents are carried by a different Cl^- channel.

NONSELECTIVE CATION CHANNELS

Introduction

Nonselective cation (NSC) channels are ion channels that are equally permeable to Na^+ and K^+ and thus have a reversal potential near 0 mV. Under physiological ionic gradients, opening of NSC channels results predominantly in Na^+ influx and membrane depolarization.

Channel Classification

NSC channels were the first channels to be described. In 1951, Fatt & Katz described a large nonselective increase of ion permeability induced by ACh at the muscle end plate (53). NSC channels encompass a large group of channels, ranging from the nicotinic ACh receptor to gap junctions. The group includes ligand-gated NSC channels, mechanosensitive NSC channels, the cGMP-gated NSC channel involved in olfactory and visual signal transduction, bacterial porins, and gap junction NSC channels, Ca^+-regulated NSC channels, ATP-gated NSC channels, and receptor-regulated NSC channels. In gastrointestinal myocytes, only receptor and Ca^{2+}-regulated NSC channels have been described, and this section is limited to these groups. The term NSC channel is used interchangeably with receptor and Ca^{2+}-regulated NSC channels.

Channel Structure

NSC channels that express currents similar to those found in gastrointestinal myocytes have not been cloned yet. The structure of the nicotinic ACh receptor, a NSC channel, is well understood; however, it is not known if nicotinic ACh receptors are found in gastrointestinal myocytes.

Single Channel Conductance

Inoue et al (54) determined the conductance of an ACh-activated NSC channel from guinea pig ileal longitudinal myocyte on-cell patches. The channel conductance was 20–25 pS, with a Na^+/K^+ permeability ratio of 1/0.3–0.4. The channel was voltage dependent with a bell-shaped current-voltage relationship. Similar experiments were performed on canine gastric pyloric myocytes (55). ACh (10 μM) activated a NSC channel with a unitary conductance of 30 pS.

In cultured guinea pig ileum longitudinal smooth muscle cells, a 12 pS NSC channel was identified (inside-out patches, 150 mM KCl in pipette and bath). The channel was voltage dependent with half-maximal activation at $\approx$7 ms and a 60 mV change required to increase P_o *e*-fold. The permeability ratios (P_x/P_K) for Na^+, Ca^{2+}, and Li^+ were 1, 0.86, and 1.17, respectively. The NSC channel was insensitive to Ca^{2+} (1 mM) and was blocked by Cs^+ and Ba^{2+}. Angiotensin II (100 nM) increased P_o, an effect blocked by the angiotensin II antagonist Sar^1-Leu^8-Ang II (200 nM) (56).

An 80 pS NSC channel was identified from *Bufo marinus* gastric myocytes (on-cell patches 120 NaCl bath, 130 CsCl pipette). The channel was insensitive to voltage from −60 to +60 mV, activated by caffeine, and permeable to Ca^{2+} in the presence of extracellular Na^+ (56a).

Whole-Cell Current Kinetics and Regulation

Two types of whole-cell NSC currents have been described in the gastrointestinal tract. One is a baseline current that is present under unstimulated conditions, and the other is a NSC current induced by activation of muscarinic receptors. The currents are similar and may represent degrees of activation of the same channels. There may, however, be more than one type of NSC current in myocytes. In canine pyloric myocytes (55), ACh-activated a NSC current that was more noisy than the baseline current and was blocked by Cs^+, which is usually permeable through NSC currents. P_K/P_{Na} of the ACh-activated current was 1.7. The data suggest that ACh-activated a second NSC current.

Two currents carried by external Na^+ (presumably NSC currents) were recorded from longitudinal myocytes of guinea pig ileum (57). One current was activated by ACh (10 μM) and relaxed to a steady state within 200 ms of activation. The other was activated by substance P (SP), did not relax over a longer time period, and increased in size with hyperpolarization. The difference in inactivation time constants, voltage dependence, and differential response to SP and ACh led the authors to suggest the presence of two separate currents. Also, in canine colonic myocytes, substance P and neurokinin A, on the one hand, and Ach, on the other hand, activated NSC currents with different I-V relationships (58).

A NSC current in gastrointestinal myocytes was first described by Benham et al in 1985 in rabbit jejunal longitudinal myocytes (59). The current-voltage relationship obtained from the whole-cell NSC current was U shaped, with an increase in inward current at about −40 to −30 mV and then a decrease in current as the current direction changes to an outward direction at about 0 mV. The U-shaped current-voltage relationship may reflect a voltage dependence of the open probability combined with a change in driving force, with a larger driving force at −30 mV compared with no driving force at 0 mV. It may also be due to Ca^{2+} effects. However, nifedipine did not affect the shape of the current-voltage relationship, which supports the former explanation (60). Steady-state activation curves were obtained for longitudinal myocytes from guinea pig ileum (61). The ACh-activated NSC current had a half-maximal activation voltage of −58 mV.

BLOCKERS Chen et al (62) determined the effects of numerous ion-channel blockers on NSC current from longitudinal myocytes of guinea pig ileum. Cesium aspartate was used in the internal solution to inhibit K^+ currents, and ACh (10 μM) was used to stimulate the NSC current. The K^+ channel blockers, TEA (10 mM), procaine (5 mM), 4-AP (5 mM), and quinine (10 μM), inhibited the current by ≈45, 90, 75, and 90%, respectively (at a holding potential of −50 mV). Caffeine (10 mM), known to release Ca^{2+} from intracellular stores, inhibited the current by 45%, most likely through a direct effect on the NSC channel. The Ca^{2+}-activated NSC channel blockers, flufenamic acid, niflumic acid, and DCDPC, blocked the NSC current with ≈IC_{50}s of 32, 100, and 30 μM. These results point to the need for care in interpreting pharmacological experiments on whole-cell currents made up of a mixture of channel types, as the blockers may not be specific. Similar results were obtained by Kim et al (63). In this study, quinidine, 4-AP, and TEA inhibited NSC current in guinea pig gastric myocytes. The IC_{50}s for 4-AP and TEA were 3.3 and 4.1 mM, respectively. Quinidine at 2 μM appeared to be a somewhat specific blocker for the carbachol-induced NSC current, blocking ≈11% of inward Ca^{2+} current, ≈15% of the voltage-dependent K^+ current (at 30 mV), and ≈11% of the Ca^{2+}-activated K^+ current (at 45 mV) compared with near-complete block of the carbachol-induced NSC current.

CALCIUM The NSC current recorded from several regions of the gastrointestinal tract is Ca^{2+} regulated but not directly Ca^{2+} activated. The ACh-activated NSC is sensitive to internal Ca^{2+}, although the NSC current itself does not appear to be directly activated by a rise in intracellular Ca^{2+}. An increase in intracellular Ca^{2+} to ≈ 1 μM in most gastrointestinal myocytes does not markedly alter the size of the NSC (64), but the response to ACh is markedly enhanced by a rise in intracellular Ca^{2+}. In voltage-clamp experiments where depolarization was used to elicit Ca^{2+} entry through Ca^{2+} channels, the effects of ACh on the NSC current were enhanced (65, 66). This enhancement was blocked by L-type Ca^{2+} channel blockers such as nifedipine and nitrendipine (65) and by replacing extracellular Ca^{2+} with Ba^{2+} or Sr^{2+}, suggesting it was specifically due to Ca^{2+} entry from L-type Ca^{2+} channels. Release of Ca^{2+} from intracellular stores may also be involved in the enhancement of the ACh-activated NSC current by Ca^{2+}. If caffeine or ryanodine is used to deplete intracellular Ca^{2+} stores, the effects of ACh on the NSC current are blunted (65, 67). Use of heparin to block IP_3 release of Ca^{2+} from intracellular stores markedly reduces the rise in intracellular Ca^{2+} evoked by ACh (66). As a rise in intracellular Ca^{2+} is not sufficient to activate the NSC in most preparations, it appears that either ACh binding to its receptor or activation of a G protein is necessary before Ca^{2+} can activate the NSC.

ACH AND G PROTEINS The effects of muscarinic stimulation have been extensively studied in gastrointestinal smooth muscle. At a channel level, muscarinic stimulation has been shown to modulate Ca^{2+} channels (see above), K^+ channels (see below), and NSC channels. The effects of ACh on a NSC current were first reported (59) in rabbit jejunal myocytes. The effects of ACh on the NSC current appear to be mediated by pertussis toxin-sensitive G proteins. Inoue & Isenberg in 1990 (64) examined the effect of G-protein activation on guinea pig ileal longitudinal myocytes. A K^+-free pipette solution was used to isolate the NSC current and cells were clamped at −50 mV. GTP-γS (100 μM) activated the inward current, and ACh (300 μM), applied after GTP-γS, was without effect. Also, GDP-βS, an inhibitor of G-protein activation, inhibited the effects of ACh on the NSC current. These results suggest that the effects of ACh are mediated by a G protein. The NSC current was blocked by pertussis toxin. Similar results were obtained by Komori et al (68), who also showed that histamine activated the NSC current by the same pertussis toxin-sensitive G-protein mechanism. Activation of a NSC current by ACh has now been reported for rabbit jejunal myocytes (59); guinea pig myocytes (69); canine pyloric, jejunal, and colonic myocytes (24, 55, 67, 70); *Bufo marinus* myocytes; opossum esophageal myocytes (43); and mouse anococcygeus myocytes (72). The carbachol-activated NSC current in guinea pig myocytes was inhibited by activation of PKC (73).

pH The ACh-activated NSC current in longitudinal myocytes from guinea pig ileum is pH sensitive (61). Acidification of the extracellular solution to a pH of 6.0 doubled the ACh-activated NSC current, and alkalization to a pH of 7.75 halved the ACh-activated NSC current. The effects of pH were secondary to an increase in H^+ conductance because no effect of pH change was seen in the absence of ACh or to changes in intracellular [Ca^{2+}]; the same effects were observed with 20 mM BAPTA in the pipette. These results suggest a direct modulation of the NSC current by H^+. The effects of pH on the ACh-activated NSC current could be described with a Hill-type equation with an apparent pK_a of 7.4 and a Hill coefficient of ≈1. Acidification shifted the peak of the inward current-voltage relationship to the left, and steady-state activation shifted from a half-maximal activation voltage of −58 mV at pH 7.4 to −68 mV at a pH of 7.0.

POTASSIUM CHANNELS

Introduction

Most excitable cells, including gastrointestinal smooth muscle cells, express several types of K^+ channels, with the most common being delayed rectifier and Ca^{2+}-activated types. Other K^+ channel types include A-type, inward rectifier, and ATP-sensitive channels. Given the large diversity of K^+ channels, even within their subgroups, each type of K^+ channel is discussed separately.

DELAYED RECTIFIER K^+ CHANNELS

Introduction

Delayed rectifier K^+ channels have been found in all smooth muscles studied. The term delayed rectifier was coined to describe a K^+ channel that opens after a brief delay in response to a depolarization, and it is now loosely applied to K^+ channels that are not Ca^{2+} activated, do not inactivate rapidly, and do not show inward rectification regardless of whether there is a delay in activation. Many delayed rectifiers K^+ channels are open at the resting membrane potential of gastrointestinal smooth muscle and hence contribute to setting the membrane potential. Opening of a delayed rectifier K^+ channel would pull the membrane potential toward E_K, usually ≈−80 mV. The membrane potential of gastrointestinal smooth muscle cells is usually positive to E_K. The membrane potential is therefore set by the combination of K^+ channels and other channels open at the resting membrane potential, such as chloride and NSC channels.

Channel Classification

The first K^+ channel to be sequenced was the A-type K^+ channel from *Drosophila*. The *shaker* locus on the X chromosome encodes for a gene whose cDNA clones resulted in expression of functional A-type K^+ channels, the *shaker* K^+ channel. Probes from the *shaker* locus were then used to identify related K^+ channels, called *shal*, *shab*, and *shaw*. In the progression from *shaker* to *shaw*, inactivation lengthens and the channels become more like delayed rectifier channels. A myriad of delayed rectifier K^+ channels have now been cloned, as well as subunits that do not express a functional K^+ channel on their own but modify the behavior of other K^+ channels. Delayed rectifier K^+ channels are now classified by their gene family into nine families of α-subunits, K_V1–K_V9, as well as K_VLQT1. Additional families are likely to be expressed in the future. K_V1–K_V4 and K_V7 are electrically active; K_V5, 6, 8, and 9 are electrically silent but when combined with the electrically active subunits alter their electrical behavior. Also in the current classification are β-subunits $K_V\beta$-1, $K_V\beta$-2, and $K_V\beta$-4, which are cytoplasmic subunits with little homology with α-subunits but modify their behavior. The current classification is maintained at http://qlink.queensu.ca/~4jch3/Kchseq.htm. In gastrointestinal smooth muscle, $cK_V1.2$ and $cK_V1.5$ have been cloned from canine gastrointestinal myocytes (74, 75). $cK_V1.2$ had a single channel conductance of 14 pS (symmetrical 140 mM K^+). The macroscopic current resulting from expression of $cK_V1.2$ increased with voltages positive to −40 mV. The current had a fast activation time (time to half-peak = 7.4 ms), exhibited slow and incomplete inactivation, was blocked by 4-AP (IC_{50} of 75 μM), and was resistant to TEA (11% block by 10 mM). Based on its electrophysiological and pharmacological characteristics, $cK_V1.2$ was thought to be most closely similar to $I_{dK(f)}$ in the native colonic circular smooth muscle whole-cell current (see below). The single channel conductance (symmetrical 140 mM K^+) of $cK_V1.5$ was 10 pS. Like $cK_V1.2$, the macroscopic current resulting from expression of $cK_V1.5$ increased with voltages positive to −40 mV. The current had a fast activation time (time to half-peak = 5.5 ms), exhibited slow and incomplete inactivation, was blocked by 4-AP (IC_{50} of 211 μM), and was resistant to TEA (less than a 10% block by10 mM). Based on the electrophysiological and pharmacological characteristics, $cK_V1.5$ closely resembled $cK_V1.2$, suggesting that $I_{dK(f)}$ is made up of more than one channel type or that the native current is made up of $K_V1.2$ and $cK_V1.5$ heterotetramers (76).

Channel Structure

Delayed rectifier K^+ channels are made up of at least four identical α-subunits. Each subunit has six membrane spanning regions. α-subunits need to be expressed together or with β-subunits to approximate native delayed rectifier current.

Single Channel Conductance

Several different single channel conductances have been reported for different delayed rectifier channels. In gastric myocytes from *Rana pipiens* and *Bufo marinus*, two channels were identified with conductances of 15 and 40 pS. The 40 pS channel was blocked by quinidine (100 μM) and the 15 pS channel by TEA, but not by quinidine (77). Also in *Bufo marinus* gastric myocytes, a 20 pS channel was characterized that was responsive to stretch and fatty acids, suggesting it was a stretch-activated K^+ channel (78).

In rabbit longitudinal jejunal myocytes, a 50 pS (internal $K^+ = 5.9$ mM, external $K^+ = 126$ mM) delayed rectifier K^+ channel was identified. The channel was insensitive to Ca^{2+} and blocked by cytoplasmic TEA (5–10 mM). Mean open time was 16.4 ms and mean closed time within a burst was 6.4 ms. As activation times were slow and open probability began to increase around −45 mV, it is likely that this channel type does not contribute significantly to the membrane potential, and action potentials can occur without activation of this channel type (79). In the small intestine, a 186 pS K^+ channel was identified in neonatal mouse myocytes from an explant. Channel activity was not affected by buffering Ca^{2+} with EGTA, was not blocked by intracellular ATP, and single channel gating was inhibited by 4-AP (100 μM). Also, the ensemble current turned on after a brief delay, leading the authors to suggest that it was a delayed rectifier K^+ channel.

In colonic circular myocytes, 19- and 90-pS channels (symmetrical 140 mM K^+) were identified that had delayed-rectifier properties (80). The 19-pS channel was inhibited by 4-AP (10 mM), TEA (10 mM), and was not Ca^{2+} dependent. Most channel openings were clustered at the beginning of depolarizing pulses, suggesting substantial inactivation. Inactivation was, however, never complete, with channel openings still resolvable at steady state depolarized voltages. The 90-pS channel was variably sensitive to 4-AP, TEA, and Ca^{2+}, suggesting a class rather than a single channel type. Protein kinase A activated both channel types, but at −60 mV (a physiological membrane potential), only the 19-pS channel was activated. VIP (100 nM) activated the 19-pS channel increasing open probability, mean open time, and mean burst duration (18). Also, in canine colonic myocytes there is 4-pS K^+ activated by nitric oxide but not by voltage, suggesting it may not be a delayed rectifier K^+ channel (82).

Whole-Cell Current Kinetics and Regulation

Whole-cell delayed rectifier current kinetics were studied in human and canine jejunal circular smooth muscle cells at 24°C. In both, activation was not voltage dependent (83, 84). Activation time was 90 ± 25 ms and 80 ± 25 ms, respectively. Deactivation was weakly voltage dependent, with a τ of 10 ± 3 ms at −140 mV and 40 ± 32 ms at −60 mV for canine myocytes and a τ of 13 ± 4 ms at −80 mV and 22 ± 11 ms at −40 mV for human myocytes. The current was not dependent on holding voltage (10% decrease in current at 0 mV compared with −60 mV). Less than 15% inactivation was noted over 2 s. The open probability of the delayed rectifier K^+ channels contributing to the whole-cell

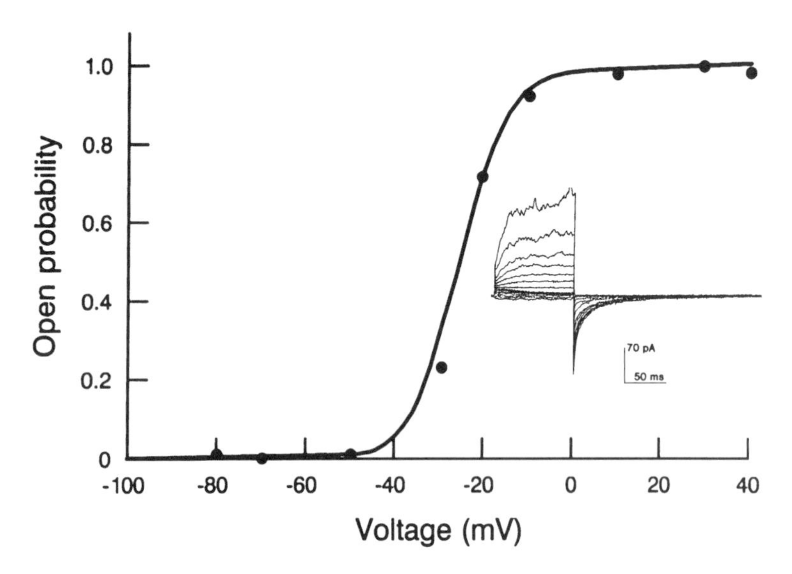

Figure 2 Open probability of the delayed rectifier channels carrying the whole-cell current. Normalized tail currents were obtained from tail currents (*inset*) of canine jejunal circular smooth muscle cells with 150 KCl in the bath. Open probability began to increase at −60 mV (83).

current was determined from tail current protocols generated in 150 mM KCl (Figure 2). The open probability of the canine delayed rectifier current began to increase at about −60 mV and reached unitary open probability at 0 mV. The human delayed rectifier current began to increase at about −70 mV and reached unitary open probability at 10 mV. Therefore the currents would be expected to contribute to the membrane potential of human and canine jejunal circular smooth muscle myocytes. In human myocytes, quinidine (100 μM) blocked a substantial portion of the whole-cell current and depolarized the membrane potential to near 0 mV, again suggesting that the whole-cell delayed rectifier K^+ current is a major determinant of the membrane potential.

The whole-cell delayed rectifier current in canine colonic circular myocytes included three components discernible by their TEA and 4-AP sensitivities (85). Time to half-maximal activation of the control current was 26 ± 4 ms. TEA (10 mM) blocked 50% of the outward current and the time to half-maximal activation of the residual current was 17 ± 2 ms. In contrast, 4-AP blocked 35% of the outward current and the time to half-maximal activation of the residual current was 40 ± 8 ms, suggesting that 4-AP blocked a fast activation component of the whole-cell delayed rectifier current ($I_{dK(f)}$) and TEA a slow-activating component ($I_{dK(s)}$). 4-AP block was use dependent but not frequency or voltage dependent, suggesting that the slowing of activation times by 4-AP was not the result of a state-dependent block but rather block of a component of the whole-cell current. The third component of the whole-cell delayed rectifier current was revealed by block with TEA (10 mM) in the pipette. In the absence of TEA, the current inactivated by only 10% during a 20 s pulse to −50 mV and in the presence of intracellular TEA by 80%, suggesting the presence of a low inactivation threshold current ($I_{dK(n)}$). This current was insensitive to 4-AP and sensitive to external TEA.

PHOSPHORYLATION The delayed rectifier current in guinea pig taenia coli myocytes was activated by phosphorylation (86). The membrane permeant form of cAMP, dibutyryl cAMP, increased the K^+ current, and H-8 (a protein kinase A inhibitor) inhibited the effect of dibutyryl cAMP. Calyculin A also increased outward K^+ current, suggesting that the delayed rectifier type current is regulated by protein kinase A-mediated phosphorylation. At the single channel level, the 20 and 90 pS delayed rectifier channels identified in colonic myocytes were also activated by protein kinase A. Application of the catalytic subunit of protein kinase A (10 U/ml) to inside-out patches activated both channels (80).

VIP In canine colon circular smooth muscle cells, VIP increased a charybdotoxin (ChTX)-insensitive, voltage-dependent K^+ current (81). VIP is known to relax gastrointestinal smooth muscle and is an inhibitory neurotransmitter found in enteric nerves. At a single channel level, VIP activated a 20 pS 4-AP-sensitive K^+ channel, suggesting that the delayed rectifier 20 pS channel may underlie the effects of VIP in colonic smooth muscle.

FENAMATES AND FLUOXETINE The delayed rectifier current characterized (83, 84) in human and canine jejunal circular smooth muscle cells is sensitive to fenamates, which are nonsteroidal antiinflammatory drugs in clinical use. Use of these drugs is associated with gastrointestinal motility disturbances in up to a third of patients. Flufenamic acid and mefenamic acid, both fenamates, activated the delayed rectifier current at concentrations equivalent to therapeutic blood levels. Similarly, fluoxetine, a commonly prescribed antidepressant (Prozac®), and its metabolite norfluoxetine had profound effects on the delayed rectifier current in both human and canine jejunal circular smooth muscle cells (129). Fluoxetine inhibited the current at concentrations equivalent to therapeutic blood levels and at higher concentrations stimulated a Ca^{2+}-activated ChTX sensitive current by increasing intracellular Ca^{2+} levels.

LOW-MOLECULAR-WEIGHT OXIDES Low-molecular-weight oxides regulate colonic and jejunal myocyte delayed rectifier current. In colonic circular myocytes, nitric oxide (NO) and sodium nitroprusside activate an 80 pS delayed rectifier channel (82). As the effects of nitric oxide are often mediated through activation of cGMP-dependent protein kinase, the effects of the membrane-permeant form of cGMP, dibutyryl cGMP, were tested on the K^+ channel. Dibutyryl cGMP increased P_o in cell-attached patches. However, in inside-out patches, NO still increased the open probability of the 80 pS channel, raising the possibility of a direct action on the channel. As patches may contain cytoplasmic components, an indirect effect of NO cannot be ruled out. NO also activated two other K^+ channels, a voltage-insensitive $\approx$4-pS channel and a Ca^{2+}-activated 250-pS channel. NO may therefore contribute to several phases of the inhibitory response in the gastrointestinal tract. At the resting membrane potential, the 4 pS and 80 pS channels may be modulated by NO released from enteric nerves, while under conditions where the muscle is depolarized or intracellular Ca^{2+} is raised, such as at the peak of the slow wave, the 250 pS Ca^{2+}-activated K^+ channel may be activated.

Carbon monoxide (CO) is another low-molecular-oxide putative messenger in the gastrointestinal tract. Exogenous CO activates the delayed rectifier current in both human and canine jejunal circular smooth muscle cells, resulting in a cyclic oscillation in the membrane potential (87, 88). The enzyme that produces CO, heme oxygenase, was found in a subpopulation of enteric neurons and interstitial cells of Cajal (89), raising the possibility that CO released from nerves and interstitial cells modulates smooth muscle delayed rectifier activity and membrane potential.

A-TYPE K^+ CHANNELS

Introduction

A fast-inactivating K^+ current was first described in molluscan neurons (90). Characteristic properties of this current include a steep holding voltage dependence, with near-complete inactivation at -50 mV, fast kinetics of activation and inactivation, and high sensitivity to block by 4-AP. In neurons, A-type K^+ currents are mostly inactivated at the resting membrane potential and activated during and after hyperpolarization to slow the rate of pacemaker depolarization, modulating the action potential frequency. The role of an A-type K^+ current in gastrointestinal smooth muscle is less clear. The A-type K^+ current in guinea pig colonic myocytes and esophageal myocytes is not completely inactivated at the resting membrane potential and may therefore contribute to the membrane potential, modulating the generation of action potentials by opposing the inward Ca^{2+} current (91, 92).

Channel Classification

A-type K^+ channels are now classified by their gene family into the K_V subfamilies, with most falling into the K_V1 subfamily. K^+ channels with A-type characteristics have not yet been reported in gastrointestinal smooth muscle.

Channel Structure

Recently, Doyle et al (93) used X-ray crystallography to determine the structure of KcsA, a K^+ channel from *Streptomyces lividans*. The pore region of KcsA is nearly identical to the *Drosophila shaker* K^+ channel as well as to other vertebrate voltage-gated K^+ channels. The channel is a tetramer with four identical units around a central pore. Each subunit had two transmembrane α-helices and the two α-helices are connected by the pore region (roughly 30 amino acids). One α-helix of each subunit faces outward and one faces the central pore. The selectivity filter contains two ions 7.5 Å apart and the attraction force between the selectivity filter is perfectly balanced, with repulsive forces between the two K^+ ions, allowing the channel to conduct with a high throughput and with high selectivity (93).

Single Channel Conductance

The only report of single channel recording from ion channels thought to carry an A-type K^+ current in gastrointestinal smooth muscle is from Vogalis & Lang (94). A K^+ channel with a conductance of 12–13 pS was recorded from on-cell patches of guinea pig colonic myocytes (K^+ in pipette = 130 mM, in bath 6 mM). The channel was blocked by 4-AP (5 mM) but not by TEA (5 mM), and inactivated within 50 ms. The channel was seen only following step depolarizations from a hyperpolarized voltage. Its kinetic features closely resembled the whole-cell A-type current recorded from guinea pig colonic myocytes, suggesting it carried the whole-cell current (91).

Although the cloned K^+ channels from canine colon, $cK_V1.2$ and $cK_V1.5$, fall in the *shaker* family of K^+ channels, the expressed channels do not exhibit rapid inactivation and are not considered A-type K^+ channels.

Whole-Cell Current Kinetics and Regulation

The first description of an A-type K^+ current in gastrointestinal myocytes was from rat ileal myocytes (95). Two major currents were found in newborn and adult rat ileal myocytes: a delayed rectifier type current, and a fast-inactivating current labeled I_{fo}. At a holding voltage of -80 mV, step depolarizations to -40 mV revealed an outward current that peaked within 10 ms and inactivated rapidly. Activation was voltage dependent, with a time to peak of 10.8 ± 0.9 ms at -30 mV and 6.7 ± 1.2 ms at 20 mV. I_{fo} decay was well fit with a single exponential, with a time constant of 17–33 ms. Recovery from inactivation was also well fit with a single exponential. Recovery from inactivation was voltage dependent, with a time constant of 28 ms at -120 mV and 90 ms at -80 mV. Current kinetics were dependent on external $[Ca^{2+}]$, with an increase in peak current and a 16-mV shift in the hyperpolarized direction when Ca^{2+} was removed from the bath. I_{fo} was weakly TEA sensitive and 4-AP sensitive. 4-AP (1 mM) blocked 40% of the outward current.

In rabbit esophageal muscularis mucosae myocytes, a transient outward K^+ current was recorded using the nystatin perforated patch technique (96). The transient K^+ inactivated over a period of about 50 ms. However, the current was Ca^{2+} dependent and blocked by TEA (5 mM), suggesting it was not an A-type K^+ current.

In esophageal circular myocytes (92) and in guinea pig colonic myocytes (91), overlap of steady-state activation and inactivation curves reveals a window current between −60 and −30 mV, suggesting that the A-type K^+ current can contribute to electrophysiological events at voltages approximating the membrane potential. A-type K^+ currents have also been reported in guinea pig ileum, human jejunum, and rat distal colonic myocytes (97–99).

In guinea pig colonic myocytes the A-type current is blocked by arachidonic acid (1–10 μM). Block by arachidonic acid was not dependent on protein kinases, G proteins, or indomethacin. Arachidonic acid was the most potent blocker of all fatty acids tested. As arachidonic acid had the most unsaturated double bonds (4) of the fatty acids tested, it was suggested that arachidonic acid blocked A-type K^+ channels through a stereospecific mechanism (100).

Ca^{2+}-ACTIVATED K^+ CHANNELS

Introduction

Ca^{2+}-activated K^+ channels are a diverse group of K^+ channels that share a common property: an increase in open probability as internal Ca^{2+} rises. Three subgroups of Ca^{2+}-activated K^+ channels can be identified based on their single channel conductance: large conductance (BK), intermediate conductance (IK_{Ca}), and small conductance (SK_{Ca}).

BK may contribute to repolarization after an excitable event. ChTX has little effect on basal electrical or mechanical activity of gastrointestinal smooth muscle in most preparations, which suggests that, at rest, BK does not contribute significantly to mechanical activity or membrane potential. However, in a study of the effects of ChTX on guinea pig ileum, longitudinal muscle ChTX induced spike-like depolarizations, increased spontaneous activity, and inhibited nerve stimulation-evoked membrane hyperpolarization, which suggests BK in this preparation was constitutively active (101). Also, when gastrointestinal smooth muscle strips are activated by ACh, ChTX increases electrical slow-wave duration and amplitude and increases contractile activity, suggesting that BK plays a role in the control of excitability of gastrointestinal smooth muscle to counter large unopposed effects of excitatory neurotransmitters.

IK_{Ca} and SK_{Ca} may play central roles in the generation of inhibitory junction potentials (IJPs). IJPs are membrane hyperpolarizations accompanied by muscle relaxation evoked by inhibitory neurotransmitter release from enteric nerves. Abnormalities in IJPs have been implicated in constipation and other gastrointestinal motility disorders. Recent evidence suggests that ATP-activated IK_{Ca} and SK_{Ca} are present in gastrointestinal smooth muscle cells and, based on their pharmacology, generate IJPs (102, 103).

BK channels have a conductance of ≈80–250 pS, are activated by micromolar concentrations of Ca^{2+}, regulated by voltage, and blocked by ChTX. IK_{Ca} have a conductance of ≈40 pS, have higher sensitivity to Ca^{2+} than BK, are voltage insensitive, and are blocked by apamin and millimolar concentrations of TEA. SK_{Ca} have a conductance of 5–10 pS, have a higher sensitivity to internal Ca^{2+} than BK, are voltage insensitive, and are blocked by apamin but are resistant to millimolar TEA.

Channel Structure

BK is made up of α- and β-subunits. Both have been cloned in canine colonic smooth muscle (cslo-α and cslo-β) (104). The α-subunit has a M_r of 62,000 and when expressed alone can conduct K^+ and is voltage and Ca^{2+} sensitive. The β-subunit has a M_r of 22,000, and both NH_2 and COOH terminals are cytoplasmic. The β-subunit has a site for phosphorylation by protein kinase A. Expression of the β-subunit alone does not lead to the appearance of a functional ion channel, but expression of both subunits together shifts the voltage dependence of activation by ≈50 mV as well as increases Ca^{2+} sensitivity.

Single Channel Conductance

BK channels in gastrointestinal smooth muscle have conductances varying from 100 to 220 pS (reviewed in 105). Larger and smaller conductances have been reported in other cells. The slope conductance of the cloned BK channel composed of the α-subunit alone or of the α- and β-subunits together was 207–215 pS at 1 μM free Ca^{2+}. TEA (100–500 μM) produced a characteristic flickery block and an apparent decrease in unitary current. ChTX and iberiotoxin completely blocked channel openings, features characteristic of BK.

IK_{Ca} have been studied in murine ileal and colonic myocytes and SK_{Ca} in murine ileal myocytes. In the ileum, IK_{Ca} and SK_{Ca} were identified in cell-attached patches (bath K^+ = 2.5 mM, pipette K^+ 2.5 mM), with an external Ca^{2+} concentration of 150 nM. The conductance of the IK_{Ca} was 39 pS and of the SK_{Ca} estimated at 10 pS. IK_{Ca} and SK_{Ca} were activated by the P2Y agonist 2-MeSATP (20–50 μM). SK_{Ca} was not blocked by 2 mM TEA in the pipette and IK_{Ca} was only partly blocked by apamin. In the colon, SK_{Ca} were recorded from inside-out patches. In symmetrical K^+ solutions (140 mM), the channel conductance at a bath [Ca^{2+}] 100 nM was 5 pS. The P_o was increased by caffeine, ATP, 2-MeSATP (10 μM), and UTP (1 mM). In inside-out patches, at 10 nM external Ca^{2+} little activity of SK_{Ca} was noted. Open probability increased as bath Ca^{2+} concentration increased with a 50% effective concentration of Ca^{2+} of 500 nM. The channel showed no voltage or time dependence.

Whole-Cell Current Kinetics and Regulation of BK

A signature of the whole-cell current produced by BK channels is noise. As the single channel conductance is large, the whole-cell current often appears to be noisy. Another feature of BK is fast deactivation on stepping to hyperpolarized voltages, giving rise to fast tail currents, with τ of a few ms.

CALCIUM DEPENDENCE BK channel activity is dependent on intracellular Ca^{2+} concentration. In a study in excised patches from canine gastric myocytes (106), a change in Ca^{2+} concentration from 100 nM to 1 μM at the inner surface of the patch resulted in an a ~100 mV negative shift in the voltage for half-maximal activation. At a holding voltage of 0 mV, activation had a Hill coefficient of 3.4, suggesting Ca^{2+} cooperativity in the activation of the channel. In similar experiments carried out in canine colonic myocytes (107), a change of the Ca^{2+} concentration from 100 nM to 1 μM resulted in a 130-mV shift in the voltage for half-maximal activation. At +50 mV, activation had a Hill coefficient of 5.3, again suggesting high cooperativity in the activation of the colonic channel by Ca^{2+}.

Substance P (SP) activates BK in rabbit longitudinal colonic myocytes through an increase in intracellular $[Ca^{2+}]$ (108). SP (10^{-12} M) activated a BK channel with a conductance of ≈165 pS (pipette = 126 mM K^+) in on-cell patches and 198 pS in inside-out patches (pipette and bath K^+ = 126 mM). The P_o increased tenfold when Ca^{2+} was increased from 50 nM to 5 μM, and TEA (10 mM) blocked the channel. Activation of BK by SP was dependent on extracellular Ca^{2+} as nifedipine decreased the P_o.

Nitric oxide (NO) activates Ca^{2+}-dependent K^+ currents in esophageal circular myocytes as well as colonic myocytes. Sin-1 and sodium nitroprusside, NO donors, activated a whole-cell K^+ current, and activation was blocked by cyclopiazonic acid, a sarcoplasmic reticulum (SR) Ca^{2+}-pump inhibitor. This suggests that activation depends on release of Ca^{2+} from the SR (109). NO activates a 250 pS Ca^{2+}-activated channel in on-cell patches from canine colon circular myocytes (82).

VOLTAGE DEPENDENCE Activation of BK by voltage is intimately linked to Ca^{2+}. Ca^{2+} may alter the voltage sensor, which alters the binding of Ca^{2+} to BK. BK is strongly voltage dependent. At constant intracellular $[Ca^{2+}]$, BK is activated by depolarization and closed by hyperpolarization. In experiments carried out on coexpressed α- and β-subunits from canine colonic myocytes in

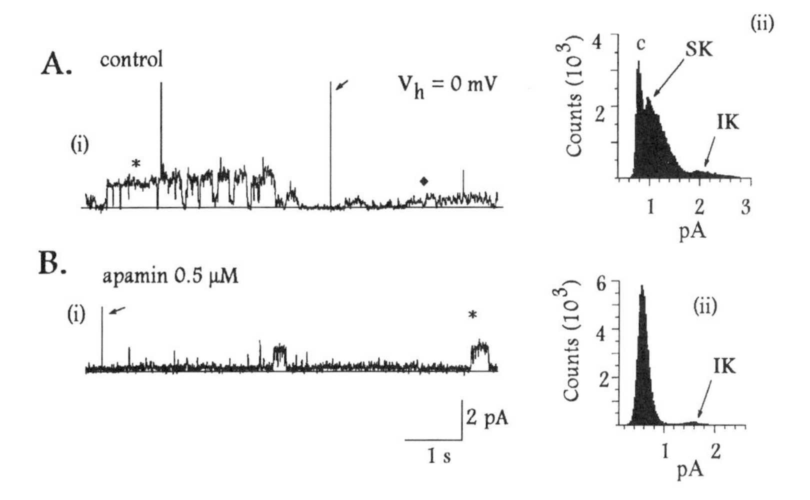

Figure 3 BK (*arrow*), IK_{Ca} (*) and SK_{Ca} (♦) channels recorded from a cell-attached patch from mouse ileum (*panel A*). Apamin (0.5 μM, *panel B*) blocked SK_{Ca} but not BK or IK_{Ca} (102).

inside-out patches, with a bath [Ca^{2+}] of 1 μM, the macroscopic current began to activate at 0 mV and reached full open probability at ≈100 mV (104).

Whole-Cell Kinetics and Regulation of IK_{Ca} and SK_{Ca}

At a single channel level, IK_{Ca} and SK_{Ca} in murine ileal myocytes were found to be activated by ATP and blocked by apamin (Figure 3). These features were used to identify the whole-cell current correlate (102). The whole-cell current, recorded using the amphotericin perforated patch technique, was blocked by apamin and activated by ATP. It had an initial transient outward component and a sustained outward component. Apamin (0.5 μM) blocked about 70% of the sustained current at +50 mV. ATP increased both the initial transient outward component and the sustained outward component of the whole-cell current and apamin blocked the increase in current evoked by ATP. The current-voltage relationship revealed initial outward currents at voltages positive to −50 mV. The current was dependent on intracellular [Ca^{2+}]. In traditional whole-cell experiments, the initial transient outward current was not seen, and at 150 nM (but not at 85 nM internal Ca^{2+}) an apamin-sensitive current was present. Similar experiments were carried out in murine colonic myocytes (103). ATP (1 mM) activated a K^+ conductance with initial activation seen at about −80 mV and little or no voltage dependence. Similarly, the putative P2Y receptor agonist 2-MeSATP (100 μM) and UDP (1 mM) activated a whole-cell current with characteristics similar to that activated by ATP. Apamin (300 nM) blocked about 44% of the current stimulated by ATP.

ATP-SENSITIVE AND INWARDLY RECTIFYING POTASSIUM CHANNELS

Introduction

In this family there are two main types of K^+ channels: ATP-sensitive (K_{ATP}) and inward rectifier (K_{IR}). K_{IR} channels have not been found in gastrointestinal smooth muscle, and it is unclear whether K_{ATP} channels are expressed in gastrointestinal smooth muscle cells. However, as K_{ATP} channel modulators do have effects on ionic currents in these cells, this review focuses on K_{ATP} channels. K_{ATP} channels show weak inward rectification and are sensitive to ATP. A decrease in intracellular ATP, such as would occur with metabolic inhibition or hypoxia, activates K_{ATP} channels and an increase in ATP closes them. K_{ATP} channels link K^+ flux across a cell membrane to the metabolic state of the cells. Characteristic features of K_{ATP} channels are that they are inhibited by sulfonylureas such as glibenclamide and tolbutamide and activated by cromakalim, minoxidil, pinacidil, and diazoxide (reviewed in 110).

Channel Classification

K_{ATP} and K_{IR} channels have similar structures and are classified into $K_{IR}1$ to $K_{IR}6$ subfamilies. Inward rectifier K^+ channels fall into $K_{IR}1$ to $K_{IR}3$ (K_{IR}). $K_{IR}4$ are ATP-dependent K^+ channels and $K_{IR}6$ ATP-sensitive K^+ channels (K_{ATP}).

Channel Structure

Both K_{ATP} and K_{IR} channels share a similar structure with two transmembrane domains in each subunit. It appears that, like the *shaker* K_V channel, four subunits aggregate to form a functional channel. K_{ATP} channels are made up of $K_{IR}6$ subfamily subunits that associate with the sulfonylurea receptor. The sulfonylurea receptor belongs to the ATP-binding cassette ATPase superfamily.

Single Channel Conductance

No single channel studies on K_{ATP} channels in the gastrointestinal tract have been reported. In vascular smooth muscle, unitary conductance can be divided into two groups, a small conductance family (15–50 pS) and a large conductance family (100–258 pS) (reviewed in 110).

Whole-Cell Current Kinetics and Regulation

Some of the first evidence for the presence of K_{ATP} channels in gastrointestinal smooth muscle came from a study of the effects of sulfonylureas and glibenclamide on a guinea pig longitudinal smooth muscle/myenteric plexus preparation (111). Cromakalim and its isomer lemakalim activate a whole-cell K^+ current in canine colonic myocytes (112). Activation was inhibited by the sulfonylurea glyburide. However, a subsequent study showed that the predominant effects of cromakalim and lemakalim were on a Ca^{2+}-activated K^+ channel, questioning the presence of K_{ATP} in canine colonic myocytes (113).

In rabbit esophageal muscularis mucosa myocytes, lemakalim (10 μM) activates a whole-cell current that is ATP sensitive and Ca^{2+} independent (114). The current-voltage relationship of this current showed a substantial inward current compatible with K_{ATP}. Carbachol, via the M_3 receptor and PMA (membrane permeant PKC activator) inhibited the current, an effect attenuated by tyrosine kinase inhibitors. These results suggest that K_{ATP} is present in rabbit esophageal muscularis mucosa myocytes.

SODIUM CHANNELS

Introduction

The presence of Na^+ channels in gastrointestinal smooth muscle is controversial. The main function of Na^+ channels in excitable cells is to generate the rapid upstroke of the action potential, resulting in a rapid depolarization. Na^+ channels also play a role in the generation of pacemaker and subthreshold potentials. In gastrointestinal smooth muscle, the upstroke of the action potential is predominantly due to Ca^{2+} entry and therefore Na^+ channels are not essential in the generation of the action potential. However, some data suggest that Na^+ channels can be found in gastrointestinal smooth muscle, although their physiological role is presently unclear.

Channel Classification

Excitable-membrane sodium channels can be classified based on their sensitivity to tetrodotoxin (TTX), the paralytic poison derived from fish of the order Tetraodontiformes. TTX selectively blocks Na^+ channels with varying kinetics, defining two main types of Na^+: fast TTX-sensitive and slow TTX-insensitive.

Channel Structure

The basic structure of a Na^+ channel is of four homologous protein domains thought to be arranged around a central pore.

Single Channel Conductance

Single channel Na^+ currents have not been measured from gastrointestinal smooth muscle.

Whole-Cell Current Kinetics and Regulation

Ohya et al reported that, in rabbit ileal longitudinal smooth muscle cells, removal of extracellular Ca^{2+} unmasked a Na^+ current at depolarized potentials. The current was revealed when extracellular Ca^{2+} was reduced to 100 nM. However, the current was TTX insensitive and blocked by Ca^{2+} channel blockers, suggesting that it was due to Na^+ influx through Ca^{2+} channels rather than through a Na^+ channel (115). Inoue et al (54) studied single channel activity evoked by ACh in single guinea pig ileum smooth muscle cells. In their experiments the pipette solution contained Mg^{2+} (5 mM) and no Ca^{2+}. ACh activated atropine-sensitive channels with a single channel conductance of 20–25 pS and a permeability ratio of $Na^+ : K^+$ of 1.0 : 0.3–0.4. The permeability ratio suggests a NSC channel, although removal of external Na^+ resulted in loss of channel activity over a wide range of membrane potential (−30 to −80 mV), suggesting that in physiological ionic environments the channel was predominantly Na^+ selective. Although the channel appears to function as a Na^+ channel, it is still considered a NSC channel (54).

A TTX-sensitive Na^+ current was recorded from rat ileum single smooth muscle cells in nominally Ca^{2+}-free solution (32) and from rat fundus smooth muscle cells (116, 117). The strongest evidence for expression of Na^+ channels in gastrointestinal smooth muscle was provided by Xiong et al (118). Single adult rat and human colonic smooth muscle cells were patch clamped in the presence of 4-AP in the bath solution and Cs^{2+} in the pipette solution to block K^+ currents. Cells were held at −100 mV and step depolarized. At voltages positive to −40 mV two components of an inward current were observed: The slower component was was blocked by nifedipine and Ni^{2+}, suggesting it was carried by Ca^{2+} channels; the other fast component was blocked by TTX, unaffected by 0 mM external Ca^{2+}, nifedipine or Ni^{2+}, and disappeared when external Na^+ was substituted with choline, suggesting that it was a Na^+ current (Figure 4). The Na^+ current had half-inactivations of −74.5 and −69.5 mV, and slope factors of 12.2 and 7.6 mV in rat and human cells, respectively. Half-activation was −36.1 and −21.8 mV, with slope factors of 5.8 and 7.6 mV in rat and human cells, respectively. As the activation and steady-state inactivation curves overlapped between −60 and −30 mV, a substantial window current was present. The incidence of the Na^+ current was higher in the proximal colon (16 of 22 human cells) when compared with the distal colon (7 of 32 cells). The uneven distribution of Na^+ current raises an interesting question: Were the Na^+ currents recorded from cells derived from colonic muscularis propria or from contaminant cells? The most likely source of contaminant cell is smooth muscle cells from the muscularis mucosae and interstitial cells of Cajal (ICC). Contamination is unlikely because the muscularis mucosae was removed in

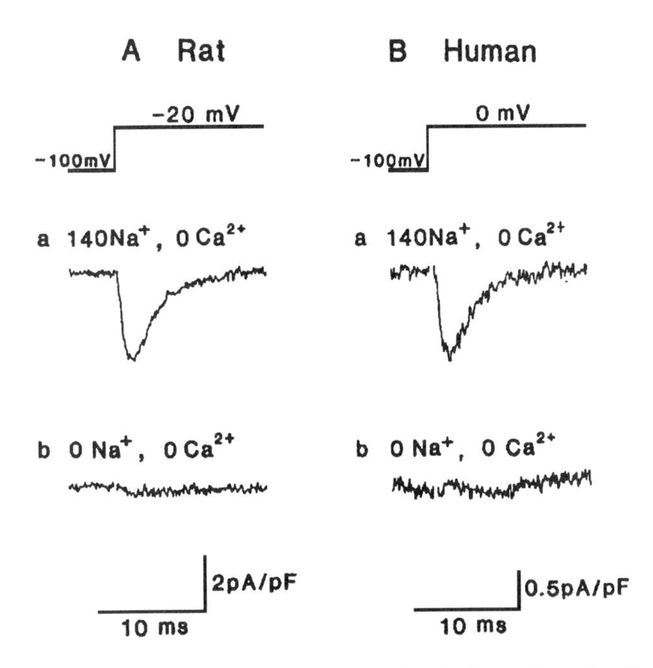

Figure 4 Na^+ currents recorded from rat (*A*) and human (*B*) colonic smooth muscle cells. Removal of Na^+ ions from the bath resulted in loss of the Na^+ current (118).

these experiments and the interstitial cells of Cajal occupy less than 3% of the smooth muscle volume.

IONIC CURRENTS IN INTERSTITIAL CELLS OF CAJAL

Introduction

It has recently been established that ICC generate the electrical slow wave recorded from muscle cells in muscle strip preparations (120, 121). ICC express c-Kit, a tyrosine receptor kinase, that is required for the development of a subpopulation of ICC. Mice partly lacking c-Kit do not have ICC associated with the myenteric plexus in the small intestine, unlike normal controls. No slow wave can be recorded from the small intestine of these mice and intestinal peristalsis is markedly altered and inefficient (120, 121). ICC may serve not only to generate the slow wave but also to amplify neuronal input to gastrointestinal smooth muscle cells. Loss of ICC has been implicated in human motility disorders such as hypertrophic infantile stenosis (122), Hirshsprung's disease (123), severe constipation, and intestinal pseudo-obstruction (124) and in inflammatory bowel disease (125). It is therefore of great interest to determine the ionic conductances of ICC as they appear to be central to the regulation of gastrointestinal motility. As relatively little is known about ionic currents in ICC, they are grouped together.

Ion Channels

Initial patch clamp recording of ICC were performed in dog colon (126). ICC were isolated from the submucosal surface of the circular muscle layer, known to be a pacemaker region of the colon. Ca^{2+}-activated K^+ channels with a similar conductance (218 ± 25 pS) to colonic circular smooth muscle myocytes were present in on-cell patches. The voltage- and Ca^{2+}-dependence of Ca^{2+}-activated K^+ channels in ICC were also similar to colonic myocytes. Ca^{2+} currents were also studied in this preparation. Inward Ca^{2+} current activated within 5 ms and was blocked by nifedipine (1 μM). The current-voltage relationships of the whole-cell inward current revealed initial activation at -60 mV, with a peak at 0 mV, although initial activation was more negative in the figure shown (-70 mV). Steady-state activation and inactivation curves revealed a window current, suggesting a sustained Ca^{2+} influx.

The ionic current in canine colonic ICC was further studied and compared with canine colonic myocytes using both standard whole-cell recording techniques and the perforated patch clamp technique. Outward current in standard whole-cell recordings (1 mM EGTA in pipette) activated to peak within 14 ms and inactivated by 60% within 500 ms. The outward current was resistant to 4-AP (1 mM), unlike the current recorded for canine colonic myocytes, and also inactivated faster. Inward current from canine colonic ICC was studied with the perforated patch clamp technique. Inward current activated at 10 mV negative to inward current of canine colonic myocytes and peaked 10–30 mV more negative than canine colonic myocytes. The current-voltage relationship showed a distinct hump at negative voltages, and the current was more dependent on holding voltage than its counterpart was in colonic myocytes. A comparison of steady-state inactivation curves between ICC and myocytes showed that at -30 mV only 13% of the peak current (at -80 mV) remained, compared with 55% for colonic myocytes. The hump was sensitive to nickel (40 μM) and insensitive to nifedipine (1 μM). These electrophysiological and pharmacological data suggest the presence of a low voltage-activated T-type-like Ca^{2+} channel current, supporting a role for ICC as pacemaker cells.

In ICC isolated from normal human jejunal circular smooth muscle, a study on inward Ca^{2+} currents also revealed a hump in the current-voltage relationships of the whole-cell current at negative voltages, with a second inward peak around 0 mV, suggesting the presence of both an L-type Ca^{2+} channel current and a second Ca^{2+} current with a more negative activation possibly T-type-like. However, at very negative holding voltages (−90 mV), a similar but less pronounced hump in the current-voltage relationship was seen in some human jejunal circular smooth muscle cells. Hence, the difference in Ca^{2+} channels in ICC and myocytes in the human jejunum may be quantitative and not qualitative (130).

For ICC to act as pacemakers, they must generate rhythmic changes in membrane conductances. The membrane conductances in newborn BALB/c mice were determined from ICC maintained in culture for at least two days in the presence of the natural ligand for c-Kit, stem cell factor (127). At a holding voltage of −40 mV, voltage clamp experiments showed a rhythmic oscillation in current paralleled by changes in voltage under current clamp. The current appeared to be carried by Cl^- as it was blocked by the Cl^- channel blocker 4-acetamido-4-isothiocyanatostilbene-2,2′-disulfonic acid (SITS, 300 μM) and the reversal potential tracked the Cl^- equilibrium potential. Another component of the rhythmic current with faster kinetics than the Cl^- current was present but was not studied. In contrast, in a study on rhythmic activity in ICC from adult mouse small intestine, rhythmic inward currents were recorded with a frequency of 6/min (128). The current-voltage relationship reversed at +10–20 mV, suggesting a nonselective cation current. Which ionic conductance or conductances underlie the rhythmic changes in whole-cell current is therefore still unclear. Clearly, ionic conductances in ICC, especially in humans, will be a topic of intense investigation in the coming years.

ACKNOWLEDGMENTS

The author thanks Kristy Zodrow for secretarial assistance. The work was supported in part by National Insitutes of Health grant DK 52766.

Literature Cited

1. McDonald TF, Pelzer S, Trautwein W, Pelzer DJ. 1994. Regulation and modulation of calcium channels in cardiac, skeletal, and smooth muscle cells. *Physiol. Rev.* 74:365–507
2. Singer D, Biel M, Lotan I, Flockerzi V, Hofmann F, Dascal N. 1991. The roles of the subunits in the function of the calcium channel. *Science* 253:1553–57
3. Yoshino M, Yabu H. 1985. Single Ca channel currents in mammalian visceral smooth muscle cells. *Pflügers Arch.* 404: 285–86
4. Yoshino M, Someya T, Nishio A, Yabu H. 1988. Whole-cell and unitary Ca channel currents in mammalian intestinal smooth muscle cells: evidence for the existence of two types of Ca channels. *Pflügers Arch.* 411:229–31
5. Inoue Y, Xiong ZL, Kitamura K, Kuriyama H. 1989. Modulation produced by nifedipine of the unitary Ba current of dis-

persed smooth muscle cells of the rabbit ileum. *Pflügers Arch.* 414:534–42
6. Rich A, Kenyon JL, Hume JR, Overturf K, Horowitz B, Sanders KM. 1993. Dihydropyridine-sensitive calcium channels expressed in canine colonic smooth muscle cells. *Am. J. Physiol.* 264:C745–54
7. Farrugia G, Rich A, Rae JL, Sarr MG, Szurszewski JH. 1995. Calcium currents in human and canine jejunal circular smooth muscle cells. *Gastroenterology* 109:707–17
8. Cavalie A, McDonald TF, Pelzer D, Trautwein W. 1985. Temperature-induced transitory and steady-state changes in the calcium current of guinea pig ventricular myocytes. *Pflügers Arch.* 405:294–96
9. Ganitkevich VYa, Shuba MF, Smirnov SV. 1987. Calcium-dependent inactivation of potential-dependent calcium inward current in an isolated guinea pig smooth muscle cell. *J. Physiol.* 392:431–49
10. Rich A, Farrugia G, Rae JL, Szurszewski JH. 1994. Temperature dependence of a inward calcium current in canine jejunal circular smooth muscle cells. *Gastroenterology* 107(4):1219 (Abstr.)
11. Farrugia G. 1997. G-protein regulation of an L-type calcium channel current in canine jejunal circular smooth muscle. *J. Membr. Biol.* 160:39–46
12. Ohya Y, Kitamura K, Kuriyama H. 1987. Modulation of ionic currents in smooth muscle balls of the rabbit intestine by intracellularly perfused ATP and cyclic AMP. *Pflügers Arch.* 408:465–73
13. Romanin C, Grosswagen P, Schindler H. 1991. Calpastatin and nucleotides stabilize cardiac calcium channel activity in excised patches. *Pflügers Arch.* 418(12):86–92
14. Katzka DA, Morad M. 1989. Properties of calcium channels in guinea pig gastric myocytes. *J. Physiol.* 413:175–97
15. McCarron JG, McGeown JG, Walsh JV Jr, Fay FS. 1997. Modulation of high- and low-voltage-activated calcium currents in smooth muscle by calcium. *Am. J. Physiol.* 273:C883–92
16. England S, McFadzean I. 1995. Inhibition of voltage-dependent Ca^{2+}-current by alpha-adrenoceptor agonists in smooth muscle cells. *Eur. J. Pharmacol.* 288:355–64
17. Koh SD, Sanders KM. 1996. Modulation of Ca^{2+} current in canine colonic myocytes by cyclic nucleotide-dependent mechanisms. *Am. J. Physiol.* 271:C794–803
18. Yabu H, Yoshino M, Usuki T, Someya T, Obara K, et al. 1990. Modification by calyculin A of inward Ca currents in smooth muscle cells isolated from guinea pig taenia coli. *Prog. Clin. Biol. Res.* 327:623–26
19. Ward SM, Vogalis F, Blondfield DP, Ozaki H, Fusetani N, et al. 1991. Inhibition of electrical slow waves and Ca^{2+} currents of gastric and colonic smooth muscle by phosphatase inhibitors. *Am. J. Physiol.* 261:C64–70
20. Lang RJ, Ozolins IZ, Paul RJ. 1991. Effects of okadaic acid and ATP gamma S on cell length and Ca^{2+}-channel currents recorded in single smooth muscle cells of the guinea pig taenia caeci. *Br. J. Pharmacol.* 104:331–36
21. Obara K, Yabu H. 1993. Dual effect of phosphatase inhibitors on calcium channels in intestinal smooth muscle cells. *Am. J. Physiol.* 264:C296–301
22. Sims SM, Singer JJ, Walsh JV Jr. 1985. Cholinergic agonists suppress a potassium current in freshly dissociated smooth muscle cells of the toad. *J. Physiol.* 367:503–29
23. Wade GR, Barbera J, Sims SM. 1996. Cholinergic inhibition of Ca^{2+} current in guinea pig gastric and tracheal smooth muscle cells. *J. Physiol.* 491:307–19
24. Lee HK, Bayguinov O, Sanders KM. 1993. Role of nonselective cation current in muscarinic responses of canine colonic muscle. *Am. J. Physiol.* 265:C1463–71
25. Farrugia G, Macielag MJ, Peeters TL, Sarr MG, Galdes A, Szurszewski JH. 1997. Motilin and OHM-11526 activate a calcium current in human and canine jejunal circular smooth muscle. *Am. J. Physiol.* 273:G404–12
26. Hagiwara N, Irisawa H, Kameyama M. 1988. Contribution of two types of calcium currents to the pacemaker potentials of rabbit sino-atrial node cells. *J. Physiol.* 395:233–53
27. Peres-Reyes E, Cribbs LL, Daud A, Lacerda AE, Barclay J, et al. 1998. Molecular characterization of a neuronal low-voltage-activated T-type calcium channel. *Nature* 391:896–900
28. Yoshino M, Someya T, Nishio A, Yabu H. 1988. Whole-cell and unitary Ca channel currents in mammalian intestinal smooth muscle cells: evidence for the existence of two types of Ca channels. *Pflügers Arch.* 411(2):229–31
29. Yabu H, Yoshino M, Someya T, Totsuka M. 1989. Two types of Ca channels in smooth muscle cells isolated from guinea pig taenia coli. *Adv. Exp. Med. Biol.* 255:129–34

30. Yoshino M, Someya T, Nishio A, Yazawa K, Usuki T, Yabu H. 1989. Multiple types of voltage-dependent Ca channels in mammalian intestinal smooth muscle cells. *Pflügers Arch.* 414(4):401–9
31. Yamamoto Y, Hu SL, Kao CY. 1989. Inward current in single smooth muscle cells of the guinea pig taenia coli. *J. Gen. Physiol.* 93(3):521–50
32. Smirnov SV, Zholos AV, Shuba MF. 1992. Potential-dependent inward currents in single isolated smooth muscle cells of the rat ileum. *J. Physiol.* 454:549–71
33. Xiong Z, Sperelakis N, Noffsinger A, Fenoglio-Preiser C. 1993. Changes in calcium channel current densities in rat colonic smooth muscle cells during development and aging. *Am. J. Physiol.* 265: C617–25
34. Ward SM, Sanders KM. 1992. Upstroke component of electrical slow waves in canine colonic smooth muscle due to nifedipine-resistant calcium current. *J. Physiol.* 455:321–37
35. Morel JL, Drobecq H, Sautiere P, Tartar A, Mironneau J, et al. 1997. Purification of a new dimeric protein from *Cliona vastifica* sponge, which specifically blocks a non-L-type calcium channel in mouse duodenal myocytes. *Mol. Pharmacol.* 51(6):1042–52
36. Jentsch TJ, Gunther W. 1997. Chloride channels: an emerging molecular picture. *BioEssays* 19(2):117–26
37. Mayer EA, Sun XP, Supplisson S, Kodner A, Regoli M, Sachs G. 1991. Neurokinin receptor-mediated regulation of $[Ca]_i$ and Ca-sensitive ion channels in mammalian colonic muscle. *Ann. NY Acad. Sci.* 632:439–41
38. Deleted in proof
39. Byrne NG, Large WA. 1987. Action of noradrenaline on single smooth muscle cells freshly dispersed from the rat anococcygeus muscle. *J. Physiol.* 389:513–25
40. Ito S, Ohta T, Nakazato Y. 1993. Inward current activated by carbachol in rat intestinal smooth muscle cells. *J. Physiol.* 470:395–409
41. Ohta T, Ito S, Nakazato Y. 1993. Chloride currents activated by caffeine in rat intestinal smooth muscle cells. *J. Physiol.* 465:149–62
42. Akbarali HI, Giles WR. 1993. Ca^{2+} and Ca^{2+}-activated Cl^- currents in rabbit oesophageal smooth muscle. *J. Physiol.* 460:117–33
43. Wang Q, Akbarali HI, Hatakeyama N, Goyal RK. 1996. Caffeine- and carbachol-induced Cl^- and cation currents in single opossum esophageal circular muscle cells. *Am. J. Physiol.* 271:C1725–34
44. Crist JR, He XD, Goyal RK. 1991. Chloride-mediated inhibitory junction potentials in opossum esophageal circular smooth muscle. *Am. J. Physiol.* 261: G752–62
45. Farrugia G. 1997. Activation of a chloride current by volume in canine jejunal circular smooth muscle cells. *Gastroenterology* 112:A730 (Abstr.)
46. Sun XP, Supplisson S, Torres R, Sachs G, Mayer E. 1992. Characterization of large-conductance chloride channels in rabbit colonic smooth muscle. *J. Physiol.* 448:355–82
47. Sun XP, Supplisson S, Mayer E. 1993. Chloride channels in myocytes from rabbit colon are regulated by a pertussis toxin-sensitive G protein. *Am. J. Physiol.* 264:G774–85
48. Nilius B, Eggermont J, Voet T, Buyse G, Manolopoulos V, Droogmans G. 1997. Properties of volume-regulatied anion channels in mammalian cells. *Prog. Biophys. Mol. Biol.* 68(1):69–119
49. Xu WX, Kim SJ, So I, Kang TM, Rhee JC, Kim KW. 1997. Volume-sensitive chloride current activated by hyposmotic swelling in antral gastric myocytes of the guinea pig. *Pflügers Arch.* 435(1):9–19
50. Duan D, Winter C, Cowley S, Hume JR, Horowitz B. 1997. Molecular identification of a volume-regulated chloride channel. *Nature* 390:417–21
51. Farrugia G. 1998. Role of the cytoskeleton in volume activation of an anion current in canine jejunal circular smooth muscle cells. *Gastroenterology* 114(4):A751
52. Farrugia G, Sarr MG. 1998. Properties of a volume-activated chloride current in human jejunal circular smooth muscle cells. *Neurogastroenterol. Motil.* 10(1):70
53. Fatt P, Katz B. 1951. An analysis of the end plate potential recorded with an intracellular electrode. *J. Physiol.* 115:320–70
54. Inoue R, Kitamura K, Kuriyama H. 1987. Acetylcholine activates single sodium channels in smooth muscle cells. *Pflügers Arch.* 410(12):69–74
55. Vogalis F, Sanders KM. 1990. Cholinergic stimulation activates a non-selective cation current in canine pyloric circular muscle cells. *J. Physiol.* 429:223–36
56. Nouailhetas VL, Aboulafia J, Frediani-Neto E, Ferreira AT, Paiva AC. 1994. A Na^+-sensitive cation channel modulated by angiotensin II in cultured intestinal myocytes. *Am. J. Physiol.* 266:C1538–43
56a. Guerrero A, Fay FS, Singer JJ. 1994. Caffeine activates a Ca^{2+}-permeable, nonse-

lective cation channel in smooth muscle cells. *J. Gen. Physiol.* 104(2):375–94
57. Nakazawa K, Inoue K, Fujimori K, Takanaka A. 1990. Difference between substance P- and acetylcholine-induced currents in mammalian smooth muscle cells. *Eur. J. Pharmacol.* 179(3):453–56
58. Lee HK, Shuttleworth CW, Sanders KM. 1995. Tachykinins activate nonselective cation currents in canine colonic myocytes. *Am. J. Physiol.* 269:C1394–401
59. Benham CD, Bolton TB, Lang RJ. 1985. Acetylcholine activates an inward current in single mammalian smooth muscle cells. *Nature* 316:345–47
60. Inoue R, Isenberg G. 1990. Effect of membrane potential on acetylcholine-induced inward current in guinea pig ileum. *J. Physiol.* 424:57–71
61. Inoue R, Waniishi Y, Ito Y. 1995. Extracellular H^+ modulates acetylcholine-activated nonselective cation channels in guinea pig ileum *Am. J. Physiol.* 268: C162–70
62. Chen S, Inoue R, Ito Y. 1993. Pharmacological characterization of muscarinic receptor-activated cation channels in guinea pig ileum. *Br. J. Pharmacol.* 109(3):793–801
63. Kim SJ, Ahn SC, So I, Kim KW. 1995. Quinidine blockade of the carbachol-activated nonselective cationic current in guinea pig gastric myocytes. *Br. J. Pharmacol.* 115(8):1407–14
64. Inoue R, Isenberg G. 1990. Acetylcholine activates nonselective cation channels in guinea pig ileum through a G protein. *Am. J. Physiol.* 258:C1173–78
65. Inoue R, Isenberg G. 1990. Intracellular calcium ions modulate acetylcholine-induced inward current in guinea pig ileum. *J. Physiol.* 424:73–92
66. Pacaud P, Bolton TB. 1991. Relation between muscarinic receptor cationic current and internal calcium in guinea pig jejunal smooth muscle cells. *J. Physiol.* 441:477–99
67. Sims SM. 1992. Cholinergic activation of a non-selective cation current in canine gastric smooth muscle is associated with contraction. *J. Physiol.* 449:377–98
68. Komori S, Kawai M, Takewaki T, Ohashi H. 1992. GTP-binding protein involvement in membrane currents evoked by carbachol and histamine in guinea pig ileal muscle. *J. Physiol.* 450:105–26
69. Inoue R, Chen S. 1993. Physiology of muscarinic receptor-operated nonselective cation channels in guinea pig ileal smooth muscle. In *Nonselective Cation Channels: Pharmacology, Physiology and Biophysics*, ed. D Siemen, J Hescheler, pp. 261–68. Basle: Birkhause Verlag
70. Rich A, Farrugia G, Szurszewski JH. 1998. Muscarinic stimulation of a nonselective cation current in circular smooth muscle cells from canine jejunum. *Neurogastroenterol. Motil.* 10(1):93 (Abstr.)
71. Deleted in proof
72. Wayman CP, McFadzean I, Gibson A, Tucker JF. 1996. Inhibition by sodium nitroprusside of a calcium store depletion-activated non-selective cation current in smooth muscle cells of the mouse anococcygeus. *Br. J. Pharmacol.* 118(8):2001–8
73. Ahn SC, Kim SJ, So I, Kim KW. 1997. Inhibitory effect of phorbol 12,13 dibutyrate on carbachol-activated nonselective cationic current in guinea pig gastric myocytes. *Pflügers Arch.* 434(4):505–7
74. Hart PJ, Overturf KE, Russell SN, Carl A, Hume JR, et al. 1993. Cloning and expression of a Kv1.2 class delayed rectifier K^+ channel from canine colonic smooth muscle. *Proc. Natl. Acad. Sci. USA* 90(20):9659–63
75. Overturf KE, Russell SN, Carl A, Vogalis F, Hart PJ, et al. 1994. Cloning and characterization of a Kv1.5 delayed rectifier K^+ channel from vascular and visceral smooth muscles. *Am. J. Physiol.* 267:C1231–38
76. Russell SN, Overturf KE, Horowitz B. 1994. Heterotetramer formation and charybdotoxin sensitivity of two K^+ channels cloned from smooth muscle. *Am. J. Physiol.* 267:C1729–33
77. Wong BS. 1989. Quinidine blockade of calcium-activated potassium channels in dissociated gastric smooth muscle cells. *Pflügers Arch.* 414(4):416–22
78. Ordway RW, Petrou S, Kirber MT, Walsh JV Jr, Singer JJ. 1995. Stretch activation of a toad smooth muscle K^+ channel may be mediated by fatty acids. *J. Physiol.* 484:331–37
79. Benham CD, Bolton TB. 1983. Patch-clamp studies of slow potential-sensitive potassium channels in longitudinal smooth muscle cells of rabbit jejunum. *J. Physiol.* 340:469–86
80. Koh SD, Sanders KM, Carl A. 1996. Regulation of smooth muscle delayed rectifier K^+ channels by protein kinase A. *Pflügers Arch.* 432(3):401–12
81. Shuttleworth CW, Koh SD, Bayginov O, Sanders KM. 1996. Activation of delayed rectifier potassium channels in canine proximal colon by vasoactive intestinal peptide. *J. Physiol.* 493:651–63

82. Koh SD, Campbell JD, Carl A, Sanders KM. 1995. Nitric oxide activates multiple potassium channels in canine colonic smooth muscle. *J. Physiol.* 489:735–43
83. Farrugia G, Rae JL, Szurszewski JH. 1993. Characterization of an outward potassium current in canine jejunal circular smooth muscle and its activation by fenamates. *J. Physiol.* 468:297–310
84. Farrugia G, Rae JL, Sarr M, Szurszewski JH. 1993. A potassium whole cell current in jejunal human circular smooth muscle. *Am. J. Physiol.* 265:G873–79
85. Carl A. 1995. Multiple components of delayed rectifier K^+ current in canine colonic smooth muscle. *J. Physiol.* 484: 339–53
86. Yabu H, Obara K, Usuki T. 1992. Calcium and potassium channel regulation by protein phosphorylation in smooth muscle cells of guinea pig taenia coli. In *Advances in Experimental Medicine and Biology*, ed. GB Frank, CP Bianchi, HEDJ ter Keurs, 311:41–52. New York: Plenum
87. Farrugia G, Rae JL, Sarr M, Szurszewski JH. 1993. Activation of whole cell currents in isolated human jejunal circular smooth muscle by carbon monoxide. *Am. J. Physiol.* 264:G1184–89
88. Farrugia G, Miller SM, Rich A, Liu X, Maines MD, et al. 1998. Distribution of heme oxygenase and effects of exogenous carbon monoxide in canine jejunum. *Am. J. Physiol.* 274:G350–58
89. Miller SM, Farrugia G, Schmalz PF, Ermilov LG, Maines MD, Szurszewski JH. 1998. Heme oxygenase 2 is present in interstitial cell networks of the mouse small intestine. *Gastroenterology* 114(2):239–44
90. Hagiwara S, Kusano K, Saito N. 1961. Membrane changes of Onchidium nerve cell in potassium-rich media. *J. Physiol.* 155:470–89
91. Vogalis F, Lang RJ, Bywater RA, Taylor GS. 1993. Voltage-gated ionic currents in smooth muscle cells of guinea pig proximal colon. *Am. J. Physiol.* 264:C527–36
92. Akbarali HI, Hatakeyama N, Wang Q, Goyal RK. 1995. Transient outward current in opossum esophageal circular muscle. *Am. J. Physiol.* 268:G979–87
93. Doyle DA, Cabral JM, Pfuetzner RA, Kuo A, Gulbais JM, et al. 1998. The structure of the potassium channel: molecular basis of K^+ conduction and selectivity. *Science* 280:69–77
94. Vogalis F, Lang RJ. 1994. Identification of single transiently opening ("A-type") K channels in guinea pig colonic myocytes. *Pflügers Arch.* 429(2):160–64
95. Smirnov SV, Zholos AV, Shuba MF. 1992. A potential-dependent fast outward current in single smooth muscle cells isolated from the newborn rat ileum. *J. Physiol.* 454:573–89
96. Akbarali HI. 1993. K^+ currents in rabbit esophageal muscularis mucosae *Am. J. Physiol.* 264:G1001–7
97. Duridanova DB, Boev KK. 1995. Three components of potassium outward current in cells isolated from the circular layer of guinea pig ileum. *Gen. Physiol. Biophys.* 14(2):125–37
98. Duridanova DB, Gagov HS, Damyanov D, Boev KK. 1997. Two components of potassium outward current in smooth muscle cells from the circular layer of human jejunum. *Gen. Physiol. Biophys.* 16(1):49–58
99. Xiong Z, Sperelakis N, Noffsinger A, Fenoglio-Preiser C. 1995. Potassium currents in rat colonic smooth muscle cells and changes during development and aging. *Pflügers Arch.* 430(4):563–72
100. Nagano N, Imaizumi Y, Watanabe M. 1997. Effects of arachidonic acid on A-type potassium currents in smooth muscle cells of the guinea pig. *Am. J. Physiol.* 272:C860–69
101. Hong SJ, Roan YF, Chang CC. 1997. Spontaneous activity of guinea pig ileum longitudinal muscle regulated by Ca^{2+}-activated K^+ channel. *Am. J. Physiol.* 272:G962–71
102. Vogalis F, Goyal RK. 1997. Activation of small conductance Ca^{2+}-dependent K^+ channels by purinergic agonists in smooth muscle cells of the mouse ileum. *J. Physiol.* 502:497–508
103. Koh SD, Dick GM, Sanders KM. 1997. Small-conductance Ca^{2+}-dependent K^+ channels activated by ATP in murine colonic smooth muscle. *Am. J. Physiol.* 273:C2010–21
104. Vogalis F, Vincent T, Qureshi I, Schmalz F, Ward MW, et al. 1996. Cloning and expression of the large-conductance Ca^{2+}-activated K^+ channel from colonic smooth muscle. *Am. J. Physiol.* 271: G629–39
105. Carl A, Lee HK, Sanders KM. 1996. Regulation of ion channels in smooth muscles by calcium. *Am. J. Physiol.* 271:C9–34
106. Carl A, McHale NG, Publicover NG, Sanders KM. 1990. Participation of Ca^{2+}-activated K^+ channels in electrical activity of canine gastric smooth muscle. *J. Physiol.* 429:205–21
107. Carl A. Sanders KM. 1989. Ca^{2+}-activated K channels of canine colonic myocytes. *Am. J. Physiol.* 257:C470–80

108. Mayer EA, Loo DD, Kodner A, Reddy SN. 1989. Differential modulation of Ca^{2+}-activated K^+ channels by substance P. *Am. J. Physiol.* 257:G887–97
109. Jury J, Boev KR, Daniel EE. 1996. Nitric oxide mediates outward potassium currents in opossum esophageal circular smooth muscle. *Am. J. Physiol.* 270: G932–38
110. Quayle JM, Nelson MT, Standen NB. 1997. ATP-sensitive and inwardly rectifying potassium channels in smooth muscle. *Physiol. Rev.* 77(4):1165–232
111. Zini S, Ben-Ari Y, Ashford ML. 1991. Characterization of sulfonylurea receptors and the action of potassium channel openers on cholinergic neurotransmission in guinea pig isolated small intestine. *J. Pharmacol. Exp. Ther.* 259(2):566–73
112. Post JM, Stevens RJ, Sanders KM, Hume JR. 1991. Effect of cromakalim and lemakalim on slow waves and membrane currents in colonic smooth muscle. *Am. J. Physiol.* 260:C375–82
113. Carl A, Bowen S, Gelband CH, Sanders KM, Hume JR. 1992. Cromakalim and lemakalim activate Ca^{2+}-dependent K^+ channels in canine colon. *Pflügers Arch.* 421(1):67–76
114. Hatakeyama N, Wang Q, Goyal RK, Akbarali HI. 1995. Muscarinic suppression of ATP-sensitive K^+ channel in rabbit esophageal smooth muscle. *Am. J. Physiol.* 268:C877–85
115. Ohya Y, Terada K, Kitamura K, Kuriyama H. 1986. Membrane currents recorded from a fragment of rabbit intestinal smooth muscle cell. *Am. J. Physiol.* 251: C335–46
116. Muraki K, Imaizumi Y, Watanabe M. 1991. Sodium currents in smooth muscle cells freshly isolated from stomach fundus of the rat and ureter of the guinea pig. *J. Physiol.* 442:351–75
117. Yamamoto Y, Fukuta H, Suzuki H. 1993. Blockade of sodium channels by divalent cations in rat gastric smooth muscle. *Jpn. J. Physiol.* 43(6):785–96
118. Xiong Z, Sperelakis N, Noffsinger A, Fenoglio-Preiser C. 1993. Fast Na^+ current in circular smooth muscle cells of the large intestine. *Pflügers Arch.* 423(56):485–91
119. Morgan KG, Angel F, Schmalz PF, Szurszewski JH. 1985. Intracellular electrical activity of muscularis mucosae of the dog stomach. *Am. J. Physiol.* 249: G256–63
120. Ward SM, Burns AJ, Torihashi S, Sanders KM. 1994. Mutation in the proto-oncogene c-kit blocks development of interstitial cells and electrical rhythmicity in murine intestine. *J. Physiol.* 480:91–97
121. Huizinga JD, Thuneberg L, Kluppel M, Malysz J, Mikkelsen HB, Bernstein A. 1995. W/kit gene required for interstitial cells of Cajal and for intestinal pacemaker activity. *Nature* 373:347–49
122. Vanderwinden JM, Liu H, DeLaet MH, Vanderhaeghen JJ. 1996. Study of the interstitial cells of Cajal in infantile hypertrophic pyloric stenosis. *Gastroenterology* 111:279–88
123. Vanderwinden JM, Rumessen JJ, Liu H, Descamps D, DeLaet MH, Vanderhaeghen JJ. 1996. Interstitial cells of Cajal in human colon and in Hirschsprung's disease. *Gastroenterology* 111(4):901–10
124. Isozaki K, Hirota S, Miyagawa J, Taniguchi M, Shinomura Y, Matsuzawa Y. 1997. Deficiency of c-kit$^+$ cells in patients with a myopathic form of chronic idiopathic intestinal pseudo-obstruction. *Am. J. Gastroenterol.* 92(2):332–34
125. Rumessen JJ. 1996. Ultrastructure of interstitial cells of Cajal at the colonic submuscular border in patients with ulcerative colitis. *Gastroenterology* 111(6): 1447–55
126. Langton P, Ward SM, Carl A, Norell MA, Sanders KM. 1989. Spontaneous electrical activity of interstitial cells of Cajal isolated from canine proximal colon. *Proc. Natl. Acad. Sci. USA* 86(18):7280–84
127. Tokutomi N, Maeda H, Tokutomi Y, Sato D, Sugita M, et al. 1995. Rhythmic Cl^- current and physiological roles of the intestinal c-kit-positive cells. *Pflügers Arch.* 431(2):169–77
128. Thomsen L, Robinson T, Lee J, Farraway L, Huizenga JD. 1998. Characterization of spontaneous electrical activity in isolated interstitial cells of Cajal. *Neurogastroenterol. Motil.* 10(1):A104 (Abstr.)
129. Farrugia G. 1996. Modulation of ionic currents in isolated canine and human jejunal circular smooth muscle cells by fluoxetine. *Gastroenterology* 110:1438–45
130. Rich A, Farrugia G, Sarr MG, Szurszewski JH. 1998. Calcium currents in intestinal cells from human jejunum. *Gastroenterology* 114(4):A826

Annu. Rev. Physiol. 1999. 61:85–115

EXCITATION-CONTRACTION COUPLING IN GASTROINTESTINAL AND OTHER SMOOTH MUSCLES

T. B. Bolton, S. A. Prestwich, A. V. Zholos, and D. V. Gordienko
Department of Pharmacology and Clinical Pharmacology, St George's Hospital Medical School, London SW17 0RE, United Kingdom;
e-mail: t.bolton@sghms.ac.uk

KEY WORDS: ultrastructure, ion channels, calcium events, signal transduction, sarcoplasmic reticulum

ABSTRACT

The main contributors to increases in $[Ca^{2+}]_i$ and tension are the entry of Ca^{2+} through voltage-dependent channels opened by depolarization or during action potential (AP) or slow-wave discharge, and Ca^{2+} release from store sites in the cell by the action of IP_3 or by Ca^{2+}-induced Ca^{2+}-release (CICR). The entry of Ca^{2+} during an AP triggers CICR from up to 20 or more subplasmalemmal store sites (seen as hot spots, using fluorescent indicators); Ca^{2+} waves then spread from these hot spots, which results in a rise in $[Ca^{2+}]_i$ throughout the cell. Spontaneous transient releases of store Ca^{2+}, previously detected as spontaneous transient outward currents (STOCs), are seen as sparks when fluorescent indicators are used. Sparks occur at certain preferred locations—frequent discharge sites (FDSs)—and these and hot spots may represent aggregations of sarcoplasmic reticulum scattered throughout the cytoplasm. Activation of receptors for excitatory signal molecules generally depolarizes the cell while it increases the production of IP_3 (causing calcium store release) and diacylglycerols (which activate protein kinases). Activation of receptors for inhibitory signal molecules increases the activity of protein kinases through increases in cAMP or cGMP and often hyperpolarizes the cell. Other receptors link to tyrosine kinases, which trigger signal cascades interacting with trimeric G-protein systems.

0066-4278/99/0315-0085$08.00

INTRODUCTION

Excitation in its original sense as applied to nerve and skeletal muscle meant the discharge of an action potential. In smooth muscles (SMs) contraction—or, indeed, relaxation of existing tone—may occur with or without a change in potential across the cell membrane (plasmalemma), although under physiological conditions it seems likely that changes in membrane potential normally accompany changes in tension. In SMs, including those of the gastrointestinal tract, the electrical change triggering contraction is an action potential or some form of slower potential change (of which the "slow wave" is one example); the initiation of contraction by changes in the membrane potential has been termed electromechanical coupling (195). The change in membrane potential generally reflects changes in the conductance of the plasmalemma which, if not myogenic, are caused by activation of receptors by signal molecules or by stretch. Whether an action potential and/or a slow wave triggers contraction, it is likely that it is the entry of calcium through voltage-dependent channels which initiates the contractile process, although it is possible that sometimes depolarization itself plays a part. Because calcium is strongly buffered in the SM cell (buffering ratio, 30-227) (10, 63, 99, 100) the amount of entering calcium may be insufficient to raise the ionized calcium concentration, $[Ca^{2+}]_i$, throughout the cytoplasm to the required level for contraction so that in many cases calcium-induced calcium release (CICR) is necessary. Conversely, relaxation of existing tension or tone is associated with hyperpolarization; this may inhibit existing action potential discharge or simply reduce the probability of voltage-dependent calcium channels being in the open state, both of which reduce voltage-dependent calcium entry.

However, a wider definition of excitation-contraction coupling has been suggested for SMs which includes, besides electromechanical coupling, stimuli causing contraction which are not associated with electrical change in the membrane. Such mechanisms have been termed pharmacomechanical coupling (196, 197); this process involves activation of receptors which often increase $[Ca^{2+}]_i$ by releasing calcium from intracellular stores. Pharmacomechanical coupling generally involves the phospholipase C (PLC)/inositol-1,4,5-trisphosphate (IP_3)/diacylglycerol (DAG) system and often a number of other mechanisms by which SM tension can be modulated or even initiated through GTP-binding proteins (G proteins), phosphorylation and dephosphorylation reactions, and possibly others. Since pharmacomechanical coupling does not by definition involve an electrical event in the membrane, it might be argued that it does not strictly fall within the definition of excitation, although it has been deemed to do so in SM by custom and use. There are now many examples of synergism or interaction between pharmacomechanical and electromechanical mechanisms.

As in other muscles, calcium is believed to be the crucial signal for tension generation or shortening of the SM cell. However, important differences exist between SM and striated muscles; cardiac and skeletal muscle owe their striped appearance under the light microscope to the regular alternating arrangement of actin, myosin, and other contractile proteins, which gives rise to optically anisotropic bands. Other features of their ultrastructure reflect this repeating pattern of the contractile proteins: Calcium release, calcium sparks, and the arrangement of the calcium stores are also organized on the same repeating, sarcomeric pattern (45, 184). The ultrastructure of SMs is very different from that of striated muscles, and it should not therefore come as any surprise that the control of the contraction process is also very different; actin, myosin, and associated contractile proteins show no regular repeat or sarcomeric pattern; the sarcoplasmic (endoplasmic) reticulum (SR), which is believed to be the major site of calcium stores, also shows no regular periodic arrangement but is scattered in the cytoplasm. Also, myosin-actin interaction in SMs involves a calcium-calmodulin–controlled phosphorylation of the myosin light chain, quite unlike the troponin-regulated system of striated muscles. In addition, it is believed that there is some thin-filament regulation of contraction through the phosphorylation of two proteins, caldesmon and calponin, which reduces their inhibitory influence on actin-myosin interaction (5, 44; but see 156). Although SM generally contracts more slowly than skeletal muscle, it can exhibit shortening to 25% of its resting length (56) and, despite these differences from striated muscles, at optimum length it generates comparable force per cross-sectional area to striated muscle but has one-third of its myosin content; it does not show fatigue (41) and maintains tension at a much lower energy cost (167).

ULTRASTRUCTURE

A knowledge of the arrangement of the components of the contractile system and the mechanisms for the local control of calcium movements within the cell are essential for an understanding of the process of excitation-contraction coupling in SMs. While there are quantitative variations in SM structure, and occasionally special features, the basic arrangement of the contractile proteins and other intracellular organelles as seen in fixed specimens with the electron microscope is similar in all mammalian SMs, as has been known for more than 20 years (8, 40, 58, 60). The fusiform SM cell in its relaxed state is generally less than 5 μm wide [transverse sections of guinea pig taenia caeci cells in the fully relaxed state have an average area of about 10 μm^2, increasing about fivefold under conditions of extreme shortening (56)], and are up to 500 μm long, although in some situations, such as small blood vessels, they are much shorter, 20–50 μm (59). Thick myosin filaments 2.2 μm long are orientated roughly parallel to the long axis; the thinner and more numerous [about 10–12 times (range, 5 to 27)] (41, 58) actin filaments run parallel to the myosin filaments. Recent measurements indicate that they are 1.35 μm long (41). They are inserted either into dense bodies scattered within the cytoplasm or into dense bands (attachment plaques) inserted on the internal surface of the plasmalemma. Dense bodies and bands contain α-actinin and have been compared to the Z-line in striated muscles; they differ in that dense bands, but not bodies, contain vinculin (192). Tension or shortening of the contractile filaments pulls on the dense bands, causing invagination of the surface membrane at these points.

Between the sites of attachment of the dense bands are rows of flask-like caveolae intracellulares of uncertain function; two proteins, dystrophin and caveolin, are associated with the region containing these caveolae (158). Caveolin interacts with heterotrimeric G proteins, and three caveolin isomers encoded by separate genes have been identified (198, 206). Intramembranous particles have been described as surrounding the necks of caveolae (57). Especially in phasic SMs, the caveolae commonly have associated with them (within 100 nm or so of the surface plasmalemma) a network of SR tubes and fenestrated sacs in which calcium is believed to be stored. The SR contains the calcium storage proteins calsequestrin and calreticulin (136, 223) and phospholamban, a regulatory protein of the SR calcium pump (SERCA) (52, 173); SERCA can also be regulated in some SMs by direct phosphorylation by calmodulin-dependent kinase (72). The gap between the base of the caveolae and the SR membrane is shown by electron microscopy of fixed tissues to be frequently less than 20 nm, and a similar gap may separate the plasmalemma from the SR membrane in regions where caveolae are absent (40, 55); sometimes small feet are seen bridging this gap (40). Another SR, deeper within the cytoplasm, is often found extending from or associated with the Golgi apparatus or nucleus or arranged in collections of lamellae within the cytoplasm. Connections between superficial (subplasmalemmal) and deep (central) SR do occur (40, 55, 157). It is claimed that phasic SMs (e.g. vas deferens) have mainly subplasmalemmal SR, whereas tonic SMs (e.g. aorta) have small but well-developed deep SR (40, 123, 157). Mitochondria, also implicated in calcium uptake and storage (42, 70), are scattered within the cytoplasm.

Present evidence favors the idea that there are two distinguishable regions of the SM plasmalemma, one serving a force-transmission function and the other representing the site of ion exchange through channel and pump activities (158); the latter is associated with the rows of caveolae intracellulares. These two regions are arranged as roughly alternating longitudinal bands on the SM cell surface (58). When labeled antibodies were used, vinculin, a component of the dense bands to which the contractile proteins are anchored, was found not to be colocalized with either the Na/Ca exchanger or the Na/K pump. However, these were colocalized with each other and the Na/Ca exchanger also colocalized with calsequestrin (141), a calcium-binding protein found particularly in the subplasmalemmal SR (157, 215). It had been suggested on the basis of calcium oxalate precipitation experiments that the caveolae are the sites of calcium extrusion (170), and more recently immunocytochemical experiments have supported this (53). A body of indirect evidence supports the idea that calcium released from the plasmalemmal side of the superficial SR into the narrow subplasmalemmal space between it and the plasmalemma may be extruded by the plasmalemma Na/Ca exchanger rather than escaping into the general cytoplasm (116, 214). It seems possible that the caveola-rich regions between dense bands represent regions of the SM plasmalemma where ion channels and pumps are found; calcium entering through voltage-dependent channels may trigger CICR from the SR in these regions since colocalization of plasmalemmal calcium channels and SR ryanodine receptors (RyRs) in bladder SMs has been demonstrated by using fluorescent antibodies (33). Caveola-rich regions may also be the location of receptors linked to ion channels and to the PLC/IP_3 system, since the superficial SR has also been shown by immunogold staining to be rich in IP_3 receptors (54, 157, 215).

Besides actin and myosin filaments, there are also intermediate filaments containing desmin (skeletin; reported to be replaced by vimentin in vascular smooth muscle) (123), which are considered to be part of the cytoskeletal system. These insert into both dense bodies and bands. In addition, there are a number of other proteins that can be extracted from the muscle and that are considered to be part of the cytoskeletal system, although some of these have been implicated in the control of the contractile process; these include α-actinin, filamin, gelsolin, laminin, vinculin, and vimentin (200); filamin and gelsolin have been suggested to inhibit the action of caldesmon on actin filaments and thus to facilitate contraction (39, 74). Suggestions that distinct cytoskeletal and contractile protein domains exist were not borne out by studies of actin isoform distribution (41).

PLASMALEMMAL ION CHANNELS

Gastrointestinal SM generally shows slow waves of potential change; sometimes it is a matter of arbitrary definition whether a transient potential change should be regarded as an action potential or a slow wave. The form of potential changes recorded from some SMs can be variable, and graded transitions between overt action potentials and slow waves are frequent; in other cases, the form of potential change can be quite characteristic for a particular SM. The ion channel events underlying slow-wave changes are poorly understood.

The action potential in mammalian SMs of many types involves mainly an influx of calcium through voltage-dependent calcium channels, but in some SMs, sodium channels make a substantial contribution to the upstroke of the action potential. Although during the repolarization phase of the action potential there is partial inactivation and deactivation of the calcium channels, this phase is due mainly to the opening of a variety of potassium channels. These include delayed-rectifier (K_V) and calcium-activated large conductance (BK_{Ca}) channels. Other potassium channels also contribute to the form of the electrical activity in some SMs or under some conditions: These include small conductance calcium-activated (SK_{Ca}), inward-rectifier (K_{IR}), and A-type (K_A) potassium channels, potassium channels sensitive to the internal concentrations of ATP and nucleoside diphosphates (K_{ATP}), and an M-current (K_M) in toad gastric muscle. A cation channel activated by hyperpolarization (I_f) causes inward rectification. Chloride channels have also been described (202); some of these are calcium activated (Cl_{Ca}) (117). Following their discovery in other tissues (see e.g. 9) volume-activated chloride channels have recently been found in vascular smooth muscle (151, 242) and are likely to be of widespread occurrence.

Activation of receptors may open potassium (BK_{Ca}, SK_{Ca}, or K_{ATP}) or chloride channels (201) to alter excitability and tension. Receptors for excitatory substances often open cationic channels, close potassium channels (K_M), or, by raising $[Ca^{2+}]_i$, open Cl_{Ca} channels; all cause depolarization. BK_{Ca} channels may also be opened, and this presumably acts to limit the depolarization where it occurs. Cationic channels opened by stretch, $[Ca^{2+}]_i$, or caffeine and potassium channels opened by fatty acids have also been described (for reviews, see 21, 130).

The properties of ion channels in the plasmalemma largely determine the form of electrical activity shown by smooth muscles; most gastrointestinal muscles discharge action potentials or slow waves, and these reflect the activities of their plasmalemmal ion channels modified by cell-cell interactions and by the presence of membrane pumps, which are electrogenic. At present, detailed reconstructions of the form of membrane electrical activity in SMs are few (115). There is information on the types of channels present in SMs, but there are many SMs, and probably much remains to be discovered.

Calcium Channels

The voltage-dependent calcium current in many SMs is not a homogeneous current, since components with differing properties can be distinguished by holding at different potentials; thus, low-threshold and a high-threshold currents are sometimes distinguished. These are sometimes equated with transient, T, and longer-lasting, L, currents as described for other cell types, which are rapidly and more slowly inactivating and show different sensitivities to blockers such as Ni^{2+} and dihydropyridines, respectively (see e.g. 2, 15). The channel events underlying the calcium current(s) have usually been investigated by using high concentrations of Ba^{2+} on the outside of cell-attached patches; under these conditions, single-channel currents corresponding to conductances around 5–10 pS and 20–30 pS have often been described (175, 217, 240), with the occasional presence of channels of an intermediate (about 15-pS) conductance (51). Exceptional single-channel recordings have been made with as little as 0.5 mM calcium in the recording pipette, and the conductance of the 20–30-pS channel in the physiological range, between 1 and 2 mM calcium, was 5–8 pS (103). The largest-conductance channels are believed to be responsible for the L-type current and the smallest for the T-type current, and it has sometimes been possible to demonstrate this by reconstruction of the global currents from single-channel events by repeated voltage steps. The role of channels with the intermediate conductance is obscure. Although differences of these types can be discerned in some visceral SMs (237), it is seldom possible to unambiguously equate the activity of the small- and large-conductance channels with the T- and L-type whole-cell currents (217, 240), and variations in pharmacological properties of the currents are also found (2). It seems possible that modulation of calcium channel properties can occur as a result of metabolic processes in the cell; added to this, there are different sensitivities to blocking agents for reasons which are as yet obscure but are probably related to the expression of modulating systems in some SMs and not others; in addition, differences in channel structure possibly caused by combinations of different channel subunits (175) and alternative splicing of the genes (228) are involved.

Heterogeneity of the calcium current is by no means the rule, and in several gastrointestinal SMs the calcium current appears homogeneous in that different components cannot be distinguished by the use of different holding potentials (4, 185, 241). The calcium current has been suggested to play an important role in slow-wave generation in canine colonic SM: A nifedipine-resistant component has been implicated in the initiation of slow waves, and a second, sustained, nifedipine-sensitive component of the same current is believed to be responsible for calcium entry into the cell during the plateau (219, 220, 226). The ionic mechanisms underlying the electrical rhythms of gastrointestinal SMs will be considered elsewhere in this volume (see chapters by G Farrugia and by K Sanders & B Horowitz, this volume). Although a number of ion channel types have been identified in gastrointestinal SMs, which exhibit slow-wave and action potential discharge, the exact contributions of these (and other) channels to the components of the slow wave and to the bursts of action potentials that slow waves sometimes exhibit are not known (179); in multicellular preparations, there is also the unquantified role of groups of cells with differing properties, such as the interstitial cells of Cajal (see e.g. 86, 209).

Receptor activation can frequently modulate the voltage-dependent calcium current in many SM cell types via a G-protein mechanism and/or phosphorylation. The G protein involved in guinea pig ileum has been described as pertussis toxin sensitive by some (171) and insensitive by others (212). In canine and human jejunum, motilin increased the calcium current (49); introducing cholera toxin or GTPγS into the cell via the pipette during single-cell recording potentiated the calcium current, which was not inhibited by pertussis toxin, suggesting the involvement of an α-protein subunit (α_s) (47). Potentiation of the calcium current in canine colon involved a cAMP-dependent mechanism, suggesting that the effects of cholera toxin and GTPγS may occur via adenylyl cyclase stimulation (106).

Potassium Channels

Some potassium channels are open at the resting membrane potential; these include the inward rectifier (152) and noninactivating (46) channels. In gastrointestinal SMs, a number of potassium currents can be activated by changes in potential; these include an A-current (218), calcium-activated current (3, 30, 37, 50, 222, 236, 245), and more than one type of delayed-rectifier current (29, 75, 140, 163).

Large-conductance calcium-activated potassium channels (BK_{Ca}) seem almost ubiquitously distributed in SM cells. They are characterized by a conductance of about 120 pS in quasi-physiological potassium gradients and about 250 pS in symmetrical high-potassium solutions. They are blocked by charybdotoxin and iberiotoxin in low concentrations and by tetraethylammonium (IC_{50}, about 0.5 mM; higher concentrations will nonspecifically block other potassium channels). The synergism exerted by the combination of depolarization and a rise in $[Ca^{2+}]_i$ on their opening probability (14) would seem to make them ideally suited to open and repolarize the membrane following the opening of calcium channels at the upstroke of the action potential. They have been suggested to terminate the slow wave in SMs of the canine colon (32).

BK_{Ca} channels also open in response to an increase in $[Ca^{2+}]_i$ close to the plasmalemma as a result of a spontaneous transient release of calcium from stores in the cell. The resulting simultaneous opening of up to 100 BK_{Ca} channels is seen as a spontaneous transient outward current (STOC) in voltage-clamped cells held at potentials positive to E_K (12). The opening of BK_{Ca} channels can play an important role in the responses to a number of inhibitory hormones and transmitters that cause their open probability to increase, producing hyperpolarization (see below).

Following the isolation from bovine tracheal SM (65) of BK_{Ca} and cloning of its β-subunit (104), the channel has been cloned from canine colonic SM (222).

Studies have also been done on two cloned contributors to the delayed-rectifier current, $K_V1.2$ (75) and $K_V1.5$ (163).

Other Ion Channels

Sodium channels have been found in several gastrointestinal and other SMs. They carry a voltage-dependent inward current that is transient and generally lasts less than 10 ms; the major inward current in cells showing sodium currents is carried by calcium and is much longer-lasting. The sodium currents show different sensitivities to tetrodotoxin, with IC_{50} as follows: rat ileum, 4.5 nM (193); rat colon, 130 nM; human colon, 14 nM (235); rat fundus, 870 nM; guinea pig ureter, 11 nM (146); and human myometrium, <100 nM (243). Differences in channel activation and inactivation ranges were also noticed, reinforcing the idea that voltage-dependent sodium channels of SM are a heterogeneous group.

Channels activated, and some inactivated, by stretch of the membrane have been reported. Stretch has been applied mostly by negative pressure to the pipette during whole-cell tight-seal recording, although sometimes single cells have been stretched between micropipettes (230, 231). Usually the channels activated allow cations to pass, and their opening is facilitated by hyperpolarization (229). Sometimes hyperpolarization-activated channels open more readily in stretched cells (80). Stretch has also been described to increase the current through voltage-dependent calcium channels (238). Stretch also activates a potassium channel, possibly via the release of fatty acids (161). Some cation channels are inactivated by stretching (81).

SIGNAL TRANSDUCTION MECHANISMS INVOLVING ION CHANNELS

Many receptors found on SMs of the gastrointestinal tract exert their effects on the cell through heterotrimeric G-proteins. These in turn modulate the activity of enzymes (such as PLC, and protein kinases) and ion channels. Some, such as the P2X-receptor (a purinoceptor), combine a ligand-binding site and an ion channel (159). Many receptors for growth factors have tyrosine kinase activity, and some have been implicated in regulation of $[Ca^{2+}]_i$ (76, 178). Receptors can be divided conveniently into those binding signal molecules that cause contraction (excitatory receptors) and those binding signal molecules that cause relaxation (inhibitory receptors). The actions of signal molecules on ion channels in SM have been recently reviewed (11, 31).

Excitatory Receptors

These are commonly associated with G proteins, which link the activated receptors to intracellular effector mechanisms. Many types of excitatory receptor are linked through G_q, G_{11}, G_{14}, or G_{16} to PLC-β, which, from phosphatidylinositol-1,4-bisphosphate, generates DAG and IP_3. IP_3 acts on receptors on the SR and possibly elsewhere to release calcium; this causes a rise in $[Ca^{2+}]_i$, which has secondary effects on other, calcium-activated or -modulated, channels, i.e. potassium, chloride, and sometimes cation channels. Increased opening probability of the latter two causes depolarization, which allows more calcium to enter through voltage-dependent calcium channels, often because of increased action potential discharge (31). DAG stimulates the activity of protein kinase C (PKC), which in turn phosphorylates a number of proteins involved in signal transduction and contraction (85, 155, 224) and modulates the activity of some types of channel (77, 137, 216). Changes in the membrane potential can apparently affect the activity of PLC-β and the rate of IP_3 production (62, 97), as first shown by Best & Bolton (16).

The isoform PLC-γ is linked to receptors for growth factors which have intrinsic tyrosine kinase activity; activation of some G-protein-coupled receptors has been reported to cause phosphorylation of PLC-γ in vascular SM (174). A rise in $[Ca^{2+}]_i$ stimulates PLA_2 (145) or PLD (190), generating arachidonic acid or DAG (via phosphatidic acid), respectively; in addition to an effect of $[Ca^{2+}]_i$, PLA_2 activity (145) and PLD activity (190) can be regulated by several other pathways. Arachidonic acid, besides being a precursor for prostaglandins and related eicosanoids, has actions of its own on channel function (149, 162, 186), on tyrosine kinase activity (see e.g. 26), and on myosin phosphorylation (195). Phosphatidic and arachidonic acids can activate PLC-γ (174). In recent years a large number of small GTPases have been identified that are involved in cell signaling through downstream kinase cascades. Interactions between these signaling systems and trimeric G-protein systems are now being described (see e.g. 20).

A common effect of the activation of G-protein-linked excitatory receptors is the opening of cation channels. The most extensively studied cation channel in SM is found in the longitudinal muscle of the rabbit and guinea pig ileum (13, 93, 248). This current has an unusual current-voltage relationship: from its reversal potential at 0 mV to about -50 mV, the current increases in proportion to the increase in the electromotive force, but as negativity is further increased, the current progressively declines. Cation currents with similar current-voltage relationships have been found in canine gastric corpus (187), pylorus (221), and colonic muscle (120). In guinea pig ileum, the opening of the cation channels is gated by receptor activation via a pertussis toxin-sensitive G-protein link (94, 108), but opening probability is strongly increased by an increase in $[Ca^{2+}]_i$ (93). In rat ileum and canine gastric fundus, the cation current may be gated by a rise in $[Ca^{2+}]_i$ concentration (96, 187). Single-channel conductance in canine colon SM was 30 pS (221). Submaximal activation of muscarinic receptors in guinea pig ileum results in oscillations of the cation current as a result of synchronous oscillations of $[Ca^{2+}]_i$ brought about by what appears to be alternating unloading and loading of calcium stores through the action of IP_3 (107, 249).

Activation of other receptors such as histamine may elicit a cationic current (108). Caffeine has been described to open a cationic channel directly (73). In many vascular muscles, cation channels are commonly opened by activation of excitatory receptors (6). Sometimes cation channels themselves allow significant amounts of calcium to enter: ATP opens cation channels, admitting calcium in bladder SM (183).

The release of calcium from stores within the cell produced when the PLC/IP_3 system is stimulated has secondary effects on calcium-activated plasmalemma ion channels. The opening of calcium-activated cation channels has already been mentioned. In some gastrointestinal muscles, the rise in $[Ca^{2+}]_i$ also causes the opening of calcium-activated chloride (96, 225) and calcium-activated potassium (129, 188, 225) channels. Regulation of ion channels in SM by calcium has recently been reviewed (31).

A number of other effects on SM ion channels have been described. An A-type potassium current in colon and other SMs was blocked by arachidonic acid (149). Inhibition of an M-type potassium current due to activation of excitatory receptors caused depolarization, an effect mediated by DAG and so far described only for toad gastric SM (36). Mammalian gastrointestinal SM potassium currents have also been described as being inhibited by excitatory receptor activation (114); in tracheal and colonic SM, BK_{Ca} channels are inhibited through a pertussis toxin-sensitive G protein (38, 110, 111). In bladder and esophagus SM, an ATP-sensitive potassium current is inhibited (24, 77).

Inhibitory Receptors

Inhibitory receptors (which cause relaxation or reduction in tension generation) are described as working largely through cAMP and cGMP kinases, which in turn phosphorylate channels, enzymes, or membrane pumps. These actions reduce $[Ca^{2+}]_i$ by reducing calcium entry (through opening potassium channels and hyperpolarization) and by increasing calcium sequestration in stores and calcium extrusion from the cell (139, 173), possibly by increasing sodium-calcium exchange (142). In addition, effects on the relationship between tension generation and $[Ca^{2+}]_i$ are likely (194; reviewed in 109). The actions of nitric oxide (147) and carbon monoxide (48, 210) were believed to be mediated via activation of guanylate cyclase to increase the cGMP concentration (84). Three types of potassium channels in canine colon, one of which was BK_{Ca}, were opened by nitric oxide, partially through an increase in the cGMP concentration (105). Some inhibitory receptors, such as those activated by calcitonin gene-related peptide or β-adrenoceptor agonists, presumably accelerate the phosphorylation of the K_{ATP} (172, 244), BK_{Ca} (126), and delayed rectifier channels (1) by PKA through an increase in cAMP concentrations. In vascular muscle, increased opening of BK_{Ca} channels may be mediated by both cGMP phosphorylation (176, 207) and G-protein mechanisms (121); PKC activation causes inhibition (137). In tracheal SM, G_s protein mediated cAMP-dependent phosphorylation of BK_{Ca} channels and an increase in opening probability occur in response to β-adrenoceptor activation (112, 177). In toad gastric muscle, β-receptor activation gates an M-type current inhibited by excitatory muscarinic receptor activation (189).

CALCIUM-INTRACELLULAR EVENTS

Elementary Calcium Release Events

Brief spontaneous transient increases in $[Ca^{2+}]_i$ as a result of release from stores were first detected in muscle cells by the opening of calcium-activated potassium channels, which gave rise to STOCs in voltage-clamped SM cells (12, 160). Spontaneous transient increases in $[Ca^{2+}]_i$ were later detected in cardiac (34) and skeletal (211) muscle by monitoring the fluorescence of the calcium indicator dye, fluo-3, introduced into the cell. The spontaneous localized transient increase in light emission from the fluorescent calcium indicator fluo-3 has been termed a calcium spark (34). In enzymatically dispersed SM cells from the longitudinal layer of the small intestine, the rise time of the spark is about 40 ms and sparks decay to half their maximum size within about 55 ms; thus, the total event lasts about 200 ms at room temperature. Their width at half-maximum amplitude was about 2 μm, and the increase in resting fluorescence was 1.75-fold (69). In vascular SM cells, the rise time was about 20 ms and the peak increase in resting fluorescence was 3-fold, which decayed to half-maximum size in about 25–50 ms (7, 138, 150). However, in intestinal SM cells, spontaneous calcium events shorter and smaller than sparks were observed, casting doubt on the notion that the spark is the elementary calcium event (69).

STOCs in voltage-clamped single SM cells represent the opening of a few to a hundred calcium-activated large-conductance potassium channels (BK_{Ca} channels) (12). STOCs are believed to represent periodic discharges of calcium from the calcium stores within the cell; the stores are generally superficially situated, but in any case the cells in the relaxed state are seldom more than 5 μm wide, so that sparks, because they are around 2 μm wide at half-maximum size, will be sufficiently close to the membrane to raise the free-calcium concentration above the threshold for the opening of substantial numbers of BK_{Ca} channels (138, 150). The evidence that STOCs arise in this way has been recently reviewed (23). STOCs can be up to 1 nA in size, which represents the opening of perhaps as many as 100 BK_{Ca} channels simultaneously, and they last less than 100 ms at half-maximum size (12, 23, 160). Recently, we have observed in small mesenteric artery cells spontaneous transient inward currents (STICs) due to Cl_{Ca} channel opening, which were related to sparks (TB Bolton & DV Gordienko, unpublished data).

The frequency of STOCs is strongly increased by depolarizing the cell (160), and it has been argued that they represent a response to overload of the calcium stores (12, 23), although there may also be a contribution from an increased sensitivity of the BK_{Ca} channels to internal ionized calcium brought about by the depolarization (14). In cardiac muscle, the frequency of sparks increased as the calcium loading of the SR was increased (34).

Calcium-Induced Calcium Release

CICR involves a process whereby a rise in $[Ca^{2+}]_i$ triggers further calcium release from SR stores; this may happen when calcium enters the cell through voltage-dependent channels or when IP_3 releases stored calcium, and it is probably important for the propagation of intracellular calcium waves. It has been suggested that $[Ca^{2+}]_i$ must exceed 1 μM for CICR to occur (87); the relationship of RyRs to the source of the calcium flux will be crucial in achieving this threshold concentration. cADP-ribose may play a role in CICR (102). In single isolated enzyme-treated SM cells, CICR may be impaired compared to its action on the intact tissue. Depolarization of small intestine SM cells under voltage clamp evoked an inward followed by a transient outward current; the latter was abolished by acetylcholine or by caffeine, which deplete store calcium, suggesting that calcium entering through voltage-dependent channels releases stored calcium, which acts to open BK_{Ca} channels, transiently contributing to the outward current (12, 246, 247). CICR has also been described in bladder SM (61). The existence of CICR in portal vein SM cells has been denied (99), despite the findings in an earlier report (71). Evidence for limited CICR in coronary artery SM cells was found (63). Caffeine and acetylcholine also abolish STOCs, implying that sparks in SM arise by calcium release from the same store as that acted upon by entering calcium (12). In a careful study of calcium waves in cultured SM cells, Blatter & Wier (19) found that caffeine treatment abolished propagation of the wave and concluded that CICR was crucial for this process.

Calcium Waves

A calcium wave may be defined as a transient rise in intracellular $[Ca^{2+}]_i$ which propagates within the cell. The velocity of propagation of calcium waves has been described to be in the range 10–50 $\mu m \cdot s^{-1}$ (19, 90, 127, 153, 233), although recently higher values, up to 260 $\mu m \cdot s^{-1}$, have been obtained (69); in these studies, the contribution of plasmalemmal electrical events was uncertain because the membrane potential was not controlled by voltage clamp. Since SM cells are often electrically excitable, as action potentials or slow waves propagate over the plasmalemma, they will give rise to propagating calcium waves within the cell as a result of calcium entering through voltage-dependent calcium channels and triggering CICR from the subplasmalemmal SR. Action potentials propagate at about 5 $cm \cdot s^{-1}$ (113), and slow waves propagate at about 1/10 of this velocity (180, 205). The much greater velocity of plasmalemma electrical events in SMs compared with intracellular calcium waves raises the question of the physiological importance of intracellular propagation of calcium waves in these long narrow cells.

In an SM tissue where action potential propagation occurs at 5 $cm \cdot s^{-1}$, all parts of a single cell longitudinally orientated within the tissue will be excited on average within 10 ms even if the cell is 500 μm long. There will follow a phase of calcium entry into the depolarized cell, which will last some tens of milliseconds; during this phase, CICR will occur from superficial stores beneath the plasmalemma (91, 92). It seems likely from work on longitudinal SM of guinea pig ileum that entering calcium may release further calcium from sites which, during the period of observation, have frequently discharged calcium sparks and have been referred to as frequent-discharge sites (FDSs) (69). These may be the same sites as those referred to as "hot spots," where $[Ca^{2+}]_i$ first rises in the cell during the upstroke of the action potential (91). There are several FDSs, or hot spots, in any confocal plane through the cell, and it is from these that calcium waves spread throughout the cell (69, 91). The velocity of the calcium wave (30–260 $\mu m \cdot s^{-1}$) implies the presence of CICR since it is too high to be explained by simple diffusion; however, the calcium release sites involved in the calcium wave were not previously discharged by the entering calcium, yet are discharged by calcium release from an adjacent store site during calcium wave propagation (22).

Estimates of intracellular calcium wave propagation velocity perpendicular to the plasmalemma in single contracted SM cells of the guinea pig small intestine, using the line-scan mode of confocal microscopy, gave values in the range 50–75 $\mu m \cdot s^{-1}$ at room temperature (69; TB Bolton & DV Gordienko, unpublished results). In relaxed cells, no part of the cell is more than about 2 μm from the plasmalemma; this situation changes drastically upon contraction, and the question arises whether the SM cell has some special feature of the arrangement of the SR calcium stores such that rapid radial calcium wave propagation can still occur when the cell is strongly contracted. Under some conditions, for example when the muscarinic receptor is activated, intracellular calcium waves may conceivably influence membrane electrical activity through ion channels (K^+, Cl^-, or cation-selective) modulated or activated by calcium (115). These results and others indicate that, on occasions, not only do plasmalemmal electrical events trigger intracellular calcium waves but these in turn may also alter plasmalemmal electrical activity in the SM cell.

In SM cells, calcium waves that propagated through the cell could often be seen to originate from sites at which sparks were discharged (69). Although it is attractive to suppose that calcium waves and more general increases in calcium concentrations in the cell are composed of multiple elementary events (28), this is difficult to test since sparks can be discerned only when the rise in calcium concentration during a wave is small or modest. The spark probably represents a brief opening of one or a small cluster of ryanodine channels, which release calcium from the SR (34). Open times of channels are generally not constant but are exponentially distributed with one (or perhaps more than one) mean open time; therefore, it is odd that the sparks should be relatively constant in size. Clearly, some mechanism exists that confers this property; it could involve a threshold and an all-or-none (positive-feedback) process. When conditions change, such as they might during a calcium wave when the ionized-calcium concentration in the vicinity of the channel greatly increases, the mean open time may increase or more complex changes in channel kinetics may occur. Unfortunately, it is at just such times that it is difficult to visualize the component sparks, if they exist, and under these conditions calcium efflux through the open channel may be greater, perhaps proportional to the increase in channel open time, although with large increases in calcium efflux the calcium gradient might be expected to decline. RyR channels from skeletal and cardiac muscle increase their probability of the open state when [Ca^{2+}] is increased; whether the mean open time remains constant but the frequency of opening increases (as would be predicted if the spark were the elemental or quantal event underlying all SR calcium releases) has not been resolved (118, 191).

SARCOPLASMIC RETICULUM

Ryanodine Receptor/Calcium Release Channel

Three isoforms of the RyR have been cloned and sequenced. Several alternatively spliced forms are known for each isoform. All have been described to be present in SMs, although the identity of the RyR types in individual SMs is just now beginning to be explored (66, 67, 123, 154). The RyR includes a cation channel which, after isolation and reconstitution in bilayers, was found to be 7.4 times more permeable to calcium than to potassium (234). Two types of RyR function are believed to exist: In skeletal muscle, a direct coupling of membrane depolarization to RyR channel opening is brought about by an association between a voltage- and dihydropyridine-sensitive calcium channel and the RyR; in cardiac muscle, a process of CICR occurs whereby calcium entering through these calcium channels triggers further calcium release through RyRs from the SR stores (203, 250). At present, such evidence as exists favors the notion that the situation in SM resembles that in cardiac muscle; however, a direct coupling such as that in skeletal muscle has by no means been eliminated as a possibility in all SMs, perhaps especially those which have been shown to have large inward sodium currents (see above).

Spliced variants of the isoforms designated RyR1, RyR2, and RyR3 have been identified in various SMs including esophagus, stomach, and small intestine (presumably in the SM of these organs). There is likely to be a tissue-specific distribution of these isoforms, but the physiological significance of this is not yet apparent (67, 119, 128, 154). RyRs are distributed on both superficial and deep SR (123).

Few electrophysiological studies exist concerning the behavior in bilayers of the isolated RyR channel from SMs (78, 239), but the evidence suggests that the channel probably behaves similarly to those from cardiac and skeletal muscles, where ryanodine and its analogs cause the channel to open and then be fixed in a partially open state or, at higher concentrations, to be blocked (208). Some SMs such as myometrium do not respond to caffeine by releasing calcium (124, 181, 182); this has been suggested to result from the expression of RyR3, which was observed to be insensitive to caffeine (66; but see 135).

Caffeine or ryanodine can act on the RyR to deplete or reduce the amount of calcium in the stores and block CICR (246, 247), slowing the recovery of $[Ca^{2+}]_i$ following a calcium load (61). Application of ryanodine, which opens calcium channels in the SR (83), or inhibition of SERCA by cyclopiazonic acid (144, 169, 213) or thapsigargin (169; but see 134) generally causes a rise in $[Ca^{2+}]_i$ and often in tension (213) in SM cells. It seems likely that the SR calcium pump is continuously active, perhaps especially if channels are opened in the SR through which calcium can escape to increase $[Ca^{2+}]_i$ in its vicinity (199). Treatment with ryanodine and then caffeine results in a persistent increase in $[Ca^{2+}]_i$ and tension in SM of gastric antrum (35); this treatment probably fixes the RyR channels in the open state so that no calcium can be stored. Readmission of calcium to SMs where the calcium stores have been depleted causes contraction which is delayed compared to when the calcium stores are full, presumably because calcium is first taken up to fill the empty stores and this initially reduces the amounts reaching the contractile proteins (82, 214). Superficial stores fill more rapidly than deeper ones (27, 64). However, treatment with caffeine or ryanodine to deplete SR calcium stores does not accelerate the removal of a calcium load in toad gastric myocytes (133), and a similar result was obtained, after treatment with cyclopiazonic acid or thapsigargin, which should inhibit filling of the SR stores (134).

The postulated vectorial transport of calcium by the plasmalemma (116, 214) presumably depends on calcium being present in the superficial SR and its continual extrusion from this into the 10-nm space between the plasmalemma (or caveolar) membrane and superficial SR outer membrane; from here it is suggested to bind to the Na^+/Ca^{2+} exchanger and to be extruded to the exterior. When the calcium stores under the plasmalemma are rendered inoperative, it would be expected that the total capacity of processes to remove calcium from the cell would be reduced, and the $[Ca^{2+}]_i$ deep in the cell (which represents an equilibrium between these processes and calcium entering the cell) would be expected to rise. However, the $[Ca^{2+}]_i$ immediately below the plasmalemma, between it and the superficial SR, would be predicted to fall when the SR calcium store is depleted, since vectorial calcium transport to the exterior will cease; the predicted fall in subplasmalemmal $[Ca^{2+}]_i$ provides an explanation for the reduction in calcium-activated potassium current evoked upon depolarization when ryanodine (204), cyclopiazonic acid (98), or thapsigargin (61) is applied to SM cells, as well as the depolarization of the resting potential (125, 213) if this current normally makes a contribution. Conversely, an increase in this current is seen when SERCA is stimulated by nitric oxide, sodium nitroprusside, or sin-1 (98), which are believed to increase cGMP; membrane-permeable analogs of cGMP have a similar effect. If calcium-activated potassium channels can make a contribution to the resting membrane potential, they also provide an explanation for the relaxation caused by sodium nitroprusside and other nitric oxide donors (68, 168, 169). However, the relaxant effect of β-receptor activation is unaffected by ryanodine depletion of the calcium stores, suggesting that cAMP does not modulate SERCA (83).

Some observations are not consistent with the vectorial transport of calcium via superficial SR stores and Na/Ca exchanger to the exterior. Following a calcium load (induced by opening of voltage-dependent calcium channels) applied to single voltage-clamped toad gastric SM cells, the rate of fall of $[Ca^{2+}]_i$ is not affected by cyclopiazonic acid, thapsigargin, caffeine, or ryanodine (133, 134). It is, however, decreased under conditions where the ability of the Na/Ca exchanger to extrude calcium would be impaired, such as when the sodium gradient is reversed or abolished. These results argue that Na/Ca exchange is important quantitatively in removing a calcium load, at least in some SMs (but not guinea pig colonic SM, 132), and that most of the calcium it extrudes does not pass obligatorily through the superficial SR calcium stores.

When the calcium stores are empty, calcium entry may increase owing to activation of a calcium entry pathway (calcium release-activated channels), which is insensitive to organic calcium entry blockers. A similar effect can be produced if calcium stores are depleted by activating receptors, which increases IP_3 production, or if cyclopiazonic acid or thapsigargin is used to inhibit SERCA (148, 164, 169, 227).

Mitochondria also play a significant role in the calcium economy of the SM cell. They take up calcium following a calcium load applied to the cell, and this process is slowed by mitochondrial inhibitors or inhibitors of calmodulin-dependent PKII (42, 70, 133, 134).

Inositol Trisphosphate Calcium Release Channel

When many G-protein-linked receptors are activated, IP_3 is formed in increased amounts through stimulation of PLC activity. Three types of IP_3 receptor have been reported to be present in SM (95, 143). IP_3 receptors are distributed on both superficial and deep SR (157), and in intestinal SM about 10 times more IP_3 receptors than RyRs were found by cell fractionation and binding studies (232). The action of IP_3 on its receptor is blocked by heparin, which does not block and may potentiate, the opening of RyR receptors. In bilayers, the IP_3 receptor calcium channel has a conductance in quasi-physiological calcium gradients, of 30–50 pS, depending on whether a lipid bilayer was seeded with purified receptor (131) or with a microsomal preparation containing the receptor (17). SM microsomes from canine aorta gave a lower value under different conditions (43). It has been calculated that the current through the channel under physiological conditions might be 0.5 pA (17). Its opening in response to IP_3 is potentiated by low and inhibited by high concentrations of calcium (17, 18, 88). Cytoplasmic calcium and IP_3 synergize in opening the IP_3-receptor channel (79). ATP also potentiates the opening of the channel (89). The potentiating effect of SR luminal $[Ca^{2+}]$ on IP_3-mediated calcium release may contribute to the phenomenon whereby the long-lasting application of submaximally effective concentrations of IP_3 does not release all stored calcium (so-called quantal calcium release) even if SERCA is inhibited by thapsigargin and the $[Ca^{2+}]_i$ is heavily buffered (166). In such experiments, it is necessary to be certain that all SR calcium pumps have been completely inhibited, because the simultaneous operation of the SERCA pump with the opening of calcium channels in the SR can produce an equilibrium situation (199); this has been suggested to provide an explanation for the phenomenon of quantal release in the case of the RyR. A number of other explanations have been proffered for quantal release (25, 166). Further properties of the IP_3 receptor channel have been reviewed (17).

In single cells, oscillations of $[Ca^{2+}]_i$ can be observed in response to activation of G-protein-linked receptors that generate IP_3. These oscillations can also be observed when the membrane potential of single cells is voltage clamped; therefore, the oscillation presumably does not involve potential-dependent plasmalemma channels but originates in the interior of the cell and involves the SR. The oscillations in response to muscarinic receptor activation can be monitored by the change in size of the cationic current, which is modulated by $[Ca^{2+}]_i$. Photolytic release of IP_3 from an inert precursor at different times with respect to the oscillations of $[Ca^{2+}]_i$ suggested that IP_3 was able to release calcium from the SR when $[Ca^{2+}]_i$ was low (and the level of calcium in the SR high) and was not able to release it when $[Ca^{2+}]_i$ was high (and the level of calcium in the SR lower) (107, 249). It seemed possible that while IP_3 production may be steady, the release of a small amount of calcium from the SR results in a potentiation of the action of IP_3 on the SR and further calcium release; a regenerative system is thereby formed which may release most of the SR calcium content, at which point calcium release will cease and $[Ca^{2+}]_i$ will fall as the SR fills (107). Essentially similar conclusions have been reached on the basis of other types of experiment (90).

It has been suggested that IP_3 receptors occur in clusters and that some form of concerted opening of the channels within a cluster occurs to produce "puffs;" smaller increases in $[Ca^{2+}]_i$ that were detected ("blips") could represent openings of single IP_3 receptor calcium channels (165). Binding studies indicate that in intestinal SM there are about 10 times more IP_3 receptors than RyRs (232). However, the relationship between these and their locations on the SR or elsewhere is imperfectly known or understood. In guinea pig longitudinal intestinal muscle, where IP_3-mediated oscillations in $[Ca^{2+}]_i$ readily occur in response to activation of various plasmalemma receptors, similar oscillations are not seen in response to caffeine (107, 249). The STOC frequency may be increased by lower concentrations of caffeine, and STOCs may be regarded as a type of (irregular) oscillation; more regular oscillations occur in other SMs in response to caffeine (101, 122). Possibly, calcium potentiates the opening of RyR channels at a higher concentration than is required to potentiate the opening of IP_3 calcium channels in the SR.

SUMMARY AND CONCLUSIONS

Contraction or tension generation by SMs generally involves some form of depolarization of the membrane, which admits more calcium into the cell through voltage-dependent calcium channels; hyperpolarization has the opposite effect and is associated with relaxation of existing tension. In gastrointestinal SMs, depolarization occurs through the discharge of action potentials or slow waves, although slower depolarization may occur on occasion. Receptor activation triggers other mechanisms that raise $[Ca^{2+}]_i$: the most important of these is the PLC/IP_3/DAG system; calcium may also enter through channels opened by receptor activation or stretch. Receptors for excitatory signal molecules are mostly G protein coupled and may modulate ion channel activity directly (and thus electrical activity) or via phosphorylation. In addition, a number of receptors are known to activate tyrosine kinases directly without the intervention of G proteins and to interact with G protein-coupled systems. Although a change in $[Ca^{2+}]_i$ is the most important mechanism for the control of tension, other G protein- and kinase-mediated mechanisms are able to modulate or even perhaps initiate tension generation, or to inhibit it, producing relaxation.

The plasmalemma of the SM cell appears to have two domains: One of these acts as an anchor site for the contractile proteins, and the other may be the location of most of the ion channels and ion pumps; the latter has the caveolae and is related to the SR. These two domains exist as parallel longitudinal stripes on the plasmalemma. SR is reported to be superficially located in phasic SMs but to be more extensive and located centrally in tonic SMs, which do not readily generate action potentials and generally show only slow changes in potential.

The rise in $[Ca^{2+}]_i$ produced by calcium entry into the cell, or perhaps by the action of IP_3 produced as a result of receptor activation, may trigger further calcium release from calcium stores in the cell by a CICR process. The main calcium stores are believed to exist in the SR, although mitochondria also have a storage role. The SR has both RyRs and IP_3 receptors. Spontaneous calcium discharges (sparks) occur in certain preferred locations, the FDSs; sparks give rise to STOCs and/or STICs. Recent evidence suggests that in phasic SMs generating action potentials and/or slow waves, RyRs are located in relation to calcium fluxes such that, during calcium entry through voltage-dependent calcium channels, a high $[Ca^{2+}]_i$ is achieved in their vicinity, resulting in CICR. Calcium entering the cell through voltage-dependent calcium channels triggers calcium release first from hot spots, which may be identical to FDSs; from these, a calcium wave spreads to other parts of the cell by CICR. IP_3 receptors, when activated, may create sufficient calcium flux from the SR for CICR also to occur.

The level of $[Ca^{2+}]_i$ can feed back to affect plasmalemmal electrical activity by increasing the probability of opening of calcium-activated K^+, Cl^+, and cation channels. There is also evidence that the state of filling of the calcium stores in the SR may modulate calcium-activated K^+ channel activity in the plasmalemma and that when SR calcium storage is increased, the outward BK_{Ca} current is also increased. These effects may be manifestations of the vectorial transport of calcium by the SR to the exterior across the narrow gap between it and the plasmalemma, although not all observations are consistent with this interpretation.

ACKNOWLEDGMENT

During the writing of this review, the authors' work was supported by the U.K. Medical Research Council and The Wellcome Trust.

Literature Cited

1. Aiello EA, Walsh MP, Cole WC. 1995. Phosphorylation by protein kinase A enhances delayed rectifier K^+ current in rabbit vascular smooth muscle cells. *Am. J. Physiol.* 268:H926–34
2. Akaike N, Kanaide H, Takeshi K, Nakamura M, Sadoshima J-I, Tomoike H. 1989. Low-voltage activated calcium current in rat aorta smooth muscle cells in primary culture. *J. Physiol.* 416:141–60
3. Akbarali HI. 1993. K^+ currents in rabbit esophageal muscularis mucosae. *Am. J. Physiol.* 264:G1001–7
4. Akbarali HI, Giles WR. 1993. Ca^{2+}- and Ca^{2+}-activated Cl^- currents in rabbit oesophageal smooth muscle. *J. Physiol.* 460:117–33
5. Allen BG, Walsh MP. 1994. The biochemical basis of the regulation of smooth-muscle contraction. *Trends Biochem. Sci.* 19:362–68
6. Amédée T, Benham CD, Bolton TB, Byrne NG, Large WA. 1990. Potassium, chloride and non-selective cation conductances opened by noradrenaline in rabbit ear artery cells. *J. Physiol.* 423:551–68
7. Arnaudeau S, Macrez-Leprêtre N, Mironneau J. 1996. Activation of calcium sparks by angiotensin II in vascular myocytes. *Biochem. Biophys. Res. Commun.* 222:809–15
8. Bagby RM. 1983. Organization of contractile/cytoskeletal elements. In *Biochemistry of Smooth Muscle*, ed. NL Stephens, pp. 1–84. Boca Raton, FL: CRC
9. Bakhramov A, Fenech C, Bolton TB. 1995. Chloride current activated by hypotonicity in cultured human astrocytoma cells. *Exp. Physiol.* 80:373–89
10. Becker PL, Singer JJ, Walsh JV, Fay FS. 1989. Regulation of calcium concentration in voltage-clamped smooth muscle cells. *Science* 244:211–14
11. Beech DJ. 1997. Actions of neurotransmitters and other messengers on Ca^{2+} channels and K^+ channels in smooth muscle cells. *Pharmacol. Ther.* 73:91–119
12. Benham CD, Bolton TB. 1986. Spontaneous transient outward currents in single visceral and vascular smooth muscle cells of the rabbit. *J. Physiol.* 381:385–406
13. Benham CD, Bolton TB, Lang RJ. 1985. Acetylcholine activates an inward current in single mammalian smooth muscle cells. *Nature* 316:345–47
14. Benham CD, Bolton TB, Lang RJ, Takewaki T. 1986. Calcium-activated potassium channels on single smooth muscle cells of rabbit jejunum and guinea-pig mesenteric artery. *J. Physiol.* 371:45–67
15. Benham CD, Hess P, Tsien RW. 1987. Two types of calcium channels in single smooth muscle cells from rabbit ear artery studied with whole-cell and single-channel recordings. *Circ. Res.* 61:10–16 (Suppl. I)
16. Best L, Bolton TB. 1986. Depolarization of guinea-pig visceral smooth muscle causes hydrolysis of inositol phospholipids. *Naunyn-Schmiedeberg's Arch. Pharmacol.* 333:78–82
17. Bezprozvanny I, Ehrlich BE. 1995. The inositol 1,4,5-trisphosphate ($InsP_3$) receptor. *Membr. Biol.* 145:205–16
18. Bezprozvanny I, Watras J, Ehrlich BE. 1991. Bell-shaped calcium-response curves of Ins(1,4,5)P_3 and calcium-gated channels from sarcoplasmic reticulum of cerebellum. *Nature* 351:751–54
19. Blatter LA, Wier WG. 1992. Agonist-induced $[Ca^{2+}]_i$ waves and Ca^{2+}-induced Ca^{2+} release in mammalian vascular smooth muscle cells. *Am. J. Physiol.* 263:H576–86
20. Bokoch GM. 1996. Interplay between Ras-regulated and heterotrimeric GTP binding proteins: lifestyles of the big and little. *FASEB J.* 10:1290–95
21. Bolton TB, Beech DJ. 1992. Smooth muscle potassium channels: their electrophysiology and function. In *Potassium Channel Modulators: Pharmacological, Molecular and Clinical Aspects*, ed. AH Weston, TC Hamilton, pp. 144–80. London: Blackwell
22. Bolton TB, Gordienko DV. 1998. Confocal imaging of calcium release events in single smooth muscle cells. *Acta Physiol. Scand.* In press
23. Bolton TB, Imaizumi Y. 1996. Spontaneous transient outward currents in smooth muscle cells. *Cell Calcium* 20:141–52
24. Bonev AD, Nelson MT. 1993. Muscarinic inhibition of ATP-sensitive K^+ channels by protein kinase C in urinary bladder smooth muscle. *Am. J. Physiol.* 265:C1723–28
25. Bootman M. 1994. Questions about quantal Ca^{2+} release. *Curr. Biol.* 4:169–72
26. Buckley BJ, Whorton AR. 1995. Arachidonic acid stimulates tyrosine phosphorylation in vascular cells. *Am. J. Physiol.* 269:C1489–95
27. Buryi VA, Gordienko DV, Shuba MF.

1994. Two kinds of spatially separated caffeine-sensitive calcium stores in smooth muscle cells from guinea-pig mesenteric artery. In *The Resistance Arteries*, ed. W Halpern, J Bevan, J Brayden, H Dustan, M Nelson, G Osol, pp. 71–82. Totowa, NJ: Humana
28. Cannell MB, Cheng H, Lederer WJ. 1995. The control of calcium release in heart muscle. *Science* 268:1045–49
29. Carl A. 1995. Multiple components of delayed rectifier K^+ current in canine colonic smooth muscle. *J. Physiol.* 484: 339–53
30. Carl A, Kenyon JL, Uemura D, Fusetani N, Sanders KM. 1991. Regulation of Ca^{2+}-activated K^+ channels by protein kinase A and phosphatase inhibitors. *Am. J. Physiol.* 261:C387–92
31. Carl A, Lee HK, Sanders KM. 1996. Regulation of ion channels in smooth muscles by calcium. *Am. J. Physiol.* 271:C9–34
32. Carl A, Sanders KM. 1989. Ca^{2+}-activated K channels of canine colonic myocytes. *Am. J. Physiol.* 257:C470–80
33. Carrington WA, Lynch RM, Moore EDW, Isenberg G, Fogarty KE, Fay FS. 1995. Superresolution three-dimensional images of fluorescence in cells with minimal light exposure. *Science* 268:1483–87
34. Cheng H, Lederer WJ, Cannell MB. 1993. Calcium sparks: elementary events underlying excitation-contraction coupling in heart muscle. *Science* 262:740–44
35. Chowdhury JU, Pang Y-W, Huang S-M, Tsugeno M, Tomita T. 1995. Sustained contraction produced by caffeine after ryanodine treatment in the circular muscle of the guinea-pig gastric antrum and rabbit portal vein. *Br. J. Pharmacol.* 114: 1414–18
36. Clapp LH, Sims SS, Singer JJ, Walsh JV. 1992. Role for diacylglycerol in mediating the actions of Ach on M-current in gastric smooth muscle cells. *Am. J. Physiol.* 263:C1274–81
37. Cole WC, Sanders KM. 1989. Characterization of macroscopic outward currents of canine colonic myocytes. *Am. J. Physiol.* 257:C461–69
38. Cole WC, Sanders KM. 1989. G proteins mediate suppression of Ca^{2+}-activated K current by acetylcholine in smooth muscle cells. *Am. J. Physiol.* 257:C596–600
39. Dabrowska R, Hinssen H, Galazkiewicz B, Nowak E. 1996. Modulation of gelsolin-induced actin-filament severing by caldesmon and tropomyosin and the effect of these proteins on the actin activation of myosin Mg^{2+}-ATPase activity. *Biochem. J.* 315:753–59
40. Devine CE, Somlyo AV, Somlyo AP. 1972. Sarcoplasmic reticulum and excitation-contraction coupling in mammalian smooth muscles. *J. Cell Biol.* 52:690–718
41. Drew JS, Murphy RA. 1997. Actin isoform expression, cellular heterogeneity, and contractile function in smooth muscle. *Can. J. Physiol. Pharmacol.* 75:869–77
42. Drummond RM, Fay FS. 1996. Mitochondria contribute to calcium removal in smooth muscle cells. *Pflügers Arch.* 431:473–82
43. Ehrlich BE, Watras J. 1988. Inositol 1,4,5-trisphosphate activates a channel from smooth muscle sarcoplasmic reticulum. *Nature* 336:583–86
44. El-Mezgueldi M. 1996. Calponin. *Int. J. Biochem. Cell Biol.* 28:1185–89
45. Escobar AL, Monck JR, Fernandez JM, Vergara JL. 1994. Localization of the site of Ca^{2+} release at the level of a single sarcomere in skeletal muscle fibres. *Nature* 367:739–41
46. Evans AM, Osipenko ON, Gurney AM. 1996. Properties of a novel K^+ current that is active at resting potential in rabbit pulmonary artery smooth muscle cells. *J. Physiol.* 496:407–20
47. Farrugia G. 1997. G-protein regulation of an L-type calcium channel current in canine jejunal circular smooth muscle. *J. Membr. Biol.* 160:39–46
48. Farrugia G, Irons WA, Rae JL, Sarr MG, Szurszewski JH. 1993. Activation of whole cell currents in isolated human jejunal circular smooth muscle cells by carbon monoxide. *Am. J. Physiol.* 264:G1184–89
49. Farrugia G, Macielag MJ, Peters TL, Sarr MG, Galdes A, Szurszewski JH. 1997. Motilin and OHM-11526 activate a calcium current in human and canine jejunal circular smooth muscle. *Am. J. Physiol.* 273:G404–12
50. Farrugia G, Rae JL, Sarr MG, Szurszewski JH. 1993. Potassium current in circular smooth muscle of human jejunum activated by fenamates. *Am. J. Physiol.* 265:G873–79
51. Farrugia G, Rich A, Rae JL, Sarr MG, Szurszewski JH. 1995. Calcium currents in human and canine jejunal circular smooth muscle cells. *Gastroenterology* 109:707–17
52. Ferguson DG, Young EF, Raeymaekers L, Kranias EG. 1988. Localization of phospholamban in smooth muscle using immunogold electron microscopy. *J. Cell Biol.* 107:555–62

53. Fujimoto T. 1993. Calcium pump of the plasma membrane is localized in caveolae. *J. Cell Biol.* 120:1147–57
54. Fujimoto T, Nakade S, Miyawaki A, Mikoshiba K, Ogawa K. 1992. Localization of inositol 1,4,5-trisphosphate receptor-like protein in plasmalemmal caveolae. *J. Cell Biol.* 119:1507–13
55. Gabella G. 1971. Caveolae intracellulares and sarcoplasmic reticulum in smooth muscle. *J. Cell Sci.* 8:601–9
56. Gabella G. 1976. Structural changes in smooth muscle cells during isotonic contraction. *Cell Tissue Res.* 170:187–201
57. Gabella G. 1978. Inpocketings of the cell membrane (caveolae) in the rat myocardium. *J. Ultrastruct. Res.* 65:135–47
58. Gabella G. 1981. Structure of smooth muscles. In *Smooth Muscle: An Assessment of Current Knowledge*, ed. E Bulbring, AF Brading, AW Jones, T Tomita, pp. 1–46. London: Edward Arnold
59. Gabella G. 1983. Asymmetric distribution of dense bands in muscle cells of mammalian arterioles. *J. Ultrastruct. Res.* 84:24–33
60. Gabella G. 1989. Structure of intestinal musculature. In *Handbook of Physiology: The Gastrointestinal System*, ed. JD Wood, pp. 103–39. New York: Oxford Univ. Press
61. Ganitkevich VY, Isenberg G. 1992. Contribution of Ca^{2+}-induced Ca^{2+} release to the $[Ca^{2+}]_i$ transients in myocytes from guinea-pig urinary bladder. *J. Physiol.* 458:119–37
62. Ganitkevich VY, Isenberg G. 1993. Membrane potential modulates inositol 1,4,5-trisphosphate-mediated Ca^{2+} transients in guinea-pig coronary myocytes. *J. Physiol.* 470:35–44
63. Ganitkevich VY, Isenberg G. 1995. Efficacy of peak Ca^{2+} currents (I_{Ca}) as triggers of sarcoplasmic reticulum Ca^{2+} release in myocytes from the guinea-pig coronary artery. *J. Physiol.* 484:287–306
64. Ganitkevich VY, Isenberg G. 1996. Dissociation of subsarcolemmal from global cytosolic $[Ca^{2+}]$ in myocytes from guinea-pig coronary artery. *J. Physiol.* 490:305–18
65. Garcia-Calvo M, Knaus H-G, McManus OB, Giangiacomo KM, Kaczorowski GJ, Garcia ML. 1994. Purification and reconstitution of the high-conductance, calcium-activated potassium channel from tracheal smooth muscle. *J. Biol. Chem.* 289:676–82
66. Giannini G, Clementi E, Ceci R, Marziali G, Sorrentino V. 1992. Expression of a ryanodine receptor-Ca^{2+} channel that is regulated by TGF-β. *Science* 257:91–94
67. Giannini G, Conti A, Mammarella S, Scrobogna M, Sorrentino V. 1995. The ryanodine receptor/calcium channel genes are widely and differentially expressed in murine brain and peripheral tissues. *J. Cell Biol.* 128:893–904
68. Gibson A, McFadzean I, Tucker JF, Wayman C. 1994. Variable potency of nitrergic-nitrovasodilator relaxations of the mouse anococcygeus against different forms of induced tone. *Br. J. Pharmacol.* 113:1494–1500
69. Gordienko DV, Bolton TB, Cannell MB. 1998. Variability in spontaneous subcellular calcium release in guinea-pig ileum smooth muscle cells. *J. Physiol.* 507:707–20
70. Greenwood IA, Helliwell RM, Large WA. 1997. Modulation of Ca^{2+}-activated Cl^- currents in rabbit portal vein smooth muscle by an inhibitor of mitochondrial Ca^{2+} uptake. *J. Physiol.* 505:53–64
71. Grégoire G, Loirand G, Pacaud P. 1993. Ca^{2+} and Sr^{2+} entry induced Ca^{2+} release from the intracellular Ca^{2+} store in smooth muscle cells of rat portal vein. *J. Physiol.* 474:483–500
72. Grover AK, Xu A, Samson SE, Narayanan N. 1996. Sarcoplasmic reticulum Ca^{2+} pump in pig coronary artery smooth muscle is regulated by a novel pathway. *Am. J. Physiol.* 271:C181–87
73. Guerrero A, Fay FF, Singer JJ. 1994. Caffeine activates a Ca^{2+}-permeable nonselective cation channel in smooth muscle cells. *J. Gen. Physiol.* 104:375–94
74. Gusev NB, Pritchard K, Hodgkinson JL, Marston SB. 1994. Filamin and gelsolin influence Ca^{2+}-sensitivity of smooth muscle thin filaments. *J. Muscle Res. Cell Motil.* 15:672–81
75. Hart PJ, Overturf KE, Russell SN, Carl A, Hume JR, et al. 1993. Cloning and expression of a $K_V1.2$ class delayed rectifier K^+ channel from canine colonic smooth muscle. *Proc. Natl. Acad. Sci. USA* 90:9659–63
76. Hatakeyama N, Mukhopadhyay D, Goyal RK, Akbarali HI. 1996. Tyrosine kinase-dependent modulation of calcium entry in rabbit colonic muscularis mucosae. *Am. J. Physiol.* 270:C1780–89
77. Hatakeyama N, Wang Q, Goyal RK, Akbarali HI. 1995. Muscarinic suppression of ATP-sensitive K^+ channel in rabbit esophageal smooth muscle. *Am. J. Physiol.* 268:C877–85

78. Herrmann-Frank A, Darling E, Meissner G. 1991. Functional characterization of the Ca^{2+}-gated Ca^{2+} release channel of vascular smooth muscle sarcoplasmic reticulum. *Pflügers Arch.* 418:353–59
79. Hirose K, Kadowaki S, Iino M. 1998. Allosteric regulation by cytoplasmic Ca^{2+} and IP_3 of the gating of IP_3 receptors in permeabilized guinea-pig vascular smooth muscle cells. *J. Physiol.* 506:407–14
80. Hisada T, Ordway RW, Kirber MT, Singer JJ, Walsh JV. 1991. Hyperpolarization-activated cationic channels in smooth muscle cells are stretch sensitive. *Pflügers Arch.* 417:493–99
81. Hisada T, Walsh JV, Singer JJ. 1993. Stretch-inactivated cationic channels in single smooth muscle cells. *Pflügers Arch.* 422:393–96
82. Hisayama T, Takayanagi I. 1988. Ryanodine: its possible mechanism of action in the caffeine-sensitive calcium store of smooth muscle. *Pflügers Arch.* 412:376–81
83. Hisayama T, Takayanagi I, Okamoto Y. 1990. Ryanodine reveals multiple contractile and relaxant mechanisms in vascular smooth muscle: simultaneous measurements of mechanical activity and of cytoplasmic free Ca^{2+} level with fura-2. *Br. J. Pharmacol.* 100:677–84
84. Hobbs AJ. 1997. Soluble guanylate cyclase: the forgotten sibling. *Trends Pharmacol. Sci.* 18:484–91
85. Horowitz A, Menice CB, Laporte R, Morgan KG. 1996. Mechanisms of smooth muscle contraction. *Physiol. Rev.* 76:967–1002
86. Huizinga JD, Thuneberg L, Vanderwinden J-M, Rumessen JJ. 1997. Interstitial cells of Cajal as targets for pharmacological intervention in gastrointestinal motor disorders. *Trends Pharmacol. Sci.* 18:393–403
87. Iino M. 1989. Calcium-induced calcium release mechanism in guinea pig taenia caeci. *J. Gen. Physiol.* 94:363–83
88. Iino M. 1990. Biphasic Ca^{2+} dependence of inositol 1,4,5-trisphosphate-induced Ca release in smooth muscle of the guinea-pig taenia caeci. *J. Gen. Physiol.* 95:1103–22
89. Iino M. 1991. Effects of adenine nucleotides on inositol 1,4,5-trisphosphate-induced calcium release in vascular smooth muscle cells. *J. Gen. Physiol.* 98: 681–98
90. Iino M, Yamazawa T, Miyashita Y, Endo M, Kasai H. 1993. Critical intracellular Ca^{2+} concentration for all-or-none Ca^{2+} spiking in single smooth muscle cells. *EMBO J.* 12:5287–91
91. Imaizumi Y, Torii Y, Ohi Y, Nagano N, Atsuki K, et al. 1998. Ca^{2+} images and K^+ current during depolarization in smooth muscle cells of the guinea-pig vas deferens and urinary bladder. *J. Physiol.* 510: 705–19
92. Imaizumi Y, Torii Y, Ooi Y, Muraki K, Bolton TB, et al. 1997. Ca^{2+} imaging by fast scanning confocal microscopy during action potential in smooth muscle cells. *Biophys. J.* 72:A343 (Abstr.)
93. Inoue R, Isenberg G. 1990. Intracellular calcium ions modulate acetylcholine-induced inward current in guinea-pig ileum. *J. Physiol.* 424:73–92
94. Inoue R, Isenberg G. 1990. Acetylcholine activates nonselective cation channels in guinea pig ileum through a G protein. *Am. J. Physiol.* 258:C1173–78
95. Islam MO, Yoshida Y, Koga T, Kojima M, Kangawa K, Imai S. 1996. Isolation and characterization of vascular smooth muscle inositol 1,4,5-trisphosphate receptor. *Biochem. J.* 316:295–302
96. Ito S, Ohta T, Nakazato Y. 1993. Inward current activated by carbachol in rat intestinal smooth muscle cells. *J. Physiol.* 470:395–409
97. Itoh T, Seki N, Suzuki S, Ito S, Kajikuri J, Kuriyama H. 1992. Membrane hyperpolarization inhibits agonist-induced synthesis of inositol 1,4,5-trisphosphate in rabbit mesenteric artery. *J. Physiol.* 451:307–28
98. Jury J, Boev KR, Daniel EE. 1996. Nitric oxide mediates outward potassium currents in opossum esophageal circular smooth muscle. *Am. J. Physiol.* 270: G932–38
99. Kamishima T, McCarron JG. 1996. Depolarization-evoked increases in cytosolic calcium concentration in isolated smooth muscle cells of rat portal vein. *J. Physiol.* 492:61–74
100. Kamishima T, McCarron JG. 1997. Regulation of cytosolic Ca^{2+} concentration by Ca^{2+} stores in single smooth muscle cells from rat cerebral arteries. *J. Physiol.* 501:497–508
101. Kang TM, So I, Kim KW. 1995. Caffeine- and histamine-induced oscillations of $K_{(Ca)}$ current in single smooth muscle cells of rabbit cerebral artery. *Pflügers Arch.* 431:91–100
102. Kannan MS, Fenton AM, Prakash YS, Sieck GC. 1996. Cyclic ADP-ribose stimulates sarcoplasmic reticulum release in porcine coronary artery smooth muscle. *Am. J. Physiol.* 270:H801–6

103. Klockner U. 1996. Voltage-dependent L-type calcium channels in smooth muscle cells. In *Smooth Muscle Excitation*, ed. TB Bolton, T Tomita, pp. 1–12. London: Academic
104. Knaus H-G, Folander K, Garcia-Calvo M, Garcia ML, Kaczorowski GJ, et al. 1994. Primary sequence and immunological characterization of β-subunit of high conductance Ca^{2+}-activated K^+ channel from smooth muscle. *J. Biol. Chem.* 269:17274–78
105. Koh SD, Campbell JD, Carl A, Sanders KM. 1995. Nitric oxide activates multiple potassium channels in canine colonic smooth muscle. *J. Physiol.* 489:735–43
106. Koh SD, Sanders KM. 1996. Modulation of Ca^{2+} current in canine colonic myocytes by cyclic nucleotide-dependent mechanisms. *Am. J. Physiol.* 271:C794–803
107. Komori S, Kawai M, Pacaud P, Ohashi H, Bolton TB. 1993. Oscillations of receptor-operated cationic current and internal calcium in single guinea-pig ileal smooth muscle cells. *Pflügers. Arch.* 424:431–38
108. Komori S, Kawai M, Takewaki T, Ohashi H. 1992. GTP-binding protein involvement in membrane currents evoked by carbachol and histamine in guinea-pig ileal muscle. *J. Physiol.* 450:105–26
109. Kotlikoff MI, Kamm KE. 1996. Molecular mechanisms of β-adrenergic relaxation of airway smooth muscle. *Annu. Rev. Physiol.* 58:115–41
110. Kume H, Graziano MP, Kotlikoff MI. 1992. Stimulatory and inhibitory regulation of calcium-activated potassium channels by guanine nucleotide-binding proteins. *Proc. Natl. Acad. Sci. USA* 89: 11051–55
111. Kume H, Kotlikoff MI. 1991. Muscarinic inhibition of single K_{Ca} channels in smooth muscle cells by a pertussis-sensitive G protein. *Am. J. Physiol.* 261: C1204–9
112. Kume H, Takai A, Tokuno H, Tomita T. 1989. Regulation of Ca^{2+}-dependent K^+-channel activity in tracheal myocytes by phosphorylation. *Nature* 341:152–54
113. Kuriyama H. 1970. Effects of ions and drugs on the electrical activity of smooth muscle. In *Smooth Muscle*, ed. E Bulbring, AF Brading, AW Jones, T Tomita, pp. 366–95. London: Edward Arnold
114. Lammel E, Deitmer P, Noack T. 1991. Suppression of steady membrane currents by acetylcholine in single smooth muscle cells of the guinea-pig gastric fundus. *J. Physiol.* 432:259–82
115. Lang RJ, Rattray-Wood CA. 1996. A simple mathematical model of the spontaneous electrical activity in a single smooth muscle myocyte. In *Smooth Muscle Excitation*, ed. TB Bolton, T Tomita, pp. 391–402. London: Academic
116. Laporte R, Laher I. 1997. Sarcoplasmic reticulum-sarcolemma interactions and vascular smooth muscle tone. *J. Vasc. Res.* 34:325–43
117. Large WA, Wang Q. 1996. Characteristics and physiological role of the Ca^{2+}-activated Cl^- conductance in smooth muscle. *Am. J. Physiol.* 271:C435–54
118. Laver DR, Curtis BA. 1996. Response of ryanodine receptor channels to Ca^{2+} steps produced by rapid solution exchange. *Biophys. J.* 71:732–41
119. Ledbetter MW, Preiner JK, Louis CF, Mickelson JR. 1994. Tissue distribution of ryanodine receptor isoforms and alleles determined by reverse transcription polymerase chain reaction. *J. Biol. Chem.* 269:31544–51
120. Lee HK, Bayguinov O, Sanders KM. 1993. Role of nonselective cation current in muscarinic responses of canine colonic muscle. *Am. J. Physiol.* 265:C1463–71
121. Lee M-Y, Chung S, Bang H-W, Baek KJ, Uhm D-Y. 1997. Modulation of large conductance Ca^{2+}-activated K^+ channel by $G\alpha_h$ (transglutaminase II) in the vascular smooth muscle cell. *Pflügers. Arch.* 433:671–73
122. Lee SH, Earm YE. 1994. Caffeine induces periodic oscillations of Ca^{2+}-activated K^+ current in pulmonary arterial smooth muscle cells. *Pflügers Arch.* 426:189–98
123. Lesh RE, Nixon GF, Fleischer S, Airey JA, Somlyo AP, Somlyo AV. 1998. Localization of ryanodine receptors in smooth muscle. *Circ. Res.* 82:175–85
124. Lynn S, Morgan JM, Gillespie JI, Greenwell JR. 1993. A novel ryanodine sensitive calcium release mechanism in cultured human myometrial smooth muscle cells. *FEBS Lett.* 330:227–30
125. Maggi CA, Giuliani S, Santicioli P. 1995. Effect of the Ca^{2+}-ATPase inhibitor, cyclopiazonic acid, on electromechanical coupling in the guinea-pig ureter. *Br. J. Pharmacol.* 114:127–37
126. Maggi CA, Giuliani S, Zagorodnyuk V. 1996. Calcitonin gene-related peptide (CGRP) in the circular muscle of guinea-pig colon: role as inhibitory transmit-

ter and mechanisms of relaxation. *Regul. Peptides* 61:27–36

127. Mahoney MG, Slakey LI, Hepler PK, Gross DJ. 1993. Independent modes of propagation of calcium waves in smooth muscle cells. *J. Cell Sci.* 104:1101–7
128. Marziali G, Rossi D, Giannini G, Charlesworth A, Sorrentino V. 1996. cDNA cloning reveals a tissue specific expression of alternatively spliced transcripts of the ryanodine receptor type 3 (RyR3) calcium release channel. *FEBS Lett.* 394:76–82
129. Mayer EA, Loo DDF, Kodner A, Reddy SN. 1989. Differential modulation of Ca^{2+}-activated K^+ channels by substance P. *Am. J. Physiol.* 257:G887–97
130. Mayer EA, Sun XP, Willenbucher RF. 1992. Contraction coupling in colonic smooth muscle. *Annu. Rev. Physiol.* 54: 395–414
131. Mayrleitner M, Chadwick CC, Timerman AP, Fleischer S, Schindler H. 1991. Purified IP_3 receptor from smooth muscle forms an IP_3 gated and heparin sensitive Ca^{2+} channel in planer bilayers. *Cell Calcium* 12:505–14
132. McCarron JG, Muir TC. 1998. Role of Na^+/Ca^{2+} exchange in the regulation of the cytosolic Ca^{2+} concentration ($[Ca^{2+}]_i$) in guinea-pig colonic myocytes. *J. Physiol.* 509:110p (Abstr.)
133. McGeown JG, Drummond RM, McCarron JG, Fay FS. 1996. The temporal profile of calcium transients in voltage-clamped gastric myocytes from *Bufo marinus*. *J. Physiol.* 497:321–36
134. McGeown JG, McCarron JG, Drummond RM, Fay FS. 1998. Calcium-calmodulin-dependent mechanisms accelerate calcium decay in gastric myocytes from *Bufo marinus*. *J. Physiol.* 506:95–197
135. McPherson PS, Kim Y-K, Valdivia H, Knudson CM, Takekura H, et al. 1991. The brain ryanodine receptor: a caffeine-sensitive calcium release channel. *Neuron* 7:17–25
136. Milner RE, Baksh S, Shemanko C, Carpenter MR, Smillie L, et al. 1991. Calreticulin, and not calsequestrin, is the major calcium binding protein of smooth muscle sarcoplasmic reticulum and liver endoplasmic reticulum. *J. Biol. Chem.* 266:7155–65
137. Minami K, Fukuzawa K, Nakaya Y. 1993. Protein kinase C inhibits the Ca^{2+}-activated K^+ channel of cultured porcine coronary artery smooth muscle cells. *Biochem. Biophys. Res. Commun.* 190:263–69
138. Mironneau J, Arnaudeau S, Macrez-Leprêtre N, Boittin FX. 1996. Ca^{2+} sparks and Ca^{2+} waves activate different Ca^{2+}-dependent ion channels in single myocytes from rat portal vein. *Cell Calcium* 20:153–60
139. Missiaen L, De Smedt H, Droogmans G, Himpens B, Casteels R. 1992. Calcium ion homeostasis in smooth muscle. *Pharmacol. Ther.* 56:191–231
140. Molleman A, Thuneberg L, Huizinga JD. 1993. Characterization of the outward rectifying potassium channel in a novel mouse intestinal smooth muscle cell preparation. *J. Physiol.* 470:211–29
141. Moore EDW, Etter EE, Philipson KD, Carrington WA, Fogarty KE, et al. 1993. Coupling of the Na^+/Ca^{2+} exchanger, Na^+/K^+ pump and sarcoplasmic reticulum in smooth muscle. *Nature* 365:657–60
142. Moore EDW, Fay FS. 1993. Isoproterenol stimulates rapid extrusion of sodium from isolated smooth muscle cells. *Proc. Natl. Acad. Sci. USA* 90:8058–62
143. Morgan JM, De Smedt H, Gillespie JI. 1996. Identification of three isoforms of the $InsP_3$ receptor in human myometrial smooth muscle. *Pflügers Arch.* 431:697–705
144. Munro DD, Wendt IR. 1994. Effects of cyclopiazonic acid on $[Ca^{2+}]_i$ and contraction in rat urinary bladder smooth muscle. *Cell Calcium* 15:369–80
145. Murakami M, Nakatani Y, Atsumi G-I, Inoue K, Kudo I. 1997. Regulatory functions of phospholipase A_2. *Crit. Rev. Immunol.* 17:225–83
146. Muraki K, Imaizumi Y, Watanabe M. 1991. Sodium currents in smooth muscle cells freshly isolated from stomach fundus of the rat and ureter of the guinea-pig. *J. Physiol.* 442:351–76
147. Murray JA, Shibata EF, Buresh TL, Picken H, O'Meara BW, Conkin JL. 1995. Nitric oxide modulates a calcium-activated potassium current in muscle cells from opossum esophagus. *Am. J. Physiol.* 269:G606–12
148. Murray RK, Kotlikoff MI. 1991. Receptor-activated calcium influx in human airway smooth muscle cells. *J. Physiol.* 435:123–44
149. Nagano N, Imaizumi Y, Watanabe M. 1997. Effects of arachidonic acid on A-type potassium currents in smooth muscle cells of the guinea-pig. *Am. J. Physiol.* 272:C860–69
150. Nelson MT, Cheng H, Rubart M, Santana LF, Bonev AD, et al. 1995. Relaxation of

arterial smooth muscle by calcium sparks. *Science* 270:633–37
151. Nelson MT, Conway MA, Knot HJ, Brayden JE. 1997. Chloride channel blockers inhibits myogenic tone in rat cerebral arteries. *J. Physiol.* 502:259–64
152. Nelson MT, Quayle JM. 1995. Physiological roles and properties of potassium channels in arterial smooth muscle. *Am. J. Physiol.* 268:C799–822
153. Neylon CB, Hoyland J, Mason WT, Irvine RF. 1990. Spatial dynamics of intracellular calcium in agonist-stimulated vascular smooth muscle cells. *Am. J. Physiol.* 259:C675–86
154. Neylon CB, Richards SM, Larsen MA, Agrotis A, Bobik A. 1995. Multiple types of ryanodine receptor/Ca^{2+} release channels are expressed in vascular smooth muscle. *Biochem. Biophys. Res. Commun.* 215:814–21
155. Nishizuka Y. 1995. Protein kinase C and lipid signaling for sustained cellular responses. *FASEB J.* 9:484–96
156. Nixon GF, Iizuka K, Haystead CMM, Haystead TAJ, Somlyo AP, Somlyo AV. 1995. Phosphorylation of caldesmon by mitogen-activated protein kinase with no effect on Ca^{2+} sensitivity in rabbit smooth muscle. *J. Physiol.* 487:283–89
157. Nixon GF, Mignery GA, Somlyo AV. 1994. Immunogold localization of inositol 1,4,5-trisphosphate receptors and characterization of ultrastructural features of the sarcoplasmic reticulum in phasic and tonic smooth muscle. *J. Muscle Res. Cell Motil.* 15:682–700
158. North AJ, Galazkiewicz B, Byers TJ, Glenney JR, Small JV. 1993. Complementary distributions of vinculin and dystrophin define two distinct sarcolemma domains in smooth muscle. *J. Cell Biol.* 120:1159–67
159. North RA. 1996. Families of ion channels with two hydrophobic segments. *Curr. Opin. Cell Biol.* 8:474–83
160. Ohya Y, Kitamura K, Kuriyama H. 1987. Cellular calcium regulates outward currents in rabbit intestinal smooth muscle cell. *Am. J. Physiol.* 252:C401–10
161. Ordway RW, Petrou S, Kirber MT, Walsh JV, Singer JJ. 1995. Stretch activation of a toad smooth muscle K^+ channel may be mediated by fatty acids. *J. Physiol.* 484:331–37
162. Ordway RW, Walsh JV, Singer JJ. 1989. Arachidonic acid and other fatty acids directly activate potassium channels in smooth muscle cells. *Science* 244:1176–79
163. Overturf KE, Russell SN, Carl A, Vogalis F, Hart JH, et al. 1994. Cloning and characterization of a K_V 1.5 delayed rectifier K^+ channel from vascular and visceral smooth muscles. *Am. J. Physiol.* 267:C1231–38
164. Pacaud P, Bolton TB. 1991. Relation between muscarinic receptor cationic current and internal calcium in guinea-pig jejunal smooth muscle cells. *J. Physiol.* 441:477–99
165. Parker I, Yao Y. 1996. Ca^{2+} transients associated with openings of inositol trisphosphate-gated channels in *Xenopus* oocytes. *J. Physiol.* 491:663–68
166. Parys JB, Missiaen L, De Smedt H, Sienaert I, Casteels R. 1996. Mechanisms responsible for quantal Ca^{2+} release from inositol trisphosphate-sensitive calcium stores. *Pflügers Arch.* 432:359–67
167. Paul RJ, Gluck E, Ruegg JC. 1976. Cross bridge ATP utilization in arterial smooth muscle. *Pflügers Arch.* 361:297–99
168. Petkov G, Duridanova D, Gagov H, Boev K. 1994. Effects of sodium nitroprusside on the electrical and contractile activity of cat gastric antrum. *C. R. Acad. Bulg. Sci.* 47:61–64
169. Petkov GV, Boev KK. 1996. The role of sarcoplasmic reticulum and sarcoplasmic reticulum Ca^{2+}-ATPase in the smooth muscle tone of the cat gastric fundus. *Pflügers Arch.* 431:928–35
170. Popescu LM, Diculescu I, Zelck U, Ionescu N. 1974. Ultrastructural distribution of calcium in smooth muscle cells of guinea-pig taenia coli. *Cell Tissue Res.* 154:357–78
171. Pucovsky V, Zholos AV, Bolton TB. 1998. Muscarinic cation current and suppression of Ca^{2+} current in guinea-pig ileal smooth muscle cells. *Eur. J. Pharmacol.* 346:323–30
172. Quayle JM, Bonev AD, Brayden JE, Nelson MT. 1994. Calcitonin gene-related peptide activated ATP-sensitive K^+ currents in rabbit arterial smooth muscle via protein kinase A. *J. Physiol.* 475:9–13
173. Raeymaekers L, Wuytack F. 1993. Ca^{2+} pumps in smooth muscle cells. *J. Muscle Res. Cell Motil.* 14:141–57
174. Rhee SG, Bae YS. 1997. Regulation of phosphoinositide-specific phospholipase C isoenzymes. *J. Biol. Chem.* 272:15045–48
175. Rich A, Kenyon JL, Hume JR, Overturf K, Horowitz B, Sanders KM. 1993. Dihydropyridine-sensitive calcium channels expressed in canine colonic smooth muscle cells. *Am. J. Physiol.* 264:C745–54

176. Robertson BE, Schubert R, Hescheler J, Nelson MT. 1993. cGMP-dependent protein kinase activates Ca-activated K channels in cerebral artery smooth muscle cells. *Am. J. Physiol.* 265:C299–303
177. Sadoshima J-I, Akaike N, Kanaide H, Nakamura M. 1988. Cyclic AMP modulates Ca-activated K channel in cultured smooth muscle cells of rat aortas. *Am. J. Physiol.* 255:H754–59
178. Salvo JD, Nelson SR, Kaplan N. 1997. Protein tyrosine phosphorylation in smooth muscle: a potential coupling mechanism between receptor activation and intracellular calcium. *Proc. Soc. Exp. Biol. Med.* 214:285–301
179. Sanders KM. 1992. Ionic mechanisms of electrical rhythmicity in gastrointestinal smooth muscles. *Annu. Rev. Physiol.* 54:439–53
180. Sanders KM, Publicover NG. 1989. Electrophysiology of the gastric musculature. In *Handbook of Physiology: The Gastrointestinal System*, ed. SG Schultz, pp. 187–216. New York: Oxford Univ. Press
181. Savineau J-P. 1988. Caffeine does not contract skinned uterine fibers with a functional calcium store. *Eur. J. Pharmacol.* 149:187–90
182. Savineau J-P, Mironneau J. 1990. Caffeine acting on pregnant rat myometrium: analysis of its relaxant action and its failure to release Ca^{2+} from intracellular stores. *Br. J. Pharmacol.* 99:261–66
183. Schneider P, Hopp HH, Isenberg G. 1991. Ca^{2+} influx through ATP-gated channels increments $[Ca^{2+}]_i$ and inactivates I_{Ca} in myocytes from guinea-pig urinary bladder. *J. Physiol.* 440:479–96
184. Shacklock PS, Wier WG, Balke CW. 1995. Local Ca^{2+} transients (Ca^{2+} sparks) originate at transverse tubules in rat heart cells. *J. Physiol.* 487:601–8
185. Shimada T. 1993. Voltage-dependent calcium channel current in isolated gallbladder smooth muscle cells of guinea-pig. *Am. J. Physiol.* 264:G1066–76
186. Shimada T, Somlyo AP. 1992. Modulation of voltage-dependent Ca channel current by arachidonic acid and other long chain fatty acids in rabbit intestinal smooth muscle. *J. Gen. Physiol.* 100:27–44
187. Sims SM. 1992. Cholinergic activation of a non-selective cation current in canine gastric smooth muscle is associated with contraction. *J. Physiol.* 449:377–98
188. Sims SM, Vivaudou MB, Hillemeier C, Biancani P, Walsh JV, Singer JJ. 1990. Membrane currents and cholinergic regulation of K^+ current in esophageal smooth muscle cells. *Am. J. Physiol.* 258:G794–802
189. Sims SS, Clapp LH, Walsh JV, Singer JJ. 1990. Dual regulation of M current in gastric smooth muscle cells: β-adrenergic-muscarinic antagonism. *Pflügers Arch.* 417:291–302
190. Singer WD, Brown HA, Sternweis PC. 1997. Regulation of eukaryotic phosphatidylinositol-specific phospholipase C and phospholipase D. *Annu. Rev. Biochem.* 66:475–509
191. Sitsapesan R, Montgomery RAP, Williams AJ. 1995. New insights into the gating mechanisms of cardiac ryanodine receptors revealed by rapid changes in ligand concentration. *Circ. Res.* 77:765–72
192. Small JV, Sobieszek A. 1983. Contractile and structural proteins of smooth muscle. In *Biochemistry of Smooth Muscle*, ed. NL Stephens, 1:85–140. Boca Raton, FL: CRC
193. Smirnov SV, Zholos AV, Shuba MF. 1992. Potential-dependent inward currents in single isolated smooth muscle cells of the rat ileum. *J. Physiol.* 454:549–71
194. Smith TK, Ward SM, Zhang L, Buxton ILO, Gerthoffer WT, et al. 1993. β-adrenergic inhibition of electrical and mechanical activity in canine colon: role of cAMP. *Am. J. Physiol.* 264:G708–17
195. Somlyo AP, Somlyo AV. 1994. Signal transduction and regulation in smooth muscle. *Nature* 372:231–36
196. Somlyo AV, Somlyo AP. 1968. Electromechanical and pharmacomechanical coupling in vascular smooth muscle. *J. Pharmacol. Exp. Ther.* 159:129–45
197. Somlyo AV, Vinall P, Somlyo AP. 1969. Excitation-contraction coupling and electrical events in two types of vascular smooth muscle. *Microvasc. Res.* 1:354–73
198. Song KS, Scherer PE, Tang Z, Okamoto T, Li S, et al. 1996. Expression of caveolin-3 in skeletal, cardiac, and smooth muscle cells. Caveolin-3 is a component of the sarcolemma and co-fractionates with dystrophin and dystrophin-associated glycoproteins. *J. Biol. Chem.* 271:15160–65
199. Steenberger JM, Fay FS. 1996. The quantal nature of calcium release to caffeine in single smooth muscle cells results from activation of the sarcoplasmic reticulum Ca^{2+}-ATPase. *J. Biol. Chem.* 271:1821–24

200. Stromer MH. 1995. Immunocytochemistry of the muscle cell cytoskeleton. *Microsc. Res. Tech.* 31:95–105
201. Sun XP, Supplison S, Mayer E. 1993. Chloride channels in myocytes from rabbit colon are regulated by a pertussis toxin-sensitive G protein. *Am. J. Physiol.* 264:G774–85
202. Sun XP, Supplison S, Torres R, Sach G, Mayer E. 1992. Characterization of large-conductance chloride channels in rabbit colonic smooth muscle. *J. Physiol.* 448:355–82
203. Sutko JL, Airey JA. 1996. Ryanodine receptor Ca^{2+} release channels: does diversity in form equal diversity in function? *Physiol. Rev.* 76:1027–71
204. Suzuki M, Muraki K, Imaizumi Y, Watanabe M. 1992. Cyclopiazonic acid, an inhibitor of the sarcoplasmic reticulum Ca^{2+} pump, reduces Ca^{2+}-dependent K^+ currents in guinea-pig smooth muscle cells. *Br. J. Pharmacol.* 107:134–40
205. Szurszewski JH. 1987. Electrical basis for gastrointestinal motility. In *Physiology of the Gastrointestinal Tract*, ed. LR Johnson, pp. 383–422. New York: Raven 2nd ed.
206. Tang Z, Scherer PE, Okamoto T, Song K, Chu C, et al. 1996. Molecular cloning of caveolin-3, a novel member of the caveolin gene family expressed predominantly in muscle. *J. Biol. Chem.* 271:2255–61
207. Taniguchi J, Furukawa K-I, Shigekawa M. 1993. Maxi K^+ channels are stimulated by cyclic guanosine monophosphate-dependent protein kinase in canine coronary smooth muscle cells. *Pflügers Arch.* 423:167–72
208. Tinker A, Sutko JL, Ruest L, Deslongchamps P, Welch W, et al. 1996. Electrophysiological effects of ryanodine derivatives on the sheep cardiac sarcoplasmic reticulum calcium-release channel. *Biophys. J.* 70:2110–19
209. Torihashi S, Ward SM, Nishikawa S-I, Nishi K, Kobayashi S, Sanders KM. 1995. c-kit-dependent development of interstitial cells and electrical activity in the murine gastrointestinal tract. *Cell Tissue Res.* 280:97–111
210. Trischmann U, Klockner U, Isenberg G, Utz J, Ullrich V. 1991. Carbon monoxide inhibits depolarization-induced Ca rise and increases cyclic GMP in visceral smooth muscle cells. *Biochem. Pharmacol.* 41:237–41
211. Tsugorka A, Rios E, Blatter LA. 1995. Imaging elementary events of calcium release in skeletal muscle cells. *Science* 269:1723–26
212. Unno T, Komori S, Ohashi H. 1995. Inhibitory effect of muscarinic receptor activation on Ca^{2+} channel current in smooth muscle cells of guinea-pig ileum. *J. Physiol.* 484:567–81
213. Uyama Y, Imaizumi Y, Watanabe M. 1992. Effects of cyclopiazonic acid, a novel Ca^{2+}-ATPase inhibitor, on contractile responses in skinned ileal smooth muscle. *Br. J. Pharmacol.* 106:208–14
214. van Breemen C, Chen Q, Laher I. 1995. Superficial buffer barrier function of smooth muscle sarcoplasmic reticulum. *Trends Pharmacol. Sci.* 16:98–105
215. Villa A, Podini P, Panzeri MC, Soling HD, Volpe P, Meldolesi J. 1993. The endoplasmic-sarcoplasmic reticulum of smooth muscle: immunocytochemistry of vas deferens fibers reveals specialized subcompartments differently equipped for the control of Ca^{2+} homeostasis. *J. Cell Biol.* 121:1041–51
216. Vivaudou MB, Clapp LH, Walsh JV, Singer JJ. 1988. Regulation of one type of Ca^{2+} current in smooth muscle cells by diacylglycerol and acetylcholine. *FASEB J.* 2:2497–504
217. Vivaudou MB, Singer JJ, Walsh JV. 1991. Multiple types of Ca^{2+} channels in visceral smooth muscle cells. *Pflügers Arch.* 418:144–52
218. Vogalis F, Lang RJ, Bywater RAR, Taylor GS. 1993. Voltage-gated ionic currents in smooth muscle cells of guinea-pig proximal colon. *Am. J. Physiol.* 264:C527–36
219. Vogalis F, Publicover NG, Hume JH, Sanders KM. 1991. Relationship between calcium current and cytosolic calcium in canine gastric smooth muscle. *Am. J. Physiol.* 260:C1012–18
220. Vogalis F, Publicover NG, Sanders KM. 1992. Regulation of calcium current by voltage and cytoplasmic calcium in canine gastric smooth muscle. *Am. J. Physiol.* 262:C691–700
221. Vogalis F, Sanders KM. 1990. Cholinergic stimulation activates a non-selective cation current in canine pyloric circular muscle cells. *J. Physiol.* 429:223–36
222. Vogalis F, Vincent T, Qureshi I, Schmalz F, Ward MW, et al. 1996. Cloning and expression of the large-conductance Ca^{2+}-activated K^+ channel from colonic smooth muscle. *Am. J. Physiol.* 271: G629–39
223. Volpe P, Martini A, Furlan S, Meldolesi J. 1994. Calsequestrin is a component of smooth muscles: the skeletal- and

cardiac-muscle isoforms are both present, although in highly variable amounts and ratios. *Biochem. J.* 301:465–69
224. Walsh MP, Horowitz A, Clément-Chomienne O, Andrea JE, Allen BG, Morgan KG. 1996. Protein kinase C mediation of Ca^{2+}-independent contractions of vascular smooth muscle. *Biochem. Cell Biol.* 74:485–502
225. Wang Q, Akbarali HI, Hatakeyama N, Goyal RK. 1996. Caffeine- and carbachol-induced Cl^- and cation currents in single opossum esophageal circular smooth muscle cells. *Am. J. Physiol.* 271: C1725–34
226. Ward SM, Sanders KM. 1992. Upstroke component of electrical slow wave in canine colonic smooth muscle due to nifedipine-resistant calcium current. *J. Physiol.* 455:321–37
227. Wayman CP, Gibson A, McFadzean I. 1998. Depletion of either ryanodine- or IP_3-sensitive calcium stores activates capacitative calcium entry in mouse anococcygeus smooth muscle cells. *Pflügers Arch.* 435:231–39
228. Welling A, Ludwig A, Zimmer S, Klugbauer N, Flockerzi V, Hofmann F. 1997. Alternatively spliced IS6 segments of the α_{1C} gene determine the tissue-specific dihydropyridine sensitivity of cardiac and vascular smooth muscle L-type Ca^{2+} channels. *Circ. Res.* 81:526–32
229. Wellner M-C, Isenberg G. 1993. Properties of stretch-activated channels in myocytes from the guinea-pig urinary bladder. *J. Physiol.* 466:213–27
230. Wellner M-C, Isenberg G. 1994. Stretch effects on whole-cell currents of guinea-pig urinary bladder myocytes. *J. Physiol.* 480:439–48
231. Wellner M-C, Isenberg G. 1995. cAMP accelerates the decay of stretch-activated currents in guinea-pig urinary bladder myocytes. *J. Physiol.* 482:141–56
232. Wibo M, Godfraind T. 1994. Comparative localization of inositol 1,4,5-trisphosphate and ryanodine receptors in intestinal smooth muscle: an analytical subfractionation study. *Biochem. J.* 297: 415–23
233. Wier WG, Blatter LA. 1991. Ca^{2+}-oscillations and Ca^{2+}-waves in mammalian cardiac and vascular smooth muscle cells. *Cell Calcium* 12:241–54
234. Williams AJ. 1992. Ion conductance and discrimination in the sarcoplasmic reticulum ryanodine receptor/calcium release channel. *J. Muscle Res. Cell Motil.* 13:7–26
235. Xiong Z, Sperelakis N, Noffsinger A, Fenoglio-Preiser C. 1993. Fast Na^+ current in circular smooth muscle cells of the large intestine. *Pflügers Arch.* 423:485–91
236. Xiong A, Sperelakis N, Noffsinger A, Fenoglio-Preiser C. 1995. Potassium currents in rat colonic smooth muscle cells and changes during development and aging. *Pflügers Arch.* 430:563–72
237. Xiong Z, Sperelakis N, Noffsinger A, Fenoglio-Preiser C. 1995. Ca^{2+} currents in human colonic smooth muscle cells. *Am. J. Physiol.* 269:G378–85
238. Xu WX, Kim SJ, So I, Kang TM, et al. 1996. Effect of stretch on calcium channel currents recorded from the antral circular myocytes of guinea-pig stomach. *Pflügers Arch.* 432:159–64
239. Xu L, Lai FA, Cohn A, Etter E, Guerrero A, et al. 1994. Evidence for a Ca^{2+}-gated ryanodine-sensitive Ca^{2+} release channel in visceral smooth muscle. *Proc. Natl. Acad. Sci. USA* 91:3294–98
240. Yabu H, Yoshino M, Someya T, Totsuka M. 1990. Two types of Ca channels in smooth muscle cells isolated from guinea-pig taenia coli. *Adv. Exp. Med. Biol.* 255:129–34
241. Yamamoto Y, Hu SL, Kao CY. 1989. Inward current in single smooth muscle cells of the guinea-pig taenia coli. *J. Gen. Physiol.* 93:521–50
242. Yamazaki J, Duan D, Janiak R, Kuenzli K, Horowitz B, Hume JR. 1998. Functional and molecular expression of volume-regulated chloride channels in canine vascular smooth muscle cells. *J. Physiol.* 507:729–36
243. Young RC, Herndon-Smith L. 1991. Characterization of sodium channels in cultured human uterine smooth muscle cells. *Am. J. Obstet. Gynecol.* 164:175–81
244. Zhang L, Bonev AD, Mawe GM, Nelson MT. 1994. Protein kinase A mediates activation of ATP-sensitive K^+ currents by CGRP in gallbladder smooth muscle. *Am. J. Physiol.* 267:G494–99
245. Zhang L, Bonev AD, Nelson MT, Mawe GM. 1993. Ionic basis of the action potential of guinea-pig gallbladder smooth muscle cells. *Am. J. Physiol.* 265:C1552–61
246. Zholos AV, Baidan LV, Shuba MF. 1991. Properties of the late transient outward current in isolated intestinal smooth muscle cells of the guinea-pig. *J. Physiol.* 443:555–74
247. Zholos AV, Baidan LV, Shuba MF. 1992. Some properties of Ca^{2+}-induced Ca^{2+}

release mechanism in single visceral smooth muscle cell of guinea-pig. *J. Physiol.* 457:1–25
248. Zholos AV, Bolton TB. 1994. G-protein control of voltage dependence as well as gating of muscarinic metabotropic channels in guinea-pig ileum. *J. Physiol.* 478:195–202
249. Zholos AV, Komori S, Ohashi H, Bolton TB. 1994. Ca^{2+} inhibition of inositol trisphosphate-induced release in single smooth muscle cells of guinea-pig small intestine. *J. Physiol.* 481:97–109
250. Zucchi R, Ronca-Testoni S. 1997. The sarcoplasmic reticulum Ca^{2+} channel/ryanodine receptor: modulation by endogenous effectors, drugs and disease states. *Pharmacol. Rev.* 49:1–51

Annu. Rev. Physiol. 1999. 61:117–42

THE ENTERIC NERVOUS SYSTEM AND REGULATION OF INTESTINAL MOTILITY

W. A. A. Kunze and J. B. Furness
Department of Anatomy and Cell Biology, University of Melbourne, Parkville, Victoria 3052, Australia; e-mail: w.kunze@anatomy.unimelb.edu.au

KEY WORDS: afferent neurons, neural integration, synaptic transmission, sensory transduction, enteric reflexes

ABSTRACT

The enteric nervous system exerts local control over mixing and propulsive movements in the small intestine. When digestion is in progress, intrinsic primary afferent neurons (IPANs) are activated by the contents of the intestine. The IPANs that have been physiologically characterized are in the intrinsic myenteric ganglia. They are numerous, about 650/mm length of small intestine in the guinea pig, and communicate with each other through slow excitatory transmission to form self-reinforcing assemblies. High proportions of these neurons respond to chemicals in the lumen or to tension in the muscle; physiological stimuli activate assemblies of hundreds or thousands of IPANs. The IPANs make direct connections with muscle motor neurons and with ascending and descending interneurons. The circular muscle contracts as an annulus, about 2–3 mm in minimum oral-to-anal extent in the guinea pig small intestine. The smooth muscle cells form an electrical syncytium that is innervated by about 300 excitatory and 400 inhibitory motor neurons per mm length. The intrinsic nerve circuits that control mixing and propulsion in the small intestine are now known, but it remains to be determined how they are programmed to generate the motility patterns that are observed.

INTRODUCTION

The patterns of motility of the gastrointestinal tract include mixing and propulsive movements, which are more or less confined to regions, and organized

0066-4278/99/0315-0117$08.00

patterns of movement such as swallowing and esophageal peristalsis, migrating complexes, vomiting, and defecation, which involve large sections of the digestive tract. In general, mixing and propulsive movements in the small and large intestines are generated and controlled locally through a restricted part of the nervous system, the enteric nervous system. The enteric nervous system is nevertheless subject to modification of its activity by signals emanating from the central nervous system and from other gut regions. In this review, the mechanisms by which the enteric nervous system determines the motility patterns of the small intestine are discussed.

Considerable progress has been made in unravelling the circuitry of the enteric nervous system and identifying the physiological properties of its major components in the small intestine. It is still a long step to explain how the activity of the enteric nervous system is itself integrated and how the effects of the enteric nervous system are enmeshed with the roles of other parts of the nervous and endocrine systems to direct the movements of the stomach and intestines.

PATTERNS OF MOTILITY

Two patterns of activity are recognized in the mammalian small intestine, the activity of the interdigestive state and the fed pattern of activity. The interdigestive pattern is characterized by the migrating myoelectric complex (MMC), which passes along the intestine every 80–110 min in humans. The complex takes about 6–10 min to pass any point in the intestine, and as it passes, that region undergoes intense rhythmic contractions of the circular muscle. These contractions are propagated through the region occupied by the migrating complex at a greater speed than the complex itself propagates. The migrating complex is also referred to as phase III activity. It is followed by a period of less intense activity (phase IV), then by relative quiescence (phase I) and by irregular contractions (phase II) that are interrupted by the reoccurrence of phase III activity. In continuously feeding animals, such as sheep and guinea pigs, the MMC passes down the intestine at regular intervals even when the animal is digesting. However, in intermittent feeders, such as humans and dogs, the MMC and the other cycles of the interdigestive state disappear soon after a meal is taken, to be replaced by the fed pattern of activity, which consists of ongoing phasic contractile activity (Figure 1). The contractions are highly irregular, so it is difficult to define their frequency, which is approximately 12–15 contractions per min.

Both the interdigestive pattern and the fed pattern are generated through the enteric nervous system but are modified by extrinsic nerves. The MMC cycle is still observed after bilateral infracardiac vagotomy, removal of prevertebral sympathetic ganglia, severing of the splanchnic nerves, or total extrinsic

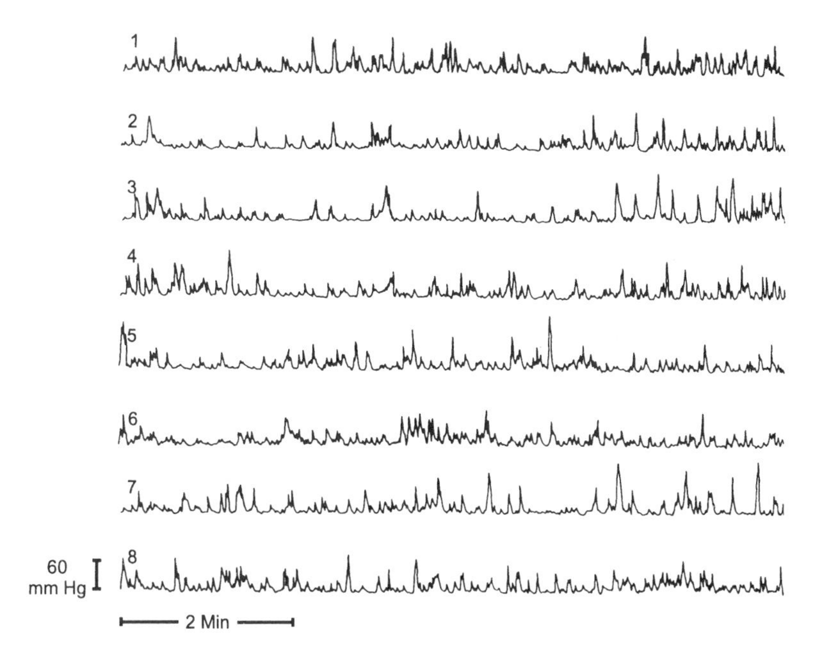

Figure 1 Typical fed contractile activity in the normal human small intestine, recorded in vivo. Intraluminal pressures were recorded at eight points, each 3 cm apart. (From Reference 113 with permission.)

denervation of a region of small intestine by autotransplantation (1–5). However, it is abolished from a segment of intestine that is infused through the vasculature with tetrodotoxin (which blocks action potential conduction in neurons) or hexamethonium (which blocks a substantial component of fast excitatory transmission between enteric neurons) (6). Similarly, the fed activity occurs after total vagotomy, sympathectomy, or neural isolation of a segment of intestine but is abolished by hexamethonium (1, 2, 7). The continuity of the enteric nervous system is necessary for the orderly progress of the MMC; if the myenteric plexus is interrupted surgically or if the small intestine is cut through and then rejoined, the MMC does not always pass the lesion and ectopic MMCs occur on the anal side (8, 9).

The fed pattern of activity both mixes and propels the contents. In one human study, about 45% of individual contractions did not propagate and about 35% propagated for less than 9 cm (10). The nonpropagating contractions probably correspond to the mixing or segmentation activity described by Cannon (11). The propagated contractions are peristaltic waves that die out after a short distance.

INTRINSIC REFLEXES THAT CONTRIBUTE TO MOTILITY PATTERNS

Many strategies have been used to reduce the complex movements of the intestine to underlying stereotyped responses to defined stimuli. The often unstated assumptions are that the complex patterns observed in vivo are the consequence of many superimposed responses to local variations in the volume and physicochemical properties of the contents of the intestine and that the local reflexes, by themselves, are relatively simple. The earliest attempts to detect reflexes that underlie intestinal motility patterns involved either studying segments of intestine removed from an animal (e.g. 12) or exteriorizing the intestine of a sedated animal and applying reproducible stimuli (e.g. 13).

Simplified approaches have permitted conclusions to be drawn about the natural stimuli that elicit reflexes and the stereotyped responses of the musculature to stationary stimuli. In most of these studies, any propulsion of contents that involves luminal constriction has been referred to as peristalsis or peristaltic reflex. Although peristalsis is thus rather loosely defined, it is a useful shorthand for propulsive activity. Bayliss & Starling (13) defined peristalsis more stringently as consisting of a contraction of the circular muscle oral to a bolus in the lumen (the ascending excitatory reflex) and relaxation on the anal side (the descending inhibitory reflex). Mall (12) deduced that irritation of the mucosa by a bolus was the stimulus for peristalsis. This was demonstrated under more defined conditions by stroking the mucosa of the opened intestine, which elicited circumferential contraction and muscle depolarization oral plus relaxation and hyperpolarization anal (14–16). The same types of responses can be elicited by distorting the villi by gentle pressure (17). When care is taken to avoid mechanical stimulation of the mucosa, polarized reflexes are also elicited by local application to the mucosa of hypertonic salt solutions, short-chain fatty acids, bile salts, or inorganic acid (14, 18). The early experiments of Bayliss & Starling (13) demonstrated ascending excitatory and descending inhibitory reflexes in response to distension, but in these experiments, like many that followed, the mucosa was also mechanically distorted. Nevertheless, distending stimuli that are applied with no mucosa present, or in ways that avoid mucosal distortion, also cause excitation oral and inhibition anal to the stimulus (19–22).

If the intestine is chronically denervated, so that endings of extrinsic neurons degenerate, and then removed from the animal, the stereotyped ascending excitatory and descending inhibitory reflexes, elicited by distension or mucosal distortion, and believed to contribute to peristalsis, are found to be unaffected (23, 24).

Thus, three types of stimuli, distension, mechanical distortion of the mucosa, and change in luminal chemistry, can independently elicit polarized reflex responses, excitation oral and relaxation anal, in the intestine. In vivo, all of these stimuli are present at the same time and will affect successive sites in the intestine to different degrees and with varying intensities over time, as the intestine mixes and absorbs its contents, as more material arrives from the stomach, pancreas, gallbladder, and the intestine itself, and as digestive enzymes do their work. Moreover, the movements elicited by the reflexes themselves have local effects on tension-sensitive neurons, as we discuss later in this review. In the small intestine, the local reflexes spread and mix the contents, so it is not surprising that peristaltic movements progress for only short distances.

As we discuss in more detail below, all the neural elements for the peristaltic reflexes are in the intestine; these are the intrinsic primary afferent neurons, interneurons, and motor neurons. The pathways that carry the reflexes orally and anally along the intestine are in the myenteric plexus.

INTRINSIC NEURONS OF THE SMALL INTESTINE

Intensive studies over about the last 20 years have led to the identification of all major neuronal types in the enteric nervous system in one region, the small intestine of the guinea pig, and this has become a model of the organization of enteric nerve circuits. From these studies, rudimentary circuits for stereotyped motility reflexes, the ascending excitatory and descending inhibitory reflexes, have been drawn (25) (Figure 2). These circuits depict the neurons as being in series, whereas numerous connections between neurons mean that they act as assemblies, with both in-parallel and in-series connections. How these assemblies are arranged and how they may be expected to operate is a major focus of this review.

Some aspects of the circuit organization differ between species. One difference is in the distributions of the groups of nerve cell bodies (ganglia) of the enteric nervous system. The myenteric ganglia seem to be similarly arranged in all mammals, ranging from the mouse and guinea pig to large mammals such as the pig and human. They form a single plexus between the longitudinal and circular layers of the external muscle. In small animals, the submucosal ganglia form a single layer and are concerned mainly with control of transmucosal water and electrolyte transport and local blood flow. In large mammals, the submucosal ganglia form layers that are identified as inner, outer, and in some cases intermediate plexuses (26). The inner and outer submucosal plexuses differ in their organization and the types of neurons that they contain. Some data suggest that the outer submucosal plexus (closest to the circular muscle) shares control of the external muscle with the myenteric plexus.

A second difference is in the chemical coding of neurons. Enteric neurons contain combinations of transmitters, transmitter-related molecules, and other

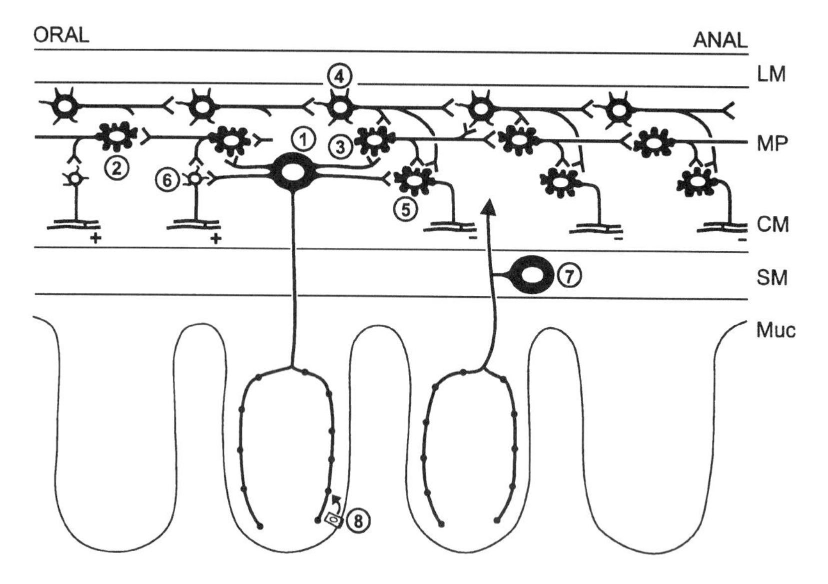

Figure 2 Simplified, in-series representation of enteric circuits for motility reflexes. 1, IPAN with cell body in the myenteric plexus; 2, ascending cholinergic interneuron; 3, descending interneuron in the local reflex pathway; 4, descending interneuron of the migrating myoelectric complex pathway; 5, inhibitory-muscle motor neuron; 6, excitatory muscle motor neuron; 7, IPAN with cell body in the submucosal plexus; 8, enteroendocrine cell that releases excitant of the mucosal endings of IPANs; LM, longitudinal muscle; MP, myenteric plexus; CM, circular muscle; SM, submucosa; Muc, mucosa.

regulatory molecules, such as calcium-binding proteins. The combinations form a code that identifies functional subgroups of neurons (27, 28). There are substantial differences in the codes between species and even between regions in the same species. Nevertheless, the variations are not in the primary neurotransmitters of the neurons, which appear to be well conserved between regions and species (27). In this review, we concentrate on the primary transmitters and consider chemical codes only where they are pertinent to distinguishing neurons or determining their places in circuits.

Motor Neurons

Extensive physiological studies have revealed that the muscle layers of the stomach and intestine are dually innervated by excitatory and inhibitory motor neurons, whose cell bodies are in the gut wall. In the stomach these neurons can be conveniently activated by stimulation of the vagus, and in other regions they can be activated by electrodes placed around or across the gut wall.

Mainly because appropriate antagonists were available, it was soon recognized that a primary transmitter of excitatory motor neurons is acetylcholine. However, pharmacological block of cholinergic transmission to the muscle does not completely abolish excitatory transmission; residual transmission, blocked by antagonists of tachykinin receptors, occurs (29, 30). That these two components of transmission are from a single neuron type is concluded from immunohistochemical studies demonstrating that the muscle is innervated by one class of excitatory neuron that is immunoreactive for both choline acetyltransferase (ChAT), through which acetylcholine is synthesized, and tachykinins. This colocalization has been demonstrated in the stomach and intestine of several species, including humans (28, 31, 32). The excitatory motor neurons project to the circular muscle just internal to their cell bodies, and they also project to muscle that is more oral. The axons run circumferentially, following the direction of the muscle cells. In the small intestine, many of the fibers are in a dense layer, the deep muscular plexus, near the boundary of the circular muscle with the submucosa (33).

Similar to the excitatory motor neurons, the inhibitory neurons have cotransmitters, but the relative roles of these transmitters are not properly resolved (27). In fact, the relative roles of different substances appear to vary considerably between gut regions and between species (27). The substances that can contribute to transmission include NO, ATP, vasoactive intestinal peptide (VIP), and pituitary adenylyl cyclase-activating peptide (PACAP). Of these, NO is most frequently implicated as a primary transmitter (34). The inhibitory neurons project axons to the muscle close to and anal to their cell bodies; most supply the muscle within about 2 mm anal, but some extend their axons for many millimeters anal (35, 36).

Effects on the muscle from both the excitatory and inhibitory motor neurons are relayed at least in part via the interstitial cells of Cajal (ICC), which are electrically coupled to the muscle (see review by B Horowitz, SM Ward & KM Sanders, this volume). The ICC have receptors both for the inhibitory transmitter, NO (37, 38), and for the excitatory tachykinin transmitters (39–41). In the canine colon, electrical stimulation of inhibitory motor neurons elicits inhibitory junction potentials of reduced amplitude when the ICC are removed (42). A similar dependence on ICC was demonstrated by comparison of inhibitory transmission in the stomach of normal mice and mutants that lack ICC in the muscle (43). In this study, the component of transmission that was mediated via NO did not occur without the presence of ICC. Disruption of ICC by treating neonatal rats with antibodies to kit, a receptor tyrosine kinase on the ICC, impaired excitatory and inhibitory transmission to the circular muscle of the ileum and abolished transmission to colonic circular muscle (44).

Interneurons

Evidence for the existence of interneurons in the myenteric plexus comes from structural studies that show the existence of neurons with cell bodies in myenteric ganglia and terminals in ganglia lying anal or oral; the observation has been confirmed by physiological and pharmacological studies, some of which are reviewed below. In the guinea pig small intestine, there is one class of ascending interneurons and three (perhaps four) classes of descending interneurons (28). The chemistries, projections, and connections of these neurons are discussed in a later section.

It is difficult to study interneurons physiologically, except by recording from them directly, which is technically demanding and not always feasible. In those cases where direct recordings have been made, the interneurons have responded to reflex stimuli with fast excitatory postsynaptic potentials (EPSPs) (45). However, some deductions concerning the pharmacology of transmission from interneurons can be made by using divided organ bath experiments, in which compartments are separately perfused with drug-containing solutions.

The use of divided organ baths with pharmacologically isolated compartments indicates that, in ascending pathways, transmission between interneurons and transmission between interneurons and excitatory muscle motor neurons is cholinergic, occurring via nicotinic receptors (46, 47). In contrast, descending reflexes are resistant to the nicotinic antagonist hexamethonium (15, 47), but it is not yet known which transmitters are used for fast excitatory synaptic transmission between the descending interneurons or between interneurons and inhibitory motor neurons. A possible candidate is ATP, acting through P2 purinoreceptors (48). Stimulation of bundles of axons within nerve strands in the guinea pig ileum elicits fast EPSPs that exhibit a mixed pharmacology. A small proportion of the EPSPs is blocked by hexamethonium. The residual fast EPSPs, in the presence of hexamethonium, are blocked or significantly reduced in amplitude by the P2 receptor antagonist PPADS (48). The noncholinergic EPSPs are also inhibited by desensitization of purinoreceptors with α,β-methylene ATP and by the relatively nonspecific purinoreceptor antagonist suramin (49). Some fast EPSPs had components that were not blocked by a combination of hexamethonium and PPADS. Among possible transmitters of noncholinergic fast EPSPs are 5-hydroxytryptamine (5-HT) and glutamate (48, 50).

Intrinsic Primary Afferent Neurons

The first neurons in the intrinsic nerve circuits that are activated by appropriate stimuli are the intrinsic primary afferent neurons (IPANs). These have been studied in detail only in the small intestine of the guinea pig, where they are morphologically Dogiel type II neurons and electrophysiologically AH neurons. For a time, there was debate about whether IPANs exist at all. The alternative hypothesis was that the first neurons that were activated when reflexes were initiated in the gut were spinal afferent neurons, with cell bodies in dorsal root ganglia. According to this hypothesis, neurons within the gut wall would be activated via axon reflexes in the ends of spinal afferent neurons. There is in fact good evidence that axon reflexes of spinal afferent neurons are necessary for reflexes in response to distension in the colon of the rat (51). Because distension reflexes occur in the small intestine after the severed ends of extrinsic nerves have degenerated (see above), they must depend on IPANs.

Intracellular microelectrodes have been used to record from Dogiel type II neurons in the guinea pig small intestine, and the neurons were shown to be excited by sensory stimuli. Adequate stimuli to excite these neurons from the mucosa include acid, short-chain neutralized fatty acid, and 5-HT (52, 53). The effectiveness of 5-HT is of interest because it has been suggested that this substance is an essential intermediate in reflexes initiated from the mucosa (54–56). The reason to propose an intermediate compound is that the luminal chemicals are separated from the afferent nerve endings by the mucosal epithelium (Figure 2). 5-HT is present in numerous enterochromaffin cells in the epithelium and is an effective stimulant of intestinal reflexes. Furthermore, reflexes from the mucosa are attenuated by 5-HT receptor antagonists (54–56). The chemoresponsive IPANs that innervate the mucosa exhibit brief bursts of action potentials when chemicals are pressure-ejected onto the mucosa (53). Whether they would maintain their response if the chemical stimulant remained in contact with the mucosa has not been tested. However, if the mucosa is retained with the rest of the intestinal wall in vitro there is continuing action potential discharge of some IPANs for several hours (57). This discharge may arise because the mucosa deteriorates in vitro and releases active substances, including 5-HT. Whatever the mechanism, it does imply that the neurons are capable of maintained discharge and suggests that they could be more or less continuously active in vivo. Other data suggest that the reflexes elicited by mucosal distortion could also be mediated by 5-HT release. The amplitudes of reflex responses were reduced by 50–70% by antagonists of 5-HT_3 receptors applied at the site of initiation of the reflexes by mucosal distortion (16).

Responses to tension generated by muscle contraction have been recorded with intracellular microelectrodes from IPANs that have cell bodies in the myenteric plexus. Stretch of the intestine by only 20% beyond the slack width was sufficient to excite some neurons, and most neurons were excited by 40% stretch (58). However, it was not the stretch per se that stimulated the neurons but the contraction of muscle cells in response to the stretch. It is well established that intestinal smooth muscle cells have stretch-activated channels and that stretch of the muscle causes their excitation (59, 60). The dependence of the neural response on the generation of tension in the muscle was demonstrated by the use of isoproterenol or nicardipine to prevent contraction; with either of these drugs present, the IPANs were not excited when the muscle was stretched by 40%. Conversely, if the muscle was not stretched but was held at its resting length and tension was generated in the muscle by application of the calcium channel stimulant Bay K 8864, tension-responsive IPANs were activated (WAA Kunze, unpublished observations).

There must also be IPANs that respond to stretch without the need for the muscle to contract, because reflexes are evoked at the onset of distension stimuli despite the muscle being paralyzed with nicardipine (21). The responses in paralyzed tissue are undiminished by extrinsic denervation (24).

There is also evidence for IPANs with cell bodies in submucosal ganglia. When the mucosal villi were mechanically disturbed, the cell bodies of responsive neurons expressed the immediate-early gene product, c-Fos (54). These neurons may be important for reflexes evoked by mechanical stimulation of the mucosa, although mucosal mechanical stimulation can also activate some myenteric IPANs (53). It is also notable that mucosal stimulation evokes secretory and vascular reflexes. The secretomotor reflexes in the colon are observed in the absence of the myenteric ganglia, and so they almost certainly involve submucosal IPANs (61–63). Further studies are required to determine whether activation of these neurons contributes to motility reflexes; in the present review, they are not included in the analysis of reflex circuits for motility control.

NUMBERS AND DENSITIES OF OCCURRENCE OF NEURONS

Current knowledge allows us to quantify the relation between the numbers of neurons and the sizes of the regions that are stimulated and that react to stimuli and thus might be considered to form reflex units. It is partly a consideration of these numbers that leads to the hypothesis that enteric neurons act in assemblies. Two other considerations are the large extent of overlap of sensory fields of individual neurons and the high density of innervation of the muscle and its electrical coupling.

Counts of the numbers of calbindin-immunoreactive (IR) nerve cells provide a suitable starting point to calculate nerve cell densities and relative numbers. These cells stain strongly, and calbindin has been used as a standard marker by several authors. There are 522 ± 10 myenteric calbindin-IR nerve cells per mm length of guinea pig ileum (64), and calbindin-IR nerve cells make up 20–24% of myenteric nerve cells (28, 65). Thus, in total there are around 2,500 nerve cells per mm. Calbindin neurons make up 80% of all myenteric IPANs (Dogiel type II neurons) (66, 67). Thus, there is a total of about 650 myenteric IPANs per mm.

Calculations of the relative numbers of nerve cells belonging to separate classes by different laboratories have yielded similar values (25, 28). The numbers of inhibitory muscle motor neurons can be estimated with some precision. In the ileum, nitric oxide synthase (NOS) is in both the motor neurons and some descending interneurons. The interneurons, but not the inhibitory motor neurons, are also immunoreactive for ChAT, which is in 14% of the NOS neurons (68). Of the ileal neurons, 19% contain NOS; therefore, 86% of 19% (16%) are inhibitory motor neurons and 3% are descending interneurons. Using an analysis of patterns of colocalization of chemical markers, Costa et al (28) estimated that inhibitory motor neurons were 17% and NOS-IR interneurons were $\leq$5% of all myenteric neurons. The excitatory circular muscle motor neurons were calculated to make up 12% of neurons, and ascending interneurons were calculated to make up 5% (28, 69).

Since there are 2,500 nerve cells per mm length of gut, from the percentages above, 1 mm contains the cell bodies of 400 inhibitory motor neurons and 300 excitatory motor neurons to the circular muscle, as well as the cell bodies of about 120 ascending and 120 ChAT/NOS descending interneurons. A large proportion of the remaining neurons are longitudinal muscle motor neurons, which account for about 500 nerve cell bodies per mm. There are also small populations of ChAT/somatostatin (SOM) (4%), ChAT/5-HT (2%), and possibly ChAT/VIP (3%), descending interneurons (28). As discussed below, the ChAT/SOM and ChAT/5-HT descending interneurons do not seem to be directly involved in local motility reflexes. Some IPANs (about 10%) have long, anally directed axons that probably contribute to descending reflexes (70).

NUMBERS OF NEURONS INVOLVED IN REFLEX RESPONSES: ASSEMBLIES OF NEURONS

When the human or feline small intestine is examined in vivo by cineradiography, annular contractions (1–2 cm long in human) are found to occur during mixing and greater lengths are contracted during peristaltic movements (11, 71). During propulsion in the guinea pig and rat small intestine, it is consistently observed that the circular muscle is contracted for lengths of 10–15 mm (72–75). If the lesser value, 10 mm, is used for calculation this is a length that contains 6,500 IPANs and 3,000 excitatory circular-muscle motor neurons in the small intestine in the guinea pig. The degree to which there are heterogeneities in the chemical content of the lumen, and therefore the lengths over which chemical stimuli may vary, does not seem to be known. Nevertheless, considering the mixing activity of the gut, the lengths of intestine that are likely to be affected by variation in the chemical contents of the lumen are probably at least several centimeters, suggesting that large assemblies of neurons are activated chemically from the lumen. In the digestive state, the intestine is constantly filled with fluid containing nutrient chemicals and bile salts, so that all the responsive IPANs that project to the mucosa could potentially be activated.

Assemblies of Intrinsic Primary Afferent Neurons

In the guinea pig small intestine, all neurons with the morphology of IPANs (Dogiel type II neurons) project to the mucosa (67, 76). Moreover, they have considerable overlap in their fields of supply; retrograde tracing indicates that each villus is supplied by the axons of 65 IPANs with cell bodies in the myenteric ganglia (76). By mapping regions of mucosa from which IPANs can be electrically activated, it was concluded that each projects to a circumferentially oriented strip of mucosa, about 2 mm in oral-to-anal width and 8–12 mm^2 in area (77), which contains about 80–120 villi. It is not possible to say whether all of the Dogiel type II neurons respond to chemical stimulation from the lumen. To record from these neurons, it is necessary to remove part of the mucosa (53). About 50% of the neurons respond to electrical stimulation of the remaining, intact mucosa. Thus, perhaps in these experiments only 50% of IPANs have mucosally projecting axons that are intact in the test regions. Of the neurons that responded to focal electrical stimulation of the mucosal surface, 60% responded to chemicals (acid, base, or fatty acid) applied to the mucosa (53). This may underestimate the proportion of neurons that are chemoresponsive, because it is not possible to be certain that the stimulus reached the nerve ending or that the appropriate chemical was tested in each case. In tissue that was stretched to excite stretch-activated IPANs with cell bodies in the myenteric plexus, about 80% of neurons responded to a 40% increase in the circumference of the intestine (58). About 70% of the neurons that respond to stretch do so directly; these neurons are probably also excited via synaptic connections from the IPAN assembly, as are other IPANs that are not directly activated (see below).

SYNAPTIC INTERACTIONS BETWEEN IPANS The myenteric IPANs respond to stimulation of their synaptic inputs with slow EPSPs, but fast excitatory synaptic inputs to these neurons are rarely seen in the guinea pig small intestine, and when they are recorded, fast EPSPs are of low amplitude (66, 78). This absence of fast EPSPs applies to the guinea pig small intestine and does not necessarily apply to other regions or to the small intestine in other species. For the reasons that are elaborated in this paragraph, the major origin of the slow EPSPs is likely to be other myenteric IPANs. The axons of Dogiel type II neurons give rise to very dense networks of varicose terminals, which appear to surround all nerve cell bodies in their own and adjacent ganglia (64, 79). By electron microscopy, these terminals are seen to form synapses on nerve cell bodies, including the cell bodies of IPANs (80). Moreover, when the cell bodies of two IPANs were impaled with microelectrodes and action potentials were evoked by stimulus pulses passed through one electrode, the other IPAN responded with slow EPSPs (81). Pharmacological experiments support the conclusion that the origins of slow EPSPs in IPANs are synapses made on them by other IPANs. In the guinea pig small intestine, Dogiel type II neurons are immunoreactive for tachykinins, and antagonists of tachykinin receptors block the slow EPSPs in these cells (82). The conclusion that slow EPSPs in IPANs arise from other IPANs is consistent with the results of experiments in which the axons of ascending and descending interneurons were severed (83). In areas between lesions, where the severed axons of interneurons had degenerated but endings of IPANs remained, slow EPSPs of usual amplitude were recorded in the cell bodies of IPANs. Thus, data from several experimental approaches all indicate that the IPANs form interconnected networks, and because transmission at the connections between IPANs is excitatory, these networks would be self-reinforcing (Figure 3). That

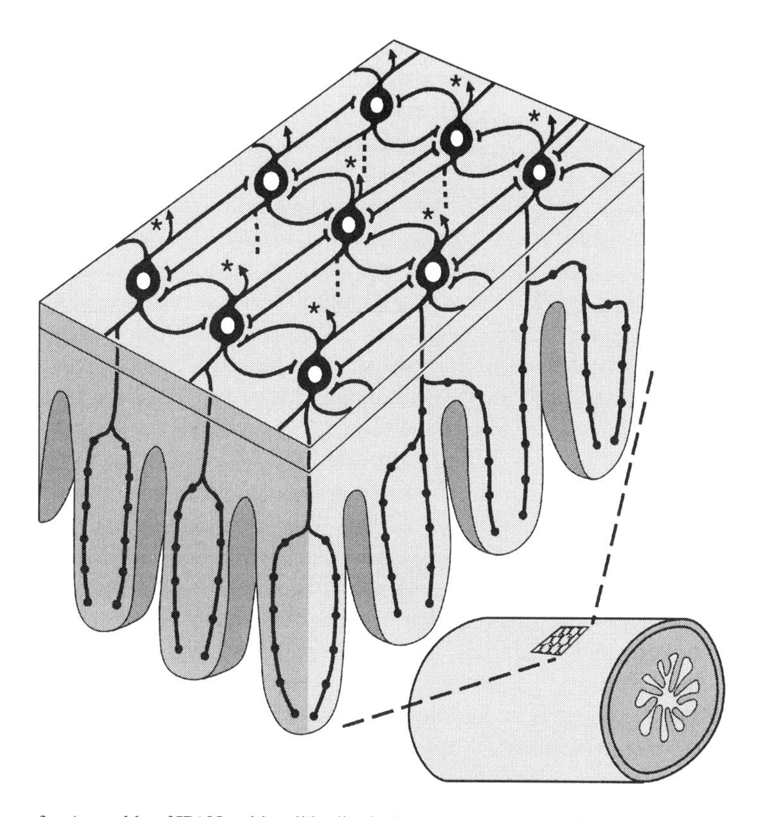

Figure 3 Assembly of IPANs with cell bodies in the myenteric plexus. Such a group comes from a small area of the intestinal wall; there are 6,500 nerve cell bodies per 10 mm length of intestine. The IPANs connect with each other through slow excitatory transmission. They provide outputs to other neurons [interneurons and motor neurons (*asterisks*)].

Dogiel type II neurons form such networks was earlier deduced by Wood (84), but at that time the Dogiel type II neurons had not been shown to be IPANs.

A 10-mm length of guinea pig small intestine contains about 6,500 myenteric IPANs. If this length is contracting and there are fatty acids in the lumen, or perhaps other nutrients that could activate the IPANs, a high proportion of these neurons would be expected to react directly by firing action potentials. Moreover, many IPANs in the region, whether they were directly activated or not, would be excited synaptically.

It is thus concluded that assemblies of several thousand myenteric IPANs respond together when changes in muscle tension and lumenal chemistry occur. Mucosal distortion probably also contributes to activation of submucosal IPANs at the same time.

Assemblies of Interneurons

Activity is conducted orally and anally along the intestine via interneurons. In the small intestine of the guinea pig, there is one class of ascending interneuron and three (or four) classes of descending interneurons (28). Both pharmacological data (15, 46, 47) and immunohistochemical data (36) indicate that the ascending interneurons are cholinergic. They are also immunoreactive for calretinin (28), which can be used to locate them by electron microscopy. Electron microscopy shows that these calretinin immunoreactive neurons connect with each other to form ascending chains and that they receive inputs from myenteric IPANs (69, 85) (Figure 4). Of the inputs to the ascending interneurons, about 70% are from calbindin immunoreactive IPANs and 15% are from other ascending interneurons (85). Physiological and electron microscopic analyses both demonstrate that the ChAT/calretinin ascending interneurons provide inputs to muscle motor neurons (15, 46, 85).

Most, probably all, descending interneurons are also cholinergic, as indicated by their immunoreactivity for ChAT, but transmission in local reflexes is not purely cholinergic because, as mentioned above, it is only partly blocked by antagonists of cholinergic transmission. A component of fast excitatory transmission is blocked by PPADS, an antagonist of purinergic (ATP) receptors (48); therefore, it is possible that acetylcholine and ATP are cotransmitters at some synapses of descending interneurons. The classes of descending interneuron are those immunoreactive for ChAT/SOM; those immunoreactive for ChAT/NOS, VIP, plus other substances; those immunoreactive for ChAT/5-HT; and a little-studied group immunoreactive for ChAT/VIP (28). The ChAT/5-HT neurons do not make connections with the inhibitory muscle motor neurons (86), and pharmacological studies, which show a lack of effect of receptor antagonists, suggest that 5-HT is not a transmitter in local descending motility reflexes (87). Electron microscopy studies show that the ChAT/SOM neurons receive very few inputs from IPANs but that over 80% of their inputs are from other

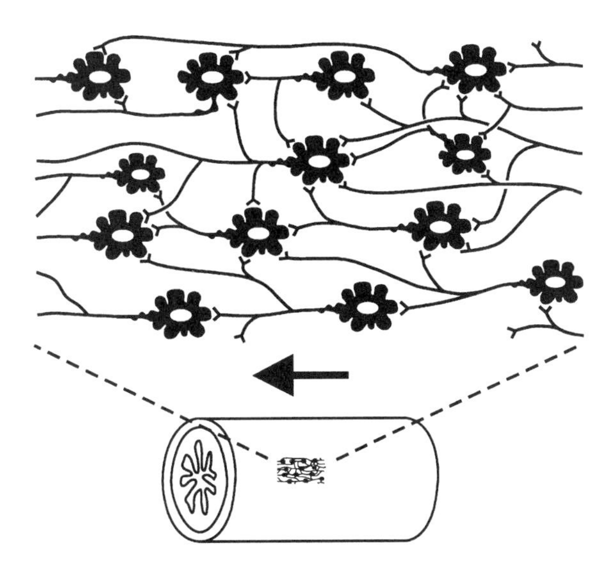

Figure 4 Assembly of interneurons. The interneurons make multiple excitatory connections with each other to form ascending and descending chains that run along the intestine. The neurons depicted come from a small region of myenteric plexus; the direction of propagation is indicated by the arrow. In total, the cell bodies of about 120 ascending and 300 descending interneurons are found in 1 mm length of intestine.

ChAT/SOM neurons. On the basis of these observations, it has been suggested that ChAT/SOM descending interneurons are a conduit for the passage of migrating myoelectric complexes along the guinea pig intestine (88). This is consistent with the results of electrophysiological studies, which show that the majority of ChAT/SOM neurons receive inputs from oral regions, but only one-sixth receive local inputs that are activated by stimulation circumferential to the cell body (89). Thus, the ChAT/NOS neurons are the ones most likely to be directly involved in local descending inhibitory reflexes. The ChAT/NOS interneurons form descending chains (90), as do the other descending interneurons (86, 91), and pharmacological studies indicate that the NOS neurons are involved in descending reflexes (92).

A very high proportion (over 90%) of S neurons (interneurons and motor neurons) respond when the intestine is distended (93), and around 50% respond to mucosal distortion (45).

Assemblies of Motor Neurons

Both physiological and structural studies indicate that the circular muscle of the intestine is innervated by dense arrays of nerve fibers that run circumferentially, more or less parallel to the long axes of the circular muscle cells. These axons influence the muscle cells as a group, because the cells are electrically coupled to each other. The motor unit of the intestinal circular muscle could thus be regarded as a circumferential strip that is electrically closely coupled and its innervating neurons. In the guinea pig small intestine, the minimum widths of contractile rings are about 2–3 mm (73). Thus, an annulus about 2–3 mm wide, innervated by axons arising from about 600–900 excitatory and 800–1,200 inhibitory motor neurons, could be regarded as a motor unit. The numbers of axons supplying the circular muscle have been counted per muscle cell and per millimeter of oral-to-anal length. In the deep muscular plexus, there are 2,500 axons per mm length of intestine (94), which represents two-thirds of the fibers that innervate the muscle (33). Thus, there are about 3,700 axons innervating 1 mm of intestinal length, corresponding to 7,500–11,000 in a motor unit 2–3 mm wide. Quantitative electron-microscopic analysis indicates that about half the axons are from excitatory neurons and about half are from inhibitory neurons (95). These quantitative data indicate that the processes of individual neurons branch within the circular muscle. The ratio of axons detected in single cross sections of the muscle to the corresponding nerve cells in the same length is about 12 for the excitatory neurons and 9 for the inhibitory neurons. The majority of excitatory motor neurons project very short distances along the length of the intestine; about 80% of the cell bodies of neurons supplying a 2-mm band of intestine are located adjacent to the muscle strip, and the remainder are found up to about 8 mm anally (36). The axons of inhibitory neurons project anally, so that the cell bodies providing a muscle strip lie oral to the strip, about 40% within 2 mm and the remainder spread out for up to 14 mm oral to the strip (36). In view of the large numbers of axons that innervate a neuromuscular unit, it is not surprising that it is difficult to fractionate, by varying the stimulus strength, the electrical events (junction potentials) in the muscle that are caused by nerve stimulation (35).

The idea of an annulus as a motor unit is consistent with the observation that the muscle undergoes annular contractions and relaxations (11, 96). The intensity of the contraction or relaxation of the muscle would depend on the numbers of neurons that are activated and the frequency with which they fire. Although a strip 2–3 mm wide might be regarded as the smallest motor unit of the circular muscle of the guinea pig small intestine, the annular contractions of the small intestine usually occupy 10–15 mm (72–75).

The muscle motor neurons are not assemblies in the same sense as assemblies of IPANs and interneurons that are connected to each other synaptically. However, since their activity is determined by transmission from the IPANs and interneurons, they are recruited as populations, and because they innervate electrically coupled smooth muscle, their summed rather than individual effects are manifested in muscle contraction and relaxation.

RECIPROCAL INTERACTIONS BETWEEN IPANs AND THE MUSCLE

The activity in IPANs has the end effect of changing muscle tension, but muscle tension is itself an activator of many IPANs. Thus, the IPANs and muscle have a reciprocal relationship. Increased tension in the muscle activates a proportion of IPANs, whereas they are unloaded (that is their propensity to be activated is reduced) by muscle relaxation. This implies that when reflexes are generated by activating IPANs in a small region, the consequent contraction on the oral side will activate IPANs in that region, whereas the relaxation anally will unload (deactivate) IPANs (Figure 5). If IPANs were responsive to changes in tissue length rather than changes in tension, the opposite effects would ensue. At the site of the distension, a local accommodation reflex occurs (97–99) in which inhibitory motor neurons are activated. Thus, the effect of the distension in exciting IPANs could be reduced (*a*) by unloading of the IPANs in the distended area as a consequence of the muscle relaxation caused by the accommodation reflex, (*b*) by descending inhibition caused by excitation of tension-sensitive IPANs on the oral side, or (*c*) by inhibition of ascending reflexes by unloading of IPANs in the relaxed region on the anal side (Figure 5). When reflexes are quickly evoked by distension, the output to the muscle is not maintained (100), even though many IPANs continue to fire action potentials (58). This implies that there is a diminution of the effectiveness of transmission somewhere in the circuit, beyond the IPANs. This could be caused by rundown of synaptic transmission, which has been described for fast EPSPs at enteric neuroneural synapses, or it could be because inhibitory mechanisms come into play after some delay. It also could arise because different populations of IPANs are activated by quick stretch and by sustained stretch.

Exactly how the interactions between neurons and muscle translate into the movements of the intestine cannot be stated without a more accurate knowledge of the mechanical events and their timing. However, the initial contraction orally, relaxation on the anal side and relaxation at the site of distension can be anticipated to push the contents of the distended region anally, where the interaction of the contents with the gut wall, through its chemical nature, distortion of the mucosa, and distending effect, can set off further reflexes (Figure 5).

The fact that IPANs are excited by tension generated in the muscle may be one reason why it is necessary to have inhibitory neurons to the muscle rather than relaxing the muscle simply by lowering activity in excitatory neurons (as, for example, occurs in arteries that receive only an excitatory, vasoconstrictor innervation). If the excitation were simply reduced, the lengthening of muscle in the dilating segments of intestine could lead to stretch-activated contraction of the muscle and further excitation of IPANs. However, if lengthening is caused

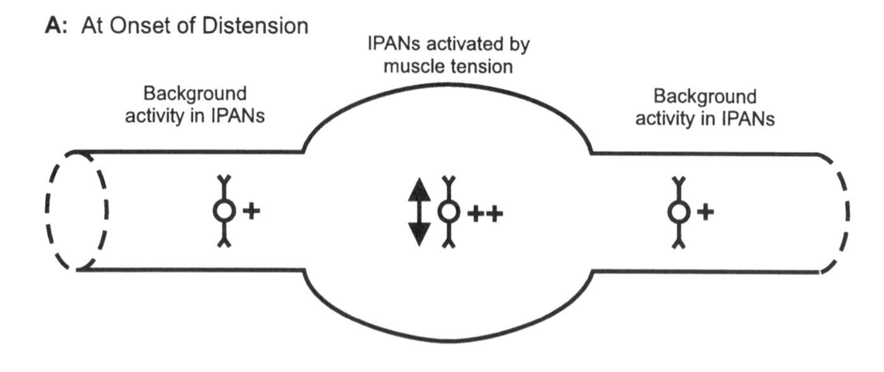

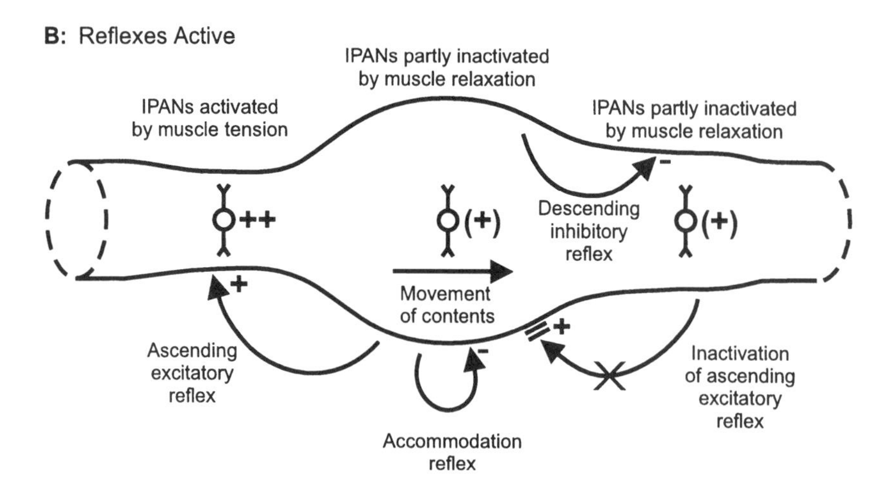

Figure 5 Schematic representation of the probable reciprocal interactions between the circular muscle and IPANs. At the onset of distension, the muscle reacts to stretch by contracting and imposes tension on IPANs that causes them to fire action potentials. This results in changes in muscle tension via enteric reflexes, which in turn changes IPAN activity.

by inhibitory neurons acting on the muscle, it is not associated with reactive muscle contraction and excitation of IPANs.

SERIAL CONNECTIONS BETWEEN ASSEMBLIES OF NEURONS

The assemblies of neurons that are described in this review are connected in series, as depicted in Figure 6. At each point along the intestine, there is input

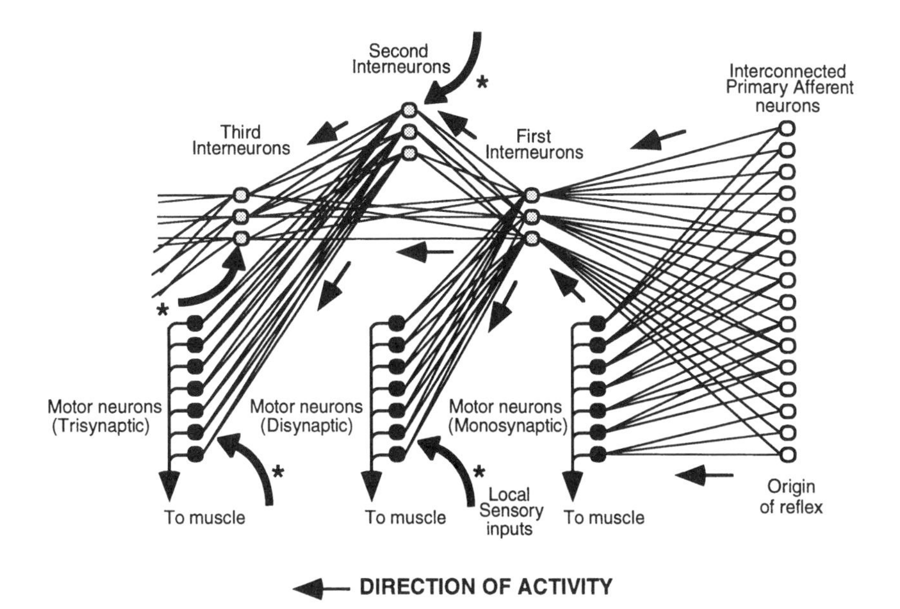

Figure 6 Connections of neurons in ascending reflex pathways in the small intestine. Assemblies of IPANs make monosynaptic connections with assemblies of motor neurons and ascending interneurons. Then the reflex is connected through polysynaptic pathways to further assemblies of motor neurons. At successive points, the reflex pathways receive input from additional assemblies of local IPANs (*arrows with asterisks*). (From Reference 114 with permission.)

to the chains of interneurons that run orally and anally, and at each point there is output from the chains to motor neurons and thence to the muscle. At short distances, there is evidence for monosynaptic reflexes not involving interneurons, and at greater distances, there are polysynaptic pathways involving several interneurons.

LIMITS TO UNDERSTANDING

As we hope the preceding discussion makes clear, the present state of knowledge allows the substrate for the generation of enteric reflexes to be defined, that substrate being the enteric neurons, their patterns of connection, their physiological properties, and the pharmacology of the transmission between them and to the muscle. However, it is not known how the circuits are programmed to generate the motility patterns. To fully understand the system, it is necessary to determine how the activities of neurons lead to the complex mixing movements of the small intestine, to the anal progression of the contents, and to migrating myoelectric complexes. That is, it is necessary to determine the patterns of activity in the assemblies of neurons and how these patterns are regulated.

INTRINSIC SECRETOMOTOR AND VASCULAR REFLEXES

The same types of stimuli (distension, mucosal distortion, and chemicals in the lumen) cause secretory and blood flow changes, in addition to motility changes in the small intestine, and there is experimental evidence that these functions vary together (101).

Secretomotor reflexes are initiated physiologically by chemical or mechanical interaction of luminal contents with the mucosa or pathologically by toxins, such as cholera toxin or enterotoxins, in the lumen (62, 63). In the small intestine, an important physiological stimulus appears to be the presence of nutrients, such as glucose. Enteric reflexes also cause bicarbonate secretion in response to duodenal acidification (102). The enteric secretomotor circuits consist of IPANs with their endings in the mucosa and an integrating circuitry in the myenteric and submucous plexuses that feeds back to secretomotor neurons with cell bodies in the submucosal ganglia. In some cases, for example in cholera toxin-induced secretion, the reflex pathways involve the myenteric ganglia (103), whereas reflexes initiated by mechanical stimuli can be mediated entirely through the submucosal plexus (61–63). There are two types of secretomotor neurons: cholinergic and noncholinergic. The noncholinergic neurons appear to mediate most of the local reflex response, and they utilize VIP or a related peptide as their primary transmitter (63, 104). The secretomotor neurons stimulate the epithelial cells to secrete chloride ions into the lumen.

Local vasodilator reflexes are elicited in the small intestine by mechanical or chemical irritation of the mucosa, and substantial evidence indicates that the vasodilator neurons are intrinsic to the intestine and that transmission from them is predominantly noncholinergic (105, 106). It is presumed that the first neurons in these reflexes are the IPANs, but this has not been directly shown. In fact, of the reflexes in the intestine, the vasomotor reflexes are the least extensively studied. Observation of the changes in the diameter of submucous blood vessels after single neurons were stimulated provides direct evidence for both cholinergic and noncholinergic vasodilator neurons with their cell bodies in the submucous plexus (107, 108). Immunohistochemical studies confirm that separate cholinergic and noncholinergic neurons innervate intestinal arterioles (109). It is probable that a primary transmitter for noncholinergic transmission is VIP (106, 110, 111).

Histochemical studies suggest that the same neurons have axons that branch to supply both the secretory epithelium and arterioles; hence, some secretomotor and vasodilator reflexes may share the same final neurons (112). This makes physiological sense, because the secreted water and electrolyte come indirectly from the vasculature. However, it is not known whether the same, different, or overlapping populations of IPANs contribute to motility, secretomotor, and vasomotor reflexes. Thus, some of the IPANs that have been recorded from and whose responses have been related to motility control in the earlier part of this review may be concerned primarily with other aspects of control of the intestine.

CONCLUSIONS

The identities of intrinsic primary afferent neurons, interneurons, and motor neurons in the enteric nervous system have now been determined. For each type, there is considerable knowledge of its functional place in the enteric nerve circuits, including its neurochemistry, pharmacology of transmission, projections, connections, and cellular physiology. It is apparent that the neurons operate in assemblies. In the guinea pig small intestine, a contracting unit of 10 mm contains on the order of 6,500 intrinsic primary afferent neurons in myenteric ganglia, 1,200 ascending and 3,000 descending interneurons (maybe 1,200 of the descending interneurons are in local reflexes), 4,000 inhibitory motor neurons to the circular muscle, and 3,000 excitatory motor neurons to the circular muscle. High proportions of these are active during motility reflexes.

None of the neurons within particular functional groups appear to act independently. The IPANs connect with each other through slow synaptic excitation and thus constitute a self-reinforcing network. Likewise, the ascending and descending interneurons form interconnecting chains. Finally, the motor neurons innervate a muscle that is an electrical syncytium. Thus, each class of neuron must be considered to act as a neuronal assembly. A challenge that lies ahead is to determine how the activity in these assemblies of neurons results in the movements of the intestine that are observed.

ACKNOWLEDGMENTS

We thank Paul Bertrand, Joel Bornstein, Alan Lomax, and Evan Thomas for their helpful advice and constructive criticism. The figures were prepared by Siobhan Lavin, who also assisted with the collation of references; we are most grateful for her contribution. The work from our laboratory that contributes to this review was supported by the National Health and Medical Research Council of Australia (Grant 963213).

Literature Cited

1. Marik F, Code CF. 1975. Control of the interdigestive myoelectric activity in dogs by the vagus nerves and pentagastrin. *Gastroenterology* 69:387–95
2. Weisbrodt NW, Copeland EM, Moore EP, Kearley RW, Johnson LR. 1975. Effect of vagotomy on electrical activity of the small intestine of the dog. *Am. J. Physiol.* 228:650–54
3. Code CF, Marlett JA. 1975. The interdigestive myoelectric complex of the stomach and small bowel of dogs. *J. Physiol.* 246:289–309
4. Sarr MG, Kelly KA. 1981. Myoelectric activity of the autotransplanted canine jejunoileum. *Gastroenterology* 81:303–13
5. Hashmonai M, Go VLW, Szurszewski JH. 1987. Effect of total sympathectomy and decentralization on migrating motor complexes. *Gastroenterology* 92:978–86
6. Sarna S, Stoddard C, Belbeck L, McWade D. 1981. Intrinsic nervous control of migrating myoelectric complexes. *Am. J. Physiol.* 241:G16–23
7. Cannon WB. 1906. The motor activities of the stomach and small intestine after splanchnic and vagus section. *Am. J. Physiol.* 17:429–42
8. Matsumoto T, Sarna SK, Condon RE, Cowles VE, Frantzides C. 1986. Differential sensitivities of morphine and motilin to initiate migrating motor complex in isolated intestinal segments. Regeneration of intrinsic nerves. *Gastroenterology* 90:61
9. Galligan JJ, Furness JB, Costa M. 1989. Migration of the myoelectric complex after interruption of the myenteric plexus: intestinal transection and regeneration of enteric nerves in the guinea pig. *Gastroenterology* 97:1135–46
10. Dusdicker NS, Summers RW. 1979. Patterns of smooth muscle contractions in the jejunum. *Gastroenterology* 76:1126–35
11. Cannon WB. 1902. The movements of the intestines studied by means of the Roentgen rays. *Am. J. Physiol.* 6:251–77
12. Mall F. 1896. A study of the intestinal contraction. *Johns Hopkins. Hosp. Rep* 1:37–75
13. Bayliss WM, Starling EH. 1899. The movements and innervation of the small intestine. *J. Physiol.* 24:99–143
14. Hukuhara T, Yamagami M, Nakayama S. 1958. On the intestinal intrinsic reflexes. *Jpn. J. Physiol.* 8:9–20
15. Smith TK, Furness JB. 1988. Reflex changes in circular muscle activity elicited by stroking the mucosa: an electrophysiological analysis in the isolated guinea-pig ileum. *J. Auton. Nerv. Syst.* 25:205–18
16. Neya T, Mizutani M, Yamasato T. 1993. Role of 5-HT_3 receptors in peristaltic reflex elicited by stroking the mucosa in the canine jejunum. *J. Physiol.* 471:159–73
17. Yuan SY, Furness JB, Bornstein JC, Smith TK. 1991. Mucosal distortion by compression elicits polarized reflexes and enhances responses of the circular muscle to distension in the small intestine. *J. Auton. Nerv. Syst.* 35:219–26
18. Baldwin MV, Thomas JE. 1975. The intestinal intrinsic mucosal reflex: a possible mechanism of propulsive motility. In *Functions of the Stomach and Intestine*, ed. M Friedman, pp. 75–91. Baltimore: University Park Press
19. Costa M, Furness JB. 1976. The peristaltic reflex: an analysis of nerve pathways and their pharmacology. *Naunyn-Schmiedeberg's Arch. Pharmacol.* 294:47–60
20. Grider JR. 1989. Identification of neurotransmitters regulating intestinal peristaltic reflex in humans. *Gastroenterology* 97:1414–9
21. Smith TK, Bornstein JC, Furness JB. 1990. Distension-evoked ascending and descending reflexes in the circular muscle of guinea-pig ileum: an intracellular study. *J. Auton. Nerv. Syst.* 29:203–17
22. Tsuji S, Anglade P, Ozaki T, Sazi T, Yokoyama S. 1992. Peristaltic movement evoked in intestinal tube devoid of mucosa and submucosa. *Jpn. J. Physiol.* 42:363–75
23. Langley JN, Magnus R. 1905. Some observations of the movements of the intestine before and after degenerative section of the mesenteric nerves. *J. Physiol.* 33:34–51
24. Furness JB, Johnson PJ, Pompolo S, Bornstein JC. 1995. Evidence that enteric motility reflexes can be initiated through entirely intrinsic mechanisms in the guinea-pig small intestine. *Neurogastroenterol. Motil.* 7:89–96
25. Furness JB, Bornstein JC, Pompolo S, Young HM, Kunze WAA, Kelly H. 1994. The circuitry of the enteric nervous system. *Neurogastroenterol. Motil.* 6:241–53
26. Timmermans J-P, Scheuermann DW, Stach W, Adriaensen D, De Groodt-Lasseel MHA. 1990. Distinct distribution of CGRP-, enkephalin-, galanin-, neuromedin U-, neuropeptide Y-, somatostatin-,

substance P-, VIP- and serotonin-containing neurons in the two submucosal ganglionic neural networks of the porcine small intestine. *Cell Tissue Res.* 260:367–79
27. Furness JB, Young HM, Pompolo S, Bornstein JC, Kunze WAA, McConalogue K. 1995. Plurichemical transmission and chemical coding of neurons in the digestive tract. *Gastroenterology* 108:554–63
28. Costa M, Brookes SJH, Steele PA, Gibbins I, Burcher E, Kandiah CJ. 1996. Neurochemical classification of myenteric neurons in the guinea-pig ileum. *Neuroscience* 75:949–67
29. Grider JR. 1989. Tachykinins as transmitters of ascending contractile component of the peristaltic reflex. *Am. J. Physiol.* 257:709–14
30. Holzer P. 1989. Ascending enteric reflex: multiple neurotransmitter systems and interactions. *Am. J. Physiol.* 256:540–45
31. Schemann M, Schaaf C, Mäder M. 1995. Neurotransmitter coding of enteric neurones in the guinea pig stomach. *J. Comp. Neurol.* 353:161–78
32. Porter AJ, Wattchow DA, Brookes SJH, Schemann M, Costa M. 1996. Choline actyltransferase immunoreactivity in the human small and large intestine. *Gastroenterology* 111:401–8
33. Gabella G. 1972. Innervation of the intestinal muscular coat. *J. Neurocytol.* 1: 341–62
34. Stark ME, Szurszewski JH. 1992. Role of nitric oxide in gastrointestinal and hepatic function and disease. *Gastroenterology* 103:1928–49
35. Bornstein JC, Costa M, Furness JB, Lang RJ. 1986. Electrophysiological analysis of projections of enteric inhibitory motor neurones in the guinea-pig small intestine. *J. Physiol.* 370:61–74
36. Brookes SJH, Steele PA, Costa M. 1991. Identification and immunohistochemistry of cholinergic and non-cholinergic circular muscle motor neurons in the guinea-pig small intestine. *Neuroscience* 42:863–78
37. Young HM, McConalogue K, Furness JB, De Vente J. 1993. Nitric oxide targets in the guinea-pig intestine identified by induction of cyclic GMP immunoreactivity. *Neuroscience* 55:583–96
38. Shuttleworth CW, Xue C, Ward SM, De Vente J, Sanders KM. 1993. Immunohistochemical localization of 3′,5′-cyclic guanosine monophosphate in the canine proximal colon responses to nitric oxide and electrical stimulation of enteric inhibitory neurons. *Neuroscience* 56:513–22
39. Vigna SR, Bowden JJ, McDonald DM, Fisher J, Okamoto A, et al. 1994. Characterization of antibodies to the rat substance P (NK-1) receptor and to a chimeric substance P receptor expressed in mammalian cells. *J. Neurosci.* 14:834–45
40. Sternini C, Su D, Gamp PD, Bunnett NW. 1995. Cellular sites of expression of the neurokinin-1 receptor in the rat gastrointestinal tract. *J. Comp. Neurol.* 358:531–40
41. Portbury AL, Furness JB, Young HM, Southwell BR, Vigna SR. 1996. Localisation of NK1 receptor immunoreactivity to neurons and interstitial cells of the guinea-pig gastrointestinal tract. *J. Comp. Neurol.* 367:342–51
42. Huizinga JD, Berezin I, Daniel EE, Chow E. 1990. Inhibitory innervation of colonic smooth muscle cells and interstitial cells of Cajal. *Can. J. Physiol. Pharmacol.* 68: 447–54
43. Burns AJ, Lomax AEJ, Torihashi S, Sanders KM, Ward SM. 1996. Interstitial cells of Cajal mediate inhibitory neurotransmission in the stomach. *Proc. Natl. Acad. Sci. USA* 93:12008–13
44. Torihashi S, Ward SM, Nishikawa S-I, Nishi K, Kobayashi S, Sanders KM. 1995. c-*kit*-dependent development of interstitial cells and electrical activity in the murine gastrointestinal tract. *Cell Tissue Res.* 280:97–111
45. Bornstein JC, Furness JB, Smith TK, Trussell DC. 1991. Synaptic responses evoked by mechanical stimulation of the mucosa in morphologically characterized myenteric neurons of the guinea-pig ileum. *J. Neurosci.* 11:505–18
46. Tonini M, Costa M. 1990. A pharmacological analysis of the neuronal circuitry involved in distension-evoked enteric excitatory reflex. *Neuroscience* 38:787–95
47. Johnson PJ, Bornstein JC, Yuan SY, Furness JB. 1996. Analysis of contributions of acetylcholine and tachykinins to neuroneuronal transmission in motility reflexes in the guinea-pig ileum. *Br. J. Pharmacol.* 118:973–83
48. Lepard KJ, Messori E, Galligan JJ. 1997. Purinergic fast excitatory postsynaptic potentials in myenteric neurons of guinea pig: distribution and pharmacology. *Gastroenterology* 113:1522–34
49. Galligan JJ, Bertrand PP. 1994. ATP mediates fast synaptic potentials in enteric neurons. *J. Neurosci.* 14:7563–71
50. Liu M-T, Rothstein JD, Gershon MD, Kirchgessner AL. 1997. Glutamatergic

enteric neurons. *J. Neurosci.* 17:4764–84
51. Grider JR, Jin J-G. 1994. Distinct populations of sensory neurons mediate the peristaltic reflex elicited by muscle stretch and mucosal stimulation. *J. Neurosci.* 14:2854–60
52. Kunze WAA, Bornstein JC, Furness JB. 1995. Identification of sensory nerve cells in a peripheral organ (the intestine) of a mammal. *Neuroscience* 66:1–4
53. Bertrand PP, Kunze WAA, Bornstein JC, Furness JB, Smith ML. 1997. Analysis of the responses of myenteric neurons in the small intestine to chemical stimulation of the mucosa. *Am. J. Physiol.* 273:G422–35
54. Kirchgessner AL, Tamir H, Gershon MD. 1992. Identification and stimulation by serotonin of intrinsic sensory neurons of the submucosal plexus of the guinea pig gut: activity-induced expression of Fos immunoreactivity. *J. Neurosci.* 12:235–48
55. Foxx-Orenstein AE, Grider JR. 1996. Regulation of colonic propulsion by enteric excitatory and inhibitory neurotransmitters. *Am. J. Physiol.* 271:G433–37
56. Grider JR, Kuemmerle JF, Jin J-G. 1996. 5-HT released by mucosal stimuli initiates peristalsis by activating 5-HT_4/5-HT_{1p} receptors on sensory CGRP neurons. *Am. J. Physiol.* 270:G778–82
57. Kunze WAA, Bertrand PP, Furness JB, Bornstein JC. 1997. Influence of the mucosa on the excitability of myenteric neurons. *Neuroscience* 76:619–34
58. Kunze WAA, Furness JB, Bertrand PP, Bornstein JC. 1998. Intracellular recording from myenteric neurons of the guinea-pig ileum that respond to stretch. *J. Physiol.* 506:827–42
59. Bülbring E. 1955. Correlation between membrane potential, spike discharge and tension in smooth muscle. *J. Physiol.* 128: 200–21
60. Kirber MT, Walsh JV Jr, Singer JJ. 1988. Stretch-activated ion channels in smooth muscle: a mechanism for the initiation of stretch-induced contraction. *Pflügers Arch.* 412:339–45
61. Diener M, Rummel W. 1990. Distension-induced secretion in the rat colon: mediation by prostaglandins and submucosal neurons. *Eur. J. Pharmacol.* 178:47–57
62. Frieling T, Wood JD, Cooke HJ. 1992. Submucosal reflexes: distention-evoked ion transport in the guinea-pig distal colon. *Am. J. Physiol.* 263:G91–96
63. Cooke HJ, Reddix RA. 1994. Neural regulation of intestinal electrolyte transport. In *Physiology of the Gastrointestinal Tract*, ed. LR Johnson, pp. 2083–132. New York: Raven
64. Furness JB, Trussell DC, Pompolo S, Bornstein JC, Smith TK. 1990. Calbindin neurons of the guinea-pig small intestine: quantitative analysis of their numbers and projections. *Cell Tissue Res.* 260:261–72
65. Young HM, Furness JB, Sewell P, Burcher EF, Kandiah CJ. 1993. Total numbers of neurons in myenteric ganglia of the guinea-pig small intestine. *Cell Tissue Res.* 272:197–200
66. Iyer V, Bornstein JC, Costa M, Furness JB, Takahashi Y, Iwanaga T. 1988. Electrophysiology of guinea-pig myenteric neurons correlated with immunoreactivity for calcium binding proteins. *J. Auton. Nerv. Syst.* 22:141–50
67. Song Z-M, Brookes SJH, Costa M. 1991. Identification of myenteric neurons which project to the mucosa of the guinea-pig small intestine. *Neurosci. Lett.* 129:294–98
68. Li ZS, Furness JB. 1998. The immunohistochemical localization of cholinergic markers in putative intrinsic primary afferent neurons of the guinea-pig small intestine. *Cell Tissue Res.* In Press
69. Pompolo S, Furness JB. 1993. Origins of synaptic inputs to calretinin immunoreactive neurons in the guinea-pig small intestine. *J. Neurocytol.* 22:531–46
70. Brookes SJH, Song Z-M, Ramsay GA, Costa M. 1995. Long aboral projections of Dogiel type II, AH neurons within the myenteric plexus of the guinea pig small intestine. *J. Neurosci.* 15:4013–22
71. Corraziari E, Torsoli A. 1985. Radiology. In *An Illustrated Guide to Gastrointestinal Motility*, ed. D Kumar, D Wingate, pp. 165–82. Edinburgh: Churchill Livingstone. 727 pp.
72. Hukuhara T, Neya T. 1968. The movements of the colon of rats and guinea pigs. *Jpn. J. Physiol.* 18:551–62
73. Schulze-Delrieu K, Brown BP, Custer-Hagen T. 1991. Contraction and accommodation of guinea pig duodenum in vitro. *Am. J. Physiol.* 261:364–72
74. Waterman SA, Tonini M, Costa M. 1994. The role of ascending excitatory and descending inhibitory pathways in peristalsis in the isolated guinea-pig small intestine. *J. Physiol.* 481:223–32
75. Benard T, Bouchoucha M, Dupres M, Cugnenc P-H. 1997. In vitro analysis of rat intestinal wall movements at rest and during propagated contraction: a new method. *Am. J. Physiol.* 273:G776–84
76. Song Z-M, Brookes SJH, Costa M. 1994. All calbindin-immunoreactive myenteric

neurons project to the mucosa of the guinea-pig small intestine. *Neurosci. Lett.* 180:219–22
77. Bertrand PP, Kunze WAA, Bornstein JC, Furness JB. 1998. Electrical mapping of the projections of intrinsic primary afferent neurons to the mucosa of the guinea-pig small intestine. *Neurogastroenterol. Motil.* In Press
78. Bornstein JC, Furness JB, Kunze WAA. 1994. Electrophysiological characterization of myenteric neurons: How do classification schemes relate? *J. Auton. Nerv. Syst.* 48:1–15
79. Bornstein JC, Hendriks R, Furness JB, Trussell DC. 1991. Ramifications of the axons of AH-neurons injected with the intracellular marker biocytin in the myenteric plexus of the guinea pig small intestine. *J. Comp. Neurol.* 314:437–51
80. Pompolo S, Furness JB. 1988. Ultrastructure and synaptic relationships of calbindin-reactive, Dogiel type II neurons, in myenteric ganglia of guinea-pig small intestine. *J. Neurocytol.* 17:771–82
81. Kunze WAA, Furness JB, Bornstein JC. 1993. Simultaneous intracellular recordings from enteric neurons reveal that myenteric AH neurons transmit via slow excitatory postsynaptic potentials. *Neuroscience* 55:685–94
82. Johnson PJ, Bornstein JC, Burcher E. 1998. Roles of neuronal NK_1 and NK_3 receptors in synaptic transmission during motility reflexes in the guinea-pig ileum. *Br. J. Pharmacol.* In Press
83. Bornstein JC, North RA, Costa M, Furness JB. 1984. Excitatory synaptic potentials due to activation of neurons with short projections in the myenteric plexus. *Neuroscience* 11:723–31
84. Wood JD. 1994. Physiology of the enteric nervous system. In *Physiology of the Gastrointestinal Tract*, ed. LR Johnson, pp. 423–82. New York: Raven
85. Pompolo S, Furness JB. 1995. Sources of inputs to longitudinal muscle motor neurons and ascending interneurons in the guinea-pig small intestine. *Cell Tissue Res.* 280:549–60
86. Young HM, Furness JB. 1995. An ultrastructural examination of the targets of serotonin-immunoreactive descending interneurons in the guinea-pig small intestine. *J. Comp. Neurol.* 356:101–14
87. Yuan SY, Bornstein JC, Furness JB. 1994. Investigation of the role of 5-HT_3 and 5-HT_4 receptors in ascending and descending reflexes to the circular muscle of guinea-pig small instestine. *Br. J. Pharmacol.* 112:1095–100
88. Pompolo S, Furness JB. 1998. Quantitative analysis of inputs to somatostatin immunoreactive descending interneurons in the myenteric plexus of the guinea-pig small intestine. *Cell Tissue Res.* In Press
89. Stebbing MJ, Bornstein JC. 1996. Electrophysiological mapping of fast excitatory synaptic inputs to morphological and chemically characterised myenteric neurons of guinea-pig small intestine. *Neuroscience* 73:1017–28
90. Young HM, Furness JB, Povey JB. 1995. Analysis of connections between nitric oxide synthase neurons in the myenteric plexus of the guinea-pig small intestine. *J. Neurocytol.* 24:257–63
91. Mann PT, Southwell BR, Young MH, Furness JB. 1997. Appositions made by axons of descending interneurons in the guinea-pig small intestine, investigated by confocal microscope. *J. Chem. Neuroanat.* 12:151–64
92. Yuan SY, Bornstein JC, Furness JB. 1995. Pharmacological evidence that nitric oxide may be a retrograde messenger in the enteric nervous system. *Br. J. Pharmacol.* 114:428–32
93. Hirst GDS, Holman ME, McKirdy HC. 1975. Two descending nerve pathways activated by distension of guinea-pig small intestine. *J. Physiol.* 244:113–27
94. Wilson AJ, Llewellyn-Smith IJ, Furness JB, Costa M. 1987. The source of the nerve fibres innervating the circular muscle and forming the deep muscular plexus in the guinea-pig small intestine. *Cell Tissue Res.* 247:497–504
95. Llewellyn-Smith IJ, Furness JB, Gibbins IL, Costa M. 1988. Quantitative ultrastructural analysis of enkephalin-, substance P-, and VIP-immunoreactive nerve fibers in the circular muscle of the guinea-pig small intestine. *J. Comp. Neurol.* 272: 139–48
96. Bass P, Code CF, Lambert EH. 1961. Motor and electric activity of the duodenum. *Am. J. Physiol.* 201:287–91
97. Bayliss WM, Starling EH. 1900. The movements and innervation of the small intestine. *J. Physiol.* 26:125–38
98. Furness JB, Costa M. 1977. The participation of enteric inhibitory nerves in accommodation of the intestine to distension. *Clin. Exp. Pharmacol. Physiol.* 4:37–41
99. Waterman SA, Costa M, Tonini M. 1994. Accommodation mediated by enteric inhibitory reflexes in the isolated guinea-pig small intestine. *J. Physiol.* 474:539–46
100. Smith TK, Bornstein JC, Furness JB. 1991. Interaction between reflexes evoked by distention and mucosal stimulation:

electrophysiological studies of guinea-pig ileum. *J. Auton. Nerv. Syst.* 34:69–76
101. Greenwood B, Davison JS. 1987. The relationship between gastrointestinal motility and secretion. *Am. J. Physiol.* 252:G1–7
102. Flemström G. 1994. Gastric and duodenal mucosal secretion of bicarbonate. In *Physiology of the Gastrointestinal Tract*, ed. LR Johnson, pp. 1285–309, New York: Raven
103. Cassuto J, Siewert A, Jodal M, Lundgren O. 1983. The involvement of intramural nerves in cholera toxin induced intestinal secretion. *Acta Physiol. Scand.* 117:195–202
104. Reddix R, Kuwahara A, Wallace L, Cooke HJ. 1994. Vasoactive intestinal polypeptide: a transmitter in submucous neurons mediating secretion in guinea pig distal colon. *J. Pharmacol. Exp. Ther.* 269: 1124–29
105. Vanner S, Jiang M-M, Surprenant A. 1993. Mucosal stimulation evokes vasodilation in submucosal arterioles by neuronal and nonneuronal mechanisms. *Am. J. Physiol.* 264:G202–12
106. Vanner S, Surprenant A. 1996. Neural reflexes controlling intestinal microcirculation. *Am. J. Physiol.* 271:G223–30
107. Neild TO, Shen K-Z, Surprenant A. 1990. Vasodilatation of arterioles by acetylcholine released from single neurones in the guinea-pig submucosal plexus. *J. Physiol.* 420:247–65
108. Vanner S, Surprenant A. 1991. Cholinergic and noncholinergic submucosal neurons dilate arterioles in guinea pig colon. *Am. J. Physiol.* 261:G136–44
109. Li ZS, Fox-Threlkeld JET, Furness JB. 1998. Innervation of intestinal arteries by axons with immunoreactivity for the vesicular acetylcholine transporter (VAChT). *J. Anat.* 192:107–17
110. Furness JB, Costa M. 1987. *The Enteric Nervous System*, Edinburgh: Churchill Livingstone
111. Jodal M, Lundgren O. 1989. Neurohormonal control of gastrointestinal blood flow. In *Handbook of Physiology*, sect. 6: *The Gastrointestinal System*, Vol. I, ed. JD Wood, pp. 1667–711. Washington, DC: Am. Physiol. Soc.
112. Furness JB, Costa M, Rokaeus A, McDonald TJ, Brooks B. 1987. Galanin-immunoreactive neurons in the guinea-pig small intestine: their projections and relationships to other enteric neurons. *Cell Tissue Res.* 250:607–15
113. Summers RW, Anuras S, Green J. 1983. Jejunal manometry patterns in health, partial intestinal obstruction, and pseudo-obstruction. *Gastroenterology* 85:1290–300
114. Furness JB, Bornstein JC, Kunze WAA, Bertrand PP, Kelly H, Thomas EA. 1996. Experimental basis for realistic large scale computer simulation of the enteric nervous system. *Clin. Exp. Pharmacol. Physiol.* 23:786–92

Annu. Rev. Physiol. 1999. 61:143–67

MECHANISMS OF CARDIAC PAIN

R. D. Foreman
Department of Physiology, The University of Oklahoma Health Sciences Center, Oklahoma City, Oklahoma 73190; e-mail: robert-foreman@ouhsc.edu

KEY WORDS: visceral pain, heart, cortex, sympathetic afferents, vagus, spinal cord

ABSTRACT

Angina pectoris often results from ischemic episodes that excite chemosensitive and mechanoreceptive receptors in the heart. Ischemic episodes release a collage of chemicals, including adenosine and bradykinin, that excites the receptors of the sympathetic and vagal afferent pathways. Sympathetic afferent fibers from the heart enter the upper thoracic spinal cord and synapse on cells of origin of ascending pathways. This review focuses on the spinothalamic tract, but other pathways are excited as well. Excitation of spinothalamic tract cells in the upper thoracic and lower cervical segments, except C7 and C8 segments, contributes to the anginal pain experienced in the chest and arm. Cardiac vagal afferent fibers synapse in the nucleus tractus solitarius of the medulla and then descend to excite upper cervical spinothalamic tract cells. This innervation contributes to the anginal pain experienced in the neck and jaw. The spinothalamic tract projects to the medial and lateral thalamus and, based on positron emission tomography studies, activates several cortical areas, including the anterior cingulate gyrus (BA 24 and 25), the lateral basal frontal cortex, and the mesiofrontal cortex.

INTRODUCTION

Patients with ischemic heart disease usually seek medical care when they experience the symptom of cardiac pain called angina pectoris. Heberden (1), who experienced angina pectoris, described its most typical manifestation as retrosternal with a crushing, burning, or squeezing characteristic. Pain may radiate to the throat, neck, or ulnar aspect of the left arm, sometimes reaching to the little finger. Less often, it radiates to the neck and jaw or either the right or both arms. Intensity and pain location vary from person to person and from time

0066-4278/99/0315-0143$08.00

to time. Angina pectoris may also be associated with the subjective sensation of anguish and fear of impending death.

Pain, however, is an inconsistent indicator of the presence or absence of transient myocardial ischemia because angina pectoris may consist of a continuum of conditions. These conditions may span a spectrum of patients, from those revealing no signs of coronary artery disease with a hypersensitive cardiac neural network producing angina pectoris, to those manifesting severe coronary artery disease with a hyposensitive cardiac neural network and no angina pectoris. One explanation for variation between painful and nonpainful effects of myocardial ischemia may be that angina pectoris occurs late in the ischemic cascade (2, 3). The typical sequence after onset of ischemia is left ventricular dysfunction, electrocardiographic changes, and then onset of pain. Thus, some ischemic episodes may end before the onset of angina pectoris. When pain is present in patients, its character is similar for reversible episodes of myocardial ischemia, acute myocardial infarction, and other causes (4). Nevertheless, pain can serve as a protective reaction and warning signal that may become alarming and sometimes disabling.

Coronary artery occlusion and chemical stimulation of receptors excite both sympathetic and vagal afferent fibers that may be responsible for transmitting the signals that give rise to pain from the heart during ischemia. The purpose of this review is to explain how these two afferent pathways from the heart contribute to the painful experience of angina pectoris. This review addresses how sympathetic afferent fibers contribute primarily to the usual areas of pain referral, including the chest and arm. Neural mechanisms are also discussed, to explain how vagal afferents contribute more to the pain sensed in the neck and jaw. This chapter also reviews factors activating afferent endings and their pathways, processing of information in the spinal cord, ascending pathways that transmit nociceptive information to the thalamus and brainstem, and processing of information in the limbic and cortical regions that contribute to the perception of angina pectoris. Not enough space is available to discuss how spinal and central processing could occur to contribute to silent myocardial ischemia; however, other reviews have addressed this important issue (5–8).

AFFERENT PATHWAYS TRANSMITTING NOXIOUS INFORMATION

Surgical interventions of sympathetic afferent pathways abolished or relieved angina pectoris (9–11). These procedures include removal of the superior cervical ganglia and stellate ganglia or the cervical thoracic trunk, and the sympathetic chain; and dorsal rhizotomy from the level of the lower cervical to the middle thoracic spinal cord. A summary of these studies shows that 50–60% of patients report complete relief from angina whereas 30–40% report partial relief and approximately 10–20% report no relief at all (12). Surgical interventions show that sympathetic afferents contribute to most of the pain experienced during angina pectoris. This does not eliminate the possibility that other afferent pathways are involved. Partial success in some of these patients could also be attributed to incomplete surgical sympathectomies. After surgical intervention of sympathetic afferents was completed, pain was occasionally unmasked in the neck and jaw or patients continued to experience pain in these regions during ischemic episodes. It was proposed that the vagus nerve may be contributing to that painful experience. Although patients experienced this pain, it was more tolerable than the pain they experienced when sympathetic afferent pathways were intact.

Characterization and Localization of Sensory Endings

The anatomical organization and functional characteristics of sensory nerve endings that may contribute to angina pectoris have been studied. However, much more research is required to understand how these endings contribute to variable consequences of ischemia and other forms of heart disease that lead to pain. Afferent fibers in the heart have diffuse or compact uncapsulated sensory nerve endings that are branched and found primarily in the epicardium (13, 14). The myocardium does not appear to contain sensory endings, but mixed myelinated and unmyelinated nerves forming bundles are traced through connective tissues of the septa between the muscles (13). Reflex activation of renal nerves shows that sympathetic afferent endings in the ventricle generally appear to be close to the epicardial surface whereas vagal afferent endings are closer to the endocardial surface (15, 16). It is also proposed, based on reflex responses, that sympathetic afferent fibers may be distributed over the wall of the left ventricle whereas vagal afferent fibers are distributed preferentially to the inferoposterior wall (17–20). Anatomical studies show that dorsal root afferent fibers innervate predominantly the anterior portion of the left ventricle, and nodose ganglion afferent fibers are concentrated in the inferoposterior wall (21, 22). Although these findings agree with the reflex responses, this homogeneity could not be confirmed when recordings were made directly from nodose ganglion afferent fibers (23) and cardiac sensitive dorsal root ganglion cells of sympathetic afferent fibers (24). Thus, reflexes may evoke responses that do not necessarily define how pain is generated from nociceptors in the heart. Direct recordings of afferent fibers agree with observations made in patients that patterns of anginal pain do not vary with different ischemic sites in the heart (4, 25). The emerging field of the intrinsic nervous system of the heart adds to the complexity about the processing of afferent information arising from the heart (26, 27). Much more needs to be learned before we understand how this processing of afferent information locally affects symptomatic and asymptomatic episodes of myocardial ischemia.

Excitation of terminal sensory nerve endings may occur because of at least two separate processes (28). One process may have a channel-linked receptor, producing a spatially precise, immediate, and rapid response. The other process may result from a nonchannel–linked receptor causing synaptic modulation that is slow and requires several hundred milliseconds to produce its effect. This process most likely involves G-proteins and enzymatic reactions mediating changes in the metabolism of the neuron and producing modulatory processes that are spatially diffuse.

Visceral Sensory Encoding

Intensity and specificity theories have been proposed to describe stimulus transduction in visceral afferent fibers (29). The specificity theory accounts for receptor encoding mechanisms responding to specific stimulus intensities. This theory is based on the idea that one population of receptors responds to low-intensity innoxious stimuli and another population responds to noxious stimuli. The intensity theory describes receptors that respond to a wide range of stimulus intensities. These receptors discharge at low frequencies and, as the stimulus intensity increases, increase their discharge rate until frequency reaches a threshold, producing pain sensations. Both theories have supporters (29). Recently, studies have shown that both specific nociceptors and intensity receptors exist in the esophagus and urinary bladder (30–32), but the existence of these two types has not been clearly delineated for the heart. Separation of sympathetic afferents into intensity and specificity categories is attractive, but the concern is that the curves of individual receptors show a continuum of responses when each stimulus response curve is plotted. Also, the number of nociceptive-specific fibers may be far fewer than those that participate in intensity coding.

Adequate Stimuli for Angina Pectoris

Debates about mechanical and chemical mechanisms to activate sensory receptors generating pain symptoms have continued for years. The mechanical hypothesis centered on the idea that distension of the ventricular wall resulted in pain (33). Clinical studies showing that painful and painless episodes of transient ischemia are produced by similar patterns of ventricular dilation do not support this hypothesis (3). In addition, acute ventricular failure, valvuloplasty, and myocardial biopsy all produce nonpainful ventricular dilation. Thus, the general sense is that mechanical stimulation does not play a major role in the pain associated with myocardial ischemia (3).

Both mechanosensitive and chemosensitive sympathetic afferent fibers exist in the heart. Mechanosensitive endings display a regular pattern of activity with each cardiac cycle and respond vigorously and immediately to gentle movement of a fine probe or bristle on the receptor field (34). Chemosensitive endings discharge irregularly and infrequently without cardiac modulation (35). A common feature of these two classes of cardiac afferent fibers is that both respond to bradykinin; however, only chemosensitive endings are sensitized with prostaglandins, especially PGE_1 (36, 37). After sensitization, bradykinin increases the magnitude and duration of chemosensitive endings but does not affect mechanosensitive endings. Because chemical stimuli activate mechanosensitive endings, they are classified as polymodal receptors (34). These receptors discharge spontaneously when hemodynamic conditions are normal and possess some degree of sensitivity (34). Their activity increases during coronary artery occlusion or intracoronary injections of small amounts of bradykinin. Malliani (34) argues that cardiac nociception occurs when a spatially restricted population of polymodal nociceptors is strongly excited. Based on recent evidence, however, it appears that chemical effects of these neurons are far more dramatic than are mechanical effects for producing pain of angina pectoris. Thus, chemosensitive endings are better candidates for carrying information that leads to pain perception. Often the environment around receptors is sensitized because the release of chemicals changes the responsivity of the afferent endings.

Silent Nociceptors and Receptor Sensitization

Activation of silent nociceptors during myocardial ischemia also may contribute to angina pectoris. These receptors were first identified in joints (38), but they have also been observed in the urinary bladder (32) and just recently were recorded in the heart (39). The main characteristic of these receptors is that they do not become activated until an organ or tissue is inflamed. Studies of the urinary bladder show that a population of unmyelinated and small myelinated bladder afferent fibers respond weakly, if at all, to intense bladder distension under normal conditions, but the rate of discharge increases dramatically after acute inflammation. In a preliminary study (39), silent receptors in the left ventricle responded to ischemia and bradykinin, but to date no one has created inflammatory conditions in the heart to activate these receptors. Possibly symptomatic and asymptomatic symptoms may occur because there may be variability in the inflammation that may or may not activate silent nociceptors. Thus, a population of fibers in the heart may be activated when the heart undergoes inflammation resulting from myocardial ischemia. Indeed, the heart does become inflamed during some of these ischemic episodes and changes the characteristics of the fibers to respond to the stimulus. Sensitization of nociceptors after injury or inflammation occurs when prostaglandins, leukotrienes, substance P, and other chemical mediators are released from local tissue damage. It is possible that intimal rupture or erosion of thrombosed coronary atherosclerotic plaques releases sensitizing chemicals that inflame the adventitia of coronary arteries, activate silent nociceptors, and sensitize chemosensitive receptors (40–42). The release of substances such as substance P may sensitize nociceptors to intensify the pain experience felt in patients who are infused with substance P and adenosine (43). Future studies will need to find out if sympathetic afferent fibers are sensitized during inflammation of the heart.

Chemical Stimulation of Sensory Endings

Unmyelinated sympathetic afferent fibers respond vigorously to chemical substances such as bradykinin, potassium, adenosine, acids, and veratridine when applied to the epicardial surface and injected directly into coronary arteries (36, 44–50). Several chemicals have been examined for their role in activating afferent fibers during myocardial ischemia; however, bradykinin has long been used as a chemical of choice to produce nociceptive responses. Bradykinin is an endogenous algesic chemical that results in pain in animals (51, 52) and in humans, particularly in the cutaneous receptor fields (53–60). Early reports suggest that bradykinin is increased in the effluent of the coronary sinus following coronary artery occlusion (61, 62). However, occlusion of the left anterior descending coronary artery with percutaneous transluminal coronary angioplasty occlusion elicits signs of myocardial ischemia, but no bradykinin was detected in the coronary sinus (63). Human studies and animal experiments (64) show that bradykinin, by itself, may not be sufficient to produce or mimic the pain of angina pectoris. Intracoronary injection of bradykinin in patients does not lead to angina-like pain (65, 66). These patients describe an unspecific discomfort or pain that is sensed over the whole body. Only a few patients experienced chest pain. It is likely that a collage of substances, including bradykinin, adenosine, lactate, and potassium, excite cardiac receptors that transmit nociceptive information to the central nervous system. Pagani et al used this information, coupled with the finding that conscious dogs do not respond in any specific way to pain with bradykinin injections, to formulate or reformulate the intensity hypothesis (67). They suggested that a specific code be based on a specific spatial temporal activation sequence where a discrete limited amount of myocardium is activated. Sylvén proposes an alternative hypothesis based on the nonlinear sensitive dependence of angina pectoris on initial conditions (68). He proposes that a model should be based on the deterministic, chaotic dynamics rather than require classical mechanical and cause/effect relationships. The variability of the pain sensation and its lack of direct relationship with myocardial ischemia shows that a complex system may be operating in a way not yet discovered because little is known about receptor characteristics of the heart and how they are influenced by their environment.

Recent studies have shown that adenosine may be an important component of the chemicals contributing to cardiac pain. Adenosine causes anginal-like pain in healthy volunteers (69) and in patients suffering from ischemic heart disease and those having angina pectoris (70) without any electrocardiographic changes. A dose-dependent relationship exists between adenosine and pain intensity (71). The adenosine receptor antagonist theophylline counteracted the pain experience, and inhibition of the cellular uptake of adenosine with dipyridamole increased pain. Intracoronary infusion of adenosine in patients with chronic stable angina causes pain that mimics many aspects of the pain experienced during daily life episodes of patients with transient myocardial ischemia (72). This pain most likely originates from the heart because a similar dose of adenosine infused into the right atrium did not evoke any pain.

Excitation of sympathetic afferent fibers with adenosine strongly supports the results of human and receptor studies. The first report of the excitatory effects of adenosine on cardiac sympathetic afferents of the third thoracic rami or the sympathetic chain was done by Uchida & Murao (48). In a more detailed study, afferent fibers responding to coronary artery occlusion are excited when adenosine is applied to the epicardium (73). These results show that adenosine activates afferent fibers that very likely are important for transmitting information that leads to pain perception. In contrast, Pan & Longhurst (74) show that afferent fibers cannot be activated by adenosine but only by bradykinin; therefore, they argue that other mechanisms account for activation of the receptors by adenosine. Differences in anesthesia, animal preparation for exposing the heart, length of coronary occlusion, and sites for recording afferent activity might contribute to the conflicting results between these two studies. Support for activation of cardiac sympathetic afferent fibers with adenosine also comes from the work of Huang et al (24), who show that adenosine also excites dorsal root ganglion cells that respond to coronary occlusion. Thus, there is strong evidence to suggest that sympathetic afferent pathways are activated by adenosine and can play an important role in generation of angina pectoris.

Surface membrane P1 receptors have at least two subtypes (A1 and A2) that adenosine stimulates to produce cardiac effects (75). Several studies suggest that A1 receptors are the primary mediators of the effects of endogenous adenosine on pain (76, 68); however, Huang et al (24) suggest that A1- and A2-receptor effects and substance P receptors are present on sensory nerve endings in the epicardium of the ventricle.

SPINAL CORD PROCESSING OF VISCERAL INFORMATION

Sympathetic afferent fibers from the heart and coronary arteries have their cell bodies generally in the dorsal root ganglia of the C8 to T9 spinal segments.

The major concentration, however, is found between the T2 and T6 segments (77, 78). These dorsal root ganglion cells have axons entering the tract of Lissauer and terminating in the same segment or ascending and descending a few segments before they penetrate into the spinal cord (77). Axons course over the dorsal rim of the gray matter and terminate primarily in lamina I, whereas others slide along the lateral edge of the gray matter and terminate primarily in laminae V, VII, and X. It should be noted that the density of visceral termination sites is much less than those of the somatic afferent fibers. Diffuse pain experienced with cardiac ischemia may occur because sympathetic afferent axons are a small percentage of the fibers that enter the spinal cord, and they have a broad rostral to caudal distribution. This extensive and diffuse arrangement of visceral afferent fibers innervates second-order neurons in several segments, thus contributing to the diffuse and poorly localized nature of angina pectoris.

Central Sensitization of Visceral Afferent Information

Continual bombardment of neurons in the gray matter of the spinal cord can activate mechanisms in cells of the spinal cord that provide a functional substrate for hyperalgesic states resulting from injury to visceral organs. The primary focus of the previous studies was to study central sensitization for somatic components, but the visceral effects lagged behind (79). Studies of other visceral organs provide insight into the changes that may occur in the thoracic segments of the spinal cord during angina pectoris. Repeated noxious balloon distensions of the colorectal region in humans evoke painful responses that increase pain sensitivity and expand the area of pain referral to the overlying somatic areas of the body (80). Animal models support the findings observed in human studies. Recordings made from neurons in the lower thoracic gray matter during gall bladder distension show that some neurons respond only to somatic input and not to the visceral stimulus whereas another population responds to both somatic input and distension (81). The somatic receptive field enlarges only for spinal neurons that receive input from noxious stimulation of the gall bladder. Thus, the conditioning visceral stimulus is selective because only those neurons responsive to a visceral afferent input change their sensitization to the somatic input. An additional important characteristic of these responsive neurons is that the somatic referral of visceral pain that produced the changes tends to outlast the duration of the noxious visceral stimulus. This observation correlates well with the clinical experience that hyperalgesia is felt after the painful episode has passed. These results raise the possibility that central sensitization of spinothalamic tract (STT) cells and neurons in the gray matter can intensify the pain experience resulting from cardiac pain.

ASCENDING PATHWAYS TRANSMITTING NOXIOUS CARDIAC INFORMATION The gray matter is made up of cells serving as interneurons and as the origin of ascending pathways that transmit visceral information to areas of the brain processing sensory information and participating in pain perception (Figure 1). Of the ascending pathways, the STT is the most studied system for transmitting visceral afferent information to the brain. Axons of STT cells generally cross over to the contralateral side within one or two segments and then ascend generally in the anterolateral quadrant. Recent studies, however, have shown that some axons remain on the ipsilateral side and some are in the dorsolateral quadrant (82). Visceral information from the upper thoracic segments usually converges with input from somatic structures and ascends to the lateral and medial thalamus (83–86).

Spinothalamic Tract Organization and Characteristics of Angina Pectoris: Chest and Arm

Patients with angina pectoris express three main clinical characteristics to describe their symptoms: (*a*) Pain from the heart is generally referred to somatic structures innervated by the same spinal segments that innervate the heart (87); (*b*) pain of angina pectoris is referred to proximal and axial body areas but generally not to distal limbs (88); and (*c*) angina pectoris is generally felt as deep and not superficial or cutaneous pain (89). In this section, neurophysiological mechanisms are described to support the patient observations of the referred pain associated with myocardial ischemia and other cardiac diseases.

VISCEROSOMATIC CONVERGENCE Electrophysiological studies show that electrical stimulation of cardiopulmonary afferent fibers excites STT cells in the T1 to T6 segments of the spinal cord (90). Approximately 80% of the cells recorded in these segments are strongly activated with cardiopulmonary afferent stimulation, and all these cells receive convergent input from somatic structures. It is interesting that cardiopulmonary afferent stimulation has little effect on the activity of cells in the C7 and C8 segments, where the major innervation is to the distal forelimb and hand. This fits with the clinical observations that anginal pain is usually not referred to the hand and distal forelimb (91–93). Thus, lack of responsiveness of these cells agrees with clinical observations. Once past the cervical enlargement, STT cells of the C5–C6 segments are again primarily excited by cardiopulmonary sympathetic afferent and somatic stimulation. In these segments, cardiopulmonary afferent stimulation excited approximately 60% of the cells and inhibited 16%. Somatic fields for these cells are primarily from the chest. An interesting feature of these segments is that they do not receive cardiac input directly from their dorsal root ganglion cells; in fact, the afferent input is a few segments away. Some evidence suggests that cardiopulmonary afferent fibers may activate cell bodies of a propriospinal path where it directly or indirectly makes synaptic connection with STT cells in the cervical region (94). It is also possible that afferent branches of the T2 and

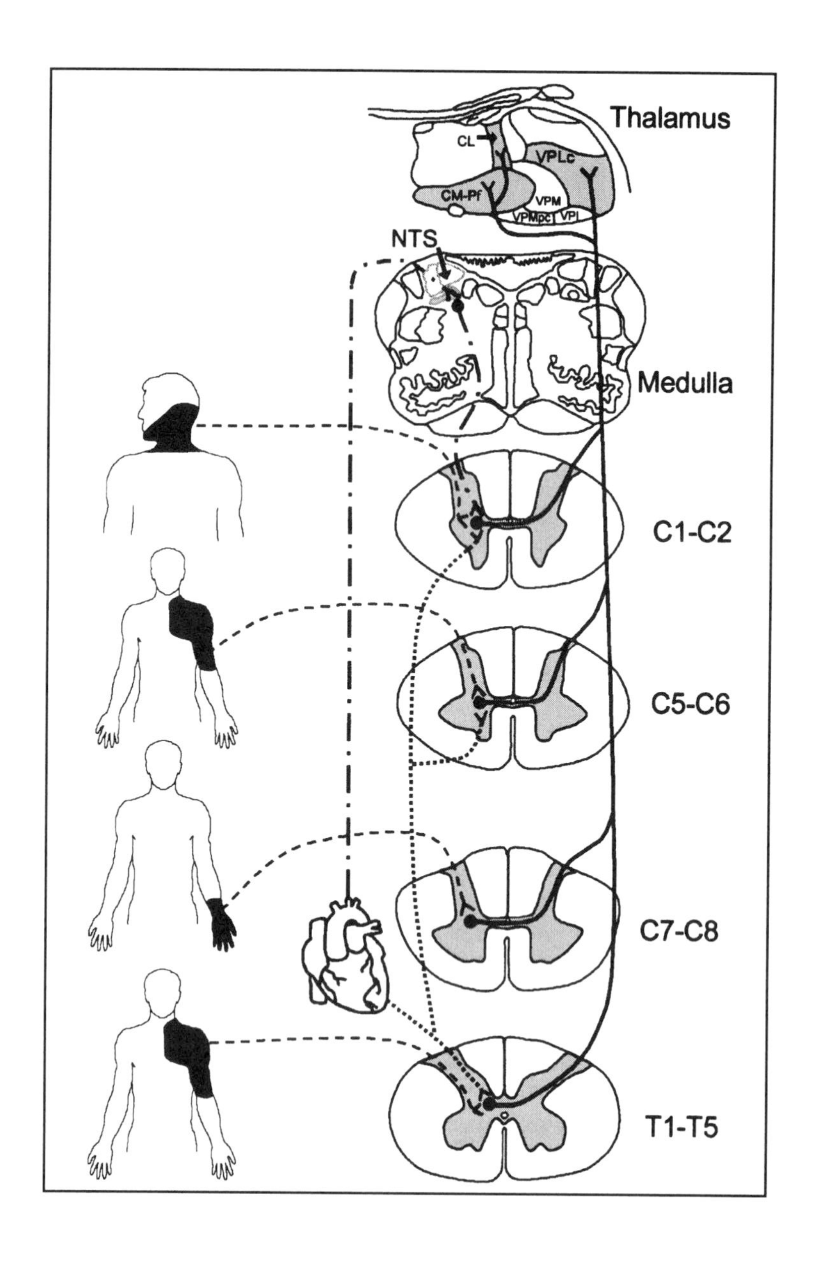
Thalamus
CL
VPLc
CM-Pf
VPM
VPMpc
VPl
NTS
Medulla
C1-C2
C5-C6
C7-C8
T1-T5

T3 sympathetic fibers may travel in the zone of Lissauer for several segments (95). Thus, convergence of visceral and somatic input onto a common pool of STT cells provides a substrate for explaining the referral of pain to somatic structures.

PROXIMAL AND AXIAL SOMATIC INVOLVEMENT Neurophysiological mechanisms also provide a basis for the proximal nature of the referred pain of angina pectoris. Electrophysiological studies of the STT show that cardiopulmonary afferent input most commonly excites cells with proximal somatic receptive fields (90). Cardiopulmonary input strongly excites approximately 80% of the STT cells with proximal somatic receptor fields but only weakly excites 35% of the cells with distal somatic input. Thus, the relationship of cells with excitatory visceral input and proximal axial fields is highly significant. These neurophysiological observations support the human studies that angina pectoris is most commonly felt in the proximal and axial regions of the left arm and chest. The frequency distribution of angina pectoris shows that the chest is involved more than 95% of the time, and the pain radiates 30–60% of the time to the left proximal shoulder and less involvement occurs down the arm (92, 96).

DEEP, DULL, DIFFUSE, ACHING PAIN The final characteristic of angina pectoris is the deep, diffuse, dull nature of the symptoms. These sensations are comparable to muscle pain. That is, the pain is typically deep and aching and is often associated with referred muscle hyperalgesia. The similarity of muscle pain and visceral pain was shown in patients who suffer frequently from angina pectoris referred unilaterally to the chest and radiating down the inner aspect of the left arm (89). These patients were asked to compare their sensations of angina pectoris with those provoked when a hypertonic saline solution was injected into the interspinus ligament of the left eighth cervical or first thoracic spinal segment. These patients explained that the pain was felt in the upper interscapular region, over the left chest, and then radiated down the inside aspect of the left arm. These patients stated that the onset, continuation, segmental

←

Figure 1 Schematic diagram showing functional organization to explain characteristics of referred pain of angina pectoris in the chest and arm (C5–C6, T1–T5) and the neck and jaw (C1–C2). The spinothalamic tract (*solid line*) ascends from each of the spinal segments to the lateral (VPLc, caudal ventral posterolateral nucleus) and medial (CL, nucleus centralis lateralis; CM-Pf, centrum medianum-parafascicularis nucleus) nuclei of the thalamus. Afferent pathways from the somatic structures (*dashed line*) and the cardiopulmonary sympathetic afferent fibers (*dotted line*) and vagal fibers (*dotted/dashed line*) converge on cell bodies of the spinothalamic tract. Blackened regions on the figures represent somatic fields. NTS, nucleus tractus solitarius; VPM, ventral posteromedial nucleus; VPI, ventral posteroinferior nucleus; VPMpc, ventral posteromedial nucleus, parvocellular part.

localization, and character closely mimicked their anginal pectoris. The pain is diffuse, continuous, and difficult to describe, although it can be identified as causing suffering (89).

Human studies show that referred muscle hyperalgesia resulting from a diseased visceral organ is a common presentation in the clinic (97). Although this section focuses on the results of hyperalgesia from different visceral organs, the possibility of hyperalgesia resulting from angina pectoris should also be considered. Patients suffering pain caused by calculosis of the upper urinary tract experience muscular hyperalgesia with less involvement of overlying cutaneous structures (98, 99). Experimental studies also show that stimulation of the ureter results in muscular hyperalgesia and central sensitization of dorsal horn cells (100–102). Their results show that muscle and deep structures make contributions to referred pain resulting from visceral diseases, and cutaneous pain plays a much smaller role. Muscle hyperalgesia associated with visceral pain leads to the suggestion that the STT plays a role in processing sensations associated with muscle changes resulting from cardiac pain. This led to the hypothesis that STT cells excited by visceral stimulus are more likely to be excited with deep, i.e. muscle, input than cutaneous input (90, 103). This hypothesis was tested by recording STT cell activity during stimulation of cardiopulmonary afferent fibers and pinching the skin and muscle of somatic receptor fields in the hands and the proximal arm and chest (90). In the hand and fingers, the strongest response of STT cells is elicited when the skin alone is pinched and does not increase when skin and muscle are stimulated together. In these neurons, cardiopulmonary afferent fiber stimulation minimally increases cell activity to approximately 10% of the maximal response to cutaneous stimulation. When STT cells receive their input primarily from the proximal arm and chest region, they are most often excited powerfully during muscle stimulation. Their overall response reaches 88% of the maximal somatic response that can be elicited from all neurons with proximal somatic input. Cutaneous stimulation alone only achieves less than 33% of the maximal somatic response. These muscle responsive cells are strongly excited during cardiopulmonary afferent stimulation, with their activity reaching 68% of the maximal somatic response. These observations provided support for our hypothesis that muscle and visceral afferent fiber input converged most commonly onto the same STT cells, whereas cells with primarily cutaneous input were not very responsive to the visceral stimulus. Thus, converging input from deep tissue and visceral afferent fibers onto STT cells may provide a basis for explaining why visceral pain, such as that resulting from myocardial ischemia, is felt predominantly as a deep or localized suffering pain, generally in proximal structures such as muscles, tendons, and ligaments. It also supports the idea that some hyperalgesia may remain after episodes of angina pectoris.

Spinothalamic Tract Organization and Characteristics of Angina Pectoris: Neck and Jaw Pain

Surgical sympathectomy reduces the incidence of refractory angina pectoris, but pain referred to the neck and jaw sometimes remains or appears after extensive sympathectomy. This pain led to the suggestion that vagal afferent fibers, which commonly are thought to transmit non-nociceptive sensory information, may produce referred pain associated with myocardial ischemia (9, 12, 10). A particularly interesting study would be one that noted the incidence of jaw or neck pain in patients who are quadriplegic because of a lower cervical segment injury and who have coronary artery disease. Presumably these patients would not have sympathetic afferent input to the upper cervical segments, thereby eliminating the sympathetic component as a factor in jaw pain. Stimulation of the vagal or sympathetic afferent fibers and chemical stimulation of the heart excites STT neurons in the C1–C3 segments (104, 105). Thus, these afferent pathways are candidates for transmitting noxious cardiac information to these segments. Vagal stimulation serves as a more potent stimulus than the input from cardiopulmonary afferent fibers. Vagal stimulation markedly increases cell activity with C-fiber input more often than does cardiopulmonary afferent stimulation. Somatic receptive fields for these C1–C3 STT neurons are found most commonly on the neck, jaw, ear, and upper arm. Overlapping terminations of primary afferent fibers from different regions could explain why the receptive fields of the head and upper body have variable locations. Somatic fields from the ipsilateral neck and/or shoulder regions enter the spinal cord at the upper cervical dorsal root ganglia (106). The more caudal somatic fields may result from projections of somatic afferent fibers from the C5–C7 segments on the upper cervical segments (107, 108). Although cardiopulmonary afferent input seems to play a subordinate role, this pathway nevertheless excites neurons in the C1–C3 segments. These cells are far removed from the entry zone of the cardiac afferent fibers, which is primarily in the T2–T6 dorsal root ganglia (109, 77). Most likely, cardiac afferent input enters the spinal cord and ascends in a pathway in the ventrolateral quadrant and synapses on these C1–C3 neurons (110). Such a pathway likely exists in monkeys as well as in rats. This suggestion is based on information that excitation of the T1–T5 STT cells by splanchnic nerve stimulation is abolished when the ventrolateral part of the cord is cut rostral to the T7 segment (111). The splanchnic nerve has its primary point of entry in the T9–T11 segments of the spinal cord. Thus, it is likely that this pool of neurons in the C1–C3 segments of the spinal cord provides a neural substrate for referred pain originating from the heart and being perceived in the neck and jaw region. The exact mechanism has not been defined to explain why some patients feel neck and jaw pain with angina and others do not.

OTHER ASCENDING PATHWAYS FOR TRANSMITTING VISCERAL INFORMATION

The Anterolateral Pathways

Other ascending tracts besides the STT in the anterolateral quadrant of the spinal cord may be important for transmission of noxious information that ascends to the brain and leads to the perception of pain (112–114). A prominent pathway is the parabrachial region of the pons, which that may serve as an important relay for processing visceral somatic nociceptive information. A major projection of axons originates from lamina I and enters the lateral parabrachial area (115–118). This information is relayed to the amygdala (119), the ventromedial nucleus, and the retrochiasmatic area of the hypothalamus (120). This system might contribute to the emotional-affective behavioral and autonomic reactions to noxious events. Future studies need to address similarities and differences of information transmitted via the parabrachial relay versus the medial thalamic relay nucleus for cardiac input.

Other pathways, including the spinoreticular pathway (121) and the spinomesencephalic (122, 123), spinosolitary (124), and spinohypothalamic tracts (125), may all be involved with conveying visceral information from the heart, but much less is known about the visceral responsiveness of these pathways. Future studies will help to determine how these particular pathways contribute to the overall cardiac pain experience during myocardial ischemia.

The Dorsal Column Pathway

Recent studies also suggest that the dorsal column pathways play an important role in transmitting nociceptive visceral information, particularly from pelvic organs (126–130). The role of the dorsal columns became known when it was shown that eight patients were successfully relieved of their pelvic cancer pain following a midline lesion of the dorsal column at the T10 spinal level (131). This limited myelotomy only penetrated the dorsal columns and not other areas of the spinal cord. In animal studies, gentle or noxious stimulation of reproductive organs or noxious colorectal distension excited gracile nucleus neurons that most likely reach this pathway via the postsynaptic dorsal column pathway (126, 130). The limited dorsal column lesion also reduced their response of cells in the ventroposterolateral nucleus of the thalamus in rats, showing that visceral input could be transmitted via the dorsal columns (127). Less work has been done for the afferent input from the heart. Recordings from neurons of the ventroposterolateral nucleus of the thalamus show that both STT and dorsal column pathways play a role in transmitting information from the heart and thoracic region to the thalamus (132). Thus, multiple ascending pathways transmit visceral information, but the content of the coded visceral messages in the somatic information that each pathway contributes to the processing of the thalamus must be evaluated to understand their respective roles in sculpting visceral sensation. In comparison to the STT tract neurons, a smaller percentage of cells of the cuneothalamic neurons respond with significantly fewer evoked action potentials and a shorter latency to activation (133). Furthermore, most cuneothalamic neurons respond primarily to innocuous somatic stimuli whereas STT neurons respond primarily or solely to noxious pinches of somatic fields. Neurons that responded to cardiopulmonary input most often have somatic fields on the proximal arm and chest. Thus, differences in neuronal responses to noxious stimulation of the cardiopulmonary afferent fibers suggest that a dorsal column pathway and the ventrolateral pathways to the ventroposterolateral thalamus may play different roles in the transmission and integration of pain associated with coronary artery disease. Much more work needs to be done to understand how these different contributions can explain the characteristics of cardiac pain.

SUPRASPINAL PROCESSING OF CARDIAC NOCICEPTIVE INFORMATION

Thalamus

LATERAL THALAMUS The lateral thalamus is composed primarily of the ventroposterolateral and posteromedial nuclei. Cells of the lateral thalamus relay information to the primary somatosensory cortex and possibly to the secondary somatic cortex (Figure 2). Little information exists about processing of visceral information in the somatosensory cortex, but there is some evidence to suggest that this information can project to this region (134–136). This region is important for processing information that would be interpreted as sensory discriminative because it refers to the capacity to analyze location, intensity, and duration of the nociceptive stimulus (137, 138).

MEDIAL THALAMUS Ascending pathways carrying visceral and somatic input also project to the medial thalamus (Figure 2). The medial thalamus is primarily the centralis lateralis and centrum medianum-parafascicularis nuclei (139, 140). These nuclei send information to the association cortex, including the insular cortex, amygdala, and cingulate gyrus (141–144). These nuclei may be primarily responsible for the motivational affective components of pain, including autonomic adjustments (145–147, 137).

Higher Central Integration

Information on higher central integration is sketchy. Much less is known about processing of noxious visceral information in cortical structures. The

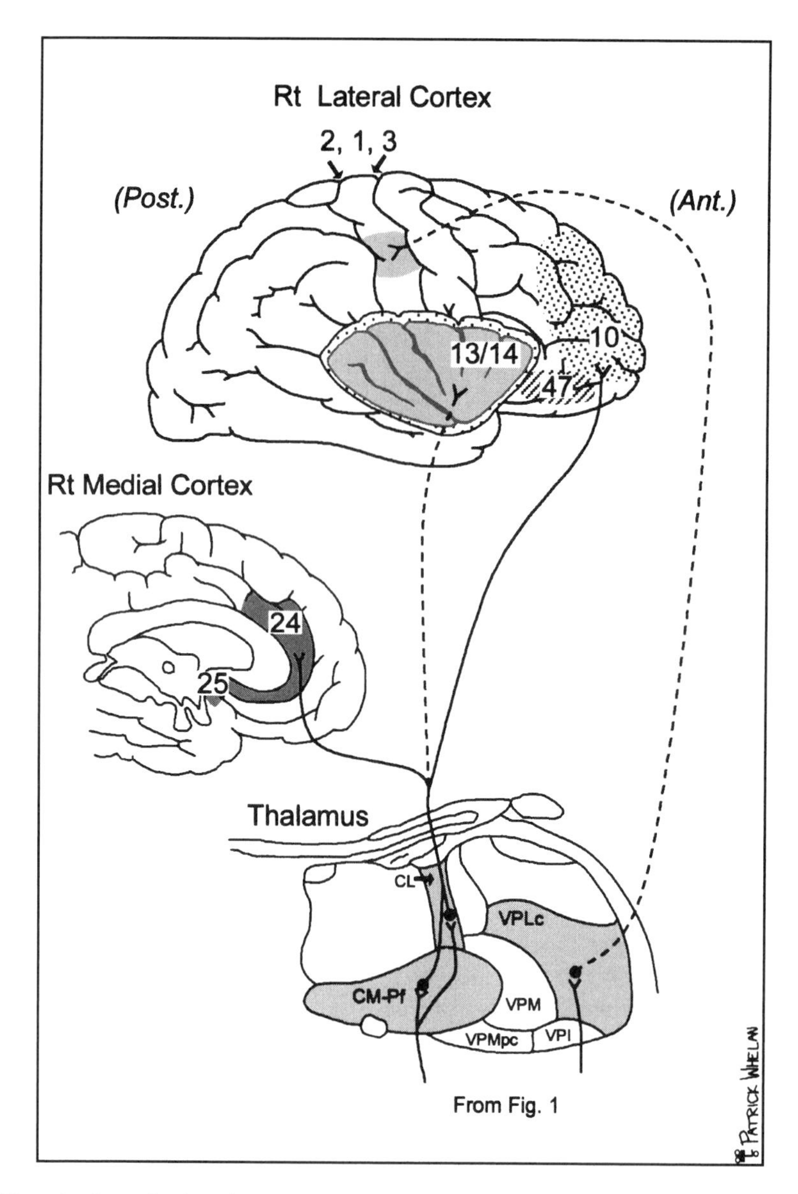

Figure 2 Generalization of supraspinal organization of cardiac nociceptive (*solid line*) and other noxious visceral (*dashed line*) afferent inputs in the cortex from the lateral and medial thalamus. This organization is based primarily on positron emission tomography studies (151, 148–150, 152). Brodmann's Area (BA) 2,1,3, postcentral gyrus; 10, medial orbitofrontal cortex; 13/14, anterior insula; 24, anterior cingulate gyrus; 25, ventral cingulate gyrus; and 47, lateral basal frontal cortex. Post., posterior; Ant., anterior. Abbreviations for the thalamus are defined in the legend of Figure 1.

information described here resulted from positron emission tomography (PET) studies and functional magnetic resonance imaging in patients. To date, few laboratories have used PET studies to determine the cortical areas that are involved with angina pectoris (148, 149, 150). In addition, these techniques were used to study brain blood flow changes resulting from gastrointestinal distension in healthy volunteers (151) and patients with irritable bowl syndrome (152). Far more studies with PET have been done to examine brain responses during noxious somatic stimulation (153).

Ascending pathways transmit noxious somatic and cardiac information to the lateral and medial thalamus (83) as well as to both the reticular formation and the thalamus (121). In addition, convergent input from the dorsal column postsynaptic pathway transmits information at least to the lateral thalamus (127). Cells of the lateral thalamus respond to cardiac afferent input (132, 154). Other visceral stimuli, such as colorectal distension and urinary bladder distension, also excite the VPL neurons (136, 128). Human studies also suggest that thalamic nuclei are activated during angina pectoris (149).

Cells of the lateral thalamus project primarily to somatosensory cortex, particularly areas 1 and 3 (Figure 2). This region of the cortex is activated during painful esophageal distension in healthy patients (151). Nonpainful distension produces bilateral activation of the central sulcus, and the response is intensified during painful esophageal distension. Activation of these areas contributes to the spatial localization and encoding intensity discrimination of the stimulus. It should be noted that this area did not show changes in patients with irritable bowel syndrome and angina pectoris (152, 149). Because visceral information changes cell activity, it is possible that angina pectoris reaches the region, but the effects are not observed because excitation of one pool of neurons is counterbalanced by inhibition of another pool of neurons. Thus, activity of visceral input from myocardial ischemia cannot be ruled out for this region of the cortex.

The medial thalamus projects its information to those areas of the cortex that are important for cognitive-evaluative and affective-motivational aspects of the pain experience (Figure 2). Angina pectoris increases thalamic blood flow bilaterally, but the sensitivity of PET is not sufficient to identify the specific nuclei involved. Based on previous studies, angina pectoris most likely activates the medial thalamus. Noxious visceral information resulting from angina pectoris projects bilaterally to the ventral cingulate cortex (BA 25) [BA stands for Brodmann's areas (see 155–157 for a description of these areas) and the numbers identify surface regions of the cortex], the lateral basal frontal cortex (BA 47), and the mesial orbitofrontal cortex (BA 10) (149). The ventral cingulate gyrus increases its blood flow [in the 1994 study of Rosen et al (148), the increase occurred only in the left gyrus, but a bilateral increase was reported in their 1996 study (149)]. Other visceral studies have shown that the anterior cingulate gyrus (BA 24) is strongly activated by a visceral stimulus (151, 152). The 1994 study of Rosen et al (148) shows a decrease in regional blood flow in BA 24 whereas the later study shows that blood flow in this region increased, although the change was substantially less than for BA 25. These results, in general, show that the anterior cingulate gyrus appears to be activated during noxious visceral stimulation. This region of the gyrus is most closely related to visceromotor responses (158). In rats, this general area connects with the nucleus of the solitary tract (159), dorsal motor nucleus of the vagus, and sympathetic thoracic intermediolateral cell columns (160). This region generates affective and cognitive responses to pain (161).

Angina pectoris also activates the prefrontal (BA 47) and mesial orbitofrontal (BA 10) cortices. This general area is also activated in patients with irritable bowel syndrome (152). In general, noxious cardiac information may cause responses in these regions as a consequence of planning that has resulted from behavioral and attentional organization (153, 162–164). This general area may also be associated with emotional vocalization and verbalization (158), as well as recall of negative affectively charged memories (152). In contrast, esophageal pain in healthy volunteers did not activate this region (151). The reason for this difference is unclear, but one difference may be that chronic pain patients use this region to plan a strategy that helps them to cope with their pain whereas healthy patients are not required to evoke these behavioral patterns.

The insular cortex is another important association area for coordinating visceral sensory and motor information that project from thalamic nuclei, the nucleus of the solitary tract, via the parabrachial nucleus and via reciprocal efferent projections to these areas (165–167). Painful esophageal distention activated the insular cortices (151). It is therefore somewhat surprising that angina pectoris did not evoke activity in this region, even though angina is a visceral stimulus and cardiovascular afferent fibers innervate the insula (165). One reason for the difference may be that esophageal pain is an acute stimulus and angina pectoris is a chronic condition.

A number of discrepancies and differences exist among the studies that have been done using PET and magnetic resonance imaging scans to examine the effects of visceral input. Future studies must be done to elucidate the spatial and temporal processing of neural mechanisms that underlie the changes observed with this technology. These studies, however, have provided an important catalyst to study these areas in the future using electrophysiological, neuroanatomical, and inmunocytochemical techniques as well as refined PET scans and other research strategies. Elucidation of how these areas function will facilitate ways to treat chronic pain of visceral origin.

ACKNOWLEDGMENTS

I thank Ms. Carrie Hulka for typing the manuscript and Mr. Patrick Whelan for preparing the figures. This work was supported by the National Institutes of Health grants HL22732, HL52986, and NS35471 and by the Presbyterian Health Foundation.

Literature Cited

1. Heberden W. 1971. Some account of a disorder of the breast. 1772. *Med. Trans.* 2:59–67. Cited in *Arch. Med.* 128:782
2. Nesto RW, Kowalchuk GJ. 1987. The ischemic cascade: temporal sequence of hemodynamic, electrocardiographic and symptomatic expressions of ischemia. *Am. J. Cardiol.* 57:23–30C
3. Davies G, Bencivelli W, Chierchia S, Fragasso G, Crea F, et al. 1988. Sequence and magnitude of ventricular volume changes in painful and painless myocardial ischemia. *Circulation* 78:310–19
4. Eriksson B, Vuorisalo D, Sylvén C. 1994. Quality and intensity of chest pains in patients treated in coronary care. *J. Intern. Med.* 235:473–78
5. Foreman RD, Chandler MJ. 1994. Vagal afferent modulation of cardiac pain. In *Vagal Control of the Heart: Experimental Basis and Clinical Implications*, ed. MN Levy, PJ Schwartz, pp. 345–68. New York: Futura
6. Maseri A, ed. 1995. *Ischemic Heart Disease*. New York: Churchill Livingstone
7. Cohn PF. 1989. *Silent Myocardial Ischemia and Infarction*. New York: Marcel Dekker
8. Droste C, Roskamm H. 1990. Pain perception and endogenous pain modulation in angina pectoris. In *Silent Myocardial Ischemia: A Critical Appraisal*, ed. JJ Kellermann, E Braunwald, 37:142–64. Basel: Karger
9. Lindgren I, Olivecrona H. 1947. Surgical treatment of angina pectoris. *J. Neurosurg.* 4:19–39
10. White JC, Bland EF. 1948. The surgical relief of severe angina pectoris. Methods employed and end results in 83 patients. *Medicine* 27:1–42
11. White JC. 1957. Cardiac pain. Anatomic pathways and physiological mechanisms. *Circulation* 16:644–55
12. Meller ST, Gebhart GF. 1992. A critical review of the afferent pathways and the potential chemical mediators involved in cardiac pain. *Neuroscience* 48(3):501–24
13. Miller MR, Kasahara M. 1964. Studies on the nerve endings in the heart. *Am. J. Anat.* 115:217–33
14. Khabarova AY. 1961. *The Afferent Innervation of the Heart*. New York: Consult. Bur.
15. Barber MJ, Mueller TM, Davies BG, Zipes DP. 1984. Phenol topically applied to canine left ventricular epicardium interrupts sympathetic but not vagal afferents. *Circ. Res.* 55:532–44
16. Minisi AJ, Thames MD. 1991. Activation of cardiac sympathetic afferents during coronary occlusion: evidence for reflex activation of the sympathetic nervous system during transmural myocardial ischemia in the dog. *Circulation* 84:357–67
17. Thames MD, Klopfenstein HS, Abboud FM, Mark AL, Walker JL. 1978. Preferential distribution of inhibitory cardiac receptors with vagal afferents to the inferoposterior wall of the left ventricle activated during coronary occlusion in the dog. *Circ. Res.* 43:512–19
18. Walker JL, Thames MD, Abboud FM, Mark AL, Klopfenstein HS. 1978. Preferential distribution of inhibitory cardiac receptors in left ventricle of the dog. *Am. J. Physiol.* 235:H188–92
19. Thames MD, Abboud FM. 1979. Inhibition of renal sympathetic nerve activity during myocardial ischemia mediated by left ventricular receptors with vagal afferents in dogs. *J. Clin. Invest.* 63:395–402
20. Minisi AJ, Thames MD. 1993. Distribution of left ventricular sympathetic afferents demonstrated by reflex responses to transmural myocardial ischemia and to intracoronary and epicardial bradykinin. *Circulation* 87:240–46
21. Quigg M. 1991. Distribution of vagal

afferent fibers of the guinea pig heart labeled by anterograde transport of conjugated horseradish peroxidase. *J. Auton. Nerv. Syst.* 36:13–24
22. Quigg M, Elfvin LG, Aldskogius H. 1988. Distribution of cardiac sympathetic afferent fibers in the guinea pig heart labeled by anterograde transport of wheat germ agglutinin-horseradish peroxidase. *J. Auton. Nerv. Syst.* 25:107–18
23. Armour JA, Huang MH, Pelleg A, Sylvén C. 1994. Activity of in situ canine nodose ganglion cardiac afferent neurons responsive to mechanoreceptor and/or chemoreceptor inputs. *Cardiovasc. Res.* 28:1218–25
24. Huang MH, Sylvén C, Horackova M, Armour JA. 1995. Ventricular sensory neurons in canine dorsal root ganglia: effects of adenosine and substance P. *Am. J. Physiol.* 269:R318–24
25. Pasceri V, Cianflone D, Finocchiaro ML, Crea F, Maseri A. 1995. Relation between myocardial infarction site and pain location in Q wave acute myocardial infarction. *Am. J. Cardiol.* 75:224–30
26. Armour JA. 1994. Peripheral autonomic neuronal interactions in cardiac regulation. In *Neurocardiology*, ed. JA Armour, JL Ardell, pp. 219–244. New York: Oxford Univ. Press
27. Ardell JL. 1994. Structure and function of mammalian intrinsic cardiac neurons. In *Neurocardiology*, ed. JA Armour, JL Ardell, pp. 95–114. New York: Oxford Univ. Press
28. Alberts B, Bray D, Lewis J, Raff M, Roberts K, Watson JD. 1989. *Molecular Biology of the Cell*. New York: Garland
29. Cervero F, Jänig W. 1992. Visceral nociceptors: a new world order. *Trends Neurosci.* 15:374–78
30. Sengupta JN, Kauvar D, Goyal RK. 1989. Characteristics of vagal esophageal tension-sensitive afferent fibers in the opossum. *J. Neurophysiol.* 61:1001–10
31. Sengupta JN, Saha JK, Goyal RK. 1990. Stimulus-response function studies of esophageal mechanosensitive nociceptors in sympathetic afferents of opossum. *J. Neurophysiol.* 64:796–812
32. Häbler H-J, Jänig W, Koltzenburg M. 1990. Activation of unmyelinated afferent fibres by mechanical stimuli and inflammation of the urinary bladder in the cat. *J. Physiol.* 425:545–62
33. Colbeck EH. 1903. Angina pectoris: a criticism and a hypothesis. *Lancet* 1:793–95
34. Malliani A. 1982. Cardiovascular and sympathetic afferent fibers. *Rev. Physiol. Biochem. Pharmacol.* 94:11–74
35. Casati R, Lombardi F, Malliani A. 1979. Afferent sympathetic unmyelinated fibres with left ventricular endings in cats. *J. Physiol.* 292:135–48
36. Baker DG, Coleridge HM, Coleridge JCG, Nerdrum T. 1980. Search for a cardiac nociceptor: stimulation by bradykinin of sympathetic afferent nerve endings in the heart of cat. *J. Physiol.* 306:519–36
37. Nerdrum T, Baker DG, Coleridge HM, Coleridge JCG. 1986. Interaction of bradykinin and prostaglandin E1 on cardiac pressor reflex and sympathetic afferents. *Am. J. Physiol.* 250:R815–22
38. Schmidt RF, Schaible H-G, Messinger K, Heppelmann B, Hanesch U, Pawlak M. 1994. Silent and active nociceptors: structure, functions, and clinical implications. In *Progress in Pain Research and Management*, ed. GF Gebhart, DL Hammond, TS Jensen, pp. 213–50. Seattle: Int. Assoc. Study of Pain
39. Pan H-L, Averill D. 1998. Functional properties of silent cardiac sympathetic afferents in cats. *FASEB J.* 12(5):3994 (Abstr.)
40. Kohchi K, Takebayashi S, Hiroki T, Nobuyoshi M. 1985. Significance of adventitial inflammation of the coronary artery in patients with unstable angina: results at autopsy. *Circulation* 71(4):709–16
41. Van Der Wall AC, Becker AE, Van Der Loos CM, Das PK. 1994. Site of intimal rupture or erosion of thrombosed coronary atherosclerotic plaques is characterized by an inflammatory process irrespective of the dominant plaque morphology. *Circulation* 89:36–44
42. Crea F, Biasucci LM, Buffon A, Liuzzo G, Monaco C, et al. 1997. Role of inflammation in the pathogenesis of unstable coronary artery disease. *Am. J. Cardiol.* 80(5A):10–16E
43. Gaspardone A, Crea F, Tomai F, Iamele M, Crossman DC, et al. 1994. Substance P potentiates the algogenic effects of intraarterial infusion of adenosine. *J. Am. Coll. Cardiol.* 24(2):477–82
44. Coleridge HM, Coleridge JCG. 1980. Cardiovascular afferents involved in regulation of peripheral vessels. *Annu. Rev. Physiol.* 42:413–27
45. Uchida Y, Murao S. 1974. Potassium-induced excitation of afferent cardiac sympathetic nerve fibers. *Am. J. Physiol.* 226:603–7
46. Uchida Y, Murao S. 1974. Afferent sympathetic nerve fibers originating in the left atrial wall. *Am. J. Physiol.* 227:753–58

47. Uchida Y, Murao S. 1974. Bradykinin-induced excitation of afferent cardiac sympathetic nerve fibers. *Jpn. Heart J.* 15: 84–91
48. Uchida Y, Murao S. 1975. Acid-induced excitation of afferent cardiac sympathetic nerve fibers. *Am. J. Physiol.* 228:27–33
49. Brown AM, Malliani A. 1971. Spinal sympathetic reflexes initiated by coronary receptors. *J. Physiol.* 212:685–705
50. Lombardi F, Della Bella P, Casati R, Malliani A. 1981. Effects of intracoronary administration of bradykinin on the impulse activity of afferent sympathetic unmyelinated fibers with left ventricular endings in the cat. *Circ. Res.* 48:69–75
51. Besson JM, Guilbaud G, Lombard MC. 1974. Effects of bradykinin intra-arterial injection into the limbs upon bulbar and mesencephalic reticular unit activity. *Adv. Neurol.* 4:207–15
52. Guzman F, Braun C, Lim RKS. 1962. Visceral pain and the pseudoaffective response to intra-arterial injection of bradykinin and other algesic agents. *Arch. Int. Pharmacodyn. Ther.* 136:353–83
53. Armstrong D, Dry RML, Keele CA, Markham JW. 1953. Observations on chemical excitation of cutaneous pain in man. *J. Physiol.* 120:326–51
54. Armstrong D, Jepson JB, Keele CA, Stewart JW. 1957. Pain producing substance in human inflammatory exudates and plasma. *J. Physiol.* 135:350–70
55. Bleehen T, Keele CA. 1977. Observations on the algogenic actions of adenosine compounds on the human blister base preparation. *Pain* 3:367–77
56. Chahl LA. 1979. Pain induced by inflammatory mediators. In *Mechanisms of Pain and Analgesic Compounds*, ed. RF Beers, EG Bennett, pp. 273–84. New York: Raven
57. Chahl LA, Kirk EJ. 1975. Toxins which produce pain. *Pain* 1:3–49
58. Elliott DF, Horton EW, Lewis GP. 1960. Actions of pure bradykinin. *J. Physiol.* 153:473–80
59. Keele CA, Armstrong D. 1969. *Substances Producing Pain and Itch*. London: Arnold
60. Lim KS, Guzman F. 1968. Manifestations of pain in analgesic evaluation in animals and man. In *Pain*, ed. A Soulairac, J Cohn, J Charpentier, pp. 119–52. London: Academic
61. Hashimoto K, Hirose M, Furukawa S, Hayakawa H, Kimura E. 1977. Changes in hemodynamics and bradykinin concentration in coronary sinus blood in experimental coronary artery occlusion. *Jpn. Heart J.* 18:679–89
62. Kimura E, Hashimoto K, Furukawa S, Hayakawa H. 1973. Changes in bradykinin level in coronary sinus blood after the experimental occlusion of coronary artery. *Am. Heart J.* 85:635–47
63. Eldar M, Hollander G, Schulhoff N, Ohlstein E, Greengart A, et al. 1992. Bradykinin level in the great cardiac vein during balloon angioplasty of the left anterior descending coronary artery. *Am. J. Cardiol.* 70:1621–23
64. Euchner-Wamser I, Meller ST, Gebhart GF. 1994. A model of cardiac nociception in chronically instrumented rats: behavioral and electrophysiological effects of pericardial administration of algogenic substances. *Pain* 58:117–28
65. Rafflenbeul W, Bassenge E, Lichtlen P. 1989. Competition between endothelium-dependent and nitrogylcerin-induced coronary vasodilation. *Z. Kardiol.* 78(Suppl. 2):45–47
66. Schaefer S, Valente RA, Laslett LJ, Longhurst JC. 1996. Cardiac reflex effects of intracoronary bradykinin in humans. *J. Invest. Med.* 44(4):160–67
67. Pagani M, Pizzinelli P, Furlan R, Guzzetti S, Rimoldi O, et al. 1985. Analysis of the pressor sympathetic reflex produced by intracoronary injections of bradykinin in conscious dogs. *Circ. Res.* 56:175–83
68. Sylvén C. 1993. Mechanisms of pain in angina pectoris—a critical review of the adenosine hypothesis. *Cardiovasc. Drugs Ther.* 7:745–59
69. Sylvén C, Beermann B, Jonzon B, Brandt R. 1986. Angina pectoris-like pain provoked by intravenous adenosine in healthy volunteers. *Br. Med. J.* 293:227–30
70. Sylvén C, Beermann B, Edlund A, Lewander R, Jonzon B, Mogensen L. 1988. Provocation of chest pain in patients with coronary insufficiency using the vasodilator adenosine. *Eur. Heart J.* 9(Suppl. N):6–10
71. Sylvén C, Borg G, Brandt R, Beermann B, Jonzon B. 1988. Dose-effect relationship of adenosine provoked angina pectoris-like pain—a study of the psychophysical power function. *Eur. Heart J.* 9:89–91
72. Crea F, Pupita G, Galassi AR, El-Tammi H, Kaski JC, et al. 1990. Role of adenosine in pathogenesis of anginal pain. *Circulation* 81:164–72
73. Gnecchi-Ruscone T, Montano N, Contini M, Guazzi M, Lombardi F, Malliani A. 1995. Adenosine activates cardiac sympathetic afferent fibers and potentiates the

excitation induced by coronary occlusion. *J. Auton. Nerv. Syst.* 53:175–84
74. Pan H-L, Longhurst JC. 1995. Lack of a role of adenosine in activation of ischemically sensitive cardiac sympathetic afferents. *Am. J. Physiol.* 269:H106–13
75. Burnstock G. 1989. Vascular control by purines with emphasis on the coronary system. *Eur. Heart J.* 10:15–21
76. Thames MD, Kinugawa T, Dibner-Dunlap ME. 1993. Reflex sympathoexcitation by cardiac sympathetic afferents during myocardial ischemia. Role of adenosine. *Circulation* 87:1698–704
77. Kuo DC, Oravitz JJ, de Groat WC. 1984. Tracing of afferent and efferent pathways in the left inferior cardiac nerve of the cat using retrograde and transport of horseradish peroxidase. *Brain Res.* 321:111–18
78. Vance WH, Bowker RC. 1983. Spinal origins of cardiac afferents from the region of the left anterior descending artery. *Brain Res.* 258:96–100
79. Woolf CF. 1994. The dorsal horn; state-dependent sensory processing and the generation of pain. In *Textbook of Pain*, ed. PD Wall, R Melzack, pp. 101–12. Edinburgh: Churchill Livingstone
80. Ness TJ, Metcalf AM, Gebhart GF. 1990. A psychophysiological study in humans using phasic colonic distention as a noxious visceral stimulus. *Pain* 43:377–86
81. Cervero F, Laird JMA, Pozo MA. 1992. Selective changes of receptive field properties of spinal nociceptive neurones induced by visceral noxious stimulation in the cat. *Pain* 51:335–42
82. Apkarian AV, Hodge CJ Jr. 1989. Primate spinothalamic pathways II. The cells of origin of the dorsolateral and ventral spinothalamic pathways. *J. Comp. Neurol.* 288:474–92
83. Ammons WS, Girardot M-N, Foreman RD. 1985. T2–T5 spinothalamic neurons projecting to medial thalamus with viscerosomatic input. *J. Neurophysiol.* 54:73–89
84. Ammons WS, Girardot M-N, Foreman RD. 1985. Effects of intracardiac bradykinin on T2–T5 medial spinothalamic cells. *Am. J. Physiol.* 249:R147–52
85. Blair RW, Weber RN, Foreman RD. 1981. Characteristics of primate spinothalamic tract neurons receiving viscerosomatic convergent inputs in T3–T5 segments. *J. Neurophysiol.* 46:797–811
86. Blair RW, Weber RN, Foreman RD. 1982. Responses of thoracic spinothalamic neurons to intracardiac injection of bradykinin in the monkey. *Circ. Res.* 51:83–94
87. Ruch TC. 1961. Pathophysiology of pain. In *Neurophysiology*, ed. TC Ruch, HD Patton, JW Woodbury, AL Towe, pp. 350–68. Philadelphia: Saunders
88. Bonica JJ. 1990. *Management of Pain*, pp. 133–79. London: Lea & Febiger
89. Lewis T. 1942. *Pain*. New York: Macmillan
90. Hobbs SF, Chandler MJ, Bolser DC, Foreman RD. 1992. Segmental organization of visceral and somatic input onto C_3–T_6 spinothalamic tract cells of the monkey. *J. Neurophysiol.* 68:1575–88
91. Harrison TR, Reeves TJ. 1968. Patterns and causes of chest pain. In *Principles and Problems of Ischemic Heart Disease*, pp. 197–204. Chicago: Year Book Med.
92. Sampson JJ, Cheitlin MD. 1971. Pathophysiology and differential diagnosis of cardiac pain. *Prog. Cardiovasc. Dis.* 23:507–31
93. Procacci P, Zoppi M. 1989. Heart pain. In *Textbook of Pain*, pp. 410–19. Edinburgh: Churchill Livingstone
94. Nowicki D, Szulczyk P. 1986. Longitudinal distribution of negative cord dorsum potentials following stimulation of afferent fibres in the left inferior cardiac nerve. *J. Auton. Nerv. Syst.* 18:185–97
95. Sugiura Y, Terul N, Hosoya Y. 1989. Difference in distribution of central terminals between visceral and somatic unmyelinated (C) primary afferent fibers. *J. Neurophysiol.* 62:834–40
96. Bennet JR, Atkinsson M. 1966. The differentiation between oesophageal and cardiac pain. *Lancet* 2:1123–27
97. Giamberardino MA, Valente R, Vecchiet L. 1993. Muscular hyperalgesia of renal/ureteral origin. In *New Trends in Referred Pain and Hyperalgesia*, ed. L Vecchiet, D Albe-Fessard, L Lindblom, pp. 149–60. New York: Elsevier
98. Giamberardino MA, de Bigotina P, Martegiani C, Vecchiet L. 1994. Effects of extracorporal shock-wave lithotripsy on referred hyperalgesia from renal/ureteral calculosis. *Pain* 56:77–83
99. Vecchiet L, Giamberardino MA, Dragani L, Albe-Fessard D. 1989. Pain from renal/ureteral calculosis: evaluation of sensory thresholds in the lumbar area. *Pain* 36:289–95
100. Giamberardino MA, Dalal A, Valente R, Vecchiet L. 1996. Changes in activity of spinal cells with muscular input in rats with referred muscular hyperalgesia from ureteral calculosis. *Neurosci. Lett.* 203:89–92

101. Giamberardino MA, Valente R, Affaitati G, Vecchiet L. 1997. Central neuronal changes in recurrent visceral pain. *Int. J. Clin. Pharmacol. Res.* 17(2/3):63–66
102. Laird JMA, Roza C, Cervero F. 1996. Spinal dorsal horn neurons responding to noxious distension of the ureter in anesthetized rats. *J. Neurophysiol.* 76(5):3239–48
103. Foreman RD. 1993. Spinal mechanisms of referred pain. In *New Trends in Referred Pain and Hyperalgesia*, ed. L Vecchiet, D Albe-Fessard, U Lindblom, pp. 47–57. New York: Elsevier
104. Chandler MJ, Zhang J, Foreman RD. 1996. Vagal, sympathetic and somatic sensory inputs to upper cervical (C1–C3) spinothalamic tract neurons in monkeys. *J. Neurophysiol.* 76(4):2555–67
105. Chandler MJ, Zhang J, Foreman RD. 1995. Pericardial injections of inflammatory chemicals excite upper cervical (C1–C3) spinothalamic tract (STT) cells in monkeys. *Soc. Neurosci.* 21(1):2604 (Abstr.)
106. Hekmatpanah J. 1961. Organization of tactile dermatomes, C1 in cat. *J. Neurophysiol.* 264:582–86
107. Shriver JE, Stein BM, Carpenter MB. 1968. Central projections of spinal dorsal roots in the monkey: I. Cervical and upper thoracic dorsal roots. *Am. J. Anat.* 123:27–74
108. Webster KE, Kemplay SK. 1987. Distribution of primary afferent fibres from the forelimb of the rat to the upper cervical spinal cord in relation to the location of spinothalamic neuron populations. *Neurosci. Lett.* 76:18–24
109. Hopkins DA, Armour JA. 1989. Ganglionic distribution of afferent neurons innervating the canine heart and cardiopulmonary nerves. *J. Auton. Nerv. Syst.* 26: 213–22
110. Zhang J, Chandler MJ, Miller KE, Foreman RD. 1997. Cardiopulmonary sympathetic afferent input does not require dorsal column pathways to excite C1–C3 spinal cells in rats. *Brain Res.* 771:25–30
111. Ammons WS, Blair RW, Foreman RD. 1984. Greater splanchnic excitation of primate T1–T5 spinothalamic neurons. *J. Neurophysiol.* 51:592–603
112. White JC, Sweet WM. 1969. *Pain and the Neurosurgeon. A Forty-year Experience*, p. 560. Springfield: Thomas
113. Vierck CJ, Greenspan JD, Ritz LA, Yeomans DC. 1986. The spinal pathways contributing to the ascending conduction and the descending modulation of pain sensations and reactions. In *Spinal Afferent Processing*, ed. TL Yaksh, pp. 275–329. New York: Plenum
114. Gybels JM, Sweet WH, eds. 1989. *Neurosurgical Treatment of Persistent Pain.* New York: Karger
115. Blomqvist A, Ma W, Berkley KJ. 1989. Spinal input to the parabrachial nucleus in the cat. *Brain Res.* 480:29–36
116. Cechetto DF, Standaert DG, Saper CB. 1985. Spinal and trigeminal dorsal horn projections to the parabrachial nucleus in the rat. *J. Comp. Neurol.* 240:153–60
117. McMahon SB, Wall PD. 1985. Electrophysiological mapping of brainstem projections of spinal cord lamina I cells in the rat. *Brain Res.* 333:19–26
118. Panneton WM, Burton H. 1985. Projections from the paratrigeminal nucleus and the medullary and spinal dorsal horn to the peribrachial area in the cat. *Neuroscience* 15:779–98
119. Bernard JF, Huang GF, Besson JM. 1994. The parabrachial area: electrophysiological evidence for an involvement in visceral nociceptive processes. *J. Neurophysiol.* 71:1646–60
120. Bester H, Menendez L, Besson JM, Bernard JF. 1995. Spino (trigemino) parabrachiohypothalamic pathway: electrophysiological evidence for an involvement in pain processes. *J. Neurophysiol.* 73:568–85
121. Foreman RD, Blair RW, Weber RN. 1984. Viscerosomatic convergence onto T2–T4 spinoreticular, spinoreticular-spinothalamic, and spinothalamic tract neurons in the cat. *Exp. Neurol.* 85: 597–619
122. Yezierski RP, Broton JG. 1991. Functional properties of spinomesencephalic tract (SMT) cells in the upper cervical spinal cord of the cat. *Pain* 45:187–96
123. Yezierski RP, Schwartz RH. 1986. Response and receptive-field properties of spinomesencephalic tract cells in the cat. *J. Neurophysiol.* 55:76–96
124. Menétrey D, Basbaum AI. 1987. Spinal and trigeminal projections to the nucleus of the solitary tract: a possible substrate for somatovisceral and viscerovisceral reflex activation. *J. Comp. Neurol.* 255:439–50
125. Burstein R. 1996. Somatosensory and visceral input to the hypothalamus and limbic system. *Prog. Brain Res.* 107:257–67
126. Al-Chaer ED, Lawand NB, Westlund KN, Willis WD. 1996. Pelvic visceral input into the nucleus gracilis is largely mediated by the postsynaptic dorsal column pathway. *J. Neurophysiol.* 76(4):2675–90

127. Al-Chaer ED, Lawand NB, Westlund KN, Willis WD. 1996. Visceral nociceptive input into the ventral posterolateral nucleus of the thalamus: a new function for the dorsal column pathway. *J. Neurophysiol.* 76(4):2661–74
128. Al-Chaer ED, Westlund KN, Willis WD. 1997. Sensitization of postsynaptic dorsal column neuronal responses by colon inflammation. *Neuroreport* 8(15):3267–73
129. Apkarian AV, Brüggemann JST, Airapetian LR. 1995. A thalamic model for true and referred visceral pain. In *Visceral Pain, Progress in Pain Research and Management*, ed. GF Gebhart, pp. 217–59. Seattle: Int. Assoc. Study of Pain
130. Berkley KJ, Hubscher CH. 1995. Are there separate central nervous system pathways for touch and pain? *Nature Med.* 1:766–73
131. Hirshberg RM, Al-Chaer ED, Lawand NB, Westlund KN, Willis WD. 1996. Is there a pathway in the posterior funiculus that signals visceral pain? *Pain* 67:291–305
132. Chandler MJ, Foreman RD. 1997. Pathways and characterization of excitatory cardiopulmonary sympathetic afferent (CPSA) input to ventroposterolateral (VPL) thalamic cells in primates. *Soc. Neurosci.* 23(2):9151 (Abstr.)
133. Chandler MJ, Zhang J, Foreman RD. 1998. Cardiopulmonary sympathetic input excites primate cuneothalamic neurons: comparison with spinothalamic tract neurons. *J. Neurophysiol.* In press
134. Brüggemann J, Shi T, Apkarian AV. 1997. Viscero-somatic neurons in the primary somatosensory cortex (SI) of the squirrel monkey. *Brain Res.* 756(1–2):297–300
135. Follett KA, Dirks B. 1994. Characterization of responses of primary somatosensory cerebral cortex neurons to noxious visceral stimulation in the rat. *Brain Res.* 656(1):27–32
136. Chandler MJ, Hobbs SF, Fu Q-G, Kenshalo DR, Blair RW, Foreman RD. 1992. Responses of neurons in ventroposterolateral nucleus of primate thalamus to urinary bladder distention. *Brain Res.* 571:26–34
137. Melzack R, Wall PD. 1982. *The Challenge of Pain*. New York: Basic Books
138. Price DD, Dubner R. 1977. Neurons that subserve the sensory-discriminative aspects of pain. *Pain* 3:307–38
139. Boivie J. 1979. An anatomical reinvestigation of the termination of the spinothalamic tract in the monkey. *J. Comp. Neurol.* 186:343–70
140. Mehler WR, Feferman ME, Nauta WJH. 1960. Ascending axon degeneration following anterolateral cordotomy. An experimental study in the monkey. *Brain* 83:718–51
141. Bentivoglio M, Macchi C, Albanese A. 1981. The cortical projections of the thalamic intralaminar nuclei as studies in cat and rat with the multiple-fluorescence retrograde tracing technique. *Neurosci. Lett.* 26:5–10
142. Berendse HW, Groenewengen VH. 1991. Restricted cortical termination fields of the midline and intralaminar thalamic nuclei in the rat. *Neuroscience* 42:73–102
143. Herkenham M. 1980. Laminar organization of thalamic projections to the rat neocortex. *Science* 207:532–35
144. Sadikot AF, Parent A, Francois C. 1990. The center median and parafascicular thalamic nuclei project respectively to the sensorimotor and associate limbic striatal territories in the squirrel monkey. *Brain Res.* 510:161–65
145. Albe-Fessard D, Besson JM. 1973. Convergent thalamic and cortical projections. The non-specific system. In *Handbook of Sensory Physiology*, ed. A Iggo, pp. 489–560. Berlin: Springer-Verlag
146. Casey KL, Jones EG. 1978. Supraspinal mechanisms: an overview of ascending pathways: brainstem and thalamus. *Neurosci. Res. Prog. Bull.* 16:103–18
147. Melzack R, Casey KL. 1968. Sensory, motivational and central control determinants of pain. In *The Skin Senses*, ed. DR Kenshalo, pp. 423–43. Springfield, IL: Thomas
148. Rosen SD, Paulesu E, Frith CD, Frackowiak RSJ, Davies GJ, et al. 1994. Central nervous pathways mediating angina pectoris. *Lancet* 344:147–50
149. Rosen SD, Paulesu E, Nihoyannopoulos P, Tousoulis D, Frackowiak RS, et al. 1996. Silent ischemia as a central problem: regional brain activation compared in silent and painful myocardial ischemia. *Ann. Int. Med.* 124:939–49
150. Hautvast RW, Ter Horst GJ, DeJong BM, DeJongste MF, Blanksma PK, et al. 1997. Relative changes in regional cerebral blood flow during spinal cord stimulation in patients with refractory angina pectoris. *Eur. J. Neurosci.* 9(6):1178–83
151. Aziz Q, Andersson JL, Valind S, Sundin A, Hamdy S, et al. 1997. Identification of human brain loci processing esophageal sensation using positron emission tomography. *Gastroenterology* 113(1):50–59
152. Silverman DH, Munakata JA, Ennes H, Mandelkern MA, Hoh CK, Mayer EA.

1997. Regional cerebral activity in normal and pathological perception of visceral pain. *Gastroenterology* 112(1):64–72
153. Derbyshire SWG, Jones AKP, Gyullai F, Clark S, Townsend D, Firestone LL. 1997. Pain processing during three levels of noxious stimulation produces differential patterns of central activity. *Pain* 73:431–45
154. Horie H, Yokota T. 1990. Responses of nociceptive VPL neurons to intracardiac injection of bradykinin in the cat. *Brain Res.* 516:161–64
155. Crosby IC, Humphrey T, Lauer EW. 1962. *Correlative Anatomy of the Nervous System*, pp. 440–518. New York: Macmillan
156. Jones EG. 1987. Brodmann's areas. In *Encyclopedia of Neuroscience*, ed. G Adelman, pp. 180–81. Boston: Birkhäuser
157. Lynch JC. 1997. The cerebral cortex. In *Fundamental Neuroscience*, ed. DE Haines, pp. 455–70. Edinburgh: Churchill Livingstone
158. Devinsky O, Morrell MJ, Vogt BA. 1995. Contributions of anterior cingulate cortex to behaviour. *Brain* 118:279–306
159. Terreberry RR, Neafsey EJ. 1983. Rat medial frontal cortex: a visceral motor region with a direct projection to the solitary nucleus. *Brain Res.* 278:245–49
160. Hurley KM, Herbert H, Moga NM, Saper CB. 1991. Efferent projections of the inferolimbic cortex of the rat. *J. Comp. Neurol.* 308:249–76
161. Vogt BA, Sikes RW, Vogt LJ. 1994. Anterior cingulate cortex and the medial pain system. In *Neurobiology of Cingulate Cortex and Limbic Thalamus*, ed. BA Vogt, M Gabriel, pp. 313–44. Boston: Birkhäuser
162. Hsieh J-C, Belfrage M, Stone-Elander S, Hansson P, Ingvar M. 1995. Central representation of chronic ongoing neuropathic pain studies by positron emission tomography. *Pain* 63:225–36
163. Hsieh J-C, Ståhle-Bäckdahl M, Hägermark O, Stone-Elander S, Rosenquist G, Ingvar M. 1995. Traumatic nociceptive pain activates the hypothalamus and the periaqueductal gray: a positron emission tomography study. *Pain* 64:303–14
164. Hsieh J-C, Hannerz J, Ingvar M. 1996. Right-lateralised central processing for pain of nitroglycerin-induced cluster headache. *Pain* 67:59–68
165. Cechetto DF, Saper CB. 1990. Role of cerebral cortex in autonomic function. In *Central Regulation of Autonomic Function*, ed. AD Loewy, KM Spyer, pp. 208–23. New York: Oxford Univ. Press
166. Saper CB. 1982. Reciprocal parabrachial-cortical connections in the rat. *Brain Res.* 242:33–40
167. Mesulam MM, Mufson EF. 1985. The insula of Reil in man and monkey. Architectonics, connectivity and function. In *Cerebral Cortex*, ed. A Peters, EG Jones, pp. 179–226. New York: Plenum

Annu. Rev. Physiol. 1999. 61:169–92

DESENSITIZATION OF G-PROTEIN–COUPLED RECEPTORS IN THE CARDIOVASCULAR SYSTEM

M. Bünemann, K. B. Lee, R. Pals-Rylaarsdam, A. G. Roseberry, M. M. Hosey
Department of Molecular Pharmacology & Biological Chemistry, Northwestern University Medical School, Chicago, Illinois 60611; e-mail: mhosey@nwu.edu

KEY WORDS: protein phosphorylation, G-protein–coupled receptor kinases, arrestins, internalization, down regulation

ABSTRACT

Multiple mechanisms exist to control the signaling and density of G-protein-coupled receptors (GPRs). Upon agonist binding and receptor activation, a series of reactions participate in the turn off or desensitization of GPRs. Many GPRs are phosphorylated by protein kinases and consequently uncoupled from G proteins. In addition, many GPRs are sequestered from the cell surface and become inaccessible to their activating ligands. Both receptor:G protein uncoupling and receptor sequestration may involve the participation of arrestins or other proteins. A model for receptor regulation has been developed from studies of the β-adrenergic receptor. However, recent studies suggest that other GPRs important in the cardiovascular system, such as the muscarinic cholinergic receptors that regulate heart rate, might be regulated by mechanisms other than those that regulate the β-adrenergic receptors. This review summarizes our current understanding of the processes involved in the desensitization of GPRs.

INTRODUCTION

Desensitization is a complex process that plays an important role in turning off receptor-mediated signal transduction pathways. The goal of this chapter is to review our current understanding of the molecular events associated with the short- and long-term desensitization of G-protein–coupled receptors (GPRs) that play important roles in the cardiovascular system.

0066-4278/99/0315-0169$08.00

Turning Off the Signals

Signal transduction pathways that turn on also need to turn off, to ensure that signaling can be achieved in a spatiotemporal manner that allows precise regulation of cell function. In addition to mechanisms that allow for removal of agonists from receptors, multiple intracellular mechanisms contribute to signal termination in the superfamily of GPRs. Many of these events involve regulation of the GPRs (1), while others occur downstream of the receptors. These signal termination events are commonly referred to as desensitization, which we define herein as the attenuation of receptor signaling despite the continued presence of stimulus. Many GPRs in the cardiovascular system desensitize to physiological or pharmacological stimuli or both (Table 1), including the β-adrenergic receptors (β-AR) and the muscarinic cholinergic receptors (mAChR) that play critical roles in the regulation of cardiac function (2–4). Desensitization of GPRs in the cardiovascular system also can be associated with pathological conditions. For example, circulating antibodies in patients with Chagas' disease that mimic the effects of acetylcholine (5, 6) induce a decrease in the affinity

Table 1 Desensitization of cardiovascular G-protein-coupled receptors

Receptor	Signaling[a]	Desensitization	Cell line(s)	Reference
α_{1B}-AR	PI	Fast	COS7	95, 96
α_{2A}-AR	↓AC	Fast	COS7, CHO	65, 97, 98
α_{2B}-AR	↓AC	Fast	CHO	97, 99
β_1-AR	↑AC	Fast	SK-N-MC, HEK293, CHO, CHW	100, 101
β_2-AR	↑AC	Fast	S49 lymphoma	102
Adenosine A1	↓AC, KCh	Slow	DDT_1 MF2	103, 104
Adenosine A2a	↑AC	Fast	CHO	104, 105
Adenosine A3	↓AC, KCh	Fast	CHO	106
Angiotensin II-1A	PI	Fast	HEK293	107
Bradykinin	PI	Fast	HF15	108
Endothelin ET-A	PI	Fast	CHO, human epithelial	60, 109
Endothelin ET-B	PI	Fast	CHO	60, 110
m2 mAChR	↓AC, KCh, PI	Fast	Heart, HEK293, CHO	59, 111–114
m3 mAChR	PI	Fast	CHO	115
m4 mAChR	↓AC, KCh	Fast	CHO	88
PAF[b]	PI	Fast	RBL-2H3	116
Thrombin	PI, ↓AC	Fast	Rat-1 fibroblasts	61
Sphingolipid	KCh	Fast	Atrial myocytes	117
Vasopressin V1	PI	No	HEK293	118
Vasopressin V2	PI	Fast	COS.M6, HEK293	118

[a]↑AC, activation of adenylyl cyclase; ↓AC, inhibition of adenylyl cyclase; PI, production of phosphoinositides; KCh, activation of potassium channels.
[b]Platelet-activating factor.

of the m2 mAChR for agonist and promote internalization of the receptors (7). These events are hypothesized to be associated with the pathological changes in the cardiovascular and autonomic nervous system in Chagas' disease that culminate in autonomic denervation and congestive heart failure (CHF) (8).

Molecular Events Associated with Desensitization of GPRs

The molecular events underlying the rapid phases of desensitization of GPRs have been studied in some detail, and a general description of the types of events that are involved is described in Figure 1. While many of the details have not been entirely elucidated, current evidence suggests that the initial, most rapid phase of desensitization occurs with a time course of seconds to minutes after exposure to an agonist and involves agonist-induced phosphorylation of the GPRs and subsequent uncoupling of the receptors from G proteins (Figure 1, *step 2*). In many cases the uncoupling of GPRs from G proteins requires binding of adaptor proteins to the phosphorylated receptors (9).

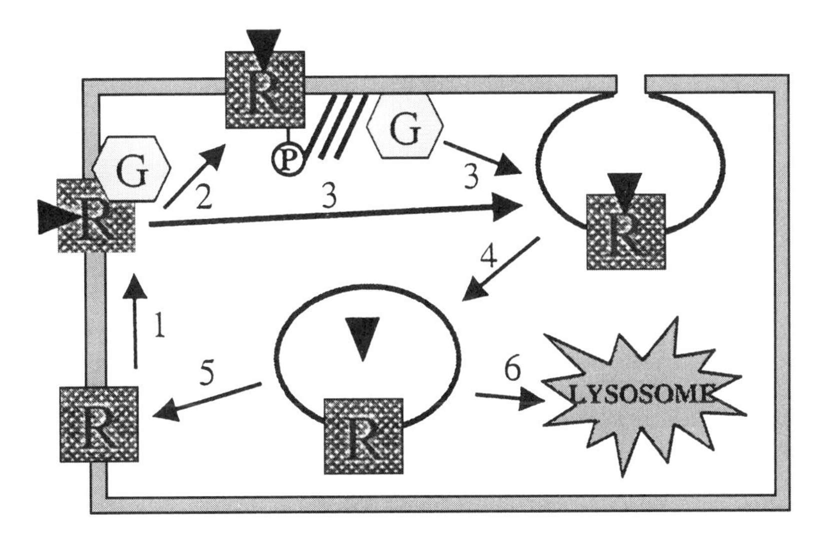

Figure 1 Model for acute desensitization and regulation of GPRs. Agonist binding to GPRs activates heterotrimeric G proteins (*step 1*). Activation is followed by phosphorylation of the GPR and consequent inhibition of the GPR–G-protein interaction (*step 2*). The GPRs can traffic to endocytic vesicles in a phosphorylation-dependent or -independent manner (*step 3*) and are internalized from the cell surface by endocytosis (*step 4*). The internalized GPRs can then recycle back to the plasma membrane (*step 5*) or be targeted to lysosomes for degradation (*step 6*). In addition, for certain GPRs (especially those with large ligands, such as polypeptide hormones), ligand removal occurs after endocytosis, and the ligands are destroyed in lysosomes.

A second event that commonly occurs on a slightly slower time course (several minutes to hours) is the sequestration or internalization of receptors away from the cell surface (Figure 1, *step 3, 4*). This step may be facilitated by phosphorylation of the GPRs (Figure 1, *step 2*), although phosphorylation-independent internalization may also occur. In some cases, internalization is irreversible, and the internalized receptors are targeted for degradation. Such is the case with the thrombin receptor (10, 11). However, more frequently, internalization is reversible, and sequestered receptors return to the cell surface (Figure 1, *step 5*).

A third process associated with desensitization is down regulation, a term used here to describe the process in which there is a net decrease in the total number of receptors; this is often caused by a destruction of the receptor protein in lysosomes (Figure 1, *step 6*). This process is usually the slowest and the least well understood, and recovery requires new protein synthesis. However, signals or machinery additional to those used for endocytosis may be necessary for down regulation to occur, since down regulation does not necessarily follow once receptors have been internalized (12). However, in certain cases, such as was recently observed for the β_2-AR, evidence indicates that the same adaptor proteins that play a role in internalization are also required for down regulation (13).

Several studies indicate that a variety of processes are used in cells to achieve rapid receptor–G-protein uncoupling, receptor internalization, and down regulation. Although these three types of events may be a common theme in the desensitization of GPRs, these events appear to be regulated by multiple types of signals and regulatory proteins for different receptor types. We review the evidence for the widely accepted model of regulation that has been developed for the β_2-AR and consider the data that suggest that other modes of regulation may be operative with other GPRs. Recent studies highlight the fact that there are marked differences in the regulation of various types of GPRs and demonstrate the need to study the mechanisms underlying the regulation of different GPRs. Much of the work we discuss has been performed with heterologously expressed GPRs, where the systems involved in the regulation of these receptors have been dissected using various molecular biological approaches. Because of the difficulties in using similar approaches in native cells, such as cardiac myocytes (which can be transfected only with low efficiency), it has been difficult to similarly dissect the regulatory pathways in native cells. Newer approaches with recombinant viruses and viruses to carry in cDNAs, as well as transgenic mice, are beginning to allow insights into native systems. Meanwhile, one must carefully compare data obtained from native cells with those obtained from heterologous expression systems to ensure that the data from the later systems provide a true reflection of the physiological events involved.

DESENSITIZATION CAN BE HOMOLOGOUS OR HETEROLOGOUS

Homologous desensitization is considered to be strictly agonist dependent, and thus only activated receptors desensitize (2). This type of desensitization is teleologically pleasing in that the process turns off only those receptors that are activated and leaves nonactivated receptors ready to function. In contrast, in heterologous desensitization the activation of one receptor can result in reduced responses to activation of other unrelated receptors, particularly when there is activation of signaling pathways or effectors common to the receptor types affected (2). The underlying mechanisms can be either the desensitization of common downstream signaling molecules (e.g. inactivation of G proteins or effectors) or the heterologous desensitization of other nonactivated receptors. Thus, while homologous desensitization requires agonist-occupied receptors, heterologous desensitization occurs in the absence of agonist occupancy. In both cases phosphorylation of GPRs has been strongly linked to desensitization (Table 2). However, very different mechanisms appear to be involved.

Table 2 Agonist-dependent phosphorylation of cardiovascular GPRs in whole cells

Receptor	Cell	Kinase	Reference
α_{1B}-AR	COS7	Endogenous, GRK2, 5, 6	96
α_{2A}-AR	COS7, CHO	Endogenous, heparin-sensitive	65, 97, 98
α_{2B}-AR	CHO	GRK2, 3	97, 99
α_{2C}-AR	CHO		99
β_1-AR	HEK293	Endogenous, GRK	100, 101
β_2-AR	S49, erythrocytes, many others	GRK1, 2, 3, 4, 5, 6, PKA	102, 119, see 47
Adenosine A1	DDT_1 MF2		103
Adenosine A2a	NG-108	GRK2?	104
Adenosine A3	CHO	Endogenous, GRKs 2, 3, 5	120
Angiotensin II-1A	HEK293	Endogenous, PKC, GRKs 2, 3, 5	20
Bradykinin	HF15	Unknown (not PKC)	108
Endothelin ET-A	293	Endogenous GRK, GRKs 2, 5, 6	60
Endothelin ET-B	293	Endogenous GRK, GRKs 2, 5, 6	60
m2 mAChR	Heart, HEK293, COS7, BHK	GRK2, other GRKs?, PKC	59, 111, 113, 121, 122
m3 mAChR	CHO	Casein kinase 2?	115, 123
PAF	RBL-2H3		116
Thrombin	Rat-1	GRK3	61
Vasopressin V1	HEK293	PKC	124
Vasopressin V2	COS.M6, HEK293		118

Heterologous Desensitization and Roles of Second Messenger-Activated Protein Kinases

Phosphorylation and regulation of GPRs by second messenger-activated protein kinases have been demonstrated for many GPRs and are most commonly suggested to play a role in heterologous desensitization of GPRs (2). The best-studied example of heterologous desensitization occurs with the β_2-AR, which is an excellent substrate for cyclic-AMP (cAMP)-dependent protein kinase (PKA) (14, 15). In most instances, phosphorylation of GPRs by second messenger-regulated protein kinases does not appear to be greatly influenced by agonist occupancy. For example, agonist occupancy of the β_2-AR was suggested to have only modest effects on the rate, but not the extent, of PKA-mediated phosphorylation (16). Early studies suggested that any condition that elevates intracellular cAMP results in phosphorylation of the β_2-AR by PKA and uncoupling of the receptors from the stimulatory G protein G_s and adenylyl cyclase (AC) activation (15, 17). More recently, new evidence has suggested that PKA-dependent phosphorylation of the β_2-AR can strengthen the coupling of the receptor to the inhibitory G-protein G_i (18) and promote activation of the MAP kinase pathway through a process that has been suggested to be pertussis toxin sensitive and to require receptor endocytosis (19). Thus, although PKA-mediated phosphorylation of the β_2-AR turns off signaling through the receptor's normal partner, G_s, at the same time as it helps to couple the receptor to an inhibitory G protein. This unique series of events points to the necessity for future studies to determine whether unappreciated mechanisms of receptor signaling and signal termination also may be occurring with other GPRs.

Several other cardiovascular GPRs also have been suggested to be regulated by second messenger-activated kinases, in particular by members of the protein kinase C (PKC) family. Many studies have utilized pharmacological regulators of PKC to imply a role for this enzyme family in GPR regulation; however, such studies can be difficult to interpret because the effects may be occurring on the receptors or on downstream signaling proteins, or both. Nevertheless, if receptor phosphorylation is directly measured, the effects of PKC activators and inhibitors can be studied. Indeed, studies of the angiotensin II-type 1A receptor have shown that this receptor can be phosphorylated by PKC when heterologously expressed in HEK293 cells (20). This phosphorylation seems to be responsible for desensitization of these receptors induced by low (1 nM) agonist concentrations (21). Desensitization induced by high agonist concentrations (100 nM), however, was unaffected by inhibitors of PKC (21).

Another approach to ascertain whether GPRs are regulated by second messenger-activated kinases has been to determine whether the purified receptors are phosphorylated and regulated by these kinases. Indeed, studies with purified and reconstituted m2 mAChR have demonstrated that these receptors can be stoichiometrically phosphorylated by purified PKC in vitro and that this phosphorylation results in reduced ability of the receptors to activate G proteins (22). Interestingly, the PKC-mediated phosphorylation or the m2 mAChR was inhibited by G_i-G_0, and this inhibition was relieved by guanosine triphosphate (GTP) analogs (22). This suggested that the m2 mAChR complexed to G proteins might not be a target for PKC; however, neither this concept nor the functional consequences of PKC-mediated phosphorylation of the m2 mAChR has been studied in intact cells.

Homologous Desensitization and G-Protein–Coupled Receptor Kinases

Homologous desensitization appears to involve phosphorylation of the GPRs by a unique family of "G-protein–coupled receptor kinases" (GRKs) (23). GRKs exhibit an exquisite specificity for agonist-activated members of the GPR superfamily; nonactivated receptors, or antagonist-liganded receptors, are usually not phosphorylated at significant rates by the GRKs. There are hundreds to thousands of GPRs, and only a handful of GRKs, suggesting that different GRKs recognize different subsets of GPRs as substrates in vivo. Six GRKs have been identified from mammalian cDNA libraries: GRK1 (rhodopsin kinase), GRK2 and GRK3 (formerly referred to as the β-adrenergic receptor kinases β-ARK1 and β-ARK2), GRK4, GRK5, and GRK6 (23). GRK1 and 4 are believed to be localized in a tissue-specific manner (to the retina-pineal gland and testis, respectively) (23), which would largely limit their interaction with many types of GPRs. In contrast, the other GRKs are more widely distributed, and in the cardiovascular system, GRK2, 3, and 5 have been suggested to regulate a number of GPRs.

Regulation of GRK Activity

Although it was originally assumed that GRKs are constitutively active, recent studies suggest that multiple factors regulate these enzymes in a manner that is not completely understood. Lipid modification or regulation of GRKs occurs by various means. GRK1 is isoprenylated (24, 25), whereas GRK4 and 6 are palmitoylated (26, 27). GRK5 is regulated by an autophosphorylation mechanism that is stimulated by phospholipids (28). GRK2 and 3 require phospholipids for activity (29, 30). A PH domain in the C terminus is likely to be the site of regulation of GRK2 and GRK3 by phospholipids (31, 32). The phospholipid requirement of GRK2 and 3 had been obscured by the use of purified receptors reconstituted in phospholipid vesicles as substrates for the GRKs. However, once receptors were solubilized in noninhibitory detergents, or reconstituted into a pure neutral phospholipid (phosphatidylcholine) that was unable to support kinase activation, it became clear that charged phospholipids are required for agonist-dependent phosphorylation of receptors by GRK2 and 3 (29, 30). Among lipids tested, phosphatidylinositols PIP_2 and PIP were found to be the most potent activators of GRK2 (30). GRK2 and 3 are also regulated by $G\beta\gamma$ subunits (33–35). Whereas phospholipids alone can activate GRK2 and 3 (29, 30), stimulation by $G\beta\gamma$ requires the simultaneous presence of phospholipids (30, 36). One hypothesis is that the $G\beta\gamma$ subunits play a role in recruiting the cytosolic GRKs to the membrane environment of their receptor substrates and the membrane phospholipids that are required for kinase activation. The translocation of GRK2 and 3 to the plasma membrane has been observed and can be blocked by overexpression of the C-terminal $G\beta\gamma$-binding domain of GRK2 (37). In addition to phospholipids and $G\beta\gamma$ subunits, the GRKs may be regulated by the GPRs themselves. The strongest evidence for this comes from studies of rhodopsin kinase and the visual receptor rhodopsin (38, 39). However, studies of the β_2-AR (40) and the mAChR (41) suggest a similar scenario may be operative for GRK2. Other potential regulators include calmodulin (42).

ROLES OF GRKS IN THE REGULATION OF GPRS

The β-Adrenergic Receptor Model

Several different classes of GPRs that are expressed in the cardiovascular system have been directly tested as substrates for GRKs both in vitro and in intact cells or transgenic mice. These include several subtypes of α- and β-adrenergic receptors, mAChRs, angiotensin II receptors, bradykinin, vasopressin, thrombin, lipid, and endothelin receptors (see Table 2). Of these, the β_2-AR has been the most extensively studied, and much of the regulation that was first discovered for the visual receptor rhodopsin (43–46), which is the best understood GPR, has been shown to have its counterpart in the β_2-AR system. Because of the striking similarities in the regulation of rhodopsin and the β_2-AR, the β_2-AR system has served as a model for the regulation of other nonvisual GPRs (47). The events involved are summarized in Figure 2. In brief, upon ligand binding, the β_2-AR activates G_s and the released $G\beta\gamma$ helps to recruit GRK2 or 3 to the membrane where these kinases phosphorylate the receptor on its C terminus in an agonist-dependent manner (2) (Figure 2, *step 2*). Subsequently, proteins known as arrestins bind to the phosphorylated GPRs and arrest signaling (Figure 2, *step 3*) by precluding further receptor–G-protein interactions (2, 9, 23). Of the four known forms of arrestins, two (arrestin 1 and cone-arrestin) are expressed in the visual system (48, 49), whereas arrestin 2 and 3 (50, 51) are widely expressed and most likely participate in the regulation of the β_2-AR and other GPRs. In addition to causing receptor–G-protein uncoupling, clathrin-binding motifs present in the C-terminal domains of arrestin 2 and 3

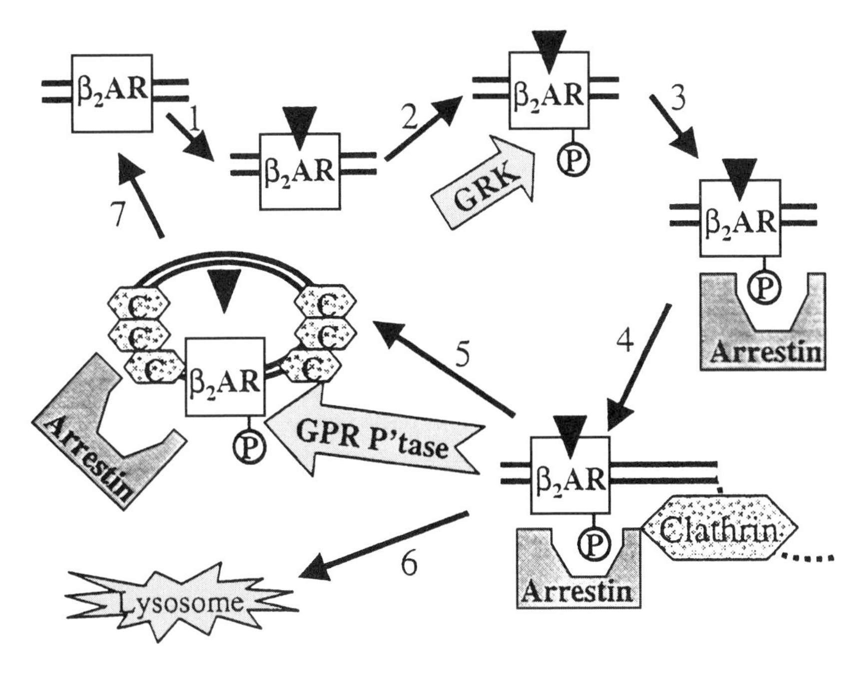

Figure 2 Model for β_2-AR regulation. Agonist binding to the β_2-AR (*step 1*) leads to receptor phosphorylation by a GRK (*step 2*). Arrestin proteins bind to the phosphorylated β_2-AR (*step 3*) and cause uncoupling from G proteins. Additionally, arrestins act as adaptors to deliver the β_2-AR to clathrin-coated pits (*step 4*) for endocytosis to endosomes (*step 5*) or lysosomes (*step 6*). In endosomes, arrestin dissociates from the receptor, and a GPR phosphatase dephosphorylates the receptor. This resensitizes the β_2-AR, which recycles back to the plasma membrane (*step 7*). Targeting to lysosomes (*step 6*) leads to β_2-AR degradation.

facilitate targeting of the β_2-AR into clathrin-coated vesicles (1, 52) (Figure 2, *step 4*). Internalization of the β_2-AR is inhibited by a dominant-negative mutant of dynamin (53), a motor protein that surrounds the necks of clathrin-coated pits and drives the pinching off of the vesicles in the process of classical receptor-mediated endocytosis (54). Internalization of the β_2-AR is thought to be required to allow for receptor resensitization; the acidic environment of the endosomes is believed to result in a conformational change that allows dephosphorylation of the receptor by a specific member of the phosphatase 2a family (55, 56) (Figure 2, *step 5*). Following dephosphorylation, the resensitized receptor returns to the plasma membrane via an unknown pathway (Figure 2, *step 7*). Alternatively, the internalized β_2-AR may be degraded in the lysosomes (Figure 2, *step 6*). In certain cells, this down-regulation of the β_2-AR is inhibited by dominant-negative constructs of arrestin and dynamin

(13), suggesting that this down-regulation is a consequence of arrestin-mediated internalization.

It should be emphasized that phosphorylation of the β_2-AR is required for both R–G uncoupling and receptor internalization (57). In vitro studies showed that binding of arrestin 2 to the β_2-AR required phosphorylation of the β_2-AR by a GRK and led to R–G uncoupling (17); interestingly, phosphorylation of the β_2-AR by PKA did not allow for arrestin 2 binding, suggesting that specific residues need to be phosphorylated for arrestin to bind (17).

Regulation of Other GPRS by GRKs

Several recent studies have examined the specificity of different GRK subtypes for a given GPR. The m2 and m3 mAChRs have been shown to be phosphorylated in vitro by several members of the GRK family (58). In addition, GRK2 has been implicated in causing phosphorylation of the m2 mAChR in intact cells and has been shown to be important in causing the desensitization of the ability of this receptor to attenuate AC (59). The endothelin (ET_A and ET_B) receptors were shown to be preferentially phosphorylated by GRK2 when these kinases were overexpressed in HEK293 cells (60). Furthermore, the thrombin receptor has been shown to be preferentially regulated by GRK3 (61). On the other hand, angiotensin II type 1a receptors seem to be substrates for GRK 2, 3, and 5 (20, 62). These studies suggest that GRKs exhibit specific functions in GPR regulation by a variety of mechanisms. One degree of specificity may be defined by the avidity of the kinase–substrate interaction, whereas, for those GPRs that are substrates for multiple GRKs, specificity may be defined by the cellular complement of GRKs in any given cell.

Identification of the Sites of Phosphorylation in GPRs

An important test of the hypothesis that phosphorylation of GPRs is critical for desensitization can be made by identifying the phosphorylation sites in GPRs and testing whether ablation of these putative sites affects the events associated with desensitization. Extensive analysis of rhodopsin has demonstrated that three residues in the C terminus undergo rapid phosphorylation (43) (Figure 3). The β_2-AR is the only other GPR whose phosphorylation has been analyzed by amino acid sequencing; multiple phosphorylation sites in the C terminus were identified (Figure 3) after in vitro phosphorylation with GRK2 (63). The phosphorylated residues identified in the β_2-AR and rhodopsin do not fall into any type of consensus sequence, although they are found in relatively acidic domains (Figure 3). The sites of phosphorylation in other GPRs that undergo phosphorylation on their C terminus, including the somatostatin receptor type 3 (64), have been determined by site-directed mutagenesis (Figure 3). Other GPRs undergo phosphorylation on their third cytoplasmic domains (i3 loops). The α_{2A}-AR (65) and m2 mAChR (66) are phosphorylated on S–T-rich motifs

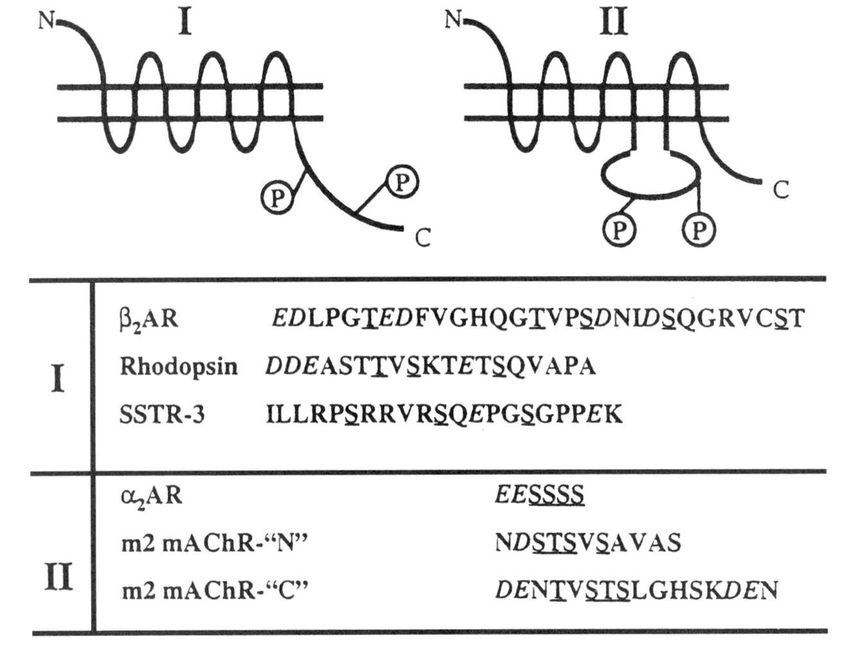

I	β_2AR	EDLPGTEDFVGHQGTVPSDNIDSQGRVCST
	Rhodopsin	DDEASTTVSKTETSQVAPA
	SSTR-3	ILLRPSRRVRSQEPGSGPPEK
II	α_2AR	EESSSS
	m2 mAChR-"N"	NDSTSVSAVAS
	m2 mAChR-"C"	DENTVSTSLGHSKDEN

Figure 3 Identified sites of phosphorylation in cardiovascular GPRs. Group I encompasses GPRs whose sites of phosphorylation are found within the carboxyl terminus of the receptor, including the β_2-AR (63), somatostatin 3 receptor (64), and rhodopsin (45). Group II indicates GPRs that contain phosphorylation sites within their intracellular third loops, including the α_{2A}AR (65) and m2 mAChR (66).

in acidic domains in their i3 loops (Figure 3). For the α_{2A}-AR (65) each serine seems to play a role as mutations in each partially disrupted desensitization. Similar S–T-rich motifs are present in other GPRs. For example, all of the mAChR subtypes (67–69) contain small S–T-rich motifs in acidic environs that are similar to those identified in the m2 mAChR (Figure 3). Conceivably these motifs play critical roles in the regulation of other subtypes of GPRs.

Physiological Roles of GRK-Mediated Regulation of GPRs

The physiological relevance of agonist-induced desensitization of GPRs in intact organisms is difficult to determine because of obvious experimental limitations such as systemic side effects of drug applications. However, recent studies with transgenic animals, as well as observations made in pathophysiological conditions, have demonstrated that GRKs may play an important role in regulation of β-AR responsiveness of the heart. GRK2 knock-out mice were found to be embryonic lethal at age 15 day (70). Embryos at this age showed severe defects in cardiac development and most likely died of cardiac failure, indicating an important role for GRK2 in the early cardiac development. Transgenic mice overexpressing GRK2 showed a diminished β-AR responsiveness (71), whereas in the same study, an increase in basal cardiac function, as well as an increased sensitivity to β-AR agonists, was observed upon overexpression of the C-terminal portion of GRK2 (β-ARK1 inhibitor), which is known to inhibit endogenous GRK2 (72). These data support the hypothesis that GRK2 may play an important role in regulation of β-AR responsiveness under both physiological and pathophysiological conditions. As for the latter, in a rabbit model of CHF, a reduction of β-AR density, impaired AC stimulation by β-AR agonists, and an increase in GRK2 expression and activity were observed (73). Furthermore, the β-AR signaling in myocytes from these rabbits was restored by adenovirus-mediated expression of β_2-AR or the β-ARK1-inhibitor (73), indicating an important role for GRK2 in CHF. GRK5 also may play a physiological role in the phosphorylation of the β_2-AR because cardiac-specific overexpression of GRK5 in transgenic mice resulted in an enhanced desensitization of the β_2-AR (74).

How Good Is the β_2-AR as a "Prototypical" Model for Regulation of Other GPRs?

Pioneering studies from the Lefkowitz, Caron, and Benovic laboratories, as well as others, have provided extremely important insights into the molecular events that mediate desensitization of the β_2-AR (2). However, it is important to test other GPRs to understand how well the model developed from these studies fits other GPRs. As a first step, one can ask whether agonist-dependent phosphorylation is required for receptor regulation. A critical need for agonist-dependent phosphorylation of GPRs to allow for R–G uncoupling and receptor internalization has been shown for a variety of receptors including the m2 mAChR, as reported from our lab (59, 66). Tables 1–3 contain information regarding the phosphorylation, desensitization, internalization, and down-regulation characteristics for several varieties of GPRs found throughout the cardiovascular system.

Because the role of phosphorylation of the β_2-AR is to allow for the binding of arrestins and subsequent R–G uncoupling and internalization, the next question is whether arrestins participate in the desensitization or internalization of other GPRs, or in both. The implication is that any GPR that interacts physiologically with arrestins might desensitize and internalize in a manner similar to the β_2-AR. Recently, studies using green fluorescent protein-tagged arrestin 2 suggested that a large number of GPRs might be regulated in an arrestin-dependent manner (75). Nevertheless, the desensitization and trafficking of GPRs in response to agonists in the absence of overexpressed arrestins has not been extensively examined.

Table 3 Internalization and down-regulation of cardiovascular GPRs

Receptor	Internalization		Down-regulation		Reference
	Percent/time	Cell line	Observed?	Cell line	
α_{1B}-AR	12%/25 min	Bovine aorta	No	HEK293	125–127
α_{2A}-AR	0%/30 min	DDT1-MF2	25%/24 h	CHO	128
α_{2B}-AR	26%/30 min	CHO	25%/24 h	CHO	128
α_{2C}-AR	35%/30 min	CHO	No decrease in heart disease	CHO	128
β_1-AR	none	CHO		—	129, 130
β_2-AR	75%/5 min	1231N1	90%/24 h	12321N1	14, 131–134
	55%/20 min	A431, CHO			
Adenosine A1	50%	DDT1-MF2	40–50%/7 day	DDT1-MF2, guinea pig heart	106, 135, 136
Angiotensin II-1A	60%/15 min	COS-7			137
Bradykinin	40%/5 min	Rat-1			138
Endothelin ET-A	No	CHO			109
Endothelin ET-B	Yes	CHO			109
m1 mAChR	55%/30 min	U293	No	U293	82a
	30%/1 h	HEK-tsA201	75%/24 h	B82	
	20%/2 h	CHO			139–142
m2 mAChR	50%/60 min	HEK-tsA201	75%/24 h	Heart, B82	59, 122
	80%/60 min	CHO	87%/6 h	Chick heart	141–143
	70%/4–6 h	Chick heart	No	HEK	
	40%/60 min	COS			
	20%/60 min	BHK			
m3 mAChR	60%/2 h	U293	60%/24 h	CHO	144, 145
	22%/1 h	HEK-tsA201			82a
	20%/2 h	CHO			142
m4 mAChR	70%/10 min	CHO			146
	35%/60 min	HEK-tsA201			82a
PAF	Yes	Human PMN			147
Thrombin	85%/1 min	HEK, CHRF-288	Yes	HEK, CHRF-288	11
Vasopressin V1	80%	HEK293			148
Vasopressin V2	60%/40 min	HEK293			118

Arrestin-Dependent and -Independent Pathways for Regulation of GPRs

The m2 mAChR is one of several other cardiovascular GPRs that have been studied in some detail. This receptor couples to G_i and G_o and mediates attenuation of AC and activation of inwardly rectifying K^+ channels in atrial myocytes (76). Results from several laboratories have demonstrated a critical role for GRK-mediated phosphorylation in the regulation of m2 mAChRs (4, 77). Furthermore, arrestins 2 and 3 can bind to m2 mAChRs in vitro and in vivo (78–80), and correlations exist to suggest that arrestins may play a role in uncoupling of the m2 mAChR from G-proteins. For example, phosphorylation of the serine and threonine residues in the TVSTS motif at residues 307–311 is required for desensitization of the m2 mAChR-mediated attenuation of adenylyl cyclase in intact cells (66) and for arrestin binding to the m2 mAChR in vitro (81). However, it is uncertain whether arrestins play a role in the desensitization and internalization of the m2 mAChR in intact cells. Whereas one study has demonstrated that overexpression of arrestin 2 can enhance desensitization of the m2 mAChR, this was observed only in the presence of overexpressed GRK2 (82). Other results have suggested that the m2 mAChR might be regulated in a different manner from that predicted by the β_2-AR model. For example, the preferred pathway of internalization of the m2 mAChR in HEK cells is an arrestin-independent pathway that does not require dynamin (81). Similar results have been obtained for the angiotensin II type 1A receptor (53). The behavior of the m2 mAChR and Ang II 1A receptors in HEK cells contrasts markedly with that of the β_2-AR that internalizes in these same HEK cells via an arrestin-dependent, dynamin-dependent pathway (53). Yet another variation on the theme has been uncovered in studies of the m1, m3, and m4 mAChR, which internalize in HEK cells in an arrestin-independent, dynamin-dependent pathway (82a). Thus, there appear to be at least three different modes of agonist-dependent internalization of GPRs that have been observed to date (Figure 4): (*a*) arrestin-, dynamin-, and clathrin-dependent internalization (example, β_2-AR) (52, 53); (*b*) arrestin-independent, dynamin-dependent internalization (m1, m3, and m4 mAChR; 82a); and (*c*) arrestin-independent, dynamin-independent internalization (m2 mAChR, angiotensin II-type 1A receptor) (53, 81).

Although the identity of the non-clathrin-dependent pathways remains unknown, it is interesting that certain GPRs have been suggested to associate with caveolae. The endothelin type A receptor (83) and the bradykinin B2 receptors in smooth muscle cells (84) have been shown to localize to caveolae. In addition, evidence suggests that m2 mAChR may localize to caveolae in cardiac myocytes (85). Because dynamin has now been shown to participate in caveolae function (86, 87), internalization via caveolae would be expected to be dynamin dependent and should be disrupted by the use of a dominant negative dynamin (86). Conceivably, the arrestin-independent, dynamin-dependent pathway observed with the m1, m3, or m4 mAChRs might reflect involvement of caveolae, whereas the arrestin-independent, dynamin-independent pathway detected in studies of the m2 mAChR requires the participation of yet another type of internalization machinery. Obviously, there is unanticipated diversity in the pathways mediating regulation of different GPRs (Figure 4).

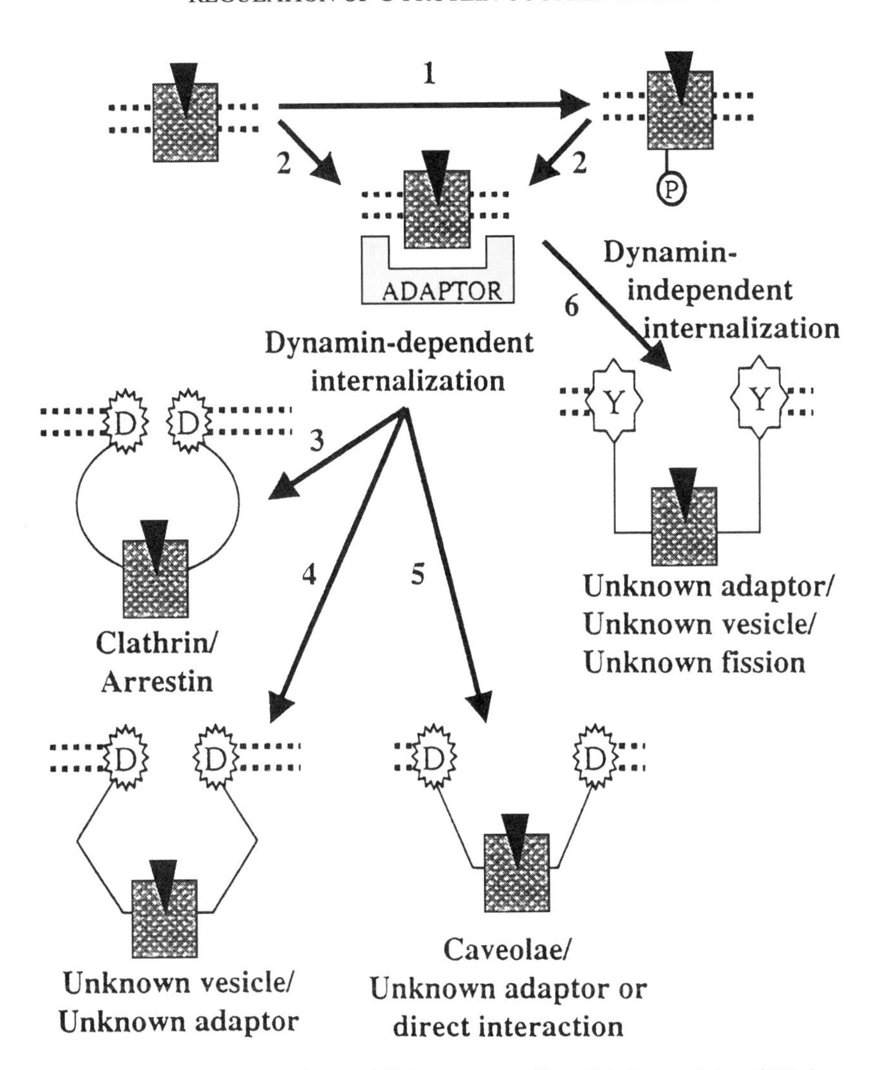

Figure 4 Multiple potential pathways of GPR endocytosis. Ligand binding can induce GPR phosphorylation (*step 1*) and binding of adaptors (*step 2*); adaptors might also bind in a phosphorylation-independent manner. Subsequently, the adaptors deliver the receptors to different types of endocytic machinery that can internalize the GPRs via dynamin-dependent (*steps 3–5*) or -independent (*step 6*) pathways. Dynamin-dependent internalization can occur by GPR delivery to different types of vesicles by various adaptors, including: (*step 3*) arrestin-dependent delivery to clathrin-coated pits; (*step 4*) an unknown adaptor brings GPRs to unknown vesicles; (*step 5*) either an unknown adaptor brings GPRs to caveolae or the GPRs directly interact with caveolin in caveolae. Other GPRs are internalized in a dynamin-independent manner through a process that might involve unidentified adaptor(s) and unknown vesicle(s) (*step 6*). (D, Dynamin; Y, unknown vesicle fission protein).

Although most of the studies cited above are concerned with receptor internalization, the results prompt questions about the mechanisms of receptor–G-protein uncoupling. If arrestins are not mediating receptor internalization, do they participate in causing R–G-protein uncoupling? Or, to put it another way, if arrestins bind to the GPRs to cause R–G-protein coupling, what would preclude the bound arrestin from moving the GPRs to clathrin-coated pits? Conceivably, other phosphorylation-dependent protein-protein interactions occur that direct the receptors to nonclathrin or noncaveolae endocytic machinery. The identification of the steps involved in non-arrestin-mediated regulation of GPRs is a challenge for future studies.

Roles of Internalization

Traditionally, sequestered receptors have been thought to be unable to signal as they are removed from their normal complement of G-proteins and effectors and are commonly not accessible to their ligands. However, a recent study suggests that internalization of the β_2-AR might play a role in delivering receptors to intracellular compartments where they might participate in alternative signaling pathways (19). An additional role of internalization of the β_2-AR has been postulated to allow for dephosphorylation and consequent resensitization (55). However, the role of internalization for other GPRs is not known. Indeed, in marked contrast to what is postulated for the β_2-AR, for the m4 mAChR, internalization is thought to prolong desensitization because resensitization is faster when internalization is blocked (88). At least in certain systems, internalization does not cause desensitization. For example, in studies of the m2 mAChR, certain manipulations were found to completely block receptor–G-protein uncoupling whereas internalization was unaffected (59, 66). Studies with the visual system, in which internalization does not occur, have suggested that dephosphorylation precedes arrestin dissociation (89); this process has not been studied in other systems.

Roles of Down-Regulation

Down-regulation of GPRs as a result of prolonged agonist exposure has been widely described for cardiovascular GPRs (Table 3) and is well known to be a side effect of long-term treatment with drugs that act as receptor agonists. Down-regulation may be a sensitive mechanism to allow cells to adapt their physiological responses to long-lasting changes in the concentration of agonists. For example, the long-term agonist treatment of m2 mAChR in atrial myocytes has been shown to cause down-regulation of these receptors (3). Interestingly, this process occurred in the presence of agonist concentrations far below the K_d. Furthermore, other indirect evidence suggested that the m2 mAChR might be down-regulated chronically in vivo as a result of their frequent exposure to the physiological agonist acetylcholine (90).

The molecular events involved in down-regulation of GPRs are poorly understood. Major scenarios in which down-regulation may occur include a decrease in new GPR synthesis, an increase in the rate of GPR degradation, or both. It has been hypothesized that trafficking of GPRs from early endosomes to lysosomes, in which the receptors can be degraded, might be a mechanism for agonist-induced down-regulation (91). Whether internalization of GPRs directly contributes to their down-regulation appears to depend either on the specific GPR or on the internalization pathway utilized by the receptor. For example, in studies of heterologously expressed m2 mAChR in HEK293 cells, rapid uncoupling and internalization of the receptors occur (59, 66, 81), but the receptors do not appreciably down-regulate (92). On the other hand, when β_2-AR are expressed in the same cell line, extensive down-regulation occurs and the machinery used for internalization appears to be required for down-regulation (13). In addition to degradation of GPRs, a decrease in GPR synthesis indicated by reduced mRNA levels has been implicated in the down-regulation of several GPRs (93, 94). Obviously regulation of receptor number in the cell is a complex process that can be regulated at a number of different levels.

In conclusion, the process of GPR regulation is only just beginning to be understood. Although significant progress has been made and new insights have suggested that multiple pathways of regulation occur, the steps of the regulatory pathways examined here have only begun to be analyzed. Unexpected complexity has been observed at every step. Many questions remain concerning the events associated with homologous and heterologous desensitization of GPRs.

Literature Cited

1. Ferguson SS, Downey WE, Colapietro AM, Barak LS, Menard L, et al. 1996. Role of beta-arrestin in mediating agonist-promoted G protein-coupled receptor internalization. *Science* 271:363–66
2. Freedman NJ, Lefkowitz RJ. 1996. Desensitization of G protein-coupled receptors. *Rec. Prog. Horm. Res.* 51:319–51
3. Bünemann M, Brandts B, Pott L. 1996. Down-regulation of muscarinic M2 receptors linked to K^+ current in cultured guinea-pig atrial myocytes. *J. Physiol.* 494:351–62
4. Hosey MM, DebBurman SK, Pals-Rylaarsdam R, Richardson RM, Benovic JL. 1996. The role of G-protein coupled receptor kinases in the regulation of muscarinic cholinergic receptors. *Prog. Brain Res.* 109:169–79
5. Goin JC, Perez-Leiros C, Borda E, Sterin-Borda L. 1994. Modification of cholinergic-mediated cellular transmembrane signals by the interaction of human Chagasic IgG with cardiac muscarinic receptors. *Neuroimmunomodulation* 1: 284–91
6. Goin JC, Borda E, Perez-Leiros C, Storino R, Sterin-Borda L. 1994. Identification of antibodies with muscarinic cholinergic activity in human Chagas'

disease: pathological implications. *J. Auton. Nerv. Syst.* 47:45–52
7. Perez-Leiros CP, Sterin-Borda L, Borda ES, Goin JC, Hosey MM. 1997. Desensitization and sequestration of human m2 muscarinic acetylcholine receptors by autoantibodies from patients with Chagas' disease. *J. Biol. Chem.* 272:12989–93
8. Acosta AM, Santos-Buch CA. 1985. Autoimmune myocarditis induced by *Trypanosoma cruzi. Circulation* 71:1255–61
9. Sterne-Marr R, Benovic JL. 1995. Regulation of G protein-coupled receptors by receptor kinases and arrestins. *Vitam. Horm.* 51:193–234
10. Shapiro MJ, Trejo J, Zeng D, Coughlin SR. 1996. Role of the thrombin receptor's cytoplasmic tail in intracellular trafficking: distinct determinants for agonist-triggered versus tonic internalization and intracellular localization. *J. Biol. Chem.* 271:32874–80
11. Hoxie JA, Ahuja M, Belmonte E, Pizarro S, Parton R, et al. 1993. Internalization and recycling of activated thrombin receptors. *J. Biol. Chem.* 268:13756–63
12. Hein L, Meinel L, Pratt RE, Dzau VJ, Kobilka BK. 1997. Intracellular trafficking of angiotensin II and its AT1 and AT2 receptors: evidence for selective sorting of receptor and ligand. *Mol. Endocrinol.* 11:1266–77
13. Gagnon AW, Kallal L, Benovic JL. 1998. Role of clathrin-mediated endocytosis in agonist-induced down-regulation of the beta2-adrenergic receptor. *J. Biol. Chem.* 273:6976–81
14. Stadel JM, Strulovici B, Nambi P, Lavin TN, Briggs MM, et al. 1983. Desensitization of the beta-adrenergic receptor of frog erythrocytes: recovery and characterization of the down-regulated receptors in sequestered vesicles. *J. Biol. Chem.* 258:3032–38
15. Lohse MJ, Benovic JL, Caron MG, Lefkowitz RJ. 1990. Multiple pathways of rapid beta 2-adrenergic receptor desensitization: delineation with specific inhibitors. *J. Biol. Chem.* 265:3202–11
16. Benovic JL, Pike LJ, Cerione RA, Staniszewski C, Yoshimasa T, et al. 1985. Phosphorylation of the mammalian beta-adrenergic receptor by cyclic AMP-dependent protein kinase: regulation of the rate of receptor phosphorylation and dephosphorylation by agonist occupancy and effects on coupling of the receptor to the stimulatory guanine nucleotide regulatory protein. *J. Biol. Chem.* 260:7094–101
17. Lohse MJ, Andexinger S, Pitcher J, Trukawinski S, Codina J, et al. 1992. Receptor-specific desensitization with purified proteins. Kinase dependence and receptor specificity of beta-arrestin and arrestin in the beta 2-adrenergic receptor and rhodopsin systems. *J. Biol. Chem.* 267:8558–64
18. Daaka Y, Luttrell LM, Lefkowitz RJ. 1997. Switching of the coupling of the beta 2-adrenergic receptor to different G proteins by protein kinase A. *Nature* 390: 88–91
19. Daaka Y, Luttrell LM, Ahn S, Della Rocca GJ, Ferguson SS, et al. 1998. Essential role for G protein-coupled receptor endocytosis in the activation of mitogen-activated protein kinase. *J. Biol. Chem.* 273: 685–88
20. Oppermann M, Freedman NJ, Alexander RW, Lefkowitz RJ. 1996. Phosphorylation of the type 1A angiotensin II receptor by G protein-coupled receptor kinases and protein kinase C. *J. Biol. Chem.* 271:13266–72
21. Balmforth AJ, Shepherd FH, Warburton P, Ball SG. 1997. Evidence of an important and direct role for protein kinase C in agonist-induced phosphorylation leading to desensitization of the angiotensin AT1A receptor. *Br. J. Pharmacol.* 122:1469–77
22. Richardson RM, Ptasienski J, Hosey MM. 1992. Functional effects of protein kinase C-mediated phosphorylation of chick heart muscarinic cholinergic receptors. *J. Biol. Chem.* 267:10127–32
23. Chuang TT, Iacovelli L, Sallese M, De Blasi A. 1996. G protein-coupled receptors: heterologous regulation of homologous desensitization and its implications. *Trends Pharmacol. Sci.* 17:416–21
24. Inglese J, Glickman JF, Lorenz W, Caron MG, Lefkowitz RJ. 1992. Isoprenylation of a protein kinase: requirement of farnesylation/alpha-carboxyl methylation for full enzymatic activity of rhodopsin kinase. *J. Biol. Chem.* 267:1422–25
25. Inglese J, Koch WJ, Caron MG, Lefkowitz RJ. 1992. Isoprenylation in regulation of signal transduction by G-protein-coupled receptor kinases. *Nature* 359:147–50
26. Stoffel RH, Randall RR, Premont RT, Lefkowitz RJ, Inglese J. 1994. Palmitoylation of G protein-coupled receptor kinase, GRK6: Lipid modification diversity in the GRK family. *J. Biol. Chem.* 269: 27791–94
27. Premont RT, Macrae AD, Stoffel RH, Chung N, Pitcher JA, et al. 1996. Characterization of the G protein-coupled recep-

tor kinase GRK4. Identification of four splice variants. *J. Biol. Chem.* 271:6403–10
28. Kunapuli P, Gurevich VV, Benovic JL. 1994. Phospholipid-stimulated autophosphorylation activates the G protein-coupled receptor kinase GRK5. *J. Biol. Chem.* 269:10209–12
29. Onorato JJ, Gillis ME, Liu Y, Benovic JL, Ruoho AE. 1995. The beta-adrenergic receptor kinase (GRK2) is regulated by phospholipids. *J. Biol. Chem.* 270:21346–53
30. DebBurman SK, Ptasienski J, Benovic JL, Hosey MM. 1996. G protein-coupled receptor kinase GRK2 is a phospholipid-dependent enzyme that can be conditionally activated by G protein beta gamma subunits. *J. Biol. Chem.* 271:22552–62
31. Touhara K, Koch WJ, Hawes BE, Lefkowitz RJ. 1995. Mutational analysis of the pleckstrin homology domain of the beta-adrenergic receptor kinase: differential effects on G beta gamma and phosphatidylinositol 4,5-bisphosphate binding. *J. Biol. Chem.* 270:17000–5
32. Mahadevan D, Thanki N, Singh J, McPhie P, Zangrilli D, et al. 1995. Structural studies on the PH domains of Db1, Sos1, IRS-1, and βARK1 and their differential binding to G beta gamma subunits. *Biochemistry* 34:9111–17
33. Haga K, Haga T. 1992. Activation by G protein beta gamma subunits of agonist- or light-dependent phosphorylation of muscarinic acetylcholine receptors and rhodopsin. *J. Biol. Chem.* 267:2222–27
34. Pitcher JA, Inglese J, Higgins JB, Arriza JL, Casey PJ, et al. 1992. Role of beta gamma subunits of G proteins in targeting the beta-adrenergic receptor kinase to membrane-bound receptors. *Science* 257:1264–67
35. Kim CM, Dion SB, Benovic JL. 1993. Mechanism of beta-adrenergic receptor kinase activation by G proteins. *J. Biol. Chem.* 268:15412–18
36. Pitcher JA, Touhara K, Payne ES, Lefkowitz RJ. 1995. Pleckstrin homology domain-mediated membrane association and activation of the beta-adrenergic receptor kinase requires coordinate interaction with G beta gamma subunits and lipid. *J. Biol. Chem.* 270:11707–10
37. Daaka Y, Pitcher JA, Richardson M, Stoffel RH, Robishaw JD, et al. 1997. Receptor and G-$\beta\gamma$ isoform-specific interactions with G protein-coupled receptor kinases. *Proc. Natl. Acad. Sci. USA* 94: 2180–85
38. Palczewski K, Buczylko J, Kaplan MW, Polans AS, Crabb JW. 1991. Mechanism of rhodopsin kinase activation. *J. Biol. Chem.* 266:12949–55
39. Shi W, Osawa S, Dickerson CD, Weiss ER. 1995. Rhodopsin mutants discriminate sites important for the activation of rhodopsin kinase and Gt. *J. Biol. Chem.* 270:2112–19
40. Chen CY, Dion SB, Kim CM, Benovic JL. 1993. Beta-adrenergic receptor kinase: agonist-dependent receptor binding promotes kinase activation. *J. Biol. Chem.* 268:7825–31
41. Haga K, Kameyama K, Haga T. 1994. Synergistic activation of a G protein-coupled receptor kinase by G protein-$\beta\gamma$ subunits and mastoparan or related peptides. *J. Biol. Chem.* 269:12594–99
42. Pronin AN, Satpaev DK, Slepak VZ, Benovic JL. 1997. Regulation of G protein-coupled receptor kinases by calmodulin and localization of the calmodulin binding domain. *J. Biol. Chem.* 272:18273–80
43. Ohguro H, Palczewski K, Ericsson LH, Walsh KA, Johnson RS. 1993. Sequential phosphorylation of rhodopsin at multiple sites. *Biochemistry* 32:5718–24
44. Ohguro H, Johnson RS, Ericsson LH, Walsh KA, Palczewski K. 1994. Control of rhodopsin multiple phosphorylation. *Biochemistry* 33:1023–28
45. Ohguro H, Van Hooser JP, Milam AH, Palczewski K. 1995. Rhodopsin phosphorylation and dephosphorylation in vivo. *J. Biol. Chem.* 270:14259–62
46. Ohguro H, Rudnicka-Nawrot M, Buczylko J, Zhao X, Taylor JA, et al. 1996. Structural and enzymatic aspects of rhodopsin phosphorylation. *J. Biol. Chem.* 271: 5215–24
47. Lefkowitz RJ, Pitcher J, Krueger K, Daaka Y. 1998. Mechanisms of beta-adrenergic receptor desensitization and resensitization. *Adv. Pharmacol.* 42:416–20
48. Craft CM, Whitmore DH. 1995. The arrestin superfamily: cone arrestins are a fourth family. *FEBS Lett.* 362:247–55
49. Palczewski K, Rispoli G, Detwiler PB. 1992. The influence of arrestin (48K protein) and rhodopsin kinase on visual transduction. *Neuron* 8:117–26
50. Lohse MJ, Benovic JL, Codina J, Caron MG, Lefkowitz RJ. 1990. Beta-arrestin: a protein that regulates beta-adrenergic receptor function. *Science* 248:1547–50
51. Attramadal H, Arriza JL, Aoki C, Dawson TM, Codina J, et al. 1992. Beta-arrestin2, a novel member of the arrestin/beta-arrestin gene family. *J. Biol. Chem.* 267: 17882–90

52. Goodman OB Jr, Krupnick JG, Santini F, Gurevich VV, Penn RB, et al. 1996. Beta-arrestin acts as a clathrin adaptor in endocytosis of the beta 2-adrenergic receptor. *Nature* 383:447–50
53. Zhang J, Ferguson SSG, Barak LS, Menard L, Caron MG. 1996. Dynamin and beta-arrestin reveal distinct mechanisms for G protein-coupled receptor internalization. *J. Biol. Chem.* 271:18302–05
54. Urrutia R, Henley JR, Cook T, McNiven MA. 1997. The dynamins: redundant or distinct functions for an expanding family of related GTPases? *Proc. Natl. Acad. Sci. USA* 94:377–84
55. Pitcher JA, Payne ES, Csortos C, DePaoli-Roach AA, Lefkowitz RJ. 1995. The G-protein-coupled receptor phosphatase: a protein phosphatase type 2A with a distinct subcellular distribution and substrate specificity. *Proc. Nat. Acad. Sci. USA* 92: 8343–47
56. Krueger KM, Daaka Y, Pitcher JA, Lefkowitz RJ. 1997. The role of sequestration in G protein-coupled receptor resensitization: regulation of β_2-adrenergic receptor dephosphorylation by vesicular acidification. *J. Biol. Chem.* 272:5–8
57. Ferguson SS, Barak LS, Zhang J, Caron MG. 1996. G-protein-coupled receptor regulation: role of G-protein-coupled receptor kinases and arrestins. *Can. J. Physiol. Pharmacol.* 74:1095–110
58. Debburman SK, Kunapuli P, Benovic JL, Hosey MM. 1995. Agonist-dependent phosphorylation of human muscarinic receptors in *Spodoptera frugiperda* insect cell membranes by G protein-coupled receptor kinases. *Mol. Pharmacol.* 47:224–33
59. Pals-Rylaarsdam R, Xu Y, Witt-Enderby P, Benovic JL, Hosey MM. 1995. Desensitization and internalization of the m2 muscarinic acetylcholine receptor are directed by independent mechanisms. *J. Biol. Chem.* 270:29004–11
60. Freedman N, Ament AS, Oppermann M, Stoffel RH, Exum ST, et al. 1997. Phosphorylation and desensitization of human endothelin A and B receptors: evidence for G protein-coupled receptor kinase specificity. *J. Biol. Chem.* 272:17734–43
61. Ishii K, Chen J, Ishii M, Koch WJ, Freedman NJ, et al. 1994. Inhibition of thrombin receptor signaling by a G-protein coupled receptor kinase: functional specificity among G-protein coupled receptor kinases. *J. Biol. Chem.* 269:1125–30
62. Ishizaka N, Alexander RW, Laursen JB, Kai H, Fukui T, et al. 1997. G protein-coupled receptor kinase 5 in cultured vascular smooth muscle cells and rat aorta: regulation by angiotensin II and hypertension. *J. Biol. Chem.* 272:32482–88
63. Fredericks ZL, Pitcher JA, Lefkowitz RJ. 1996. Identification of the G protein-coupled receptor kinase phosphorylation sites in the human beta 2-adrenergic receptor. *J. Biol. Chem.* 271:13796–803
64. Roth A, Kreienkamp HJ, Meyerhof W, Richter D. 1997. Phosphorylation of four amino acid residues in the carboxyl terminus of the rat somatostatin receptor subtype 3 is crucial for its desensitization and internalization. *J. Biol. Chem.* 272:23769–74
65. Eason MG, Moreira SP, Liggett SB. 1995. Four consecutive serines in the third intracellular loop are the sites for beta-adrenergic receptor kinase-mediated phosphorylation and desensitization of the alpha 2A-adrenergic receptor. *J. Biol. Chem.* 270:4681–88
66. Pals-Rylaarsdam R, Hosey MM. 1997. Two homologous phosphorylation domains differentially contribute to desensitization and internalization of the m2 muscarinic acetylcholine receptor. *J. Biol. Chem.* 272:14152–58
67. Peralta EG, Ashkenazi A, Winslow JW, Smith DH, Ramachandran J, et al. 1987. Distinct primary structures, ligand-binding properties and tissue-specific expression of four human muscarinic acetylcholine receptors. *EMBO J.* 6:3923–29
68. Bonner TI, Buckley NJ, Young AC, Brann MR. 1987. Identification of a family of muscarinic acetylcholine receptor genes. *Science* 237:527–32
69. Bonner TI, Young AC, Brann MR, Buckley NJ. 1988. Cloning and expression of the human and rat m5 muscarinic acetylcholine receptor genes. *Neuron* 1:403–10
70. Jaber M, Koch WJ, Rockman H, Smith B, Bond RA, et al. 1996. Essential role of beta-adrenergic receptor kinase 1 in cardiac development and function. *Proc. Natl. Acad. Sci. USA* 93:12974–79
71. Koch WJ, Rockman H-A, Samama P, Hamilton RA, Bond RA, et al. 1995. Cardiac function in mice overexpressing the beta-adrenergic receptor kinase or a βARK inhibitor. *Science* 268:1350–53
72. Koch WJ, Inglese J, Stone WC, Lefkowitz RJ. 1993. The binding site for the beta gamma subunits of heterotrimeric G proteins on the beta-adrenergic receptor kinase. *J. Biol. Chem.* 268:8256–60
73. Akhter SA, Skaer CA, Kypson AP, McDonald PH, Peppel KC, et al. 1997.

Restoration of beta-adrenergic signaling in failing cardiac ventricular myocytes via adenoviral-mediated gene transfer. *Proc. Natl. Acad. Sci. USA* 94:12100–5
74. Rockman HA, Choi DJ, Rahman NU, Akhter SA, Lefkowitz RJ, et al. 1996. Receptor-specific in vivo desensitization by the G protein-coupled receptor kinase-5 in transgenic mice. *Proc. Natl. Acad. Sci. USA* 93:9954–59
75. Zhang J, Barak LS, Winkler KE, Caron MG, Ferguson SS. 1997. A central role for beta-arrestins and clathrin-coated vesicle-mediated endocytosis in beta 2-adrenergic receptor resensitization: differential regulation of receptor resensitization in two distinct cell types. *J. Biol. Chem.* 272: 27005–14
76. Zang WJ, Yu XJ, Honjo H, Kirby MS, Boyett MR. 1993. On the role of G protein activation and phosphorylation in desensitization to acetylcholine in guinea-pig atrial cells. *J. Physiol.* 464:649–79
77. Haga T, Haga K, Kameyama K, Tsuga H. 1995. Phosphorylation and sequestration of muscarinic receptors. In *Molecular Mechanisms of Muscarinic Acetylcholine Receptor Function*, pp. 227–45. Austin: RG Landes
78. Gurevich VV, Richardson RM, Kim CM, Hosey MM, Benovic JL. 1993. Binding of wild-type and chimeric arrestins to the m2 muscarinic cholinergic receptor. *J. Biol. Chem.* 268:16879–82
79. Gurevich VV, Dion SB, Onorato JJ, Ptasienski J, Kim CM, et al. 1995. Arrestin interactions with G protein-coupled receptors: direct binding studies of wild-type and mutant arrestins with rhodopsin, beta 2-adrenergic, and m2 muscarinic cholinergic receptors. *J. Biol. Chem.* 270: 720–31
80. Gurevich VV, Pals-Rylaarsdam R, Benovic JL, Hosey MM, Onorato JJ. 1997. Agonist-receptor-arrestin, an alternative ternary complex with high agonist affinity. *J. Biol. Chem.* 272:28849–52
81. Pals-Rylaarsdam R, Gurevich VV, Lee KB, Ptasienski JA, Benovic JL, et al. 1997. Internalization of the m2 muscarinic acetylcholine receptor. Arrestin-independent and -dependent pathways. *J. Biol. Chem.* 272:23682–89
82. Schlador ML, Nathanson NM. 1997. Synergistic regulation of m2 muscarinic acetylcholine receptor desensitization and sequestration by G protein-coupled receptor kinase-2 and beta-arrestin-1. *J. Biol. Chem.* 272:18882–90
82a. Lee KB, Pals-Rylaarsdam R, Benvoic JL, Hosey MM. 1998. Arrestin-independent internalization of the m1, m3, and m4 subtypes of muscarinic cholinergic receptors. *J. Biol. Chem.* 273:12967–72
83. Chun M, Liyanage UK, Lisanti MP, Lodish HF. 1994. Signal transduction of a G protein-coupled receptor in caveolae: colocalization of endothelin and its receptor with caveolin. *Proc. Natl. Acad. Sci. USA* 91:11728–32
84. de Weerd WF, Leeb-Lundberg LM. 1997. Bradykinin sequesters B2 bradykinin receptors and the receptor-coupled Gα subunits Gαq and Gαi in caveolae in DDT1 MF-2 smooth muscle cells. *J. Biol. Chem.* 272:17858–66
85. Feron O, Smith TW, Michel T, Kelly RA. 1997. Dynamic targeting of the agonist-stimulated m2 muscarinic acetylcholine receptor to caveolae in cardiac myocytes. *J. Biol. Chem.* 272:17744–48
86. Oh P, McIntosh DP, Schnitzer JE. 1998. Dynamin at the neck of caveolae mediates their budding to form transport vesicles by GTP-driven fission from the plasma membrane of endothelium. *J. Cell. Biol.* 141:101–14
87. Henley JR, Krueger EWA, Oswald BJ, McNiven MA. 1998. Dynamin-mediated internalization of caveolae. *J. Cell. Biol.* 141:85–99
88. Bogatkewitsch GS, Lenz W, Jakobs KH, Van Koppen CJ. 1996. Receptor internalization delays m4 muscarinic acetylcholine receptor resensitization at the plasma membrane. *Mol. Pharmacol.* 50:424–29
89. Palczewski K, McDowell JH, Jakes S, Ingebritsen TS, Hargrave PA. 1989. Regulation of rhodopsin dephosphorylation by arrestin. *J. Biol. Chem.* 264:15770–73
90. Bünemann M, Brandts B, Pott L. 1997. In vivo downregulation of M2 receptors revealed by measurement of muscarinic K current in cultured guinea-pig atrial myocytes. *J. Physiol.* 501:549–54
91. Kallal L, Gagnon AW, Penn RB, Benovic JL. 1998. Visualization of agonist-induced sequestration and down-regulation of a green fluorescent protein-tagged beta 2-adrenergic receptor. *J. Biol. Chem.* 273:322–28
92. Tsuga H, Kameyama K, Haga T, Honma T, Lameh J, et al. 1998. Internalization and down-regulation of human muscarinic acetylcholine receptor m2 subtypes: role of third intracellular m2 loop and G protein-coupled receptor kinase 2. *J. Biol. Chem.* 273:5323–30
93. Habecker BA, Wang H, Nathanson NM. 1993. Multiple second-messenger path-

ways mediate agonist regulation of muscarinic receptor mRNA expression. *Biochemistry* 32:4986–90
94. Danner S, Lohse MJ. 1997. Cell type-specific regulation of beta2-adrenoceptor mRNA by agonists. *Eur. J. Pharmacol.* 331:73–8
95. Diviani D, Lattion AL, Larbi N, Kunapuli P, Pronin A, et al. 1996. Effect of different G protein-coupled receptor kinases on phosphorylation and desensitization of the alpha1B-adrenergic receptor. *J. Biol. Chem.* 271:5049–58
96. Diviani D, Lattion AL, Cotecchia S. 1997. Characterization of the phosphorylation sites involved in G protein-coupled receptor kinase- and protein kinase C-mediated desensitization of the alpha1B-adrenergic receptor. *J. Biol. Chem.* 272:28712–19
97. Kurose H, Lefkowitz RJ. 1994. Differential desensitization and phosphorylation of three cloned and transfected alpha 2-adrenergic receptor subtypes. *J. Biol. Chem.* 269:10093–99
98. Liggett SB, Ostrowski J, Chesnut LC, Kurose H, Raymond JR, et al. 1992. Sites in the third intracellular loop of the alpha 2A-adrenergic receptor confer short term agonist-promoted desensitization. Evidence for a receptor kinase-mediated mechanism. *J. Biol. Chem.* 267:4740–46
99. Jewell-Motz EA, Liggett SB. 1996. G protein-coupled receptor kinase specificity for phosphorylation and desensitization of alpha2-adrenergic receptor subtypes. *J. Biol. Chem.* 271:18082–87
100. Zhou XM, Fishman PH. 1991. Desensitization of the human beta 1-adrenergic receptor: involvement of the cyclic AMP-dependent but not a receptor-specific protein kinase. *J. Biol. Chem.* 266:7462–68
101. Freedman NJ, Liggett SB, Drachman DE, Pei G, Caron MG, et al. 1995. Phosphorylation and desensitization of the human beta 1-adrenergic receptor. Involvement of G protein-coupled receptor kinases and cAMP-dependent protein kinase. *J. Biol. Chem.* 270:17953–61
102. Strasser RH, Sibley DR, Lefkowitz RJ. 1986. A novel catecholamine-activated adenosine cyclic 3′,5′-phosphate independent pathway for beta-adrenergic receptor phosphorylation in wild-type and mutant S49 lymphoma cells: mechanism of homologous desensitization of adenylate cyclase. *Biochemistry* 25:1371–77
103. Ramkumar V, Kwatra M, Benovic JL, Stiles GL. 1993. Functional consequences of A1 adenosine-receptor phosphorylation by the beta-adrenergic receptor kinase. *Biochim. Biophys. Acta* 1179:89–97
104. Mundell SJ, Benovic JL, Kelly E. 1997. A dominant negative mutant of the G protein-coupled receptor kinase 2 selectively attenuates adenosine A2 receptor desensitization. *Mol. Pharmacol.* 51:991–98
105. Palmer TM, Gettys TW, Jacobson KA, Stiles GL. 1994. Desensitization of the canine A2a adenosine receptor: delineation of multiple processes. *Mol. Pharmacol.* 45:1082–94
106. Palmer TM, Harris CA, Coote J, Stiles GL. 1997. Induction of multiple effects on adenylyl cyclase regulation by chronic activation of the human A3 adenosine receptor. *Mol. Pharmacol.* 52:632–40
107. Oppermann M, Diverse-Pierluissi M, Drazner MH, Dyer SL, Freedman NJ, et al. 1996. Monoclonal antibodies reveal receptor specificity among G-protein-coupled receptor kinases. *Proc. Natl. Acad. Sci. USA* 93:7649–54
108. Blaukat A, Alla SA, Lohse MJ, Muller-Esterl W. 1996. Ligand-induced phosphorylation/dephosphorylation of the endogenous bradykinin B2 receptor from human fibroblasts. *J. Biol. Chem.* 271: 32366–74
109. Cramer H, Muller-Esterl W, Schroeder C. 1997. Subtype-specific desensitization of human endothelin ETA and ETB receptors reflects differential receptor phosphorylation. *Biochemistry* 36:13325–32
110. Oles M, Ewert M, Meyer T, Pott L. 1997. Rapid down regulation of Ca^{2+} signals induced by endothelin-1 in a human bronchial epithelial cell line. *Cell Calcium* 21:221–31
111. Richardson RM, Hosey MM. 1992. Agonist-induced phosphorylation and desensitization of human m2 muscarinic cholinergic receptors in Sf9 insect cells. *J. Biol. Chem.* 267:22249–55
112. Kwatra MM, Leung E, Maan AC, McMahon KK, Ptasienski J, et al. 1987. Correlation of agonist-induced phosphorylation of chick heart muscarinic receptors with receptor desensitization. *J. Biol. Chem.* 262:16314–21
113. Kwatra MM, Benovic JL, Caron MG, Lefkowitz RJ, Hosey MM. 1989. Phosphorylation of chick heart muscarinic cholinergic receptors by the beta-adrenergic receptor kinase. *Biochemistry* 28:4543–47
114. Dell'Acqua ML, Carroll RC, Peralta EG. 1993. Transfected m2 muscarinic acetylcholine receptors couple to $G\alpha_{i2}$ and $G\alpha_{i3}$ in Chinese hamster ovary cells: activation and desensitization of the phospholi-

pase C signaling pathway. *J. Biol. Chem.* 268:5676–85

115. Tobin AB, Nahorski SR. 1993. Rapid agonist-mediated phosphorylation of m3-muscarinic receptors revealed by immunoprecipitation. *J. Biol. Chem.* 268: 9817–23
116. Ali H, Richardson RM, Tomhave ED, DuBose RA, Haribabu B, et al. 1994. Regulation of stably transfected platelet activating factor receptor in RBL-2H3 cells: role of multiple G proteins and receptor phosphorylation. *J. Biol. Chem.* 269:24557–63
117. Bünemann M, Liliom K, Brandts BK, Pott L, Tseng JL, et al. 1996. A novel membrane receptor with high affinity for lysosphingomyelin and sphingosine 1-phosphate in atrial myocytes. *EMBO J.* 15:5527–34
118. Innamorati G, Sadeghi H, Eberle AN, Birnbaumer M. 1997. Phosphorylation of the V2 vasopressin receptor. *J. Biol. Chem.* 272:2486–92
119. Sibley DR, Peters JR, Nambi P, Caron MG, Lefkowitz RJ. 1984. Desensitization of turkey erythrocyte adenylate cyclase: Beta-adrenergic receptor phosphorylation is correlated with attenuation of adenylate cyclase activity. *J. Biol. Chem.* 259:9742–49
120. Palmer TM, Benovic JL, Stiles GL. 1995. Agonist-dependent phosphorylation and desensitization of the rat A3 adenosine receptor: evidence for a G-protein-coupled receptor kinase-mediated mechanism. *J. Biol. Chem.* 270:29607–13
121. Kwatra MM, Hosey MM. 1986. Phosphorylation of the cardiac muscarinic receptor in intact chick heart and its regulation by a muscarinic agonist. *J. Biol. Chem.* 261:12429–32
122. Tsuga H, Kameyama K, Haga T, Kurose H, Nagao T. 1994. Sequestration of muscarinic acetylcholine receptor m2 subtypes: facilitation by G protein-coupled receptor kinase (GRK2) and attenuation by a dominant-negative mutant of GRK2. *J. Biol. Chem.* 269:32522–27
123. Tobin AB, Keys B, Nahorski SR. 1996. Identification of a novel receptor kinase that phosphorylates a phospholipase C-linked muscarinic receptor. *J. Biol. Chem.* 271:3907–16
124. Innamorati G, Sadeghi H, Birnbaumer M. 1998. Transient phosphorylation of the V1a vasopressin receptor. *J. Biol. Chem.* 273:7155–61
125. Fonseca MI, Button DC, Brown RD. 1995. Agonist regulation of alpha 1B-adrenergic receptor subcellular distribution and function. *J. Biol. Chem.* 270: 8902–9
126. Jagadeesh G, Tian WN, Deth RC. 1991. Agonist-induced modulation of agonist binding to alpha 1-adrenoceptors in bovine aorta. *Eur. J. Pharmacol.* 208:163–70
127. Cowlen MS, Toews ML. 1987. Effects of agonist and phorbol ester on adrenergic receptors of DDT1 MF-2 cells. *J. Pharmacol. Exp. Ther.* 243:527–33
128. Eason MG, Liggett SB. 1992. Subtype-selective desensitization of alpha 2-adrenergic receptors: Different mechanisms control short and long term agonist-promoted desensitization of alpha 2C10, alpha 2C4, and alpha 2C2. *J. Biol. Chem.* 267:25473–79
129. Bohm M, Lohse MJ. 1994. Quantification of beta-adrenoceptors and beta-adrenoceptor kinase on protein and mRNA levels in heart failure. *Eur. Heart J.* 15:30–4
130. Engelhardt S, Bohm M, Erdmann E, Lohse MJ. 1996. Analysis of beta-adrenergic receptor mRNA levels in human ventricular biopsy specimens by quantitative polymerase chain reactions: progressive reduction of beta 1-adrenergic receptor mRNA in heart failure. *J. Am. Coll. Cardiol.* 27:146–54
131. Waldo GL, Northup JK, Perkins JP, Harden TK. 1983. Characterization of an altered membrane form of the beta-adrenergic receptor produced during agonist-induced desensitization. *J. Biol. Chem.* 258:13900–8
132. von Zastrow M, Kobilka BK. 1992. Ligand-regulated internalization and recycling of human beta 2-adrenergic receptors between the plasma membrane and endosomes containing transferrin receptors. *J. Biol. Chem.* 267:3530–38
133. Waldo GL, Doss RC, Perkins JP, Harden TK. 1984. Use of a density shift method to assess beta-adrenergic receptor synthesis during recovery from catecholamine-induced down-regulation in human astrocytoma cells. *Mol. Pharmacol.* 26: 424–29
134. Yu SS, Lefkowitz RJ, Hausdorff WP. 1993. Beta-adrenergic receptor sequestration: a potential mechanism of receptor resensitization. *J. Biol. Chem.* 268:337–41
135. Ciruela F, Saura C, Canela EI, Mallol J, Lluis C, et al. 1997. Ligand-induced phosphorylation, clustering, and desensitization of A1 adenosine receptors. *Mol. Pharmacol.* 52:788–97
136. Dennis DM, Shryock JC, Belardinelli

L. 1995. Homologous desensitization of the A1-adenosine receptor system in the guinea pig atrioventricular node. *J. Pharmacol. Exp. Ther.* 272:1024–35
137. Hunyady L, Bor M, Balla T, Catt KJ. 1994. Identification of a cytoplasmic Ser-Thr-Leu motif that determines agonist-induced internalization of the AT1 angiotensin receptor. *J. Biol. Chem.* 269:31378–82
138. Prado GN, Taylor L, Polgar P. 1997. Effects of intracellular tyrosine residue mutation and carboxyl terminus truncation on signal transduction and internalization of the rat bradykinin B2 receptor. *J. Biol. Chem.* 272:14638–42
139. Lameh J, Philip M, Sharma YK, Moro O, Ramachandran J, et al. 1992. Hm1 muscarinic cholinergic receptor internalization requires a domain in the third cytoplasmic loop. *J. Biol. Chem.* 267:13406–12
140. Maeda S, Lameh J, Mallet WG, Philip M, Ramachandran J, et al. 1990. Internalization of the Hm1 muscarinic cholinergic receptor involves the third cytoplasmic loop. *FEBS Lett.* 269:386–88
141. Wei HB, Yamamura HI, Roeske WR. 1994. Down-regulation and desensitization of the muscarinic M1 and M2 receptors in transfected fibroblast B82 cells. *Eur. J. Pharmacol.* 268:381–91
142. Koenig JA, Edwardson JM. 1996. Intracellular trafficking of the muscarinic acetylcholine receptor: importance of subtype and cell type. *Mol. Pharmacol.* 49: 351–59
143. Halvorsen SW, Nathanson NM. 1981. In vivo regulation of muscarinic acetylcholine receptor number and function in embryonic chick heart. *J. Biol. Chem.* 256:7941–48
144. Moro O, Lameh J, Sadee W. 1993. Serine- and threonine-rich domain regulates internalization of muscarinic cholinergic receptors. *J. Biol. Chem.* 268:6862–65
145. Yang J, Williams JA, Yule DI, Logsdon CD. 1995. Mutation of carboxyl-terminal threonine residues in human m3 muscarinic acetylcholine receptor modulates the extent of sequestration and desensitization. *Mol. Pharmacol.* 48:477–85
146. Van Koppen CJ, Sell A, Lenz W, Jakobs KH. 1994. Deletion analysis of the m4 muscarinic acetylcholine receptor: Molecular determinants for activation of but not coupling to the Gi guanine-nucleotide–binding regulatory protein regulate receptor internalization. *Eur. J. Biochem.* 222:525–31
147. O' Flaherty JT, Jacobson DP, Redman JF. 1992. Regulation of platelet-activating-factor receptors and the desensitization response in polymorphonuclear neutrophils. *Biochem. J.* 288:241–48
148. Fishman JB, Dickey BF, Bucher NL, Fine RE. 1985. Internalization, recycling, and redistribution of vasopressin receptors in rat hepatocytes. *J. Biol. Chem.* 260: 12641–46

Annu. Rev. Physiol. 1999. 61:193–217

REGULATION OF NATRIURETIC PEPTIDE SECRETION BY THE HEART

G. Thibault,[1] F. Amiri,[2] and R. Garcia[2]
[1]Laboratory of Cell Biology of Hypertension and [2]Laboratory of Experimental Hypertension and Vasoactive Peptides, Clinical Research Institute of Montreal and University of Montreal, Montreal, Quebec, Canada H2W 1R7;
e-mail: Thibaug@ircm.umontreal.ca

KEY WORDS: atrial stretch, endothelin, α_1-adrenergic agonists, intracellular calcium, prostaglandins

ABSTRACT

Secreted by the heart, more specifically by atrial cardiomyocytes under normal conditions but also by ventricular myocytes during cardiac hypertrophy, natriuretic peptides are now considered important hormones in the control of blood pressure and salt and water excretion. Studies on natriuretic peptide secretagogues and their mechanisms of action have been complicated by hemodynamic changes and contractions to which the atria are constantly subjected. It now appears that atrial stretch through mechano-sensitive ion channels, adrenergic stimulation via α_{1A}-adrenergic receptors, and endothelin via its ET_A receptor subtype are major triggering agents of natriuretic peptide release. With several other stimuli, such as angiotensin II and β-adrenergic agents, modulation of natriuretic peptide release appears to be linked to local generation of prostaglandins. In all cases, intracellular calcium homeostasis, controlled by several ion channels, is considered a key element in the regulation of natriuretic peptide secretion.

INTRODUCTION

Atrial natriuretic peptide (ANP) was discovered in 1981 and brain natriuretic peptide (BNP) was purified in 1988 (1). Natriuretic peptides (NP) generated much interest in the understanding of cardiovascular physiology because they are key regulators in the homeostasis of salt and water excretion and in the

0066-4278/99/0315-0193$08.00

maintenance of blood pressure (2). Both NPs are synthesized, stored in secretory granules, and secreted mainly by atrial myocytes under normal conditions. However, during various cardiac pathologies, ventricular myocytes undergo important phenotypic modifications, reexpress several fetal genes including ANP and BNP, and secrete them into the circulation. It is thus crucial to understand which are the humoral agents that trigger NP secretion and how these agents mediate their intracellular action through signal transduction pathways. This review represents an up-to-date compilation of the most important factors affecting NP secretion. However, given the exhaustive reviews 6 years ago on the same subject by Ruskoaho et al (3, 4), we focus mainly on reports published after 1991.

FACTORS AFFECTING NATRIURETIC PEPTIDE SECRETION IN VIVO AND IN VITRO

Hemodynamic Factors

The first few years of research on the release mechanisms of ANP focused mainly on determining which hemodynamic maneuvers were capable of triggering ANP release into the circulation. Later, the investigation was dedicated to unraveling the intracellular mechanisms involved in that release. One of the first stimuli found to release ANP was blood volume expansion (for review see Ruskoaho 3), but the precise role of local paracrine factors was unknown. Bilateral atrial appendectomy completely prevented ANP release in volume-expanded dogs (5), which indicates that in small and large mammals, most of the ANP released upon volume expansion comes from the atria. The activation of several local paracrine factors have been invoked as related to ANP release following volume expansion. Thus, it has been reported (6) that ANP release during volume expansion in rats is almost completely blocked by the combined administration of losartan, an AT_1 (angiotensin type I receptor) antagonist, and bosentan, an ET_A/ET_B (endothelin ET_A receptor subtype/endothelin ET_B receptor subtype) antagonist. Moreover, volume expansion in conscious dogs induced a significant ANP release that was potentiated by a low-dose infusion of endothelin (ET) but was not modified by a calcium channel antagonist (7). This suggests that, by activating the phosphoinositide pathway, locally produced ET participates in the ANP release induced by volume expansion. However, angiotensin II (ANG II) and ET are not the only factors that may mediate a local cardiac paracrine effect. In fact, the administration of N^G-nitro-L-arginine methyl ester (L-NAME), a selective nitric oxide (NO) synthase inhibitor, increased plasma ANP and potentiated ANP release by volume expansion in the conscious rats without additional changes in atrial pressure (8). These results suggest that in addition to ET and ANG II, the induction of local NO by volume expansion may negatively regulate ANP release. A caveat is necessary, however: Most of the agents administered may induce hemodynamic changes (blood pressure, atrial pressure, heart rate) that per se may activate local mediators, thus making their effect on ANP release indirect.

Most early observations in human and experimental in vivo and in vitro models have demonstrated the importance of an increased atrial contraction rate on ANP release. This enhancement of ANP release by heart rate was explained, in vivo, by an increased mean atrial pressure. Later, however, it was found that passive atrial distention (stretch) was not the most important mechanism of ANP release during an enhanced atrial rate; instead, the ratio of atrial wall tension and wall stress may be more important. Recently, it was reported that during pacing tachycardia in open-chest pig models, no increase in atrial dimensions was observed, but ANP release was stimulated by an increased atrial pressure during atrial systole (9). This suggests again that passive atrial distention may not be the most important stimulus for ANP release during an atrial tachycardia. By using the isolated perfused beating rabbit atria, it was demonstrated that the enhanced ANP release during atrial pacing was coincident with an increased atrial stroke volume and an increase in the transmural transport of extracellular fluid (10). This indicates that increases in wall tension and wall stress could be the most important factors affecting ANP release during tachycardia. To avoid any indirect effect of hemodynamic changes on ANP release, primary cultured neonatal rat atrial myocytes were electrically paced to contract (11), and it was found that ANP release was associated with a cytoplasmic Ca^{2+} elevation and inhibited by nifedipine and ryanodine and by a Ca^{2+}/calmodulin-dependent protein kinase II inhibitor. This suggests that ANP release regulation by pacing depends on the calcium transients and calmodulin (11).

Passive atrial stretch remains an important stimulus for ANP release in both atria (12) and ventricles (13) in isolated organ perfusion. Exactly which mechanisms aid stretch in stimulating ANP release have started to become unraveled during the last few years. Schiebinger & Greening (12) reported that ET but not arginine vasopressin (AVP) or norepinephrine (NE) enhanced the ANP release provoked by stretch in isolated perfused rat atria. The concomitant effect of the infused ET during in vitro atrial stretch was later confirmed (14), and subsequently it was found that the stretch-induced ANP release was significantly reduced by BQ-123, an ET_A receptor antagonist. This strongly suggests that ANP release during stretch is, at least in part, mediated by locally stimulated ET formation acting in a paracrine fashion. On the other hand, in a similar experimental model, an increase in local NO activity significantly reduces not only stretch-stimulated ANP release but the enhancing effect of ET on ANP secretion during stretch as well (15). Thus, it seems that ANP secretion during atrial

Table 1 Effects of inhibitors of intracellular signaling pathways on three major secretagogues of NP release[a]

Determinants	Stretch	α_{1A}-Adrenergic agonists	Endothelin
Calcium channel antagonists	± (16, 113, 116, 132)	↓(67, 68, 133)	↓(123, 133–135)
Calcium SR release inhibitors	↓(92, 132, 136)	± (67)	± (123)
Low extracellular calcium	± (70, 113, 132, 137)	↓(67)	↓(123, 133)
Prostaglandin synthesis inhibitors	NA	NA	↓(138)
Protein kinase C inhibitors	↓(97, 116)	↓(68, 139)	↓(114, 140)
Cyclic AMP inhibitors	± (118)	± (68)	NA
Calmodulin inhibitors	↓(115, 118, 132)	↓(68, 139)	↓(114, 141)
Pacing	↑(9, 142, 143)	NA	↑(11)

[a]NA, No result available; ±, results not conclusive.

stretch is regulated by a reciprocal interaction between ET and NO. The intracellular effects of ET and the role of intracellular Ca^{2+} concentration ($[Ca^{2+}]_i$) on ANP release are discussed later. Ca^{2+} also seems to be involved in the stretch-induced ANF secretion. Thus, it has been reported that during stretch-induced ANP release in isolated perfused rat atria, high extracellular Ca^{2+} concentrations induced a higher ANP release than did low extracellular Ca^{2+} (16). The stretch-induced ANP release was blocked by gadolinium, a stretch-activated ion channel blocker, but not by diltiazem, an L-type calcium channel selective blocker (17), which suggests that stretch-activated channels mediate ANP release during atrial stretch. Intracellular Ca^{2+} transients are also important in the stretch-secretion coupling process because blocking ryanodine-sensitive intracellular Ca^{2+} stores also inhibits stretch-induced ANP secretion (18). Therefore, it seems that atrial passive stretch and wall stress are the main factors involved in the release of ANP induced by hemodynamic changes (Table 1). Locally induced vasoactive agents, such as ET and NO, could be the paracrine mediators of ANP secretion, and Ca^{2+} transport seems to be an important signal in ANP secretion.

Vasoactive Agents

ANGIOTENSIN II ANG II has the ability to induce ANP release through the AT_1 receptor (19) by activation of protein kinase C (PKC) and rise of $[Ca^{2+}]_i$

in rat atrial tissue (20). It has also been suggested that this pathway involves a cyclooxygenase product (21). The ability of ANG II to increase plasma ANP levels could also be mediated by the ability of this hormone to increase left or right atrial pressure (22). In support of this, it has been demonstrated that ANG II–induced ANP release is mediated by hemodynamic changes, particularly by an elevation of left ventricular end-diastolic pressure rather than right atrial pressure (23), thus causing the observed increase in afterload (24). However, there is no consensus on the hemodynamic effect of ANG II in stimulating ANP secretion, because it has been shown that ANG II has the ability to directly stimulate ANP release in isolated rabbit hearts independently of hemodynamic changes (25). In addition, the effect of ANG II was not changed by L-NMMA (N^G-nomethyl-L-arginine, a nitric oxide synthase inhibitor) (26) but was decreased by the administration of a cyclooxygenase inhibitor, indomethacin, which suggests that the basal secretion mechanism requires prostaglandin (PG) production (27). Moreover, it has been demonstrated by Itoh et al that the brain renin-angiotensin system has the ability to modulate ANP secretion in response to volume expansion by stimulating AVP secretion (28). Furthermore, these authors have also suggested that the brain renin-angiotensin system and brain ANP have an antagonistic relationship that could be involved in the regulation of blood pressure and body fluid homeostasis (29).

ENDOTHELINS Shortly after its discovery, ET was shown to be a potent stimulator of ANP release in isolated rat atria (30–32), independent of systemic arterial and right atrial pressures (33) and other hemodynamic changes (34) (see Table 1). It was demonstrated that this effect is mediated via the ET_A receptor (35–37). Furthermore, it was suggested that ANP synthesis requires only PKC activation (38) whereas its secretion is dependent primarily on Ca^{2+} transients and calmodulin kinase (11). However, it seems that ET-dependent ANP secretion is regulated differently in each of the atrial chambers. In the left atria, ANP secretion is stimulated by ET-2 and ET-3 but not ET-1, and it is not affected by cyclooxygenase inhibition by aspirin (39). In contrast, in the right atrium, ANP secretion is stimulated by ET-1 and ET-2 but not ET-3, and it is reduced by cyclooxygenase inhibition (39). These authors concluded that in right atrial cells, ANP secretion is regulated by PG-mediated response to PKC activation whereas the secretory mechanisms in the right atria are different (39). As mentioned earlier, ANG II via the AT_1 receptor is also a secretagogue of ANP (19). However, it has been recently proposed that ET via the ET_A receptors is a more important factor in the regulation of mechanical-stretch–induced ANP release than is ANG II via the AT_1 receptor (6). Moreover, Skvorak & Dietz (15) showed that ANP secretion is regulated by a simultaneous increase in ET production and decrease in NO production. Even though the physiological role of ET-induced ANP secretion remains to be determined, the ANP secretory response to ET is also stretch-enhanced (40), which suggests that the ANP response to ET is increased in volume-expanded states (12).

VASOPRESSIN Similar to ANG II and ET, AVP when administered in vivo increases plasma ANP levels (12, 41). This effect is mediated by the vasopressinergic V_1 receptor subtype (42) and requires both PKC activation and Ca^{2+} influx (43, 44). Furthermore, it has been shown that AVP-induced ANP secretion is greatly enhanced in volume-expanded states (12), in hypoxic hypertensive rats (45), and in AVP-deficient Brattleboro and pithed rats (46, 47). Moreover, it was recently demonstrated that in addition to stimulating ANP secretion, AVP can also inhibit ANP release through the production of NO (26). AVP, as a vasoactive agent, can increase blood pressure, resulting in an increase in atrial pressure. Thus, it was unclear whether AVP-induced ANP secretion was due to a direct atrial effect or mediated by an elevation in atrial pressure. However, when AVP was used to increase cardiac afterload by increasing atrial pressure and diameter, ANP secretion was not induced (48).

NITRIC OXIDE First discovered in 1980 as the endothelium-derived relaxing factor (49) and later identified (50), NO has been implicated in numerous functions, such as maintenance of volume and pressure homeostasis. Recently, several investigators have suggested that stimulation of NO by ET, AVP, and acetylcholine may be responsible for the inhibitory effects of these agents on ANP secretion (15, 26). Furthermore, it has been implied that this inhibitory effect of NO occurs during stretch-stimulated but not basal ANP release (15). This is partially supported by Leskinen et al, who demonstrated that acute inhibition of NO formation by L-NAME enhanced stretch-induced ANP release but also increased basal plasma ANP levels in vivo (8).

ADRENOMEDULLIN Adrenomedullin (ADM), a novel and potent hypotensive peptide (51), has been detected in rat cardiac atrium (52), and similarly to the many other vasoactive peptides, it seems to modulate ANP secretion in a negative fashion by causing a dose-dependent increase in cAMP (53). Furthermore, it has been suggested that both ADM and ANP might be responsible for glucocorticoid-induced vasodilation (54).

PROSTAGLANDINS In recent years, considerable evidence has been accumulated that points toward a role for PGs in modulating ANP release. Cyclooxygenase inhibition by indomethacin was shown to abolish ANP release caused by increased atrial tension (55) but did not have any effect on basal ANP release from isolated atria or from atrial slices (56, 57). In addition, indomethacin administration also abolished ANP release to AVP (56), platelet-activating factor (58), corticotropin-releasing factor (59), isoproterenol (57), the PKC activator

4-phorbol 12-myristate 13-acetate (PMA) (60), Ca^{2+} ionophores (61), and L-type voltage-operated Ca^{2+}-channel activators (44). Furthermore, the influence of PGs on ANP release has also been documented in rats with global ischemia via leukotrienes generated through the lipoxygenase pathway (62). Of all the PGs, it has been shown that $PGF_{2\alpha}$ and PGE_2, which are secreted by the mammalian myocardium, are stimulators of ANP release in both cultured neonatal rat atrial and ventricular cells (63). This effect was not mediated through a cAMP-dependent mechanism but does appear to be calmodulin-dependent, at least for $PGF_{2\alpha}$ (64). However, these results are not supported by others, who have found that $PGF_{2\alpha}$ and not PGE_2 is able to stimulate ANP secretion (65). Moreover, it has been demonstrated that it is PGE_2 that mediates the isoproterenol-induced ANP release by cAMP formation and protein kinase A (PKA) activation (66).

Neurohumoral Factors

Although atrial stretch is considered the most important mechanism involved in ANF release, the role that several neurohumoral factors may have on ANP secretion has been extensively investigated. Early in vitro and in vivo studies looking at the effect of α- and β-adrenergic agents on ANP release have produced contradictory results (3). Most of the in vivo effects of those agents on ANP release have been attributed to being a consequence of their hemodynamic effects. Most authors have agreed that α-adrenergic stimulation induced both an in vitro and an in vivo ANP release. More recently, it was reported that α-adrenergic stimulation of isolated perfused atria (67) or cultured atrial myocytes (68) increased the rate of ANP secretion, which in the absence of any hemodynamic effects suggests a direct stimulatory role of α-adrenergic receptors (see Table 1). This stimulatory effect was inhibited by a PKC inhibitor (68), but an influx of extracellular Ca^{2+} was necessary for a full secretory response (67, 68). On the other hand, basal and α_1-stimulated ANP secretory rate was reduced by β-adrenergic stimulation (68). The secretory ANP stimulation by α-adrenergic agents is accompanied by an increased expression of ANP mRNA (69).

The results of β-adrenergic stimulation by isoproterenol on ANP secretion have been more conflictive. Whereas isoproterenol inhibits basal or α-adrenergic–stimulated ANP secretion by cultured atrial myocytes (68), it also induced a transient increase in ANP release by superfused rat atria (70), which could be mediated by cAMP (57) and, at least in part, by PGs (57, 66). It has been also reported that clonidine stimulates ANP release by rat atrial sections and by rat perfused heart (71). The effect of clonidine was mimicked by a synthetic analog and inhibited by efaroxan, a selective imidazoline receptor antagonist, and by yohimbine. This suggests that the clonidine ANP-stimulatory effect may be mediated by α_2-adrenergic and imidazoline receptors. It thus seems well established that α-adrenergic stimulation increases ANP release. In contrast, the reports on the β-adrenergic effect on ANP secretion are contradictory and do not exclude the possibility that the increases in ANP release by superfused atria during β-adrenergic stimulation is not secondary to changes in the contraction force.

The results from several models of interrupting the central and peripheral nervous systems to study their role on ANP release have not been conclusive. Pithed rats, cardiac denervation, and peripheral pharmacological and surgical blockade have not clarified whether the central and peripheral nervous systems have a direct, nonhemodynamically driven role on ANP secretion. Nor have more recent studies yielded more enlightening results. Complete cardiac denervation in baboons by orthotopic autotransplantation of the heart did not modify plasma ANP basal levels but almost completely abolished ANP responses to changes in central venous pressure (72). On the other hand, transplanted denervated heart patients subjected to an acute volume expansion secreted more ANP than did their controls, which suggests an inhibitory role of cardiac nerves on ANP release in humans (73). To further confound the role of cardiac nerves on ANP secretion, Singer et al (74) reported that in human transplant recipients subjected to low- or high-sodium diets, ANP release was no different from that in healthy subjects. The different behavior of cardiac transplant recipients may not be due only to a species difference; it also could reflect incomplete deinnervation, such as during orthotopic transplantation in the baboon (72). Activation of neuronal sodium channels or atrial electrical stimulation in isolated perfused, paced rat heart increased ANP secretion (75), which suggests that stimulation of cardiac sympathetic nerves stimulates ANP release. Changes in myocardial contractile force or hemodynamics during stimulation cannot, however, be ruled out. Stereotactically applied electrical stimulation of several central nervous sympathetic nuclei also stimulated ANP secretion (76), but as in the preceding study, an indirect hemodynamically mediated effect cannot be excluded. Clinical and experimental evidence suggests involvement of the nervous system in the regulation of ANP secretion, but it is not conclusive.

Ischemia-Hypoxia

Cardiac ischemia has been shown to be a potent stimulus for ANP release in both humans and in vivo and in vitro experimental models. It is thought that its effect on ANP secretion is mainly mediated by hemodynamic changes. In isolated rat heart during ischemia, ANP can be secreted by the ventricles (77), but it is released mainly by atria (78). However, when regional ischemia is not accompanied by atrial distention, ANF secretion is blunted (78), which suggests that ischemia per se may not have a direct effect on ANP release. Others, using a similar in vitro model, have reported that reduced coronary blood flow and decreased oxygen to the myocardium may not be the primary triggers affecting

ANP release during ischemia; however, changes in myocardial temperature could be (79). ANP release during ischemia showed a positive linear correlation with the atrial and ventricular lactate/pyruvate ratio and a negative correlation with atrial and ventricular phosphorylation potential. This suggests that ANP secretion during myocardial ischemia is related to energy metabolism changes (80). Others have presented evidence that the enhanced ANP release during ischemia by isolated perfused rat heart is completely blocked by the addition of cyclooxygenase and lipoxygenase inhibitors. This suggests a prostanoid- and leukotriene-mediated ANP release during myocardial ischemia (62).

Similarly to ischemia, hypoxia is an effective stimulator of ANP release in humans and animal experimental models, but the mechanisms remain unclear. Atrial stretch secondary to pulmonary vasoconstriction and the consequent increased pulmonary vascular resistance triggered neural reflexes, and metabolic factors have been the primary candidates (3). It recently has been demonstrated that the increased ANP release by perfused rat heart during hypoxia was nearly abolished by the treatment with either BQ-123, an ET_A antagonist, or indomethacin. This suggests that locally ET-induced PGs may be responsible for the increased ANP secretion during anoxia. More evidence supports a hemodynamic rather than a direct effect of anoxia on ANP release and synthesis. The intracellular mechanisms have not yet been fully explored, but a paracrine role for ET and PG has been suggested.

Hormonal Factors

Early in ANP research, it was established that glucocorticoids increased ANP synthesis and release both in vivo and in vitro (41, 81–83). Since Ruskoaho's review (3), little new information on this particular topic has been reported. The infusion of corticotropin releasing factor (CRF) into isolated perfused rat heart induced a short-term increase of ANP release, which was accompanied by an increased coronary flow and a transient inotropic positive effect (84). This suggests a hemodynamic effect of CRF on ANP secretion. However, more recently it has been reported that in cultured neonatal rat cardiac myocytes, CRF produced a time- and dose-dependent increase in ANP secretion, which suggests a direct effect (85). This effect was blunted by a cAMP-dependent protein kinase and PKC inhibitors, which suggests that as with other previously discussed stimuli, the direct effect of CRF may be mediated by a PKC pathway.

Triiodothyronine (T_3) has been shown to increase the in vivo release of ANP and its in vitro secretion and synthesis, which suggests that, apart from its known cardiovascular hemodynamic effects, thyroid hormone may participate directly in the regulation of ANP gene expression. The exact mechanisms have not been defined though. More recent reports on thyroid hormone and ANP have not added much to our understanding of the effect of those hormones on ANP release and synthesis, and they tend to extend previous work rather than provide original thoughts. Thus, it has been reported that the in vivo administration of large doses of T_3 to rats [50 μg/100 g (body weight)/day] increases plasma ANP levels during the first 24 h after administration, falls subsequently below baseline, and rises to control levels by day 4. Atrial ANP content and the density of atrial-specific granules followed an opposite temporal pattern (86). T_3 administration induced important hemodynamic changes, which may explain its effect on ANP. As discussed above, volume expansion stimulates ANP release, which is markedly blunted in hypophysectomized rats and completely restored by daily thyroxine administration (87). Thyroxine replacement therapy in patients with severe hypothyroidism, normal cardiac function, and low plasma ANP concentrations restored plasma ANP levels, which suggests that the direct effect is not mediated by hemodynamic changes (88). For the moment, there is no clear evidence that the increase in ANP plasma levels during thyroid administration is not mainly due to hemodynamic changes.

The effect of sex hormones on ANP release and synthesis has not been extensively investigated. In rats chronically treated (10 days) with either estradiol or testosterone, estradiol increased basal secretion of ANP by isolated perfused heart but had no effect on stretch-induced ANP release. On the other hand, testosterone did not affect basal concentration of ANP and abolished the stretch-induced secretion of ANP (89). Orchiectomy significantly increased both plasma ANP levels and atrial ANP content. Testosterone replacement restored plasma ANP to control levels but atrial ANP content remained elevated (90). It was suggested that testosterone may regulate both release and synthesis of ANP, but other metabolic or hemodynamic effects have not been explored. So far, little is known about the effect of sex hormones on ANP release and synthesis but most evidence suggests a hemodynamic rather than a direct effect.

OTHER STIMULI The effect of aging on basal or stimulated ANP levels has been contradictory. It has been demonstrated that stretched isolated perfused atria from young and aged rats secreted equal (91) or lower (92, 93) amounts of ANP. In chronically catheterized conscious rats, acute volume expansion induced an equal secretion of ANP in young and older rats, whereas it was higher in the ventricles of the older group even though atrial ANP content was equal in both age groups (94). Atrial distention of perfused hearts from genetically hypertensive rats released less ANP than those from normotensive animals, and this release impairment was progressive with age (95). In humans, an acute volume load induced a higher ANP release in older than in younger normotensive subjects (96). Basal plasma ANP levels may be equal (94) or higher in older animals (97) when compared with controls. Thus the effect of age on plasma ANP levels or ANP release is not unanimously accepted. Whether the discrepancy is due to differences in atrial compliance or to unknown factors remains to be elucidated.

Calcitonin gene–related peptide (CGRP) is secreted by nerve endings and may affect the cardiovascular system (98). On isolated paced perfused atria, CGRP causes a dose-related secretion of ANP with a parallel increase in the developed tension (99, 100). The fact that the CGRP-stimulated secretion was cAMP-dependent suggests that secretion is independent of the force of contraction. CGRP may thus be another possible regulator of NP secretion.

Bolus injection of CRF in perfused isolated heart leads to a modest release over basal of NP (59, 84). However, the cardiac hemodynamics were considerably affected by CRF, and NP release may thus reflect an alteration in heart performance. NP release by CRF was blocked by indomethacin, which suggests an indirect participation of PGs. On cultured neonatal ventricular myocytes, CRF was shown to increase ANP and BNP release (85). However, the experiments were performed over a 24-h period and protein synthesis was also observed. CRF may thus affect NP release through de novo protein synthesis rather than by regulated secretion. These data indicate that CRF may not be a direct secretagogue of NP.

Platelet-activating factor (PAF), a phospholipid derivative, has been documented as an antihypertensive agent because of its vasorelaxant effect. On isolated perfused heart, PAF produces a potent dose-dependent and long-lasting secretion of NP (58, 101), which was blocked by indomethacin and meclofenamate. This suggests PGs are implicated. Indeed, injection of PAF produced a rapid rise in $PGF_{1\alpha}$ that was immediately followed by NP release. PAF was also able to induce NP secretion from neonatal ventricular myocytes through a cAMP-dependent mechanism (102). Whether this stimulation of ventricular myocytes is mediated by PGs or can be reproduced in atrial myocytes remains to be determined.

Relaxin, a reproductive peptide released by the corpus luteum, can significantly affect the cardiovascular system. Considering the fact that relaxin receptors are present in cardiac atrium, it was questioned whether this peptide can modulate NP secretion. Relaxin produced a marked increase in NP release in isolated perfused heart (103), and this response was characterized by slow onset but long duration without modification of cardiac hemodynamics. PKC and PKA inhibitors were able to reduce relaxin-induced NP secretion, which suggests that protein phosphorylation was involved.

Ouabain is a potent inhibitor of Na^+-K^+ ATPase, and its presence in the mammalian circulation is still disputed (103a,b). Blockade of ATP-dependent Na^+ extrusion from isolated superfused atria by ouabain leads to an unbalanced intracellular Na^+ that increases cytosolic Ca^{2+} and, as a consequence, causes an increased accumulation of NP in the perfusion fluid (104).

INTRACELLULAR SIGNALING MECHANISMS AFFECTING NATRIURETIC PEPTIDE SECRETION

Several experimental models have been used to investigate the intracellular signaling mechanisms controlling NP secretion in cardiac cells. The most appropriate model appears to be the isolated perfused heart and, of less extent, the isolated atria, because they represent systems that are close to the in vivo situation. However, because these tissues consist of different cell types and NP can be released by both atrial and ventricular myocytes, due to paracrine interactions it may be difficult to evaluate the real contribution of myocytes and dissect the signaling pathways involved. In that sense, cultures of adult myocytes represent a better system. Because adult myocytes are difficult to isolate and undergo structural and biochemical changes in long-term culture (105), most investigators have preferred to work with primary cultures of ventricular and atrial neonatal cardiac cells. Although both cell types synthesize NP during embryogenesis, the fetal gene program is rapidly lost in ventricular myocytes immediately after birth. Therefore, ventricular myocytes, prepared from newborn rats, exhibit a limited amount of secretory granules (106, 107); thus, NP release is modulated by both a regulated and a constitutive pathway, whereas in atrial myocytes NP release is mostly the consequence of a regulated pathway (108, 109). Considering that atrial and ventricular myocytes have different abilities to secrete NP, it may be misleading to generalize from one cell type to the other the results we present hereafter on intracellular signaling mechanisms.

Intracellular Calcium Homeostasis

$[Ca^{2+}]_i$ is a key element in the mechanisms regulating the secretion of several hormones. Elevation of $[Ca^{2+}]_i$ activates several Ca^{2+}-dependent proteins that are then able to trigger granule movement and fusion to cellular membrane and the subsequent release of the granule content into the extracellular milieu. Several experiments have demonstrated that changes of $[Ca^{2+}]_i$ induced by drugs are able to affect either positively or negatively the secretion of NP by atrial myocytes. A major difference between atrial myocytes and other endocrine cells is that cardiac myocytes exhibit rapid $[Ca^{2+}]_i$ fluctuations during the Ca^{2+}-dependent contraction. This parameter complicates the interpretion of the experimental results because beating and quiescent atrial myocytes may behave differently in their response to NP secretagogues. As reviewed by Ruskoaho (3), enhanced calcium influx in spontaneously beating or paced cardiac tissues causes a modest increase in NP, whereas in quiescent atria or arrested cultured atrial myocytes, an augmented $[Ca^{2+}]_i$ has no effect or slightly decreases NP secretion. This review therefore focuses on new available data that may have resolved these issues.

Recent experiments performed with isolated hearts or atria showed that perfusion with Ca^{2+}-free buffer, supplemented or not with EGTA, produced divergent results on basal and stimulated NP secretion. Data in nonbeating cardiac tissues indicated that omission of extracellular Ca^{2+} may augment (57, 110) basal NP secretion, whereas in paced tissues secretion was decreased (67). Cultured cardiac cells exhibit spontaneous beating and the omission of extracellular Ca^{2+} caused a diminution of basal secretion (68, 109, 111). When cardiac tissues were stimulated by either atrial distention (stretch), adrenergic agents, ouabain, or ET, the removal of extracellular Ca^{2+} provoked a decreased NP secretion (16, 57, 67, 68, 104, 111, 112), except in two studies (112, 113) where the atrial tissue was quiescent. Consequently, either the addition of extracellular Ca^{2+} (16) or the utilization of the Ca^{2+} ionophore A23187 (20) or of the dihydropyridine-sensitive Ca^{2+} channel agonists, Bay K 8644 (11, 38, 114, 115), all of which increase $[Ca^{2+}]_i$, augmented both basal and stimulated NP secretion. Conversely, if the entry of Ca^{2+} into cardiac cells is blocked by different types of L-type Ca^{2+} channel antagonists, such as verapamil, nifedipine, nitrendipine, isradipine, and diltiazem, it is expected that basal and stimulated NP secretion should be decreased. Indeed, the dihydropyridine family of Ca^{2+} blockers were, in general, able to inhibit NP secretion when stimulated by a variety of agents (11, 43, 67, 68, 102, 104, 114, 115). Surprisingly, diltiazem, a benzothiazepine, was unable to affect either the basal or the stretch and ANG II–stimulated NP secretion (20, 112, 116, 117). Verapamil, belonging to a different class of Ca^{2+} channel antagonist, was shown to affect the basal (109) but not the stretch-stimulated secretion (118). The observed action of the different Ca^{2+} antagonists was reported in paced and nonbeating cardiac tissues and cultures, and clearly a comparison of the efficacy of the different families of L-type Ca^{2+} channel antagonists blocking the secretion of NP needs to be documented. Lanthanum, a nonspecific Ca^{2+} channel blocker, inhibited the secretion of NP stimulated by either ouabain or osmolarity in perfused atria (104, 119). However, $NiCl_2$, a preferential T-type Ca^{2+} channel antagonist, was unable to decrease stretch-activated NP secretion (17).

The entry of Ca^{2+} into the cell can originate from pathways other than voltage-dependent Ca^{2+} channels. Stretch-activated ion channels are permeable to monovalent and divalent cations when the cell membrane is mechanically stressed. At micromolar concentrations, gadolinium, $GdCl_3$, can inhibit nonselective mechano-sensitive channels without affecting voltage-dependent channels. $GdCl_3$ dose-dependently inhibited NP release in isolated beating and noncontracting perfused atria stretched by an increased intra-atrial pressure (17) and can even suppress the up-regulation of NP mRNA expression by stretch (16). Ca^{2+}-permeable mechano-sensitive channels thus appear important in the regulation of NP secretion by atrial distention. Further experiments are needed to confirm these important results on stretch-activated secretion.

ATP-dependent K^+ (K^+_{ATP}) channels may also affect Ca^{2+} influx into cardiac cells. Thus, glibenclamide, an inhibitor of K^+_{ATP} channels, was able to block the stretch-activated NP release in a perfused atrial preparation (112). On the other hand, in the same study, pinacidil, a K^+_{ATP} channel opener, was unable to affect basal NP secretion, whereas on cultured neonatal atrial myocytes, pinacidil decreased basal secretion.

Other mechanisms, such as Na^+-H^+ exchanger and Na^+-K^+-Cl^- cotransport, have been considered potential regulators of Ca^{2+} influx. However, bumetanide, an inhibitor of the Na^+-K^+-Cl^- cotransport, was ineffective in reducing NP secretion stimulated by osmolarity or by ouabain (104, 119). Only 5-(N,N-hexamethylene) amiloride, an Na^+-H^+ exchanger inhibitor, was able to inhibit ouabain-activated NP release (104).

The mechanisms related to NP secretion may be activated not only through Ca^{2+} influx but also by Ca^{2+} from the intracellular storage pool. The sarcoplasmic reticulum (SR) is particularly rich in Ca^{2+} and the generation of intracellular inositol 1,4,5-trisphosphate (IP_3) by various humoral agents causes a rapid release of Ca^{2+} into the cytoplasm. Ryanodine can prevent Ca^{2+} release from SR and is thus a useful agent to determine the contribution of SR to $[Ca^{2+}]_i$. Ryanodine was ineffective in inhibiting NP secretion mediated by phenylephrine, ET, or osmolarity (11, 67, 111), but it was effective in inhibiting ouabain, PAF, stretch, and pacing-stimulated secretion (11, 18, 102, 104). This suggests that some secretagogues act through an SR-dependent Ca^{2+} release whereas others do not need stored intracellular Ca^{2+}. Thapsigargin, an inhibitor of Ca^{2+} ATPase that restores SR Ca^{2+} pool, leads to Ca^{2+} accumulation in the cytoplasm. Thapsigargin affected neither basal nor ET-stimulated NP release by cultured neonatal atrial myocytes (111).

The homeostasis of $[Ca^{2+}]_i$ is a complex process regulated by several pumps and channels. The influx of Ca^{2+} is certainly a major contributor to the signal that triggers NP secretion. Since in vivo atrial myocytes are always submitted to constant contractions and $[Ca^{2+}]_i$ oscillations, static experiments, in which atria or cultured cardiomyocytes are quiescent, may not be adequate for fully understanding all the implications that Ca^{2+} may have in the regulation of NP secretion.

Inositol Trisphosphate Production and Protein Kinase C Activation

Several NP secretagogues bind to receptors belonging to the seven transmembrane domain family linked to G proteins. The activation of those receptors results in activation of phospholipase C and hydrolysis of phosphatidylinositol

4,5-bisphosphate generating IP_3 and 1,2-diacylglycerol (DAG). Generated IP_3, which possesses a short life, interacts then with an IP_3-gated Ca^{2+} channel on the SR releasing stored Ca^{2+}. On the other hand, in the presence of Ca^{2+}, membrane-inserted DAG binds and activates PKC.

Generation of IP_3 has been documented as an important second messenger in the transduction pathway involved in the regulation of NP secretion (3). In atrial myocytes, ET-1, α_1-adrenergic agents, ANG II, AVP, and muscarinic-cholinergic agents were all recognized as potent activators of IP_3 production and thus modulators of NP secretion. The results, which have been published since 1991, have only refined this signaling pathway.

Phenylephrine activates IP_3 generation in neonatal ventricular myocytes (115, 120, 121). The production of IP_3 was blocked by 5-methyluradipil and (+)-niguldipine, two α_{1A} adrenergic receptor antagonists (120). α_{1A}-Adrenergic receptor stimulation was later confirmed with adult atrial cardiac myocytes (68). However, at about the same time, another group observed that in perfused rabbit atria, adrenergic stimulation was inhibited by β-adrenergic antagonist (57). The reason for this discrepancy is unknown but may be related to the experimental model because in atrial tissue NP secretion was blocked by indomethacin, which implies the local generation of PGs. Through α_{1A}-adrenergic receptor stimulation, phenylephrine was found to cause important phenotypic modifications such as increase in cell size and up-regulation of ANP gene expression (120). However, the temporal pattern of IP_3 production by adrenergic agents was different from its generation by ET (121). Thus, whereas the stimulation by phenylephrine was sustained and lasted for several hours, the response to ET was of shorter duration although of comparable initial level. Consequently, NP expression to adrenergic stimulation remained higher than with ET. The shorter duration of ET action may be explained by a desensitization of ET receptors (37). ET-stimulated NP secretion by neonatal and adult atrial myocytes was associated with activation of the ET_A receptor (35–37). As documented (122), this G protein-coupled receptor is linked to hydrolysis of phosphatidyl inositol. Blockade of ET_A receptor with the antagonist BQ-123 was associated with a significant decrease of IP_3 formation and a parallel inhibition of ANP secretion (36).

ANG II acts through AT_1, a G protein-coupled receptor. In rat perfused atrial slices, ANG II induces NP release concomitantly with the generation of IP_3 within 5 min (19). This response was blocked by losartan, an AT_1 antagonist, but not by PD 123319, an AT_2 antagonist. However, the minimal ANG II concentration required to induce a significant IP_3 response was 10^{-8} M, a concentration 10-fold higher than the affinity of ANG II to the AT_1 receptor. Considering the lack of consistency on ANG II-stimulated NP secretion, these results may imply an indirect action of ANG II through generation of PGs or other substances (21, 27).

Finally, pacing is a powerful stimulus of NP release. Electrical stimulation of cultured neonatal atrial myocytes induces a rapid release of ANP (11). However, IP_3 production was absent in these experiments, indicating that Ca^{2+} influx alone, induced by pacing, can cause ANP secretion, probably through a Ca^{2+}-dependent calmodulin mechanism (11).

The role of IP_3 and subsequent release of Ca^{2+} from SR on the secretion of NP should be exemplified by the use of ryanodine. Ryanodine blocks the release of Ca^{2+} from SR and, therefore, should inhibit any potential action of IP_3 on NP secretion. Unfortunately, nobody has ever looked closely at the relationship that may exist between IP_3, Ca^{2+} release, and ryanodine. Partial results from different sources indicated that ryanodine was unable to decrease the ET- or phenylephrine-stimulated NP secretion (11, 67, 111, 123).

Little data are available on the generation of DAG in relation to NP secretion. Not much attention was brought to this second messenger, probably for several reasons: DAG is produced in equimolar concentrations with IP_3; the measurement of DAG is a relatively complicated assay; and phorbol ester is a membrane-permeable substitute that activates PKC. In one study, it was found that the formation of DAG was parallel to the ET- and phenylephrine-stimulated NP secretion (121).

The involvement of PKC in the regulation of NP release was mostly investigated indirectly by the use of tumor-promoting phorbol ester derivatives (phorbol-12,13-didecanoate, phorbol-12,13-dibutyrate, phorbol-12-myristate-13-acetate) or by inhibitors of PKC such as chelerythrine, staurosporine, H-7, calphostin C, and CGP 41251. Because of their chemical structure, phorbol esters are substitutes of DAG and activate PKC, presumably through the same binding site. Inhibitors of PKC are generally specific, except for staurosporine and H-7, which can also affect PKA and PKG. The addition of phorbol ester to cultures of neonatal atrial and ventricular myocytes triggered secretion of NP (11, 38, 68, 124) as well as an up-regulation of the expression of NP mRNAs (125), implying that PKC activation results in the phosphorylation of proteins closely associated with intracellular mechanisms of NP secretion (114). Indeed, most of the studies also agreed that the inhibition of PKC, which had been activated by several factors such as ET, thrombin, stretch, α-adrenergic agents, ANG II, acidic FGF, AVP, neurokines, or relaxin, resulted in a decreased NP release (21, 43, 68, 103, 114, 116, 117, 126–128).

More direct proof of the action of PKC is now available. ET caused a dose-dependent increase in the activity of PKC as measured by the phosphorylation of p80 (111). Substance P caused the rapid translocation of the PKC α isoform from the cytoplasm to the membrane (117). Transfection of neonatal ventricular myocytes with an expression vector bearing PKC β led to a enhanced expression of BNP. Finally, an interesting experiment was performed by Larsen et al (129), who—by treating newborn atrial myocytes with staurosporine or

H-7—observed a translocation of ANP secretory granules from the perinuclear region to the cell periphery with a concomitant decrease of ANP release. This suggests that PKC is not required for the translocation of secretory granules but rather may be necessary in the mechanisms related to the fusion of secretory granules to the cellular membrane. Taken together, these results indicate that PKC isoforms are involved in the secretion of NP as well as in the regulation of their expression. However, additional experiments are needed to further delineate which isoforms of PKC are involved and which are the steps in the secretion of ANP regulated by PKC.

Cyclic AMP

cAMP is formed intracellularly upon activation of adenylyl cyclase by agonists binding to G protein-coupled receptors. cAMP can then activate cAMP-dependent protein kinases (PKA) that phosphorylates several proteins. β-Adrenergic agents are potent stimulants of adenylyl cyclase. Isoproterenol raised cAMP levels in cardiac tissues in parallel with an increased NP secretion (57, 66). This effect has been reproduced by a cell-permeable cAMP analogue (dibutyryl cAMP) or by forskolin, a direct activator of adenylyl cyclase. However, in these experiments, it was also shown that isoproterenol caused synthesis of PGs, which, by themselves, can enhance cAMP. In favor of a PG-mediated NP secretion, indomethacin, quinacrine, and diclofenac, inhibitors of PGs synthesis, could block NP release (57, 124). In addition, H-89, an inhibitor of PKA, decreased NP secretion (66). In the same experimental model, the authors also demonstrated that phorbol ester, as previously shown, induced NP secretion and increased PGs and cAMP (124). It must be pointed out that the experiments on PG-mediated NP secretion were all conducted in cultured neonatal ventricular myocytes or in perfused atria, and the results have not been reproduced in atrial myocytes. Indeed, in neonatal atrial myocytes, ADM increased cAMP and decreased ANP secretion and expression (53). Stretched atrial myocytes and ANG II–stimulated perfused atria were insensitive to the addition of IBMX, an inhibitor of cyclic nucleotide phosphodiesterase, or of H-89. As discussed by Ruskoaho (3), the intracellular production of cAMP may have both positive and negative effects on NP secretion by cardiac cells. Therefore, the question of the real implication of cAMP as a second messenger in NP secretion remains open. However, these results raise another point about the significance of PGs as a NP secretagogue, an issue that needs to be clarified in atrial myocytes that represent NP secretory cells more appropriately than ventricular myocytes.

Calmodulin and Calmodulin Kinase

Once calmodulin binds 4 mol of Ca^{2+}, it associates and activates a family of Ca^{2+}/calmodulin-dependent protein kinases (CaMK). The role of calmodulin and the activation of CaMK II in the NP secretion by cardiac cells have been established mainly by using antagonists of calmodulin (W-7, calmidazolium, trifuoperazine) and inhibitors of CaMK II (KN-62). It has been reported that, generally, both types of agents are potent inhibitors of NP secretion when cardiac cells or tissues are stimulated by stretch, pacing, phenylephrine, ANG II, or ET (11, 20, 68, 111, 114, 115, 118). In most cases, the inhibition reaches 100%, which suggests that calmodulin and CaMK II are important relays in the transduction mechanism. In addition, it has been shown that some Ca^{2+}-binding proteins, namely calmodulin and annexin V and VI, can be found in association with atrial secretory granules (130, 131). It is thus surprising that these results have not stimulated much interest from the investigators to better understand how calmodulin and its related kinases are involved in the mechanisms of NP secretion.

CONCLUSION

The key elements required to understand the factors controlling secretion of NP by cardiac cells are now on the table. However, several questions remain to be explored. First, the fact that NP release by atrial myocytes is of the regulated type whereas in ventricular myocytes it is of the constitutive type questions the role of NP secretagogues in ventricular myocytes. Comparison between the secretory properties of these two cell types is required. Second, the phenotypic modifications of ventricular myocytes during heart diseases turn on NP synthesis, and ventricles become an important source of NP. Whether ventricular constitutive secretion is modified into a regulated one, and which secretagogues are involved, remain to be investigated. Third, the role of PGs in the control of NP secretion is intriguing. Where and how these PGs are generated deserve further exploration. Finally, the links among PKC, CaMK, and Ca^{2+} and the mechanisms of translocation and fusion of secretory granules, remain to be established.

Literature Cited

1. Koller KJ, Goedfdel DV. 1992. Molecular biology of the natriuretic peptides and their receptors. *Circulation* 86:1081–88
2. Brenner BM, Ballermann BJ, Gunning ME, Zeidel ML. 1990. Diverse biological actions of atrial natriuretic peptide. *Physiol. Rev.* 70:665–99
3. Ruskoaho H. 1992. Atrial natriuretic peptide: synthesis, release, and metabolism. *Pharmacol. Rev.* 44:479–602
4. Ruskoaho H, Kinnunen P, Mantymaa P, Uusimaa P, Taskinen T, et al. 1991. Cellular signals regulating the release of ANF. *Can. J. Physiol. Pharmacol.* 69: 1514–24
5. Stewart JM, Dean R, Brown M, Diasparra D, Zeballos GA, et al. 1992. Bilateral atrial appendectomy abolishes

increased plasma atrial natriuretic peptide release and blunts sodium and water excretion during volume loading in conscious dogs. *Circ. Res.* 70:724–32
6. Leskinen H, Vuolteenaho O, Ruskoaho H. 1997. Combined inhibition of endothelin and angiotensin II receptors blocks volume load-induced cardiac hormone release. *Circ. Res.* 80:114–23
7. Donckier J, Hanet C, Galanti L, Stoleru L, Van Mechelen H, et al. 1992. Low-dose endothelin-1 potentiates volume-induced secretion of atrial natriuretic factor. *Am. J. Physiol.* 263:H939–44
8. Leskinen H, Vuolteenaho O, Leppaluoto J, Ruskoaho H. 1995. Role of nitric oxide on cardiac hormone secretion: effect of N^{G}-nitro-L-arginine methyl ester on atrial natriuretic peptide and brain natriuretic peptide release. *Endocrinology* 136:1241–49
9. Christensen G, Leistad E. 1997. Atrial systolic pressure, as well as stretch, is a principal stimulus for release of ANF. *Am. J. Physiol.* 272:H820–26
10. Cho KW, Kim SH, Kim CH, Seul KH. 1995. Mechanical basis of ANP secretion in beating atria: atrial stroke volume and ECF translocation. *Am. J. Physiol.* 268:R1129–36
11. McDonough PM, Stella SL, Glembotski CC. 1994. Involvement of cytoplasmic calcium and protein kinases in the regulation of atrial natriuretic factor secretion by contraction rate and endothelin. *J. Biol. Chem.* 269:9466–72
12. Schiebinger RJ, Greening KM. 1992. Interaction between stretch and hormonally stimulated atrial natriuretic peptide secretion. *Am. J. Physiol.* 262:H78–83
13. Kinnunen P, Vuolteenaho O, Uusimaa P, Ruskoaho H. 1992. Passive mechanical stretch releases atrial natriuretic peptide from rat ventricular myocardium. *Circ. Res.* 70:1244–53
14. Skvorak JP, Nazian SJ, Dietz JR. 1995. Endothelin acts as a paracrine regulator of stretch-induced atrial natriuretic peptide release. *Am. J. Physiol.* 269:R1093–98
15. Skvorak JP, Dietz JR. 1997. Endothelin and nitric oxide interact to regulate stretch-induced ANP secretion. *Am. J. Physiol.* 273:R301–6
16. Laine M, Id L, Vuolteenaho O, Ruskoaho H, Weckstrom M. 1996. Role of calcium in stretch-induced release and mRNA synthesis of natriuretic peptides in isolated rat atrium. *Pflügers Arch. Eur. J. Physiol.* 432:953–60
17. Laine M, Arjamaa O, Vuolteenaho O, Ruskoaho H, Weckstrom M. 1994. Block of stretch-activated atrial natriuretic peptide secretion by gadolinium in isolated rat atrium. *J. Physiol.* 480:553–61
18. Laine M, Weckstrom M, Vuolteenaho O, Arjamaa O. 1994. Effect of ryanodine on atrial natriuretic peptide secretion by contracting and quiescent rat atrium. *Pflügers Arch. Eur. J. Physiol.* 426:276–83
19. Soualmia H, Barthelemy C, Masson F, Maistre G, Eurin J, Carayon A. 1997. Angiotensin II-induced phosphoinositide production and atrial natriuretic peptide release in rat atrial tissue. *J. Cardiovasc. Pharmacol.* 29:605–11
20. Soualmia H, Masson F, Barthelemy C, Maistre G, Carayon A. 1996. Cellular mechanism of angiotensin II-induced atrial natriuretic peptide release in rat right atrial tissue. *Life Sci.* 58:1621–29
21. Church DJ, Braconi S, Van der Bent V, Vallotton MB, Lang U. 1994. Protein kinase C-dependent prostaglandin production mediates angiotensin II-induced atrial-natriuretic peptide release. *Biochem. J.* 298:451–56
22. Dietz JR. 1988. The effect of angiotensin II and ADH on the secretion of atrial natriuretic factor. *Proc. Soc. Exp. Biol. Med.* 187:366–69
23. Lachance D, Garcia R. 1988. Atrial natriuretic factor release by angiotensin II in the conscious rat. *J. Hypertension* 11: 502–8
24. Lachance D, Garcia R. 1989. Atrial natriuretic factor release during angiotensin II infusion in right and left atrial appendectomized rats. *J. Hypertens.* 7:293–98
25. Focaccio A, Volpe M, Ambrosio G, Lembo G, Pannain S, et al. 1993. Angiotensin II directly stimulates release of atrial natriuretic factor in isolated rabbit hearts. *Circulation* 87:192–98
26. Melo LG, Sonnenberg H. 1996. Effect of nitric oxide inhibition on secretion of atrial natriuretic factor in isolated rat heart. *Am. J. Physiol.* 270:H306–11
27. Melo LG, Sonnenberg H. 1995. Requirement for prostaglandin synthesis in secretion of atrial natriuretic factor from isolated rat heart. *Regul. Pept.* 60:79–87
28. Itoh H, Nakao K, Yamada T, Morii N, Shiono S, et al. 1988. Brain renin-angiotensin. Central control of secretion of atrial natriuretic factor from the heart. *Hypertension* 11:I57–61
29. Itoh H, Nakao K, Yamada T, Morii N, Shiono S, et al. 1988. Central interaction

of the brain atrial natriuretic polypeptide (ANP) system and the brain renin-angiotensin system in ANP secretion from heart—evidence for possible brain-heart axis. *Can. J. Physiol. Pharmacol.* 66:255–61
30. Hu JR, Berninger UG, Lang RE. 1988. Endothelin stimulates atrial natriuretic peptide (ANP) release from rat atria. *Eur. J. Pharmacol.* 158:177–78
31. Stasch JP, Hirth-Dietrich C, Kazda S, Neuser D. 1989. Endothelin stimulates release of atrial natriuretic peptides in vitro and in vivo. *Life Sci.* 45:869–75
32. Fukuda Y, Hirata Y, Taketani S, Kojima T, Oikawa S, et al. 1989. Endothelin stimulates accumulations of cellular atrial natriuretic peptide and its messenger RNA in rat cardiocytes. *Biochem. Biophys. Res. Commun.* 164:1431–36
33. Ohman KP, Hoffman A, Keiser HR. 1990. Endothelin-induced vasoconstriction and release of atrial natriuretic peptides in the rat. *Acta Physiol. Scand.* 138:549–56
34. Horio T, Kohno M, Takeda T. 1993. Cosecretion of atrial and brain natriuretic peptides stimulated by endothelin-1 from cultured rat atrial and ventricular cardiocytes. *Metab. Clin. Exp.* 42: 94–96
35. Thibault G, Doubell AF, Garcia R, Lariviere R, Schiffrin EL. 1994. Endothelin-stimulated secretion of natriuretic peptides by rat atrial myocytes is mediated by endothelin A receptors. *Circ. Res.* 74: 460–70
36. Irons CE, Murray SF, Glembotski CC. 1993. Identification of the receptor subtype responsible for endothelin-mediated protein kinase C activation and atrial natriuretic factor secretion from atrial myocytes. *J. Biol. Chem.* 268: 23417–21
37. Leite MF, Page E, Ambler SK. 1994. Regulation of ANP secretion by endothelin-1 in cultured atrial myocytes: desensitization and receptor subtype. *Am. J. Physiol.* 267:H2193–203
38. Suzuki E, Hirata Y, Kohmoto O, Sugimoto T, Hayakawa H, et al. 1992. Cellular mechanisms for synthesis and secretion of atrial natriuretic peptide and brain natriuretic peptide in cultured rat atrial cells. *Circ. Res.* 71:1039–48
39. Miller H III, Lee D, Rice T, Southerland C. 1996. In rats, atrial natriuretic peptide secretion is regulated differently in the right and left atria. *Endocr. Res.* 22:43–57
40. Mantymaa P, Leppaluoto J, Ruskoaho H. 1990. Endothelin stimulates basal and stretch-induced atrial natriuretic peptide secretion from the perfused rat heart. *Endocrinology* 126:587–95
41. Lachance D, Garcia R, Gutkowska J, Cantin M, Thibault G. 1986. Mechanisms of release of atrial natriuretic factor. I. Effect of several agonists and steroids on its release by atrial minces. *Biochem. Biophys. Res. Commun.* 135:1090–98
42. Jin HK, Chen YF, Yang RH, McKenna TM, Jackson RM, Oparil S. 1989. Vasopressin lowers pulmonary artery pressure in hypoxic rats by releasing atrial natriuretic peptide. *Am. J. Med. Sci.* 298:227–36
43. Van der Bent V, Church DJ, Vallotton MB, Meda P, Kem DC, et al. 1994. $[Ca^{2+}]_i$ and protein kinase C in vasopressin-induced prostacyclin and ANP release in rat cardiomyocytes. *Am. J. Physiol.* 266:H597–605
44. Matsubara H, Hirata Y, Yoshimi H, Takata S, Takagi Y, et al. 1988. Role of calcium and protein kinase C in ANP secretion by cultured rat cardiocytes. *Am. J. Physiol.* 255:H405–9
45. Jin H, Yang RH, Chen YF, Jackson R, Oparil S. 1987. Arginine vasopressin lowers pulmonary arterial pressure in rat adapted to chronic hypoxia. *Am. J. Med. Sci.* 30:274–78
46. Ruskoaho H, Taskinen T, Pesonen A, Vuolteenaho O, Leppaluoto J, Tuomisto L. 1989. Atrial natriuretic peptide in plasma, atria, ventricles, and hypothalamus of Long-Evans and vasopressin-deficient Brattleboro rats. *Endocrinology* 124:2595–603
47. Ruskoaho H, Vakkuri O, Arjamaa O, Vuolteenaho O, Leppaluoto J. 1989. Pressor hormones regulate atrial-stretch-induced release of atrial natriuretic peptide in the pithed rat. *Circ. Res.* 64:482–92
48. Stewart JM, Wang J, Singer A, Zeballos GA, Ochoa M, et al. 1990. Regulation of plasma ANF after increases in afterload in conscious dogs. *Am. J. Physiol.* 259:H1736–42
49. Furchgott RF, Zawadski J. 1980. The obligatory role of endothelial cells in the relaxation of arterial smooth muscle by acetylcholine. *Nature* 288:373–76
50. Palmer RMJ, Ferrige AG, Moncada S. 1987. Nitric oxide release accounts for the biological activity of endothelium-derived relaxing factor. *Nature* 327:524–26

51. Kitamura K, Kangawa K, Kawamoto M, Ichiki Y, Nakamura S, et al. 1993. Adrenomedullin: a novel hypotensive peptide isolated from human pheochromocytoma. *Biochem. Biophys. Res. Commun.* 192:553–60
52. Sakata J, Shimokubo T, Kitamura K, Nishizono M, Iehiki Y, et al. 1994. Distribution and characterization of immunoreactive rat adrenomedullin in tissue and plasma. *FEBS Lett.* 352:105–8
53. Sato A, Canny BJ, Autelitano DJ. 1997. Adrenomedullin stimulates cAMP accumulation and inhibits atrial natriuretic peptide gene expression in cardiomyocytes. *Biochem. Biophys. Res. Commun.* 230:311–14
54. Nishimori T, Tsujino M, Sato K, Imai T, Marumo F, Hirata Y. 1997. Dexamethasone induced up regulation of adrenomedullin and atrial natriuretic peptides genes in cultured rat ventricular myocytes. *J. Mol. Cell. Cardiol.* 29: 2125–30
55. Norman AW, Litwack G. 1987. Prostaglandins. In *Hormones*, pp. 645–80. Orlando: Academic
56. Zongazo MA, Carayon A, Masson F, Maistre G, Noe E, et al. 1991. Effects of arginine vasopressin and extracellular osmolarity on atrial natriuretic peptide release by superfused rat atria. *Eur. J. Pharmacol.* 209:45–55
57. Azizi C, Carayon A, Masson F, Noe E, Barthelemy C, et al. 1993. Mechanisms of isoproterenol-induced atrial natriuretic peptide release from superfused rabbit atria. *Am. J. Physiol.* 265:H1283–88
58. Rayner TE, Chen BN, McLoughlin JW, Menadue MF, Norman RJ, Oliver JR. 1993. Prostaglandin F2 alpha mediates platelet-activating factor-stimulated atrial natriuretic factor release from the isolated rat heart. *Endocrinology* 133: 1108–15
59. Haug C, Grunt M, Schmid S, Steinbach G, Metzele A, et al. 1994. Effect of corticotropin releasing factor on atrial natriuretic peptide release from the isolated perfused rat heart. *Arzneim. Forsch.* 44:579–82
60. Church DJ, Van der Bent V, Vallotton MB, Lang U. 1994. Role of prostaglandin-mediated cyclic AMP formation in protein kinase C-dependent secretion of atrial natriuretic peptide in rat cardiomyocytes. *Biochem. J.* 303:217–25
61. Bloch KD, Zamir N, Lichtstein D, Seidman CE, Seidman JG. 1988. Ouabain induces secretion of proatrial natriuretic factor by rat atrial cardiocytes. *Am. J. Physiol.* 255:E383–87
62. Chen BN, Rayner TE, Menadue MF, McLennan PL, Oliver JR. 1993. Effect of ischaemia and role of eicosanoids in release of atrial natriuretic factor from rat heart. *Cardiovasc. Res.* 27:1576–79
63. Gardner DG, Schultz HD. 1990. Prostaglandins regulate the synthesis and secretion of the atrial natriuretic factor. *J. Clin. Invest.* 86:52–59
64. Kovacic-Milivojevic B, Schultz HD, Gardner DG. 1991. Arachidonic acid metabolites regulate the secretion of atrial natriuretic peptide in cultured rat atrial cardiocytes. *Can. J. Physiol. Pharmacol.* 69:1493–99
65. Lai J, Jin H, Yang R, Winer J, Li W, et al. 1996. Prostaglandin F2 alpha induces cardiac myocyte hypertrophy in vitro and cardiac growth in vivo. *Am. J. Physiol.* 271:H2197–208
66. Azizi C, Barthelemy C, Masson F, Maistre G, Eurin J, Carayon A. 1995. Myocardial production of prostaglandins: its role in atrial natriuretic peptide release. *Eur. J. Endocrinol.* 133:255–59
67. Schiebinger RJ, Parr HG, Cragoe EJ Jr. 1992. Calcium: its role in alpha 1-adrenergic stimulation of atrial natriuretic peptide secretion. *Endocrinology* 130:1017–23
68. Ambler SK, Leite MF. 1994. Regulation of atrial natriuretic peptide secretion by alpha 1-adrenergic receptors: the role of different second messenger pathways. *J. Mol. Cell. Cardiol.* 26:391–402
69. Hanford DS, Thuerauf DJ, Murray SF, Glembotski CC. 1994. Brain natriuretic peptide is induced by alpha 1-adrenergic agonists as a primary response gene in cultured rat cardiac myocytes. *J. Biol. Chem.* 269:26227–33
70. Agnoletti G, Rodella A, Cornacchiari A, Panzali AF, Harris P, Ferrari R. 1992. Isoproterenol induces release of atrial natriuretic peptide from rat atrium in vitro. *Am. J. Physiol.* 262:H285–92
71. Mukaddam-Daher S, Lambert C, Gutkowska J. 1997. Clonidine and ST-91 may activate imidazoline binding sites in the heart to release atrial natriuretic peptide. *Hypertension* 30:83–87
72. Pepino P, Volpe M, Rose EA, Panza A, Lembo G, et al. 1992. Effect of complete cardiac denervation on atrial natriuretic factor release in baboons. *J. Surg. Res.* 53:43–47
73. Geny B, Piquard F, Follenius M, Mettauer B, Schaefer A, et al. 1993. Role of

cardiac innervation in atrial natriuretic peptide secretion in transplanted heart recipients. *Am. J. Physiol.* 265:F112–18
74. Singer DR, Markandu ND, Buckley MG, Miller MA, Sagnella GA, et al. 1994. Blood pressure and endocrine responses to changes in dietary sodium intake in cardiac transplant recipients. Implications for the control of sodium balance. *Circulation* 89:1153–59
75. Jiao JH, Baertschi AJ. 1993. Neural control of the endocrine rat heart. *Proc. Natl. Acad. Sci. USA* 90:7799–803
76. Jiao JH, Guyenet PG, Baertschi AJ. 1992. Lower brain stem controls cardiac ANF secretion. *Am. J. Physiol.* 263: H198–207
77. Uusimaa PA, Peuhkurinen KJ, Hassinen IE, Vuolteenaho O, Ruskoaho H. 1992. Ischemia stimulates the release of atrial natriuretic peptide from rat cardiac ventricular myocardium in vitro. *Life Sci.* 50:365–373
78. Arad M, Zamir N, Horowitz L, Oxman T, Rabinowitz B. 1994. Release of atrial natriuretic peptide in brief ischemia-reperfusion in isolated rat hearts. *Am. J. Physiol.* 266:H1971–78
79. Focaccio A, Ambrosio G, Enea I, Russo R, Balestrieri P, et al. 1995. Influence of O2 deprivation, reduced flow, and temperature on release of ANP from rabbit hearts. *Am. J. Physiol.* 268:H2352–57
80. Uusimaa PA, Peuhkurinen KJ, Vuolteenaho O, Ruskoaho H, Hassinen IE. 1992. Role of myocardial redox and energy states in ischemia-stimulated release of atrial natriuretic peptide. *J. Mol. Cell. Cardiol.* 24:191–205
81. Garcia R, Debinski W, Gutkowska J, Kuchel O, Thibault G, et al. 1985. Gluco- and mineralocorticoids may regulate the natriuretic effect and the synthesis and release of atrial natriuretic factor by the rat atria in vivo. *Biochem. Biophys. Res. Commun.* 131:806–14
82. Gardner DG, Hane S, Trachewsky D, Schenk D, Baxter JD. 1998. Atrial natriuretic peptide mRNA is regulated by glucocorticoids in vivo. *Biochem. Biophys. Res. Commun.* 139:1047–54
83. Gardner DG, Gertz BJ, Deschepper CF, Kim DY. 1988. Gene for the rat atrial natriuretic peptide is regulated by glucocorticoids in vitro. *J. Clin. Invest.* 82: 1275–81
84. Grunt M, Haug C, Duntas L, Pauschinger P, Maier V, Pfeiffer EF. 1992. Dilatory and inotropic effects of corticotropin-releasing factor (CRF) on the isolated heart. Effects on atrial natriuretic peptide (ANP) release. *Horm. Metab. Res.* 24:56–9
85. Tojo K, Sato S, Tokudome G, Ohta M, Kawaguchi Y, et al. 1996. Stimulation by corticotropin-releasing factor of atrial natriuretic peptide and brain natriuretic peptide secretions from cultured neonatal rat cardiomyocytes. *Biochem. Biophys. Res. Commun.* 225:340–46
86. Cavallini G, Clerico A, Del Chicca M, De Tata V, Gori Z, Bergamini E. 1992. Effects of the administration of thyroid hormone on the plasma levels of atrial natriuretic peptides and on atrial myoendocrine cells in the rat: an immunochemical, ultrastructural, and stereological study. *J. Endocrinol. Invest.* 15: 727–34
87. Zamir N, Slover M, Ohman KP. 1993. Thyroid hormone restores atrial stretch-induced secretion of atrial natriuretic peptide in hypophysectomized rats. *Horm. Metab. Res.* 25:152–5
88. Bernstein R, Midtbo K, Urdal P, Morkrid L, Smith G, et al. 1998. Serum N-terminal pro-atrial natriuretic factor 1–98 before and during thyroxine replacement therapy in severe hypothyroidism. *Thyroid.* 7:415–19
89. Deng Y, Kaufman S. 1993. The influence of reproductive hormones on ANF release by rat atria. *Life Sci.* 53:689–96
90. Hwu CM, Tsai SC, Lau CP, Pu HF, Wang TL, et al. 1993. Increased concentrations of atrial and plasma atrial natriuretic peptide in castrated male rats. *Life Sci.* 52:205–12
91. Tummala PE, Dananberg J, Grekin RJ. 1992. Alterations in the secretion of atrial natriuretic factor in atria from aged rats. *Hypertension* 20:85–88
92. Laine M, Weckstrom M, Vuolteenaho O, Arjamaa O. 1994. Effect of ryanodine on atrial natriuretic peptide secretion by contracting and quiescent rat atrium. *Pflug. Arch. Eur. J. Physiol.* 426:276–83
93. Pollack JA, Skvorak JP, Nazian SJ, Landon CS, Dietz JR. 1997. Alterations in atrial natriuretic peptide (ANP) secretion and renal effects in aging. *J. Gerontol. Ser. A* 52:B196–202
94. Reckelhoff JF, Morris M, Baylis C. 1992. Basal and stimulated plasma atrial natriuretic peptide (ANP) concentrations and cardiac ANP contents in old and young rats. *Mech. Aging Dev.* 63: 177–81
95. Opie LH, Owen P, du Toit E, Norton GG. 1998. Decreased rates of release of atrial

natriuretic peptide from isolated hearts from aging hypertensive rats. *Am. J. Hypertens.* 5:748–53

96. Legault L, van Nguyen P, Holliwell DL, Leenen FH. 1992. Hemodynamic and plasma atrial natriuretic factor responses to cardiac volume loading in young versus older normotensive humans. *Can. J. Physiol. Pharmacol.* 70:1549–54
97. Wu SQ, Kwan CY, Tang F. 1997. The efffect of aging on ANP levels in the plasma, heart, and brain of rats. *J. Gerontol. Ser. A* 52:B250–54
98. Bell D, McDermott BJ. 1996. Calcitonin gene-related peptide in the cardiovascular system: characterization of receptors populations and their (patho)physiological significance. *Pharmacol. Rev.* 44:479–602
99. Schiebinger RJ, Santora AC. 1989. Stimulation by calcitonin gene-related peptide of atrial natriuretic peptide secretion in vitro and its mechanism of action. *Endocrinology* 124:2473–79
100. Yamamoto A, Kimura S, Hasui K, Fujisawa Y, Tamaki T, et al. 1988. Calcitonin gene-related peptide (CGRP) stimulates the release of atrial natriuretic peptide (ANP) from isolated rat atria. *Biochem. Biophys. Res. Commun.* 155:1452–58
101. Rayner TE, Menadue MF, Oliver JR. 1991. Platelet-activating factor stimulates the release of atrial natriuretic factor from the rat heart. *J. Endocrinol.* 130: 281–88
102. Church DJ, Van der Bent V, Vallotton MB, Capponi AM, Lang U. 1994. Calcium influx in platelet activating factor-induced atrial natriuretic peptide release in rat cardiomyocytes. *Am. J. Physiol.* 266:E403–9
103. Toth M, Taskinen P, Ruskoaho H. 1996. Relaxin stimulates atrial natriuretic peptide secretion in perfused rat heart. *J. Endocrinol.* 150:487–95

103a. Hamlyn JM, Manunta P. 1992. Ouabain, digitalis-like factors and hypertension. *J. Hypertens.* 10(Suppl. 7):S99–111

103b. Gudmundsson AO, Herlitz H, Jonsson O, Nancler J, Wikstraud J, Berglund G. 1984. Blood pressure, intraerythrocyte content, and transmembrane fluxes of sodium during normal and high salt intake in subjects with and without a family history of hypertension: evidence against a sodium-transport inhibitor. *J. Cardioten. Pharmacol.* 6(Suppl.1):S35–41

104. Schiebinger RJ, Cragoe EJ, Jr. 1993. Ouabain. A stimulator of atrial natriuretic peptide secretion and its mechanism of action. *Circ. Res.* 72:1035–43
105. Nag AC, Cheng M. 1981. Adult mammalian cardiac muscle cells in culture. *Tissue Cell* 13:515–23
106. Hassall CJ, Wharton J, Gulbenkian S, Anderson JV, Frater J, et al. 1988. Ventricular and atrial myocytes of newborn rats synthesise and secrete atrial natriuretic peptide in culture: light- and electron-microscopical localisation and chromatographic examination of stored and secreted molecular forms. *Cell Tissue Res.* 251:161–69
107. Larsen TH, Huitfeldt HS, Myking O, Saetersdal T. 1993. Microtubule-associated distribution of specific granules and secretion of atrial natriuretic factor in primary cultures of rat cardiomyocytes. *Cell Tissue Res.* 272:201–10
108. Bloch KD, Seidman JG, Naftilan JD, Fallon JT, Seidman CE. 1986. Neonatal atria and ventricles secrete atrial natriuretic factor via tissue-specific secretory pathways. *Cell* 47:695–702
109. De Young MB, Keller JC, Graham RM, Wildey GM. 1994. Brefeldin A defines distinct pathways for atrial natriuretic factor secretion in neonatal rat atrial and ventricular myocytes. *Circ. Res.* 74:33–40
110. Cho KW, Kim SH, Seul KH, Hwang YH, Kook YJ. 1994. Effect of extracellular calcium depletion on the two-step ANP secretion in perfused rabbit atria. *Regul. Pept.* 52:129–37
111. Doubell AF, Thibault G. 1994. Calcium is involved in both positive and negative modulation of the secretory system for ANP. *Am. J. Physiol.* 266:H1854–63
112. Kim SH, Cho KW, Chang SH, Kim SZ, Chae SW. 1997. Glibenclamide suppresses stretch-activated ANP secretion: involvements of K^+ATP channels and L-type Ca^{2+} channel modulation. *Pflug. Arch. Eur. J. Physiol.* 434:362–72
113. Deng Y, Lang R. 1992. The influence of calcium on ANF release in the isolated rat atrium. *Can. J. Physiol. Pharmacol.* 70:1057–60
114. Irons CE, Sei CA, Hidaka H, Glembotski CC. 1992. Protein kinase C and calmodulin kinase are required for endothelin-stimulated atrial natriuretic factor secretion from primary atrial myocytes. *J. Biol. Chem.* 267:5211–16
115. McDonough PM, Glembotski CC. 1992. Induction of atrial natriuretic factor and myosin light chain-2 gene expression in cultured ventricular myocytes by electrical stimulation of contraction. *J. Biol. Chem.* 267:11665–68

116. Kinnunen P, Vuolteenaho O, Ruskoaho H. 1993. Mechanisms of atrial and brain natriuretic peptide release from rat ventricular myocardium: effect of stretching. *Endocrinology* 132:1961–70
117. Church DJ, Arkinstall SJ, Vallotton MB, Chollet A, Kawashima E, Lang U. 1996. Stimulation of atrial natriuretic peptide release by neurokinins in neonatal rat ventricular cardiomyocytes. *Am. J. Physiol.* 270:H935–44
118. Gardner DG, Wirtz H, Dobbs LG. 1992. Stretch-dependent regulation of atrial peptide synthesis and secretion in cultured atrial cardiocytes. *Am. J. Physiol.* 263:E239–44
119. Schiebinger RJ, Joseph CM, Li Y, Cragoe EJ Jr. 1995. Mechanism of hyperosmolality stimulation of ANP secretion: its dependency on calcium and sodium. *Am. J. Physiol.* 268:E476–83
120. Knowlton KU, Michel MC, Itani M, Shubeita HE, Ishihara K, et al. 1993. The alpha 1A-adrenergic receptor subtype mediates biochemical, molecular, and morphologic features of cultured myocardial cell hypertrophy. *J. Biol. Chem.* 268:15374–80
121. McDonough PM, Brown JH, Glembotski CC. 1993. Phenylephrine and endothelin differentially stimulate cardiac PI hydrolysis and ANF expression. *Am. J. Physiol.* 264:H625–30
122. Sokolovsky M. 1993. Functional coupling between endothelin receptors and multiple G-proteins in rat heart myocytes. *Recept. Channels.* 1:295–304
123. Schiebinger RJ, Gomez-Sanchez CE. 1990. Endothelin: a potent stimulus of atrial natriuretic peptide secretion by superfused rat atria and its dependency on calcium. *Endocrinology* 127:119–25
124. Church DJ, Van der Bent V, Vallotton MB, Lang U. 1994. Role of prostaglandin-mediated cyclic AMP formation in protein kinase C-dependent secretion of atrial natriuretic peptide in rat cardiomyocytes. *Biochem. J.* 303:217–25
125. LaPointe MC, Sitkins JR. 1993. Phorbol ester stimulates the synthesis and secretion of brain natriuretic peptide from neonatal rat ventricular cardiocytes: a comparison with the regulation of atrial natriuretic factor. *Mol. Endocrinol.* 7:1284–96
126. Glembotski CC, Irons CE, Krown KA, Murray SF, Sprenkle AB, Sei CA. 1993. Myocardial alpha-thrombin receptor activation induces hypertrophy and increases atrial natriuretic factor gene expression. *J. Biol. Chem.* 268:20646–52
127. Tokola H, Salo K, Vuolteenaho O, Ruskoaho H. 1994. Basal and acidic fibroblast growth factor-induced atrial natriuretic peptide gene expression and secretion is inhibited by staurosporine. *Eur. J. Pharmacol.* 267:195–206
128. Magga J, Vuolteenaho O, Tokola H, Marttila M, Ruskoaho H. 1997. Involvement of transcriptional and posttranscriptional mechanisms in cardiac overload-induced increase of B-type natriuretic peptide gene expression. *Circ. Res.* 81:694–702
129. Larsen TH, Myking O, Lillehaug JR, Saetersdal T. 1993. Inhibition and downregulation of protein kinase C in cultured atrial myocytes: effects on distribution of specific granules and secretion of atrial natriuretic peptide. *Mol. Cell. Endocrinol.* 94:173–81
130. Doubell AF, Bester AJ, Thibault G. 1991. Annexins V and VI: major calcium-dependent atrial secretory granule-binding proteins. *Hypertension* 18: 648–56
131. Doubell AF, Lazure C, Tremblay J, Thibault G. 1994. Identification of a calcium-dependent atrial secretory binding protein as calmodulin. *Cardiovasc. Res.* 28:705–9
132. Katoh S, Toyama J, Aoyama M, Miyamoto N, Seo H, et al. 1990. Mechanisms of atrial natriuretic peptide (ANP) secretion by rat hearts perfused in vitro—Ca2(+)-dependent signal transduction for ANP release by mechanical stretch. *Jpn. Circ. J.* 54:1283–94
133. Sei CA, Glembotski CC. 1990. Calcium dependence of phenylephrine-, endothelin-, and potassium chloride-stimulated atrial natriuretic factor secretion from long term primary neonatal rat atrial cardiocytes. *J. Biol. Chem.* 265: 7166–72
134. Fukuda Y, Hirata Y, Yoshimi H, Kojima T, Kobayashi Y, et al. 1988. Endothelin is a potent secretagogue for atrial natriuretic peptide in cultured rat atrial myocytes. *Biochem. Biophys. Res. Commun.* 155:167–72
135. Lew RA, Baertschi AJ. 1992. Endothelium-dependent ANF secretion in vitro. *Am. J. Physiol.* 263:H1071–77
136. Kuroski-de Bold ML, de Bold AJ. 1991. Stretch-secretion coupling in atrial cardiocytes. Dissociation between atrial natriuretic factor release and mechanical activity. *Hypertension* (Suppl. III) 18: 169–78

137. Page E, Goings GE, Power B, Upshaw-Earley J. 1990. Basal and stretch-augmented natriuretic peptide secretion by quiescent rat atria. *Am. J. Physiol.* 259:C801–18
138. Skvorak JP, Sutton ET, Rao PS, Dietz JR. 1996. Mechanism of anoxia-induced atrial natriuretic peptide release in the isolated rat atria. *Am. J. Physiol.* 271:R237–43
139. Ishida A, Tanahashi T, Okumura K, Hashimoto H, Ito T, et al. 1988. A calmodulin antagonist (W-7) and a protein kinase C inhibitor (H-7) have no effect on atrial natriuretic peptide release induced by atrial stretch. *Life Sci.* 42:1659–67
140. Pitkanen M, Mantymaa P, Ruskoaho H. 1991. Staurosporine, a protein kinase C inhibitor, inhibits atrial natriuretic peptide secretion induced by sarafotoxin, endothelin and phorbol ester. *Eur. J. Pharmacol.* 195:307–15
141. Gardner DG, Newman ED, Nakamura KK, Nguyen KP. 1991. Endothelin increases the synthesis and secretion of atrial natriuretic peptide in neonatal rat cardiocytes. *Am. J. Physiol.* 261:E177–82
142. Riddervold F, Smiseth OA, Hall C, Groves G, Risoe C. 1991. Rate-induced increase in plasma atrial natriuretic factor can occur independently of changes in atrial wall stretch. *Am. J. Physiol.* 260:H1953–58
143. Nishimura K, Ban T, Saito Y, Nakao K, Imura H. 1990. Atrial pacing stimulates secretion of atrial natriuretic polypeptide without elevation of atrial pressure in awake dogs with experimental complete atrioventricular block. *Circ. Res.* 66:115–22

Annu. Rev. Physiol. 1999. 61:219–42

MYOBLAST CELL GRAFTING INTO HEART MUSCLE: Cellular Biology and Potential Applications

P. D. Kessler
Peter Belfer Cardiac Laboratory, Division of Cardiology, Johns Hopkins University School of Medicine, Baltimore, Maryland 21205;
e-mail: pkessler@welchlink.welch.jhu.edu

B. J. Byrne
Gene Therapy Center, Department of Molecular Genetics and Microbiology and Department of Pediatrics, University of Florida College of Medicine, Gainesville, Florida 32610; e-mail: byrne@college.med.ufl.edu

KEY WORDS: skeletal muscle, cardiomyocytes, cell transplantation, cardiac regeneration, transdifferentiation

ABSTRACT

This review surveys a wide range of cellular and molecular approaches to strengthening the injured or weakened heart, focusing on strategies to replace dysfunctional, necrotic, or apoptotic cardiomyocytes with new cells of mesodermal origin. A variety of cell types, including myogenic cell lines, adult skeletal myoblasts, immortalized atrial cells, embryonic and adult cardiomyocytes, embryonic stem cells, teratoma cells, genetically altered fibroblasts, smooth muscle cells, and bone marrow–derived cells have all been proposed as useful cells in cardiac repair and may have the capacity to perform cardiac work. We focus on the implantation of mesodermally derived cells, the best developed of the options. We review the developmental and cell biology that have stimulated these studies, examine the limitations of current knowledge, and identify challenges for the future, which we believe are considerable.

0066-4278/99/0315-0219$08.00

INTRODUCTION

Techniques that introduce new myogenic cells into the heart, induce the replication of myocardial cells in situ, or allow cells resident in the heart to convert to a myogenic phenotype have great potential for treating heart failure and cardiomyopathy. The ultimate goal of this work is to repair, replace, or enhance the biological function of damaged cells in order to strengthen the weakened heart. Cell implantation may also provide a "platform" for the stable local delivery of recombinant proteins.

These studies have been an active area of investigation since the introduction of exogenous cells in canine heart was first reported (1). These investigators demonstrated the successful grafting and subsequent myodifferentiation of autologous canine myoblasts (satellite cells) in canine cryoinjury (1, 2). Subsequent investigations utilized immortalized myogenic cells in rodents (3–5). A concern that skeletal muscle cells could not appropriately communicate with the underlying myocardium (a matter of some controversy) led to an extension of this approach to fetal cardiomyocyte grafts, which form intercalated disks and gap junctions with native myocardium (6, 7).

Alternate approaches to generating cardiac substitutes have utilized immortalized atrial cell lines (8), and genetically selected embryonic stem cells (9). Alternative cell sources have been considered, including smooth muscle cells, bone marrow–derived cells, and embryonal carcinoma cells (10–13). Other strategies have focused on inducing undamaged cardiomyocytes to replicate or identify "cardiogenic master genes" that might program a cell present in the heart (fibroblasts, smooth muscle, or endothelial cells) or grafted cells (e.g. fibroblasts or myoblasts) to convert into cardiomyocytes. The goal of each of these interventions is to generate a cell that can perform cardiac work, respond appropriately to adjacent cardiomyocytes and nonmyocyte cells, and exhibit a favorable response to physiological and pathophysiological stimuli. Successful cardiac tissue engineering would provide a valuable alternative therapy for end-stage heart failure (reviewed in 14).

CONGESTIVE HEART FAILURE

Why develop cell transplantation for heart disease? Loss and dysfunction of cardiomyocytes are characteristics of chronic heart disease, including ischemic heart disease, hypertensive heart disease, and idiopathic cardiomyopathy. These deficits in cardiomycyte number lead to heart failure, which is a consequence of either primary or secondary irreversible cell loss. The molecular basis for the syndrome of congestive heart failure is a lack of stem cells in the heart and the inability of the damaged heart cells to undergo repair or divide (15–17). Cell transplantation strategies have been designed to replace damaged cells with cells that can perform cardiac work.

There is a pressing need for novel therapies to treat heart failure (18). This condition affects an estimated 4.8 million Americans, and 400,000 new cases are diagnosed each year. The use of angiotensin-converting enzyme inhibitors and of beta-adrenergic blockers has improved survival in these patients (19–21). Additionally, new mechanical-assist devices, experimental surgical procedures, and xenotransplantation approaches are currently being developed (22–25), yet mortality remains high, with greater than 50% of all patients succumbing within 5 years of initial diagnosis (26). The utility of cardiac transplantation is limited by a shortage of donor hearts, the complications of immunosuppression, and the failure of grafted organs. The idea of transplanting single cells instead of entire organs has a number of attractive attributes and is dependent on an ever-expanding understanding of the molecular basis of skeletal myogenesis and early events in cardiogenesis, which are briefly reviewed below.

DEVELOPMENTAL AND CELL BIOLOGY

Stem Cells

Mammalian embryos consist of pluripotent cells that have the capacity to form an entire organism. This capability of forming multiple cell lineages becomes progressively restricted with development, through a process known as determination. Determined stem cells give rise to cells of a specific lineage (e.g. pluripotent hematopoetic progenitor cells give rise to various blood lineages), whereas committed progenitor cells (e.g. myoblasts or embryonic cardiomyocytes) have a more limited fate. The subsequent differentiation of committed cells can occur autonomously, without environmental influence.

Vertebrates respond to injury though activation of committed progenitor cells or stem cells (e.g. bone marrow) or through proliferation of differentiated cells (liver or endothelial cells) (reviewed in 27, 28). In skeletal muscle, committed progenitor cells (adult myoblasts, satellite cells) located below the basal lamina are induced to proliferate in response to injury (29). Skeletal muscle development or repair occurs along an orderly pathway, with commitment of stem cells to myogenic lineage (myoblasts), proliferation of myoblasts, and fusion of myoblasts to form myotubes. In the mammalian heart, a population of self-renewing cells (stem cells) is not present, and there is compelling evidence that the proliferative capacity of adult cardiomyocytes is limited (15, 16, 30), although dissenting views have been presented (31). Following injury or infarction, there is no evidence of DNA synthesis (15). In contrast, regeneration of heart tissue does occur in the amphibian axolotl (see section on urodele amphibians below) (32, 33).

Skeletal Myogenesis

Despite the obvious similarity of cardiac and skeletal muscle, both being striated muscle, there are fundamental differences between the two types of tissues, including morphology, mechanism of excitation-contraction coupling, embryological origin, and response to injury. Skeletal myogenesis involves activation of muscle-specific gene expression and withdrawal from the cell cycle. Although proliferation and differentiation are mutually exclusive in skeletal myocytes, differentiated cardiomyocytes can proliferate up to birth (30).

The idea that a master regulator controls skeletal muscle myogenesis has its origin in the work of Holzer and coworkers (34–36). They observed that the nucleoside analogue bromodeoxyuridine (BrdU) reversibly inhibited myogenesis in vitro. The muscle differentiation gene *myoD* was identified by 5-azacytidine–induced hypomethylation experiments as the target that bound BrdU (37, 38) and has led to the identification of the family of myogenic determination factor(s). Forced expression of members of this family has led to the activation of myogenesis in fibroblasts, chondrocytes, and mesenchymal stem cells (e.g. C3H10T1/2). This effect was able to cross embryonic borders: The ectopic expression of myogenic determination factor(s) in cells of ectodermal [retinal pigment epithelial cells, keratinocytes (39)] or endodermal lineage [liver cells (40)] led to differentiation into skeletal muscle. Similarly, conversion of nonmyogenic cells to a myogenic phenotype occurred following the expression of the transcription factor MEF2A, or of the 3′ untranslated region of muscle tropomysin (41, 42). Additionally, coculture of fibroblasts with the myogenic cells leads to conversion of fibroblasts into differentiated cells (43). The identification of factors that direct cells to a skeletal muscle phenotype has demonstrated a high degree of plasticity in differentiated cells that had been previously unappreciated and leads to the possibility that a similar strategy might be adopted to convert nonmyocyte cells into cardiomyocytes. However, BrdU does not inhibit cardiac differentiation, and not suprisingly, attempts to identify a myoD homologue in heart have not been successful (44).

Formation of the Vertebrate Heart

The components of the circulatory system, heart, blood vessels, and blood cells are all of mesodermal origin. The formation of the heart consists of two stages: (*a*) specification and differentiation of cardiomyocytes, and (*b*) formation of a mature, four-chambered heart (morphogenesis). Readers should consult these excellent reviews for further details (45–48).

Cardiogenesis involves complex interactions with growth factors, intrinsic and extrinsic signaling molecules, and the cellular matrix. The primitive heart tube develops from two clusters of mesodermal cells (anterior lateral plate mesoderm) that are organized in a bilaterally symmetric fashion as precardiac mesoderm in the gastrula stage (49). The endothelium of the heart is derived from a distinct population of cells, at the edge of the two cardiac fields (50). These precardiac fields are brought together in the midline after gastrulation to form a two-layered heart tube with endocardial and myocardial layers.

Mesodermal populations that give rise to the primitive heart are influenced by inductive factors secreted by anterior endoderm. In *Drosophila*, mutations in a transforming growth factor (TGF)-β/bone morphogenic protein (BMP)-like molecule (decaplentaplegic) or the fibroblast growth factor (FGF) receptor (heartless) are associated with an absence of the dorsal vessel, the heart homologue (51, 52). Similarly, mutations in *tinman*, a homeobox gene, also lead to absence of the dorsal vessel (53). The anterior mesoderm in chicken gastrula-stage embryos undergoes cardiac differentiation following exposure to the TGF-β family members BMP-2 and BMP-4 (54), and posterior mesoderm (which is not normally cardiogenic) can be converted to cardiogenic material by the combination of BMP2 and FGF4 (55). Although the precise signals and receptors have not been identified in most of these systems, these studies stress the role of instructive stimuli derived from the endoderm in the specification of cells that form the heart or define the dorsal-ventral coordinates of the cells that give rise to the heart.

The zinc-finger transcription factors GATA-4 and Nkx2.5, a vertebrate homologue of *tinman*, are both expressed in early cardiac progenitor cells (56, 57) and can induce the expression of cardiac genes. Neither of these transcription factors functions like the basic helix-loop-helix myogenic regulator, MyoD, to induce cardiogenesis. Ectopic expression of Nkx2.5 in murine embryonic mesenchymal cells (C3H10T1/2) does not lead to cardiac specification and cardiogenesis (58). Forced expression of Nkx2.5 in *Xenopus* and zebrafish embryos produces an increase in cell number in the developing heart and heart size (59), and the activation of myosin heavy chain expression in ectopic cells has also been observed in zebrafish (60). Similarly, overexpression of the homeobox gene *ladybird* causes the hyperplasia of dorsal vessel precursors in *Drosophila* (61). Targeted disruption of Nkx-2.5 in mice and mutations in humans suggest partial redundancy within the Nk gene family (62, 63), further indicating that other members of the family may be identical to *Drosophila tinman* (64–66), responsible for the initial commitment to the cardiac lineage. Despite expression of GATA-4 in early cardiogenic regions, mice that contain a homozygous inactivation of this gene contain differentiated cardiomyocytes (67, 68). Similar genetic strategies in mice have led to the identification of an array of genes, some of which show unexpected involvement in the thickening of the vertebrate heart: neuregulin, N-myc, gp130, and transcription factor enhancer 1 (69–73).

These data suggest the existence of a vast array of regulatory proteins that have the potential to convert noncardiac cells into embryonic cardiac cells. The process will likely involve genetic information that is intrinsic to the mesodermal lineage and inductive signals from endoderm. However, the lack of a permissive cell type for use in monitoring the conversion to the cardiac phenotype (e.g C3H10T1/2) and an apparent lack of dominance of the cardiac phenotype in heterokaryons (74) have made it difficult to adapt the approach used by Davis et al (37). to screen these candidates for the cardiac master gene. Furthermore, the proteins that have been implicated by their expression in early cardiogenic regions may assign mesenchymal cells to a cardiogenic lineage and may function relatively late in cardiogenesis. Alternatively, there may be not unique factors but a combination of factors, or a stochastic pattern of expression that occurs uniquely in early cardiac development.

APPROACHES TO AUGMENTING CELL NUMBER IN THE HEART

Given the lack of regenerative capacity in the mammalian heart, strategies have been proposed to augment cardiac cell numbers using autologous, allogeneic, xenogeneic, immortalized, or transdifferentiated cells. There is an important unanswered question with each strategy: How will the transplanted cells respond to physiological and pathophysiological stimuli?

Transdifferentiation

Transdifferentiation is a fascinating biological phenomenon with potential applications in cardiac tissue engineering [see review by Brockes (75)]. The process of transdifferentiation involves the conversion of a committed, differentiated, or specialized cell to another differentiated cell type with a distinctly different phenotype. The pre- and postdifferentiated state must be clearly identifiable and distinct, and there must be a relationship between precursor cells and their progeny. It has been suggested that a single switch in the commitment program is responsible for these changes in phenotype (75).

TRANSDIFFERENTIATION IN URODELE MUSCLE Urodele amphibians (including newt and axolotl) are the only adult vertebrates capable of regenerating limbs. The animal heals the wound, cells beneath the epidermis dedifferentiate, and regeneration occurs by local formation of a growth zone (blastema) that proliferates to form a new limb (75, 76). Newt myotubes lack reserve cells, and the regeneration involves reversal of the differentiated state instead of recruitment of satellite cells. It has been suggested that the environment of the growth zone leads to destabilization of the differentiated state (75). Myotubes implanted beneath the site of transection are able to revert from multinucleate structures to give rise to mononucleate progeny. When newt myotubes are shifted to high serum, they reenter the cell cycle, whereas in mammals (77), serum-induced cell cycle reentry occurs only in the retinoblastoma protein null mice (78). Although newt myotubes are not lacking in retinoblastoma protein, exposure to serum may lead to inactivation of the protein (77). In addition, innervation is important for limb regeneration because the denervated limb cannot initiate the process of regeneration (79). Cardiac regeneration occurs in newts, and it is possible that this ability was lost in higher vertebrates because of selective pressures (75). It would be an enormous advance if such a transformation could be engineered in mammals (32, 33, 80).

TRANSDIFFERENTIATION IN MAMMALIAN MUSCLE There are numerous examples of transdifferentiation into and from muscle cells. The electric organs of fish transdifferentiate from muscle (81), and smooth muscle in the external musculature of the mouse esophagus transdifferentate to striated muscle (82). Expression of the adipogenic transcription factors PPARγ and C/EBPα in murine G8 myoblasts blocks muscle differentiation and promotes adipocyte differentiation (83). It is interesting to speculate that fat cells observed within the heart or skeletal muscle in obesity, mitochondrial myopathies, fatty right ventricle, and right ventricular dysplasia (84) may result from transdifferentiation.

POSSIBLE TARGETS FOR TRANSDIFFERENTIATION Smooth muscle cells, endothelial cells, mesenchymal stem cells (see section on mesenchymal stem cells), and fibroblasts have a differing developmental origin and represent cell types that might be transdifferentiated into cells capable of performing work. By analogy to the studies of Choi et al (39) and Weintraub et al (40, 85), forced expression of MyoD was utilized to attempt to convert cardiac fibroblasts into skeletal myotubes in situ (86). Although skeletal myogenesis was initiated, myofibrillogenesis did not occur (86). Alternative cell types have not been tested to date, although it is informative that the skeletal muscle differentiation program is a fundamentally incompatible aspect of the cardiac phenotype because forced expression of myoD or myogenic regulatory factor (myf5) in transgenic animals results in cardiomyopathy or death (87, 88).

Proliferation of Cardiomyoctyes In Situ

Reversal of the terminal differentiation of uninjured cardiomyocytes represents an additional strategy for manipulating the cardiac repair process (18). The general feasibility of this approach was suggested by the observation that mice expressing the oncoprotein simian virus 40 T antigen (SV40-Tag) develop unilateral right atrial tumors (rhabdomyosarcomas) consisting of highly differentiated atrial cells (89, 90). Oncoproteins immortalize by an interaction with cell cycle proteins; therefore, these studies suggested that cardiomyocyte growth might be reactivated in adult cells through the manipulating the cell cycle (91, 92) or by alternative means to enhance the replicative potential of cardiomyocytes (93). This novel approach has begun to be tested. Expression of the E1A oncoprotein or the transcription factor E2F-1 in neonatal cardiomyocytes induced DNA synthesis and triggered apoptosis (91, 94). The cardiac restricted expression of cyclin D produced multinucleated cardiomyocytes in trangenic mice (92). We expect this approach to be actively developed in the next few years, with a caveat that this approach will require a tightly regulated system of gene expression because of concerns regarding neoplastic transitions in these altered cells.

Introducing New Cells into the Cardiac Environment

The introduction of new cells into myocardium is the best studied of the strategies for myocardial repair and is the focus for the remainder of the review. This strategy assumes that grafted cells demonstrate a normal response to physiological stimuli. Fundamental questions common to all cell sources are identification and survival of grafted cells, differentiation of implanted cells, host-cell interactions, and mechanical and electrical coupling of implanted cells. Although use of fetal cells in studies has proven important, it remains ethically controversial. Important issues that remain unanswered include the ideal source for cells (allogeneic or autologous) and the role of genetic enhancements of the grafted cells or recipient bed as a means of enhancing the survival of grafted cells or of engineering a more favorable response to hypertrophy or ischemia.

CARDIOMYOCYTE GRAFTING The possibility of transplanting cardiac muscle cells grown in culture was first explored by Steinhelper et al (95) and Delcarpio et al (96). Atrial tumors were isolated from transgenic mouse tumors produced by atrial expression of SV40 large T antigen. The tumors were propagated as subcutaneous tumors in syngeneic animals to generate a cell line that has the characteristics of differentiated atrial cells, called AT-1 cells (95, 96). Grafts of these cells into the ventricle demonstrated retained mitotic activity and long-term survival AT-1 cells, without the formation of gap junctions with native myocardium (8). A cell line derived from AT-1 cells, called HL-1 (97), has been introduced into normal and infarcted pig myocardium. These cells formed stable grafts when grafted within the normal porcine myocardium, with formation of adherens junctions and gap junctions, but they failed to survive in a myocardial infarction model (98).

It was also demonstrated that embryonic cardiomyocytes could be grafted into murine and canine hearts (6, 7). Intercalated disk formation, gap junctions, and connexin-43 staining were observed at interfaces between grafted cells and host myocardium, confirming stable incorporation of grafted cells into the myocardium. Similar close associations with intercalated disk formation were observed when human fetal cardiomyocytes were grafted into normal porcine myocardium (99), or when murine fetal cardiomyocytes were labeled with an adenoviral vector prior to transplantation (100).

When the grafting studies were extended to include models of myocardial injury, fetal human and rat cardiomyocytes formed stable grafts within the myocardial scar up to 65 days after transplantation for myocardial infarction (101). These studies demonstrated that the cardiac environment was hospitable for grafts across species and demonstrated an angiogenic response to the grafting process that may be related to autocrine substances released from grafted cells (98; see also 102). In coronary occlusion/reperfusion, grafting of fetal cardiomyocytes was associated with improved left ventricular function as assessed by echocardiography (103). Similarly, grafts of fetal rat cardiomyocytes, administered 4 weeks after cryoinjury of the left ventricle, were associated with improved function, when assessed in the excised heart, and with limited myocardial scar expansion (102, 104). Therefore, in the absence of mechanical or electrical coupling (as the grafted cells were encased in scar), the presence of cells exerted favorable effects on ventricular function and geometry. In contrast, Connold et al (105) identified gap junctions between grafted cells and damaged myocardium. Nevertheless, the contractile effects of cardiomyocytes, passive mechanical properties of the graft, or effects on angiogenesis may have contributed to the beneficial effect of cardiomyocyte transplants in myocardial infarction. An ethical objection to the use of fetal tissues may be addressed by the development of human embryonic stem cells and the genetic selection of cardiomyocytes from these stem cells (see 9).

GRAFTING OF SKELETAL MYOBLASTS The use of skeletal muscle as a passive graft to rebuild the heart dates from Leriche & Fontaine (106), who used a passive graft of skeletal muscle to repair a cardiac defect. The modern experimental surgical procedure, dynamic cardiomyoplasty, provided evidence that autologous grafts of skeletal muscle grafts could be adapted to perform cardiac work and enhance cardiac function. In this experimental surgery, vascularized grafts of left latissimus dorsi muscle were wrapped around the epicardial surface of the heart in the orthotopic position and rhythmically stimulated with a pacemaker to condition the muscle (24). This ability of skeletal muscle to transform into indefatigable muscle was based on the biochemical and physiological plasticity of skeletal muscle (reviewed in 107). Chronic electrical stimulation of fast-twitch skeletal muscle induces the expression of slow-twitch isoforms of contractile and sarcoplasmic reticulum proteins, including myosin heavy chain, calcium ATPase (SERCA2a), and the slow-twitch/cardiac protein phospholamban (108–111). These proteins contribute to the slower contraction and relaxation rates of slow-twitch skeletal and cardiac muscle fibers. The plasticity of skeletal muscle in response to electrical depolarization, and the clinical experience with dynamic cardiomyoplasty, suggested that individual myoblasts might be converted to muscle fibers that are capable of performing cardiac work.

The initial experiments determined the fate of myogenic cells grafted into the hearts of syngeneic animals (3–5) or autologous satellite cells grafted into heart (1, 2, 112, 113). Myogenic cell lines were used because they had been extensively characterized, and they proliferate in culture as pure populations. Myogenic cells derived from rodents, such as L6 and BCH1, have been produced by treatment with chemical mutagens and form tumors in vivo. The C2C12 mouse myogenic cell line, however, was generated by spontaneous immortalization of rodent muscle (114). Murine C2C12 myoblasts enter the resting phase of the cell cycle in response to lowered levels of serum and remain mitotically quiescent, thus recapitulating myogenic differentiation. Potential problems associated with the use of these cells include the potential for tumor formation (115) and genetic drift of the cell line.

Grafts of autologous cells minimize the risks of neoplasia and immune rejection associated with allogeneic or xenogeneic cells. However, immunomodulation to allow the survival of allogeneic or xenogeneic cells can be achieved using conventional immunosupressive agents (102) or strategies to induce donor-specific tolerance (116). Protocols for the growth and maintenance of autologous skeletal myoblasts isolated from adult muscle were established (117). These primary cultures can be expanded in large numbers up to 10^{17} cells per clone. However, they can contain 50% nonmyogenic cells (118) and generally require adenoviral vectors to efficiently label (113, 119). In contrast, myogenic cell lines can be easily modified with plasmid DNA to contain a genetic marker or transgene (115, 120).

Transmural and arterial delivery of myoblasts Successful delivery and long-term survival of skeletal myoblast grafts in the myocardium have been achieved by intramural implantation (1–4) and arterial delivery (5, 113, 118). Both approaches might be adapted for use for myoblast transfer in patients. Implanting myoblasts into the wall of the heart is relatively simple: Cells are suspended in phosphate-buffered saline or medium and then directly injected into the ventricular wall using a small-gauge needle. Although scar formation is observed at the injection site in mice, in larger animals the needle path is often difficult to identify.

Arterial delivery was achieved with a transventricular injection in small rodents (5) or by selective coronary injection in larger rodents (113). Arterial delivery of skeletal myoblasts has several advantages over direct infiltration into the myocardium, notably an approach that parallels endovascular methods in clinical practice. It is likely that adult myoblasts (satellite cells) do not normally migrate into the bloodstream (121). However, arterial delivery of L6 skeletal myoblasts to rat skeletal muscle had been demonstrated, confirming the capacity of immortalized myoblasts to cross the endothelium into the muscle interstitium (122). Additionally, myogenic progenitor cells may be mobilized from bone marrow and traverse the circulation to reach injured muscle (see discussion of mesenchymal stem cells below) (12), and following the vascular delivery of endothelial cells and mesenchymal stem cells, engraftment of vascularized organs occurs (123, 124).

The fate of skeletal myoblasts following their introduction into the arterial circulation of the heart was predicted to be analogous to intraventricularly injected tumor cells. Murine melanoma cells arrest in the coronary capillaries and undergo lysis within 5 min (125, 126). In studies performed by Robinson et al (5), within seconds of injection into the ventricular cavity, genetically labeled C2C12 cells were distributed throughout the left and right coronaries, entrapped in the lumina of small capillaries. One week after injection, the cells were no longer found in the capillaries but appeared to be integrated into the myocardial interstitium; 72% of the animals injected continued to show labeled cells for as long as 6 months (5). No histological evidence of myocardial thrombosis or infarction was observed, and electrocardiograms of sham-injected and myoblast-injected animals appeared similar.

Differentiation of implanted cells Skeletal muscle develops along an orderly pathway, with commitment of stem cells to the myogenic lineage (myoblasts), proliferation of myoblasts, and fusion to form myotubes. Following introduction in the heart, primary myoblasts (113, 118) and myogenic cell lines (3, 5) parallel the normal developmental process for myoblasts, with cell cycle exit and myogenic differentiation (as assessed by proliferating cell nuclear antigen (PCNA) staining) (5), the expression of fast-twitch skeletal muscle isoforms of myosin heavy chain (3, 118), SERCA1 (5), and formation of myofibrils (3, 5, 118). SERCA1 expression was present for at least 6 months after implantation. These findings suggested that the cardiac environment was permissive for myogenic differentiation. Myogenic differentiation occurred when cross-species transplants were performed with immunodeficient recipients (SW Robinson, PD Kessler, unpublished data).

Alteration in the phenotype of implanted cells to a slow-twitch phenotype Phospholamban is expressed in cardiac cells and slow-twitch skeletal muscle. The induction of phospholamban expression during electrical stimulation of skeletal muscle has been reported (110, 111). Robinson et al (5) identified myoblast-derived cells that coexpressed phospholamban and the fast-twitch marker, SERCA1. Murry et al (118) also identified primary rat myotube cells that expressed a slow-twitch isoform of myosin heavy chain. The mechanism for the induction of slow-twitch gene expression in these grafted cells is unknown. In view of the induction of the slow-twitch phenotype in skeletal muscle grafts encased in scar, an aspect of the cardiac milieu altered the developmental program of the implanted cells, switching them to a slow-twitch phenotype rather than to a cardiac phenotype.

Electromechanical coupling of implanted cells Cardiac cells are electrically coupled to adjacent cells via specialized gap junctions, composed of hexamers of the protein connexin-43, that allow the exchange of ions and small molecules between adjacent cells (127, 128). Gap junctions are found in virtually every cell type in mammals; adult skeletal muscle fibers are a notable exception. These junctions have been identified in developing avian and rodent muscle fibers and primary cultures of these cells (129–131), and connexin-43 has been identified in cultured L6 myoblasts prior to fusion (132). In addition, connexin-40 is expressed in neonatal fibers (133).

When skeletal myoblasts were introduced into normal murine heart or cryoinjured rat heart, analysis of the graft-host myocardium junction failed to demonstrate evidence for mechanical or electrical coupling between skeletal and cardiac cells (3, 118). In unpublished studies, neither connexin-43 staining nor structures that resemble intercalated disks between host myocardium and intramural grafts of genetically labeled C2C12 myoblasts were observed (SW Robinson, PD Kessler unpublished information). Interestingly, Murry et al (118) described structures resembling adherens junctions and tight junctions within the grafts. The observed junctions may represent couplings between two adjacent myoblast-derived structures, or between myoblast-derived structures and smooth muscle (10), fibroblasts (134), or perhaps putative intracardiac mesenchymal stem cells (see below) (135, 136). That junction formation was not consistently observed among myoblast-derived cells (3, 5) may be due to differences in species, in animal model, or between primary and immortalized cells. The electrical couplings observed by Murray et al (118) may be similar to the low-resistant junctions described during the fusion of myoblasts in vitro (130, 131).

Putative electrical coupling when C2C12 myoblasts are delivered via the arterial circulation That coupling between intramurally delivered skeletal myoblasts and host myocardium has not been observed when myoblasts are infiltrated into the ventricular wall may be due to the formation of a scar tissue that effectively isolates grafted cells from host cells. Dense scar is described in cryoinjury and may isolate implanted cells from surrounding myocardium

(1, 2, 118, 137). The intramural injection of myoblasts into uninjured rodent heart is accompanied by a transient increase in cardiac lactate dehydrogenase (LDH) isoenzymes, consistent with myocardial injury (3).

When myoblasts were delivered via the arterial circulation, connexin-43 was immunolocalized to some sites of donor and host cell contact (5). Fine-structure analysis demonstrated electron-dense thickenings at cell-cell interfaces, consistent with spot desmosomal junctions. Surpringly, this observation is not novel. Terasaki et al (10) identified desmosomes and fascia adherens junctions between cardiomyocytes and subendocardial smooth muscle cells in situ. We observed structures in several independent cell pairs that resembled intercalated disks, and observed a structure at the interface of the two different cell types, that appeared to be a gap junction (5). Taken together, these data suggest that components of an electrical coupling system might be present in some engrafted cells that survive 5–6 months. Confirmation of electrical coupling will require demonstration of the transfer of small tracer molecules between myoblast-derived cells and cardiomyocytes.

Functional effects of myoblast grafting More relevant to the problem of myocardial repair has been the experience with grafting primary cells into injured myocardium. Primary myoblasts have been grafted into the cryoinjured myocardium of dogs, rabbits, and rats (1, 2, 118, 137). This injury approximates a myocardial infarction, without subsequent aneurysm formation. Collectively, these studies clearly demonstrated the long-term survival and differentiation of implanted cells. Importantly, functional improvement in left ventricular function after myocardial injury was observed (118, 137).

In contrast to experience with myoblast grafting into skeletal muscle (138), there have been few estimates of the efficiency of myoblast grafting into heart. In fact, grafted cells frequently failed to survive in rabbit cryoinjury (137). Arterial injection of myoblasts was relatively inefficient (5). After an injection of 10^6 cells, about 50,000 would be expected to partition to the coronary circulation, which receives about 5% of the cardiac output in mice (126). In fact, in our hands, only about 700 LacZ-positive cells were present in the heart 1 week after injection (5). In contrast to these results, when Taylor and coworkers (113) performed selective coronary injections of myoblasts in rabbits, they were able to achieve high-efficiency delivery to the myocardium via the coronary circulation. The mechanism for the translocation of myoblasts is unknown, and it may be favorably affected by transient ischemia related to capillary plugging.

Unanswered questions There are many unanswered questions about this approach. Although some workers have suggested that an implanted cell undergoes transdifferentiation into a cell that has a cardiac phenotype (1), the existing evidence supports conversion of implanted muscle to a slow-twitch phenotype

(5, 118). It may be advisable to manipulate implanted cells so they remain mononuclear to enhance the number of surviving cells (34), or perhaps a delay of myogenic differentiation may elicit a cardiac phenotype. It is unlikely that heterokaryons form between cardiac and skeletal muscle, and in fact they may not be advantageous (74). Although specialization of the multiple nuclei of the myotube is well understood (139, 140), it is unclear if similar specialization will develop for myotubes that differentiate within the cardiac environment.

MESENCHYMAL STEM CELLS (MARROW STROMAL CELLS) The bone marrow contains, in addition to blood-forming progenitors, cells that have the properties of stem cells (reviewed in 141, 142). These cells are referred to as marrow stromal cells or mesenchymal stem cells (MSCs). It has been hypothesized that MSCs derived from the marrow of post-natal animals can serve as a continuing source of progenitor cells that give rise to mesodermal tissue, such as cartilage, bone, muscle, fat, and tendon (141–143). These adherent cells have been shown to be multipotential, and under appropriate culture conditions they differentiate into osteoblasts, adipocytes, chondroblasts, and skeletal muscle. MSCs are similar to the murine mesenchymal stem cell line, C3H10T1/2. Following treatment with 5-azacytidine, C3H10T1/2 and MSCs are capable of differentiating into multiple lineages, including muscle, cartilage, and fat cells (144–146). C3H10T1/2 cells also show osteogenic, adipogenic, and chondrogenic differentiation upon exposure to BMP-2 and BMP-4 (147).

In contrast to the hematopoetic and endothelial stem cells, MSCs are derived from somatic mesoderm. There is no evidence for a common stem cell that gives rise to hematopoetic and stromal progenitors (148). In vivo, MSCs can form cartilage or bone after implantation in ceramic cubes (141), or they can become incorporated into normal or dystrophic skeletal muscle fibers (12, 149). More homogenous populations of these cells have been prepared recently, and they have been explored as a vehicle for cell-based gene therapy and cellular repair (124, 149–151). Marrow-derived cell populations have an advantage as an autologous cell source, as they are easy to isolate and may be unaffected by systemic disease.

After systemic injection, MSCs can repopulate a number of organs (150). Following a systemic injection, MSCs were detected in lung, cartilage, and bone, but not heart (150). More recently, it has been suggested that bone marrow stromal cells or another population of cells present in the marrow may participate in skeletal muscle regeneration (12, 149). In murine muscle regeneration, bone marrow–derived cells migrated to the site of muscle injury and were incorporated into muscle fibers (12). This supplemental repair program may be important in states that are characterized by impaired satellite cell function, such as aging or myopathy (see above).

Might MSC be present in extramedullary sites? There is evidence that MSCs or MSC-like cells may be present in heart. The cardiomyocyte cell line, H9C2, isolated from cardiac fibroblasts demonstrates aspects of the cardiac and skeletal phenotype (152). Recently, cells were isolated from neonatal rats that had the potential to differentiate into several mesodermal phenotypes, including binucleate cardiomyocytes, and that behave like MSCs (135). Also isolated were MSC-like cells from the skeletal muscle of neonatal rats (153) and embryonic chicken (136), and similar cells have been isolated from the atria and ventricles of chick heart (154). Moreover, a recent abstract reported that 5-azacytidine induced conversion of murine bone marrow stromal cells into cardiomyocyte-like cells (155). Clones were derived that formed a syncythium in vitro, which beat synchronously, and expressed cardiac markers, including Nkx2.5 and GATA-4. Further confirmation of these findings is eagerly awaited, but collectively these data and those of Warejcka et al (135) suggest an interesting possibility: An MSC or another stem cell, resident in bone marrow or heart, might be converted into a cardiomyocyte-like cell when placed in the proper environmental context. This possibility has been stimulated by the notion that progenitor cells for nonhematopoetic tissues (endothelial or myogenic precursor cells) are present in bone marrow and participated in repair processes in the adult vertebrate (12, 156). Most interestingly, studies by Eisenberg et al (157–159) suggest that a pluripotent cell exists during early development that has the capacity to differentiate into endothelium, hematopoetic cells, or cardiomyocytes. We do not know if this cell population overlaps with the population of MSCs, although embryological considerations suggest they may not. We have begun to evaluate bone marrow–derived cells as a source for cells that might be adapted for cardiac repair. Toward these ends we have demonstrated the survival of MSCs when grafted into the heart (11; C Toma, P Gruber, PD Kessler, BJ Byrne, M Pittenger, unpublished information), and we anticipate this may be a fruitful area of research in the future.

CLINICAL IMPLICATIONS

Implanted Cells as a Platform for Protein Delivery

The utility of genetically modified C2C12 cells as a platform to deliver recombinant TGF-β1 has been demonstrated (4). Myoblasts are able to process a variety of recombinant proteins with proper posttranslational modification of secretory proteins (160). Recombinant myoblast transfer to the heart might be useful for local expression of neurotrophic factors and angiogenic factors and may avoid the potentially harmful effects of systemic delivery of these proteins (160). Transcriptional regulation remains one of the greatest challenges when such a strategy is used. A potential advantage of placing extra cells in the implantation site is that fine control of the amount of gene expression may be achieved by selective elimination of some of the implanted cells using suicide genes engineered into the cell.

Genetic Alteration of Cells and Environment

The ability to genetically alter implanted cells or the environment may have profound effects on the results of cell transplantation. The inactivation of the interferon-γ receptor in murine myoblasts by homologous recombination suggests the possibility of engineering myoblasts with a favorable profile for myocardial repair or gene transfer (161). Insights into the mechanism of translocation of cells across the capillary bed may allow us to engineer cells designed for enhanced cell transfer.

Methods of gene transfer that have been utilized to genetically modify myoblasts include plasmid DNA, retrovirus, adenovirus, and adeno-associated virus vectors (5, 118, 162, 163). Cells engineered to overexpress metaloproteinases might allow for enhanced myoblast egress from the circulation, or reduce fibroblast and matrix deposition, which may encase the grafted cells. Alternatively, immunomodulatory molecules, such as the CD 95 (Fas) ligand expressed on allogeneic cells, may allow for the long-term engraftment of genetically dissimilar cells (164).

Methods to Deliver Cells in the Clinical Setting

In order to enhance cellular graft survival and improve the region of distribution in the myocardium, several technical challenges will have to be met. Given the ability to isolate sufficient quantities of syngeneic donor cells, the first obstacle to successful tissue repair with myogenic cells will be the method of delivery of the cells. Placement of the cells in the myocardium may be accomplished by a direct epicardial injection into pre-identified zones of ischemic risk or cardiomyocyte loss. Presumably, such a procedure would be done at the time of another cardiac intervention, such as revascularization surgery or implantation of a ventricular assist device. An alternative approach to epicardial delivery is via thoracoscopy. Over the past few years, minimally invasive surgery has transformed the approach to a number of surgical procedures. Surgical expertise and interest in minimally invasive surgery has increased with the development of new protocols and techniques to perform a variety of such procedures, including coronary artery bypass surgery and valve-replacement surgery (165). These new methods allow the surgeon to work on the heart through a small incision between the ribs. The further development of endoscopic techniques will allow for the introduction of cells into the heart without a median sternotomy. Alternatively, endovascular techniques, using modification of the transmyocardial revascularization technique, might be utilized to deliver cells to the heart. Steerable catheters may be utilized to enter the endocardium to place endocardial plugs ("myocardial sodding"). If placed closely together, and allowing for a small degree of cellular proliferation, these plugs might result in a mechanical benefit for the heart tissue. Finally, direct arterial delivery of cells (5, 113) via the coronary circulation might be attempted. Once the cells are implanted into the interstitial space, strategies to enhance transdifferentiation of implanted cells may be necessary, whereas this approach will be unnecessary if cardiomyocyte-like cells are implanted. One of the strongest signals for transdifferentiation may be the mechanical or electrical environment of the working heart.

Phase I clinical trials of cell implantation in the damaged heart could easily be achieved in patients undergoing placement of left ventricular assist devices or ventricular reduction surgeries (22, 23). Patients undergoing left ventricular assist device placement have intractable heart failure and are candidates for cardiac transplantation. Therefore, the implanted cells can be reexamined when the transplantation surgery is performed and the explanted heart is available for detailed histologic examination. This ambitious program for clinical development will depend on further demonstration of the efficacy and safety of grafting in preclinical models.

CONCLUSION

This review chronicles the current state of the art for the grafting of mesodermally derived cells. Collectively, the findings suggest that myoblasts can form stable grafts in the heart and that signals originating in this environment may alter the phenotype of skeletal muscle–derived cells. Further studies are needed to characterize the interactions between implanted cells and native myocardium, and to develop methods to enhance this interaction. The success of this approach will require the integration of a number of disciplines: molecualr biology, bioengineering, matrix and tissue engineering, gene therapy, medicine, and surgery. Promising areas for research in the next millenium include identification of factors that can maximize grafted cell survival and strategies that might convert cells into cardiomyocytes.

ACKNOWLEDGMENTS

This review is dedicated to Doug Fambrough on the 25th anniversary of his description of the electrical coupling of differentiating muscle cells (130). We thank Dr. Doris Taylor for sharing her work in press.

Literature Cited

1. Marelli D, Desrosiers C, El-Alfy M, Kao RL, Chiu RCJ. 1992. Cell transplantation for myocardial repair: an experimental approach. *Cell Transplant.* 1:383–90
2. Chiu RCJ, Zibaitis A, Kao RL. 1995. Cellular cardiomyoplasty: myocardial regeneration with satellite cell implantation. *Ann. Thorac. Surg.* 60:12–18
3. Koh GY, Klug MG, Soonpaa MH, Field LJ. 1993. Differentiation and long-term survival of C2C12 myoblast grafts in heart. *J. Clin. Invest.* 92:1548–54
4. Koh GY, Kim SJ, Klug MG, Park K, Soonpaa MH. 1995. Targeted expression of transforming growth factor-beta 1 in intracardiac grafts promotes vascular endothelial cell DNA synthesis. *J. Clin. Invest.* 95:114–21
5. Robinson SW, Cho PC, Levitsky HI, Olson JL, Hruban RH, et al. 1996. Arterial delivery of genetically labeled skeletal myoblasts to the murine heart: long-term survival and phenotypic modification of implanted myoblasts. *Cell Transplant.* 5: 77–91
6. Soonpaa MH, Koh GY, Klug MG, Field LJ. 1994. Formation of nascent intercalated disks between grafted fetal cardiomyocytes and host myocardium. *Science* 264:98–101
7. Koh GY, Soonpaa MH, Klug MG, Pride HP, Cooper BJ, et al. 1995. Stable fetal cardiomyocyte grafts in the hearts of dystrophic mice and dogs. *J. Clin. Invest.* 96:2034–42
8. Koh GY, Soonpaa MH, Klug MG, Field LJ. 1993. Long-term survival of AT-1 cardiomyocyte grafts in syngeneic myocardium. *Am. J. Physiol.* 264:H1727–33
9. Klug MG, Soonpaa MH, Koh GY, Field LJ. 1996. Genetically selected cardiomyocytes from differentiating embryonic stem cells form stable intracardiac grafts. *J. Clin. Invest.* 98:216–24
10. Terasaki F, James TN, Hayashi T. 1993. Electron microscopic demonstration of intracellular junctions between subendocardial smooth muscle and myocardium in the sheep heart. *Am. Heart J.* 126:399–405
11. Robinson SW, Acker MA, Byrne BJ, Kessler PD. 1997. Implantation of skeletal myoblast-derived cells. In *Cellular Cardiomyoplasty: Myocardial Repair with Cell Implantation*, ed. RL Kao, RCJ Chiu, pp. 81–107. Austin, TX: Landes Biosci.
12. Ferrari G, Cusella-De AG, Coletta M, Paolucci E, Stornaiuolo A, et al. 1998. Muscle regeneration by bone marrow-derived myogenic progenitors. *Science* 279:1528–30
13. Angello JC, Stern HM, Hauschka SD. 1997. P19 embryonal carcinoma cells: a model system for studying neural tube induction of skeletal myogenesis. *Dev. Biol.* 192:3–98
14. Soonpaa MH, Daud AI, Koh GY, Klug MG, Kim KK, et al. 1995. Potential approaches for myocardial regeneration. *Ann. NY Acad. Sci.* 752:446–54
15. Soonpaa MH, Field LJ. 1998. Survey of studies examining mammalian cardiomyocyte DNA synthesis. *Circ. Res.* 83:15–26
16. Soonpaa MH, Field LJ. 1997. Assessment of cardiomyocyte DNA synthesis in normal and injured adult mouse hearts. *Am. J. Physiol.* 272:H220–26
17. Soonpaa MH, Field LJ. 1994. Assessment of cardiomyocyte DNA synthesis during hypertrophy in adult mice. *Am. J. Physiol.* 266:H1439–45
18. Cohn JN, Bristow MR, Chien KR, Colucci WS, Frazier OH, et al. 1997. Report of the National Heart, Lung, and Blood Institute Special Emphasis Panel on Heart Failure Research. *Circulation* 95:766–70
19. Cohn JN, Johnson G, Ziesche S, Cobb F, Francis G, et al. 1991. A comparison of enalapril with hydralazine-isosorbide dinitrate in the treatment of chronic congestive heart failure. *N. Engl. J. Med.* 325:303–10
20. Colucci WS, Packer M, Bristow MR, Gilbert EM, Cohn JN, et al. 1996. Carvedilol inhibits clinical progression in patients with mild symptoms of heart failure. US Carvedilol Heart Failure Study Group. *Circulation* 94:2800–6
21. Packer M, Bristow MR, Cohn JN, Colucci WS, Fowler MB, et al. 1996. The effect of carvedilol on morbidity and mortality in patients with chronic heart failure. *N. Engl. J. Med.* 334:1349–55
22. McCarthy PM, Smedira NO, Vargo RL, Goormastic M, Hobbs RE, et al. 1998. One hundred patients with the HeartMate left ventricular assist device: evolving concepts and technology. *J. Thorac. Cardiovasc. Surg.* 115:904–12
23. McCarthy PM, Starling RC, Wong J, Scalia GM, Buda T, et al. 1997. Early results with partial left ventriculectomy. *J. Thorac. Cardiovasc. Surg.* 114:755–63
24. Kass DA, Baughman KL, Pak PH,

Cho PW, Levin HR, et al. 1995. Reverse remodeling from cardiomyoplasty in human heart failure. External constraint versus active assist. *Circulation* 91:2314–18
25. Minanov OP, Artrip JH, Szabolcs M, Kwiatkowski PA, Galili U, et al. 1998. Triple immunosuppression reduces mononuclear cell infiltration and prolongs graft life in pig-to-newborn baboon cardiac xenotransplantation. *J. Thorac. Cardiovasc. Surg.* 115:998–1006
26. Packer M, Lee WH, Kessler PD, Gottlieb SS, Bernstein JL, et al. 1987. Role of neurohormonal mechanisms in determining survival in patiens with severe chronic heart failure. *Circulation* 75:IV80–92
27. Gage FH. 1998. Cell therapy. *Nature* 392: 18–24
28. Michalopoulos GK, DeFrances MC. 1997. Liver regeneration. *Science* 276: 60–66
29. Mauro A. 1961. Satellite cells of skeletal muscle fibers. *J. Biophys. Biochem. Cytol.* 9:493–97
30. Soonpaa MH, Kim KK, Pajak L, Franklin M, Field LJ. 1996. Cardiomyocyte DNA synthesis and binucleation during murine development. *Am. J. Physiol.* 271:H2183–89
31. Anversa P, Kajstura J. 1998. Myocyte cell death in the diseased heart. *Circ. Res.* 82:1231–33
32. Oberpriller JO, Oberpriller JC. 1974. Response of the adult newt ventricle to injury. *J. Exp. Zool.* 187:249–53
33. Soonpaa MH, Oberpriller JO, Oberpriller JC. 1994. Factors altering DNA synthesis in the cardiac myocyte of the adult newt, *Notophthalmus viridescens*. *Cell Tissue Res.* 275:377–82
34. Stockdale F, Okazaki K, Nameroff M, and Holtzer H. 1964. 5-Bromodeoxyuridine: effect on myogenesis in vitro. *Science* 146:533–35
35. Bischoff R, Holtzer H. 1970. Inhibition of myoblast fusion after one round of DNA synthesis in 5-bromodeoxyuridine. *J. Cell Biol.* 44:134–50
36. Weintraub H, Campbell GL, Holtzer H. 1972. Identification of a developmental program using bromodeoxyuridine. *J. Mol. Biol.* 70:337–50
37. Davis RL, Weintraub H, Lassar AB. 1987. Expression of a single transfected cDNA converts fibroblasts to myoblasts. *Cell* 51:987–1000
38. Tapscott SJ, Lassar AB, Davis RL, Weintraub H. 1989. 5-Bromo-2′-deoxyuridine blocks myogenesis by extinguishing expression of MyoD1. *Science* 245:532–36
39. Choi J, Costa ML, Mermelstein CS, Chagas C, Holtzer S, et al. 1990. MyoD converts primary dermal fibroblasts, chondroblasts, smooth muscle, and retinal pigmented epithelial cells into striated mononucleated myoblasts and multinucleated myotubes. *Proc. Natl. Acad. Sci. USA* 87:7988–92
40. Weintraub H, Tapscott SJ, Davis RL, Thayer MJ, Adam MA, et al. 1989. Activation of muscle-specific genes in pigment, nerve, fat, liver, and fibroblast cell lines by forced expression of MyoD. *Proc. Natl. Acad. Sci. USA* 86:5434–38
41. Kaushal S, Schneider JW, Nadal-Ginard B, Mahdavi V. 1994. Activation of the myogenic lineage by MEF2A, a factor that induces and cooperates with MyoD. *Science* 266:1236–40
42. L'Ecuyer TJ, Tompach PC, Morris E, Fulton AB. 1995. Transdifferentiation of chicken embryonic cells into muscle cells by the 3′ untranslated region of muscle tropomyosin. *Proc. Natl. Acad. Sci. USA* 92:7520–24
43. Salvatori G, Lattanzi L, Coletta M, Aguanno S, Vivarelli E, et al. 1995. Myogenic conversion of mammalian fibroblasts induced by differentiating muscle cells. *J. Cell Sci.* 108:2733–39
44. Chacko S, Joseph X. 1974. The effect of 5-bromodeoxyuridine (BrdU) on cardiac muscle differentiation. *Dev. Biol.* 40:340–54
45. Sucov H. Molecular insights into cardiac development. 1998. *Annu. Rev. Physiol.* 60:287–308
46. Olson EN. 1997. Things are developing in cardiology. *Circ. Res.* 80:604–6
47. Olson EN, Srivastava D. 1996. Molecular pathways controlling heart development. *Science* 272:671–76
48. Fishman MC, Chien KR, 1997. Fashioning the vertebrate heart: earliest embryonic decisions. *Development* 124:2099–117
49. Rawles ME. 1941. The heart-forming areas of the early chick blastoderm. *Physiol. Zool.* 16:22–44
50. Cohen-Gould L, Mikawa T. 1996. The fate diversity of mesodermal cells within the heart field during chicken early embryogenesis. *Dev. Biol.* 177:265–73
51. Gisselbrecht S, Skeath JB, Doe CQ, Michelson AM. 1996. Heartless encodes a fibroblast growth factor receptor (DFR1/DFGF-R2) involved in the directional migration of early mesodermal cells in the Drosophila embryo. *Genes Dev.* 10:3003–17
52. Shishido E, Ono N, Kojima T, Saigo K. 1997. Requirements of DFR1/Heartless,

a mesoderm-specific Drosophila FGF-receptor, for the formation of heart, visceral and somatic muscles, and ensheathing of longitudinal axon tracts in CNS. *Development* 124:2119–28

53. Azpiazu N, Frasch M. 1993. *tinman* and *bagpipe*: two homeo box genes that determine cell fates in the dorsal mesoderm of Drosophila. *Genes Dev.* 7:1325–40
54. Schultheiss TM, Burch JB, Lassar AB. 1997. A role for bone morphogenetic proteins in the induction of cardiac myogenesis. *Genes Dev.* 11:451–62
55. Lough J, Barron M, Brogley M, Sugi Y, Bolender DL, et al. 1996. Combined BMP-2 and FGF-4, but neither factor alone, induces cardiogenesis in non-precardiac embryonic mesoderm. *Dev. Biol.* 178:198–202
56. Lints TJ, Parsons LM, Hartley L, Lyons I, Harvey RP. 1993. Nkx-2.5: a novel murine homeobox gene expressed in early heart progenitor cells and their myogenic descendants. *Development* 119:969
57. Jiang Y, Evans T. 1996. The Xenopus GATA-4/5/6 genes are associated with cardiac specification and can regulate cardiac-specific transcription during embryogenesis. *Dev. Biol.* 174:258–70
58. Chen CY, Schwartz RJ. 1996. Recruitment of the tinman homolog Nkx-2.5 by serum response factor activates cardiac alpha-actin gene transcription. *Mol. Cell Biol.* 16:6372–84
59. Cleaver OB, Patterson KD, Krieg PA. 1996. Overexpression of the tinman-related genes XNkx-2.5 and XNkx-2.3 in Xenopus embryos results in myocardial hyperplasia. *Development* 122:3549–56
60. Chen JN, Fishman MC. 1996. Zebrafish tinman homolog demarcates the heart field and initiates myocardial differentiation. *Development* 122:3809–16
61. Jagla K, Frasch M, Jagla T, Dretzen G, Bellard F, Bellard M. 1997. Ladybird, a new component of the cardiogenic pathway in Drosophila required for diversification of heart precursors. *Development* 124:3471–79
62. Lyons I, Parsons LM, Hartley L, Li R, Andrews JE, et al. 1995. Myogenic and morphogenetic defects in the heart tubes of murine embryos lacking the homeo box gene Nkx2-5. *Genes Dev.* 9:1654–66
63. Schott JJ, Benson DW, Basson CT, Pease W, Silberbach GM, et al. 1998. Congenital heart disease caused by mutations in the transcription factor NKX2-5. *Science* 281:108–11
64. Lee KH, Xu Q, Breitbart RE. 1996. A new tinman-related gene, nkx2.7, anticipates the expression of nkx2.5 and nkx2.3 in zebrafish heart and pharyngeal endoderm. *Dev. Biol.* 180:722–31
65. Buchberger A, Pabst O, Brand T, Seidl K, Arnold HH. 1996. Chick NKx-2.3 represents a novel family member of vertebrate homologues to the Drosophila homeobox gene tinman: differential expression of cNKx-2.3 and cNKx-2.5 during heart and gut development. *Mech. Dev.* 56:151–63
66. Evans SM, Yan W, Murillo MP, Ponce J, Papalopulu N. 1995. Tinman, a Drosophila homeobox gene required for heart and visceral mesoderm specification, may be represented by a family of genes in vertebrates: XNkx-2.3, a second vertebrate homologue of tinman. *Development* 121:3889–99
67. Molkentin JD, Lin Q, Duncan SA, Olson EN. 1997. Requirement of the transcription factor GATA4 for heart tube formation and ventral morphogenesis. *Genes Dev.* 11:1061–72
68. Kuo CT, Morrisey EE, Anandappa R, Sigrist K, Lu MM, et al. 1997. GATA4 transcription factor is required for ventral morphogenesis and heart tube formation. *Genes Dev.* 11:1048–60
69. Gassmann M, Casagranda F, Orioli D, Simon H, Lai C. 1995. Aberrant neural and cardiac development in mice lacking the ErbB4 neuregulin receptor. *Nature* 378:390–94
70. Lee KF, Simon H, Chen H, Bates B, Hung MC. 1995. Requirement for neuregulin receptor erbB2 in neural and cardiac development. *Nature* 378:394–98
71. Charron J, Malynn BA, Fisher P, Stewart V, Jeannotte L, et al. 1992. Embryonic lethality in mice homozygous for a targeted disruption of the N-myc gene. *Genes Dev.* 6:2248–57
72. Yoshida K, Taga T, Saito M, Suematsu S, Kumanogoh A, et al. 1996. Targeted disruption of gp130, a common signal transducer for the interleukin 6 family of cytokines, leads to myocardial and hematological disorders. *Proc. Natl. Acad. Sci. USA* 93:407–11
73. Chen Z, Friedrich GA, Soriano P. 1994. Transcriptional enhancer factor 1 disruption by a retroviral gene trap leads to heart defects and embryonic lethality in mice. *Genes Dev.* 8:2293–301
74. Evans SM, Tai L-J, Tan VP, Newton CB, Chien KR. 1994. Heterokaryons of cardiac myocytes and fibroblasts reveal the lack of dominance of the cardiac phenotype. *Mol. Cell. Biol.* 14:4269–79
75. Brockes JP. 1997. Amphibian limb

regeneration: rebuilding a complex structure. *Science* 276:81–87
76. Brockes JP. 1994. New approaches to amphibian limb regeneration. *Trends Genet.* 10:169–73
77. Tanaka EM, Gann AA, Gates PB, Brockes JP. 1997. Newt myotubes reenter the cell cycle by phosphorylation of the retinoblastoma protein. *J. Cell Biol.* 136:155–65
78. Schneider JW, Gu W, Zhu L, Mahdavi V, Nadal-Ginard B. 1994. Reversal of terminal differentiation mediated by p107 in Rb−/− muscle cells. *Science* 264:1467–71
79. Brockes JP. 1987. The nerve dependence of amphibian limb regeneration. *J. Exp. Biol.* 132:79–91
80. Bader D, Oberpriller J. 1979. Autoradiographic and electron microscopic studies of minced cardiac muscle regeneration in the adult newt, notophthalmus viridescens. *J. Exp. Zool.* 208:177–93
81. Patterson JM, Zakon HH. 1997. Transdifferentiation of muscle to electric organ: regulation of muscle-specific proteins is independent of patterned nerve activity. *Dev. Biol.* 186:115–26
82. Patapoutian A, Wold BJ, Wagner RA. 1995. Evidence for developmentally programmed transdifferentiation in mouse esophageal muscle. *Science* 270:1818–21
83. Hu E, Tontonoz P, Spiegelman BM. 1995. Transdifferentiation of myoblasts by the adipogenic transcription factors PPAR gamma and C/EBP alpha. *Proc. Natl. Acad. Sci. USA* 92:9856–60
84. Burke AP, Farb A, Tashko G, Virmani R. 1998. Arrhythmogenic right ventricular cardiomyopathy and fatty replacement of the right ventricular myocardium: Are they different diseases? *Circulation* 97:1571–80
85. Lassar AB, Paterson BM, Weintraub H. 1986. Transfection of a DNA locus that mediates the conversion of 10T1/2 fibroblasts to myoblasts. *Cell* 47:649–56
86. Murry CE, Kay MA, Bartosek T, Hauschka SD, Schwartz SM. 1996. Muscle differentiation during repair of myocardial necrosis in rats via gene transfer with MyoD. *J. Clin. Invest.* 98:2209–17
87. Miner JH, Miller JB, Wold BJ. 1992. Skeletal muscle phenotypes initiated by ectopic MyoD in transgenic mouse heart. *Development* 114:853–60
88. Edwards JG, Lyons GE, Micales BK, Malhotra A, Factor S, et al. 1996. Cardiomyopathy in transgenic myf5 mice. *Circ. Res.* 78:379–87
89. Field LJ. 1988. Atrial natriuretic factor-SV40 T antigen transgenes produce tumors and cardiac arrhythmias in mice. *Science* 239:1029–33
90. Behringer RR, Peschon JJ, Messing A, Gartside CL, Hauschka SD, et al. 1988. Heart and bone tumors in transgenic mice. *Proc. Natl. Acad. Sci. USA* 85:2648–52
91. Kirshenbaum LA, Schneider MD. 1995. Adenovirus E1A represses cardiac gene transcription and reactivates DNA synthesis in ventricular myocytes, via alternative pocket protein- and p300-binding domains. *J. Biol. Chem.* 270:7791–94
92. Soonpaa MH, Koh GY, Pajak L, Jing S, Wang H, et al. 1997. Cyclin D1 overexpression promotes cardiomyocyte DNA synthesis and multinucleation in transgenic mice. *J. Clin. Invest.* 99:2644–54
93. Bodnar AG, Ouellette M, Frolkis M, Holt SE, Chiu CP, et al. 1998. Extension of life-span by introduction of telomerase into normal human cells. *Science* 279:349–52
94. Kirshenbaum LA, Abdellatif M, Chakraborty S, Schneider MD. 1996. Human e2f-1 reactivates cell cycle progression in ventricular myocytes and represses cardiac gene transcription. *Dev. Biol.* 179:402–11
95. Steinhelper ME, Lanson NAJ, Dresdner KP, Delcarpio JB, Wit AL, et al. 1990. Proliferation in vivo and in culture of differentiated adult atrial cardiomyocytes from transgenic mice. *Am. J. Physiol.* 259:H1826–34
96. Delcarpio JB, Lanson NAJ, Field LJ, Claycomb WC. 1991. Morphological characterization of cardiomyocytes isolated from a transplantable cardiac tumor derived from transgenic mouse atria (AT-1 cells). *Circ. Res.* 69:1591–600
97. Claycomb WC, Lanson NAJ, Stallworth BS, Egeland DB, Delcarpio JB, et al. 1998. HL-1 cells: a cardiac muscle cell line that contracts and retains phenotypic characteristics of the adult cardiomyocyte. *Proc. Natl. Acad. Sci. USA* 95:2979–84
98. Watanabe E, Smith DMJ, Delcarpio JB, Sun J, Smart FW, et al. 1998. Cardiomyocyte transplantation in a porcine myocardial infarction model. *Cell Transplant.* 7:239–46
99. Van Meter CHJ, Claycomb WC, Delcarpio JB, Smith DM, deGruiter H, et al. 1995. Myoblast transplantation in the porcine model: a potential technique for myocardial repair. *J. Thorac. Cardiovasc. Surg.* 110:1442–48

100. Gojo S, Kitamura S, Hatano O, Takakusu A, Hashimoto K, et al. 1997. Transplantation of genetically marked cardiac muscle cells. *J. Thorac. Cardiovasc. Surg.* 113:10–18
101. Leor J, Patterson M, Quinones MJ, Kedes LH, Kloner RA. 1996. Transplantation of fetal myocardial tissue into the infarcted myocardium of rat. A potential method for repair of infarcted myocardium? *Circulation* 94:II332–36
102. Li RK, Mickle DA, Weisel RD, Mohabeer MK, Zhang J, et al. 1997. Natural history of fetal rat cardiomyocytes transplanted into adult rat myocardial scar tissue. *Circulation* 96:II179–86
103. Scorsin M, Hagege AA, Marotte F, Mirochnik N, Copin H, et al. 1997. Does transplantation of cardiomyocytes improve function of infarcted myocardium? *Circulation* 96:II188–93
104. Li RK, Jia ZQ, Weisel RD, Mickle DA, Zhang J, et al. 1996. Cardiomyocyte transplantation improves heart function. *Ann. Thorac. Surg.* 62:654–60
105. Connold AL, Frischknecht R, Dimitrakos M, Vrbova G. 1997. The survival of embryonic cardiomyocytes transplanted into damaged host rat myocardium. *J. Muscle Res. Cell Motil.* 18:63–70
106. Leriche R, Fontaine R. 1933. Essai experimentale de tratment de certains infarctus du myocarde et de l'aneurisme du coer par une graffe de muscle strie. *Bull. Soc. Int. Chir.* 59:229–37
107. Jolesz F, Sreter FA. 1981. Development, innervation and activity pattern-induced changes in skeletal muscle. *Annu. Rev. Physiol.* 43:531–52
108. Acker MA, Hammond RL, Mannion JD, Salmons S, Stephenson LW. 1987. Skeletal muscle as the potential power source for a cardiovascular pump: assessment in vivo. *Science* 236:324–27
109. Briggs FN, Lee KF, Feher JJ, Wechsler AS, Ohlendieck K, et al. 1990. Ca-ATPase isozyme expression in sarcoplasmic reticulum is altered by chronic stimulation of skeletal muscle. *FEBS Lett.* 259:269–72
110. Hu P, Yin C, Zhang KM, Wright LD, Nixon TE, et al. 1995. Transcriptional regulation of the phospholamban gene and translational regulation of SERCA2 gene produces coordinate expression of these two sarcoplasmic reticulum proteins during skeletal muscle phenotypic switching. *J. Biol. Chem.* 270:11619–22
111. Leberer E, Hartner KT, Brandl CJ, Fujii J, Tada M, et al. 1989. Slow/cardiac sarcoplasmic reticulum Ca-ATPase and phospholamban are expressed in chronically stiumulated rabbit fast-twitch skeletal muscle. *Eur. J. Biochem.* 185:51–54
112. Yoon PD, Kao RL, Magovern GJ. 1995. Myocardial regeneration. Transplanting satellite cells into damaged myocardium. *Tex. Heart. Inst. J.* 22(2):119–25
113. Taylor DT, Silvesti F, Bishop SP, Annex BH, Lilly RE, et al. 1997. Delivery of primary autologous skeletal myoblasts into rabbit heart by coronary infusion: a potential approach to myocardial repair. *Proc. Am. Assoc. Physicians* 109:245–53
114. Yaffe D, Saxel O. 1977. Serial passaging and differentiation of myogenic cell lines isolated from dystrophic mouse muscle. *Nature* 270:725–27
115. Dhawan J, Pan LC, Pavlath GK, Travis MA, Lanctot AM, et al. 1991. Systemic delivery of human growth hormone by injection of genetically engineered myoblasts. *Science* 254:1509–12
116. Thomas JM, Berbanac KM, Thomas FT. 1990. The veto mechanism in transplant tolerance. *Transpl. Rev.* 5:209–29
117. Blau HM, Webster C. 1981. Isolation and characterization of human muscle cells. *Proc. Natl. Acad. Sci.USA* 78:5623–27
118. Murry CE, Wiseman RW, Schwartz SM, Hauschka SD. 1996. Skeletal myoblast transplantation for repair of myocardial necrosis. *J. Clin. Invest.* 98:2512–23
119. Jiao S, Gurevich V, Wolff JA. 1993. Long-term correction of rat model of Parkinson's disease by gene therapy. *Nature* 362:450–53
120. Barr E, Leiden JM. 1991. Systemic delivery of recombinant proteins by genetically modified myoblasts. *Science* 254: 1507–9
121. McGeachie JK, Grounds MD. 1986. Cell proliferation in denervated skeletal muscle: Does it provide a pool of potential circulating myoblasts? *Bibl. Anat.* 29:173–93
122. Neumeyer AM, DiGregorio DM, Brown RH. 1992. Arterial delivery of myoblasts to skeletal muscle. *Neurology* 42:2258–62
123. Messina LM, Podrazik RM, Whitehill TA, Ekhterae D, Brothers TE, et al. 1992. Adhesion and incorporation of lacZ-transduced endothelial cells into the intact capillary wall in the rat. *Proc. Natl. Acad. Sci. USA* 89:12018–22
124. Pereira RF, O'Hara MD, Laptev AV, Halford KW, Pollard MD, et al. 1998. Marrow stromal cells as a source of progenitor cells for nonhematopoietic tissues in transgenic mice with a phenotype of osteogenesis imperfecta. *Proc. Natl. Acad. Sci. USA* 95:1142–47

125. Weiss L, Dimitrov DS, Angelova M. 1985. The hemodynamic destruction of intravascular cancer cells in relation to myocardial metastasis. *Proc. Natl. Acad. Sci. USA* 82:5737–41
126. Weiss L. 1988. Biomechanical destruction of cancer cells in the heart. A rate regulator of hematogenous metastasis. *Invasion Metastasis* 8:228–37
127. Angst BD, Khan LU, Severs NJ, Whitely K, Rothery S, et al. Jan 1997. Associated spatial patterning of gap junctions and cell adhesion junctions during postnatal differentiation of ventricular myocardium. *Circ. Res.* 80(1):88–94
128. Beyer EC, Kister J, Paul DL, Goodenough DA, et al. 1989. Antisera directed against connexin43 pepetide react with 43kD protein localized to gap junctions in myocardium and other tissues. *J. Cell. Biol.* 108:595–605
129. Kalderon N, Epstein ML, Gilula NB. 1977. Cell-to-cell communication and myogenesis. *J. Cell. Biol.* 75:788–806
130. Rash JE, Fambrough DM. 1973. Ultrastructural and electrophysiologic correlates of cell coupling and cytoplasmic fusion during myogenesis in vitro. *Dev. Biol.* 30:166–86
131. Rash JE, Staehelin LA. 1974. Freeze-cleave demonstration of gap junctions between skeletal myogenic cells in vivo. *Dev. Biol.* 36:455–61
132. Balogh S, Naus CCG, Merrifield PA. 1993. Expression of gap junction in cultured rat L6 cells during myogenesis. *Dev. Biol.* 155:351–60
133. Dahl E, Winterhager E, Traub O, Willecke K. 1995. Expression of gap junctions genes, connexin40 and connexin43 during fetal mouse development. *Anat. Embryol.* 191:67–78
134. Chaudhari S, Delay R, Bean KG. 1989. Restoration of normal function in genetically defective myotubes by spontaneous fusion with fibroblasts. *Nature* 341:445–47
135. Warejcka DJ, Harvey R, Taylor BJ, Young HE, Lucas PA. 1996. A population of cells isolated from rat heart capable of differentiating into several mesodermal phenotypes. *J. Surg. Res.* 62:233–42
136. Young HE, Mancini ML, Wright RP, Smith JC, Black ACJ, et al. 1995. Mesenchymal stem cells reside within the connective tissues of many organs. *Dev. Dyn.* 202:137–44
137. Taylor DA, Atkins BZ, Hungspreugs P, Jones TR, Reedy MC, et al. 1998. Regenerating functional myocardium: improved performance after skeletal myoblast transplantation. *Nat. Med.* 4:929–33
138. Gussoni E, Blau HM, Kunkel LM, 1997. The fate of individual myoblasts after transplantation into muscles of DMD patients. *Nat. Med.* 3:970–77
139. Ralston E, Hall ZW. 1992. Restricted distribution of mRNA produced from a single nucleus in hybrid myotubes. *J. Cell Biol.* 119:1063–68
140. Ralston E, Hall ZW. 1989. Transfer of a protein encoded by a single nucleus to nearby nuclei in multinucleated myotubes. *Science* 244:1066–69
141. Caplan AI. 1991. Mesenchymal stem cells. *J. Orthop. Res.* 9:641–50
142. Bruder SP, Fink DJ, Caplan AI, 1994. Mesenchymal stem cells in bone development, bone repair, and skeletal regeneration therapy. *J. Cell Biochem.* 56:283–94
143. Prockop DJ. 1997. Marrow stromal cells as stem cells for nonhematopoietic tissues. *Science* 276:71–74
144. Taylor SM, Jones PA. 1979. Multiple new phenotypes induced in 10T1/2 and 3T3 cells treated with 5-azacytidine. *Cell* 17:771–79
145. Jones PA, Taylor SM. 1980. Cellular differentiation, cytidine analogs and DNA methylation. *Cell* 20:85–93
146. Wakitani S, Saito T, Caplan AI. 1995. Myogenic cells derived from rat bone marrow mesenchymal stem cells exposed to 5-azacytidine. *Muscle Nerve* 18:1417–26
147. Ahrens M, Ankenbauer T, Schroder D, Hollnagel A, Mayer H, et al. 1993. Expression of human bone morphogenetic proteins-2 or -4 in murine mesenchymal progenitor C3H10T1/2 cells induces differentiation into distinct mesenchymal cell lineages. *DNA Cell Biol.* 12:871–80
148. Waller EK, Olweus J, Lund-Johansen F, Huang S, Nguyen M, et al. 1995. The "common stem cell" hypothesis reevaluated: human fetal bone marrow contains separate populations of hematopoietic and stromal progenitors. *Blood* 85:2422–35
149. Saito T, Dennis JE, Lennon DP, Young RG, Caplan AI. 1995. Myogenic expression of mesenchymal stem cells within myotubes of mdx mice in vitro and in vivo. *Tissue Eng.* 1:327–43
150. Pereira RF, Halford KW, O'Hara MD, Leeper DB, Sokolov BP, et al. 1995. Cultured adherent cells from marrow can serve as long-lasting precursor cells for bone, cartilage, and lung in irradiated mice. *Proc. Natl. Acad. Sci. USA* 92: 4857–61

151. Azizi SA, Stokes D, Augelli BJ, DiGirolamo C, Prockop DJ. 1998. Engraftment and migration of human bone marrow stromal cells implanted in the brains of albino rats–similarities to astrocyte grafts. *Proc. Natl. Acad. Sci. USA* 95:3908–13
152. Sipido KR, Marban E. 1991. L-type calcium channels, potassium channels, and novel nonspecific cation channels in a clonal muscle cell line derived from embryonic rat ventricle. *Circ. Res.* 69:1487–99
153. Lucas PA, Warejcka DJ, Zhang LM, Newman WH, Young HE. 1996. Effect of rat mesenchymal stem cells on development of abdominal adhesions after surgery. *J. Surg. Res.* 62:229–32
154. Young HE, Ceballos EM, Smith JC, Mancini ML, Wright RP, et al. 1993. Pluripotent mesenchymal stem cells reside within avian connective tissue matrices. *In Vitro Cell Dev. Biol. Anim.* 29A:723–36
155. Makino S, Fukada K, Miyochi S, Umezawa A, Ogawa S. 1997. Establishment of a cardiomyogenic cell line from mouse bone marrow stromal cell exposed to 5-azacytidine. *Circulation Suppl.* 96:I–51 (Abstr.)
156. Asahara T, Murohara T, Sullivan A, Silver M, van der Zee R, et al. 1997. Isolation of putative progenitor endothelial cells for angiogenesis. *Science* 275:964–67
157. Eisenberg CA, Bader D. 1995. QCE-6: a clonal cell line with cardiac myogenic and endothelial cell potentials. *Dev. Biol.* 167:469–81
158. Eisenberg CA, Bader DM. 1996. Establishment of the mesodermal cell line QCE-6. A model system for cardiac cell differentiation. *Circ. Res.* 78:205–16
159. Eisenberg CA, Markwald RR. 1997. Mixed cultures of avian blastoderm cells and the quail mesoderm cell line QCE-6 provide evidence for the pluripotentiality of early mesoderm. *Dev. Biol.* 191(2):167–81
160. Blau HM, Springer MI. 1995. Muscle-mediated gene therapy. *N. Engl. J. Med.* 333:1554–56
161. Arbones ML, Austin HA, Capon DJ, Greenburg G. 1994. Gene targeting in normal somatic cells: inactivation of the interferon-gamma receptor in myoblasts. *Nat. Genet.* 6:90–97
162. Aoki M, Morishita R, Higaki J, Moriguchi A, Hayashi S, et al. 1997. Survival of grafts of genetically modified cardiac myocytes transfected with FITC-labeled oligodeoxynucleotides and the beta-galactosidase gene in the noninfarcted area, but not the myocardial infarcted area. *Gene Ther.* 4:120–27
163. Kessler PD, Podsakoff GM, Chen X, McQuiston SA, Colosi PC, et al. 1996. Gene delivery to skeletal muscle results in sustained expression and systemic delivery of a therapeutic protein. *Proc. Natl. Acad. Sci. USA* 93:14082–87
164. Sanberg PR, Borlongan CV, Saporta S, Cameron DF. 1996. Testis-derived sertoli cells survive and provide localized immunoprotection for xenografts in rat brain. *Nat. Biotechnol.* 14:1692–95
165. Mohr FW, Falk V, Diegeler A, Walther T, van Son JA, et al. 1998. Minimally invasive port-access mitral valve surgery. *J. Thorac. Cardiovasc. Surg.* 115:567–74

Annu. Rev. Physiol. 1999. 61:243–82

HEAT-SHOCK PROTEINS, MOLECULAR CHAPERONES, AND THE STRESS RESPONSE: Evolutionary and Ecological Physiology

Martin E. Feder
Department of Organismal Biology and Anatomy and Committee on Evolutionary Biology, University of Chicago, 1027 East 57th Street, Chicago, Illinois 60637; e-mail: m-feder@uchicago.edu

Gretchen E. Hofmann
Department of Biology, University of New Mexico, Albuquerque, NM 87131; e-mail: ghofmann@unm.edu

KEY WORDS: hsp, temperature, protein denaturation and folding, inducible tolerance, environmental gradients

ABSTRACT

Molecular chaperones, including the heat-shock proteins (Hsps), are a ubiquitous feature of cells in which these proteins cope with stress-induced denaturation of other proteins. Hsps have received the most attention in model organisms undergoing experimental stress in the laboratory, and the function of Hsps at the molecular and cellular level is becoming well understood in this context. A complementary focus is now emerging on the Hsps of both model and nonmodel organisms undergoing stress in nature, on the roles of Hsps in the stress physiology of whole multicellular eukaryotes and the tissues and organs they comprise, and on the ecological and evolutionary correlates of variation in Hsps and the genes that encode them. This focus discloses that (*a*) expression of Hsps can occur in nature, (*b*) all species have *hsp* genes but they vary in the patterns of their expression, (*c*) Hsp expression can be correlated with resistance to stress, and (*d*) species' thresholds for Hsp expression are correlated with levels of stress that they naturally undergo. These conclusions are now well established and may require little additional confirmation; many significant questions remain

0066-4278/99/0315-0243$08.00

unanswered concerning both the mechanisms of Hsp-mediated stress tolerance at the organismal level and the evolutionary mechanisms that have diversified the *hsp* genes.

INTRODUCTION

Although heat-shock proteins (Hsps) first achieved notoriety as gene products whose expression is induced by heat and other stresses (1, 2), discoveries of the past decade have shifted the focus of research to understanding the roles of Hsps as molecular chaperones (3–5). As a result, Hsps, their close relatives, their molecular partners, and many newly discovered proteins are now known to play diverse roles, even in unstressed cells, in successful folding, assembly, intracellular localization, secretion, regulation, and degradation of other proteins (6); failure of these activities is thought to underlie numerous and important human diseases (7). Nonetheless, many of the questions of the past either remain unanswered, awaiting the development of appropriate experimental tools, or can now be revisited with new insights gleaned from the emerging understanding of molecular chaperones. This review seeks to facilitate the examination or re-examination of Hsps as responses to natural stress in diverse organisms inhabiting environments outside the laboratory, the function of Hsps in tolerance of natural stresses, and ecological and evolutionary variation in the heat-shock system. The review sequentially considers (*a*) the principal implications of laboratory-based studies for ecological and evolutionary research on Hsps, (*b*) expression of Hsps in nature, (*c*) covariation of Hsp expression with environmental and biological gradients of stress intensity, (*d*) the consequences of Hsp expression for fitness, and (*e*) evolutionary variation in Hsps and the genes that encode them. The primary objective of this review is to redirect the focus of evolutionary and ecological research on Hsps beyond the conclusions that are now well-established and onto the many important questions that remain unanswered.

STATE OF THE LITERATURE

Established Conclusions

The relevant literature on Hsps and molecular chaperones is huge, now comprising more than 12,000 references. Even a review of the relevant reviews is difficult. For this reason, we begin by describing several well established conclusions and cite a few of the many excellent recent reviews at diverse levels of sophistication (4–6, 8–11).

The genes encoding Hsps (*hsps*) are highly conserved and occur in every species in which they have been sought. Many of these genes and their products can be assigned to families on the basis of sequence homology and typical molecular weight (6): *hsp110*, *hsp100*, *hsp90*, *hsp70*, *hsp60*, *hsp40*, *hsp10*, and small *hsp* families. Gething (6) recognizes 7 additional families and 12 genes/proteins for which families have not yet been described. In eukaryotes, many families comprise multiple members that differ in inducibility, intracellular localization, and function.

Hsps function as molecular chaperones; i.e. they interact with other proteins and, in so doing, minimize the probability that these other proteins will interact inappropriately with one another. Hsps recognize and bind to other proteins when these other proteins are in non-native conformations, whether due to protein-denaturing stress or because the peptides they comprise have not yet been fully synthesized, folded, assembled, or localized to an appropriate cellular compartment. Binding and/or release of these other proteins is often regulated by association with and/or hydrolysis of nucleotides. Typically, Hsps function as oligomers, if not as complexes of several different chaperones, co-chaperones, and/or nucleotide exchange factors. Interaction with chaperones is variously responsible for (*a*) maintaining Hsps' partner proteins in a folding-competent, folded, or unfolded state; (*b*) organellar localization, import, and/or export; (*c*) minimizing the aggregation of non-native proteins; and (*d*) targeting non-native or aggregated proteins for degradation and removal from the cell. Presumably, the last two functions are most important in coping with environmental stress.

Not all Hsps are stress-inducible, but those that are respond to a variety of stresses, including extremes of temperature, cellular energy depletion, and extreme concentrations of ions, other osmolytes, gases, and various toxic substances. Activation of various intracellular signaling pathways results in Hsp expression. All known stresses, if sufficiently intense, induce Hsp expression. Accordingly, Hsps are equally well termed stress proteins, and their expression is termed the stress response. A common aspect of these inducing stresses is that they result in proteins having non-native conformations (12), which is consistent with the function of Hsps as molecular chaperones.

Implications of the Published Literature for Ecological and Evolutionary Studies of Hsps

Space limitations necessitate that we choose among numerous equally valuable references in preparing this review. To present both the breadth and depth of research relevant to the evolutionary and ecological physiology of the heat-shock response, we have compiled a near-comprehensive bibliography of that literature, which is available electronically (13) on the World Wide Web in the Supplemental Materials Section of the main Annual Reviews site (http://www.AnnualReviews.org).

A first implication of this massive literature is that the Hsp field has long ago concluded its exploratory phase. Showing that an as-yet-unexamined species expresses Hsps in response to heat or other stresses no longer has any particular novelty.

Second, much of the work on Hsps outside the laboratory or in nonmodel organisms was undertaken before the molecular diversity of Hsps and their function as molecular chaperones was obvious. In the interim, the experimental tools for examining Hsps and the standards for such examinations have both advanced considerably. As a result, much of the earlier work on evolutionary and ecological physiology of Hsps regrettably either does not withstand current scrutiny or contributes little to issues of current interest. Several issues are obvious:

1. Many of the apparently singular Hsps of previous years, often detected by one-dimensional electrophoresis and autoradiography, are now known to represent entire families of Hsps, often with (*a*) discrete distributions within the cell (e.g. cytoplasmic-nuclear, mitochondrial, chloroplast, or endoplasmic reticulum), (*b*) different degrees of inducibility (constitutively expressed, constitutively expressed but increasing during or after stress, exclusively inducible), (*c*) differing kinetics of induction and removal from the cell, and (*d*) differing tissue specificity. Representing this diversity as a single Hsp or two Hsps ("constitutive" and "inducible") through use of nonspecific probes or lysates of whole organisms and organs can obscure phenomena of great significance (e.g. compare Refs. 14 and 15 with 16). This problem is sometimes remediable only with great difficulty. Often, highly specific probes are available only for standard model organisms, particularly at the level of proteins, and great care must be taken in applying these probes to non-standard organisms (17).

2. Inducible stress tolerance is increasingly understood to result from numerous molecular mechanisms, of which Hsps are collectively only one. Other mechanisms include synthesis of osmotic stress protectants such as polyols and trehalose, modifications of the saturation of cell membrane lipids (homeoviscous adaptation), compensatory expression of isozymes or allozymes of significant enzymes, metabolic arrest, radical scavengers (superoxide dismutase, glutathione system, cytochrome P450), and so on. Accordingly, the unambiguous attribution of stress tolerance to Hsps in general or to any specific Hsp requires more than correlative evidence (18–21). Increasingly, proof resulting from genetic or direct experimental manipulation is

becoming the standard for establishing the functional or evolutionary significance of Hsps. Again, this rising standard is often met only with great difficulty in ecological and evolutionary physiological studies, for many of the techniques for genetic and experimental manipulation are not readily applicable to the more ecologically and evolutionarily interesting species.

HSP-INDUCING STRESS IN NATURE AND NATURAL INDUCTION OF HSPS

Depending on their geographic locale, organisms in nature risk exposure to temperatures ranging from -100° to more than $100^\circ C$, and comparable extremes of chemical and gas concentration, food and water availability, hydrostatic pressure, radiation, and toxic substances of human origin. Seemingly, Hsp expression should be a common occurrence in nature. In reality, however, movement and/or other behaviors may often enable organisms to avoid Hsp-inducing stress in nature by exploiting equable microhabitats in otherwise stressful environments (22–24). Also, biochemical specializations other than Hsps may stabilize many organisms (or particular stages of their life cycles) so that environmental extremes are not particularly stressful.

Even equable environments can contain Hsp-inducing microhabitats, and even mild stresses can induce Hsps when multiple stresses act in combination. For these reasons, we can assume neither the presence nor the absence of Hsp expression in nature; for that matter, we still do not know in any comprehensive sense whether wild organisms routinely, occasionally, or seldom express inducible Hsps. A growing body of evidence, however, establishes that at least in some circumstances and taxa, Hsp induction is not solely a laboratory phenomenon.

One caution in evaluating the subsequent account is that organisms in nature seldom undergo only one stress at a time. For example, an insect larva undergoing natural heat stress in a rotting fruit may simultaneously experience intense ultraviolet radiation, desiccation, and diverse alcohols and aldehydes, among other stresses. This situation differs from that in most laboratory experimentation, which involves one or a few stresses and makes attribution of Hsp expression to a particular stress in nature more complicated.

Aquatic Temperature Stress

Due to the physical characteristics of water, the aquatic environment can be extremely stressful to its inhabitants. In general, the high specific heat and thermal conductivity of water ensure that the majority of aquatic organisms will have body temperatures equivalent to that of their surroundings. Furthermore, the relative thermal homogeneity of aquatic environments can frustrate behavioral avoidance of thermal extremes. Some aquatic ectotherms nonetheless inhabit thermally equable habitats or waters with enough thermal diversity to enable behavioral thermoregulation; our focus is on those species that do not.

In the aquatic environment, habitual exposure to Hsp-inducing thermal stress may be most common in sessile organisms that occur in shallow, stagnant water (e.g. ponds, tidepools, swamps, tidal flats) or in the intertidal zone. Corals, for example, routinely undergo thermal stress that results in bleaching, during which the corals' endosymbionts die. Even modest increases in water temperature of 1-2°C can bleach corals; these temperatures also induce Hsp expression in several species (25, 26). Marine intertidal invertebrates undergo even larger increases in body temperatures during tidal emersion (27–30). For example, during aerial exposure intertidal mussels' body temperatures exceed seawater temperatures by more than 20°C (31), resulting in Hsp expression (29). A similar phenomenon occurs in encysted brine shrimp (*Artemia*) embryos (32, 33). Even relatively mobile aquatic ectotherms such as fish may undergo heat shock in nature (34, 35). For example, gobiid fishes of the genus *Gillichthys* can become trapped in shallow water, which is heated by the sun. Summer-acclimatized fish have higher levels of Hsp90 in brain tissue than do winter-acclimatized fish (34). In addition, the threshold Hsp induction temperature for one species, *G. mirabilis*, is significantly higher in summer than in winter. These data suggest that seasonal variation in water temperature can alter the heat-shock response. More exotic venues for aquatic thermal stress include thermal effluents of power plants, hydrothermal vents, and thermal hot springs, in which temepratures can exceed 100°C (see *Hsps of Archaea*).

Terrestrial Temperature Stress

Unlike aquatic environments, terrestrial environments often offer diverse heat sources and sinks and retreats that organisms can exploit to avoid thermal stress. Thus, natural thermal stress and accompanying Hsp expression in terrestrial environments typically involve limitations in mitigating thermal extremes by movement and conflicts between thermoregulation and other needs. Salamanders, for example, which ordinarily maintain cool temperatures in nature, can inadvertently retreat beneath small sunlit rocks that become warm enough to induce *hsp70* mRNA expression (36); by abandoning these rocks to find cooler retreats they may risk immediate desiccation or even warmer temperatures.

The least equivocal case for routine exposure to Hsp-inducing temperature stress is for plants, which cannot change location except as seeds or pollen and can be limited in their ability to adjust heat exchange with the environment (37). Thus, plants in nature can become extremely hot (38). By inference, the entire range of plant heat-shock responses (8, 39) should manifest themselves in nature. Indeed, a small number of case studies document natural Hsp expression

(40–45), which can be greatest at times of day or in regions of an individual plant at which temperatures are highest (46). Plant species can differ dramatically, however, in both the magnitude and diversity of the particular Hsps that are expressed during days with especially warm weather (41). Plants should also be prone to natural cold stress (47), which ought to induce expression of Hsps (48–51).

Not surprisingly, therefore, many of the cases of natural thermal stress in animals on land involve animals that live inside or on plants (e.g. 52). *Drosophila* larvae and pupae encounter temperatures exceeding 40°C if the necrotic fruit they infest is in the sun, and express Hsp70 in response (53, 54). Presumably, other animals that cannot escape or offset intense solar heat loads will also express Hsps in nature; this hypothesis awaits systematic study. A unique case concerns desert ants, *Cataglyphis*, which voluntarily undergo body temperatures of >50°C, presumably to escape predators (55). The concentration of Hsp70 family members increases in this species before it naturally encounters high temperatures, as if in anticipation (56).

Terrestrial vertebrates are often especially effective in escaping heat stress, but both they and invertebrates are occasionally hyperthermic during intense physical activity, fever, or to conserve water. In birds and mammals, such hyperthermia activates HSF (the heat-shock transcription factor) and increases the level of Hscs (Hsp cognates, constitutively-expressed Hsps) and Hsps (57–59). Natural hypothermia of animals can be far more conspicuous than natural heat stress, involving diapause, overwintering in exposed sites, hibernation, and sometimes outright freezing. Diverse insects express Hsps in response to cold shock or during overwintering in diapause, although the identity of these Hsps, their tissue specificity, and their developmental regulation vary greatly (60–64). Some euthermic rodents express 70-kDa Hsps in response to cold ambient temperatures, possibly in tandem with nonshivering thermogenesis (65), and ground squirrels (*Spermophilus*) increase Hsp70 family members and ubiquitin-protein conjugates during hibernation (66).

In summary, laboratory studies of the heat-shock response often have proceeded far in advance of fieldwork that establishes an ecological context for their interpretation. Documentation of both natural thermal stress and Hsp expression in nature can provide this context, and a small but growing number of field studies demonstrate that such documentation is feasible.

Inducing Stresses Other than Temperature

Virtually every nonthermal stress can induce Hsps (10, 67). Rarely, however, are these nonthermal stresses ecologically relevant; the literature in this area typically focuses on chemical stressors, and the corresponding data are essentially pharmacological. Even when the stress in question is ecologically relevant, few studies of multicellular eukaryotes examine it in the field or in intact tissues and organisms. Some exceptional work, however, concerns plants and brine-shrimp (*Artemia*). The resurrection plant, a desert species, expresses Hsps in vegetative tissues during water stress; this expression is thought to contribute to desiccation tolerance (68). Similarly, rice seedlings express two proteins in the Hsp90 family upon exposure to water stress and elevated salinity (69). Embryos of the brine shrimp, one of the most hypoxia-tolerant metazoans, contain large quantities of p26, a molecular chaperone hypothesized to stabilize proteins during long bouts of anaerobic dormancy (see *Development*). Clearly, additional evolutionary physiological research in this area is sorely needed.

A recurrent theme is that thermal stress and these alternative stressors often result in different patterns of Hsp expression, indicating a diversity of regulatory mechanisms. Examples include variation in the expression of Hsp70 and ubiquitin in the *Drosophila* central nervous system under anoxia (70), and in protein expression during osmotic shock in isolated fish gill cells (71).

Bioindicators

Owing to its responsiveness to diverse forms of stress, the heat-shock response has undergone widespread application in biomonitoring and environmental toxicology (72–75). In many cases, Hsps are especially useful biomarkers because their induction is much more sensitive to stress than traditional indices such as growth inhibition. The use of Hsps as biomarkers is most widespread in aquatic toxicology. Most of the literature demonstrates elevated Hsp levels or induction of Hsps under laboratory conditions and then proposes Hsps as a potential indicator of pollutants or toxins in the environment. For example, exposing freshwater sponges to pollutants extracted from river water elevates Hsp70 levels, which increase still further when thermal stress is also imposed (76). Additional examples of Hsp expression in aquatic toxicology concern rotifers, (77), marine sponges (78), amphipods (79), polychaetes (80), mollusks (81–84), and fish (85–87). Other applications purposefully deploy organisms in potentially polluted aquatic systems as biosensors (88, 89).

In the terrestrial environment, where heavy metal contamination and pesticide or herbicide accumulation can be critical problems, common soil organisms such as invertebrates (90) are useful Hsp-biomonitors of toxicants. For example, centipedes (*Lithobius*) collected from near a smelter had higher Hsp70 levels than those collected from unpolluted areas (91). Potentially, combinations of heavy metals can induce such distinctive patterns of Hsp expression in soil nematodes that these patterns can become diagnostic fingerprints for specific toxicants in soils (92).

Some aspects of the stress response, however, present problems for the use of Hsps as biomarkers in environmental toxicology. Because so many different stresses induce Hsps, investigators may be unable to attribute changes in Hsp expression to any particular environmental stress. Organisms in the field often undergo multiple stresses simultaneously, the interaction of which can yield significant Hsp expression even when no single monitored toxicant is at harmful levels. Conversely, Hsps induced by another stress can enhance tolerance of a toxicant whose presence is being monitored. Laboratory studies support the difficulty of teasing apart environmental factors and attributing Hsp induction to a single stressor. For example, freshwater sponges exhibit greater tolerance of pollutants following a sublethal heat stress (76). Among the vertebrates, diseased fish have elevated levels of Hsps in their tissues, and disease-related expression may interfere with the use of Hsps as a biomarker (93). Thus, because numerous factors can induce Hsp expression and stress tolerance, the utility of Hsps as biomarkers of environmental toxins may be limited.

ENVIRONMENTAL AND BIOLOGICAL CORRELATES OF THE HEAT-SHOCK RESPONSE AND HEAT-SHOCK PROTEINS

Many investigators view correlations of organismal traits (e.g. Hsp expression) and environmental or biological variables (e.g. level of environmental stress, developmental stage, distinctive role in a parasitic or symbiotic relationship with another species) as prima facie evidence of biological adaptation, and thus have actively sought such correlations in terms of the heat-shock response. While the probative value of such evidence in establishing adaptation has met with skepticism (94), in this section we consider the evidence for such correlations, whatever their meaning.

Variation in the Stress Response Along Environmental Gradients of Stress

To understand how Hsps result in stress tolerance at the organismal level, many investigators have characterized the stress response along gradients that occur in nature. One central question is whether organisms from environments with little stress have a different or reduced stress response compared with organisms from environments with much stress. Little and much stress might correspond to the center and edge of a species' range, low versus high elevation, xeric and hot versus mesic and cool climate, temperate versus tropical/polar latitude, low versus high intertidal, and so on. In general, the resulting data support a correlation among Hsp expression, stress tolerance, and gradients of environmental stress. These gradients have received uneven attention, however, and their study has yielded mixed results. Comparative studies across many degrees of latitude have not produced the same results as studies of gradients on smaller scales (e.g. diurnal or microclimatic variation in stress). Currently, not a single study has examined the stress response over the entire geographical distribution of a species; thus, whether species at the extremes of their distributions have an augmented heat-shock response is yet to be determined.

The majority of multi-species comparative studies focus on three aspects of the stress response: the minimum (threshold) and maximum temperatures at which Hsps are expressed and/or are present in cells, Hsp concentrations in cells, and the diversity of the specific Hsps that are expressed. Except for the work on threshold and maximum temperatures, much of this literature is a hodgepodge of disconnected studies that are seldom comparable because of methodological differences and permit few conclusions other than that species vary in the details of their stress response. Whether this variation has environmental correlates is uncertain. A rare and exemplary exception is the work of Bosch and colleagues on species of *Hydra* (95, 96); below we discuss this and other similar work.

In general, the threshold temperature for Hsp induction is correlated with the typical temperatures at which species live, with thermophilic species having a higher threshold than psychrophilic species. For example, a relatively cold-water, northern species of mussel (*Mytilus trossulus*) has a lower threshold for Hsp70 expession than its congener, *M. galloprovincialis*, a warm-water species with a more southern distribution (97). Limpet species that occur in the upper regions of the intertidal (*Lottia digitalis* and *Lottia pelta*) induce Hsps at 3–5°C higher than the threshold for limpets that occur lower in the intertidal (*Tectura scutum*) (AL Haag & GE Hofmann, unpublished data). Subtidal species of the marine snail *Tegula* exhibit much the same pattern (98). Aggregate expression of Hsp70 family members (17) occurs at 3–4°C higher in *Drosophila melanogaster* than in *D. ambigua*, a fruit fly of Palearctic origin (56). The same study reports a similar pattern for the desert ant *Cataglyphis* and *Formica polyctena*, a red wood ant from a temperate climate. One remarkable outcome of the *Cataglyphis* study is that Hsp synthesis in the desert ants continues at temperatures up to 45°C, whereas temperatures above 39°C inhibit Hsp synthesis in the temperate species. A similar pattern (although not as extreme) is evident for desert and non-desert *Drosophila* (22). These results suggest that translation itself may have an upper thermal maximum that varies among species adapted to different temperature environments.

Antarctic organisms represent a special case of psychrophily because the temperatures they experience are both extremely cold and extremely stable. In combination, do these conditions result in the evolutionary loss of a heat-shock response? In the subtidal alga, *Plocamium cartilagineum*, heat-inducible *hsp70* and *ubiquitin* transcription still occur, although the threshold is a spectacularly cold 5°C (99). Antarctic yeast species express Hsps at much lower temperatures than does *Saccharomyces*, and at least one species lacks inducible thermotolerance (100, 101). In Antarctic fish, the picture is not as clear. Although a broadly cross-reactive anti-Hsp70 antibody can detect isoforms of Hsp70 in various tissues of the fish *Trematomus bernacchii*, heat shock temperatures from 6 to 10°C do not induce additional Hsp70 accumulation (GE Hofmann, unpublished data). A member of the *hsp70* gene family is present in two Antarctic fish species, *T. bernacchii* and *Notothenia coriiceps* (AC Whitmer & GE Hofmann, personal communication), and has been sequenced in Antarctic fish species (102). At the other extreme, some hyperthermophilic Archaea require temperatures in excess of 100°C to induce Hsp expression (see *Hsps of Archaea*).

Thermal stress gradients can be seasonal as well as geographic. In some cases, both Hsp expression and thermotolerance increase during warm seasons. The intertidal mussel *Mytilus californianus* displays significantly different Hsp induction profiles in summer than in winter, and summer-acclimatized mussels induce Hsps at a threshold temperature that is 6°C higher than the threshold in winter-acclimatized mussels (103). However, whether the accentuated Hsp expression in mussels in summer results in greater thermotolerance at the organismal level is unknown. Fish (34, 35) and intertidal invertebrates (31) also vary seasonally in Hsp expression.

In addition to work we cite elsewhere, other studies examine geographical gradients in fish (104, 105, 105a), maize (106), reptiles (107), and *Drosophila* (108); intertidal gradients in limpets (27); diurnal temperature change in *Drosophila* (109) and intertidal mussels (29); diurnal variation in spruce trees (46); and seasonal variation in insects (110).

One issue for future consideration is whether Hsps in general are specialized to function at higher temperatures than other proteins (especially enzymes), and whether homologous Hsps of species from various thermal environments have corresponding variation in thermostability of function (111). For example, that an Hsp's resistance to thermal denaturation varies according to the thermal niche of the species that expresses it has been demonstrated for only a single Hsp, alpha-crystallin (112). Another issue is how differing thresholds of Hsp expression have evolved, whether through mutations in HSF, general thermostability of proteins and cells (113), or some other mechanism (114).

The Parasitic Environment

The roles of Hsps in host-parasite interactions have received considerable attention from both clinical and biological perspectives, with the majority of the research in two general categories. First, from the perspective of the host, Hsps expressed by invading parasites are potent antigens that elicit an immune response (115–117); parasites' Hsps are thus potentially useful in generating vaccines (118). From the perspective of the parasite, the synthesis of Hsps is a cellular defense mechanism that enables the parasite to live in different thermal environments throughout its life-cycle (119). Parasites that infect mammalian and avian hosts can undergo profound changes in temperature during the transition to these hosts (with internal temperatures of 37°C or above) from ectotherm hosts or free-living stages. Induction of Hsps commonly accompanies this transition. Numerous studies have demonstrated developmentally regulated expression of Hsps in parasites; expression differs throughout the life-cycle both quantitatively and in the types of Hsps that temperature change induces. For example, mRNA transcripts for *hsp70* and *hsp83* homologues increase up to 100-fold as *Trypanosoma brucei* leaves the tsetse fly and enters a mammalian host (120). Aquatic snails release cercariae of the parasitic helminth, *Schistosoma mansoni*, into freshwater; cercariae penetrate human skin and develop into adult worms, eventually causing liver cirrhosis. The cercariae express two heat-inducible proteins that are not present in other stages (121).

Parasites that have an insect as the invertebrate vector have received much attention with regard to the developmentally regulated expression of Hsps. Examples include parasitic nematodes (122); cestode parasites (123); the malarial organism *Plasmodium* (124); *Borrelia burgdorferi*, the etiological agent of Lyme disease (125); the protist *Leishmania* (126); *Trypanosoma cruzi* (127); and *Theileria* (128).

Some parasite life cycles do not involve an animal vector; a free-living stage of the parasite occurs in water or soil and enters the host. In several cases, induction of Hsps accompanies the transition from the environment into the host. In the fungal parasite *Histoplasma capsulatum*, the temperature shift upon infection of a mammalian host cues both the transformation from a mycelial form to a budding yeast morphology and the expression of Hsps (129, 130). *Eimeria*, an intestinal parasite of numerous animals, expresses Hsp90 during infective life stages. *Eimeria* parasites are particularly interesting because this genus infects diverse hosts with correspondingly diverse body temperatures (e.g. marine fish, poultry, and cattle). However, specificity of infection is high at the species level, e.g. cattle are the exclusive host for *Eimeria bovis* (131). Whether the heat-shock response of *Eimeria* co-evolved with its speciation into these hosts is an open question.

Finally, the heat stress that infective life cycle stages of parasites experience is as diverse as their hosts. In nature, parasites of ectotherms can encounter dramatic shifts in temperature when their hosts' body temperature varies, as has been reported for parasites of reptiles, fish, and intertidal organisms (132, 133).

Symbiosis

Just as Hsps may play an important role in parasitism, in which one species maintains a close but antagonistic relationship with others, they also function in symbiosis, in which interspecific relationships can be equally close but not adversarial. Perhaps the most general example of this point concerns mitochondria and chloroplasts, which evolved from endosymbionts that colonized other cells early in the history of life. These organelles often require proteins that are encoded in the nuclear genome and synthesized by the host cell, and hence must be imported into the organelle. Hsps play diverse roles in this process in mitochondria. A cytoplasmic Hsp70 family member maintains peptides in an unfolded conformation, which enables the peptides to pass through pores in the mitochondrial membrane; a mitochondrial Hsp70 is part of the protein machinery that imports the peptide; and the Hsp60/Hsp10 apparatus participates in the folding of the imported protein (134). Several groups of primitive eukaryotes contain still other endosymbiotically derived organelles, the hydrogenosome and the nucleomorph, whose Hsps share a characteristic sequence with those of mitochondria and proteobacteria (135–138). The Hsp sequence similarities have been used to suggest that hydrogenosomes may derive from mitochondria, share a common origin with mitochondria, or represent independent colonizations of early eukaryotic cells (135–137, 139).

Aside from endosymbiotically derived organelles, the best-studied symbioses concern bacterial endosymbionts that infect insects, including aphids, flies, ants, and cockroaches. Aphids, for example, harbor the bacterium *Buchnera* in specialized cells (bacteriocytes) within a distinctive structure in the body cavity, the bacteriome (140). The bacteria express a protein, symbionin, at especially high levels, and this protein is a member of the GroEL (Hsp60) family. Other bacterial chaperones, including GroES (Hsp10) and DnaK (Hsp70), are also present at high levels (140). A similar phenomenon is evident in tsetse flies (141).

The function and significance of these high Hsp levels is enigmatic. The Hsps apparently are not a response of the endosymbionts to a novel (and therefore stressful) host environment, as the *Buchnera*/aphid symbiosis is 150–250 million years old. The endosymbionts, however, have been evolving at an especially high rate; thus, the elevated molecular chaperones could be compensating for decreased protein stability due to the accumulation of numerous amino acid substitutions (142, 143). Nonetheless, the bacteria themselves can mount a strong heat-shock response when their host undergoes stress (144). Other relevant symbioses include X-bacteria in the symbiosomes of *Amoeba* (e.g. 145), *Bradyrhizobium* and *Rhizobium* in the root nodules of nitrogen-fixing plants (146), and the zooxanthellae component of corals (26, 30). A recurrent theme is that the endosymbionts modify the amount and/or diversity of Hsps present in the symbiosis. In some cases, this modification is thought to contribute to the maintenance of the endosymbionts within the host, and in others to the augmentation of the heat-shock response of the symbiosis as a whole. Finally,

Wolbachia, a bacterial endosymbiont that infects millions of arthropod species, both interferes with the mating of infected and uninfected hosts and can alter their constitutive expression of Hsp70 and Hsp90 family members (147). Simulated natural heat stress can diminish this reproductive interference, possibly by overriding the symbiont's effect on the host Hsps.

Development

Many species exhibit characteristic and distinctive patterns of Hsp expression (or nonexpression) during the various stages of development, including gametogenesis, embryogenesis, and metamorphosis (e.g. 148–151). These patterns are often consistent with enhanced stress resistance in developmental stages that encounter unusual levels of environmental stress or during circumstances such as dormancy and diapause (see below). In other cases, developmental programs of Hsp expression ensue even in the absence of any obvious environmental stress. One common pattern is that one or more Hsps are not expressed in the initial phases of embryogenesis (152–156) or late in gametogenesis (157–161), possibly because Hsps can be harmful to developing cells (see *Deleterious Aspects of Hsps*). Parental provision of Hsps or *hsp* mRNAs can sometimes override gametic or embryonic absence of Hsp expression (162, 163); in other cases this absence presumably poses a significant problem for continued development in the face of stress (164). Stress not only can kill vulnerable developmental stages outright, but also can produce lasting damage to surviving organisms, such as the phenocopying of genetic defects; Hsps may minimize such defects (165, 166).

Adaptational analyses of the developmental expression of Hsps are diverse. Some plant seeds presumably must endure extremes of heat, desiccation, and other stresses before germinating, and some must germinate under especially challenging conditions. However, although seeds clearly undergo developmentally regulated expression of Hsps and embryos can express Hsps in response to environmental stress (167–169), few investigators have considered whether these patterns of expression are amplified or modified in species and ecotypes that naturally encounter especially challenging stress regimes (68, 170). Our state of knowledge is similar for fungal spores, which express particular Hsps in a developmentally regulated program (e.g. 171, 172). Several interesting case studies are available for animals, although a general pattern is yet to emerge. In the most spectacular example, encysted brine-shrimp (*Artemia*) embryos undergo developmental arrest, in which they may survive for years without environmental water or oxygen. The encysted embryos accumulate enormous concentrations (15% of total protein) of a small Hsp (173–177) and trehalose (178), and suppress ubiquitination of damaged proteins (179). Non-adult *D. melanogaster* infest necrotic fruit, which can become extremely warm if it is sunlit (53, 54); this species mounts a massive heat-shock response, which is greatest in the developmental stages that presumably undergo the most exposure to natural heat stress (18, 19, 180). Other flies overwinter while at a particular developmental stage, and undergo considerable Hsp expression in response to cold (60–63). Later in development, ubiquitin may assist in the degeneration of flight muscles that are no longer needed after nuptial flights of insects (181). Finally, the temperature threshold for expression of Hsps may itself undergo modification; e.g. the threshold decreases in mammalian testis, in which gametogenesis normally occurs at lower temperatures than in the core of the body (182, 183).

Aging and Senescence

As mammals age, damage to proteins progressively accumulates, and both the ability to express Hsps (e.g. Hsp or *hsp* mRNA levels after a standard exposure to heat or other stress) and stress tolerance deteriorate (184, 185). Moreover, individual Hsps can become less able to mitigate the effects of stress on proteins as mammals age (186). In ecological and evolutionary terms, whether similar Hsp-aging relationships are important or even evident in wild organisms is unknown, although these relationships occur in diverse species in the laboratory: *Drosophila* (187, 188), nematodes (189–191), and *Daphnia* (192).

These findings have provoked great interest in how Hsps potentially affect senescence and lifespan. A unifying hypothesis in the foregoing work is that protein damage, due primarily to oxidation/free radical activity, gradually accumulates during the life of a cell or organism and can lead to death if unabated; Hsps and other molecular stress responses ordinarily can mitigate this damage to some extent, and the decreasing expression of Hsps with age therefore contributes to mortality. If this hypothesis is correct, then treatments that both reduce damage to protein and increase Hsp expression (e.g. heat shock) should prolong life. In nematodes (*Caenorhabditis elegans*), some single-gene mutations that increase lifespan are associated with increased thermotolerance, but through as-yet-undescribed mechanisms (189–191). In *Drosophila*, heat shock extends lifespan (193), and this extension is enhanced in flies transformed with additional copies of the *hsp70* gene (194). Nutrient deprivation can also extend life in rodents, presumably by reducing the metabolic rate and consequently, oxidative damage to proteins; starvation, however, variously increases, decreases, or has no effect on Hsp expression (195–199).

FITNESS CONSEQUENCES OF HSP EXPRESSION

General Issues and Beneficial Aspects of Hsps

Understanding the consequences of variation in Hsps and the stress response for Darwinian fitness requires a detailed appreciation of the mechanisms by which Hsps mitigate the impact of stress on individuals in natural populations. These mechanisms are becoming well understood at the level of model proteins with which Hsps can interact, but are progressively less well understood at the level of the cell, tissue, organ, and whole organism. At the level of the model protein, various stresses clearly either directly or indirectly result in conformational change, and Hsps typically promote the reacquisition or maintenance of the native structure and function by minimizing the tendency of non-native proteins to interact inappropriately (200, 201). In cells, stress-induced conformational change, protein aggregation, and molecular chaperoning of model proteins are also well established (200–202), and many cellular components differ in stress-tolerant and stress-intolerant cells (67).

Two primary issues impede the linkage of variation in these well-established mechanisms and phenomena to variation in the fitness of individual complex multicellular eukaryotes. First, is the variation in sensitivity to stress among cells, cell types, tissues, organs, and organisms attributable to a small number of critical lesions, especially sensitive targets of stress and functions of specific Hsps in protecting or repairing these lesions/targets? Or is variation in sensitivity to stress an aggregate function of a widespread and diverse impact of stress on cellular structures, with Hsps mitigating multiple lesions in diverse ways (21)? The former alternative may be more analytically tractable than the latter. Second, given that cells and organisms may have multiple Hsps in each Hsp family, multiple Hsp families, and multiple non-Hsp mechanisms of stress mitigation, how can we unambiguously establish the contribution or importance of any particular Hsp, Hsp family, or mechanism in the complex cell, tissue, organ, or organism? Much of the published literature on the functional consequences of Hsp expression for whole organisms or the cells they comprise runs afoul of these issues. Literally thousands of studies report correlations between Hsp expression, diverse biological functions in the face of stress, and stress tolerance, but these typically conclude that their findings are at best consistent with a role of one or more Hsps in stress tolerance. Evaluating the roles of single factors in complex systems is an ongoing challenge in most areas of the biological sciences, and the heat-shock field largely has not yet deployed counterparts of the solutions that other fields have developed.

One conspicuous and major exception includes techniques and approaches, primarily drawn from molecular biology and genetics, that allow the manipulation of individual Hsps or specific genes that encode them. In rare instances, a species naturally may have an unusual genetic system (203) or a diminished suite of Hsps (95, 204) that accomplishes the same end; also, several chemical compounds may specifically inhibit one or more Hsps (e.g. 205, 206). The general implication of the resulting work (Table 1) is that, even in whole organisms or the cells they comprise, variation in single Hsps can be consequential for fitness. Some specific implications are as follows: Individual Hsps can have

Table 1 Phenotypes of multicellular eukaryotes, and the cells and tissues that they comprise, for which Hsps are necessary and/or sufficient[a]

Protein	Phenotype
Hsp10	Cellular: tolerance of ischemia (no phenotype) (308); tolerance of ischemia when co-expressed with Hsp60 (308)
Hsp27	Cellular: resistance to chemotherapeutic drugs (309); resistance to hydrogen peroxide (310, 311); resistance to hydrogen peroxide (no phenotype) (312); resistance to ultraviolet radiation (no phenotype) (312); resistance of tumor cells to monocytes (311); sensitivity to lymphokine-activated killer cells (no phenotype) (311); tolerance of hyperthermia (312–316); resistance to tumor necrosis factor (317) (310); tolerance of ischemia (318); resistance of actin polymers to cytochalasin (314); accelerated nuclear protein aggregation (319); accelerated decline of thermal radiosensitization (319)
Crystallin	Cellular: tolerance of hyperthermia (320, 321); tolerance of ischemia (318); resistance to tumor necrosis factor (310); resistance to hydrogen peroxide (310)
Hsp60	Cellular: tolerance of hyperthermia (no phenotype) (322, 323); tolerance of ischemia (no phenotype) (308, 322, 323); tolerance of ischemia when co-expressed with Hsp10 (308)
Hsp65	Cellular: tumor regression (324); loss of tumorigenicity (325) Tissue/organ: regression of malignant tumors (324)
Hsp70	Cellular: tolerance of hyperthermia (326) (316, 322, 323, 327–342); tolerance of ischemia/hypoxia (322, 323, 340, 343–345); recovery from translational and transcriptional inhibition following heat shock (335); regulation of heat-shock response (331, 346, 347); tolerance of endotoxin (348); reduced protein denaturation upon heat exposure (349); tumorigenicity (350); cell proliferation (351, 164); resistance to hydrogen peroxide (311); resistance of tumor cells to monocytes (311); sensitivity to lymphokine-activated killer cells (no phenotype) (311); escape from drug-induced cell cycle arrest (352); protein glycosylation (353); tolerance of ultraviolet radiation (354); apoptosis (351, 355, 356); resistance to apoptosis (no phenotype) (328, 329) Tissue/organ: recovery of contractility after ischemia (345, 357–359); reduction in myocardial infarct size (345, 359); reduction of hyperthermic damage to midgut (221); resistance of heart to ischemic injury (357–359); resistance of hippocampus to ischemic injury (360) Organismal: tolerance of hyperthermia (18–20, 109, 156, 203, 221, 224, 278, 361); growth and development (222); regulation of heat-shock response (361); persistence in nature (no phenotype) (277)
Hsc70	Organismal: tolerance of hyperthermia (203)
Hsp72	Cellular: apoptosis (no phenotype) (362); protection against heat-induced nuclear protein aggregation (319); protection against hypoxia (363); protection against thermal radiosensitization (319) Tissue/organ: reduction in myocardial infarct size (364)
Grp78	Cellular: protein secretion (229–231)

(*Continued*)

Table 1 (*Continued*)

Protein	Phenotype
Hsp90	Cellular: tolerance of hyperthermia (322, 323, 328, 329, 340); tolerance of ischemia (no phenotype) (322, 323, 340); apoptosis (362); apoptosis (no phenotype) (328, 329); cell proliferation and cell cycle control (365); glucocorticoid receptor function (205)
Hsp100	Organismal: host infection in *Leishmania* (126)
Hsp101	Cellular: tolerance of hyperthermia (366)
Many Hsps	Cellular: recovery of cell proliferation after heat shock (367); recovery from chromosome damage after heat shock (367–369); tolerance of hyperthermia (370, 371); tolerance of ischemia (336)
HSF	Organismal: oogenesis and development (372); thermotolerance (372, 373)

[a]In all cited work, specific Hsps have undergone experimental or natural manipulation.

pleiotropic effects, interacting with multiple systems in diverse ways. Findings from manipulations of individual Hsps usually (but not always) are consistent with the outcome of correlative studies (see above). Finally, despite the huge body of work on Hsps and the growing use of manipulative techniques, we have remarkably little physiological insight into exactly how the activity of Hsps culminates in the enhanced stress tolerance of multicellular eukaryotes and the cells and tissues that they comprise.

Interestingly, one clear conclusion that correlative studies have yielded is that Hsps cannot account for the entirety of inducible stress tolerance (207–217). Indeed, some component of inducible stress tolerance may be unrelated to protein synthesis in general (214, 218, 219).

Deleterious Aspects of Hsps

The many advantages of the heat-shock response suggest that natural selection should maximize the expression of Hsps. By contrast, the genes encoding Hsps have not undergone unlimited amplification in the genome, and the Hsps themselves are subject to strict autoregulation by multiple molecular mechanisms (220). These contrary findings suggest that Hsps can have both positive and negative impacts on fitness, and that natural selection may have acted to balance these impacts in setting the level of Hsp expression. For example, while small to moderate increases in Hsp70 levels enhance inducible thermotolerance in *Drosophila*, large increases in Hsp70 levels actually decrease thermotolerance (221); evolution thus may favor an intermediate level of Hsp70. A common theme in related work is that high levels of Hsps may be especially detrimental to cells or developmental stages in which cell growth and division proceed at high rates. *Drosophila* larvae transformed with extra copies of the *hsp70* gene have greater larva-to-adult mortality and slower development than do control larvae; these strain differences are proportional to the number of Hsp-inducing heat shocks administered to the larvae (222). Larvae naturally varying in Hsp70 expression display a similar pattern (223). *Drosophila* cells engineered to express Hsp70 constitutively at first grow more slowly than control cells, but subsequently resume control growth rates once the Hsp70 is sequestered from the cytoplasm (164); indeed, *Drosophila* embryos remove Hsp70 from their cells rapidly after heat shock (224). A yeast strain that cannot express Hsp104 grows faster than its wild-type counterpart on some media (171). More generally, most animal species that have been studied do not mount a heat-shock response during early stages of embryogenesis (see *Development*), when protein synthesis may be especially intense.

These negative effects may have at least two nonexclusive explanations (222, 225, 226): First, Hsps at high concentration could be toxic, directly interfere with ongoing processes in the cell, or otherwise alter function to the detriment of the cell (220). Second, the synthesis and degradation of Hsps could consume an intolerably large fraction of a cell's or organism's nutrient and energy stores, and/or occupy so large a fraction of the synthetic/catabolic apparatus that the processing of other essential biomolecules suffers (226–228). Consistent with the first explanation, cellular sequestration of Hsp70 is correlated with the resumption of proliferation in cells constitutively expressing this protein (164). Also, overexpression of an Hsp70 family member inhibits protein secretion and reduction increases secretion in mammalian cells in culture (229–231); excess amounts of another Hsp70 family member can promote protein aggregation in vitro (M Borrelli & J Lepock, personal communication); and Hsp70 can perturb the normal structures of nascent polypeptides (232).

Tests of the second explanation have manipulated the costs of or resources for Hsp expression. Growth of corn in nitrogen-rich soil increases the synthesis of Hsps in response to a standard heat shock (233); in plants grown in nitrogen-poor soil, other proteins may be catabolized to supply amino acids for synthesis of Hsps (234). These findings suggest that Hsp synthesis can be nitrogen-limited in plants. Starvation reduces the expression of Hsp 70 family members in mice (195). In *Drosophila* larvae, by contrast, co-expression of β-galactosidase and Hsps has no greater cost for growth and development than does expression of Hsps alone (225). Further study of this apparent trade-off of the benefits and disadvantages of Hsp expression, moreover, has the potential to link evolutionary and mechanistic views of this problem that heretofore have been separate (222, 225).

MICROEVOLUTIONARY VARIATION IN HSPS

Hsps are routinely touted as adaptations that arose and are maintained via natural selection for stress resistance. Origin and maintenance of a trait by selection require that it vary within populations, and that this intra-population variation have a genetic basis and affect the Darwinian fitness of individuals. Here we ask whether Hsps, the genes that encode them, and the factors that modify their expression display such patterns of variation and undergo stabilizing or directional selection in response to environmental stress.

First, not all intrapopulation and intraspecific variation results from genetic differences. For example, seasonal acclimatization and temperature acclimation in the laboratory can alter the minimum temperature at which *Gillichthys*, a gobiid fish, expresses an Hsp90 family member (34, 235). Seasonal acclimatization likewise affects Hsp70 levels in mussels (*Mytilus*) (103), and routine culture temperature affects the magnitude and temporal pattern of Hsp expression in HeLa cells (236). Such changes may stem from alterations in the cellular environment that modify the activation of HSF (113, 182, 236, 237). These changes, however, are not universal; laboratory thermal acclimation does not alter the thermal sensitivity of Hsp expression in fish hepatocytes in culture (238), *Drosophila* larvae (19), and mussels (103).

Even when acclimation and seasonal change are controlled, however, individuals within a population or species may vary in Hsp expression and/or the genes that determine it. Relevant research has examined this issue on two levels: direct sequence variation and restriction fragment length polymorphisms (RFLPs) (240). The sequence of *hsp70* varies among strains of the parasite *Trypanosoma* (241, 242) and the nematode *C. elegans* (243), and among conspecifics for some but not all of the mammalian *hsp70* family members (240), as does that of the 3′ untranslated region of *hsp27* in normotensive and hypertensive rats (244). RFLPs consistent with intraspecific variation either in the *hsp* genes or flanking regions are detectable in the *hsp60* and *hsp70* of the spirochete *Borrelia* (245), in multiple *hsp70* family members of mammals (240, 246, 247), and in several plant species (248–250). One putative instance of intraspecific variation in *hsp* copy number concerns *D. melanogaster*, in which at least five nearly identical copies of *hsp70* occur at two chromosomal loci. At locus 87A7, two copies are arranged as an inverted repeat (251, 252); at 87C1, two copies flank a region containing at least one additional copy (252, 253) plus numerous α/β repeats, which encode heat-inducible mRNAs of no proven function (254–257). Up to five additional *hsp70* copies have been reported, with copy number varying among strains and time of year (253, 255, 258–261). However, these reports either cannot exclude that such variation is actually in intergenic regions or that the reports are for *Drosophila* cells in culture or mutagenized laboratory strains rather than wild or even wild-type strains. The organization of the two chromosomal loci reportedly varies among natural populations (253). A less equivocal instance of evolutionary change in gene copy number concerns *Arabidopsis*, in which ecotypes vary in the number of ubiquitin-encoding repeats (262). For all of the foregoing reports, the functional significance of intraspecific variation awaits elucidation or direct verification.

Hsp expression also exhibits genetic variation among individuals of a species; often, this variation is correlated with stress resistance (248, 250, 263–271). For example, isofemale lines of *Drosophila* founded from a single wild population differ more than twofold in Hsp70 expression; this variation is correlated with thermotolerance and is heritable (180, 223). Similarly, in the pathogenic fungus *Histoplasma*, naturally temperature-insensitive strains express more *hsp70* mRNA and do so at lower temperatures than in a temperature-sensitive strain (272). In humans, fibroblasts isolated from desert-dwelling Turkmen express more Hsps and have greater thermotolerance than fibroblasts from residents of more equable climates (273); presumably, however, these peoples do not differ in body temperature.

Given that the patterns of variation necessary for natural selection occur within species, that selection can alter Hsp expression is not surprising. Laboratory evolution at high temperatures paradoxically lowers Hsp70 expression and inducible thermotolerance in *Drosophila* (19, 274), and selection for resistance to hyperthermic paralysis alters both the *hsp68* promoter and the *hsr-omega* locus in *Drosophila* (254, 275). Additional findings relevant to natural selection and its underlying genetic basis come from closely related species, some so similar that they hybridize. In the fish species *Poeciliopsis monacha* and *P. lucida*, an unusual genetic system permits the generation of hemiclonal lines in which the paternal genome varies against a constant maternal genome. Hemiclonal thermotolerance was most strongly related to Hsc70 and only secondarily to Hsp70 levels, in a pattern consistent with straightforward Mendelian inheritance of parental genotypes and adaptation to the local thermal environment. By contrast, the heat-shock response of interspecific hybrids of tomato (*Lycopersicon*) is not intermediate to the parental responses (276). Non-hybridizing congeners often exhibit a correlation among the actual or inferred incidence of thermal stress in their environment, heat-shock response, and stress tolerance. Such data are now available for diverse animals (see *Variation in the Stress Response Along Environmental Gradients of Stress*).

A particular problem with such species comparisons is that the interpretation of the observed patterns is readily confounded by phylogenetic and statistical issues. A more general problem with both laboratory evolution and species comparisons is that they describe only a supposed correlation of the heat-shock genes/proteins of interest with evolution and seldom can establish the importance of the genes/proteins of interest to evolutionary process and outcome (19, 20). Study of free-ranging organisms (277) with *hsp* transgenes (e.g. 109, 278) may contribute much to resolving these problems.

THE EVOLUTIONARY HISTORY OF HSPS AND THE GENES THAT ENCODE THEM

Hsps are among the most ancient and highly conserved of all proteins. Homologues of Hsps occur in every species in which they have been sought, and in all kingdoms of living things. Thus, Hsps represent a remarkable example of molecular "descent with modification" at the levels of gene sequence, genomic organization, regulation of gene expression, and protein structure and function. So clear are the patterns of descent and modifications that they can be used to establish the evolutionary origins and the phylogenetic affinities of the major groups of organisms.

Hsps of Archaea and Exceptional Prokaryotes

The Archaea or archaebacteria are the most extremophilic and most primitive organisms. The heat-shock response of extremophilic Archaea and nonarchaeal extremophiles occurs at remarkably high temperatures (279), e.g. 88°C in *Sulfolobus* (279) and >100°C in the hyperthermophilic species designated ES4, a heterotrophic sulfur reducer isolated from a deep-sea hydrothermal vent (280). The archaeal genome encodes homologues of most Hsps represented in other prokaryotes and eukaryotes (279), as well as their consensus promoter sequences (281). Notably, the archaeal Hsp60 homologues assemble into a dual ring-like structure, termed a rosettasome or thermosome, that resembles the structure that the chaperones GroEL and GroES form in bacteria (279, 282, 283). The archaeal structures have ATPase activity and can bind denatured proteins (282). At least some Archaea and Eubacteria differ in the number of monomers that comprise these structures (284). Surprisingly, the archaeal Hsp60s (e.g. TF55 of *Sulfolobus*) most closely resemble not a bacterial homologue, but the eukaryotic protein TCP1, which assembles into the t-complex polypeptide 1 ring complex (TRiC) in the cytosol (285, 286). Previously, Hsp60 homologues were thought to be absent from the eukaryotic cytosol. A growing body of evidence suggests that TCP1/TRiC and GroEL/GroES play comparable roles in their respective organisms and cellular compartments (287–289). Meanwhile, Trent (290) has suggested that the primary function of TF55 may be cytoskeletal, with molecular chaperoning a secondary or derived function.

Genes encoding Hsps are present even in the smallest of genomes. These include the genomes of mycoplasmas (291) and the nucleomorph, the vestigial nucleus of a phototrophic eukaryotic endosymbiont in cryptomonad algae (138). The section on symbiosis (see above) reviews the distribution of Hsps in various other organelles of endosymbiotic origin. Apparently, the problem of protein folding is ancient and ubiquitous, necessitating molecular chaperones in these diverse cases.

Large-Scale Evolution of hsp Genes

The extraordinarily conserved nature of *hsp* genes (292) has facilitated their cloning, sequencing, and comparison in diverse organisms; their evolution is now becoming understood in detail. Gupta and colleagues have undertaken the most extensive surveys of *hsp* sequences, with a particular focus on organisms deemed critical to understanding the relationships of major taxa (292–297). The interpretations resulting from these comparisons relate to hypotheses about (*a*) the origin of eukaryotic cells, the eukaryotic nucleus, and endoplasmic reticulum (292, 296); (*b*) polyphyletic versus monophyletic origin of the major bacterial groups (292–294); and (*c*) the validity of the three-domain (Archaea, bacteria, and eukaryotes) dogma (292, 294). Whereas these interpretations are controversial, if not revolutionary, and therefore have not received universal acceptance, they nonetheless clearly illustrate how comparative analyses of *hsp* genes may address fundamental issues in evolutionary history.

On a less grand scale, *hsp* gene families represent superb case studies of how one or a small number of primitive genes can diversify to encode a suite of compartment- and function-specific proteins. One of many examples is *dnaK*, a single gene in Archaea and bacteria that has become the complex multi-gene *hsp70* families of *Saccharomyces* (298), *Drosophila* (253, 299), and *Homo* (300). Another example concerns the small Hsps, which evolution recruited to become a major component of the lens of the eye: alpha crystallin (301). A growing body of work examines the discrete evolutionary events by which these changes may have occurred, including gene duplication/conversion events (302), retrotransposition, horizontal exchange of genomes, and others. New technologies promise to advance this work exponentially.

Discrete Examinations of Molecular Evolution

Ideally, a complete study of the evolutionary physiology of Hsps might examine how the following co-evolve as populations or how closely related species enter environments in which they face novel stresses: sequence (both coding and non-coding) of the gene(s) for a particular Hsp, regulation of *hsp* gene expression, the role and importance of the Hsp in stress resistance, and the intensities and durations of stress that the populations and species actually face. Much of the evolutionary physiological investigation of Hsps fails to attain this admittedly ambitious goal for one or more reasons: (*a*) The species under study are too distantly related to reconstruct the functional, environmental, and genetic events during their divergence; (*b*) molecular biology, manipulative genetics, physiology, and environmental assessment are not all possible for the species in question; or (*c*) the breadth of the techniques and approaches necessary to perform such research is too daunting for a single research program. Two case studies exemplify both how this goal could be approached and how far the field has yet to go to attain it.

The coelenterate *Hydra oligactis* and several of its congeners are the only multicellular eukaryotes reported not to express Hsps in response to heat shock and other stresses. Other congeners (e.g. *Hydra attenuata* and *H. magnipapillata*) have a well-developed stress response; these and other data for putative ancestors of *Hydra* suggest an evolutionary loss of Hsp expression in *H. oligactis* (95, 96). Physiologically and ecologically, *H. oligactis* is deficient in inducible stress tolerance and disappears from certain habitats in nature during periods of stress (95). Subsequent work suggests that, at least for Hsp70, the loss has occurred due to mutations that affect the stability of *hsp70* mRNA, as *H. oligactis* has an *hsp70* gene and expresses a heat-inducible *hsp70* mRNA in quantities similar to that in the heat-tolerant *H. magnipapillata* (96).

Dipteran insects and their ancestors have undergone an evolutionary proliferation of *hsp70* genes. Mosquitoes and *Drosophila* share a distinctly arranged duplication of the inducible *hsp70* gene (303), suggesting that this proliferation predates the original diversification of the Diptera. Within the genus *Drosophila*, all groups other than the *melanogaster* subgroup of species apparently retain the primitive copy number of two (108, 304, 305). Within the *melanogaster* subgroup, all species examined to date have four copies except for *D. melanogaster* (253), which has at least five *hsp70* copies in its haploid genome (see Microevolutionary Variation in Hsps). Curiously, *D. melanogaster* expresses no Hsp100 family members, which are critical for thermotolerance in other organisms (204, 306). The proliferation of *hsp70* copies is correlated with the ecological and biogeographic distribution of *Drosophila* species (19). Whereas most *Drosophila* species have small geographic ranges or narrow ecological niches, two of the *melanogaster* subgroup species (*simulans* and *melanogaster*) have cosmopolitan distributions, and a third (*yakuba*) is ecologically diverse throughout sub-Saharan Africa.

CONCLUSION

Ecological and evolutionary physiological analysis of heat-shock proteins may be nearing the end of its initial descriptive phase. Although accounts of spectacular levels of Hsp-mediated stress resistance and exceptional consequences of Hsp expression will continue to be newsworthy, the major patterns of Hsp expression in multicellular eukaryotes are becoming so obvious that additional descriptive work is becoming increasingly difficult to justify. Clearly, however, major questions remain unanswered. How the activities of Hsps at the molecular level culminate in organismal stress tolerance and how the *hsp* genes, their regulation, the function of the proteins they encode, and the environments faced by the organisms in which they occur all co-evolve are but two of the unresolved issues reviewed here. The perspective of evolutionary physiology can make significant contributions to the resolution of these and other issues. By placing results in actual environmental contexts, by assessing phenotypes of Hsps in the context of whole multicellular organisms, and by characterizing extant and historical variation in Hsps in natural populations and taxa, evolutionary physiologists can complement and extend a spectacular area of research that has been largely restricted to the molecular/cellular levels in the laboratory. By the same token, insights and techniques that laboratory-based investigators provide promise to continue to revolutionize the ecological and evolutionary study of Hsps. These approaches are both logical partners and necessary complements to one another (22, 307). Our understanding of Hsps has much to gain from the continued if not expanded synergy of these approaches.

ACKNOWLEDGMENTS

We thank BR Bettencourt, K Chavez, UT D'OBrador, AP Nguyen, J Meredith-Patla, and AC Whitmer for bibliographic assistance and/or editorial advice, and Susan Lindquist for founding the bibliographic database that made this review possible. Research was supported by National Science Foundation grants 97-23298 and 97-23063. Finally and most importantly, we beg the indulgence of numerous investigators whom space limitations precluded us from citing directly here; their contributions have made the field what it is today. We urge all readers contemplating research in this area to scan the complete bibliography (13) available online at http://www.AnnualReviews.org.

Literature Cited

1. Ritossa F. 1996. Discovery of the heat shock response. *Cell Stress Chaperones* 1:97–98
2. Lindquist S. 1986. The heat-shock response. *Annu. Rev. Biochem.* 55:1151–91
3. Gething MJ, Sambrook J. 1992. Protein folding in the cell. *Nature* 355:33–45
4. Morimoto RI, Tissieres A, Georgopoulos C, eds. 1994. *Heat Shock Proteins: Structure, Function and Regulation.* Cold Spring Harbor, NY: Cold Spring Harbor Lab. Press
5. Hartl FU. 1996. Molecular chaperones in cellular protein folding. *Nature* 381:571–80
6. Gething MJ, ed. 1997. *Guidebook to Molecular Chaperones and Protein-Folding Catalysts.* Oxford, UK: Oxford Univ. Press
7. Thomas PJ, Qu BH, Pedersen PL. 1995. Defective protein folding as a basis of human disease. *Trends Biochem. Sci.* 20:456–59
8. Boston RS, Viitanen PV, Vierling E. 1996. Molecular chaperones and protein folding in plants. *Plant Mol. Biol.* 32:191–222
9. Feige U, Morimoto RI, Yahara I, Polla BS, eds. 1996. *Stress-Inducible Cellular Responses.* Basel: Birkhäuser
10. Feder ME, Parsell DA, Lindquist SL. 1995. The stress response and stress proteins. In *Cell Biology of Trauma*, ed. JJ Lemasters, C Oliver, pp. 177–91. Boca Raton, FL: CRC

11. Nover L, ed. 1991. *Heat Shock Response.* Boca Raton, FL: CRC
12. Somero GN. 1995. Proteins and temperature. *Annu. Rev. Physiol.* 57:43–68
13. Feder ME, Hofmann GE. 1998. Evolutionary and ecological physiology of heat-shock proteins and the heat-shock response: a comprehensive bibliography. http://www.AnnualReviews.org
14. Stephanou G, Alahiotis SN, Christodoulou C, Marmaras VJ. 1983. Adaptation of *Drosophila melanogaster* to temperature. Heat-shock proteins and survival in *Drosophila melanogaster. Dev. Genet.* 3:299–308
15. Alahiotis SN, Stephanou G. 1982. Temperature adaptation of *Drosophila* populations. The heat shock proteins system. *Comp. Biochem. Physiol.* 73B:529–33
16. Palter KB, Watanabe M, Stinson L, Mahowald AP, Craig EA. 1986. Expression and localization of *Drosophila melanogaster* hsp70 cognate proteins. *Mol. Cell Biol.* 6:1187–203
17. Hightower LE. 1995. Desert ants. *Science* 268:1417
18. Feder ME. 1998. Engineering candidate genes in studies of adaptation: the heat-shock protein Hsp70 in *Drosophila melanogaster. Am. Nat.* In press
19. Feder ME, Krebs RA. 1998. Natural and genetic engineering of thermotolerance in *Drosophila melanogaster. Am. Zool.* 38:503–17
20. Feder ME, Krebs RA. 1997. Ecological and evolutionary physiology of heat-shock proteins and the stress response in *Drosophila*: complementary insights from genetic engineering and natural variation. In *Stress, Adaptation, and Evolution*, ed. R Bijlsma, V Loeschcke, pp. 155–73. Basel: Birkhäuser
21. Feder ME. 1996. Ecological and evolutionary physiology of stress proteins and the stress response: the *Drosophila melanogaster* model. In *Animals and Temperature: Phenotypic and Evolutionary Adaptation*, ed. IA Johnston, AF Bennett, pp. 79–102. Cambridge, UK: Cambridge Univ. Press
22. Huey RB, Bennett AF. 1990. Physiological adjustments to fluctuating thermal environments: an ecological and evolutionary perspective. In *Stress Proteins in Biology and Medicine*, ed. RI Morimoto, A Tissieres, C Georgopoulos, pp. 37–59. Cold Spring Harbor, NY: Cold Spring Harbor Lab. Press
23. Huey RB. 1991. Physiological consequences of habitat selection. *Am. Nat.* 137:S91–115
24. Bartholomew GA. 1964. The roles of physiology and behaviour in the maintenance of homeostasis in the desert environment. In *Homeostasis and Feedback Mechanisms*, ed. GM Hughes, pp. 7–29. Cambridge, UK: Cambridge Univ. Press
25. Sharp VA, Brown BE, Miller D. 1997. Heat shock protein (HSP 70) expression in the tropical reef coral *Goniopora djiboutiensis. J. Therm. Biol.* 22:11–19
26. Hayes RL, King CM. 1995. Induction of 70-kD heat shock protein in scleractinian corals by elevated temperature: significance for coral bleaching. *Mol. Mar. Biol. Biotechnol.* 4:36–42
27. Sanders BM, Hope C, Pascoe VM, Martin LS. 1991. Characterization of the stress protein response in two species of *Collisella* limpets with different temperature tolerances. *Physiol. Zool.* 64:1471–89
28. Sanders BM, Pascoe VM, Nakagawa PA, Martin LS. 1992. Persistence of the heat-shock response over time in a common *Mytilus* mussel. *Mol. Mar. Biol. Biotechnol.* 1:147–54
29. Hofmann GE, Somero GN. 1996. Protein ubiquitination and stress protein synthesis in *Mytilus trossulus* occurs during recovery from tidal emersion. *Mol. Mar. Biol. Biotechnol.* 5:175–84
30. Sharp VA, Miller D, Bythell JC, Brown BE. 1994. Expression of low molecular weight HSP 70 related polypeptides from the symbiotic sea anemone *Anemonia viridis* Forskal in response to heat shock. *J. Exp. Mar. Biol. Ecol.* 179:179–93
31. Hofmann GE, Somero GN. 1995. Evidence for protein damage at environmental temperatures: seasonal changes in levels of ubiquitin conjugates and hsp70 in the intertidal mussel *Mytilus trossulus. J. Exp. Biol.* 198:1509–18
32. Miller D, McLennan AG. 1988. The heat shock response of the cryptobiotic brine shrimp *Artemia*. I. A comparison of the thermotolerance of cysts and larvae. *J. Therm. Biol.* 13:119–24
33. Miller D, McLennan AG. 1988. The heat shock response of the cryptobiotic brine shrimp *Artemia*. II. Heat shock proteins. *J. Therm. Biol.* 13:125–34
34. Dietz TJ, Somero GN. 1992. The threshold induction temperature of the 90-kDa heat shock protein is subject to acclimatization in eurythermal goby fishes (genus *Gillichthys*). *Proc. Natl. Acad. Sci. USA* 89:3389–93
35. Fader SC, Yu Z, Spotila JR. 1994. Seasonal variation in heat shock proteins

(hsp70) in stream fish under natural conditions. *J. Therm. Biol.* 19:335–41
36. Near JC, Easton DP, Rutledge PS, Dickinson DP, Spotila JS. 1990. Heat shock protein 70 gene expression in intact salamanders *Eurycea bislineata* in response to calibrated heat shocks and to high temperatures encountered in the field. *J. Exp. Zool.* 256:303–14
37. Gates DM. 1980. *Biophysical Ecology.* New York: Springer-Verlag
38. Kee SC, Nobel PS. 1986. Concomitant changes in high-temperature tolerance and heat-shock proteins in desert succulents. *Plant Physiol.* 80:596–98
39. Nagao RT, Kimpel JA, Key JL. 1990. Molecular and cellular biology of the heat-shock response. *Adv. Genet.* 28:235–74
40. Nguyen HT, Joshi CP, Klueva N, Weng J, Hendershot KL, Blum A. 1994. The heat-shock response and expression of heat-shock proteins in wheat under diurnal heat stress and field conditions. *Aust. J. Plant Physiol.* 21:857–67
41. Hamilton EW, Heckathorn SA, Downs CA, Schwarz TE, Coleman JS, Hallberg RL. 1996. Heat shock proteins are produced by field-grown naturally occurring plants in the summer in the temperate northeast U.S. *Bull. Ecol. Soc. Am.* 77, Suppl. Part 2:180 (Abstr.)
42. Kimpel JA, Key JL. 1985. Presence of heat shock mRNAs in field grown soybeans. *Plant Physiol.* 79:672–78
43. Hernandez LD, Vierling E. 1993. Expression of low molecluar weight heat-shock proteins under field conditions. *Plant Physiol.* 101:1209–16
44. Hendershot KL, Weng J, Nguyen HT. 1992. Induction temperature of heat-shock protein synthesis in wheat. *Crop Sci.* 32:256–61
45. Burke JJ, Hatfield JL, Klein RP, Mullet JE. 1985. Accumulation of heat shock proteins in field-grown cotton. *Plant Physiol.* 78:394–98
46. Colombo SJ, Timmer VR, Colclough ML, Blumwald E. 1995. Diurnal variation in heat tolerance and heat shock protein expression in black spruce (*Picea mariana*). *Can. J. Forest Res.* 25:369–75
47. Morris GJ, Coulson G, Meyer MA, McLellan MR, Fuller BJ, et al. 1983. Cold shock—a widespread cellular reaction. *Cryo-Letters* 4:179–92
48. Danyluk J, Rassart E, Sarhan F. 1991. Gene expression during cold and heat shock in wheat. *Biochem. Cell Biol.* 69:383–91
49. Krishna P, Sacco M, Cherutti JF, Hill S. 1995. Cold-induced accumulation of hsp90 transcripts in *Brassica napus. Plant Physiol.* 107:915–23
50. Neven LG, Haskell DW, Guy CL, Denslow N, Klein PA, et al. 1992. Association of 70-kilodalton heat-shock cognate proteins with acclimation to cold. *Plant Physiol.* 99:1362–69
51. Van Berkel J, Salamini F, Gebhardt C. 1994. Transcripts accumulating during cold storage of potato (*Solanum tuberosum* L.) tubers are sequence related to stress-responsive genes. *Plant Physiol.* 104:445–52
52. Layne JR. 1991. Microclimate variability and the eurythermic natural of goldenrod gall fly (*Eurosta solidaginis*) larvae (Diptera: Tephritidae). *Can. J. Zool.* 69:614–17
53. Feder ME, Blair N, Figueras H. 1997. Natural thermal stress and heat-shock protein expression in *Drosophila* larvae and pupae. *Funct. Ecol.* 11:90–100
54. Feder ME. 1997. Necrotic fruit: a novel model system for thermal ecologists. *J. Therm. Biol.* 22:1–9
55. Wehner R, Marsh AC, Wehner S. 1992. Desert ants on a thermal tightrope. *Nature* 357:586–87
56. Gehring WJ, Wehner R. 1995. Heat shock protein synthesis and thermotolerance in *Cataglyphis*, an ant from the Sahara desert. *Proc. Natl. Acad. Sci. USA* 92:2994–98
57. Locke M, Noble EG. 1995. Stress proteins: the exercise response. *Can. J. Appl. Physiol.* 20:155–67
58. Brown IR, Rush SJ. 1996. In vivo activation of neural heat shock transcription factor HSF1 by a physiologically relevant increase in body temperature. *J. Neurosci. Res.* 44:52–57
59. Di YP, Repasky EA, Subjeck JR. 1997. Distribution of HSP70, protein kinase C, and spectrin is altered in lymphocytes during a fever-like hyperthermia exposure. *J. Cell. Physiol.* 172:44–54
60. Joplin KH, Denlinger DL. 1990. Developmental and tissue specific control of the heat shock induced 70 kDa related proteins in the flesh fly, *Sarcophaga crassipalpis. J. Insect Physiol.* 36:239–49
61. Joplin KH, Yocum GD, Denlinger DL. 1990. Cold shock elicits expression of heat shock proteins in the flesh fly *Sarcophaga crassipalpis. J. Insect Physiol.* 36:825–34
62. Yocum GD, Joplin KH, Denlinger DL. 1991. Expression of heat shock proteins

in response to high and low temperature extremes in diapausing pharate larvae of the gypsy moth *Lymantria dispar*. *Arch. Insect Biochem. Physiol.* 18:239–50
63. Lee RE, Dommel RA, Joplin KH, Denlinger DL. 1995. Cryobiology of the freeze-tolerant gall fly *Eurosta solidaginis*: overwintering energetics and heat shock proteins. *Climate Res.* 5:61–67
64. Denlinger DL, Lee RE, Yocum GD, Kukal O. 1992. Role of chilling in the acquisition of cold tolerance and the capacitation to express stress proteins in diapausing pharate larvae of the gypsy moth *Lymantria dispar*. *Arch. Insect Biochem. Physiol.* 21:271–80
65. Matz JM, LaVoi KP, Moen RJ, Blake MJ. 1996. Cold-induced heat shock protein expression in rat aorta and brown adipose tissue. *Physiol. Behav.* 60:1369–74
66. Sills NS, Gorham DA, Carey HV. 1998. Stress protein expression in a mammalian hibernator. *FASEB J.* 12:A379
67. Li GC, Nussenzweig A. 1996. Thermotolerance and heat shock proteins: possible involvement of Ku autoantigen in regulating Hsp70 expression. See Ref. 9, pp. 121–37
68. Alamillo J, Almoguera C, Bartels D, Jordano J. 1995. Constitutive expression of small heat shock proteins in vegetative tissues of the resurrection plant *Craterostigma plantagineum*. *Plant Mol. Biol.* 29:1093–99
69. Pareek A, Singla SL, Kush AK, Grover A. 1997. Distribution patterns of HSP 90 protein in rice. *Plant Sci.* 125:221–30
70. Ma E, Haddad GG. 1997. Anoxia regulates gene expression in the central nervous system of *Drosophila melanogaster*. *Brain Res. Mol. Brain Res.* 46:325–28
71. Kultz D. 1996. Plasticity and stressor specificity of osmotic and heat shock responses of *Gillichthys mirabilis* gill cells. *Am. J. Physiol.* 271:C1181–93
72. de Pomerai D. 1996. Heat-shock proteins as biomarkers of pollution. *Hum. Exp. Toxicol.* 15:279–85
73. Sanders BM, Dyer SD. 1994. Cellular stress response. *Environ. Toxicol. Chem.* 13:1209–10
74. Sanders BM. 1993. Stress proteins in aquatic organisms: an environmental perspective. *Crit. Rev. Toxicol.* 23:49–75
75. Ryan JA, Hightower LE. 1996. Stress proteins as molecular biomarkers for environmental toxicology. See Ref. 9, pp. 411–24
76. Mueller WEG, Koziol C, Kurelec B, Dapper J, Batel R, Rinkevich B. 1995. Combinatory effects of temperature stress and nonionic organic pollutants on stress protein (hsp70) gene expression in the freshwater sponge *Ephydatia fluviatilis*. *Environ. Toxicol. Chem.* 14:1203–8
77. Cochrane BJ, Irby RB, Snell TW. 1991. Effects of copper and tributylin on stress protein abundance in the rotifer *Brachionus plicatilis*. *Comp. Biochem. Physiol.* 98C:385–90
78. Krasko A, Scheffer U, Koziol C, Pancer Z, Batel R, et al. 1997. Diagnosis of sublethal stress in the marine sponge *Geodia cydonium*: application of the 70 kDa heat-shock protein and a novel biomarker, the Rab GDP dissociation inhibitor, as probes. *Aquat. Toxicol.* 37:157–68
79. Werner I, Nagel R. 1997. Stress proteins HSP60 and HSP70 in 3 species of amphipods exposed to cadmium, diazinon, dieldrin and fluoranthene. *Environ. Toxicol. Chem.* 16:2393–403
80. Ruffin P, Demuynck S, Hilbert JL, Dhainaut A. 1994. Stress protein in the polychaete annelid *Nereis diversicolor* induced by heat shock or cadmium exposure. *Biochimie* 76:423–27
81. Steinert SA, Pickwell GV. 1988. Expression of heat shock proteins and metallothionein in mussels exposed to heat stress and metal ion challenge. *Mar. Environ. Res.* 24:211–14
82. Veldhuizen Tsoerkan MB, Holwerda DA, van der Mast CA, Zandee DI. 1991. Synthesis of stress proteins under normal and heat shock conditions in gill tissue of sea mussels (*Mytilus edulis*) after chronic exposure to cadmium. *Comp. Biochem. Physiol.* 100C:699–706
83. Nascimento IA, Dickson KL, Zimmerman EG. 1996. Heat shock protein response to thermal stress in the Asiatic clam, *Corbicula fluminea*. *J. Aquat. Ecosystem Health* 5:231–38
84. Sanders BM, Martin LS, Howe SR, Nelson WG, Hegre ES, Phelps DK. 1994. Tissue-specific differences in accumulation of stress proteins in *Mytilus edulis* exposed to a range of copper concentrations. *Toxicol. Appl. Pharmacol.* 125:206–13
85. Ryan JA, Hightower LE. 1994. Evaluation of heavy-metal ion toxicity in fish cells using a combined stress protein and cytotoxicity assay. *Environ. Toxicol. Chem.* 13:1231–40
86. Dyer SD, Brooks GL, Dickson KL, Sanders BM, Zimmerman EG. 1993. Synthesis and accumulation of stress

proteins in tissues of arsenite-exposed fathead minnows *Pimephales promelas*. *Environ. Toxicol. Chem.* 12:913–24
87. Vijayan MM, Pereira C, Forsyth RB, Kennedy CJ, Iwama GK. 1997. Handling stress does not affect the expression of hepatic heat shock protein 70 and conjugation enzymes in rainbow trout treated with beta-naphthoflavone. *Life Sci.* 61:117–27
88. Van Dyk TK, Majarian WR, Konstantinov KB, Young RM, Dhurjati PS, LaRossa RA. 1994. Rapid and sensitive pollutant detection by induction of heat shock gene-bioluminescence gene fusions. *Appl. Environ. Microbiol.* 60:1414–20
89. Veldhuizen Tsoerkan MB, Holwerda DA, de Bont AM, Smaal AC, Zandee DI. 1991. A field study on stress indices in the sea mussel, *Mytilus edulis*: application of the "stress approach" in biomonitoring. *Arch. Environ. Contam. Toxicol.* 21:497–504
90. Kohler HR, Triebskorn R, Stocker W, Kloetzel PM, Alberti G. 1992. The 70 kD heat shock protein (hsp 70) in soil invertebrates: a possible tool for monitoring environmental toxicants. *Arch. Environ. Contam. Toxicol.* 22:334–38
91. Pyza E, Mak P, Kramarz P, Laskowski R. 1997. Heat-shock proteins (Hsp70) as biomarkers in ecotoxicological studies. *Ecotoxicol. Environ. Safety* 38:244–51
92. Stringham EG, Candido EPM. 1994. Transgenic hsp16-lacZ strains of the soil nematode *Caenorhabditis elegans* as biological monitors of environmental stress. *Environ. Toxicol. Chem.* 13:1211–20
93. Forsyth RB, Candido EPM, Babich SL, Iwama GK. 1997. Stress protein expression in coho salmon with bacterial kidney disease. *J. Aquat. Anim. Health* 9:18–25
94. Rose MR, Lauder GV, eds. 1996. *Adaptation*. New York/London: Academic
95. Bosch TC, Krylow SM, Bode HR, Steele RE. 1988. Thermotolerance and synthesis of heat shock proteins: These responses are present in *Hydra attenuata* but absent in *Hydra oligactis*. *Proc. Natl. Acad. Sci. USA* 85:7927–31
96. Gellner K, Praetzel G, Bosch TC. 1992. Cloning and expression of a heat-inducible hsp70 gene in two species of *Hydra* which differ in their stress response. *Eur. J. Biochem.* 210:683–91
97. Hofmann GE, Somero GN. 1996. Interspecific variation in thermal denaturation of proteins in the congeneric mussels *Mytilus trossulus* and *M. galloprovincialis*: evidence from the heat-shock response and protein ubiquitination. *Mar. Biol.* 126:65–75
98. Tomanek L, Somero GN. 1997. The effect of temperature on protein synthesis in snails of the genus *Tegula* from the sub- and intertidal zone. *Am. Zool.* 37:188A
99. Vayda ME, Yuan ML. 1994. The heat shock response of an Antarctic alga is evident at 5 degrees C. *Plant Mol. Biol.* 24:229–33
100. Berg GR, Inniss WE, Heikkila JJ. 1987. Stress proteins and thermotolerance in psychrotrophic yeasts from Arctic environments. *Can. J. Microbiol.* 33:383–89
101. Deegenaars ML, Watson K. 1997. Stress proteins and stress tolerance in an Antarctic, psychrophilic yeast, *Candida psychrophila*. *FEMS Microbiol. Lett.* 151:191–96
102. Carratu L, Maresca B. 1997. Evolutionary adaptation of hsp70 gene in Antarctic fish. *Exp. Biol. Online* 2:C5.1 (Abstr.)
103. Roberts DA, Hofmann GE, Somero GN. 1997. Heat-shock protein expression in *Mytilus californianus*: acclimatization (seasonal and tidal-height comparisons) and acclimation effects. *Biol. Bull.* 192:309–20
104. Norris CE, diIorio PJ, Schultz RJ, Hightower LE. 1995. Variation in heat shock proteins within tropical and desert species of poeciliid fishes. *Mol. Biol. Evol.* 12:1048–62
105. White CN, Hightower LE, Schultz RJ. 1994. Variation in heat-shock proteins among species of desert fishes (Poeciliidae, *Poeciliopsis*). *Mol. Biol. Evol.* 11:106–19
105a. Maresca B, Patriarcha E, Goldenberg C, Sacco M. 1988. Heat shock and cold adaptation in Antarctic fishes: a molecular approach. *Comp. Biochem. Physiol.* 90B:623–29
106. Ristic Z, Williams G, Yang G, Martin B, Fullerton S. 1996. Dehydration, damage to cellular membranes, and heat-shock proteins in maize hybrids from different climates. *J. Plant Physiol.* 149:424–32
107. Ulmasov KA, Shammakov S, Karaev K, Evgenev MB. 1992. Heat shock proteins and thermoresistance in lizards. *Proc. Natl. Acad. Sci. USA* 89:1666–70
108. Konstantopoulou I, Drosopoulou E, Scouras ZG. 1997. Variations in the heat-induced protein pattern of several *Drosophila montium* subgroup species (Diptera: Drosophilidae). *Genome* 40:132–37

109. Feder ME, Cartaño NV, Milos L, Krebs RA, Lindquist SL. 1996. Effect of engineering *Hsp70* copy number on Hsp70 expression and tolerance of ecologically relevant heat shock in larvae and pupae of *Drosophila melanogaster*. *J. Exp. Biol.* 199:1837–44
110. Nath BB, Lakhotia SC. 1989. Heat-shock response in a tropical *Chironomus*: seasonal variation in response and the effect of developmental stage and tissue type on heat shock protein synthesis. *Genome* 32:676–86
111. Hofmann GE. 1996. Molecular chaperone activity of the stress protein Hsc70 purified from an eurythermal goby, *Gillichthys mirabilis*. *Am. Zool.* 36:36A
112. McFall-Ngai M, Horwitz J. 1990. A comparative study of the thermal stability of the vertebrate eye lens: Antarctic fish to the desert iguana. *Exp. Eye Res.* 50:703–9
113. Clos J, Rabindran S, Wisniewski J, Wu C. 1993. Induction temperature of human heat shock factor is reprogrammed in a *Drosophila* cell environment. *Nature* 364:252–55
114. Carratu L, Franceschelli S, Pardini CL, Kobayashi GS, Horvath I, et al. 1996. Membrane lipid perturbation modifies the set point of the temperature of heat shock response in yeast. *Proc. Natl. Acad. Sci. USA* 93:3870–75
115. Maresca B, Kobayashi GS. 1994. Hsp70 in parasites: as an inducible protective protein and as an antigen. *Experientia* 50:1067–74
116. Kaufmann SH. 1992. The cellular immune response to heat shock proteins. *Experientia* 48:640–43
117. Polla BS. 1991. Heat shock proteins in host-parasite interactions. *Immunol. Today* 12:A38–41
118. Newport GR. 1991. Heat shock proteins as vaccine candidates. *Semin. Immunol.* 3:17–24
119. Tsuji N, Ohta M, Fujisaki K. 1997. Expression of a 70-kDa heat-shock-related protein during transformation from free-living infective larvae to the parasitic stage in *Strongyloides venezuelensis*. *Parasitol. Res.* 83:99–102
120. Van der Ploeg LH, Giannini SH, Cantor CR. 1985. Heat shock genes: regulatory role for differentiation in parasitic protozoa. *Science* 228:1443–46
121. Neumann S, Ziv E, Lantner F, Schechter I. 1993. Regulation of HSP70 gene expression during the life cycle of the parasitic helminth *Schistosoma mansoni*. *Eur. J. Biochem.* 212:589–96
122. van Leeuwen MA. 1995. Heat-shock and stress response of the parasitic nematode *Haemonchus contortus*. *Parasitol. Res.* 81:706–9
123. Ernani FP, Teale JM. 1993. Release of stress proteins from *Mesocestoides corti* is a brefeldin A-inhibitable process: evidence for active export of stress proteins. *Infect. Immun.* 61:2596–601
124. Syin C, Goldman ND. 1996. Cloning of a *Plasmodium falciparum* gene related to the human 60-kDa heat shock protein. *Mol. Biochem. Parasitol.* 79:13–19
125. Cluss RG, Boothby JT. 1990. Thermoregulation of protein synthesis in *Borrelia burgdorferi*. *Infect. Immun.* 58:1038–42
126. Hubel A, Krobitsch S, Horauf A, Clos J. 1997. The *Leishmania major* Hsp100 is required chiefly in the mammalian stage of the parasite. *Mol. Cell. Biol.* 17:5987–95
127. Giambiagi-de Marval M, Souto-Padron T, Rondinelli E. 1996. Characterization and cellular distribution of heat-shock proteins HSP70 and HSP60 in *Trypanosoma cruzi*. *Exp. Parasitol.* 83:335–45
128. Daubenberger C, Heussler V, Gobright E, Wijngaard P, Clevers HC, et al. 1997. Molecular characterisation of a cognate 70 kDa heat shock protein of the protozoan *Theileria parva*. *Mol. Biochem. Parasitol.* 85:265–69
129. Shearer GJ, Birge CH, Yuckenberg PD, Kobayashi GS, Medoff G. 1987. Heat-shock proteins induced during the mycelial-to-yeast transitions of strains of *Histoplasma capsulatum*. *J. Gen. Microbiol.* 133:3375–82
130. Maresca B. 1995. Unraveling the secrets of *Histoplasma capsulatum*. A model to study morphogenic adaptation during parasite host/host interaction. *Verh. K. Acad. Geneeskd. Belg.* 57:133–56
131. Clark TG, Abrahamsen MS, White MW. 1996. Developmental expression of heat shock protein 90 in *Eimeria bovis*. *Mol. Biochem. Parasitol.* 78:259–63
132. Tirard CT, Grossfeld RM, Volety AK, Chu FLE. 1995. Heat shock proteins of the oyster parasite *Perkinsus marinus*. *Dis. Aquat. Organisms* 22:147–51
133. Ulmasov KA, Ovezmukhammedov A, Karaev KK, Evgenev MB. 1988. Molecular mechanisms of adaptation to hyperthermia in higher organisms. III. Induction of heat-shock proteins in two *Leishmania* species. *Mol. Biol.* 22: 1583–89

134. Ryan MT, Naylor DJ, Hoj PB, Clark MS, Hoogenraad NJ. 1997. The role of molecular chaperones in mitochondrial protein import and folding. *Int. Rev. Cytol.* 174:127–93
135. Germot A, Philippe H, Le Guyader H. 1997. Evidence for loss of mitochondria in microsporidia from a mitochondrial-type HSP70 in *Nosema locustae*. *Mol. Biochem. Parasitol.* 87:159–68
136. Bui ET, Bradley PJ, Johnson PJ. 1996. A common evolutionary origin for mitochondria and hydrogenosomes. *Proc. Natl. Acad. Sci. USA* 93:9651–56
137. Sogin ML. 1997. Organelle origins: energy-producing symbionts in early eukaryotes? *Curr. Biol.* 7:R315–17
138. Hofmann CJ, Rensing SA, Hauber MM, Martin WF, Muller SB, et al. 1994. The smallest known eukaryotic genomes encode a protein gene: towards an understanding of nucleomorph functions. *Mol. Gen. Genet.* 243:600–4
139. Germot A, Philippe H, Le Guyader H. 1996. Presence of a mitochondrial-type 70-kDa heat shock protein in *Trichomonas vaginalis* suggests a very early mitochondrial endosymbiosis in eukaryotes. *Proc. Natl. Acad. Sci. USA* 93:14614–17
140. Baumann P, Moran NA, Baumann L. 1997. The evolution and genetics of aphid endosymbionts. *BioScience* 47:12–20
141. Aksoy S. 1995. Molecular analysis of the endosymbionts of tsetse flies: 16S rDNA locus and over-expression of a chaperonin. *Insect Mol. Biol.* 4:23–29
142. Moran NA, Von Dohlen CD, Baumann P. 1995. Faster evolutionary rates in endosymbiotic bacteria than in cospeciating insect hosts. *J. Mol. Evol.* 41:727–31
143. Moran NA. 1996. Accelerated evolution and Muller's rachet in endosymbiotic bacteria. *Proc. Natl. Acad. Sci. USA* 93:2873–78
144. Morioka M, Ishikawa H. 1992. Mutualism based on stress: selective synthesis and phosphorylation of a stress protein by an intracellular symbiont. *J. Biochem.* 111:431–35
145. Hong HK, Choi JY, Ahn TI. 1994. Molecular biological studies on the heat-shock responses in *Amoeba proteus*: I. Detection of heat-shock proteins. *Korean J. Zool.* 37:554–64
146. Choi EY, Ahn GS, Jeon KW. 1991. Elevated levels of stress proteins associated with bacterial symbiosis in *Amoeba proteus* and soybean root nodule cells. *Biosystems* 25:205–12
147. Feder ME, Karr TL. 1997. Evolutionarily significant consequences of the heat shock response for *Drosophila* and its endosymbiont *Wolbachia*. *Am. Zool.* 37:8A
148. Dix DJ. 1997. Hsp70 expression and function during gametogenesis. *Cell Stress Chaperones* 2:73–77
149. Lin JC, Song CW. 1993. Heat shock gene expression and development. I. An overview of fungal, plant, and poikilothermic animal developmental systems. *Dev. Genet.* 14:1–5
150. Winter J, Sinibaldi R. 1991. The expression of heat shock protein and cognate genes during plant development. *Results Prob. Cell Differ.* 17:85–105
151. Mosser DD, Duchaine J, Bourget L, Martin LH. 1993. Heat shock gene expression and development. II. An overview of mammalian and avian developmental systems. *Dev. Genet.* 14: 87–91
152. Heikkila JJ, Ohan N, Tam Y, Ali A. 1997. Heat shock protein gene expression during *Xenopus* development. *Cell. Mol. Life Sci.* 53:114–21
153. Muller WU, Li GC, Goldstein LS. 1985. Heat does not induce synthesis of heat shock proteins or thermotolerance in the earliest stage of mouse embryo development. *Int. J. Hypertherm.* 1:97–102
154. Edwards JL, Ealy AD, Monterroso VH, Hansen PJ. 1997. Ontogeny of temperature-regulated heat shock protein 70 synthesis in preimplantation bovine embryos. *Mol. Reprod. Dev.* 48: 25–33
155. Dura JM. 1981. Stage dependent synthesis of heat shock induced proteins in early embryos of *Drosophila melanogaster*. *Mol. Gen. Genet.* 184: 381–85
156. Welte MA, Tetrault JM, Dellavalle RP, Lindquist SL. 1993. A new method for manipulating transgenes: engineering heat tolerance in a complex, multicellular organism. *Curr. Biol.* 3:842–53
157. Gagliardi D, Breton C, Chaboud A, Vergne P, Dumas C. 1995. Expression of heat shock factor and heat shock protein 70 genes during maize pollen development. *Plant Mol. Biol.* 29:841–56
158. Hendrey J, Kola I. 1991. Thermolability of mouse oocytes is due to the lack of expression and/or inducibility of Hsp70. *Mol. Reprod. Dev.* 28:1–8
159. Curci A, Bevilacqua A, Mangia F. 1987. Lack of heat-shock response in preovulatory mouse oocytes. *Dev. Biol.* 123:154–60

160. Curci A, Bevilacqua A, Fiorenza MT, Mangia F. 1991. Developmental regulation of heat-shock response in mouse oogenesis: identification of differentially responsive oocyte classes during Graafian follicle development. *Dev. Biol.* 144:362–68
161. Zakeri ZF, Welch WJ, Wolgemuth DJ. 1990. Characterization and inducibility of hsp 70 proteins in the male mouse germ line. *J. Cell Biol.* 111:1785–92
162. Bedard PA, Brandhorst BP. 1986. Translational activation of maternal mRNA encoding the heat-shock protein hsp90 during sea urchin embryogenesis. *Dev. Biol.* 117:286–93
163. Gordon S, Bharadwaj S, Hnatov A, Ali A, Ovsenek N. 1997. Distinct stress-inducible and developmentally regulated heat shock transcription factors in *Xenopus* oocytes. *Dev. Biol.* 181:47–63
164. Feder JH, Rossi JM, Solomon J, Solomon N, Lindquist S. 1992. The consequences of expressing Hsp70 in *Drosophila* cells at normal temperatures. *Genes Dev.* 6:1402–13
165. Mitchell HK, Moller G, Petersen NS, Lipps-Sarmiento L. 1979. Specific protection from phenocopy induction by heat shock. *Dev. Genet.* 1:181–92
166. Welte MA, Duncan I, Lindquist S. 1995. The basis for a heat-induced developmental defect: defining crucial lesions. *Genes Dev.* 9:2240–50
167. Wehmeyer N, Hernandez LD, Finkelstein RR, Vierling E. 1996. Synthesis of small heat-shock proteins is part of the developmental program of late seed maturation. *Plant Physiol.* 112:747–57
168. Duck N, McCormick S, Winter J. 1989. Heat shock protein Hsp70 cognate gene expression in vegetative and reproductive organs of *Lycopersicon esculentum*. *Proc. Natl. Acad. Sci. USA* 86:3674–78
169. Coca MA, Almoguera C, Jordano J. 1994. Expression of sunflower low-molecular-weight heat-shock proteins during embryogenesis and persistence after germination: localization and possible functional implications. *Plant Mol. Biol.* 25:479–92
170. Helm KW, Petersen NS, Abernethy RH. 1989. Heat-shock response of germinating embryos of wheat: effects of imbibition time and seed vigor. *Plant Physiol.* 90:598–605
171. Sanchez Y, Taulien J, Borkovich KA, Lindquist S. 1992. Hsp104 is required for tolerance to many forms of stress. *EMBO J.* 11:2357–64
172. Silva AM, Juliani MH, da Costa JJ, Bonato MC. 1987. Acquisition of thermotolerance during development of *Blastocladiella emersonii*. *Biochem. Biophys. Res. Commun.* 144:491–98
173. Liang P, Amons R, Clegg JS, MacRae TH. 1997. Molecular characterization of a small heat shock/alpha-crystallin protein in encysted *Artemia* embryos. *J. Biol. Chem.* 272:19051–58
174. Liang P, Amons R, Macrae TH, Clegg JS. 1997. Purification, structure and in vitro molecular-chaperone activity of *Artemia* p26, a small heat-shock/alpha-crystallin protein. *Eur. J. Biochem.* 243:225–32
175. Jackson SA, Clegg JS. 1996. Ontogeny of low molecular weight stress protein p26 during early development of the brine shrimp, *Artemia franciscana*. *J. Exp. Biol.* 200:467–75
176. Clegg JS, Jackson SA, Liang P, MacRae TH. 1995. Nuclear-cytoplasmic translocations of protein p26 during aerobic-anoxic transitions in embryos of *Artemia franciscana*. *Exp. Cell Res.* 219:1–7
177. Clegg JS, Jackson SA, Warner AH. 1994. Extensive intracellular translocations of a major protein accompany anoxia in embryos of *Artemia franciscana*. *Exp. Cell Res.* 212:77–83
178. Clegg JS, Jackson SA. 1992. Aerobic heat shock activates trehalose synthesis in embryos of *Artemia franciscana*. *FEBS Lett.* 303:45–47
179. Anchordoguy TJ, Hand SC. 1994. Acute blockage of the ubiquitin-mediated proteolytic pathway during invertebrate quiescence. *Am. J. Physiol.* 267:R895–900
180. Krebs RA, Feder ME, Lee J. 1998. Heritability of expression of the 70-kD heat-shock protein in *Drosophila melanogaster* and its relevance to the evolution of thermotolerance. *Evolution* 52:841–47
181. Davis WL, Jacoby BH, Goodman DB. 1994. Immunolocalization of ubiquitin in degenerating insect flight muscle. *Histochem. J.* 26:298–305
182. Sarge KD, Bray AE, Goodson ML. 1995. Altered stress response in testis. *Nature* 374:126
183. Sarge KD. 1995. Male germ cell-specific alteration in temperature set point of the cellular stress response. *J. Biol. Chem.* 270:18745–48
184. Holbrook NJ, Udelsman R. 1994. Heat shock protein gene expression in response to physiologic stress and aging. See Ref. 4, pp. 577–93
185. Lee YK, Manalo D, Liu AY. 1996. Heat shock response, heat shock transcrip-

tion factor and cell aging. *Biol. Signals* 5:180–91
186. Shpund S, Gershon D. 1997. Alterations in the chaperone activity of HSP70 in aging organisms. *Arch. Gerontol. Geriatr.* 24:125–31
187. Wheeler JC, Bieschke ET, Tower J. 1995. Muscle-specific expression of *Drosophila* hsp70 in response to aging and oxidative stress. *Proc. Natl. Acad. Sci. USA* 92:10408–12
188. Marin R, Valet JP, Tanguay RM. 1993. Heat shock induces changes in the expression and binding of ubiquitin in senescent *Drosophila melanogaster*. *Dev. Genet.* 14:78–86
189. Lithgow GJ, White TM, Hinerfeld DA, Johnson TE. 1994. Thermotolerance of a long-lived mutant of *Caenorhabditis elegans*. *J. Gerontol.* 49B:270–76
190. Lithgow GJ, White TM, Melov S, Johnson TE. 1995. Thermotolerance and extended life-span conferred by single-gene mutations and induced by thermal stress. *Proc. Natl. Acad. Sci. USA* 92:7540–44
191. Lithgow GJ. 1996. Invertebrate gerontology: the *age* mutations of *Caenorhabditis elegans*. *BioEssays* 18:809–15
192. Bond JA, Gonzalez CRM, Bradley BP. 1993. Age-dependent expression of proteins in the cladoceran *Daphnia magna* under normal and heat-stress conditions. *Comp. Biochem. Physiol.* 106B:913–17
193. Khazaeli AA, Tatar M, Pletcher SD, Curtsinger JW. 1997. Heat-induced longevity extension in *Drosophila*. I. Heat treatment, mortality, and thermotolerance. *J. Gerontol.* 52A:B48–52
194. Tatar M, Khazaeli AA, Curtsinger JW. 1997. Chaperoning extended life. *Nature* 390:30
195. Dhahbi JM, Mote PL, Tillman JB, Walford RL, Spindler SR. 1997. Dietary energy tissue-specifically regulates endoplasmic reticulum chaperone gene expression in the liver of mice. *J. Nutr.* 127:1758–64
196. Heydari AR, Conrad CC, Richardson A. 1995. Expression of heat shock genes in hepatocytes is affected by age and food restriction in rats. *J. Nutr.* 125:410–18
197. Pahlavani MA, Harris MD, Moore SA, Richardson A. 1996. Expression of heat shock protein 70 in rat spleen lymphocytes is affected by age but not by food restriction. *J. Nutr.* 126:2069–75
198. Lu Q, Wallrath LL, Granok H, Elgin SC. 1993. Expression of heat shock protein 70 is altered by age and diet at the level of transcription. *Mol. Cell Biol.* 13:2909–18
199. Masoro EJ. 1996. Possible mechanisms underlying the antiaging actions of caloric restriction. *Toxicol. Pathol.* 24:738–41
200. Parsell DA, Lindquist S. 1993. The function of heat-shock proteins in stress tolerance: degradation and reactivation of damaged proteins. *Annu. Rev. Genet.* 27:437–96
201. Parsell DA, Lindquist S. 1994. Heat shock proteins and stress tolerance. See Ref. 9, pp. 457–94
202. Bensaude O, Bellier S, Dubois MF, Giannoni F, Nguyen VT. 1996. Heat-shock induced protein modifications and modulation of enzyme activities. See Ref. 9, pp. 199–219
203. diIorio PJ, Holsinger K, Schultz RJ, Hightower LE. 1996. Quantitative evidence that both Hsc70 and Hsp70 contribute to thermal adaptation in hybrids of the livebearing fishes *Poeciliopsis*. *Cell Stress Chaperones* 1:139–47
204. Feder ME, Lindquist SL. 1992. Evolutionary loss of a heat shock protein. *Am. Zool.* 32:51A (Abstr.)
205. Whitesell L, Cook P. 1996. Stable and specific binding of heat shock protein 90 by geldanamycin disrupts glucocorticoid receptor function in intact cells. *Mol. Endocrinol.* 10:705–12
206. Elia G, Santoro MG. 1994. Regulation of heat shock protein synthesis by quercetin in human erythroleukaemia cells. *Biochem. J.* 300:201–9
207. Bonham-Smith PC, Kapoor M, Bewley JD. 1987. Establishment of thermotolerance in maize by exposure to stresses other than a heat shock does not require heat shock protein synthesis. *Plant Physiol.* 85:575–80
208. Xiao CM, Mascarenhas JP. 1985. High temperature-induced thermotolerance in pollen tubes of *Tradescantia* and heat-shock proteins. *Plant Physiol.* 78:887–90
209. VanBogelen RA, Acton MA, Neidhardt FC. 1987. Induction of the heat shock regulon does not produce thermotolerance in *Escherichia coli*. *Genes Dev.* 1:525–31
210. Yocum GD, Denlinger DL. 1992. Prolonged thermotolerance in the flesh fly *Sarcophaga crassipalpis* does not require continuous expression or persistence of the 72 kDa heat-shock protein. *J. Insect Physiol.* 38:603–9
211. Boon-Niermeijer EK, Tuyl M, van de Scheur H. 1986. Evidence for two states

of thermotolerance. *Int. J. Hypertherm.* 2:93–105

212. Smith BJ, Yaffe MP. 1991. Uncoupling thermotolerance from the induction of heat shock proteins. *Proc. Natl. Acad. Sci. USA* 88:11091–94
213. Easton DP, Rutledge PS, Spotila JR. 1987. Heat shock protein induction and induced thermal tolerance are independent in adult salamanders. *J. Exp. Zool.* 241:263–67
214. Dingley F, Maynard Smith J. 1968. Temperature acclimatization in the absence of protein synthesis of *Drosophila subobscura. J. Insect Physiol.* 14:1185–94
215. Finnell RH, Van Waes M, Bennett GD, Eberwine JH. 1993. Lack of concordance between heat shock proteins and the development of tolerance to teratogen-induced neural tube defects. *Dev. Genet.* 14:137–47
216. Fisher B, Kraft P, Hahn GM, Anderson RL. 1992. Thermotolerance in the absence of induced heat shock proteins in a murine lymphoma. *Cancer Res.* 52:2854–61
217. Watson K, Dunlop G, Cavicchioli R. 1984. Mitochondrial and cytoplasmic protein syntheses are not required for heat shock acquisition of ethanol and thermotolerance in yeast. *FEBS Lett.* 172:299–302
218. Widelitz RB, Magun BE, Gerner EW. 1986. Effects of cycloheximide on thermotolerance expression, heat shock protein synthesis, and heat shock protein mRNA accumulation in rat fibroblasts. *Mol. Cell Biol.* 6:1088–94
219. Jozwiak Z, Leyko W. 1992. Role of membrane components in thermal injury of cells and development of thermotolerance. *Int. J. Radiat. Biol.* 62:743–56
220. Lindquist S. 1993. Autoregulation of the heat-shock response. In *Translational Regulation of Gene Expression 2*, ed. J Ilan, pp. 279–320. New York: Plenum
221. Krebs RA, Feder ME. 1998. Hsp70 and larval thermotolerance in *Drosophila melanogaster*: How much is enough and when is more too much? *J. Insect Physiol.* 44:1091–1101
222. Krebs RA, Feder ME. 1997. Deleterious consequences of Hsp70 overexpression in *Drosophila melanogaster* larvae. *Cell Stress Chaperones* 2:60–71
223. Krebs RA, Feder ME. 1997. Natural variation in the expression of the heat-shock protein Hsp70 in a population of *Drosophila melanogaster*, and its correlation with tolerance of ecologically relevant thermal stress. *Evolution* 51: 173–79
224. Welte MA. 1994. *Thermotolerance in Drosophila embryos: the role of hsp70 and the basis for a specific phenocopy.* Ph.D. thesis. Univ. Chicago. 230 pp.
225. Krebs RA, Feder ME. 1998. Experimental manipulation of the cost of thermal acclimation in *Drosophila melanogaster. Biol. J. Linn. Soc.* 63: 593–601
226. Hoffmann AA. 1995. Acclimation: increasing survival at a cost. *Trends Ecol. Evol.* 10:1–2
227. Calow P. 1991. Physiological costs of combating chemical toxicants: ecological implications. *Comp. Biochem. Physiol.* 100C:3–6
228. Koehn RK, Bayne BL. 1989. Towards a physiological and genetical understanding of the energetics of the stress response. *Biol. J. Linn. Soc.* 37:157–71
229. Dorner AJ, Krane MG, Kaufman RJ. 1988. Reduction of endogenous GRP78 levels improves secretion of a heterologous protein in CHO cells. *Mol. Cell Biol.* 8:4063–70
230. Dorner AJ, Wasley LC, Kaufman RJ. 1992. Overexpression of GRP78 mitigates stress induction of glucose regulated proteins and blocks secretion of selective proteins in Chinese hamster ovary cells. *EMBO J.* 11:1563–71
231. Dorner AJ, Kaufman RJ. 1994. The levels of endoplasmic reticulum proteins and ATP affect folding and secretion of selective proteins. *Biologicals* 22:103–12
232. Ryan C, Stevens TH, Schlesinger MJ. 1992. Inhibitory effects of HSP70 chaperones on nascent polypeptides. *Protein Sci.* 1:980–85
233. Heckathorn SA, Poeller GJ, Coleman JS, Hallberg RL. 1996. Nitrogen availability alters patterns of accumulation of heat stress-induced proteins in plants. *Oecologia* 105:413–18
234. Heckathorn SA, Poeller GJ, Coleman JS, Hallberg RL. 1996. Nitrogen availability and vegetative development influence the response of ribulose 1,5-bisphosphate carboxylase/oxygenase, phosphoenolpyruvate carboxylase, and heat-shock protein content to heat stress in *Zea mays* L. *Int. J. Plant Sci.* 157:588–95
235. Dietz TJ, Somero GN. 1993. Species- and tissue-specific synthesis patterns for heat-shock proteins hsp70 and hsp90 in several marine teleost fishes. *Physiol. Zool.* 66:863–80

236. Abravaya K, Phillips B, Morimoto RI. 1991. Attenuation of the heat shock response in HeLa cells is mediated by the release of bound heat shock transcription factor and is modulated by changes in growth and in heat shock temperatures. *Genes Dev.* 5:2117–27
237. Sarge KD, Cullen KE. 1997. Regulation of hsp expression during rodent spermatogenesis. *Cell. Mol. Life Sci.* 53:191–97
238. Koban M, Graham G, Prosser CL. 1987. Induction of heat-shock protein synthesis in teleost hepatocytes: effects of acclimation temperature. *Physiol. Zool.* 60:290–96
239. Deleted in proof
240. Favatier F, Bornman L, Hightower LE, Gnther E, Polla BS. 1997. Variation in *hsp* gene expression and Hsp polymorphism: Do they contribute to differential disease susceptibility and stress tolerance? *Cell Stress Chaperones* 2: 141–55
241. Engman DM, Sias SR, Gabe JD, Donelson JE, Dragon EA. 1989. Comparison of HSP70 genes from two strains of *Trypanosoma cruzi. Mol. Biochem. Parasitol.* 37:285–87
242. Engman DM, Reddy LV, Donelson JE, Kirchhoff LV. 1987. *Trypanosoma cruzi* exhibits inter- and intra-strain heterogeneity in molecular karyotype and chromosomal gene location. *Mol. Biochem. Parasitol.* 22:115–23
243. Snutch TP, Baillie DL. 1984. A high degree of DNA strain polymorphism associated with the major heat shock gene in *Caenorhabditis elegans. Mol. Gen. Genet.* 195:329–35
244. Hamet P, Kaiser MA, Sun Y, Page V, Vincent M, et al. 1996. HSP27 locus cosegregates with left ventricular mass independently of blood pressure. *Hypertension* 28:1112–17
245. Wallich R, Helmes C, Schaible UE, Lobet Y, Moter SE, et al. 1992. Evaluation of genetic divergence among *Borrelia burgdorferi* isolates by use of OspA, fla, HSP60, and HSP70 gene probes. *Infect. Immun.* 60:4856–66
246. Hamet P, Kong D, Pravenec M, Kunes J, Kren V, et al. 1992. Restriction fragment length polymorphism of *hsp70* gene, localized in the RT1 complex, is associated with hypertension in spontaneously hypertensive rats. *Hypertension* 19:611–14
247. Grosz MD, Skow LC, Stone RT. 1994. An AluI polymorphism at the bovine 70 kD heat-shock protein-1 (HSP70-1) locus. *Anim. Genet.* 25:196
248. Jorgensen JA, Nguyen HT. 1995. Genetic analysis of heat shock proteins in maize. *Theor. Appl. Genet.* 91:38–46
249. Ottaviano E, Sari Gorla M, Pe E, Frova C. 1991. Molecular markers, RFLPs and Hsps for the genetic dissection of thermotolerance in maize. *Theor. Appl. Genet.* 81:713–19
250. Dimascio JA, Sweeney PM, Danneberger TK, Kamalay JC. 1994. Analysis of heat shock response in perennial ryegrass using maize heat shock protein clones. *Crop Sci.* 34:798–804
251. Goldschmidt-Clermont M. 1980. Two genes for the major heat-shock protein of *Drosophila melanogaster* arranged as an inverted repeat. *Nucleic Acids Res.* 8:235–52
252. Ish-Horowicz D, Pinchin SM. 1980. Genomic organization of the 87A7 and 87C1 heat-induced loci of *Drosophila melanogaster. J. Mol. Biol.* 142:231–45
253. Leigh-Brown AJ, Ish-Horowicz D. 1981. Evolution of the 87A and 87C heat-shock loci in *Drosophila. Nature* 290:677–82
254. McKechnie SW, Halford MM, McColl G, Hoffmann AA. 1998. Both allelic variation and expression of nuclear and cytoplasmic transcripts of *hsr-omega* are closely associated with thermal phenotype in *Drosophila. Proc. Natl. Acad. Sci. USA* 95:2423–28
255. Ish-Horowicz D, Pinchin SM, Schedl P, Artavanis-Tsakonas S, Mirault ME. 1979. Genetic and molecular analysis of the 87A7 and 87C1 heat-inducible loci of *D. melanogaster. Cell* 18:1351–58
256. Lis JT, Ish-Horowicz D, Pinchin SM. 1981. Genomic organization and transcription of the alpha beta heat shock DNA in *Drosophila melanogaster. Nucleic Acids Res.* 9:5297–310
257. Lis JT, Prestidge L, Hogness DS. 1978. A novel arrangement of tandemly repeated genes at a major heat shock site in *D. melanogaster. Cell* 14:901–19
258. Mirault ME, Goldschmidt-Clermont M, Artavanis-Tsakonas S, Schedl P. 1979. Organization of the multiple genes for the 70,000-dalton heat-shock protein in *Drosophila melanogaster. Proc. Natl. Acad. Sci. USA* 76:5254–58
259. Craig EA, McCarthy BJ, Wadsworth SC. 1979. Sequence organization of two recombinant plasmids containing genes for the major heat shock-induced protein of *D. melanogaster. Cell* 16:575–88
260. Artavanis-Tsakonas S, Schedl P, Mirault ME, Moran L, Lis J. 1979. Genes for the 70,000 dalton heat shock protein in two

cloned *D. melanogaster* DNA segments. *Cell* 17:9–18
261. Holmgren R, Livak K, Morimoto R, Freund R, Meselson M. 1979. Studies of cloned sequences from four *Drosophila* heat shock loci. *Cell* 18:1359–70
262. Sun CW, Griffen S, Callis J. 1997. A model for the evolution of polyubiquitin genes from the study of *Arabidopsis thaliana* ecotypes. *Plant Mol. Biol.* 34:745–58
263. Ristic Z, Gifford DJ, Cass DD. 1991. Heat shock proteins in two lines of *Zea mays* L. that differ in drought and heat resistance. *Plant Physiol.* 97:1430–34
264. Colombo SJ, Colclough ML, Timmer VR, Blumwald E. 1992. Clonal variation in heat tolerance and heat shock protein expression in black spruce. *Silvae Genet.* 41:234–39
265. Fender SE, O'Connell MA. 1989. Heat shock protein expression in thermotolerant and thermosensitive lines of cotton. *Plant Cell Rep.* 8:37–40
266. Malayer JR, Hansen PJ. 1990. Differences between Brahman and Holstein cows in heat-shock induced alterations of protein synthesis and secretion by oviducts and uterine endometrium. *J. Anim. Sci.* 68:266–80
267. Otsuka Y, Takano TS, Yamazaki T. 1997. Genetic variation in the expression of the six hsp genes in the presence of heat shock in *Drosophila melanogaster*. *Genes Genetic Syst.* 72:19–24
268. Jorgensen JA, Weng J, Ho THD, Nguyen HT. 1992. Genotype-specific heat shock proteins in two maize inbreds. *Plant Cell Rep.* 11:576–80
269. Frova C, Gorla MS. 1993. Quantitative expression of maize Hsps: genetic dissection and association with thermotolerance. *Theor. Appl. Genet.* 86:213–20
270. Weng J, Nguyen HT. 1992. Differences in the heat-shock response between thermotolerant and thermosusceptible cultivars of hexaploid wheat. *Theor. Appl. Genet.* 84:941–46
271. Brown DC, Bradley BP, Tedengren M. 1995. Genetic and environmental regulation of HSP70 expression. *Mar. Env. Res.* 39:181–84
272. Caruso M, Sacco M, Medoff G, Maresca B. 1987. Heat shock 70 gene is differentially expressed in *Histoplasma capsulatum* strains with different levels of thermotolerance and pathogenicity. *Mol. Microbiol.* 1:151–58
273. Lyashko VN, Vikulova VK, Chernikov VG, Ivanov VI, Ulmasov KA, et al. 1994. Comparison of the heat shock response in ethnically and ecologically different human populations. *Proc. Natl. Acad. Sci. USA* 91:12492–95
274. Bettencourt BR, Feder ME, Cavicchi S. 1997. Laboratory evolution of Hsp70 expression in *Drosophila melanogaster*: functional consequences and molecular bases. *Am. Zool.* 37:189A (Abstr.)
275. McColl G, Hoffmann AA, McKechnie SW. 1996. Response of two heat shock genes to selection for knockdown heat resistance in *Drosophila melanogaster*. *Genetics* 143:1615–27
276. Fender SE, O'Connell MA. 1990. Expression of the heat shock response in a tomato interspecific hybrid is not intermediate between the two parental responses. *Plant Physiol.* 93:1140–46
277. Gaugler R, Wilson M, Shearer P. 1997. Field release and environmental fate of a transgenic entomopathogenic nematode. *Biol. Control* 9:75–80
278. Hashmi S, Hashmi G, Glazer I, Gaugler R. 1998. Thermal response of *Heterorhabditis bacteriophora* transformed with the *Caenorhabditis elegans* hsp70 encoding gene. *J. Exp. Zool.* 281:164–70
279. Trent JD. 1996. A review of acquired thermotolerance, heat-shock proteins, and molecular chaperones in Archaea. *FEMS Micro. Rev.* 18:249–58
280. Holden JF, Baross JA. 1993. Enhanced thermotolerance and temperature-induced changes in protein composition in the hyperthermophilic archaeon ES4. *J. Bacteriol.* 175:2839–43
281. Hamilton PT, Reeve JN. 1985. Structure of genes and an insertion element in the methane producing archaebacterium *Methanobrevibacter smithii*. *Mol. Gen. Genet.* 200:47–59
282. Waldmann T, Nimmesgern E, Nitsch M, Peters J, Pfeifer G, et al. 1995. The thermosome of *Thermoplasma acidophilum* and its relationship to the eukaryotic chaperonin TRiC. *Eur. J. Biochem.* 227:848–56
283. Phipps BM, Typke D, Heger R, Volker S, Hoffmann A, et al. 1993. Structure of a molecular chaperone from a thermophilic archaebacterium. *Nature* 361:475–77
284. Nitsch M, Klumpp M, Lupas A, Baumeister W. 1997. The thermosome: alternating alpha and beta-subunits within the chaperonin of the archaeon *Thermoplasma acidophilum*. *J. Mol. Biol.* 267:142–49
285. Lewis VA, Hynes GM, Zheng D, Saibil H, Willison K. 1992. T-complex polypeptide-1 is a subunit of a het-

eromeric particle in the eukaryotic cytosol. *Nature* 358:249–52
286. Trent JD, Nimmesgern E, Wall JS, Hartl FU, Horwich AL. 1991. A molecular chaperone from a thermophilic archaebacterium is related to the eukaryotic protein t-complex polypeptide-1. *Nature* 354:490–93
287. Hendrick JP, Hartl FU. 1995. The role of molecular chaperones in protein folding. *FASEB J.* 9:1559–69
288. Eggers DK, Welch WJ, Hansen WJ. 1997. Complexes between nascent polypeptides and their molecular chaperones in the cytosol of mammalian cells. *Mol. Biol. Cell* 8:1559–73
289. Burston SG, Clarke AR. 1995. Molecular chaperones: physical and mechanistic properties. *Essays Biochem.* 29:125–36
290. Trent JD, Kagawa HK, Yaoi T, Olle E, Zaluzec NJ. 1997. Chaperonin filaments: the archaeal cytoskeleton? *Proc. Natl. Acad. Sci. USA* 94:5383–88
291. Dascher CC, Poddar SK, Maniloff J. 1990. Heat shock response in mycoplasmas, genome-limited organisms. *J. Bacteriol.* 172:1823–27
292. Gupta RS, Singh B. 1994. Phylogenetic analysis of 70 kD heat shock protein sequences suggests a chimeric origin for the eukaryotic cell nucleus. *Curr. Biol.* 4:1104–14
293. Bustard K, Gupta RS. 1997. The sequences of heat shock protein 40 (DnaJ) homologs provide evidence for a close evolutionary relationship between the *Deinococcus thermus* group and Cyanobacteria. *J. Mol. Evol.* 45:193–205
294. Gupta RS, Bustard K, Falah M, Singh D. 1997. Sequencing of heat shock protein 70 (DnaK) homologs from *Deinococcus proteolyticus* and *Thermomicrobium roseum* and their integration in a protein-based phylogeny of prokaryotes. *J. Bacteriol.* 179:345–57
295. Gupta RS. 1995. Phylogenetic analysis of the 90 kD heat shock family of protein sequences and an examination of the relationship among animals, plants, and fungi species. *Mol. Biol. Evol.* 12:1063–73
296. Gupta RS, Aitken K, Falah M, Singh B. 1994. Cloning of *Giardia lamblia* heat shock protein HSP70 homologs: implications regarding origin of eukaryotic cells and of endoplasmic reticulum. *Proc. Natl. Acad. Sci. USA* 91:2895–99
297. Gupta RS, Singh B. 1992. Cloning of the HSP70 gene from *Halobacterium marismortui*: relatedness of archaebacterial HSP70 to its eubacterial homologs and a model for the evolution of the HSP70 gene. *J. Bacteriol.* 174:4594–605
298. Boorstein WR, Ziegelhoffer T, Craig EA. 1994. Molecular evolution of the HSP70 multigene family. *J. Mol. Evol.* 38:1–17
299. Rubin DM, Mehta AD, Zhu J, Shoham S, Chen X, et al. 1993. Genomic structure and sequence analysis of *Drosophila melanogaster* HSC70 genes. *Gene* 128:155–63
300. Tavaria M, Gabriele T, Kola I, Anderson RL. 1996. A hitchhiker's guide to the human Hsp70 family. *Cell Stress Chaperones* 1:23–28
301. de Jong WW, Leunissen JA, Voorter CE. 1993. Evolution of the alpha-crystallin/small heat-shock protein family. *Mol. Biol. Evol.* 10:103–26
302. Ohta T. 1994. Further examples of evolution by gene duplication revealed through DNA sequence comparisons. *Genetics* 138:1331–37
303. Benedict MQ, Cockburn AF, Seawright JA. 1993. The Hsp70 heat-shock gene family of the mosquito *Anopheles albimanus*. *Insect Mol. Biol.* 2:93–102
304. Drosopoulou E, Konstantopoulou I, Scouras ZG. 1996. The heat shock genes in the *Drosophila montium* subgroup: chromosomal localization and evolutionary implications. *Chromosoma* 105:104–10
305. Pardali E, Feggou E, Drosopoulou E, Konstantopoulou I, Scouras ZG, Mavragani-Tsipidou P. 1996. The Afrotropical *Drosophila montium* subgroup: Balbiani ring 1, polytene chromosomes, and heat shock response of *Drosophila vulcana*. *Genome* 39:588–97
306. Sanchez Y, Lindquist SL. 1990. HSP104 required for induced thermotolerance. *Science* 248:1112–15
307. Feder ME, Block BA. 1991. On the future of physiological ecology. *Funct. Ecol.* 5:136–44
308. Lau S, Patnaik N, Sayen MR, Mestril R. 1997. Simultaneous overexpression of two stress proteins in rat cardiomyocytes and myogenic cells confers protection against ischemia-induced injury. *Circulation* 96:2287–94
309. Huot J, Roy G, Lambert H, Chretien P, Landry J. 1991. Increased survival after treatments with anticancer agents of Chinese hamster cells expressing the human Mr 27,000 heat shock protein. *Cancer Res.* 51:5245–52

310. Mehlen P, Preville X, Chareyron P, Briolay J, Klemenz R, Arrigo AP. 1995. Constitutive expression of human hsp27, *Drosophila* hsp27, or human alpha B-crystallin confers resistance to TNF- and oxidative stress-induced cytotoxicity in stably transfected murine L929 fibroblasts. *J. Immunol.* 154:363–74
311. Jaattela M, Wissing D. 1993. Heat-shock proteins protect cells from monocyte cytotoxicity: possible mechanism of self-protection. *J. Exp. Med.* 177:231–36
312. Trautinger F, Kokesch C, Herbacek I, Knobler RM, Kindas-Mugge I. 1997. Overexpression of the small heat shock protein, hsp27, confers resistance to hyperthermia, but not to oxidative stress and UV-induced cell death, in a stably transfected squamous cell carcinoma cell line. *J. Photochem. Photobiol.* 39B:90–95
313. Rollet E, Lavoie JN, Landry J, Tanguay RM. 1992. Expression of *Drosophila*'s 27 kDa heat shock protein into rodent cells confers thermal resistance. *Biochem. Biophys. Res. Commun.* 185:116–20
314. Lavoie JN, Gingras-Breton G, Tanguay RM, Landry J. 1993. Induction of Chinese hamster HSP27 gene expression in mouse cells confers resistance to heat shock. HSP27 stabilization of the microfilament organization. *J. Biol. Chem.* 268:3420–29
315. Landry J, Chretien P, Lambert H, Hickey E, Weber LA. 1989. Heat shock resistance conferred by expression of the human HSP27 gene in rodent cells. *J. Cell Biol.* 109:7–15
316. Wissing D, Jaattela M. 1996. HSP27 and HSP70 increase the survival of WEHI-S cells exposed to hyperthermia. *Int. J. Hypertherm.* 12:125–38
317. Wang G, Klostergaard J, Khodadadian M, Wu J, Wu TW, et al. 1996. Murine cells transfected with human Hsp27 cDNA resist TNF-induced cytotoxicity. *J. Immunother. Emphasis Tumor. Immunol.* 19:9–20
318. Martin JL, Mestril R, Hilal-Dandan R, Brunton LL, Dillmann WH. 1997. Small heat shock proteins and protection against ischemic injury in cardiac myocytes. *Circulation* 96:4343–48
319. Stege GJ, Kampinga HH, Konings AW. 1995. Heat-induced intranuclear protein aggregation and thermal radiosensitization. *Int. J. Radiat. Biol.* 67:203–9
320. Blackburn R, Galoforo S, Berns CM, Ireland M, Cho JM, et al. 1996. Thermal response in murine L929 cells lacking alpha B-crystallin expression and alpha B-crystallin expressing L929 transfectants. *Mol. Cell. Biochem.* 155:51–60
321. van den Ijssel PR, Overkamp P, Knauf U, Gaestel M, de Jong WW. 1994. Alpha A-crystallin confers cellular thermoresistance. *FEBS Lett.* 355:54–56
322. Heads RJ, Yellon DM, Latchman DS. 1995. Differential cytoprotection against heat stress or hypoxia following expression of specific stress protein genes in myogenic cells. *J. Mol. Cell. Cardiol.* 27:1669–78
323. Cumming DV, Heads RJ, Watson A, Latchman DS, Yellon DM. 1996. Differential protection of primary rat cardiocytes by transfection of specific heat stress proteins. *J. Mol. Cell. Cardiol.* 28:2343–49
324. Lukacs KV, Nakakes A, Atkins CJ, Lowrie DB, Colston MJ. 1997. In vivo gene therapy of malignant tumours with heat shock protein-65 gene. *Gene Ther.* 4:346–50
325. Lukacs KV, Lowrie DB, Stokes RW, Colston MJ. 1993. Tumor cells transfected with a bacterial heat-shock gene lose tumorigenicity and induce protection against tumors. *J. Exp. Med.* 178: 343–48
326. Wischmeyer PE, Musch MW, Madonna MB, Thisted R, Chang EB. 1997. Glutamine protects intestinal epithelial cells: role of inducible HSP70. *Am. J. Physiol.* 272:G879–84
327. Angelidis CE, Lazaridis I, Pagoulatos GN. 1991. Constitutive expression of heat-shock protein 70 in mammalian cells confers thermoresistance. *Eur. J. Biochem.* 199:35–39
328. Mailhos C, Howard MK, Latchman DS. 1994. Heat shock proteins hsp90 and hsp70 protect neuronal cells from thermal stress but not from programmed cell death. *J. Neurochem.* 63:1787–95
329. Wyatt S, Mailhos C, Latchman DS. 1996. Trigeminal ganglion neurons are protected by the heat shock proteins hsp70 and hsp90 from thermal stress but not from programmed cell death following nerve growth factor withdrawal. *Brain Res. Mol. Brain Res.* 39:52–56
330. Uney JB, Staley K, Tyers P, Sofroniew MV, Kew JN. 1994. Transfection with hsp70i protects rat dorsal root ganglia neurones and glia from heat stress. *Gene Ther.* 1:S65
331. Solomon JM, Rossi JM, Golic K, McGarry T, Lindquist S. 1991. Changes in Hsp70 alter thermotolerance and heat-

shock regulation in *Drosophila. New Biol.* 3:1106–20
332. Sato K, Saito H, Matsuki N. 1996. HSP70 is essential to the neuroprotective effect of heat-shock. *Brain Res.* 740:117–23
333. Riabowol KT, Mizzen LA, Welch WJ. 1988. Heat shock is lethal to fibroblasts microinjected with antibodies against hsp70. *Science* 242:433–36
334. Mestril R, Giordano FJ, Conde AG, Dillmann WH. 1996. Adenovirus-mediated gene transfer of a heat shock protein 70 (hsp 70i) protects against simulated ischemia. *J. Mol. Cell. Cardiol.* 28:2351–58
335. Liu RY, Li X, Li L, Li GC. 1992. Expression of human hsp70 in rat fibroblasts enhances cell survival and facilitates recovery from translational and transcriptional inhibition following heat shock. *Cancer Res.* 52:3667–73
336. Nakata N, Kato H, Kogure K. 1993. Inhibition of ischaemic tolerance in the gerbil hippocampus by quercetin and anti-heat shock protein-70 antibody. *NeuroReport* 4:695–98
337. Lee YJ, Kim D, Hou ZZ, Curetty L, Borrelli MJ, Corry PM. 1993. Alteration of heat sensitivity by introduction of hsp70 or anti-hsp70 in CHO cells. *J. Therm. Biol.* 18:229–36
338. Johnston RN, Kucey BL. 1988. Competitive inhibition of hsp70 gene expression causes thermosensitivity. *Science* 242:1551–54
339. Heads RJ, Latchman DS, Yellon DM. 1994. Stable high level expression of a transfected human HSP70 gene protects a heart-derived muscle cell line against thermal stress. *J. Mol. Cell. Cardiol.* 26:695–99
340. Amin V, Cumming DV, Latchman DS. 1996. Over-expression of heat shock protein 70 protects neuronal cells against both thermal and ischaemic stress but with different efficiencies. *Neurosci. Lett.* 206:45–48
341. Khan NA, Sotelo J. 1989. Heat shock stress is deleterious to CNS cultured neurons microinjected with anti-HSP70 antibodies. *Biol. Cell* 65:199–202
342. Li GC, Li LG, Liu YK, Mak JY, Chen LL, Lee WM. 1991. Thermal response of rat fibroblasts stably transfected with the human 70-kDa heat shock protein-encoding gene. *Proc. Natl. Acad. Sci. USA* 88:1681–85
343. Williams RS, Thomas JA, Fina M, German Z, Benjamin IJ. 1993. Human heat shock protein 70 (hsp70) protects murine cells from injury during metabolic stress. *J. Clin. Invest.* 92:503–8
344. Mestril R, Chi SH, Sayen MR, O'Reilly K, Dillmann WH. 1994. Expression of inducible stress protein 70 in rat heart myogenic cells confers protection against simulated ischemia-induced injury. *J. Clin. Invest.* 93:759–67
345. Dillmann WH, Mestril R. 1995. Heat shock proteins in myocardial stress. *Z. Kardiol.* 4:87–90
346. Jacobs M, Andersen JB, Kontinen V, Sarvas M. 1993. The DNA-binding activity of the human heat shock transcription factor is regulated in vivo by Hsp70. *Mol. Cell Biol.* 13:5427–38
347. Ding XZ, Tsokos GC, Smallridge RC, Kiang JG. 1997. Heat shock gene-expression in HSP-70 and HSF1 gene-transfected human epidermoid A-431 cells. *Mol. Cell. Biochem.* 167:145–52
348. Chi SH, Mestril R. 1996. Stable expression of a human HSP70 gene in a rat myogenic cell line confers protection against endotoxin. *Am. J. Physiol.* 270:C1017–21
349. Han MY, Park YM. 1997. Reduced protein denaturation in thermotolerant cells by elevated levels of HSP70. *Korean J. Pharmacol.* 32:433–44
350. Jaattela M. 1995. Over-expression of hsp70 confers tumorigenicity to mouse fibrosarcoma cells. *Int. J. Cancer* 60: 689–93
351. Wei YQ, Zhao X, Kariya Y, Teshigawara K, Uchida A. 1995. Inhibition of proliferation and induction of apoptosis by abrogation of heat-shock protein (HSP) 70 expression in tumor cells. *Cancer Immunol. Immunother.* 40:73–78
352. Karlseder J, Wissing D, Holzer G, Orel L, Sliutz G, et al. 1996. Hsp70 overexpression mediates the escape of a doxorubicin-induced G2 cell cycle arrest. *Biochem. Biophys. Res. Commun.* 220:153–59
353. Henle KJ, Jethmalani SM, Li L, Li GC. 1997. Protein glycosylation in a heat-resistant rat fibroblast cell model expressing human HSP70. *Biochem. Biophys. Res. Commun.* 232:26–32
354. Simon MM, Reikerstorfer A, Schwarz A, Krone C, Luger TA, et al. 1995. Heat shock protein 70 overexpression affects the response to ultraviolet light in murine fibroblasts. Evidence for increased cell viability and suppression of cytokine release. *J. Clin. Invest.* 95:926–33
355. Liossis SN, Ding XZ, Kiang JG, Tsokos GC. 1997. Overexpression of

the heat shock protein 70 enhances the TCR/CD3- and Fas/Apo-1/CD95-mediated apoptotic cell death in Jurkat T cells. *J. Immunol.* 158:5668–75
356. Mosser DD, Caron AW, Bourget L, Denis-Larose C, Massie B. 1997. Role of the human heat shock protein hsp70 in protection against stress-induced apoptosis. *Mol. Cell. Biol.* 17:5317–27
357. Suzuki K, Sawa Y, Kaneda Y, Ichikawa H, Shirakura R, Matsuda H. 1997. In vivo gene transfection with heat shock protein 70 enhances myocardial tolerance to ischemia-reperfusion injury in rat. *J. Clin. Invest.* 99:1645–50
358. Plumier JC, Ross BM, Currie RW, Angelidis CE, Kazlaris H, et al. 1995. Transgenic mice expressing the human heat shock protein 70 have improved post-ischemic myocardial recovery. *J. Clin. Invest.* 95:1854–60
359. Marber MS, Mestril R, Chi SH, Sayen MR, Yellon DM, Dillmann WH. 1995. Overexpression of the rat inducible 70-kD heat stress protein in a transgenic mouse increases the resistance of the heart to ischemic injury. *J. Clin. Invest.* 95:1446–56
360. Plumier JC, Krueger AM, Currie RW, Kontoyiannis D, Kollias G, Pagoulatos GN. 1997. Transgenic mice expressing the human inducible Hsp70 have hippocampal neurons resistant to ischemic injury. *Cell Stress Chaperones* 2:162–67
361. Lee JH, Schoffl F. 1996. An Hsp70 antisense gene affects the expression of HSP70/HSC70, the regulation of HSF, and the acquisition of thermotolerance in transgenic *Arabidopsis thaliana*. *Mol. Gen. Genet.* 252:11–19
362. Galea-Lauri J, Richardson AJ, Latchman DS, Katz DR. 1996. Increased heat shock protein 90 (hsp90) expression leads to increased apoptosis in the monoblastoid cell line U937 following induction with TNF-alpha and cycloheximide: a possible role in immunopathology. *J. Immunol.* 157:4109–18
363. Nakano M, Mann DL, Knowlton AA. 1997. Blocking the endogenous increase in HSP 72 increases susceptibility to hypoxia and reoxygenation in isolated adult feline cardiocytes. *Circulation* 95:1523–31
364. Hutter JJ, Mestril R, Tam EK, Sievers RE, Dillmann WH, Wolfe CL. 1996. Overexpression of heat shock protein 72 in transgenic mice decreases infarct size in vivo. *Circulation* 94:1408–11
365. Galea-Lauri J, Latchman DS, Katz DR. 1996. The role of the 90-kDa heat shock protein in cell cycle control and differentiation of the monoblastoid cell line U937. *Exp. Cell Res.* 226:243–54
366. Schirmer EC, Lindquist S, Vierling E. 1994. An *Arabidopsis* heat shock protein complements a thermotolerance defect in yeast. *Plant Cell* 6:1899–909
367. Kutskova IUA, Mamon LA. 1996. Consequences of exposure to extreme conditions in somatic cells of *Drosophila melanogaster* under conditions of disturbed synthesis of heat shock proteins. *Genetika* 32:1406–16
368. Mamon LA, Kutskova YA. 1993. The role of the heat-shock proteins in recovery of high temperature induced damages of mitotic chromosomes in *Drosophila melanogaster*. *Genetika* 29:604–12
369. Mamon LA, Kutskova YA. 1993. The role of the heat-shock proteins in recovery of cell proliferation following high temperature treatment of *Drosophila melanogaster*. *Genetika* 29:791–98
370. Koishi M, Hosokawa N, Sato M, Nakai A, Hirayoshi K, et al. 1992. Quercetin, an inhibitor of heat shock protein synthesis, inhibits the acquisition of thermotolerance in a human colon carcinoma cell line. *Jpn. J. Cancer Res.* 83:1216–22
371. Lee YJ, Curetty L, Hou ZZ, Kim SH, Kim JH, Corry PM. 1992. Effect of pH on quercetin-induced suppression of heat shock gene expression and thermotolerance development in HT-29 cells. *Biochem. Biophys. Res. Commun.* 186:1121–28
372. Jedlicka P, Mortin MA, Wu C. 1997. Multiple functions of *Drosophila* heat shock transcription factor in vivo. *EMBO J.* 16:2452–62
373. Lee JH, Hubel A, Schoffl F. 1995. Derepression of the activity of genetically engineered heat shock factor causes constitutive synthesis of heat shock proteins and increased thermotolerance in transgenic *Arabidopsis*. *Plant J.* 8:603–12

Annu. Rev. Physiol. 1999. 61:283–310

GENETIC DISEASES AND GENE KNOCKOUTS REVEAL DIVERSE CONNEXIN FUNCTIONS

Thomas W. White and David L. Paul[1]
Departments of Cell Biology and [1]Neurobiology, Harvard Medical School, Boston, Massachusetts 02115; e-mail: twhite@warren.med.harvard.edu, dpaul@hms.med.harvard.edu

KEY WORDS: connexin, innexin, intercellular channel, gap junction

ABSTRACT

Intercellular channels present in gap junctions allow cells to share small molecules and thus coordinate a wide range of behaviors. Remarkably, although junctions provide similar functions in all multicellular organisms, vertebrates and invertebrates use unrelated gene families to encode these channels. The recent identification of the invertebrate innexin family opens up powerful genetic systems to studies of intercellular communication. At the same time, new information on the physiological roles of vertebrate connexins has emerged from genetic studies. Mutations in connexin genes underlie a variety of human diseases, including deafness, demyelinating neuropathies, and lens cataracts. In addition, gene targeting of connexins in mice has provided new insights into connexin function and the significance of connexin diversity.

INTRODUCTION

Multicellular organisms require the coordinated response of groups of cells to environmental stimuli. Intercellular channels present in gap junctions provide a simple method of synchronizing response through the direct exchange of ions, metabolites, and other messenger molecules between adjacent cells. These signaling pathways permit rapidly coordinated activities such as contraction of cardiac and smooth muscle (1, 2) and transmission of neuronal signals at electrical synapses (3–5). In addition, gap junctional communication plays a

0066-4278/99/0315-0283$08.00

role in slower physiological processes, such as cell growth and development (6–8).

Vertebrate Intercellular Channels

In vertebrates, the structural proteins comprising intercellular channels are encoded by a multigene family called the connexins (9, 10). Currently, 14 mouse connexin genes have been cloned. In addition, at least six connexin genes have been isolated from other vertebrate species (11–14) for which rodent orthologs have not yet been identified. Thus, the total number of vertebrate connexin genes is likely to exceed 20. Initially, vertebrate connexins genes were separated into two groups, α and β, on the basis of overall sequence similarities, although there are no specific protein domains that reliably define either group. A common feature of both groups of connexins is a simple gene structure in which the entire coding region is contained within one exon whereas one or two introns are located in the 5' untranslated region. Analysis of the more recently characterized connexin sequences suggests that this simple categorization scheme may need refinement. For example, rodent Cx36, skate Cx35, and perch Cx34.7 may form an entirely new subfamily. These connexins (*a*) are expressed predominantly in central nervous system neurons, (*b*) contain an intron within the coding region, and (*c*) on the basis of primary sequence do not readily fit into either the α or β groups (11, 12, 15). Similarly, mouse Cx45, initially assigned to the α group (16), forms together with human Cx46.6 and zebrafish Cx43.4 a cohort more distantly related to α connexins than β connexins are (11). It is not yet clear whether there are functional correlates to these sequence differences.

Intercellular channels are unusually complex in that they span two plasma membranes. Connexins oligomerize to form single-membrane channels (hemichannels) called connexons (17), which align in the extracellular space between two cells to complete the intercellular channel. Each connexon is comprised of six connexins arranged radially around a central pore (18, 19) and can contain either a single type of connexin (homomeric) or multiple connexins (heteromeric). Theoretically, many types of heteromeric connexons can be generated, differing in either the number or the spatial organization of the different connexin proteins. Because an intercellular channel spans two plasma membranes, adjacent cells can contribute different types of connexons, giving rise to either homotypic, heterotypic, or heteromeric intercellular channels (Figure 1). Given the existence of more than 20 connexin genes, the number of structurally and thus physiologically distinct channel types may be very large. In vivo, clear evidence for the coassembly of multiple connexin proteins into single connexons and intercellular channels has been obtained (20–25).

One consequence of the molecular diversity in the connexin family is that intercellular channels assembled from different connexin proteins have unique

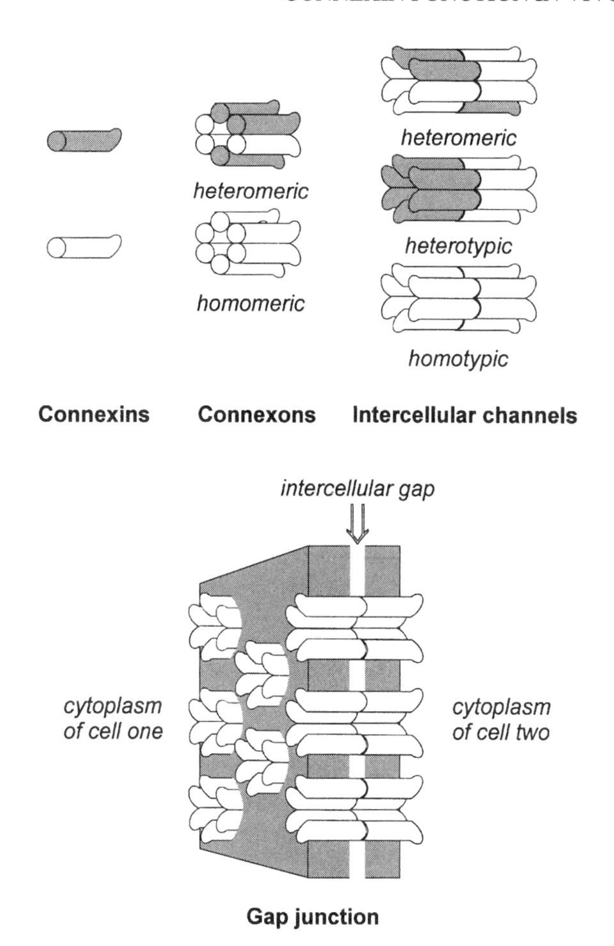

Figure 1 Organization of connexins into connexons, intercellular channels, and gap junctions. Connexin proteins oligomerize into connexons that are homomeric if they have one type of connexin or heteromeric if they contain multiple connexins. Connexons from adjacent cells align to form complete intercellular channels that span two plasma membranes. Each cell can contribute different types of connexons—giving rise to either homotypic, heterotypic, or heteromeric intercellular channels—that cluster in specialized membrane regions called gap junctions.

molecular permeabilities. Gap junctions have been historically described as relatively nonselective, permeable to a wide variety of molecules smaller than ~1200 Da (26). However, experiments carefully examining the movement of ions and dyes between cells expressing different connexins have revealed that there are connexin-dependent differences in the permeation of intercellular channels (27–29). Recently, this type of analysis has been extended to signaling molecules (30). Homomeric connexons made of Cx32 are permeable

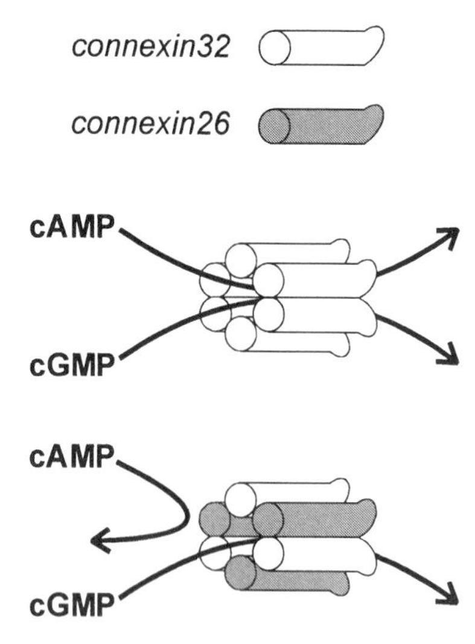

Figure 2 Isoform composition of connexin channels determines selectivity among cyclic nucleotides. Homomeric connexons made of Cx32 are permeable to both cAMP and cGMP. Heteromeric connexons containing both Cx26 and Cx32 are not permeable to cAMP but allow passage of cGMP. This is the first example of connexin-specific selectivity among second messengers (for details, see 30).

to both cAMP and cGMP, whereas heteromeric connexons composed of Cx32 and Cx26 lose permeability to cAMP but not to cGMP (Figure 2). It remains a technically daunting task to determine which molecules actually permeate intercellular channels in vivo. One recent report demonstrated that in cells metabolically labeled with [^{14}C]glucose, a significant amount of radioactive carbon exchanged through gap junctions was incorporated into ADP and/or ATP (31).

Invertebrate Gap Junction Channels

Invertebrate organisms also use gap junctional communication to coordinate activity, although connexins have never been found in invertebrate genomes. These organisms are believed to assemble intercellular channels from proteins belonging to a different gene family, originally designated OPUS, an acronym derived from the founding members ogre, passover, unc-7, and shaking-B (32). Recently, this family was renamed innexin for invertebrate analogs of the connexins (33). Because passover and shaking-B represent the same gene, there are thus far two cloned innexin genes in *Drosophila* [shaking-B/passover and lethal (1) ogre (34–36)] and at least 24 innexins in the *Caenorhabditis* genome (37–39). No vertebrate orthologs of any innexin gene have been isolated.

Innexins are predicted to encode membrane proteins with four transmembrane domains, analogous to the vertebrate connexins. However, their primary sequences show no homology with members of the connexin family (38, 39).

Several lines of evidence suggest that innexins are the channel-forming proteins comprising invertebrate gap junctions. First, some mutant phenotypes are well reconciled with the known functions of intercellular channels. For example, coordination of smooth and cardiac muscle contraction requires junctional communication, and eat-5 mutants lose synchrony of pharyngeal muscle contraction. In addition, eat-5 mutants lose detectable dye coupling, a reliable indicator of junctional communication, between anterior and posterior pharyngeal muscle groups (38). Similarly, nonlethal mutants of shaking-B fail to establish stereotypical electrical synapses in the giant fiber system. Normal appositions between interneurons and tergotrochanteral motor neurons are maintained, but normal dye coupling between these cells is not observed in the mutants (35, 40, 41).

Not all innexin mutant phenotypes are easily understood in the context of intercellular channel activity. For example, lethal alleles of ogre exhibit a significant reduction in the numbers of postembryonic neuroblasts and their offspring whereas viable alleles produce defective vision due to structural abnormalities restricted to the optic lobe (42). In addition to the lack of a clear causal relationship between these phenotypes and intercellular channel activity, the localization of the ogre gene product appears to be largely cytoplasmic, which is not consistent with its presumed role as an intercellular channel (43).

Recently, strong support for the hypothesis that innexins comprise invertebrate intercellular channels was provided by in vitro expression studies demonstrating that the lethal allele of shaking-B can form intercellular channels. Pairs of *Xenopus* oocytes injected with RNA encoding shaking-B(lethal) developed robust intercellular conductances three orders of magnitude above background (44). Another innexin, *Caenorhabditis* wxn-1, also makes intercellular channels when expressed in paired *Xenopus* oocytes (Y Landesman, TW White, TA Starich, JE Shaw, DL Paul, unpublished data). However, as seen with certain connexins (45), not all innexins are capable of inducing intercellular conductance in oocyte pairs. Shaking-B(neural), an alternatively spliced form of shaking-B expressed largely in the nervous system, failed to form active intercellular channels (44).

Surprisingly, the physiological properties of invertebrate and vertebrate intercellular channels are similar, despite the complete lack of sequence identity between connexins and innexins. One striking similarity is in the gating of these channels by voltage. Imposition of a potential difference between coupled cells results in junctional currents that generally decrease over time, reflecting a voltage-dependent closure of the intercellular channels. Two characteristic

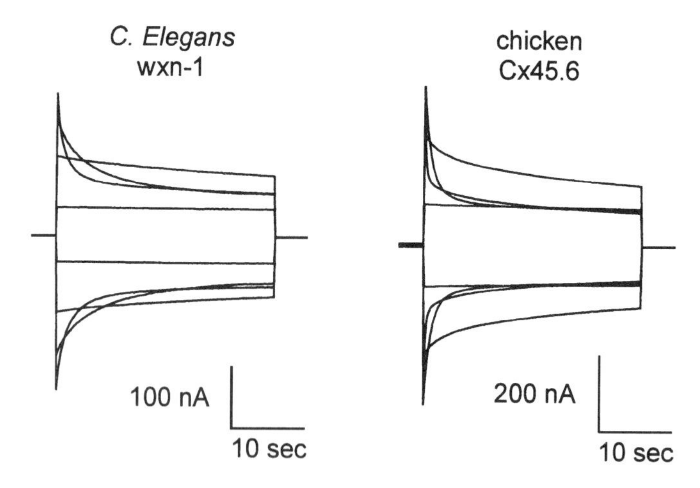

Figure 3 Similarities in the macroscopic voltage gating of innexin and connexin channels. The effect of transjunctional voltage on the junctional currents developed by oocyte pairs expressing a connexin (chicken Cx45.6) or an innexin (*Caenorhabditis elegans* wxn-1) is shown. Depolarizing voltage steps of 10, 30, 50, and 70 mV were applied to one cell of each pair. At transjunctional voltages greater than 20 mV, innexin and connexin junctional currents slowly decreased over the time of the voltage step (30 s), with similar kinetics. In both cases, the voltage-dependent closure was not complete and a substantial residual current remained. The voltage gating of the innexin channel fell well within the range of behaviors exhibited by members of the connexin family (reviewed in 140).

features of connexin voltage gating are also observed with innexins. First, the kinetics of voltage gating is unusually slow, taking several seconds for the decay in junctional currents to reach equilibrium. Second, in both cases, the voltage-dependent closure is not complete and a substantial residual current remains (Figure 3). When the activity of single channels was examined, a third similarity in gating behavior was observed. Like most ion channels, connexin and innexin channels gate between fully open states and substates on a fast time scale (1–2 ms) (46–49). However, both channel types also exhibit an unorthodox, slower gating step between the fully closed state and a substate (10–60 ms) (48, 50–52; but also see 53). Finally, connexin and innexin channels appear to be sensitive to the same classes of pharmacological agents. For example, both are closed by decreases in intracellular pH and millimolar concentrations of alkanols or halothane. Together, these data illustrate a remarkable similarity in channel properties obtained in the absence of any significant primary sequence identity.

The clarification of the identity of invertebrate intercellular channel proteins is a major advance in gap junction biology and opens up powerful genetic systems to studies of intercellular communication. Recently, a great deal of information on the physiological roles of connexins has also become available from genetic studies in vertebrates. The remainder of this review focuses on the functional roles of intercellular communication that have been elucidated from studies of connexin mutations in human hereditary disease and in mice with targeted deletion of connexin genes.

CONNEXIN MUTATIONS IN HUMAN DISEASE

Although intercellular channels have been well characterized in terms of structure and biochemistry, information regarding their biological roles is still limited. However, the association of connexin mutations with an increasing number of human pathologies, including X-linked Charcot-Marie-Tooth disease (54), sensorineural hearing loss (55), and congenital cataract (56), provides an unequivocal demonstration that gap junctional communication is crucial for diverse physiological processes. Moreover, analysis of the functional consequences of the specific connexin mutations underlying these human disorders is providing new insights into the roles of connexin diversity in vivo.

Mutations in Cx26 Cause Nonsyndromic Deafness

Genetic deafness is one of the most prevalent inherited sensory disorders, affecting about 1 in 2000 children. Both autosomal recessive (DFNB1, OMIM 220290) and autosomal dominant (DFNA3, OMIM 601544) forms of deafness were mapped near the chromosomal location of human Cx26 (57, 58). These forms of deafness are described as nonsyndromic because no other organ system exhibits defects. Because Cx26 was known to be highly expressed in cochlear cells (59), it became a likely candidate gene for these disorders. Subsequently, Kelsell and colleagues identified Cx26 coding region mutations in affected members of three families with recessive nonsyndromic deafness. In the same study, a different Cx26 mutation was identified in a pedigree with a dominant pattern of inheritance (55).

Multiple studies have confirmed that mutations in Cx26 are associated with recessive deafness (60–65). The most frequent mutation identified is a single base deletion (35delG) resulting in a frameshift and consequent premature termination of the Cx26 protein. This deletion comprises 50–70% of all mutant alleles in various ethnic populations. The prevalence of a single mutation has not been observed in other connexin-related disorders and may reflect a mutational hot spot within the Cx26 gene. Other Cx26 defects include nonsense mutations and small deletions/insertions, most of which also lead to premature termination of protein translation and the probable loss of function. In addition, recessive deafness in compound heterozygotes (individuals where each allele contains a different Cx26 mutation) has been reported. Taken together, these data reveal a tight association between mutations in Cx26 and autosomal recessive nonsyndromic deafness.

In contrast, the role of Cx26 mutations in dominant forms of deafness has been more controversial. Kelsell et al originally reported a heterozygous point mutation (M34T) in a family with dominant deafness and proposed that the mutant allele inhibited the activity of the wild-type Cx26 allele (55). This hypothesis was supported by functional expression studies using pairs of *Xenopus* oocytes programmed with connexin RNAs. The M34T variant, which does not form functional channels when expressed alone, acted as a dominant inhibitor of wild-type Cx26 channel activity when coexpressed (66). However, the ability of the M34T variant to cause dominant deafness was brought into question by the finding of heterozygous M34T mutations in individuals with normal hearing (62, 67). In light of the functional data demonstrating dominant inhibition, it is difficult to explain the normal hearing in carriers of the M34T allele. Possible mechanisms include second-site mutations that silence the allele or compensatory changes in the expression of other genes. Analysis of M34T allelic expression in carriers with normal hearing may help to resolve this issue. Regardless of its role in dominant deafness, the M34T variant can contribute to deafness in compound heterozygotes (62), which is consistent with the data demonstrating loss of channel activity.

Recently, additional Cx26 mutations linked to dominant deafness have been found. In one study, dominant deafness segregated with a heterozygous missense mutation of Cx26, causing a nonconservative amino acid substitution (R75W). The dominant inhibitory effect of the R75W variant on channel function was also demonstrated using the paired oocyte expression system (68). As in the case of M34T, the R75W mutant was unable to induce electrical conductance between adjacent cells and completely suppressed the activity of coexpressed wild-type Cx26. For comparison, a neighboring mutation (W77R) observed in a family with autosomal recessive deafness (63) was also tested. The W77R mutant also failed to induce intercellular channel activity, but it did not inhibit the ability of wild-type Cx26 to form functional channels when coexpressed, which is consistent with its recessive pattern of inheritance. An additional Cx26 point mutation (W44C) has been found in the original pedigree used to map autosomal dominant deafness (57). All 10 of the deaf individuals, but none of the 17 normal hearing individuals, of a kindred were heterozygous for the W44C allele (69). Collectively, these results indicate that heterozygous Cx26 mutations can have serious functional consequences, and they strongly support the identification of Cx26 as both the DFNB1 and DFNA3 genes.

Although the precise role of Cx26 in the etiology of nonsyndromic deafness is not known, it is likely that junctional communication influences the ionic environment of inner ear sensory epithelia. In mammals, there are no clear reports of gap junctions involving vestibular hair cells, but gap junctions and junctional communication have been well documented in other cochlear cells (70). Cells interconnected by gap junctions fall into two groups: nonsensory epithelial cells among which hair cells are dispersed, and connective tissue cells at more distal locations to the hair cells. Immunocytochemical analysis indicates that Cx26 is present in nearly every location where cochlear gap junctions have been found (59), and it is believed to be the major connexin expressed by supporting cells.

It has been proposed that serially arranged gap junctions of epithelial and connective tissue cells serve as a mechanism for recycling endolymphatic K^+ ions that pass through sensory cells during auditory transduction. The mammalian cochlea has an unusual arrangement of extracellular fluid-filled spaces, which provides a unique environment for the sensory cells. Basolateral hair cell surfaces are bathed in perilymph, which has an ionic composition similar to that of other extracellular fluids. The apices of hair cells, however, are bathed in endolymph, which has high K^+ and low Na^+ concentrations, similar to intracellular fluids. When hair cells are activated by sound, receptor potentials are generated from the flow of K^+ ions from endolymph into the hair cell. The K^+ ions are then released from hair cells into interstitial space within the organ of Corti (71), where K^+ channels in cochlear supporting cells permit uptake of these ions (72). It was proposed that junctional communication between the supporting cells facilitates recirculation of K^+ ions back to the endolymph by providing an intercellular pathway for conveyance and distal release of K^+ ions. A conceptually similar role for junctional communication has been proposed in the spatial buffering of K^+ by astrocytes in the central nervous system (73). Appropriate evaluation of this model in terms of nonsyndromic deafness awaits the development of transgenic animals with Cx26 mutations.

Human Peripheral Neuropathy and Mutations in Cx32

The first disease shown to result from mutations in a connexin is a form of Charcot-Marie-Tooth disease (CMT). CMT is a genetically heterogeneous group of neuropathies resulting in progressive degeneration of peripheral nerve, and it is characterized by distal muscle weakness and atrophy as well as impairment of sensation and deep tendon reflexes. Most forms of CMT, which affect 1 out of every 2500 people, are demyelinating syndromes associated with Schwann cell defects. Linkage studies placed the locus of an X-linked form (CMTX) near the map location assigned to Cx32 on the X chromosome. Subsequently, direct sequence analysis of the Cx32 coding region in CMTX patients revealed numerous mutations (54, 74).

The association of genetic abnormalities in Cx32 with a demyelinating disease of the peripheral nervous system was unexpected because gap junctions are extremely rare, if present at all, between adjacent myelinating Schwann cells (75). Nonetheless, immunolocalization of Cx32 reveals that Schwann cells express Cx32 and concentrate it in the uncompacted membranes adjacent to the nodes of Ranvier and at the incisures of Schmidt-Lanterman (54, 76). This distribution suggests a unique functional role for Cx32 in Schwann cells, as illustrated in Figure 4. Unlike compact myelin, the paranodal membranes and incisures enclose cytoplasm, providing continuity between the Schwann cell body and the cytoplasmic collar of the myelin sheath adjacent to the axon (Figure 4*A*). Presumably, this continuity permits diffusion of nutrients and ions between perinuclear and periaxonal Schwann cell cytoplasm and is likely to play a critical role in the transduction of signals between Schwann cell and axon. As the myelinating Schwann cell wraps the axon, the cytoplasmic continuity assumes a spiraling shape, forming the incisures and paranodes. In a large motor nerve, a Schwann cell may elaborate so many turns that the length of the spiraling pathway is too great for molecular diffusion to support the metabolic needs of the cell (77). To solve the problem, Bergoffen et al (54) proposed that a shorter, radial pathway for diffusion is generated by intracellular [reflexive (78)] gap junctions directly connecting adjacent wraps of myelin at incisures and paranodal membranes (Figure 4*B*). Cx32 mutations disrupting the normal functioning of these gap junctions could affect the diffusion of nutrients or signaling molecules between Schwann cell body and distal processes. Support for this hypothesis was obtained from recent studies using intracellular dye injection and video microscopy showing that only molecules small enough to permeate gap junctions can rapidly diffuse between adaxonal and perinuclear Schwann cell cytoplasm (79).

At least 90 different Cx32 mutations are associated with CMTX (80), which supports the identification of Cx32 as the disease-causing gene. The mutations are mostly coding region mutations but they do not cluster in any particular sequence domain. To determine the effects on channel activity, 21 different mutations have been analyzed using the paired oocyte system or transfected tissue culture cells (81–84). In about half the cases, active intercellular channels

Figure 4 Cx32 may form reflexive gap junctions within, rather than between, Schwann cells. (*A*) Schematic diagram of a myelinating Schwann cell unwrapped from the axon it invests. In compact myelin, Schwann cell cytoplasm is extruded and the cytoplasmic leaflets of the plasma membrane come into close apposition (*grey areas*). In contrast, cytoplasm is retained at incisures of Schmidt-Lanterman and paranodal membranes to maintain continuity between Schwann cell body and the cytoplasmic collar of the myelin sheath adjacent to the axon [adapted from Doyle & Colman (141)]. (*B*) Cross-sectional view of the connections formed by Cx32 at the incisures of Schmidt-Lanterman in a single Schwann cell. Cx32 is specifically localized to incisures and paranodal membranes, where intracellular (as opposed to intercellular) channels dramatically reduce the path length between Schwann cell body and periaxonal cytoplasm (adapted from 142).

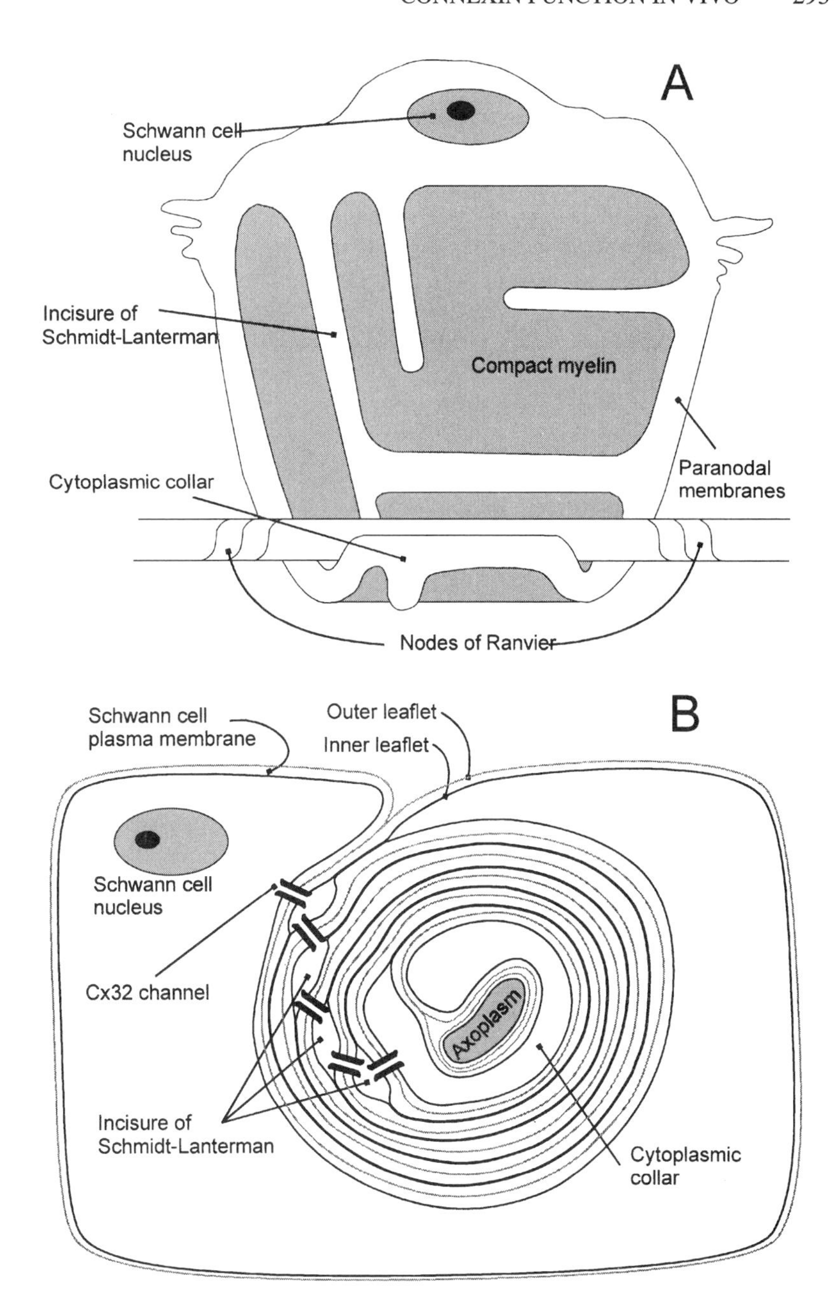
A
Schwann cell
nucleus
Incisure of
Schmidt-Lanterman
Compact myelin
Paranodal
membranes
Cytoplasmic collar
Nodes of Ranvier
B
Schwann cell
plasma membrane
Outer leaflet
Inner leaflet
Schwann cell
nucleus
Cx32 channel
Axoplasm
Incisure of
Schmidt-Lanterman
Cytoplasmic
collar

were not observed, which is consistent with a model in which complete loss of function causes the disease. However, channel activity was readily detected in 11 cases. In 9, only subtle alterations in macroscopic properties such as sensitivity to gating by pH and voltage were observed. The physiological consequence of these alterations is currently not clear. However, marked changes in functional properties in two active variants were revealed by a more detailed single-channel analysis (83). A S26L mutation exhibited a significant reduction in permeability to small solutes, whereas a M34T mutation showed a decrease in the channel open probability. These changes can be clearly interpreted as partial loss of function and are more easily reconciled with a disease phenotype.

Human Cataracts and Mutations in Cx50

Congenital cataracts are a leading cause of visual impairment or blindness, often following an autosomal dominant pattern of inheritance (85–87). A form of congenital cataract exhibiting zonular pulverulent opacities (CZP1, OMIM 116200) in an extensively studied eight-generation kindred (56, 88, 89) was recently mapped near the human Cx50 gene (90, 91). Cx50 was strongly implicated as a candidate gene for CZP1 because it is predominantly expressed in the lens (92). Sequence analysis of the coding region of Cx50 in affected members of this large pedigree revealed a C to T transition in codon 88 resulting in the nonconservative substitution of serine for proline in the second transmembrane domain (P88S). This mutation segregated with the cataract phenotype and was not detected in unaffected family members or in a control population (56).

Although the effect of this mutation on the activity of Cx50 has not yet been tested, several independent observations suggest that it is likely to result in a change in channel activity. First, the mutated proline is strictly conserved among all known connexins. Second, the same mutation in human Cx32 has been found to segregate with the peripheral neuropathy CMTX in two independent pedigrees (93, 94). Finally, in vitro mutagenesis of the equivalent proline residue in Cx26 altered channel activity. Cx26 proline mutants were no longer able to form functional homotypic channels, although they could form heterotypic channels with wild-type Cx26 or Cx32. Moreover, the heterotypic channels containing mutated Cx26 exhibited dramatically aberrant voltage gating (95). These data raise the possibility that the P88S mutation may have dominant effects on wild-type channel activity, a possibility that can be directly tested in vitro.

Mutations in Cx50 may perturb the intercellular communication that joins the cells of the lens into a functional syncytium (96). Because the lens is an avascular cyst, intercellular channels allow cells in the interior of the organ to gain access to metabolites absorbed at the surface from the aqueous humor (97).

This metabolite exchange has been proposed to maintain the precise intracellular ionic conditions necessary to prevent precipitation of the crystallins and subsequent cataract formation (98–100). Supporting this idea is the observation that mice with targeted deletions of lens connexins develop cataracts (100, 101) (see below).

Why Are the Disease Phenotypes So Restricted?

The confinement of phenotype to the lens for Cx50 mutations is reasonably consistent with its expression pattern. Cx50 is largely, although not exclusively (102–104), restricted to this organ. However, a surprising aspect of both CMTX and nonsyndromic deafness is that the connexin mutations do not cause gross functional abnormalities in multiple organ systems. Both Cx32 and Cx26 are major components of gap junctions in many cell types [for review, see Bruzzone et al (9)]. Why, then, do most cell types expressing mutated versions of these connexins appear to function normally? The explanation may be that most cells express multiple connexins. Other connexins, either normally present or up-regulated in response to the mutation, could compensate. In this scenario, myelinating Schwann cells or cochlear supporting cells may fail because either they express only one connexin or the other connexins they can produce are unable to duplicate a Cx32- or Cx26-specific function. It remains to be determined whether multiple connexins are simultaneously expressed in these cell types.

DIRECTED MUTATIONS IN CONNEXIN GENES

The analysis of connexin mutations associated with human genetic diseases has provided critical insights into their biological function. However, detailed study of disease etiology would be greatly facilitated by animal models. Potentially, such models could derive from the generation of mice with targeted disruptions of specific connexin genes. In addition, this approach could be used to examine the biological roles of connexins not yet implicated in human genetic disease. To date, seven connexin gene knockouts have been reported. In some cases the knockout phenotypes have confirmed existing hypotheses of gap junction function, and in others they have identified new questions about the role of connexin diversity in vivo.

Deletion of Cx26 Results in Embryonic Lethality

Unlike loss of function mutations of human Cx26, targeted disruption of murine Cx26 results in lethality at embryonic day 11. The failure of Cx26 knockouts to thrive was explained by postulating a role for junctional communication in transplacental movement of nutrients. It was reported that transfer of a nonmetabolizable glucose analogue across the chorioallantoic placenta from maternal to fetal blood was reduced in the knockout embryos (105). In mice, glucose must cross two adjacent cell layers, syncytiotrophoblast I and II, to be transported from maternal to fetal blood. Entry of maternal glucose into the cytoplasm of type I cells is facilitated by GLUT1 transporters in its plasma membrane. Subsequently, glucose diffuses between the two syncytiotrophoblast cell layers, presumably through intercellular channels made of Cx26. Glucose release into the fetal blood from syncytiotrophoblast II cytoplasm again utilizes the GLUT1 transporter (106). As described above, mutations in the human Cx26 gene result in hereditary deafness, not embryonic lethality. However, the human placenta contains only one syncytiotrophoblast cell layer rather than two layers connected by Cx26, as in mice. Thus, the loss of functional Cx26 presumably does not result in placental transport defects in humans.

Hepatic Abnormalities in Cx32 Knockout Mice

Although Cx32 mutations are associated with a human neuropathy, Cx32-deficient mice exhibit only subtle defects in the peripheral nervous system. However, dramatic abnormalities are present in the liver, an organ in which Cx32 is abundantly expressed. First, mobilization of glucose from glycogen stores is severely affected in these animals. Following electrical stimulation of postganglionic sympathetic neurons entering the liver at the porta hepatis, glucose release was decreased 78% in knockout animals. This lowered response was not due to decreased noradrenaline receptors or glycogen stores because normal glucose release was observed from knockout hepatocytes after vascular perfusion of either noradrenaline or glucagon (107). These data provide an example of a coordinated tissue response to external stimuli mediated by intercellular channels. Hepatocytes at the portal end of the hepatic lobule receive stimulation by sympathetic fibers that terminate at the edge of the lobule, whereas hepatocytes at the venous end of the lobule are not directly innervated. Stimulation results in the generation of intracellular 1, 4, 5-trisphosphate and release of Ca^{2+} from intracellular stores. Because both of these second messengers can pass between cells via intercellular channels (108, 109), junctional communication most likely propagates signals for glucose mobilization in hepatocytes far removed from the local noradrenaline stimulus.

Cx32 knockout mice also exhibit a 25-fold increased rate of spontaneous hepatic tumor formation. The susceptibility to tumors induced by intraperitoneal injection of the carcinogens is also markedly increased (8). These data are consistent with the hypothesis that inhibitory signals passing through intercellular channels contribute to growth control (110). Cx26, which is also present in normal hepatocyte gap junctions, is markedly reduced in the Cx32 knockout, although some Cx26 expression and channel activity persists (8, 105). It is currently unclear why the residual communication provided by Cx26 is unable to prevent the increased hepatocarcinogenesis in Cx32-deficient mice. Interestingly, no abnormalities in hepatic function, or increased incidence of cancers of any type, have been reported in humans with Cx32 mutations (CMTX, see above).

Unexpectedly, peripheral myelination in Cx32 knockout animals is only slightly affected compared with humans with essentially null mutations in Cx32 (see above). Although morphological signs of demyelination can be detected by electron microscopy, the number of affected fibers is relatively small and nerve conductance properties are altered only slightly (112). These findings are consistent with the observation that communication between the abaxonal and adaxonal aspects of Schwann cell cytoplasm in Cx32 knockouts is not qualitatively different from wild-type mice (79). Although a direct demonstration has not been made, one explanation is that murine Schwann cells express additional connexins not present in human cells. In support of this notion, Cx46 has been detected in adult rodent sciatic nerve and cultured Schwann cells (113).

Deletion of Cx37 Leads to Female Infertility

Ovarian follicular development requires complex intercellular signaling to orchestrate growth. At birth, the ovary contains primordial follicles consisting of meiotically arrested oocytes surrounded by a single layer of granulosa cells. Periodically, subsets of primordial follicles undergo further development during which oocytes increase in size while the granulosa cells proliferate, stratify, and develop a fluid-filled antrum. During this period, the innermost layer of granulosa cells extend processes through the zona pellucida, a thick extracellular matrix, to make gap junctions with the oocyte (Figure 5). Granulosa cells also make gap junctions with each other. Around the time of antrum formation, the oocyte matures enough to resume meiosis but is inhibited from doing so, presumably by surrounding granulosa cells. It has been hypothesized that gap junctions between the oocyte and granulosa cells transduce inhibitory signals, one of which is likely to be cAMP (114–117). After ovulation, meiosis resumes and the granulosa cells remaining in the follicle proliferate and differentiate into progesterone-secreting cells to form a corpus luteum. One model for control of luteinization postulates that the oocyte actively represses granulosa differentiation by releasing inhibitory factors. However, the nature of these signals and their mechanism of transduction have not been defined.

Female mice lacking Cx37 are infertile because ovulation does not occur (7). Cx37 knockouts show defects in at least three aspects of ovarian development. First, the follicle stops growing as the antrum begins to form. The extent of growth inhibition is variable, but mature follicules are never observed. Second, only a small percentage of oocytes mature sufficiently to resume meiosis. This finding suggests that growth-promoting signals from follicular cells

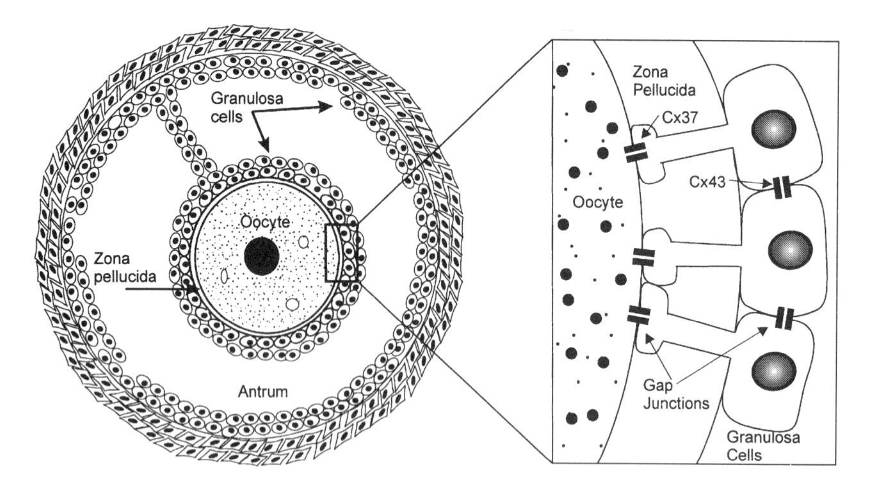

Figure 5 Cx37 is required for bidirectional signaling between oocytes and granulosa cells. In a mature ovarian follicle, the oocyte is surrounded by several layers of granulosa cells and this aggregate is suspended within a fluid-filled antrum. Granulosa cells adjacent to the oocyte extend processes through the zona pellucida and assemble intercellular junctions with the oocyte, including gap junctions that contain Cx37. In turn, granulosa cells are coupled to each other by intercellular channels containing Cx43. In Cx37 knockouts, oocyte-granulosa coupling is ablated, and granulosa-granulosa coupling persists. As a result, female mice lacking Cx37 show defects in follicular growth, oocyte maturation, and control of luteinization [adapted from Nicholson & Bruzzone (143)].

necessary for oocyte maturation permeate through gap junctions. Third, ovaries of sexually mature knockouts contain 10-fold more corpora lutea than do ovaries of wild-type. Because luteinization in normal animals occurs at ovulation when, by definition, oocyte-granulosa cell communication is lost, the premature luteinization observed in the knockout suggests that junctional communication is a major mechanism regulating corpus luteum formation.

Cx37 is readily detected in the junctions between oocyte and granulosa cell, whereas Cx43 appears to be the most abundant connexin in granulosa/granulosa junctions (7, 118). In the Cx37 knockout, gap junctions between oocyte and granulosa cells are lost and intercellular communication cannot be detected. In contrast, communication between granulosa cells is not affected. Thus, loss of only the oocyte-granulosa signaling pathway appears to account for the complex changes in ovarian development leading to infertility. One unresolved issue is the role of junctional communication in maintaining meiotic arrest. Previous models predict that meiotically competent oocytes lacking junctional communication with granulosa cells would undergo premature meiotic resumption. The fact that the majority of knockout oocytes did not mature sufficiently to become meiotically competent precludes a simple test of this model.

Aberrant Cardiac Conduction in Cx40-Deficient Mice

In the mouse, knockout studies suggest that Cx40 has an important functional role in synchronizing contraction of cardiac muscle (119, 120). Cx40 is expressed at high levels in the His-Purkinje system (121), a network of cells specialized for rapid conduction of excitation to the apical ventricular myocardium. The conduction properties in the His-Purkinje system can be monitored by three-lead electrocardiography (ECG). As diagrammed in Figure 6, each cardiac cycle is initiated in the sinoatrial node. Depolarization then spreads through the atrial myocardium from right to left and superior to inferior, causing a wave of contraction to extend down toward the ventricles. The excitatory impulse is prevented from passing to the ventricular myocardium by a thick connective tissue septum. The wave of excitation impinges on the atrioventricular (AV) node, which introduces a delay as the action potential passes slowly through the AV node cells. Subsequently, the impulse is rapidly conducted along the His-Purkinje bundles, which are insulated by subendocardial connective tissue, to excite the ventricular myocardium at the apex of the heart. The result is a wave of contraction that travels upward back through the ventricles, expelling their contents into the pulmonary artery and aorta.

Two laboratories have knocked out the Cx40 gene (119, 120) with similarities and differences in the phenotype. A representative example of an ECG taken from a wild-type and a Cx40 knockout mouse is shown in Figure 6. In these recordings, the first deflection (P wave) results from atrial depolarization. This is followed by a long PR interval, which corresponds to the slow conduction through the AV node and rapid conduction through the His-Purkinje system. The second series of positive and negative deflections (QRS complex) results from ventricular depolarization, and the last deflection (T wave) is due to ventricular repolarization. In both studies, dramatic changes in atrioventricular and intraventricular conduction were observed.

First, atrioventricular conduction was slowed in Cx40 knockouts. The interval between the start of atrial depolarization and the start of ventricular depolarization (PR interval) was ~20% longer in knockouts than in wild-type or heterozygote control animals. The PR interval reflects the time required for excitation to traverse the atrium, AV node, and His-Purkinje system. AV node conduction is typically slow and accounts for most of the interval. Because there is no Cx40 in the AV node, it is reasonable to propose that AV node conduction is unaffected in Cx40 knockouts. That being the case, the 20% difference in PR intervals most likely reflects a much greater difference in His-Purkinje conduction times between knockout and wild-type animals.

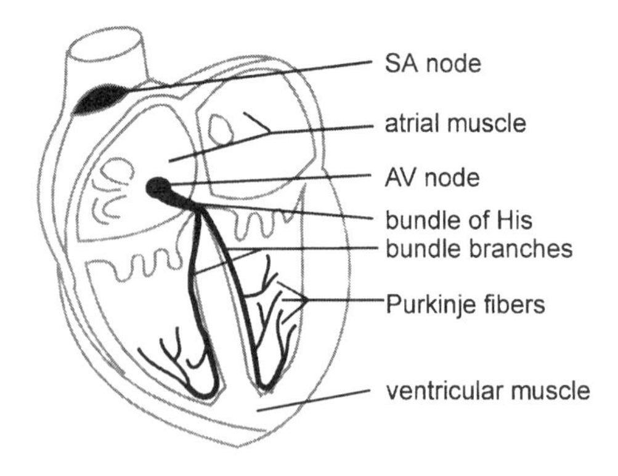

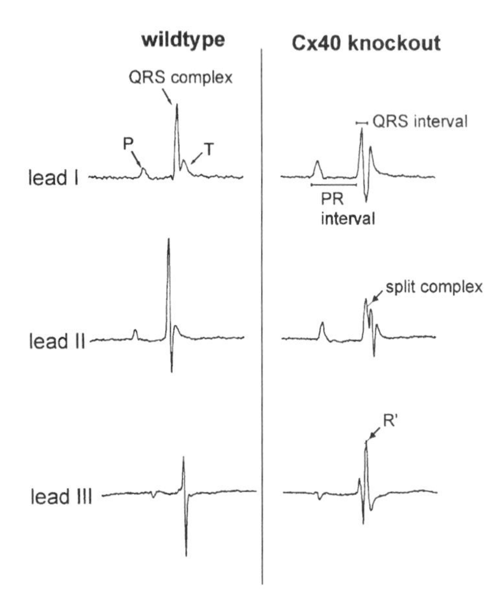

Figure 6 Slowed cardiac conduction in Cx40 knockouts. Each heartbeat is initiated in the sinoatrial node (SA) and propagates through the atrial muscle arriving at the atrioventricular (AV) node. The action potential then rapidly travels down the His bundle, its branches, and the Purkinje fibers to excite the ventricular myocardium at the apex of the heart. In an electrocardiogram (ECG), the P wave corresponds to depolarization of the atria. The PR interval is the sum of slow conduction through the AV node and rapid conduction through the His-Purkinje system. The QRS complex reflects the depolarization of the ventricles, and the T wave their repolarization. Cx40 knockout ECGs display prolonged PR intervals and QRS durations compared with wild-type ECGs, indicating that both AV and intraventricular conduction are delayed. Cx40 knockout ECGs also exhibit split QRS complexes and rSR' morphology, a possible indication of uncoordinated ventricular activation (adapted from 119).

Intraventricular conduction was also substantially delayed in Cx40 knockouts; QRS complexes were ~33% longer than wild-type control animals. The intraventricular delay was not likely to reflect slow propagation through the working myocardium because Cx40 is not expressed in ventricular muscle (122); it was more likely the result of slow conduction through Purkinje fibers, which could result in altered spatial or temporal activation of the ventricles. In support of this idea, lead II QRS complexes were also frequently split, whereas lead III complexes often exhibited rSR' morphology in which there is a second larger R wave following an S wave. Although these complex patterns can be difficult to precisely interpret, in humans they are generally indicative of asynchronous activation of right and left ventricles. Unlike the case of Cx43 (see below), elimination of only one copy of the Cx40 gene had no effect on conduction.

Significantly, the knockout phenotypes were not completely identical in the two studies. Both observed increases in P wave duration, indicating slower atrial depolarization, which is consistent with the expression of Cx40 in atrial myocytes (123). However, the difference between control and knockout was 9% in one case and 36% in the other. Another discrepancy between the studies was observed with regard to transient cardiac arrhythmia. In normal sinus rhythm, P waves are followed at a consistent interval by a QRS complex, indicating that ventricular depolarization is being triggered by impulses originating in the atrium and that conduction through the His-Purkinje system is not completely blocked. Simon et al consistently observed sinus rhythm (119), which could be explained by the presence of Cx45 in the His-Purkinje system (124). In contrast, Kirchhoff et al (120) reported a loss of sinus rhythm in 20% of the knockout animals. These differences have not been resolved but may be due to variations in the strain background or the anesthesia protocols used during the ECG measurements.

Abnormal Cardiac Development and Function in Cx43 Knockout Mice

Cx43 is widely distributed throughout vertebrate tissues. Originally characterized in myocardium (125), Cx43 is found in almost all organs in varying amounts. A targeted disruption of the Cx43 gene (126) resulted in a dramatic malformation at the origin of the pulmonary artery involving the development of labyrinthine, anomalous septae that partially or completely occlude the right ventricular outflow to the lungs. As a result, the animals are unable to oxygenate their blood independently of the placenta and they die postnatally of asphyxiation. The remainder of embryonic development is grossly normal, even though Cx43 is widely expressed throughout embryogenesis, beginning at the 8-cell stage (127). Embryonic survival is likely due to the normal coexpression of other connexin genes. For example, morula stage embryos express at least five connexins in addition to Cx43 (128).

The sensitivity of the conotruncal region of the developing heart to the lack of Cx43 has been attributed to changes in the migratory behavior of neural crest cells that express Cx43 and participate in the development of the outflow pathway (129). Neural crest cells derived from Cx43 knockouts displayed slower rates of migration in vitro whereas neural crest cells derived from transgenic lines constitutively overexpressing Cx43 showed accelerated migration. Consistent with this finding, the constitutive overexpressors also exhibited conotruncal abnormalities, although other structures that were normal in the knockout were affected (130). Finally, partial rescue of the cardiac defect was observed when the Cx43 overexpressors were bred into the Cx43 knockout line. The effect of changes in Cx43 levels in other neural crest derivatives remains to be determined.

Recently, a significant abnormality in cardiac conduction was reported for heterozygotes carrying one disrupted Cx43 allele (131, 132). Although these animals are grossly normal and otherwise healthy, ventricular conduction is 30% slower in them than in control animals. This is consistent with the fact that Cx43 protein levels are reduced by 50%, but it is nevertheless surprising because the magnitude of junctional communication was previously not believed to be a rate-limiting step. Indeed, the level of coupling necessary to entrain sinoatrial node pacemaker cells has been estimated to be only 3–5 active intercellular channels (133, 134).

Cx46 and Cx50 Provide Critical But Different Functions in Lens Physiology

The lens has two distinct types of cells: A simple cuboidal epithelium lines the anterior surface, and differentiated fibers constitute the rest of the lenticular mass. Mitotically active epithelial cells at the lens equator differentiate to give rise to the lens fibers, which lose intracellular organelles and accumulate high concentrations of soluble proteins known as crystallins (135). These cellular properties, together with an elastic capsule and zonular fibers, result in the optical transparency, high refractive index, and elasticity necessary for accommodation. With the loss of cellular organelles, the fibers lose the ability to support oxidative phosphorylation and an active metabolism. Gap junctional communication joins all the cells of the lens into a functional syncytium, and it is likely that this intercellular communication allows the metabolically active epithelium to maintain the precise intracellular ionic conditions necessary to prevent precipitation of the crystallins and cataract formation (98–100). In support of this hypothesis, both Cx46 and Cx50 knockout mice develop cataracts, although the nature of the defects is distinctly different in each case.

Cx46 knockout mice exhibit a progressive "senile-type" cataractogenesis. Lens growth and development are normal, but after the mice reach three weeks of age, lens opacities appear. In adult animals, aberrant proteolysis of crystallins was observed, which may have contributed to their conversion to insoluble forms associated with cataractogenesis (101). Because Cx46 and Cx50 have a similar, if not identical, distribution in lens fibers (25), presumably both connexins contribute to intercellular channels joining fibers. The ability of lens fibers to communicate in Cx46 knockouts was not directly tested, although it may persist because Cx50 distribution was unaffected in Cx46 knockout lenses (101). Thus, cataracts in the Cx46 knockout could develop either from a reduction in the absolute number of intercellular channels, or because the presence of Cx46 provided an activity not obtainable from Cx50 alone. The first possibility would be supported if targeted disruption of the Cx50 and Cx46 genes produced the same phenotype, whereas the second possibility could result in different phenotypes.

Deletion of the Cx50 gene by homologous recombination results in reduced growth of the lens and eye and the appearance of zonular pulverulent nuclear cataracts (100a). The microphthalmia most likely results from the retardation of lens growth, as studies of chick eye development following extirpation of the lens demonstrated that the growth of the eye is dependent on the lens (137). Similarly, ablation of the lens by transgenic expression of toxic genes results in reduced eye growth in mice (138, 139). In turn, the reduction in lens size resulted from a transient inhibition of growth rate during the first postnatal week. The mechanism whereby Cx50 intercellular channels stimulate fiber growth and differentiation remains to be determined.

Cx50 knockout mice develop cataracts in the first postnatal week, providing a model to study the early cellular events associated with human congenital cataracts that result from mutations in Cx50 (described above). Injection of gap junction permeable tracers into Cx50 knockout lenses before cataracts had formed demonstrated the persistence of intercellular communication between epithelial cells, between fiber cells, and between the epithelium and fibers. These results suggested that intercellular communication per se was not sufficient to prevent cataractogenesis, but that intercellular channels incorporating the unique properties of Cx50 were required. In contrast to the Cx46 knockout (101), the deletion of Cx50 did not provoke aberrant proteolysis of crystallins, although their conversion to insoluble forms led to lens opacity.

Comparison of the Cx46 and Cx50 knockout studies strongly suggests that the channel diversity resulting from the expression of two connexins in lens fibers is required for normal lens homeostasis. The restriction of the growth phenotype to loss of Cx50 but not Cx46 suggests that an early postnatal growth signal may propagate efficiently through Cx50 but not Cx46 channels. Alternatively, at the critical time in development, there could be differences in the spatial/temporal patterns of expression for Cx50 and Cx46. If Cx50 expression preceded that of Cx46 during fiber development, then differentiation could be transiently delayed until the appearance of Cx46 and the restoration of appropriate communication. Because the levels of intercellular communication were not quantitatively measured in either case, it is possible that the distinct phenoptypes result from different decreases in the absolute numbers of intercellular channels in the two knockout models. A definitive answer will await "knock-in" studies, where one of these two proteins has been replaced by the other, so that lenses in the resulting animals lack only connexin diversity and not intercellular channel quantity.

CONCLUSION

Critical functions for gap junctions have been elucidated by the discovery of disease-causing mutations in human connexins and the targeted disruption of mouse connexin genes. In addition, the realization that innexin genes encode gap junction proteins opens new avenues for studies of their biological roles. Genetic studies of intercellular communication are tempered by questions of redundancy and compensatory expression, and it is often difficult to explain the restriction, or even absence, of a phenotype following mutation of a particular gap junction gene. For example, Cx37 and Cx40 are both abundantly expressed in vascular endothelial cells, but no vascular phenotype has yet been reported for either knockout. This could be a case of redundancy, and interbreeding the Cx37- and Cx40-deficient animals may result in a more pronounced vascular phenotype. The generation of animals with multiple connexin knockouts is ongoing and will no doubt answer some of these types of questions.

The identification of connexin genes that underlie human disease will, in the short term, allow definitive genetic counseling in families carrying the mutated alleles. So far, only the Cx50 knockout mice provide a model for research into the basic mechanisms of cataract formation, as the Cx26 and Cx32 knockouts do not closely replicate the human pathologies resulting from mutations in these genes. In the case of deafness, alternative transgenic animal models might be developed using human dominant-negative Cx26 mutations. Animals expressing the dominant alleles under promoters with temporally or spatially restricted expression could overcome the embryonic lethality of Cx26 knockouts.

Finally, one of the most difficult challenges remaining will be to uncover the mechanisms whereby gene disruption leads to pathological changes. For intercellular channels, this question ultimately comes down to finding the specific molecules that no longer can pass between cells in the affected tissue.

Literature Cited

1. Weidmann S. 1952. The electrical constants of Purkinje fibres. *J. Physiol.* 118(348):362 (Abstr.)
2. Risek B, Guthrie S, Kumar N, Gilula NB. 1990. Modulation of gap junction transcript and protein expression during pregnancy in the rat. *J. Cell Biol.* 110:269–82
3. Furshpan EJ, Potter DD. 1957. Mechanism of nerve-impulse transmission at a crayfish synapse. *Nature* 180:342–43
4. Bennett MVL. 1997. Gap junctions as electrical synapses. *J. Neurocytol.* 26: 349–66
5. Brivanlou IH, Warland DK, Meister M. 1998. Mechanisms of concerted firing among retinal ganglion cells. *Neuron* 20:527–39
6. Loewenstein WR, Rose B. 1992. The cell-cell channel in the control of growth. *Semin. Cell Biol.* 3:59–79
7. Simon AM, Goodenough DA, Li E, Paul DL. 1997. Female infertility in mice lacking connexin 37. *Nature* 385:525–29
8. Temme A, Buchmann A, Gabriel HD, Nelles E, Schwarz M, Willecke K. 1997. High incidence of spontaneous and chemically induced liver tumors in mice deficient for connexin32. *Curr. Biol.* 7:713–16
9. Bruzzone R, White TW, Paul DL. 1996. Connections with connexins—the molecular basis of direct intercellular signaling. *Eur. J. Biochem.* 238:1–27
10. Goodenough DA, Goliger JA, Paul DL. 1996. Connexins, connexons, and intercellular communication. *Annu. Rev. Biochem.* 65:475–502
11. O'Brien J, Bruzzone R, White TW, al-Ubaidi MR, Ripps H. 1998. Cloning and expression of two related connexins from the perch retina define a distinct subgroup of the connexin family. *J. Neurosci.* 18:7625–37
12. O'Brien J, al-Ubaidi MR, Ripps H. 1996. Connexin 35: a gap-junctional protein expressed preferentially in the skate retina. *Mol. Biol. Cell* 7:233–43
13. Itahana K, Tanaka T, Morikazu Y, Komatu S, Ishida N, Takeya T. 1998. Isolation and characterization of a novel connexin gene, Cx-60, in porcine ovarian follicles. *Endocrinology* 139:320–29
14. Yoshizaki G, Patiño R. 1995. Molecular cloning, tissue distribution, and hormonal control in the ovary of cx41 mrna, a novel xenopus connexin gene transcript. *Mol. Reprod. Dev.* 42:7–18
15. Condorelli DF, Parenti R, Spinella F, Salinaro AT, Belluardo N, et al. 1998. Cloning of a new gap junction gene (cx36) highly expressed in mammalian brain neurons. *Eur. J. Neurosci.* 10:1202–8
16. Kumar N, Gilula NB. 1996. The gap junction communication channel. *Cell* 84:381–88
17. Musil LS. 1994. Structure and assembly of gap junctions. In *Molecular Mechanisms of Epithelial Cell Junctions: From Development to Disease*, ed. S Citi, pp. 173–94. Austin, TX: Landes
18. Sosinsky GE. 1996. Molecular organization of gap junction membrane channels. *J. Bioenerg. Biomembr.* 28:297–309
19. Unger VM, Kumar NM, Gilula NB, Yeager M. 1997. Projection structure of a gap junction membrane channel at 7 angstrom resolution. *Nature Struct. Biol.* 4:39–43
20. Jiang JX, Goodenough DA. 1996. Heteromeric connexons in lens gap junction channels. *Proc. Natl. Acad. Sci. USA* 93:1287–91
21. Konig N, Zampighi G. 1995. Purification of bovine lens cell-to-cell channels composed of connexin44 and connexin50. *J. Cell Sci.* 108:3091–98
22. Perkins G, Goodenough DA, Sosinsky G. 1997. Three-dimensional structure of the gap junction connexon. *Biophys. J.* 72:533–44
23. Nicholson B, Dermietzel R, Teplow D, Traub O, Willecke K, Revel JP. 1987. Two homologous protein components of hepatic gap junctions. *Nature* 329:732–34
24. Traub O, Look J, Dermietzel R, Brummer F, Hulser D, Willecke K. 1989. Comparative characterization of the 21-kD and 26-kD gap junction proteins in murine liver and cultured hepatocytes. *J. Cell Biol.* 108:1039–51
25. Paul DL, Ebihara L, Takemoto LJ,

Swenson KI, Goodenough DA. 1991. Connexin46, a novel lens gap junction protein, induces voltage-gated currents in nonjunctional plasma membrane of *Xenopus* oocytes. *J. Cell Biol.* 115:1077–89
26. Simpson I, Rose B, Loewenstein WR. 1977. Size limit of molecules permeating the junctional membrane channels. *Science* 195:294–97
27. Veenstra RD. 1996. Size and selectivity of gap junction channels formed from different connexins. *J. Bioenerg. Biomembr.* 28:327–37
28. Elfgang C, Eckert R, Lichtenberg-Fraté H, Butterweck A, Traub O, et al. 1995. Specific permeability and selective formation of gap junction channels in connexin-transfected HeLa cells. *J. Cell Biol.* 129:805–17
29. Cao FL, Eckert R, Elfgang C, Nitsche JM, Snyder SA, et al. 1998. A quantitative analysis of connexin-specific permeability differences of gap junctions expressed in HeLa transfectants and Xenopus oocytes. *J. Cell Sci.* 111:31–43
30. Bevans CG, Kordel M, Rhee SK, Harris AL. 1998. Isoform composition of connexin channels determines selectivity among second messengers and uncharged molecules. *J. Biol. Chem.* 273: 2808–16
31. Goldberg GS, Lampe PD, Sheedy D, Stewart CC, Nicholson BJ, Naus CC. 1998. Direct isolation and analysis of endogenous transjunctional ADP from Cx43 transfected C6 glioma cells. *Exp. Cell Res.* 239:82–92
32. Barnes TM. 1994. Opus—a growing family of gap junction proteins. *Trends Genet.* 10:303–5
33. Phelan P, Bacon JP, Davies JA, Stebbings LA, Todman MG, et al. 1998. Innexins: a family of invertebrate gap junction proteins. *Trends Genet.* 14:348–49
34. Watanabe T, Kankel DR. 1992. The l(1) ogre gene of *Drosophila melanogaster* is expressed in postembryonic neuroblasts. *Dev. Biol.* 152:172–83
35. Krishnan SN, Frei E, Swain GP, Wyman RJ. 1993. Passover: a gene required for synaptic connectivity in the giant fiber system of *Drosophila*. *Cell* 73:967–77
36. Krishnan SN, Frei E, Schalet AP, Wyman RJ. 1995. Molecular basis of intracistronic complementation in the Passover locus of *Drosophila*. *Proc. Natl. Acad. Sci. USA* 92:2021–25
37. Starich TA, Herman RK, Shaw JE. 1993. Molecular and genetic analysis of unc-7, a *Caenorhabditis elegans* gene required for coordinated locomotion. *Genetics* 133:527–41
38. Starich TA, Lee RY, Panzarella C, Avery L, Shaw JE. 1996. eat-5 and unc-7 represent a multigene family in *Caenorhabditis elegans* involved in cell-cell coupling. *J. Cell Biol.* 134:537–48
39. Barnes TM, Hekimi S. 1997. The *Caenorhabditis elegans* avermectin resistance and anesthetic response gene *unc-9* encodes a member of a protein family implicated in electrical coupling of excitable cells. *J. Neurochem.* 69: 2251–60
40. Phelan P, Nakagawa M, Wilkin MB, Moffat KG, Okane CJ, et al. 1996. Mutations in *Shaking-B* prevent electrical synapse formation in the drosophila giant fiber system. *J. Neurosci.* 16:1101–13
41. Sun YA, Wyman RJ. 1996. Passover eliminates gap junctional communication between neurons of the giant fiber system in *Drosophila*. *J. Neurobiol.* 30: 340–48
42. Lipshitz HD, Kankel DR. 1985. Specificity of gene action during central nervous system development in *Drosophila melanogaster*: analysis of the lethal (1) optic ganglion reduced locus. *Dev. Biol.* 108:56–77
43. Thomas JB, Wyman RJ, Watanabe T, Kankel DR. 1992. A mutation in *Drosophila* alters normal connectivity between two identified neurones: The l(1)ogre gene of *Drosophila melanogaster* is expressed in postembryonic neuroblasts. *Nature* 152:172–83
44. Phelan P, Stebbings LA, Baines RA, Bacon JP, Davies JA, Ford C. 1998. *Drosophila* shaking-B protein forms gap junctions in paired *Xenopus* oocytes. *Nature* 391:181–84
45. Bruzzone R, White TW, Paul DL. 1994. Expression of chimeric connexins reveals new properties of the formation and gating behavior of gap junction channels. *J. Cell Sci.* 107:955–67
46. Chanson M, Chandross KJ, Rook MB, Kessler JA, Spray DC. 1993. Gating characteristics of a stably voltage-dependent gap junction channel in rat Schwann cells. *J. Gen. Physiol.* 102: 925–46
47. Chanson M, Roy C, Spray DC. 1994. Voltage-dependent gap junctional conductance in hepatopancreatic cells of *Procambarus clarkii*. *Am. J. Physiol.* 266:C569–77
48. Bukauskas FF, Weingart R. 1994. Voltage-dependent gating of single gap

junction channels in an insect cell line. *Biophys. J.* 67:613–25
49. Veenstra RD, Wang HZ, Beyer EC, Brink PR. 1994. Selective dye and ionic permeability of gap junction channels formed by connexin45. *Circ. Res.* 75:483–90
50. Bukauskas FF, Elfgang C, Willecke K, Weingart R. 1995. Biophysical properties of gap junction channels formed by mouse connexin40 in induced pairs of transfected human HeLa cells. *Biophys. J.* 68:2289–98
51. Bukauskas FF, Peracchia C. 1997. Two distinct gating mechanisms in gap junction channels—CO_2-sensitive and voltage-sensitive. *Biophys. J.* 72:2137–42
52. Trexler EB, Bennett MVL, Bargiello TA, Verselis VK. 1996. Voltage gating and permeation in a gap junction hemichannel. *Proc. Natl. Acad. Sci. USA* 93:5836–41
53. Veenstra RD, Brink PR. 1996. Do connexin channels have a residual conductance state? *Biophys. J.* 70:1082–84
54. Bergoffen J, Scherer SS, Wang S, Scott MO, Bone LJ, et al. 1993. Connexin mutations in X-linked Charcot-Marie-Tooth disease. *Science* 262:2039–42
55. Kelsell DP, Dunlop J, Stevens HP, Lench NJ, Liang JN, et al. 1997. Connexin 26 mutations in hereditary non-syndromic sensorineural deafness. *Nature* 387:80–83
56. Shiels A, Mackay D, Ionides A, Berry V, Moore A, Bhattacharya S. 1998. A missense mutation in the human connexin50 gene (GJA8) underlies autosomal dominant "Zonular Pulverulent" cataract, on chromosome 1q. *Am. J. Hum. Genet.* 62:526–32
57. Chaib H, Lina-Granade G, Guilford P, Plauchu H, Levilliers J, et al. 1994. A gene responsible for a dominant form of neurosensory non-syndromic deafness maps to the NSRD1 recessive deafness gene interval. *Hum. Mol. Genet.* 3:2219–22
58. Mignon C, Fromaget C, Mattei MG, Gros D, Yamasaki H, Mesnil M. 1996. Assignment of connexin 26 (GJB2) and 46 (GJA3) genes to human chromosome 13q11—>q12 and mouse chromosome 14D1–E1 by in situ hybridization. *Cytogenet. Cell Genet.* 72:185–86
59. Kikuchi T, Kimura RS, Paul DL, Adams JC. 1995. Gap junctions in the rat cochlea—immunohistochemical and ultrastructural analysis. *Anat. Embryol.* 191:101–18
60. Zelante L, Gasparini P, Estivill X, Melchionda S, Dagruma L, et al. 1997. Connexin26 mutations associated with the most common form of non-syndromic neurosensory autosomal recessive deafness (DFNB1) in Mediterraneans. *Hum. Mol. Genet.* 6:1605–9
61. Denoyelle F, Weil D, Maw MA, Wilcox SA, Lench NJ, et al. 1997. Prelingual deafness: high prevalence of a 30delG mutation in the connexin 26 gene. *Hum. Mol. Genet.* 6:2173–77
62. Kelley PM, Harris DJ, Comer BC, Askew JW, Fowler T, et al. 1998. Novel mutations in the connexin 26 gene (GJB2) that cause autosomal recessive (DFNB1) hearing loss. *Am. J. Hum. Genet.* 62:792–99
63. Carrasquillo MM, Zlotogora J, Barges S, Chakravarti A. 1997. Two different connexin 26 mutations in an inbred kindred segregating non-syndromic recessive deafness—implications for genetic studies in isolated populations. *Hum. Mol. Genet.* 6:2163–72
64. Lench N, Houseman M, Newton V, Van Camp G, Mueller R. 1998. Connexin-26 mutations in sporadic non-syndromal sensorineural deafness. *Lancet* 351:415 (Lett.)
65. Estivill X, Fortina P, Surrey S, Rabionet R, Melchionda S, et al. 1998. Connexin-26 mutations in sporadic and inherited sensorineural deafness. *Lancet* 351:394–98
66. White TW, Deans MR, Kelsell DP, Paul DL. 1998. Connexin mutations in deafness. *Nature* 394:630–1 (Sci. Correspond.)
67. Scott DA, Kraft ML, Stone EM, Sheffield VC, Smith RJ. 1998. Connexin mutations and hearing loss. *Nature* 391:32 (Lett.)
68. Richard G, White TW, Smith LE, Bailey RA, Compton JG, et al. 1998. Functional defects of Cx26 due to a heterozygous missense mutation in a family with dominant deaf-mutism and palmoplantar keratoderma. *Hum. Genet.* In press
69. Denoyelle F, Lina-Granade G, Plauchu P, Bruzzone R, Chaïb H, et al. 1998. Connexin26 gene linked to a dominant deafness. *Nature.* 393:319–20 (Abstr.)
70. Kikuchi T, Adams JC, Paul DL, Kimura RS. 1994. Gap junction systems in the rat vestibular labyrinth—immunohistochemical and ultrastructural analysis. *Acta Oto-Laryngol.* 114:520–28
71. Johnstone BM, Patuzzi R, Syka J, Sykova E. 1989. Stimulus-related potassium changes in the organ of Corti of guinea-pig. *J. Physiol.* 408:77–92

72. Oesterle EC, Dallos P. 1990. Intracellular recordings from supporting cells in the guinea pig cochlea: DC potentials. *J. Neurophysiol.* 64:617–36
73. Somjen GG. 1979. Extracellular potassium in the mammalian central nervous system. *Annu. Rev. Physiol.* 41:159–77
74. Deschenes SM, Walcott JL, Wexler TL, Scherer SS, Fischbeck KH. 1997. Altered trafficking of mutant connexin32. *J. Neurosci.* 17:9077–84
75. Tetzlaff W. 1982. Tight junction contact events and temporary gap junctions in the sciatic nerve fibres of the chicken during Wallerian degeneration and subsequent regeneration. *J. Neurocytol.* 11:839–58
76. Scherer SS, Deschenes SM, Xu YT, Grinspan JB, Fischbeck KH, Paul DL. 1995. Connexin32 is a myelin-related protein in the PNS and CNS. *J. Neurosci.* 15:8281–94
77. Friede RL, Bischhausen R. 1980. The precise geometry of large internodes. *J. Neurol. Sci.* 48:367–81
78. Majack RA, Larsen WJ. 1980. The bicellular and reflexive membrane junctions of renomedullary interstitial cells: functional implications of reflexive gap junctions. *Am. J. Anat.* 157:181–89
79. Balice-Gordon RJ, Bone L, Scherer S. 1998. Functional gap junctions in the Schwann cell myelin sheath. *J. Cell Biol.* 142:1095–104
80. Scherer SS. 1997. The biology and pathobiology of Schwann cells. *Curr. Opin. Neurol.* 10:386–97
81. Bruzzone R, White TW, Scherer SS, Fischbeck KH, Paul DL. 1994. Null mutations of connexin32 in patients with X-linked Charcot-Marie-Tooth disease. *Neuron* 13:1253–60
82. Ressot C, Gomes D, Dautigny A, Pham-Dinh D, Bruzzone R. 1998. Connexin32 mutations associated with X-linked Charcot-Marie-Tooth disease show two distinct behaviors: loss of function and altered gating properties. *J. Neurosci.* 18:4063–75
83. Oh S, Ri Y, Bennett MVL, Trexler EB, Verselis VK, Bargiello TA. 1997. Changes in permeability caused by connexin 32 mutations underlie X-linked Charcot-Marie-Tooth disease. *Neuron* 19:927–38
84. Omori Y, Mesnil M, Yamasaki H. 1996. Connexin 32 mutations from X-linked Charcot-Marie-Tooth disease patients: functional defects and dominant negative effects. *Mol. Biol. Cell* 7:907–16
85. Lambert SR, Drack AV. 1996. Infantile cataracts. *Surv. Ophthalmol.* 40:427–58
86. Lund AM, Eiberg H, Rosenberg T, Warburg M. 1992. Autosomal dominant congenital cataract; linkage relations; clinical and genetic heterogeneity. *Clin. Genet.* 41:65–69
87. Scott MH, Hejtmancik JF, Wozencraft LA, Reuter LM, Parks MM, Kaiser-Kupfer MI. 1994. Autosomal dominant congenital cataract. Interocular phenotypic variability. *Ophthalmology* 101:866–71
88. Nettleship E. 1909. Seven new pedigrees of hereditary cataract. *Trans. Opthalmol. Soc. UK* 29:188–211
89. Renwick JH, Lawler SD. 1963. Probable linkage between a congenital cataract locus and the Duffy blood group locus. *Ann. Hum. Genet.* 27:67–84
90. Church RL, Wang J, Steele E. 1995. The human lens intrinsic membrane protein MP70 (Cx50) gene: clonal analysis and chromosome mapping. *Curr. Eye Res.* 14:215–21
91. Geyer DD, Church RL, Steele ECJ, Heinzmann C, Kojis TL, et al. 1997. Regional mapping of the human MP70 (Cx50; connexin 50) gene by fluorescence in situ hybridization to 1q21. 1. *Mol. Vis.* 3:13
92. White TW, Bruzzone R, Goodenough DA, Paul DL. 1992. Mouse Cx50, a functional member of the connexin family of gap junction proteins, is the lens fiber protein MP70. *Mol. Biol. Cell* 3:711–20
93. Janssen EAM, Kemp S, Hensels GW, Sie OG, Dediesmulders CEM, et al. 1997. Connexin32 gene mutations in x-linked dominant Charcot-Marie-Tooth disease (cmtx1). *Hum. Genet.* 99:501–5
94. Bort S, Nelis E, Timmerman V, Sevilla T, Cruz-Martinez A, et al. 1997. Mutational analysis of the MPZ, PMP22 and Cx32 genes in patients of Spanish ancestry with Charcot-Marie-Tooth disease and hereditary neuropathy with liability to pressure palsies. *Hum. Genet.* 99:746–54
95. Suchyna TM, Xu LX, Gao F, Fourtner CR, Nicholson BJ. 1993. Identification of a proline residue as a transduction element involved in voltage gating of gap junctions. *Nature* 365:847–49
96. Goodenough DA. 1992. The crystalline lens: a system networked by gap junctional intercellular communication. In *Seminars in Cell Biology*, ed. NB Gilula, pp. 49–58. London: Saunders Sci.
97. Goodenough DA, Dick JSB II, Lyons JE. 1980. Lens metabolic cooperation:

a study of mouse lens transport and permeability visualized with freeze-substitution autoradiography and electron microscopy. *J. Cell Biol.* 86:576–89
98. Rae JL. 1979. The electrophysiology of the crystalline lens. *Curr. Top. Eye Res.* 1:37–90
99. Goodenough DA. 1979. Lens gap junctions: a structural hypothesis for nonregulated low-resistance intercellular pathways. *Invest. Ophthalmol. Vis. Sci.* 18:1104–22
100. Mathias RT, Rae JL, Baldo GJ. 1997. Physiological properties of the normal lens. *Physiol. Rev.* 77:21–50
100a. White TW, Goodenough DA, Paul DL. 1997. Ocular abnormalities in connexin 50 knockout mice. *Mol. Biol. Cell (Suppl.)* 8:93a
101. Gong X, Li E, Klier G, Huang Q, Wu Y, et al. 1997. Disruption of α_3 connexin gene leads to proteolysis and cataractogenesis in mice. *Cell* 91:833–43
102. Gourdie RG, Green CR, Severs NJ, Thompson RP. 1992. Immonolabelling patterns of gap junction connexins in the developing and mature rat heart. *Anat. Embryol.* 185:363–78
103. Dong Y, Roos M, Gruijters T, Donaldson P, Bullivant S, et al. 1994. Differential expression of two gap junction proteins in corneal epithelium. *Eur. J. Cell Biol.* 64:95–100
104. Matic M, Petrov IN, Rosenfeld T, Wolosin JM. 1997. Alterations in connexin expression and cell communication in healing corneal epithelium. *Invest. Ophthalmol. Vis. Sci.* 38:600–9
105. Gabriel H-D, Jung D, Bützler C, Temme A, Traub O, et al. 1998. Transplacental uptake of glucose is decreased in embryonic lethal connexin26-deficient mice. *J. Cell Biol.* 140:1453–61
106. Shin BC, Suzuki T, Matsuzaki T, Tanaka S, Kuraoka A, et al. 1996. Immunolocalization of GLUT1 and connexin 26 in the rat placenta. *Cell Tissue Res.* 285:83–89
107. Nelles E, Butzler C, Jung D, Temme A, Gabriel HD, et al. 1996. Defective propagation of signals generated by sympathetic nerve stimulation in the liver of connexin32-deficient mice. *Proc. Natl. Acad. Sci. USA* 93:9565–70
108. Saez JC, Conner JA, Spray DC, Bennett MVL. 1989. Hepatocyte gap junctions are permeable to the second messenger, inositol 1, 4, 5-trisphosphate, and to calcium ions. *Proc. Natl. Acad. Sci. USA* 86:2708–12
109. Dunlap K, Takeda K, Brehm P. 1987. Activation of a calcium-dependent photoprotein by chemical signalling through gap junctions. *Nature* 325:60–62
110. Loewenstein WR. 1981. Junctional intercellular communication: the cell-to-cell membrane channel. *Physiol. Rev.* 61:829–913
111. Deleted in proof
112. Anzini P, Neuberg DHH, Schachner M, Nelles E, Willecke K, et al. 1997. Structural abnormalities and deficient maintenance of peripheral nerve myelin in mice lacking the gap junction protein connexin 32. *J. Neurosci.* 17:4545–51
113. Chandross KJ, Kessler JA, Cohen RI, Simburger E, Spray DC, et al. 1996. Altered connexin expression after peripheral nerve injury. *Mol. Cell. Neurosci.* 7:501–18
114. Gilula NB, Epstein ML, Beers WH. 1978. Cell-to-cell communication and ovulation. A study of the cumulus-oocyte complex. *J. Cell Biol.* 78:58–75
115. Cho WK, Stern S, Biggers JD. 1974. Inhibitory effect of dibutyryl cAMP on mouse oocyte maturation in vitro. *J. Exp. Zool.* 187:383–86
116. Dekel N, Beers WH. 1978. Rat oocyte maturation in vitro: relief of cyclic AMP inhibition by gonadotropins. *Proc. Natl. Acad. Sci. USA* 75:4369–73
117. Bornslaeger EA, Schultz RM. 1985. Adenylate cyclase activity in zona-free mouse oocytes. *Exp. Cell Res.* 156:277–81
118. Beyer EC, Kistler J, Paul DL, Goodenough DA. 1989. Antisera directed against connexin43 peptides react with a 43-kD protein localized to gap junctions in myocardium and other tissues. *J. Cell Biol.* 108:595–605
119. Simon AM, Goodenough DA, Paul DL. 1998. Mice lacking connexin40 have cardiac conduction abnormalities characteristic of atrioventricular block and bundle branch block. *Curr. Biol.* 8:295–98
120. Kirchhoff S, Nelles E, Hagendorff A, Krüger O, Traub O, Willecke K. 1998. Reduced cardiac conduction velocity and predisposition to arrhythmias in connexin40-deficient mice. *Curr. Biol.* 8:299–302
121. Gourdie RG, Severs NJ, Green CR, Rothery S, Germroth P, Thompson RP. 1993. The spatial distribution and relative abundance of gap-junctional connexin40 and connexin43 correlate to functional properties of components of the cardiac atrioventricular conduction system. *J. Cell Sci.* 105:985–91

122. Bruzzone R, Haefliger J-A, Gimlich RL, Paul DL. 1993. Connexin40, a component of gap junctions in vascular endothelium, is restricted in its ability to interact with other connexins. *Mol. Biol. Cell* 4:7–20
123. Gros D, Jarry-Guichard T, Tenvelde I, Demaziere A, Vankempen MJA, et al. 1994. Restricted distribution of connexin40, a gap junction protein in mammalian heart. *Circ. Res.* 74:839–51
124. Coppen SR, Dupont E, Rothery S, Severs NJ. 1998. Connexin45 expression is preferentially associated with the ventricular conduction system in mouse and rat heart. *Circ. Res.* 82:232–43
125. Beyer EC, Paul DL, Goodenough DA. 1987. Connexin43: a protein from rat heart homologous to a gap junction protein from liver. *J. Cell Biol.* 105:2621–29
126. Reaume AG, De Sousa PA, Kulkarni S, Langille BL, Zhu D, et al. 1995. Cardiac malformation in neonatal mice lacking connexin43. *Science* 267:1831–34
127. Barron DJ, Valdimarsson G, Paul DL, Kidder GM. 1989. Connexin32, a gap junction protein, is a persistent oogenetic product through preimplantation development of the mouse. *Dev. Genet.* 10:318–23
128. Davies TC, Barr KJ, Jones DH, Zhu D, Kidder GM. 1996. Multiple members of the connexin gene family participate in preimplantation development of the mouse. *Dev. Genet.* 18:234–43
129. Lo CW, Cohen MF, Huang GY, Lazatin BO, Patel N, et al. 1997. Cx43 gap junction gene expression and gap junctional communication in mouse neural crest cells. *Dev. Genet.* 20:119–32
130. Ewart JL, Cohen MF, Meyer RA, Huang GY, Wessels A, et al. 1997. Heart and neural tube defects in transgenic mice overexpressing the Cx43 gap junction gene. *Development* 124:1281–92
131. Thomas SA, Schuessler RB, Berul CI, Beardslee MA, Beyer EC, et al. 1998. Disparate effects of deficient expression of connexin43 on atrial and ventricular conduction—evidence for chamber-specific molecular determinants of conduction. *Circulation* 97:686–91
132. Guerrero PA, Schuessler RB, Davis LM, Beyer EC, Johnson CM, et al. 1997. Slow ventricular conduction in mice heterozygous for a connexin43 null mutation. *J. Clin. Invest.* 99:1991–98
133. Anumonwo JMB, Wang Z, Trabka-Janik E, Dunham B, Veenstra RD, et al. 1992. Gap junctional channels in adult mammalian sinus nodal cells. *Circ. Res.* 71:229–39
134. Verheijck EE, Wessels A, Vanginneken ACG, Bourier J, Markman MWM, et al. 1998. Distribution of atrial and nodal cells within the rabbit sinoatrial node—models of sinoatrial transition. *Circulation* 97:1623–31
135. Piatigorsky J. 1981. Lens differentiation in vertebrates. A review of cellular and molecular features. *Differentiation* 19:134–53
136. Angst BD, Khan LUR, Severs NJ, Whitely K, Rothery S, et al. 1997. Dissociated spatial patterning of gap junctions and cell adhesion junctions during postnatal differentiation of ventricular myocardium. *Circ. Res.* 80:88–94
137. Coulombre AJ, Coulombre JL. 1964. Lens development. 1. Role of the lens in eye growth. *J. Exp. Zool.* 156:39–48
138. Breitman ML, Clapoff S, Rossant J, Tsui L-C, Glode LM, et al. 1987. Genetic ablation: targeted expression of a toxin gene causes micropthalmia in transgenic mice. *Science* 238:1563–65
139. Landel CP, Zhao J, Bok D, Evans GA. 1988. Lens-specific expression of recombinant ricin induces developmental defects in the eyes of transgenic mice. *Genes Dev.* 2:1168–78
140. White TW, Bruzzone R, Paul DL. 1995. The connexin family of intercellular channel forming proteins. *Kidney Int.* 48:1148–57
141. Doyle JP, Colman DR. 1993. Glial-neuron interactions and the regulation of myelin formation. *Curr. Opin. Cell Biol.* 5:779–85
142. Paul DL. 1995. New functions for gap junctions. *Curr. Opin. Cell Biol.* 7:665–72
143. Nicholson SM, Bruzzone R. 1997. Gap junctions: getting the message through. *Curr. Biol.* 7:R340–44

Annu. Rev. Physiol. 1999. 61:311–35

LOCALIZED INTRACELLULAR CALCIUM SIGNALING IN MUSCLE: Calcium Sparks and Calcium Quarks

Ernst Niggli
Department of Physiology, University of Bern, Bühlplatz 5, 3012 Bern, Switzerland;
e-mail: niggli@pyl.unibe.ch

KEY WORDS: cardiac muscle, heart, skeletal muscle, excitation-contraction coupling, confocal microscopy

ABSTRACT

Subcellularly localized Ca^{2+} signals in cardiac and skeletal muscle have recently been identified as elementary Ca^{2+} signaling events. The signals, termed Ca^{2+} sparks and Ca^{2+} quarks, represent openings of Ca^{2+} release channels located in the membrane of the sarcoplasmic reticulum (SR). In cardiac muscle, the revolutionary discovery of Ca^{2+} sparks has allowed the development of a fundamentally different concept for the amplification of Ca^{2+} signals by Ca^{2+}-induced Ca^{2+} release. In such a system, a graded amplification of the triggering Ca^{2+} signal entering the myocyte via L-type Ca^{2+} channels is accomplished by a recruitment process whereby individual SR Ca^{2+} release units are locally controlled by L-type Ca^{2+} channels. In skeletal muscle, the initial SR Ca^{2+} release is governed by voltage-sensors but subsequently activates additional Ca^{2+} sparks by Ca^{2+}-induced Ca^{2+} release from the SR. Results from studies on elementary Ca^{2+} release events will improve our knowledge of muscle Ca^{2+} signaling at all levels of complexity, from the molecule to normal cellular function, and from the regulation of cardiac and skeletal muscle force to the pathophysiology of excitation-contraction coupling.

0066-4278/99/0315-0311$08.00

AIM OF THIS REVIEW

In this review, the results of recent experiments on subcellularly localized Ca^{2+} signals in cardiac and skeletal muscle are summarized. The aim is not only to outline what we have learned so far about fundamental properties of these cellular Ca^{2+} signaling events, but also to point out and discuss open issues where more research needs to be done. It is also speculated that the analysis of elementary Ca^{2+} signaling events may help to construct the "big picture" of cellular Ca^{2+} signaling. No attempt is made to review the immense field of cardiac and skeletal muscle excitation-contraction (EC) coupling, as several excellent reviews have been published recently (e.g. see 1–8).

INFORMATION ENCODING WITH Ca^{2+} SIGNALS

Ca^{2+} ions serve as second messengers in a variety of cell types. Cellular processes known to be regulated by Ca^{2+} include excitation-concentration coupling (EC-coupling) in muscle, excitation-secretion coupling in secretory cells (9, 10), neuronal plasticity (11–13), transmitter release and exocytosis (14, 15), and fertilization signals in oocytes (16). In addition, Ca^{2+} signals are important for the activity of many enzymes (e.g. see 17) as well as for cell differentiation, division, and growth (18). Thus, even within a given cell, Ca^{2+} signals are involved in several distinct signaling pathways. This immediately raises a question: How can the same subcellular signal be specific for a certain task and fulfill distinct roles within a particular cell? There are several possible answers. First, the information conveyed by a Ca^{2+} signal inside the cell may be encoded in different ways. From early experimental recordings of spatially averaged Ca^{2+} signals, it quickly became clear that some cells generate transient elevations of cytosolic $[Ca^{2+}]$ of variable amplitude and duration (19–22) whereas other cells were observed to produce oscillatory Ca^{2+} signals, sometimes with frequencies depending on the stimulus (9, 23, 24). Therefore, the general picture emerged that either the amplitude or the frequency of the Ca^{2+} signals could represent the biologically important information. A single transient elevation of $[Ca^{2+}]_i$ could activate downstream signals that are quite different from the cellular response during and after oscillations of $[Ca^{2+}]_i$. The demodulation of the amplitude information obviously occurs by virtue of the dose-response relationship of the Ca^{2+}-sensitive target system. Demodulation of Ca^{2+} signals in the frequency domain has remained more difficult to elucidate and is not fully understood yet. Recently, a calmodulin-dependent protein kinase has been identified as a possible demodulator for frequency-modulated Ca^{2+} signals (17). The activity of the kinase was found to be proportional to the frequency of Ca^{2+} pulses in an in vitro assay. In such a system, the protein kinase essentially acts as a low-pass filter and/or integrator for the Ca^{2+} oscillations, thereby converting the Ca^{2+} signal frequency into a steady phosphorylation signal.

Ca^{2+} SIGNALS CAN BE SPECIFICALLY TARGETED INSIDE CELLS

In some cell types, a fundamentally different mechanism for information encoding has been recognized. Using the paradigm of Ca^{2+} signals that are highly localized within a subcellular microdomain, these cells appear to be able to confine Ca^{2+} signals to a specific subcellular region or can even target it directly to a specific Ca^{2+} receptor molecule (25–27). This type of targeting offers yet another means to make subcellular Ca^{2+} signals specific by using a spatial encoding scheme. This is an obvious possibility and an easy task for cells such as neurons, in which Ca^{2+} release sites are well separated in space (15, 28). However, it came as a surprise that in muscle cells, the same general strategy can also be used. After the observation of Ca^{2+} sparks, it became clear that cardiac muscle cells can employ spatially confined Ca^{2+} signals to target information for specific subcellular sites. This is astonishing because the complex microarchitecture comprising close contacts between the invaginated T-tubular system and sarcoplasmic reticulum (SR) network does not appear to lend itself to the implementation of a signaling system that has to rely on spatially confined pulses of a rapidly diffusible messenger. However, mathematical modeling of Ca^{2+} diffusion in the relevant spatial and temporal domain suggests that large concentration gradients can be established over a limited distance and in narrow spaces, such as the diadic junction (29–34). With or without hindered diffusion of the messenger, in this case Ca^{2+}, concentration gradients on the order of several magnitudes may be expected over distances of a few nanometers (32, 35–37). Therefore, the ultrastructure of the sarcomere is sufficiently sizable to allow for local control mechanisms and to exploit the benefits of spatially confined Ca^{2+} signals.

THE PARADOX IN CARDIAC Ca^{2+} SIGNALING

The prevailing view of cardiac EC-coupling is largely based on the pioneering studies by Fabiato of skinned cardiac muscle cells (38). Several excellent and thoughtful reviews on EC-coupling have since been published (1, 3, 5, 39–41), but a few points are summarized here to set the stage for a discussion of the role of local Ca^{2+} events in cardiac Ca^{2+} signaling and EC-coupling (42, 43).

During each cardiac action potential, sarcolemmal L-type Ca^{2+} channels [dihydropyridine receptors (DHPRs)] are activated and generate an influx of Ca^{2+}

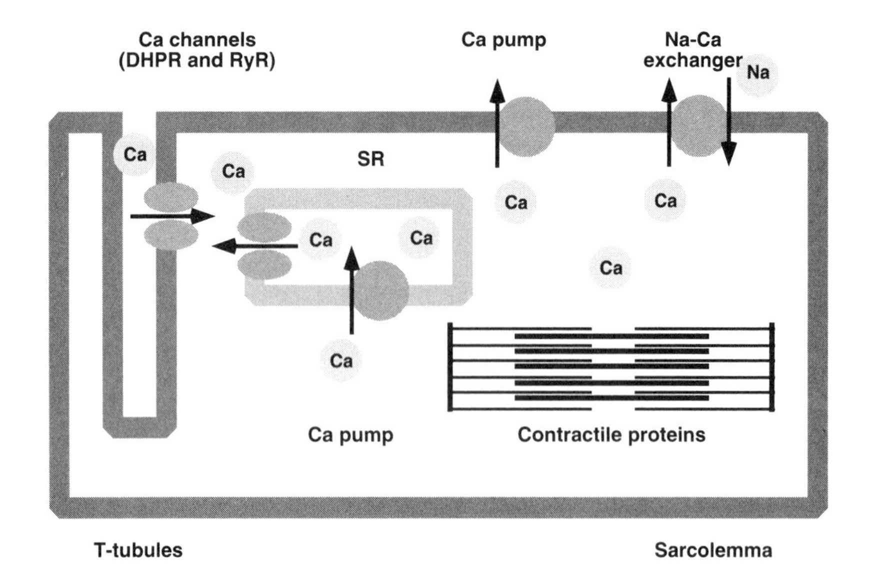

Figure 1 Schematic diagram of a cardiac myocyte (with T-tubule) and the most important elements of excitation-contraction coupling. For details see text. DHPR, dihydropyridine receptors; RyR, ryanodine receptor; SR, sarcoplasmic reticulum.

into the cytosol (see Figure 1). In most species, this initial Ca^{2+} signal is amplified severalfold by additional Ca^{2+} release from an intracellular Ca^{2+} store, the SR (e.g. see 44, 45). Ca^{2+} is released from the SR via ryanodine-sensitive Ca^{2+} release channels located in the SR membrane [ryanodine receptors (RyRs)]. Overall, the average Ca^{2+} signal exhibits a transient increase of $[Ca^{2+}]_i$ from a resting concentration of approximately 100 nM to a peak level in the range of 1 μM. The essential mechanism responsible for SR Ca^{2+} release and for the amplification of the initial trigger signal is termed Ca^{2+}-induced Ca^{2+} release (CICR) and was initially reported in a skeletal muscle SR vesicle preparation (46). After initiating cardiac force production, the $[Ca^{2+}]_i$ declines again to allow muscle relaxation. For this purpose, ATP-driven Ca^{2+} pumps and the Na-Ca exchanger, respectively, transport Ca^{2+} back into the SR or out of the cell (47).

After the initial but extensive characterization of CICR in the skinned cardiac myocyte preparation (38), numerous aspects of cardiac Ca^{2+} signaling from the molecular to the cellular level have been elucidated in several laboratories by a variety of biophysical techniques. However, one feature of CICR in cardiac muscle remained a puzzle until recently. Because the input signal for the Ca^{2+} amplification system is chemically identical to the output signal (i.e. an elevation of cytosolic $[Ca^{2+}]$), the CICR is expected to exhibit substantial positive feedback. Thus, the CICR has a tendency to be self-sustaining and should show only all-or-none responses. Indeed, Ca^{2+} signals consistent with this assumption have been detected in cardiac muscle. For example, mechanical waves as well as Ca^{2+} waves traveling along the cells or spiraling around subcellular obstacles were directly visualized with imaging techniques (48–53). These Ca^{2+} waves are driven by the CICR operating at high gain, presumably because of Ca^{2+} overload of the SR (54, 55).

In contrast, there is a large body of experimental evidence indicating that the amount of Ca^{2+} released from the SR is not all-or-none but is kept under tight control by the L-type Ca^{2+} current. In many whole-cell, patch-clamp studies, Ca^{2+} release was found to closely follow the amplitude and/or duration of L-type Ca^{2+} currents (e.g. see 44, 56, 57) or the amount of photolytic Ca^{2+} release (58). These results are more consistent with an amplification system that is tuned to exhibit little positive feedback. In summary, there were apparently contradictory results, some indicating that CICR exhibits a high gain while others suggesting the opposite. How could this discrepancy be explained?

Several studies from Eisner's laboratory revealed that the degree of positive feedback may be variable and may depend on the SR Ca^{2+} load. Local Ca^{2+} signals generated experimentally in a limited region of the myocyte were found to stay localized and not to propagate as Ca^{2+} waves unless the SR was Ca^{2+} overloaded (54, 59, 60). Likewise, other studies showed that control by L-type Ca^{2+} current over the amount of Ca^{2+} released from the SR was increasingly lost when the SR Ca^{2+} load was gradually elevated (61, 62). Taken together, these results suggest that the gain is normally low and that CICR does not exhibit all-or-none behavior under physiological conditions.

However, mathematical models of cardiac EC-coupling cast doubt about whether the observed high amplification in CICR could be accomplished with such a low-gain system. Computer models of Ca^{2+} diffusion and the CICR amplification system indicated that the observed amplification was not achievable without the threat of instabilities in any common pool system (i.e. a system in which the trigger Ca^{2+} was entering the same cytosolic Ca^{2+} pool as the Ca^{2+} released from the SR) (35). Instead, several more-stable alternatives were proposed, all of which relied on a sizable amplification of CICR that was, however, highly confined to a local subcellular Ca^{2+} release unit. Although each unit would behave in an all-or-none fashion with a very high gain, the entire system (i.e. each cell) would remain stable by virtue of the independence of these individual release units. Changes in the overall Ca^{2+} signal could then be accomplished by a recruitment process in which more or fewer release units are activated. Using this approach, a high amplification model of cardiac EC-coupling could be implemented without the problems associated with instabilities. In this model, two fundamentally different designs for the local control were explored: (*a*) a Ca^{2+} synapse model, where a single L-type Ca^{2+} channel controls an adjacent single RyR; and (*b*) a "cluster-bomb" model, in which a single L-type Ca^{2+} channel locally governs a group of RyRs that are coupled with each other by means of local CICR (i.e. coherent behavior by mutual activation within the cluster via CICR). In principle, both systems rely on a spatial coding scheme for the regulation of the Ca^{2+} signal, as described above.

INITIAL CHARACTERIZATION OF Ca^{2+} SPARKS IN CARDIAC MYOCYTES

In the early 1990s, Ca^{2+} signals possibly corresponding to the proposed local control units were initially discovered in cardiac muscle cells (63, 64) (Figure 2). This discovery was only possible because of significant advancements in the techniques available to measure and image intracellular Ca^{2+}. With the simultaneous advent of sensitive imaging technology and newly developed fluorescent Ca^{2+} indicators (65), it became feasible to record Ca^{2+} signals from single cells. Early imaging studies revealed only coarse spatial features of the Ca^{2+} concentration in cells, frequently taking the shape of Ca^{2+} waves (49, 50, 66). These Ca^{2+} signals are generally interpreted as reaction-diffusion waves (55, 67–69) driven by a regenerative amplification system, such as Ca^{2+}-induced Ca^{2+} release. The resolution of fluorescent imaging techniques was further improved with the development of laser scanning confocal instruments that allowed the imaging of the Ca^{2+} distribution on the subcellular level with near diffraction-limited optical resolution (70, 71). Confocal microscopy increases the resolution of fluorescence imaging mainly by removing out-of-focus fluorescence and enabling optical sections even within sizeable and thick specimens, such as cardiac or skeletal muscle cells.

The first observations of subcellularly localized Ca^{2+} release signals were made in freshly dissociated rat ventricular myocytes (63) and in cultured rat cardiac myocytes (64). These signaling events occurred spontaneously and at a low rate (about 100 s^{-1} in a rat ventricular myocyte). Unlike the whole-cell Ca^{2+} transient, these Ca^{2+} signals were characterized by being of short duration (about 100 ms) and having an approximate amplitude of only 170 nM and a subcellular spatial spread, for full width at half maximal amplitude, in the range of 2 μm. Pharmacological evidence indicated that these Ca^{2+} sparks corresponded to spontaneous Ca^{2+} release events from the SR via RyRs. Occasionally, these signals were also seen to spread over a short distance within the cell, giving rise to brief and abortive Ca^{2+} waves, or even to trigger Ca^{2+} waves traveling along the entire cell. At this time, it was proposed that Ca^{2+} sparks may not only be unitary events of spontaneous Ca^{2+} release but may

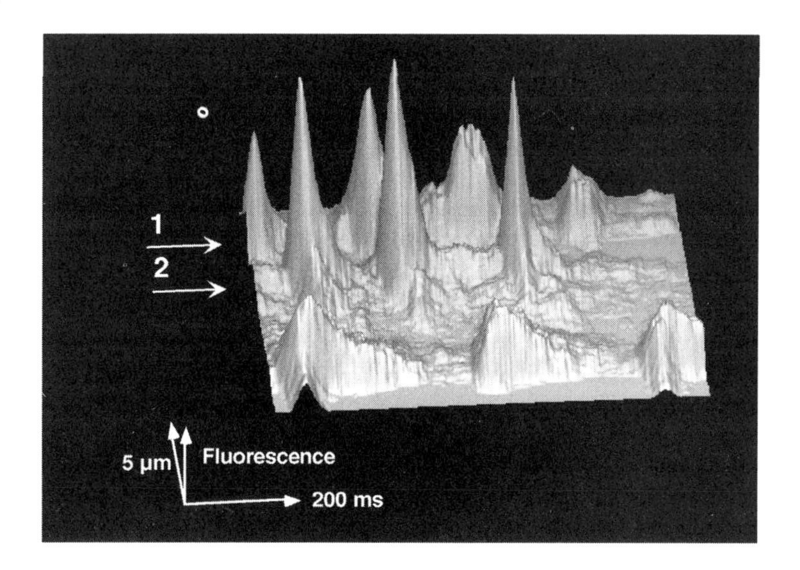

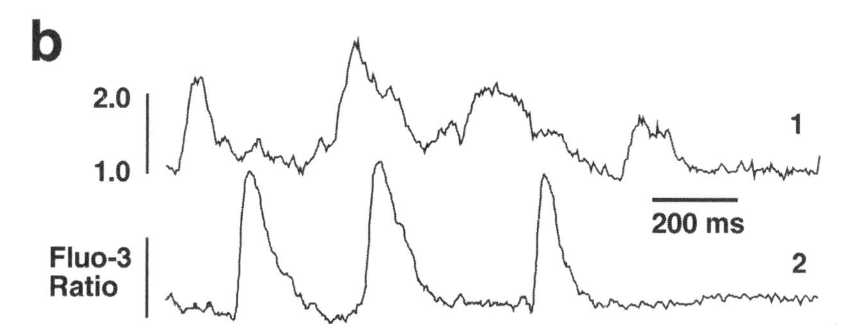

Figure 2 An example of Ca^{2+} sparks recorded in a cultured neonatal rat cardiac myocyte. (*a*) A surface plot of fluo-3 fluorescence was constructed from a confocal line scan image. Localized Ca^{2+} signals are shown along one spatial dimension whereas the other dimension corresponds to time. (*b*) Line traces of fluo-3 fluorescence recorded in two different regions (*1* and *2* in *panel a*). Several random Ca^{2+} sparks are detectable in each region and the two regions are not synchronized. (Modified from Reference 64.)

likewise represent fundamental functional units of Ca^{2+} signaling during cardiac EC-coupling (42), and possibly correspond to the opening of single SR Ca^{2+} release channels (63).

Ca^{2+} SPARKS AS FUNDAMENTAL EVENTS OF CARDIAC EC-COUPLING

The hypothesis that Ca^{2+} sparks may represent fundamental events in cardiac EC-coupling was soon confirmed experimentally in several laboratories. Because a typical Ca^{2+} transient is composed of numerous Ca^{2+} sparks, they rapidly blend into each other and cannot be resolved in a full cellular Ca^{2+} transient. However, when the number of activated L-type Ca^{2+} channels was reduced by adding a Ca^{2+} channel blocker to the superfusion solution, the previously homogeneous Ca^{2+} transient became considerably smaller and individual Ca^{2+} release events resembling the spontaneous Ca^{2+} sparks could be resolved (72–74). It was inferred that openings of L-type Ca^{2+} channels could somehow elicit Ca^{2+} sparks. As expected for Ca^{2+} signaling events that are involved in EC-coupling, Ca^{2+} sparks were predominantly found near the T-tubules, where the diadic couplings between the T-tubular sarcolemma and the SR membrane are located (75; see also 76, 77, for Ca^{2+} sparks in cardiac atrial cells lacking T-tubules).

EC-Coupling Efficiency Defined as Spark Trigger Probability

The appreciation of the Ca^{2+} spark as an elementary event of EC-coupling spurred a series of studies to examine several key properties of the link between L-type Ca^{2+} channel openings and triggering of Ca^{2+} sparks. Although the probability for spontaneous sparks in rat ventricular myocytes is low (about 100 s^{-1} per cell), openings of L-type Ca^{2+} channels greatly increase this probability during an action potential or during a voltage-clamp depolarization (78). The relationship between the L-type Ca^{2+} current and the probability of triggering a spark was analyzed (79, 80), and two major conclusions could be drawn from these results. (*a*) The probability of triggering a Ca^{2+} spark correlates with the Ca^{2+} flux through a single L-type Ca^{2+} channel and not with the average Ca^{2+} current. Therefore, given an open L-type Ca^{2+} channel, the trigger probability (and thus also the gain of CICR) is higher at more negative potentials, where the electrochemical driving force for Ca^{2+} through the L-type channels is larger. (*b*) Ca^{2+} sparks seem to be controlled by a single L-type channel. This was derived from the observation of a linear relationship between single Ca^{2+} current and Ca^{2+} release probability over the experimental voltage range.

Spark Amplitude

In the same experiments (80), the Ca^{2+} spark amplitude was found to be largely independent of the membrane potential and, thus, not to correlate with the size of the Ca^{2+} influx via the L-type Ca^{2+} channel. This finding indicates that the amount of Ca^{2+} released from the SR is more extensive than the amount required to trigger the release. The amplitude of a Ca^{2+} spark, thus, is largely governed by properties of the participating RyRs. Interestingly, Ca^{2+} sparks triggered by L-type Ca^{2+} channels were not very different from spontaneous signals. This observation has been interpreted to indicate that both may arise from the opening of a single RyR or a group of RyRs acting in concert (but see below).

It has been noted in several studies that the frequency and/or amplitude of spontaneous Ca^{2+} sparks may depend on the SR Ca^{2+} load (63, 81). This dependence was particularly noticeable in experiments where tetracaine was used to inhibit SR Ca^{2+} release, leading to massive accumulation of Ca^{2+} within the SR and to Ca^{2+} overload (82, 83). The Ca^{2+} overload was eventually able to overcome the inhibitory effect of tetracaine, giving rise to large Ca^{2+} sparks and Ca^{2+} waves.

The analysis of spark amplitudes and frequencies can be difficult and is filled with pitfalls. One reason is that not all detected Ca^{2+} sparks originate from within the plane of focus in confocal images or inside the focal cylindrical volume in confocal line-scans (84). In fact, the majority of sparks are expected to have an origin outside the focus (81, 85). However, the diffusion of Ca^{2+} into the focal plane or focal cylinder (z- or yz-dimension of approximately 1 μm) still gives rise to a detectable Ca^{2+} spark, although as an increasingly attenuated signal that eventually becomes smaller than the threshold of detection. Therefore, the observed amplitude distributions represent the convolution of the real amplitude distribution of Ca^{2+} sparks with an a priori unknown detection function, a complication that renders the analysis difficult.

Spark Decay

The decline of the local Ca^{2+} concentration after Ca^{2+} sparks is another feature that has been analyzed in some detail. Although the Ca^{2+} release flux during a spark is difficult to extract from image data (77, 86), it is assumed that Ca^{2+} is continuously released during the rise time of the spark (duration of approximately 10 ms). Once Ca^{2+} release ceases, the local [Ca^{2+}] begins to decline. Initially, it was surprising that the Ca^{2+} dissipation is more rapid after a spark than subsequent to a regular, whole-cell Ca^{2+} transient. However, in the case of a localized Ca^{2+} signal, significant Ca^{2+} diffusion out of the volume occupied by the spark can take place, whereas no net diffusion is possible when [Ca^{2+}] is elevated in the entire cytosol. In the latter case, the activity of the

Na-Ca exchanger and the SR Ca^{2+} pump are the major determinants of Ca^{2+} removal from the cytosol (47, 87, 88). For the spark decay, a minor contribution of the SR Ca^{2+} pumps and other Ca^{2+} transport processes would also be expected. Indeed, when the SR Ca^{2+} pump was stimulated with isoprenaline, the Ca^{2+} sparks were found to decline slightly faster and exhibit less spatial spread, whereas inhibition of the pump with thapsigargin had the opposite effect (89). Nonetheless, these results suggest that passive processes such as cellular Ca^{2+} buffering and diffusion are the most important factors shaping the spatiotemporal features (i.e. spatial spread and time-course) of the sparks.

Termination of Ca^{2+} Release During a Ca^{2+} Spark

Despite the large body of new information on a number of fundamental properties of localized Ca^{2+} signaling events, many questions regarding Ca^{2+} sparks remain unresolved. One intriguing example is the question of how the Ca^{2+} release during a spark is terminated. Several possibilities have been proposed. If a Ca^{2+} spark is due to a single RyR opening, termination of Ca^{2+} release would be governed by the stochastic open time of this particular channel. Reopenings triggered by Ca^{2+} released into the cleft by the same RyR channel would be unlikely because the very high local Ca^{2+} concentration is expected to return rapidly to cytosolic levels after channel closure (within microseconds) (34, 35). In a cluster of RyRs, Ca^{2+} release by mutual activation would eventually become extinguished when the stochastic closed times of all active channels overlap temporally, a mechanism termed stochastic attrition (35). As an alternative or additional mechanism, a Ca^{2+}-dependent inactivation or "adaptation" process may shut down the RyRs (86, 90–92).

Although the SR as a whole is not believed to be completely emptied with every Ca^{2+} transient (93–95), this may be different in locally active SR Ca^{2+} release units, and local depletion of stored Ca^{2+} may contribute to spark termination. Because the SR forms a well-connected network, however, local depletion may also be rapidly refilled from more distant SR Ca^{2+} release units, and therefore, depletion may only be partial and difficult to demonstrate experimentally (96). Nevertheless, CICR is known to exhibit a refractoriness that could result from one or more of the processes outlined above (52, 97).

Number of RyRs Required for a Ca^{2+} Spark

Another tempting question is how many RyR channels contribute to a Ca^{2+} spark. Taking into account Ca^{2+} currents measured with RyRs reconstituted into lipid bilayers and using estimates of the Ca^{2+} release flux during a Ca^{2+} spark, it was reckoned that a spark might arise from the opening of a single or a few RyRs (63, 72). However, these estimates necessarily involve a number of uncertainties, such as the Ca^{2+} buffering capacity of the cytosol and differences in gating and Ca^{2+} permeability of the RyR channels in situ (98). A way to address this issue experimentally would be to bypass the local control mechanism by which Ca^{2+} release is usually triggered. If the Ca^{2+} spark is an indivisible unit, in terms of either structure or function, every trigger signal capable of eliciting Ca^{2+} release from the SR should activate Ca^{2+} sparks. Because flash photolysis of caged Ca^{2+} (99) has already been successfully used to trigger CICR (58, 59, 100), photochemistry was combined with laser scanning confocal microscopy in this particular experiment. Unlike the highly local physiological trigger via a single L-type Ca^{2+} channel, flash-photolytic Ca^{2+} concentration jumps are spatially uniform within the cytosol. Spark-like SR Ca^{2+} release signals elicited with this technique would not reflect a property of the trigger itself but would arise from structural or functional features of the SR Ca^{2+} release units. Although CICR was readily evoked with flash-photolytic liberation of Ca^{2+}, the release signals were spatially uniform and no Ca^{2+} sparks could be resolved. It was proposed that a Ca^{2+} signaling event smaller than a Ca^{2+} spark may exist, the Ca^{2+} quark (101). Not surprisingly, this notion was not generally accepted because Ca^{2+} quarks were not seen and because the conclusion was essentially based on a negative result. However, there is more recent evidence supporting the existence of smaller Ca^{2+} release events; this is discussed below.

Spatially uniform Ca^{2+} release signals were also found when SR Ca^{2+} release was triggered after eliciting Na^{+} currents (presumably by activating Ca^{2+} influx via Na-Ca exchange) (29, 102, but see also 103–105). These Ca^{2+} transients were spatially uniform, similar to the flash-photolytic signals. This result is important because it confirms that the homogeneous Ca^{2+} release seen after flash-photolytic activation is not related to the photochemical technique itself but rather represents a form of SR Ca^{2+} release that is fundamentally different from Ca^{2+} sparks (106, 107).

Although the flash-photolysis illumination covers the entire cell, focusing the flash as well as light absorption by the caged compound inside thick cells (inner filtering) may lead to spatial gradients in the Ca^{2+} release. In principle, more Ca^{2+} may be released near the cell surface than in the confocal plane where the Ca^{2+} is recorded. In turn, this could trigger Ca^{2+} sparks that can blend into a uniform signal before they reach the plane of focus by diffusion.

To exclude this possibility, the two-photon excitation photolysis technique has been used to generate photolytic Ca^{2+} release within a diffraction-limited volume that was exactly located in the plane of focus and represented an almost ideal point source for Ca^{2+} (108, 109). By using this method in combination with laser scanning confocal microscopy, Ca^{2+} release events were triggered that corresponded to estimated Ca^{2+} release fluxes 20–40 times smaller than previous assessments for Ca^{2+} sparks (110).

These experimental observations again suggest that Ca^{2+} release events smaller than a Ca^{2+} spark may exist. This notion is also supported, although indirectly, by spatially homogeneous SR Ca^{2+} release signals in CHO cells overexpressing the skeletal muscle type RyR (111) and by uniform Ca^{2+} release in frog skeletal muscle when CICR was inhibited by tetracaine (85) (see below).

SKELETAL MUSCLE CELLS ALSO GENERATE Ca^{2+} SPARKS

As already pointed out, the mechanism of Ca^{2+}-induced Ca^{2+} release was initially described in an SR vesicle preparation isolated from skeletal muscle tissue (46). However, for the early EC-coupling events in skeletal muscle, CICR is not considered important. Instead, the first Ca^{2+} release events from skeletal muscle SR are initiated by a proposed mechanical link between the DHP receptors acting as voltage sensors and the RyR acting as SR Ca^{2+} release channels (6, 112–115).

The presence of a mechanical link between DHPRs and RyRs would imply a highly ordered and defined microarchitecture with at least some of these proteins exactly facing each other in the diadic cleft. Indeed, regularly ordered and matching arrangements of membrane particles have been found in both the T-tubular membrane and the SR membrane facing the T-tubule (116, 117). Unfortunately, much less is known about the analogous equivalent ultrastructure on this submicroscopic level in cardiac myocytes, particularly in mammalian species (118). Yet this information would be of crucial importance to narrow the range of possible coupling schemes in cardiac muscle cells.

In addition to voltage-induced Ca^{2+} release, skeletal muscle cells possess a functioning CICR. Both vesicular Ca^{2+} release and spontaneous Ca^{2+} waves in developing myotubes have been noted (119). In cut muscle preparations maintained under voltage-clamp conditions, the interactions of added Ca^{2+} buffers or low concentrations of caffeine with the Ca^{2+} release process have suggested the presence of a Ca^{2+} signaling component attributable to CICR. This Ca^{2+} release component would be a secondary event triggered by the initial voltage-dependent release of Ca^{2+} from the SR (115, 120–124).

When laser scanning confocal microscopy was applied in this skeletal muscle preparation, localized Ca^{2+} signals resembling Ca^{2+} sparks were detected during small depolarizing voltage steps, i.e. near the threshold of Ca^{2+} release activation (125, 126). At more positive potentials, too many rapidly fusing Ca^{2+} sparks were activated, rendering the detection of individual events impossible, comparable to the situation in cardiac Ca^{2+} transients in the absence of a blocker for the L-type Ca^{2+} channels. Interestingly, initial observations of sparks in skeletal muscle suggested the presence of an event 5- to 10-fold smaller than in cardiac myocytes.

New information recently obtained from skeletal muscle sparks may shed some light on the issue of Ca^{2+} sparks versus Ca^{2+} quarks as smallest Ca^{2+} release events, with the quark by definition corresponding to the opening of a single RyR (101). When skeletal muscle CICR was inhibited with tetracaine, the localized signals elicited by small depolarizations and resembling Ca^{2+} sparks were completely suppressed (85). Yet, $[Ca^{2+}]_i$ was still rising significantly during the voltage-clamp depolarization, most likely because of Ca^{2+} release via RyRs that were directly controlled by voltage sensors. Surprisingly, the Ca^{2+} release observed in the presence of tetracaine was spatially uniform and resembled the signals recorded from cardiac cells after flash photolysis of caged Ca^{2+}. It was concluded that even the relatively small skeletal muscle sparks are composed of several smaller precursor events (127), which may be similar to the Ca^{2+} quark proposed in cardiac cells.

A UNIFYING HYPOTHESIS FOR SR Ca^{2+} RELEASE IN STRIATED MUSCLE INCORPORATING Ca^{2+} QUARKS AND Ca^{2+} SPARKS

A New Paradox

As outlined above, the discovery of the Ca^{2+} sparks has provided an explanation for a paradox in cardiac Ca^{2+} signaling—that is, the presence of a stable cellular amplification system for Ca^{2+} signals despite the regenerativity inherent in CICR. However, with the notion that Ca^{2+} sparks are the only and the smallest elementary Ca^{2+} release events in cellular Ca^{2+} signaling, the experimental observation of homogeneous Ca^{2+} release signals (e.g. after flash-photolytic Ca^{2+} concentration jumps) remains surprising and unexplained. The existence of homogeneous SR Ca^{2+} release in both skeletal and cardiac muscle has led to the proposal that Ca^{2+} release events smaller than Ca^{2+} sparks (85) may be triggered under certain conditions, i.e. Ca^{2+} quarks (101, 110). Although additional evidence for Ca^{2+} release events smaller than Ca^{2+} sparks has been presented recently (111), the interpretation for this phenomenon has remained incomplete. In particular, the duality of elementary Ca^{2+} release events introduced a new paradox in cardiac Ca^{2+} signaling. In a sense, this paradox is similar to the one we just resolved with the Ca^{2+} sparks. But the new paradox takes place on a much smaller spatial scale. Figure 3 shows a cartoon of a diadic cleft with an L-type Ca^{2+} channel facing a group of RyRs. Assume that RyRs are grouped in clusters containing anywhere from 4 to 100 channels and that each group is under the local control of a single L-type Ca^{2+} channel. It is believed the

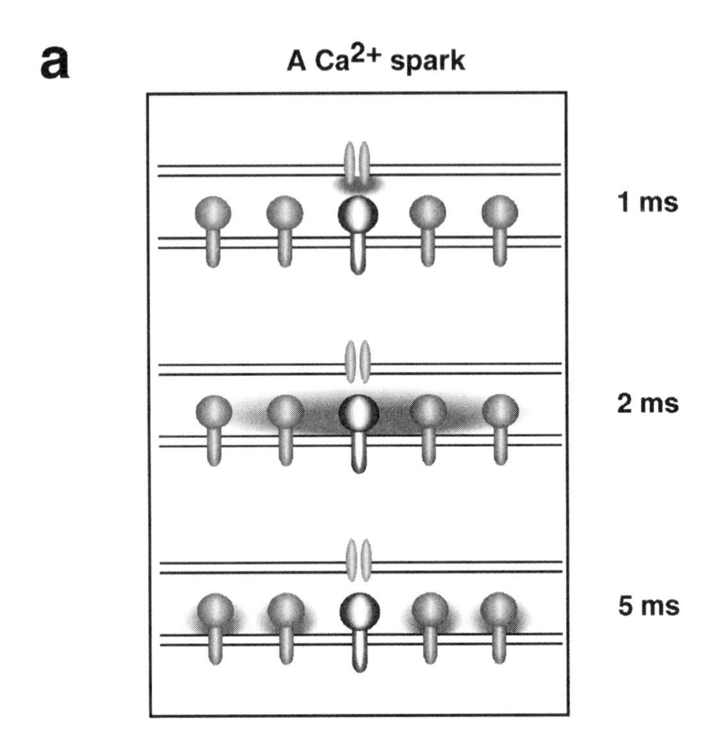
a
A Ca^{2+} spark
1 ms
2 ms
5 ms

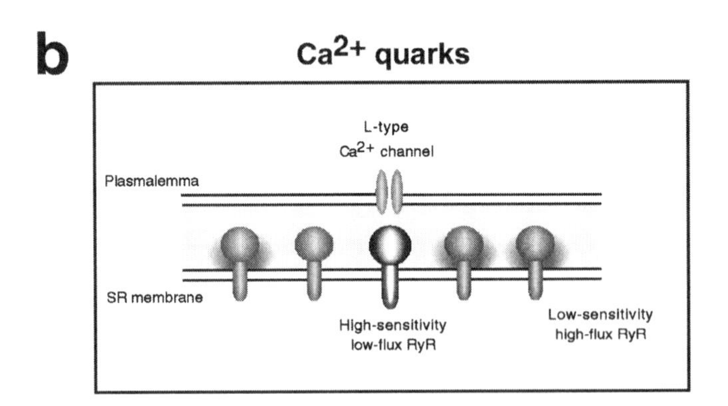
b
Ca^{2+} quarks
L-type
Ca^{2+} channel
Plasmalemma
SR membrane
High-sensitivity
low-flux RyR
Low-sensitivity
high-flux RyR

stochastic opening of a single L-type Ca^{2+} channel can provide sufficient Ca^{2+} influx into the diadic cleft to trigger a spark, i.e. to trigger at least one RyR. The Ca^{2+} flow from the SR via this single RyR is presumed to be much larger and to last longer than the L-type Ca^{2+} current [but recent bilayer experiments performed under more physiological conditions suggest a less sizeable current via the RyR (<0.5 pA) than previously estimated (98)]. Thus, the opening of the first RyR (triggered by the L-type Ca^{2+} channel) would generate a large Ca^{2+} flux into the cleft. If a single L-type Ca^{2+} channel opening provides sufficient Ca^{2+} to activate a RyR located nearby, one would expect opening of this first RyR to trigger most, if not all, neighboring Ca^{2+} release channels within the same cluster. This would result in a rapid spread of the Ca^{2+} release by local regenerativity and finally produce the Ca^{2+} signal detectable as a Ca^{2+} spark. With this notion, the opening of a single RyR within this group should always lead to an all-or-none response of the cluster (i.e. a Ca^{2+} spark), and smaller events (i.e. Ca^{2+} quarks) would not be possible. Thus, the question arises: How could a single RyR possibly open without triggering its neighbors? What mechanism(s) could uncouple two adjacent RyRs while still allowing them to respond to a smaller amount of Ca^{2+} entering via L-type Ca^{2+} channels?

Several ideas were advanced to explain this new paradox but they were incompletely conceptualized, particularly in the case of cardiac muscle. As a first possibility, it was proposed that Ca^{2+} entering via L-type Ca^{2+} channels could have preferential access to a Ca^{2+} binding site on the RyRs (128) that promotes opening of the channel pore (101). Preferential access to this site would make the RyRs more sensitive to Ca^{2+} entering from the extracellular space than to Ca^{2+} leaving the SR via neighboring RyRs. Therefore, Ca^{2+} entering via an L-type Ca^{2+} channel would directly trigger Ca^{2+} release from a group of RyRs whereas Ca^{2+} release via the RyRs themselves would not trigger neighbors under normal conditions (i.e. unless the SR were Ca^{2+} overloaded). With such a paradigm, the gain of CICR and coherence of adjacent RyRs within a given cluster would need to be very low and the experimentally observed amplification of CICR could most likely not be maintained.

←

Figure 3 Model of cardiac Ca^{2+} sparks and Ca^{2+} quarks operating in concert or Ca^{2+} quarks acting alone. (*a*) Events during a Ca^{2+} spark (for labels, see *panel b*). At $t = 1$ ms, an L-type Ca^{2+} channel located in the plasmalemma opens and a puff of Ca^{2+} enters the diadic cleft. This almost immediately triggers Ca^{2+} release from a low-sensitivity ryanodine receptor (RyR) that generates a high Ca^{2+} flux from the sarcoplasmic reticulum (SR) into the cleft. Spreading of Ca^{2+} within the cleft triggers a number of Ca^{2+} quarks from high-sensitivity, low-flux RyRs that also contribute Ca^{2+} to the spark. (*b*) A spatially homogeneous elevation of $[Ca^{2+}]$ in the diadic cleft triggers Ca^{2+} release from some of the high-sensitivity, low-flux RyRs. The Ca^{2+} concentration subsequently reached is not sufficient to activate a low-sensitivity, high-flux RyR.

As a further possibility, it was discussed how trigger signals with fundamental differences in their spatiotemporal properties might either lead to Ca^{2+} sparks or evoke only Ca^{2+} quarks (101). It is envisaged that the opening of an L-type Ca^{2+} channel acts as a point-source of Ca^{2+} and generates a very high Ca^{2+} concentration (about 100 μM) in the immediate vicinity of the channel pore (32). This high concentration would be relevant for adjacent RyRs. In contrast, photolytically released Ca^{2+} or Ca^{2+} entering via the Na-Ca exchanger would increase $[Ca^{2+}]_i$ in the diadic cleft to a much lesser extent and more uniformly. Therefore, each trigger signal has a distinct time-course and amplitude and may affect activation and inactivation of the RyR channels in a particular manner, possibly by interacting with Mg^{2+} bound to some Ca^{2+} sites (129). This general idea is supported by an experimental finding with RyRs reconstituted into lipid bilayers. In recordings at steady state, $[Ca^{2+}]$-dependent modal gating behavior of the RyRs has been described, where the prevalence of the high- and low-open probability gating modes was found to depend on the Ca^{2+} concentration (130). Related to this Ca^{2+}-dependent effect, the phenomenon of adaptation of RyRs after rapid, photolytic Ca^{2+} concentration jumps may result from shifts among several gating modes taking place before the steady state is reached (90). Thus, differences in trigger signals may result in diverse kinetics of the affected RyRs. Specifically, RyRs in the high-open probability gating mode may generate sufficient Ca^{2+} flux into the cleft to trigger neighbors and thus elicit Ca^{2+} sparks, whereas RyRs in low-open probability mode may only be able to generate Ca^{2+} quarks.

A New Hypothesis

A recent observation made in a study of skeletal muscle may provide a more viable explanation for the question of why in cardiac muscle some RyRs seem to operate alone to produce quarks whereas others act in concert to form a Ca^{2+} spark. In skeletal muscle, the explanation of the coexistence of a small precursor event with a larger SR Ca^{2+} release event is straightforward. The small events may reflect Ca^{2+} release via RyRs that are under direct control of voltage sensors whereas the Ca^{2+} sparks could result from RyRs that are not coupled with voltage sensors but that are activated by Ca^{2+} (i.e. by CICR). In other words, small precursors and Ca^{2+} sparks can easily coexist because they arise from two different populations of RyRs, only one of which is exquisitely sensitive to Ca^{2+} triggers. In frog skeletal muscle, the CICR component was selectively suppressed by tetracaine, whereas only a uniform Ca^{2+} release signal was tetracaine insensitive (85). Surprisingly, identical experiments performed with rat extensor digitorum longus muscle failed to reveal Ca^{2+} sparks; only the uniform release type was observed (131). Because the frog muscle contains both RyR-1 and RyR-3 (132) and mammalian extensor digitorum longus muscle contains only RyR-1 (133), it is tempting to speculate that only RyR-3 generates Ca^{2+} sparks in skeletal muscle. Of course, other structural or functional differences among different species may also be responsible for this observation.

Cardiac muscle is known to contain the RyR-2 isoform in abundance, but the presence of RyR-3 has now been reported as well (134). If we speculate further, it could be that in the heart, RyR-2 generates quarks and RyR-3 can trigger sparks, or vice versa. But two different isoforms are not necessarily required to form Ca^{2+} sparks and Ca^{2+} quarks. Peculiarities in the microarchitecture and vicinity of RyRs and DHPRs could be sufficient to impart functional differences to those RyRs that are adjacent and possibly connected to a DHPR, as pointed out in a recent review (135).

Figure 3 diagrams how such a system might work. There are two types of RyRs: Some are coupled to DHPRs and exhibit a low Ca^{2+} sensitivity but a high Ca^{2+} flux; others are more sensitive to trigger Ca^{2+} but allow only little Ca^{2+} efflux from the SR. In the case of a Ca^{2+} spark triggered by the opening of an L-type Ca^{2+} channel (Figure 3*a*), an initial puff of Ca^{2+} reaches the closest RyR (time, 1 ms). Opening of this low-sensitivity, high-flux RyR results in a substantial increase of $[Ca^{2+}]_i$ in the cleft (2 ms) that presumably leads to the additional activation of high-sensitivity, low-flux RyRs contributing several quarks to the spark (5 ms).

The situation is completely different when $[Ca^{2+}]$ in the cleft is elevated uniformly but to a much lesser extent, similar to the flash-photolysis experiments (Figure 3*b*). This modest elevation leads to Ca^{2+} release as Ca^{2+} quarks from some, but not all, high-sensitivity, low-flux RyRs, resulting in an additional elevation of $[Ca^{2+}]$ that does, however, not ignite neighboring RyRs (because the Ca^{2+} flux is too small). The low-sensitivity, high-flux RyR (center) remains silent.

Although this model is speculative, it integrates Ca^{2+} quarks and Ca^{2+} sparks into a system where both act in concert and synergistically. Furthermore, the model may be scrutinized experimentally with an approach combining established biophysical techniques with molecular biology techniques [e.g. knock-out animal models; for example, see (136–138)].

OUTLOOK

The discovery of elementary Ca^{2+} signaling events has been greeted with enthusiasm and has resulted in an unprecedented boost in Ca^{2+} signaling research (and probably also in sales of laser scanning confocal microscopes). In a sense, the analysis of Ca^{2+} sparks is the imaging equivalent of single membrane channel analysis that has become practicable with the patch-clamp technique (139). It is conceivable that by examining the behavior of elementary Ca^{2+} events, many aspects of Ca^{2+} signaling can be explored at or near the molecular level and inside living cells, i.e. within the natural environment of these molecules.

Not surprisingly, elementary Ca^{2+} release signals have been found in most cell types containing a Ca^{2+} signaling system with intracellular Ca^{2+} stores (i.e. sarcoplasmic or endoplasmic reticulum). In particular, it has been shown in a variety of cells that the inositol-trisphosphate (IP_3) signaling pathway utilizes subcellular elementary Ca^{2+} events arising from Ca^{2+} release via IP_3 receptor Ca^{2+} release channels located on the endoplasmic reticulum (140, 141). For example, such Ca^{2+} signals have been imaged in oocytes (142), HeLa cells (143), mast cells (144), pancreatic acinar cells (9), and several neuronal cells (e.g. 28). In these cells, a different nomenclature is sometimes used to designate corresponding Ca^{2+} events (e.g. Ca^{2+} puffs and Ca^{2+} blips). Although the precise downstream function of the local Ca^{2+} signals is not fully understood in the majority of cell types, an interesting interpretation was suggested for the functional role of Ca^{2+} sparks in smooth muscle cells (145, 146). While elevations of averaged cytosolic $[Ca^{2+}]$ lead to an increase in force, spark-like Ca^{2+} release from the endoplasmic reticulum that is preferentially located under the sarcolemma caused only local changes of $[Ca^{2+}]_i$. These local Ca^{2+} signals open Ca^{2+}-activated K^+ channels leading to spontaneous transient outward currents that hyperpolarize and relax the cell. Thus the local change of $[Ca^{2+}]$ has an effect that is the opposite of that of a global change in $[Ca^{2+}]_i$. This obviously represents a prototypical example for the consequence of spatial information encoding in Ca^{2+} signals.

Calcium sparks and quarks most likely have additional implications in cardiac muscle, where they were first discovered. Until now it was generally supposed that EC-coupling is an extremely safe and reliable mechanism: It either works or you are dead. Cardiac disorders like muscular hypertrophy and congestive heart failure were not, or were only remotely, thought to be associated with impaired EC-coupling. The report of an impaired link between Ca^{2+} influx via L-type Ca^{2+} channels and Ca^{2+} release from the SR in animal models of hypertrophy and cardiac failure was, therefore, surprising (147). Furthermore, EC-coupling could be restored to normal by beta-adrenergic stimulation, but only in hypertrophied cells and not in myocytes isolated from failing hearts. Thus Ca^{2+} signaling and cardiac EC-coupling have turned out to be more relevant clinically than was thought a few years ago. We all believe and claim (and not only in grant applications) that basic research is important for the future and benefit of humankind. Basic research work, combined with modern techniques and new model systems, will improve our understanding of the pathophysiology and disease of cardiac EC-coupling. This will permit the development of new pharmacological strategies in the foreseeable future.

SUMMARY

Intracellular Ca^{2+} is a second messenger ubiquitously used in both electrically excitable and nonexcitable cells. In muscle, properties of the cytosolic Ca^{2+} signal ultimately determine the force produced by each cell. The recent discovery of discrete and localized subcellular Ca^{2+} signaling events (Ca^{2+} sparks) has fundamentally changed our conception of Ca^{2+} signaling, primarily in muscle but also in other tissues. In addition, the existence of Ca^{2+} release events considerably smaller than Ca^{2+} sparks has been proposed, both in skeletal and in cardiac muscle (Ca^{2+} quarks). Ca^{2+} sparks as well as Ca^{2+} quarks are believed to represent elementary events of Ca^{2+} release from the SR, the intracellular Ca^{2+} store present in muscle. Ca^{2+} release occurs via a small number of Ca^{2+} release channels (RyRs) from functionally separate SR units. Although usually independent from each other, release units giving rise to Ca^{2+} sparks produce Ca^{2+}-induced Ca^{2+} release under tight and local control by Ca^{2+} influx via L-type Ca^{2+} channels in cardiac muscle and under control of voltage sensors in skeletal muscle. Ca^{2+} sparks, therefore, appear to represent the major signaling pathway for excitation-contraction coupling. Ca^{2+} quarks can be elicited by Ca^{2+} trigger signals that bypass the local control mechanism, for example with photochemical Ca^{2+} release techniques. The mutual independence of individual release units allows a graded amplification of the Ca^{2+} signal without uncontrolled regenerativity. This intricate and delicate task is accomplished by the local recruitment of a variable number of Ca^{2+} release events. Recruitment of release units, therefore, provides a cellular mechanism for the regulation of Ca^{2+} signaling. In cardiac muscle, disturbances in the regenerativity or efficiency of this local control process have been implicated in various disorders. Increased coupling between Ca^{2+} release units is known to provoke spontaneous Ca^{2+} waves that may trigger arrhythmias. A decrease in the coupling between L-type Ca^{2+} channels and Ca^{2+} release channels may be involved in clinically important changes of Ca^{2+} signaling in the course of cardiac hypertrophy and failure. Understanding, at the molecular level, how the signaling proteins communicate with each other may offer the best prospect to characterize EC-coupling and the associated cardiac disturbances, from the molecule to the patient.

ACKNOWLEDGMENTS

This work was supported by grants from the Swiss National Science Foundation (31.37417.93 and 31-50564.97) and from the Sandoz and Ciba foundations. I would like to thank Drs. M Egger, JAS McGuigan, and F DelPrincipe for thoughtful comments on the manuscript.

Literature Cited

1. Bers DM. 1991. *Excitation-Contraction Coupling and Cardiac Contractile Force*. Dordrecht, Netherlands: Kluwer
2. Timmermann M, Ashley C. 1988. Excitation-contraction coupling: bridging the gap. *J. Muscle Res. Cell. Motil.* 9:367–69
3. Fleischer S, Inui M. 1989. Biochemistry and biophysics of excitation-contraction coupling. *Annu. Rev. Biophys. Biophys. Chem.* 18:333–54
4. Rios E, Pizarro G, Stefani E. 1992. Charge movement and the nature of signal transduction in skeletal muscle excitation-contraction coupling. *Annu. Rev. Physiol.* 54:109–33
5. Callewaert G. 1992. Excitation-contraction coupling in mammalian cardiac cells. *Cardiovasc. Res.* 26:923–32
6. Melzer W, Herrmann FA, Lüttgau HC. 1995. The role of Ca^{2+} ions in excitation-contraction coupling of skeletal muscle fibres. *Biochim. Biophys. Acta* 1241:59–116
7. Dulhunty AF. 1992. The voltage-activation of contraction in skeletal muscle. *Prog. Biophys. Mol. Biol.* 57:181–223
8. Meissner G. 1994. Ryanodine receptor Ca^{2+} release channels and their regulation by endogenous effectors. *Annu. Rev. Physiol.* 56:485–508
9. Maruyama Y, Inooka G, Li YX, Miyashita Y, Kasai H. 1993. Agonist-induced localized Ca^{2+} spikes directly triggering exocytotic secretion in exocrine pancreas. *EMBO J.* 12:3017–22
10. Thorn P, Lawrie AM, Smith PM, Gallacher DV, Petersen OH. 1993. Local and global cytosolic Ca^{2+} oscillations in exocrine cells evoked by agonists and inositol trisphosphate. *Cell* 74:661–68
11. Deisseroth K, Bito H, Tsien RW. 1996. Signaling from synapse to nucleus: postsynaptic CREB phosphorylation during multiple forms of hippocampal synaptic plasticity. *Neuron* 16:89–101
12. Cummings JA, Mulkey RM, Nicoll RA, Malenka RC. 1996. Ca^{2+} signaling requirements for long-term depression in the hippocampus. *Neuron* 16:825–33
13. Frenguelli BG, Irving AJ, Collingridge GL. 1996. Ca^{2+} stores and hippocampal synaptic plasticity. *Semin. Neurosci.* 8:301–9
14. Bouron A, Reuter H. 1996. A role of intracellular Na^+ in the regulation of synaptic transmission and turnover of the vesicular pool in cultured hippocampal cells. *Neuron* 17:969–78
15. Zucker RS. 1996. Exocytosis: a molecular and physiological perspective. *Neuron* 17:1049–55
16. Galione A, Lee HC, Busa WB. 1991. Ca^{2+}-induced Ca^{2+} release in sea urchin egg homogenates: modulation by cyclic ADP-ribose. *Science* 253:1143–46
17. DeKoninck P, Schulman H. 1998. Sensitivity of CaM kinase II to the frequency of Ca^{2+} oscillations. *Science* 279:227–30
18. Tucker RW, Meade-Coburn K, Ferris D. 1990. Cell shape and increased free cytosolic calcium $[Ca^{2+}]_i$ induced by growth factors. *Cell Calcium* 11:201–9
19. Taylor SR, Rüdel R, Blinks JR. 1975. Calcium transients in amphibian muscle. *Fed. Proc.* 34:1379–81
20. Allen DG, Blinks JR. 1978. Calcium transients in aequorin-injected frog cardiac muscle. *Nature* 273:509–13
21. Baylor SM, Hollingworth S. 1988. Fura-2 calcium transients in frog skeletal muscle fibres. *J. Physiol.* 403:151–92
22. Yue DT, Marban E, Wier WG. 1986. Relationship between force and intracellular $[Ca^{2+}]$ in tetanized mammalian heart muscle. *J. Gen. Physiol.* 87:223–42
23. Woods NM, Cuthbertson KSR, Cobbold PH. 1986. Repetitive transient rises in cytoplasmic free calcium in hormone-treated hepatocytes. *Nature* 319:600–2
24. Chatton JY, Liu HY, Stucki JW. 1997. Modulation of hormone-induced calcium oscillations by intracellular pH in rat hepatocytes. *Am. J. Physiol.* 35:G954–61
25. Allbritton NL, Meyer T. 1993. Localized calcium spikes and propagating calcium waves. *Cell Calcium* 14:691–97
26. Thomas AP, Bird GSJ, Hajnóczky G,

Robb-Gaspers LD, Putney JW. 1996. Spatial and temporal aspects of cellular calcium signaling. *FASEB J.* 10:1505–17
27. Berridge MJ. 1997. Elementary and global aspects of calcium signalling. *J. Physiol.* 499:291–306
28. Eilers J, Plant T, Konnerth A. 1996. Localized calcium signalling and neuronal integration in cerebellar Purkinje neurones. *Cell Calcium* 20:215–26
29. Leblanc N, Hume JR. 1990. Sodium current-induced release of calcium from cardiac sarcoplasmic reticulum. *Science* 248:372–76
30. Lederer WJ, Niggli E, Hadley RW. 1990. Sodium-calcium exchange in excitable cells: fuzzy space. *Science* 248:283
31. Niggli E, Lipp P. 1993. Subcellular restricted spaces—significance for cell signalling and excitation-contraction coupling. *J. Muscle Res. Cell. Motil.* 14:288–91
32. Soeller C, Cannell MB. 1997. Numerical simulation of local calcium movements during L-type calcium channel gating in the cardiac diad. *Biophys. J.* 73:97–111
33. Langer GA, Peskoff A. 1997. Role of the diadic cleft in myocardial contractile control. *Circulation* 96:3761–3765
34. Amstutz C, Michailova A, Niggli E. 1996. The role of local events and diffusion in cardiac EC-coupling. *Biophys. J.* 70:A274
35. Stern MD. 1992. Theory of excitation-contraction coupling in cardiac muscle. *Biophys. J.* 63:497–517
36. Kargacin GJ. 1994. Calcium signaling in restricted diffusion spaces. *Biophys. J.* 67:262–72
37. Langer GA, Peskoff A. 1996. Calcium concentration and movement in the diadic cleft space of the cardiac ventricular cell. *Biophys. J.* 70:1169–82
38. Fabiato A. 1985. Time and calcium dependence of activation and inactivation of calcium-induced release of calcium from the sarcoplasmic reticulum of a skinned canine cardiac Purkinje cell. *J. Gen. Physiol.* 85:247–89
39. Stern MD, Lakatta EG. 1992. Excitation-contraction coupling in the heart—the state of the question. *FASEB J.* 6:3092–100
40. Wier WG. 1990. Cytoplasmic [Ca^{2+}] in mammalian ventricle: dynamic control by cellular processes. *Annu. Rev. Physiol.* 52:467–85
41. Langer GA. 1997. Chasing myocardial calcium: A 35–year perspective. *News Physiol. Sci.* 12:238–244
42. Niggli E, Lipp P. 1995. Subcellular features of calcium signalling in heart muscle: what do we learn? *Cardiovasc. Res.* 29:441–48
43. Cheng H, Lederer MR, Xiao RP, Gomez AM, Zhou YY, et al. 1996. Excitation-contraction coupling in heart: new insights from Ca^{2+} sparks. *Cell Calcium* 20:129–40
44. Barcenas-Ruiz L, Wier WG. 1987. Voltage dependence of intracellular $[Ca^{2+}]_i$ transients in guinea pig ventricular myocytes. *Circ. Res.* 61:148–54
45. Näbauer M, Callewaert G, Cleemann L, Morad M. 1989. Regulation of calcium release is gated by calcium current, not gating charge, in cardiac myocytes. *Science* 244:800–3
46. Endo M, Tanaka M, Ogawa Y. 1970. Calcium induced release of calcium from the sarcoplasmic reticulum of skinned skeletal muscle fibres. *Nature* 228:34–36
47. Bridge JHB, Smolley JR, Spitzer KW. 1990. The stoichiometric relationship between charge movement associated with I_{Ca} and I_{NaCa} in cardiac myocytes. *Science* 248:376–78
48. Kort AA, Capogrossi C, Lakatta G. 1985. Frequency, amplitude, and propagation velocity of spontaneous Ca^{2+}-dependent contractile waves in intact adult rat cardiac muscle and isolated myocytes. *Circ. Res.* 57:844–855
49. Wier WG, Cannell MB, Berlin JR, Marban E, Lederer WJ. 1987. Cellular and subcellular heterogeneity of $[Ca^{2+}]_i$ in single heart cells revealed by fura-2. *Science* 235:325–28
50. Takamatsu T, Wier WG. 1990. Calcium waves in mammalian heart: quantification of origin, magnitude, waveform, and velocity. *FASEB J.* 4:1519–25
51. Williams DA, Delbridge LM, Cody SH, Harris PJ, Morgan TO. 1992. Spontaneous and propagated calcium release in isolated cardiac myocytes viewed by confocal microscopy. *Am. J. Physiol.* 262:C731–42
52. Lipp P, Niggli E. 1993. Microscopic spiral-waves reveal positive feedback in subcellular calcium signaling. *Biophys. J.* 65:2272–76
53. Wussling MHP, Scheufler K, Schmerling S, Drygalla V. 1997. Velocity-curvature relationship of colliding spherical calcium waves in rat cardiac myocytes. *Biophys. J.* 73:1232–42
54. Trafford AW, O'Neill SC, Eisner DA. 1993. Factors affecting the propagation of locally activated systolic Ca transients in rat ventricular myocytes. *Pflügers Arch.* 425:181–83

55. Dupont G, Pontes J, Goldbeter A. 1996. Modeling spiral Ca^{2+} waves in single cardiac cells: role of the spatial heterogeneity created by the nucleus. *Am. J. Physiol.* 271:1390–99
56. Cannell MB, Berlin JR, Lederer WJ. 1987. Effect of membrane potential changes on the calcium transient in single rat cardiac muscle cells. *Science* 238: 1419–23
57. Cleemann L, Morad M. 1991. Role of Ca^{2+} channel in cardiac excitation-contraction coupling in the rat: evidence from Ca^{2+} transients and contraction. *J. Physiol.* 432:283–312
58. Niggli E, Lederer WJ. 1990. Voltage-independent calcium release in heart muscle. *Science* 250:565–68
59. O'Neill SC, Mill JG, Eisner DA. 1990. Local activation of contraction in isolated rat ventricular myocytes. *Am. J. Physiol.* 27:C1165–68
60. Trafford AW, Lipp P, O'Neill SC, Niggli E, Eisner DA. 1995. Propagating calcium waves initiated by local caffeine application in rat ventricular myocytes. *J. Physiol.* 489:319–26
61. Han S, Schiefer A, Isenberg G. 1994. Ca^{2+} load of guinea-pig ventricular myocytes determines efficacy of brief Ca^{2+} currents as trigger for Ca^{2+} release. *J. Physiol.* 480:411–21
62. Spencer I, Berlin JR. 1995. Control of sarcoplasmic reticulum calcium release during calcium loading in isolated rat ventricular myocytes. *J. Physiol.* 488:267–79
63. Cheng H, Lederer WJ, Cannell MB. 1993. Calcium sparks—elementary events underlying excitation-contraction coupling in heart muscle. *Science* 262:740–44
64. Lipp P, Niggli E. 1994. Modulation of Ca^{2+} release in cultured neonatal rat cardiac myocytes—insight from subcellular release patterns revealed by confocal microscopy. *Circ. Res.* 74:979–90
65. Minta A, Kao JPY, Tsien RY. 1989. Fluorescent indicators for cytosolic calcium based on rhodamine and fluorescein chromophores. *J. Biol. Chem.* 264:8171–78
66. Wier WG, ter Keurs HEDJ, Marban E, Gao WD, Balke CW. 1997. Ca^{2+} 'sparks' and waves in intact ventricular muscle resolved by confocal imaging. *Circ. Res.* 81:462–69
67. Jaffe LF. 1991. The path of calcium in cytosolic calcium oscillations—a unifying hypothesis. *Proc. Natl. Acad. Sci. USA* 88:9883–87
68. Backx PH, de Tombe PP, van Deen JHK, Mulder BJM, ter Keurs HEDJ. 1989. A model of propagating calcium-induced calcium release mediated by calcium diffusion. *J. Gen. Physiol.* 93:963–77
69. Dupont G, Goldbeter A. 1994. Properties of intracellular Ca^{2+} waves generated by a model based on Ca^{2+}-induced Ca^{2+} release. *Biophys. J.* 67:2191–204
70. White JG, Amos WB, Fordham M. 1987. An evaluation of confocal versus conventional imaging of biological structures by fluorescence light microscopy. *J. Cell Biol.* 105:41–48
71. Niggli E, Lederer WJ. 1990. Real-time confocal microscopy and calcium measurements in heart muscle cells: towards the development of a fluorescence microscope with high temporal and spatial resolution. *Cell Calcium* 11:121–30
72. Cannell MB, Cheng H, Lederer WJ. 1994. Spatial non-uniformities in $[Ca^{2+}]_i$ during excitation-contraction coupling in cardiac myocytes. *Biophys. J.* 67:1942–56
73. López-López JR, Shacklock PS, Balke CW, Wier WG. 1994. Local, stochastic release of Ca^{2+} in voltage-clamped rat heart cells: visualization with confocal microscopy. *J. Physiol.* 480:21–29
74. Cheng H, Cannell MB, Lederer WJ. 1995. Partial inhibition of Ca^{2+} current by methoxyverapamil (D600) reveals spatial nonuniformities in $[Ca^{2+}]_i$ during excitation-contraction coupling in cardiac myocytes. *Circ. Res.* 76:236–41
75. Shacklock PS, Wier WG, Balke CW. 1995. Local Ca^{2+} transients (Ca^{2+} sparks) originate at transverse tubules in rat heart cells. *J. Physiol.* 487:601–8
76. Hüser J, Lipsius SL, Blatter LA. 1996. Calcium gradients during excitation-contraction coupling in cat atrial myocytes. *J. Physiol.* 494:641–51
77. Blatter LA, Hüser J, Rios E. 1997. Sarcoplasmic reticulum Ca^{2+} release flux underlying Ca^{2+} sparks in cardiac muscle. *Proc. Natl. Acad. Sci. USA* 94:4176–81
78. Shorofsky SR, Izu L, Wier WG, Balke CW. 1998. Ca^{2+} sparks triggered by patch depolarization in rat heart cells. *Circ. Res.* 82:424–29
79. Cannell MB, Cheng H, Lederer WJ. 1995. The control of calcium release in heart muscle. *Science* 268:1045–49
80. López-López JR, Shacklock PS, Balke CW, Wier WG. 1995. Local calcium transients triggered by single L-type calcium channel currents in cardiac cells. *Science* 268:1042–45
81. Song LS, Stern MD, Lakatta EG, Cheng HP. 1997. Partial depletion of sarcoplasmic reticulum calcium does not prevent calcium sparks in rat ventricular myocytes. *J. Physiol.* 505:665–75

82. Györke S, Lukyanenko V, Györke I. 1997. Dual effects of tetracaine on spontaneous calcium release in rat ventricular myocytes. *J. Physiol.* 500:297–309
83. Overend CL, Eisner DA, O'Neill SC. 1997. The effect of tetracaine on spontaneous Ca^{2+} release and sarcoplasmic reticulum calcium content in rat ventricular myocytes. *J. Physiol.* 502:471–79
84. Pratusevich VR, Balke CW. 1996. Factors shaping the confocal image of the calcium spark in cardiac muscle cells. *Biophys. J.* 71:2942–57
85. Shirokova N, Rios E. 1997. Small event Ca^{2+} release: a probable precursor of Ca^{2+} sparks in frog skeletal muscle. *J. Physiol.* 502:3–11
86. Lukyanenko V, Wiesner TF, Györke S. 1998. Termination of Ca^{2+} release during Ca^{2+} sparks in rat ventricular myocytes. *J. Physiol.* 507:667–77
87. Bassani JWM, Bassani RA, Bers DM. 1994. Relaxation in rabbit and rat cardiac cells—species-dependent differences in cellular mechanisms. *J. Physiol.* 476:279–93
88. Negretti N, O'Neill SC, Eisner DA. 1993. The relative contributions of different intracellular and sarcolemmal systems to relaxation in rat ventricular myocytes. *Cardiovasc. Res.* 27:1826–30
89. Gomez AM, Cheng HP, Lederer WJ, Bers DM. 1996. Ca^{2+} diffusion and sarcoplasmic reticulum transport both contribute to $[Ca^{2+}]_i$ decline during Ca^{2+} sparks in rat ventricular myocytes. *J. Physiol.* 496:575–81
90. Györke S, Fill M. 1993. Ryanodine receptor adaptation—control mechanism of Ca^{2+}-induced Ca^{2+} release in heart. *Science* 260:807–9
91. Satoh H, Blatter LA, Bers DM. 1997. Effects of $[Ca^{2+}]_i$, SR Ca^{2+} load, and rest on Ca^{2+} spark frequency in ventricular myocytes. *Am. J. Physiol.* 41:H657–68
92. Velez P, Györke S, Escobar AL, Vergara J, Fill M. 1997. Adaptation of single cardiac ryanodine receptor channels. *Biophys. J.* 72:691–97
93. Diaz ME, Trafford AW, O'Neill SC, Eisner DA. 1997. Measurement of sarcoplasmic reticulum Ca^{2+} content and sarcolemmal Ca^{2+} fluxes in isolated rat ventricular myocytes during spontaneous Ca^{2+} release. *J. Physiol.* 501:3–16
94. Bassani JWM, Yuan WL, Bers DM. 1995. Fractional SR Ca release is regulated by trigger Ca and SR Ca content in cardiac myocytes. *Am. J. Physiol.* 37:C1313–19
95. Shannon TR, Bers DM. 1997. Assessment of intra-SR free [Ca] and buffering in rat heart. *Biophys. J.* 73:1524–31
96. DelPrincipe F, Niggli E. 1998. Paired calcium sparks triggerd by two-photon photolysis of caged calcium in isolated cardiac myocytes. *Biophys. J.* 74:A270
97. Tanaka H, Sekine T, Kawanishi T, Nakamura R, Shigenobu K. 1998. Intrasarcomere $[Ca^{2+}]$ gradients and their spatiotemporal relation to Ca^{2+} sparks in rat cardiomyocytes. *J. Physiol.* 508:145–52
98. Meija-Alvarez R, Kettlun C, Rios E, Stern M, Fill M. 1998. Unitary calcium currents through cardiac ryanodine receptors under physiological conditions. *Biophys. J.* 74:A58
99. Kaplan JH, Ellis-Davies GCR. 1988. Photolabile chelators for the rapid photorelease of divalent cations. *Proc. Natl. Acad. Sci. USA* 85:6571–75
100. Näbauer M, Morad M. 1990. Ca^{2+}-induced Ca^{2+} release as examined by photolysis of caged Ca^{2+} in single ventricular myocytes. *Am. J. Physiol.* 258:189–93
101. Lipp P, Niggli E. 1996. Submicroscopic calcium signals as fundamental events of excitation-contraction coupling in guinea-pig cardiac myocytes. *J. Physiol.* 492:31–38
102. Kohmoto O, Levi AJ, Bridge JHB. 1994. Relation between reverse sodium-calcium exchange and sarcoplasmic reticulum calcium release in guinea pig ventricular cells. *Circ. Res.* 74:550–54
103. Sham JSK, Cleemann L, Morad M. 1992. Gating of the cardiac Ca^{2+} release channel—the role of Na^+ current and Na^+-Ca^{2+} exchange. *Science* 255:850–53
104. Hobai IA, Howarth FC, Pabbathi VK, Dalton GR, Hancox JC, et al. 1997. "Voltage-activated Ca release" in rabbit, rat and guinea-pig cardiac myocytes, and modulation by internal cAMP. *Pflügers Arch.* 435:164–73
105. Santana FF, Gomez AM, Lederer WJ. 1998. Ca^{2+} flux through promiscuous cardiac Na^+ channels: slip-mode conductance. *Science* 279:1027–33
106. Lipp P, Niggli E. 1994. Sodium current-induced calcium signals in isolated guinea-pig ventricular myocytes. *J. Physiol.* 474:439–46
107. Niggli E, Lipp P. 1996. Elementary events of I_{Na}- and I_{Ca}-triggered EC-coupling. *Biophys. J.* 70:A275
108. Denk W, Strickler JH, Webb WW. 1990. Two-photon laser scanning fluorescence microscopy. *Science* 248:73–76
109. Denk W. 1994. Two-photon scanning photochemical microscopy: mapping

ligand-gated ion channel distributions. *Proc. Natl. Acad. Sci. USA* 91:6629–33
110. Lipp P, Niggli E. 1998. Fundamental calcium release events revealed by two-photon excitation photolysis of caged calcium in guinea-pig cardiac myocytes. *J. Physiol.* 508:801–9
111. Manjunatha B, Zhao JY, Zang WJ, Balke CW, Takeshima H, et al. 1997. Caffeine-induced release of intracellular Ca^{2+} from Chinese hamster ovary cells expressing skeletal muscle ryanodine receptor—effects on full-length and carboxyl-terminal portion of Ca^{2+} release channels. *J. Gen. Physiol.* 110:749–62
112. Schneider MF, Chandler WK. 1973. Voltage dependent charge movement of skeletal muscle: a possible step in excitation-contraction coupling. *Nature* 242:244–46
113. Rios E, Ma J, Gonzales A. 1991. The mechanical hypothesis of excitation-contraction (EC) coupling in skeletal muscle. *J. Muscle Res. Cell. Motil.* 12: 127–35
114. Tanabe T, Beam KG, Adams BA, Niidome T, Numa S. 1990. Regions of the skeletal muscle dihydropyridine receptor critical for excitation-contraction coupling. *Nature* 346:567–69
115. Jacquemond V, Csernoch L, Klein MG, Schneider MF. 1991. Voltage-gated and calcium-gated calcium release during depolarization of skeletal muscle fibers. *Biophys. J.* 60:867–73
116. Block BA, Imagawa T, Campbell KP, Franzini-Armstrong C. 1988. Structural evidence for direct interaction between the molecular components of the transverse tubule/sarcoplasmic reticulum junction in skeletal muscle. *J. Cell. Biol.* 107:2587–600
117. Protasi F, Franzini-Armstrong C, Allen PD. 1998. Role of ryanodine receptors in the assembly of calcium release units in skeletal muscle. *J. Cell Biol.* 140:831–42
118. Protasi F, Sun XH, Franzini-Armstrong C. 1996. Formation and maturation of the calcium release apparatus in developing and adult avian myocardium. *Dev. Biol.* 173:265–78
119. Flucher BE, Andrews SB. 1993. Characterization of spontaneous and action potential-induced calcium transients in developing myotubes in vitro. *Cell Motil. Cytoskelet.* 25:143–157
120. Simon BJ, Klein MG, Schneider MF. 1989. Caffeine slows turn-off of calcium release in voltage clamped skeletal muscle fibers. *Biophys. J.* 55:793–97
121. Csernoch L, Jacquemond V, Schneider MF. 1993. Microinjection of strong calcium buffers suppresses the peak of calcium release during depolarization in frog skeletal muscle fibers. *J. Gen. Physiol.* 101:297–333
122. Hollingworth S, Harkins AB, Kurebayashi N, Konishi M, Baylor SM. 1992. Excitation-contraction coupling in intact frog skeletal muscle fibers injected with μmolar concentrations of fura-2. *Biophys. J.* 63:224–34
123. Jong DS, Pape PC, Chandler WK, Baylor SM. 1993. Reduction of calcium inactivation of sarcoplasmic reticulum calcium release by fura-2 in voltage-clamped cut twitch fibers from frog muscle. *J. Gen. Physiol.* 102:333–70
124. Stern MD, Pizarro G, Rios E. 1997. Local control model of excitation-contraction coupling in skeletal muscle. *J. Gen. Physiol.* 110:415–40
125. Tsugorka A, Rios E, Blatter LA. 1995. Imaging elementary events of calcium release in skeletal muscle cells. *Science* 269:1723–26
126. Klein MG, Cheng H, Santana LF, Jiang YH, Lederer WJ, Schneider MF. 1996. Two mechanisms of quantized calcium release in skeletal muscle. *Nature* 379:455–58
127. Rios E, Stern MD. 1997. Calcium in close quarters: microdomain feedback in excitation-contraction coupling and other cell biological phenomena. *Annu. Rev. Biophys. Biomol. Struct.* 26:47–82
128. Wagenknecht T, Radermacher M. 1995. Three-dimensional architecture of the skeletal muscle ryanodine receptor. *FEBS Lett.* 369:43–46
129. Lamb GD, Stephenson DG. 1992. Importance of Mg^{2+} in excitation-contraction coupling in skeletal muscle. *News Physiol. Sci.* 7:270–274
130. Zahradnikova A, Zahradnik I. 1995. Description of modal gating of the cardiac calcium release channel in planar lipid membranes. *Biophys. J.* 69:1780–88
131. Shirokova N, Rios E. 1998. Local calcium release in mammalian skeletal muscle. *Biophys. J.* 74:A269
132. Ogawa Y. 1994. Role of ryanodine receptors. *Crit. Rev. Biochem. Mol. Biol.* 29:229–74
133. Conti A, Gorza L, Sorrentino V. 1996. Differential distribution of ryanodine receptor type 3 (RyR3) gene product in mammalian skeletal muscles. *Biochem. J.* 316:19–23
134. Wu G, Jeyakumar L, Barnett J, Fleischer S. 1998. Immunolocalization of RYR3 in heart. *Biophys. J.* 74:A56

135. Sutko JL, Airey JA. 1996. Ryanodine receptor Ca^{2+} release channels: does diversity in form equal diversity in function? *Physiol. Rev.* 76:1027–71
136. Buck ED, Nguyen HT, Pessah IN, Allen PD. 1997. Dyspedic mouse skeletal muscle expresses major elements of the triadic junction but lacks detectable ryanodine receptor protein and function. *J. Biol. Chem.* 272:7360–67
137. Nakai J, Ogura T, Protasi F, Franzini Armstrong C, Allen PD, Beam KG. 1997. Functional nonequality of the cardiac and skeletal ryanodine receptors. *Proc. Natl. Acad. Sci. USA* 94:1019–22
138. Ikemoto T, Komazaki S, Takeshima H, Nishi M, Noda T, et al. 1997. Functional and morphological features of skeletal muscle from mutant mice lacking both type 1 and type 3 ryanodine receptors. *J. Physiol.* 501:305–12
139. Sakmann B, Neher E. 1984. Patch clamp techniques for studying ionic channels in excitable membranes. *Annu. Rev. Physiol.* 46:455–72
140. Takei K, Stukenbrok H, Metcalf A, Mignery GA, Sudhof TC, et al. 1992. Ca^{2+} stores in Purkinje neurons: endoplasmic reticulum subcompartments demonstrated by the heterogeneous distribution of the $InsP_3$ receptor, Ca^{2+}-ATPase, and calsequestrin. *J. Neurosci.* 12:489–505
141. Marks AR. 1997. Intracellular calcium-release channels: regulators of cell life and death. *Am. J. Physiol.* 41:H597–605
142. Yao Y, Choi J, Parker I. 1995. Quantal puffs of intracellular Ca^{2+} evoked by inositol trisphosphate in xenopus oocytes. *J. Physiol.* 482:533–53
143. Bootman M, Niggli E, Berridge M, Lipp P. 1997. Imaging the hierarchical Ca^{2+} signalling system in HeLa cells. *J. Physiol.* 499:307–14
144. Horne JH, Meyer T. 1997. Elementary calcium-release units induced by inositol trisphosphate. *Science* 276:1690–93
145. Nelson MT, Cheng H, Rubart M, Santana LF, Bonev AD, et al. 1995. Relaxation of arterial smooth muscle by calcium sparks. *Science* 270:633–37
146. Gordienko DV, Bolton TB, Cannell MB. 1998. Variability in spontaneous subcellular calcium release in guinea-pig ileum smooth muscle cells. *J. Physiol.* 507:707–20
147. Gomez AM, Valdivia HH, Cheng H, Lederer MR, Santana LF, et al. 1997. Defective excitation-contraction coupling in experimental cardiac hypertrophy and heart failure. *Science* 276:800–6

Annu. Rev. Physiol. 1999. 61:337–62

ATP-SENSITIVE POTASSIUM CHANNELS: A Model of Heteromultimeric Potassium Channel/Receptor Assemblies

Susumu Seino
Department of Molecular Medicine, Chiba University Graduate School of Medicine, 1-8-1 Inohana, Chuo-ku, Chiba 260-8670, Japan;
e-mail: seino@molmed.m.chiba-u.ac.jp

KEY WORDS: inward rectifiers, sulfonylurea receptors, ATP-binding cassette protein superfamily, ADP, glibenclamide

ABSTRACT

ATP-sensitive K^+ channels (K_{ATP} channels) play important roles in many cellular functions by coupling cell metabolism to electrical activity. By cloning members of the novel inwardly rectifying K^+ channel subfamily Kir6.0 (Kir6.1 and Kir6.2) and the receptors for sulfonylureas (SUR1 and SUR2), researchers have clarified the molecular structure of K_{ATP} channels. K_{ATP} channels comprise two subunits: a Kir6.0 subfamily subunit, which is a member of the inwardly rectifying K^+ channel family; and a SUR subunit, which is a member of the ATP-binding cassette (ABC) protein superfamily. K_{ATP} channels are the first example of a heteromultimeric complex assembled with a K^+ channel and a receptor that are structurally unrelated to each other. Since 1995, molecular biological and molecular genetic studies of K_{ATP} channels have provided insights into the structure-function relationships, molecular regulation, and pathophysiological roles of K_{ATP} channels.

INTRODUCTION

ATP-sensitive potassium (K_{ATP}) channels were first discovered in cardiac myocytes (88) and were later found in many other tissues, including pancreatic

0066-4278/99/0315-0337$08.00

β-cells (12, 26, 31, 96), skeletal muscle (107), smooth muscle (108), brain (14), pituitary (18), and kidney (47), and in mitochondria (54). By linking the cell metabolic state to the membrane potential, K_{ATP} channels regulate a variety of cellular functions including insulin secretion from pancreatic β-cells, excitability of skeletal muscle and neurons, K^+ recycling in renal epithelia, and cytoprotection in cardiac and brain ischemia (10, 27, 82, 114). The activity of K_{ATP} channels is thought to be regulated by intracellular ATP and ADP (more accurately MgADP) concentrations or the ATP/ADP ratio. For example, an increase in the ATP/ADP ratio closes K_{ATP} channels, whereas a decrease in the ratio opens them.

The functional roles of K_{ATP} channels have been best characterized in pancreatic β-cells (10, 20, 27). Since the discovery of the K_{ATP} channels in pancreatic β-cells, the model of glucose-induced insulin secretion shown in Figure 1 has generally been accepted. Glucose is transported through the glucose transporter GLUT2 (17), and the subsequent metabolism of glucose produces ATP. The increase in the ATP/ADP ratio closes the K_{ATP} channels, which depolarizes the β-cell membrane and leads to the opening of the voltage-dependent calcium channels (VDCC), allowing calcium influx. The rise in intracellular calcium concentration in the β-cell triggers insulin granule exocytosis. Accordingly, the K_{ATP} channels, as ATP and ADP sensors, are key molecules in the regulation of glucose-induced insulin secretion.

In addition, sulfonylureas, widely used in the treatment of non-insulin-dependent diabetes mellitus (NIDDM), stimulate insulin secretion by closing K_{ATP} channels in pancreatic β-cells directly (13, 20, 101, 109, 119). This observation implies that the sulfonylurea receptor itself is the K_{ATP} channel or that it is a regulatory protein closely associated with the K_{ATP} channel. Until recently, the molecular basis of the K_{ATP} channel in pancreatic β-cells was not known, but the molecular cloning of members of a novel inwardly rectifying subfamily Kir6.0 (Kir6.1 and Kir6.2) (48, 52, 98) and of the sulfonylurea receptors (SUR1 and SUR2) (4, 49), which are members of the ATP-binding cassette (ABC) protein superfamily, has clarified the structure of K_{ATP} channels. Reconstitution studies have shown that differing combinations of a Kir6.0 subfamily subunit and a SUR subunit constitute K_{ATP} channels with distinct nucleotide sensitivities and pharmacological properties (49, 52, 56, 98, 130).

Traditionally, channels activated by various ligands, most of which are neurotransmitters, are called ion channel–linked receptors (also called ligand-gated ion channels or receptor-operated ion channels). The ion channel–linked receptors are thought to be channel/receptor complexes in that they have a highly specific binding site for ligands, and the channel is formed by the protein to which

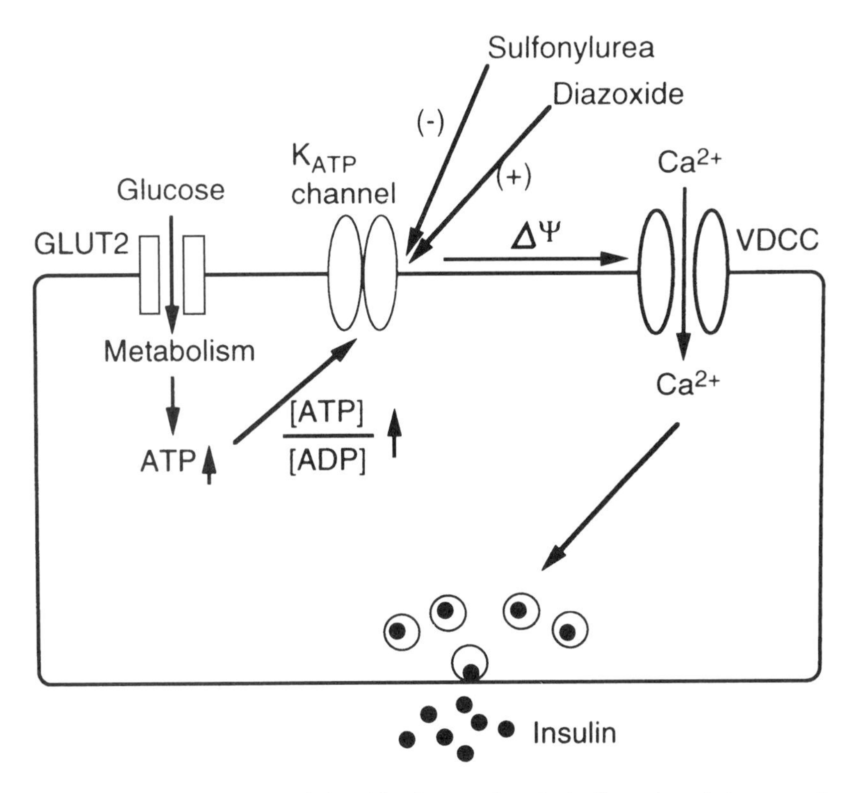

Figure 1 A model for glucose-induced insulin secretion via the K_{ATP} channels in pancreatic β-cells. The K_{ATP} channels are thought to be ATP and ADP sensors that couple glucose metabolism to electrical activity, to stimulate insulin secretion. Sulfonylureas such as tolbutamide and glibenclamide stimulate insulin secretion by inhibiting the K_{ATP} channels, and diazoxide inhibits insulin secretion by activating the channels. GLUT2: glucose transporter 2, VDCC: voltage-dependent calcium channel.

the ligands bind. These channels function as homomultimers or heteromultimers formed by structurally related (homologous) subunits (89). Voltage-gated K^+ (Kv) channel subunits and inwardly rectifying K^+ (Kir) channel subunits also function as homomultimers or heteromultimers formed by homologous subunits (15, 22, 55, 58, 59, 63, 66, 97).

K_{ATP} channels are the first example of a heteromultimeric complex assembled by an ion channel and a receptor that are structurally unrelated to each other. In this review, I describe the K_{ATP} channels as a paradigm of heteromultimeric K^+ channel/receptor assemblies and discuss the molecular and functional diversity and the pathophysiological roles of K_{ATP} channels, based on recent findings in molecular biological and molecular genetic studies. Readers are also referred to recent reviews of K_{ATP} channels (2, 11, 14a, 94, 103, 120).

THE INWARDLY RECTIFYING POTASSIUM CHANNEL SUBFAMILY Kir6.0

Since the isolation by expression cloning of the Kir channel family members, ROMK1 (Kir1.1a) (44), IRK1 (Kir2.1) (68), and GIRK1 (Kir3.1) (28), seven subfamilies (Kir1.0–Kir7.0) have been identified, based on their degree of identity (15, 29, 67, 86, 103). In contrast to the Kv channel subunits, which each have six putative transmembrane segments, Kir channel subunits each have two putative transmembrane segments, but they retain the H5 region that determines K^+ selectivity in Kv channels (58). The detailed structural and functional properties of Kir channels have been reviewed by others (15, 29, 59, 86). Here I focus on the Kir6.0 subfamily members, which are unique in that they form a heteromultimeric K^+ channel/receptor complex together with the sulfonylurea receptors to exert K^+ channel function.

Kir6.1

Using GIRK1 (Kir3.1) cDNA (28, 69) as a probe, researchers cloned uK_{ATP}-1 (currently referred to as Kir6.1) from a rat pancreatic islet cDNA library (52) (Figure 2*A*). Rat Kir6.1 is a 424-amino-acid protein that has two putative transmembrane segments. As Kir6.1 shares only 40–50% identity with previously

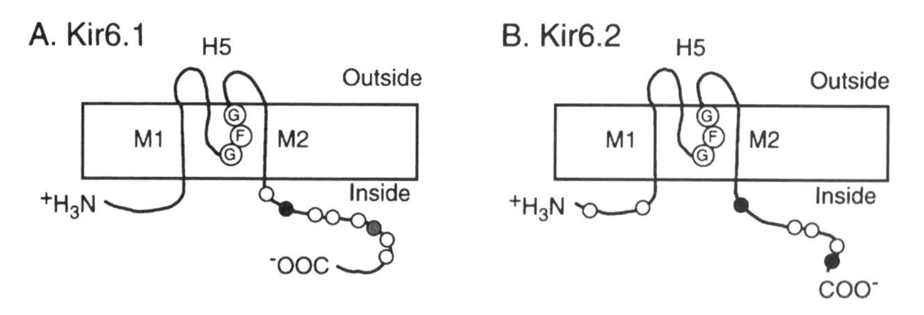

Figure 2 Proposed membrane topology of Kir6.1 (*A*) and Kir6.2 (*B*). Putative transmembrane segments (M1, M2) and the K^+ ion pore-forming region (H5) are shown. The G-Y-G motif that is critical for K^+ ion selectivity and is highly conserved among Kir channel subunits is not conserved in either Kir6.1 or Kir6.2. Instead, this motif is G-F-G in both Kir6.1 and Kir6.2. The asparagine residue in M2, a critical determinant of the rectification property, is shown. Potential protein kinase A- and protein kinase C-dependent phosphorylation sites (in human Kir6.1 and Kir6.2) are indicated by *filled circles* and *open circles*, respectively. The serine-385 (*shaded circle*) in Kir6.1 is a potential protein kinase A- and protein kinase C-dependent phosphorylation site. NH^{3+} and COO^- indicate the N- and C terminus, respectively. Single letter abbreviations for amino acids are used.

cloned Kir channel members, it represents a new subfamily, Kir6.0. The glycine-tyrosine-glycine motif in the H5 region, which is critical for K^+ ion selectivity and is highly conserved among K^+ channels (40, 58, 62), is not conserved in Kir6.1. The motif in Kir6.1 is glycine-phenylalanine-glycine. The intracellular C-terminal region in human Kir6.1 has two potential protein kinase A–dependent phosphorylation sites (threonine-234 and serine-385) and seven protein kinase C–dependent phosphorylation sites (serine-224, threonine-345, serine-354, serine-379, serine-385, serine-391, and serine-397). Kir6.1 is expressed ubiquitously, but it is not expressed in the insulin-secreting cell lines HIT-T15 (hamster-derived), RINm5F (rat-derived), and MIN6 (mouse-derived), all of which have K_{ATP} channels (32, 95; T Gonoi & S Seino, unpublished observation). A study using immunoblot analysis of subcellular fractions and electron-microscopic examination showed that Kir6.1 is present predominantly in the inner membrane of mitochondria (112). Kir6.1 protein in cardiac myocytes is upregulated by pinacidil (75), and expression of the Kir6.1 gene is induced by cardiac ischemia (5). The human *Kir6.1* gene (KCNJ8) is mapped to chromosome 12p11.23 (51).

Kir6.2

An isoform of Kir6.1, BIR (the β-cell inward rectifier, currently referred to as Kir6.2), was subsequently cloned from a human genomic library and the MIN6 cDNA library (48), using *Kir6.1* cDNA as a probe (Figure 2*B*). Kir6.2 is a 390-amino-acid protein that shares 71% amino acid identity with Kir6.1. Like Kir6.1, Kir6.2 has the glycine-phenylalanine-glycine motif in the H5 region. Unlike the strong Kir channel subunits, such as Kir2.1 and Kir3.1, which have aspartic acid in the second transmembrane segment (residue 172 of Kir2.1 and residue 173 of Kir3.1)—a crucial determinant of the rectifying property—both Kir6.1 (residue 170) and Kir6.2 (residue 160) have asparagine at the corresponding position, as is found in the weak Kir channel subunit Kir1.1a (residue 171) (45). Human Kir6.2 has two potential protein kinase A–dependent phosphorylation sites (threonine-224 and serine-372) and five protein kinase C–dependent phosphorylation sites (serine-3, serine-37, threonine-336, threonine-345, and serine-363).

Kir6.2 is expressed at high levels in pancreatic islets, MIN6, HIT-T15, and the glucagon-secreting α-cell line αTC-6 and at low levels in heart, skeletal muscle, brain, and RINm5F. In situ hybridization histochemistry and immunohistochemistry reveal that Kir6.2 is present in β-cells, α-cells, and γ-cells in pancreatic islets (111). Kir6.2 is also expressed at very low levels in pituitary and the pituitary-derived AtT-20 cell line. In situ hybridization histochemistry shows that Kir6.2 is expressed throughout rodent brain (61). Mapping of the human *Kir6.2* gene reveals that it and the *SUR1* gene are clustered at 11p15.1;

the *Kir6.2* is approximately 4.5 kbp downstream of *SUR1* (48). This observation suggests that *SUR1* and *Kir6.2* might have been coded by a single gene earlier in evolution.

THE SULFONYLUREA RECEPTORS

Sulfonylureas such as tolbutamide and glibenclamide (glyburide) are oral hypoglycemic drugs widely used in the treatment of NIDDM (13). Henquin (41) showed that tolbutamide decreased $^{86}Rb^+$ efflux from isolated rat islets. Sulfonylureas were later shown to directly inhibit the activity of K_{ATP} channels in pancreatic β-cells (109, 119). This observation raised the possibility that the receptor for sulfonylureas is the K_{ATP} channel. However, whether the sulfonylurea receptor and the K_{ATP} channel were the same protein or whether the sulfonylurea receptor was a regulatory protein closely associated with the K_{ATP} channel was controversial.

Molecular Characterization of Sulfonylurea Receptors

Using ^{3}H-labeled glibenclamide, Kramer et al (65) attempted photoaffinity labeling of the sulfonylurea receptor of plasma membranes derived from a rat β-cell tumor and found that two polypeptides with apparent molecular masses of 140 and 33 kDa were photolabeled. Since labeling of the 140-kDa polypeptide was decreased specifically by the unlabeled sulfonylureas glibenclamide and tolbutamide, Kramer et al suggested that the 140-kDa polypeptide was a component of a high-affinity sulfonylurea receptor. A 150-kDa polypeptide in pig brain microsomes was also photolabeled with ^{3}H-labeled glibenclamide (19). Using ^{125}I-labeled glibenclamide analog 5-iodo-2-hydroxyglibenclamide, researchers confirmed that a 140-kDa polypeptide is a high-affinity receptor in HIT (3). In addition to the 140-kDa polypeptide, 65-kDa, 55-kDa, and 30-kDa polypeptides were considered to be the low-affinity sulfonylurea receptors (83). However, under the conditions that led to predominant labeling of a 140-kDa polypetide by ^{3}H-labeled glibenclamide, ^{3}H-glimepiride, another sufonylurea, was specifically incorporated into a 65-kDa polypeptide in the β-cell membrane preparations, which might also represent a high-affinity sulfonylurea receptor (64). More recently, a 38-kDa polypeptide with high affinity for a glibenclamide analog was identified in HIT and cerebral cortex (102). The 38-kDa polypeptide seems to be coupled tightly to a 160- to 175-kDa polypeptide. In contrast, the majority of glibenclamide-binding protein is present in intracellular granule membrane in rat insulinoma cells (91). Recently, a 28-kDa protein binding to ^{125}I-labeled glibenclamide was isolated from the inner membrane in the mitochondria (113). Endosulfine, a putative endogenous ligand for sulfonylurea receptors, was isolated (125). Heron et al (42a) have shown that cloned α-endosulfine displaces binding of the sulfonylurea [^{3}H] glibenclamide to β-cell membrane, inhibits cloned K_{ATP} channel currents, and stimulates insulin secretion.

SUR1: High-Affinity Sulfonylurea Receptor

The structure of the sulfonylurea receptor was revealed by the cloning of a sulfonylurea receptor (currently referred to as SUR1) from HIT and RINm5F cDNA libraries et al (4). Hamster SUR1 is a 1582-amino-acid, 177-kDa protein. Rat SUR1, a 1581-amino-acid protein, has 96% amino acid identity with hamster SUR1. SUR1 has multiple putative transmembrane segments and two nucleotide binding folds (NBFs) (127) in the cytoplasmic side, indicating that as with cystic fibrosis transmembrane conductance regulator (CFTR), P-glycoprotein (P-gp), and multidrug-resistance-associated protein (MRP), SUR1 is a member of the ABC superfamily (44). Each NBF contains the Walker A and B motifs (125), which are thought to be important for nucleotide regulation of the functional activity of ABC proteins (44).

Although SUR1 was originally proposed to have 13 transmembrane segments, Tusnády et al (123) have proposed a 17-transmembrane-segment model, based on sequence alignments of SUR1 and members of the MRP gene subfamily (Figure 3*A*). The latter model suggests that like MRP, in addition to two transmembrane domains (TMD1 and TMD2), each of which consists of six transmembrane segments, SUR1 has another transmembrane domain (TMD0) consisting of five transmembrane segments in the N-terminal region. NBF-1 and NBF-2 are located in the loop between TMD1 and TMD2 and in the C terminus, respectively. There are two potential N-linked glycosylation sites in hamster, rat, and human SUR1: one in the extracellular N terminus and one in the extracellular region between the seventh and eighth transmembrane segments (123). Rat SUR1 has three potential protein kinase A–dependent phosphorylation sites, whereas hamster and human SUR1 have four such sites. SUR1 has many potential protein kinase C–dependent phosphorylation sites.

Heterologous expression of recombinant hamster and rat SUR1 in COSm6 cells exhibited high-affinity sulfonylurea-binding activities ($K_D \sim 10$ nM and 2 nM for hamster and rat SUR1, respectively) (4). SUR1 is expressed at high levels in pancreatic islets, HIT-T15, and MIN6, and at moderate to low levels in RINm5F and αTC-6. Although Northern blot analysis reveals that SUR1 is expressed at very low levels in rat brain, in situ hybridization histochemistry shows a broad distribution of SUR1 in rodent brain (52). Expression of the SUR1 gene appears to be regulated developmentally (42). SUR1-like protein is also present in plants (71).

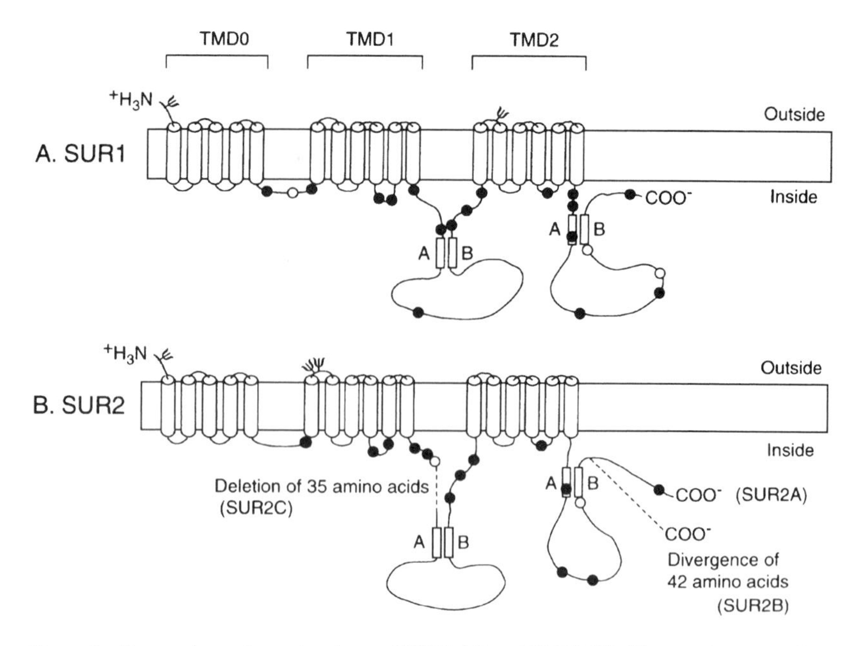

Figure 3 Proposed membrane topology of SUR1 (*A*) and SUR2 (*B*). The membrane topology is based on Tusnády et al (123). SUR is thought to have three transmembrane domains, TMD0, TMD1, and TMD3, which consist of five, six, and six transmembrane segments, respectively. Locations of potential N-linked glycosylation sites are indicated by ψ. Approximate location of potential protein kinase A- and protein kinase C-dependent phosphorylation sites (in rat SUR1 and rat SUR2A) are indicated by open circles and filled circles, respectively. NBF-1 and NBF-2 are located in the intracellular loop between TMD1 and TMD2 and in the C-terminal region, respectively. Locations of the Walker A motif (A) and Walker B motif (B) are shown by boxes. NH^{3+} and COO^- indicate the N- and C terminus, respectively.

SUR2: Low-Affinity Sulfonylurea Receptor

cDNA encoding an isoform of SUR1, SUR2 (currently referred to as SUR2A), was subsequently cloned by screening rat brain and heart cDNA libraries (49), using hamster SUR1 cDNA as a probe. Rat SUR2A is a 1545-amino-acid, 174-kDa protein that shares 68% amino acid identity with hamster SUR1. SUR2A has membrane topology similar to that of SUR1, and the Walker A and B motifs are highly conserved between the two proteins. Rat SUR2A has three potential N-linked glycosylation sites: one in the extracellular N terminus and two between the extracellular region in the seventh and eighth transmembrane segments (123). Rat SUR2A also has two potential protein kinase A–dependent phosphorylation sites: one between the eleventh and twelfth transmembrane segments and one in the intracellular C-terminal region. SUR2A also has many potential protein kinase C–dependent phosphorylation sites. The affinity of

SUR2A for sulfonylureas is approximately 500 times lower than that of SUR1 (49). SUR2A cannot be photolabeled with ^{125}I-iodoglibenclamide under the same conditions that photolabel SUR1.

Two variants of SUR2 have been identified (23, 56). One variant differs from SUR2A by 42 amino acids in the C terminus but is similar to the C terminus of SUR1 (56). The other variant has a deletion of 35 amino acids near NBF-1 of SUR2A (23). The nomenclature for these variants is in flux, but the names SUR2B and SUR2C have been proposed for the two variants, respectively (11). These variants are likely to be generated by alternative splicing of *SUR2* mRNA. SUR2A is expressed predominantly in heart and skeletal muscle (49, 56), whereas SUR2B is expressed ubiquitously (56). The human *SUR2* gene is mapped to chromosome 12p11.12 (23).

RECONSTITUTION OF ATP-SENSITIVE POTASSIUM CHANNEL CURRENTS

Expression of recombinant Kir6.2 alone in *Xenopus* oocytes or in mammalian cells such as COS-1 or HEK239 cells did not elicit significant K^+ channel currents (48). This observation is in contrast to other Kir channel subfamily subunits that show K^+ channel activities when expressed in *Xenopus* oocytes or mammalian cells. Injection of SUR1 cRNA alone in *Xenopus* oocytes did not elicit significant K^+ channel currents (4). Coinjection of SUR1 cRNA with Kir1.1a, Kir2.1, or GIRK3.4 cRNA did not generate either novel K^+ channel currents or sulfonylurea-sensitive K^+ channel currents (4). Coexpression of Kir6.2 and SUR1 mRNA at high levels in pancreatic islets and in various insulin-secreting cell lines (48) suggests that although neither Kir6.2 alone nor SUR1 alone functions as a K^+ channel, Kir6.2 and SUR1 might couple functionally to form a novel K^+ channel. Reconstitution studies with a Kir6.0 subfamily subunit and a SUR subunit in heterologous expression systems have thus far suggested that differing combinations of the Kir6.2 or Kir6.1 subunits and the SUR1, SUR2, or their variant subunits could account in part for the molecular and functional diversity of K_{ATP} channels (Table 1).

Table 1 The subunit assemblies of the reconstituted K_{ATP} channels

Type of K_{ATP} channel	α subunit[1]	β subunit[1]	Reference
Pancreatic β-cell	Kir6.2	SUR1	6, 48, 98
Cardiac and skeletal muscle	Kir6.2	SUR2A	49, 90
Smooth muscle	Kir6.2	SUR2B	56
Vascular smooth muscle	Kir6.1	SUR2B	131

[1]The Kir6.0 subfamily subunit and the SUR subunit have been proposed to be named the α-subunit and the β-subunit of K_{ATP} channels, respectively (49).

Reconstitution from the Kir6.2 and SUR1 Subunits

Coexpression of Kir6.2 and SUR1 in COS-1 cells reconstitutes weakly inwardly rectifying K^+-channel currents that have unitary conductance of approximately 76 pS in the presence of 140 mM K^+ on both sides of the membrane. ATP inhibits the reconstituted channel activity with half-maximal inhibition (Ki) at approximately 10 μM in the presence of Mg^{2+}. The reconstituted K^+ channel currents are almost completely inhibited by adenyl-5′-yl imidodiphosphate (AMP-PNP), a nonhydrolyzable ATP analog. Glibenclamide blocks the reconstituted K^+ channel currents. Diazoxide, a potent opener of the pancreatic β-cell K_{ATP} channel, stimulates the currents. Metabolic poisoning with oligomycin and 2-deoxy-glucose markedly stimulates $^{86}Rb^+$ efflux from COSm6 cells coexpressing SUR1 and Kir6.2. $^{86}Rb^+$ efflux through the reconstituted channels is inhibited by glibenclamide and stimulated by diazoxide. The K^+ channel currents reconstituted from SUR1 and Kir6.2 show the features characteristic of the K_{ATP} channels in native pancreatic β-cells (12, 26, 31, 96), indicating that the pancreatic β-cell-type K_{ATP} channel comprises the two subunits, Kir6.2, a member of the Kir channel family, and SUR1, a member of the ABC superfamily (48, 98).

Reconstitution from the Kir6.2 and SUR2A Subunits

Coexpression of Kir6.2 and SUR2A in COS-1 cells reconstitutes K^+ channel currents with rectification and single channel properties identical to those of pancreatic β-cell-type K_{ATP} (SUR1/Kir6.2) channels (49). However, burst duration and interburst interval of SUR2A/Kir6.2 channels are longer than those of SUR1/Kir6.2 channels (6, 48). SUR2A/Kir6.2 channels are 10-fold less sensitive to ATP than SUR1/Kir6.2 channels ($K_i \sim 100\ \mu$M for the SUR2A/Kir6.2 channel). The activity of SUR2A/Kir6.2 channels is almost completely inhibited by AMP-PNP. The activity of SUR2A/Kir6.2 channels is inhibited by glibenclamide only at higher concentrations than those for SUR1/Kir6.2 channels. However, SUR2A/Kir6.2 channels reconstituted in *Xenopus* oocytes (36a) are more sensitive to both ATP and glibenclamide than those reconstituted in COS-1 cells (48). The difference between the two studies might be because of the different expression system. Cromakalim and pinacidil, both potent openers of cardiac K_{ATP} channels, reactivate SUR2A/Kir6.2 channels inhibited by ATP. In contrast, diazoxide does not stimulate the activity of SUR2A/Kir6.2 channels. The channels reconstituted from Kir6.2 and SUR2A (49, 90) resemble the cardiac-muscle- and skeletal-muscle-type K_{ATP} channels (88, 128, 130), but the K_{ATP} channels in native skeletal muscles are more sensitive to ATP in the absence of Mg^{2+} (7, 126).

Reconstitution from the Kir6.2 and SUR2B Subunits

Coexpression of Kir6.2 and SUR2B in HEK239 T cells elicits weakly inwardly rectifying K^+ channel currents with unitary conductance of approximately

80 pS. ATP inhibits the activity of SUR2B/Kir6.2 channels with K_i at 68 or 300 μM in the absence or the presence of Mg^{2+}, respectively (56). In contrast to SUR2A/Kir6.2 channels, both tolbutamide and glibenclamide inhibit the activity of SUR2B/Kir6.2 channels at lower concentrations, and diazoxide stimulates the activity. These pharmacological properties are distinct from those of SUR2A/Kir6.2 channels but similar to those of smooth-muscle-type K_{ATP} channels. Because a 42-amino-acid region in the C terminus of SUR2B is similar to SUR1, the region might confer some sulfonylurea and diazoxide sensitivities. However, because the tissue distribution of SUR2B, which is ubiquitously expressed, is different from that of Kir6.2, whether the K_{ATP} channel in native smooth muscle includes the Kir6.2 subunit and the SUR2B subunit, is unclear.

Reconstitution from the Kir6.1 and SUR1 Subunits

Early reports indicated that Kir6.1 alone, when expressed heterologously in HEK239 cells, elicited ATP-sensitive K^+ channel currents, although the currents were not sensitive to sulfonylureas and diazoxide (9, 52). However, recent studies show that SUR1 is required for ATP, sulfonylurea, and diazoxide sensitivities and for functional expression of Kir6.1 channel currents when *Xenopus* oocytes (8, 35) or COSm6 cells (24) are used as expression systems. These observations suggest that the activity of the Kir6.1 channel requires a sulfonylurea receptor or other modulator of the Kir6.1 channel that is present endogenously in HEK239 cells and not in *Xenopus* oocytes or COSm6 cells (8, 103). Another possibility is that Kir6.1 requires another subunit of the Kir channel family that is expressed endogenously in HEK293 cells to form a functional K^+ channel as a heteromultimer. Although the Kir6.1 subunit plus the SUR1 subunit can reconstitute ATP-, tolbutamide-, and diazoxide-sensitive K^+ channel currents (8, 35), the occurrence of SUR1/Kir6.1 channels in native tissues has not been shown.

Reconstitution from the Kir6.1 and SUR2B Subunits

Coexpression of Kir6.1 and SUR2B produces K^+ channel currents with unitary conductance of approximately 33 pS in the presence of pinacidil (131). The activity of SUR2B/Kir6.1 channels is inhibited by ATP only at high concentrations ($>10^{-4}$ M) but is stimulated at lower concentrations (10^{-6} to $\sim 10^{-4}$ M). Similarly, GTP stimulates and inhibits channel activity at higher concentrations ($>10^{-4}$ M) and lower concentrations (10^{-6} to $\sim 10^{-4}$ M), respectively. SUR2B/Kir6.1 channel activity is stimulated by the K^+ channel openers pinacidil and nicorandil. Glibenclamide inhibits nicorandil-activated K^+ channel currents. Nucleoside diphosphates such as UDP and GDP also stimulate SUR2B/Kir6.1 channel activity. Thus the SUR2B/Kir6.1 channel is not a classical K_{ATP} channel but rather resembles the nucleotide diphosphate–dependent

K^+ channel (K_{NDP}) in vascular smooth muscle (16, 133). As described earlier, Kir6.1 is present primarily in the inner membrane of mitochondria. Because the mitochondrial K_{ATP} channel is thought to be a heteromultimer consisting of a Kir channel member (mitoKir) and a sulfonylurea receptor (mitoSUR) (33), Kir6.1 may also be a subunit of a K_{ATP} channel in the mitochondria.

PHYSICAL ASSOCIATION AND STOICHIOMETRY OF ATP-SENSITIVE POTASSIUM CHANNEL SUBUNITS

Physical Association Between the Kir6.2 and SUR1 Subunits

When Kir6.2 or Kir6.1 and SUR1 were coexpressed in COSm6 cells, both subunits were photolabeled with ^{125}I-labeled azidoglibenclamide, suggesting that Kir6.2 or Kir6.1 and SUR1 are physically associated (24). Physical association of the Kir6.2 subunit and the SUR1 subunit was confirmed by copurification of the complex of glycosylated SUR1/Kir6.2 by wheat-germ agglutinin agarose chromatography and by Ni^{2+}-agarose chromatography of hexahistidine-tagged SUR1/Kir6.2 complex (24). The majority of the Kir6.2 is associated with the glycosylated 150- to 170-kDa species of SUR1. The molecular mass of the largest highly glycosylated SUR1/Kir6.2 complex is estimated to be approximately 950 kDa, which would be reasonably consistent with four SUR1 ($\sim$170 kDa each) and four Kir6.2 ($\sim$45 kDa each) subunits. Using the specific antibody to Kir6.2, researchers were able to coimmunoprecipitate Kir6.2 and SUR1 proteins from a mixture of Kir6.2 and SUR1 subunits from in vitro–translated proteins and from COS-7 cells transfected with both subunits, providing further evidence that the Kir6.2 and the SUR1 subunits are physically associated (74).

The Subunit Stoichiometry of the SUR1/Kir6.2 Channel

The subunit stoichiometry of the SUR1/Kir6.2 channel has been determined by constructing fusion proteins of the SUR1 and Kir6.2 subunits (50). This approach was used originally to determine Kv channel subunit stoichiometry (73) and subsequently for Kir channel subunits (132). Both the $^{86}Rb^+$ permeability of the channels reconstituted from SUR1-Kir6.2 fusion protein with a 1:1 stoichiometry and their electrophysiological properties, including unitary conductance, ATP sensitivity, and glibenclamide sensitivity of the channels, are similar to those of K_{ATP} channels reconstituted from monomeric SUR1 and monomeric Kir6.2 subunits. This observation suggests that a 1:1 stoichiometry is sufficient for functional activity of the K_{ATP} channel.

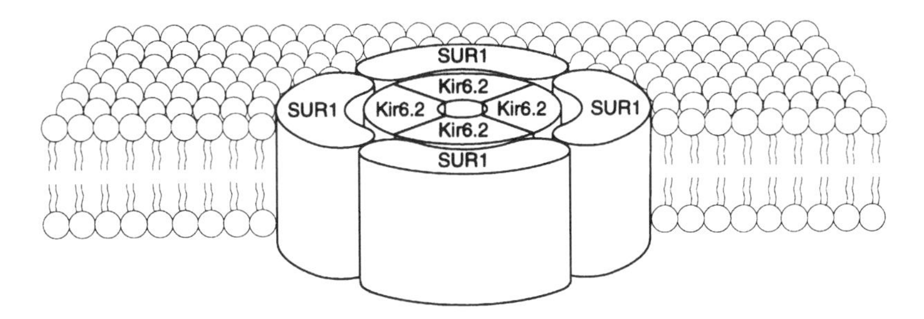

Figure 4 A model for the structure of a K_{ATP} channel. The pancreatic β-cell-type K_{ATP} channel is shown as an example. A β-cell-type K_{ATP} channel probably functions as a hetero-octamer assembled from four Kir6.2 subunits (tetramer) and four SUR1 subunits (tetramer). The K^+ ion-permeable domain is formed by a tetramer of the Kir6.2 subunit.

In addition, the channels reconstituted from the fusion protein of SUR1 and a dimeric repeat of Kir6.2 (i.e. with a SUR1:Kir6.2 stoichiometry of 1:2) show smaller $^{86}Rb^+$ efflux and K_{ATP} channel currents with less sensitivity to ATP than the channels reconstituted from the 1:1 SUR1-Kir6.2 fusion protein. The properties of this triple fusion protein are restored by supplementation with monomeric wild-type SUR1 but not completely with monomeric mutant SUR1, suggesting further that a 1:1 stoichiometry is required for function. By using similar approaches, Clement et al (24) and Shyng et al (105) also found a 1:1 stoichiometry between the SUR1 and Kir6.2 subunits. These findings, together with the biochemical findings, suggest that the pancreatic β-cell K_{ATP} channel functions as a hetero-octameric complex comprising a tetramer of the Kir6.2 subunit and a tetramer of the SUR1 subunit (24, 50, 106) (Figure 4). Based on two observations, the K_{ATP} channel pore must be formed with a tetramer of the Kir6.2 subunit, in a manner similar to other Kir channels: (*a*) mutation of asparagine at residue 160 in Kir6.2 to aspartic acid or glutamic acid increases the degree of rectification induced by Mg^{2+} or spermine (104), and (*b*) mutation of the first glycine of the glycine-phenylalanine-glycine motif to serine in the H5 region completely blocks K^+ channel currents (81).

LESSONS LEARNED FROM MUTATIONS OF THE SUR1 AND Kir6.2 SUBUNITS

Studies of naturally occurring and artificially made mutations of SUR1 and Kir6.2 have provided valuable insights into the structure-function relationships of the pancreatic β-cell K_{ATP} channel. Because pancreatic β-cell K_{ATP} channels play a critical role in the regulation of glucose-induced and sulfonylurea-induced insulin secretion, abnormalities of the genes encoding SUR1 and Kir6.2

could cause disorders of glucose homeostasis such as diabetes mellitus and hyperinsulinemic hypoglycemia. Genetic studies have shown that although neither the *SUR1* nor the *Kir6.2* gene is the major gene contributing to development of diabetes mellitus (37, 38, 53, 57, 99), both *SUR1* and *Kir6.2* gene mutations can cause familial persistent hyperinsulinemic hypoglycemia of infancy (PHHI).

Mutations in Familial Persistent Hyperinsulinemic Hypoglycemia of Infancy

PHHI is an autosomal recessive disorder of childhood characterized by severe, recurrent, and fasting hypoglycemia associated with inappropriate hypersecretion of insulin. Linkage analysis has mapped PHHI to chromosome 11p14-15.1 (34). Mutations of the *SUR1* or the *Kir6.2* gene are responsible for PHHI (1, 92). Details of each mutation have been described elsewhere (1, 30, 60, 84, 85, 87, 92, 115, 116). Here I describe three mutations that help elucidate the structure-function relationships of the β-cell K_{ATP} channel.

G1479R MUTATION OF SUR1 The mutation of glycine to arginine at 1479 in SUR1 (SUR1G1479R), which is located in the linker region between the Walker A motif and Walker B motif in NBF-2, was detected in a patient with PHHI (87). Reconstitution from SUR1G1479R and Kir6.2 in COSm6 cells elicits K^+ channel currents that are inhibited normally by ATP but are not activated by MgADP, a finding suggesting that MgADP activates the K_{ATP} channel through binding at NBF-2. The SUR1G1479R mutation also causes a reduction in the response to diazoxide.

R1437Q(23)X MUTATION OF SUR1 A guanine-to-adenine point mutation at the 3′-terminal nucleotide of exon 35 is a common mutation in PHHI. This mutation causes exon skipping and shifts the SUR1 reading frame after arginine at codon 1437. As a result, the patients have a truncated SUR1 lacking NBF-2, and the β-cells lack operational K_{ATP} channels. Reconstitution from a similarly truncated SUR1 and Kir6.2 in COS cells also fails to elicit K_{ATP} channel activity.

Y12X MUTATION OF KIR6.2 A nonsense mutation, tyrosine $\rightarrow$ stop, at codon 12 of Kir6.2 (Y12X) was found in the homozygous state in a patient with PHHI (84). Reconstitution from SUR1 and Kir6.2Y12X in COS-1 cells results in the absence of K^+ channel activity. There was no dominant-negative effect of Kir6.2Y12X on the channel activity when coexpressed with wild-type Kir6.2 and SUR1.

Transgenic Mice and Knockout Mice

Physiological consequences resulting from genetic disruption of K_{ATP} channel function have been studied in transgenic mice and mice lacking K_{ATP} channels (knockout mice).

TRANSGENIC MICE EXPRESSING A DOMINANT-NEGATIVE K_{ATP} CHANNEL IN PANCREATIC β-CELLS A substitution of the first residue of the glycine-phenylalanine-glycine motif in the H5 region of Kir6.2 (residue 132) with serine (Kir6.2G132S) blocks ionic currents (81). A $^{86}Rb^+$ efflux experiment shows that Kir6.2G132S acts as a dominant-negative inhibitor of K_{ATP} channels when coexpressed with SUR1 and wild-type Kir6.2. Studies in transgenic mice expressing Kir6.2G132S specifically in pancreatic β-cells show that the K_{ATP} channel's function is significantly impaired in pancreatic β-cells in the transgenic mice and that these mice develop hypoglycemia as neonates and hyperglycemia as adults. Apoptotic pancreatic β-cells are frequently found in these transgenic mice (81).

MICE LACKING K_{ATP} CHANNELS Mice lacking K_{ATP} channels generated by disruption of the *Kir6.2* gene (Kir6.$2^{-/-}$) have defects in both glucose-induced and tolbutamide-induced insulin secretion but have only mild impairment in glucose tolerance (80). The glucose-lowering effect of insulin is increased significantly in Kir6.$2^{-/-}$. These findings indicate that K_{ATP} channels in pancreatic β-cells are a key regulator in glucose-induced and sulfonylurea-induced insulin secretion, and they suggest that K_{ATP} channels in skeletal muscle modulate insulin action.

Studies in Site-Directed Mutagenesis

MUTAGENESIS IN NBF-1 AND NBF-2 OF SUR1 Because a SUR subunit has two NBFs, mutations of NBF-1 and/or NBF-2 might alter the nucleotide sensitivities. However, mutations of lysine residues in the Walker A motifs in NBF-1 (K719A) and/or the equivalent mutation in NBF-2 (K1384M) of SUR1 do not prevent channel inhibition by ATP (36). Mutations in the linker region between the Walker A motif and the Walker B motif of NBF-1 (G827D, G827R, and Q834H), the equivalent mutations in NBF-2 (G1479D, G1479R, G1485D, G1485R, Q1486H), or the mutation of Walker B motif of NBF-2 (D1506A) do not abolish channel inhibition by ATP (105). These studies suggest that neither NBF-1 nor NBF-2 is essential for ATP inhibition of the β-cell K_{ATP} channel.

In contrast, neither the NBF-1 mutant K719A channel nor the NBF-2 mutant K1384M channel is activated by MgADP (36). Although the mutations in the linker region and the Walker B motif of NBF-2 mostly abolish channel activation by MgADP, the equivalent mutations in NBF-1 do not interfere with channel activation by MgADP but alter the kinetic properties (105). Therefore, it is thought that both the Walker A motifs in NBF-1 and NBF-2 and the Walker B motif and the linker region in NBF-2 are essential for MgADP activation and that the Walker B motif in NBF-1 determines the kinetics of the channel response to MgADP stimulation.

A mutation in the Walker A motif in NBF-1 (K719A) abolishes channel activation by diazoxide, but a mutation in the Walker A motif in NBF-2 (K1384M) does not affect the channel activation (36). Mutations in the linker region and the Walker B motif of NBF-2 (G1479D, G1479R, G1485D, G1485R, Q1486H, and D1506A) abolish channel activation by diazoxide, and mutations in the linker region of NBF-1 (G827D, G827R, and Q834H) alter the kinetics of diazoxide activation (106). Accordingly, both NBFs are involved in activation of the pancreatic β-cell K_{ATP} channel by diazoxide.

Some mutations of NBF-1 impair expression of K_{ATP} channels on the plasma membrane, as assessed by immunoblot analysis, glibenclamide binding, $^{86}Rb^{+}$ efflux experiments, and patch-clamp recordings, whereas NBF-2 mutations do not impair expression significantly (T Gonoi & S Seino, unpublished data).

TRUNCATION OF KIR6.2 An intriguing finding is that Kir6.2 with a deletion of the last 26 amino acids (Kir6.2ΔC26) or 36 amino acids (Kir6.2ΔC36) in the C terminus, when expressed in *Xenopus* oocytes or HEK239 cells, produces K_{ATP} channel currents in the absence of SUR (122). This observation suggests that, like the N terminus of K+ channels, the C terminus of the Kir6.2 subunit might act as a blocking particle to inactivate the channel (46). Tucker et al (122) propose that the primary ATP-inhibitory site lies on the Kir6.2 subunit and that the SUR subunit increases the sensitivity of the Kir6.2 subunit to ATP (K_i from ~100 to ~10 μM) and endows the Kir6.2 subunit with sulfonylurea, diazoxide, and MgADP sensitivities.

K_{ATP} channel currents elicited by Kir6.2ΔC26 are also inhibited by GTP (117). The imidazoline phentolamine blocks K_{ATP} channel currents produced by Kir6.2ΔC26 (93). Other members of the Kir channel family—IRK3 (Kir2.3) (25) and an alternatively spliced variant of ROMK2 (Kir1.1b) with a deletion in the N terminus (79) have ATP sensitivity by themselves. However, because truncation of the C terminus of Kir6.2 has not yet been reported in native tissues, and the mutations of SUR1 detected in patients with PHHI impair K_{ATP} channel function, the SUR subunit appears to be required for functional expression of K_{ATP} channels under physiological conditions.

A MUTATION AT POSITION 160 OF KIR6.2 Mutation of the asparagine residue at position 160 in the M2 segment of Kir6.2 to a negatively charged aspartic acid (N160D) or glutamic acid (N160E) increases the degree of rectification induced by Mg^{2+} or spermine in the β-cell-type K_{ATP} channel (SUR1/Kir6.2 channel), indicating that the asparagine of the Kir6.2 subunit determines the rectification properties of the K_{ATP} channel (104).

REGULATION OF ATP-SENSITIVE POTASSIUM CHANNEL ACTIVITY BY THE SUR SUBUNIT

Regulation of ion channel activity by ABC proteins has been demonstrated (39, 76, 78, 110). Several models of a mechanism by which ABC proteins might regulate ion channel activity have been proposed (43). Physical association of SUR1 and Kir6.2 suggests that the SUR subunit directly regulates K_{ATP} channel activity by protein-protein interaction with the Kir6.0 subfamily subunit, although other proteins may also modulate the activity by interaction with the SUR subunit or the Kir6.0 subfamily subunit. As with other ABC proteins, SUR might transport a regulatory molecule to regulate the activity, but there is no evidence that SUR transports a regulatory molecule. As in CFTR (21), SUR might serve as a chaperon to guide Kir6.2 through the secretory pathway. Makhina & Nichols (77) reported that both Kir6.2 and SUR1 can independently traffic toward the plasma membrane, whereas Lorenz et al (74) suggested that SUR1 is required for proper membrane localization of Kir6.2.

ATP- and ADP-Binding Sites in K_{ATP} Channels

The Walker A and B motifs form a portion of a nucleotide-binding pocket in ABC proteins (43, 127): The lysine residue in the Walker A motif interacts with the phosphoryl moiety of the bound nucleotide, and the aspartic acid in the Walker B motif coordinates with Mg^{2+} in the MgATP complex. A biochemical study shows that SUR1 is efficiently photolabeled with 8-azido-[α-^{32}P]ATP and 8-azido-[γ-^{32}P]ATP in the absence of Mg^{2+} (124). Both mutations of the lysine in the Walker A motif (K719R, K719M) and a mutation of the aspartic acid in the Walker B motif (D854N) of SUR1 impair Mg^{2+}-independent high-affinity ATP binding (124). MgADP antagonizes ATP binding at NBF-1($IC_{50} \sim 10\ \mu M$), and a mutation of the lysine in the Walker A motif of NBF-2 (K1385M) reduces MgADP antagonism (124). Accordingly, it is thought that ATP binds to NBF-1 of SUR1 with high affinity, and MgADP, through binding to NBF-2, antagonizes the binding at NBF-1. The finding of a point mutation of NBF-2 (G1479R) in a patient with PHHI supports the possibility of MgADP antagonism through NBF-2; the mutation abolishes MgADP antagonism to ATP-inhibition of the K_{ATP} channel (87). As described earlier, a C-terminal truncation of Kir6.2 (Kir6.2ΔC26 or Kir6.2ΔC36) generates K^+ channel currents that are inhibited by ATP in the absence of SUR (122). This observation suggests that an ATP-binding site might also be present in Kir6.2. A recent study suggests that both the proximal N terminus and the proximal C terminus of Kir6.2 are involved in the inhibitory effect of ATP (121). Another study suggests that the distal part of the C terminus of Kir6.2, which includes a motif found in the ATP-binding site of ion-motif ATPases, is part of the inhibitory ATP-binding site (29a). In contrast, MgADP does not stimulate Kir6.2ΔC26 channel currents, and coexpression with SUR1 endows Kir6.2ΔC26 with MgADP sensitivity, which suggests that the ADP-binding site does not lie on Kir6.2 but on SUR1.

G-Protein Regulation of K_{ATP} Channels

The activity of K_{ATP} channels is modulated by trimeric GTP-binding (G) proteins (70, 129). Reconstitution studies have shown that the $G_{\alpha\text{-i1}}$ subunit stimulates both SUR1/Kir6.2 and SUR2A/Kir6.2 channel currents (100). In contrast, the $\beta\gamma$ subunits ($G_{\beta\gamma\text{-i1}}$ and $G_{\beta\gamma\text{-i2}}$) do not affect either SUR1/Kir6.2 or SUR2A/Kir6.2 channel currents. The study suggests that G proteins modulate the activity of K_{ATP} channels in a direct membrane-delimited pathway and that SUR is a target for the α subunit of G protein.

Models of Regulation of K_{ATP} Channel Activity by the SUR Subunit

Although the SUR subunit clearly confers sulfonylurea and diazoxide sensitivities, the mechanism by which nucleotides regulate K_{ATP} channel activity is not fully understood (11, 103, 105). A straightforward model shows SUR, not Kir6.2, conferring both ATP and MgADP sensitivities given that (*a*) SUR contains the highly conserved Walker A and B motifs in each putative NBF and there is no obvious consensus nucleotide-binding site in Kir6.1 or Kir6.2, and (*b*) either SUR1 or SUR2 (SUR2A or SUR2B) is required for functional expression of K_{ATP} channels (Figure 5*A*). ATP- and MgADP-binding experiments also support the suitability of this model. However, three findings suggest an alternative model in which ATP sensitivity is conferred primarily by Kir6.2 (11, 29a, 72,106): (*a*) SUR1 enhances the sensitivity of the channel to ATP in the absence of nucleotide hydrolysis (Figure 5*B*): (*b*) Kir6.2ΔC26 can produce K_{ATP} channel currents in the absence of SUR, although coexpression with SUR1 increases the ATP sensitivity from K_i of $\sim$100 μM to $\sim$10 μM, and (*c*) mutations in Kir6.2ΔC26 decrease the ATP sensitivity. Hydrolysis of MgATP (probably at NBF-1) might produce MgADP, which through binding to NBF-2 could stimulate the activity of the channels.

Because nonhydrolyzable analogs of ATP inhibit K_{ATP} channel activity, and ATP in the absence of Mg^{2+} inhibits K_{ATP} channel activity, nucleotide hydrolysis

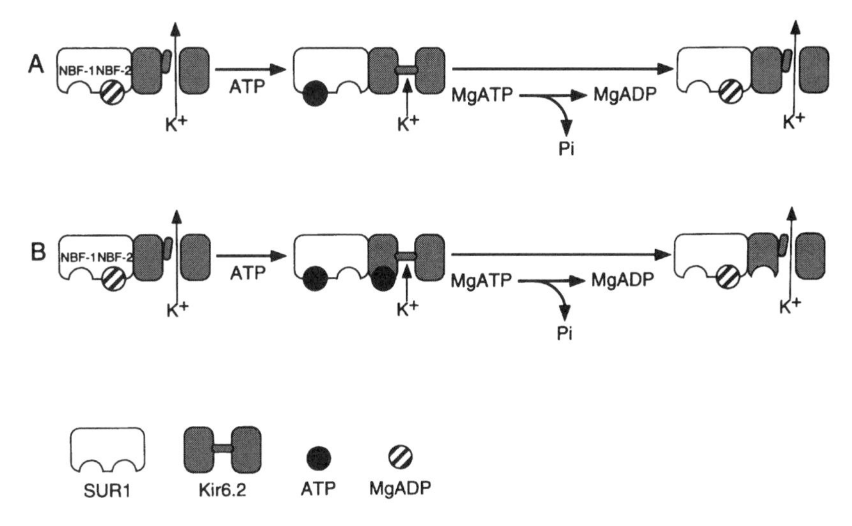

Figure 5 Models of regulation of K_{ATP} channel activity by the SUR subunit. The pancreatic β-cell-type K_{ATP} channel is shown as an example. (*A*) A model in which the SUR1 subunit confers both ATP and MgADP sensitivities. ATP binds to NBF-1 with high affinity to inhibit K_{ATP} channel activity. MgADP (produced by hydrolysis of MgATP by the SUR1 subunit or another mechanism), through binding at NBF-2, antagonizes ATP binding at NBF-1 to stimulate K_{ATP} channel activity. (*B*) A model in which the SUR1 subunit confers MgADP sensitivity and the Kir6.2 subunit confers ATP sensitivity (8, 104). ATP binds to the Kir6.2 subunit to inhibit K_{ATP} channel activity. MgADP (produced by hydrolysis of MgATP by the SUR1 subunit or another mechanism), through binding at NBF-2, stimulates K_{ATP} channel activity. The SUR1 subunit also increases the sensitivity of Kir6.2 to ATP by an unknown mechanism. The presence of a third factor that modulates the channel activity by interaction with the SUR1 subunit and/or the Kir6.2 subunit cannot be ruled out in either model.

is not required for inhibition of K_{ATP} channel activity by ATP, and binding of ATP to either SUR1 or Kir6.2 (or both) is sufficient for the inhibition. Whether SUR1 has an ATPase activity remains to be determined. The presence of a third molecule that interacts with SUR and/or Kir6.0 subfamily subunit to regulate K_{ATP} channel activity is not known.

CONCLUDING REMARKS

Molecular cloning of the sulfonylurea receptors and members of the inward rectifier subfamily Kir6.0 has made it possible to clarify the molecular basis of K_{ATP} channels, but many important questions remain: (*a*) Where are the sites of ATP and sulfonylurea binding? (*b*) What is the mechanism of channel gating? (*c*) Does a SUR subunit have ATPase activity? If it does, what is its role? (*d*) Does SUR by itself transport any molecules? (*e*) Is there a third molecule interacting with a SUR subunit or a Kir6.0 subfamily subunit? (*f*) Is there an endogenous ligand for SUR? (*g*) What are the consequences of SUR2 mutations? Answers to these questions will provide valuable insights into the structure-function relationships, molecular regulation, and pathophysiological roles of K_{ATP} channels.

ACKNOWLEDGMENTS

The author thanks the many coworkers and collaborators who were involved in the studies from our laboratory cited in this review, especially N Inagaki and T Gonoi for their major contribution to molecular biology and electrophysiology, respectively. The author also thanks M Dunne for critical reading of the manuscript; F Ashcroft, Y Kurachi, and C Nichols for providing preprints and unpublished data, and many colleagues for sending their reprints on these topics; J Kawaki for the artwork used in this review; and C Ujike for help with preparation of the manuscript. This work is supported by Scientific Research Grants from the Ministry of Education, Science, Sports, and Culture and from the Ministry of Health and Welfare, Japan.

Literature Cited

1. Aguilar-Bryan L, Bryan J. 1997. ATP-sensitive potassium channels, sulfonylurea receptors, and persistent hyperinsulinemic hypoglycemia of infancy. *Diabetes Rev.* 4:336–46
2. Aguilar-Bryan L, Clement JP IV, Gonzalez G, Kunjilwar K, Babenko A, Bryan J. 1998. Toward understanding the assembly and structure of K_{ATP} channels. *Physiol. Rev.* 78:227–45
3. Aguilar-Bryan L, Nelson DA, Vu QA, Humphrey MB, Boyd AE III. 1990. Photoaffinity labeling and partial purification of the β cell sulfonylurea receptor using a novel, biologically active glyburide analog. *J. Biol. Chem.* 265:8218–24
4. Aguilar-Bryan L, Nichols CG, Wechsler SW, Clement JP IV, Boyd AE III, et al. 1995. Cloning of the β cell high-affinity sulfonylurea receptor: a regulator of insulin secretion. *Science* 268:423–26
5. Akao M, Otani H, Takano M, Kuniyasu A, Nakayama H, et al. 1997. Myocardial ischemia induces differential regulation of K_{ATP} channel gene expression in rat hearts. *J. Clin. Invest.* 100:3053–59
6. Alekseev AE, Kennedy ME, Navarro B, Terzic A. 1997. Burst kinetics of co-expressed Kir6.2/SUR1 clones: comparison of recombinant with native ATP-sensitive K^+ channel. *J. Membr. Biol.* 159:161–68
7. Allard B, Lazdunski M, Rougier O. 1995. Activation of ATP-dependent K^+ channels by metabolic poisoning in adult mouse skeletal muscle: role of intracellular Mg^{2+} and pH. *J. Physiol.* 485:282–96
8. Ämmälä C, Moorhouse A, Ashcroft FM. 1996. The sulphonylurea receptor confers diazoxide sensitivity on the inwardly rectifying K^+ channel Kir6.1 expressed in human embryonic kidney cells. *J. Physiol.* 494:709–14
9. Ämmälä C, Moorhouse A, Gribble F, Ashfield R, Procks P, et al. 1996. Promiscuous coupling between the sulphonylurea receptor and inwardly rectifying potassium channels. *Nature* 379:545–48
10. Ashcroft FM. 1988. Adenosine 5′-triphosphate-sensitive potassium channels. *Annu. Rev. Neurosci.* 11:97–118

11. Ashcroft FM, Gribble FM. 1998. Correlating structure and function in ATP-sensitive potassium channels. *Trends Neurosci.* 21:288–94
12. Ashcroft FM, Harrison DE, Ashcroft SJH. 1984. Glucose induces closure of single potassium channels in isolated rat pancreatic β-cells. *Nature* 312:446–48
13. Ashcroft SJH, Ashcroft FM. 1992. The sulfonylurea receptor. *Biochim. Biophys. Acta* 1175:45–59
14. Ashford MLJ, Sturgess NC, Trout NJ, Gardner NJ, Hales CN. 1988. Adenosine-5′-triphosphate-sensitive ion channels in neonatal rat cultured central neurones. *Pflügers Arch.* 412:297–304

14a. Babenko AP, Aguilar-Bryan L, Bryan J. 1998. A view of SUR/Kir6.x K_{ATP} channels. *Annu. Rev. Physiol.* 60:667–87

15. Barry DM, Nerbonne JM. 1996. Myocardial potassium channels: electrophysiological and molecular diversity. *Annu. Rev. Physiol.* 58:363–94
16. Beech DJ, Zhang H, Nakao K, Bolton TB. 1993. K channel activation by nucleotide diphosphates and its inhibition by glibenclamide in vascular smooth muscle cells. *Br. J. Pharmacol.* 110:573–82
17. Bell GI, Kayano T, Buse JB, Burant CF, Takeda J, et al. 1990. Molecular biology of mammalian glucose transporters. *Diabetes Care* 13:198–208
18. Bernardi H, De Weille JR, Epelbaum J, Mourre C, Amoroso S, et al. 1993. ATP-modulated K^+ channels sensitive to antidiabetic sulfonylureas are present in adenohypophysis and are involved in growth hormone release. *Proc. Natl. Acad. Sci. USA* 90:1340–44
19. Bernardi H, Fosset M, Lazdunski M. 1988. Characterization, purification, and affinity labeling of the brain [^{3}H]glibenclamide-binding protein, a putative neuronal ATP-regulated K^+ channel. *Proc. Natl. Acad. Sci. USA* 85:9816–20
20. Boyd AE III. 1988. Sulfonylurea receptors, ion channels, and fruit flies. *Diabetes* 37:847–50
21. Bradbury NA, Jilling T, Berta G, Sorscher EJ, Bridges RJ, et al. 1992. Regulation of plasma membrane recycling by CFTR. *Science* 256:530–32
22. Christie MJ, North RA, Osborne PB, Douglass J, Adelman JP. 1990. Heteropolymeric potassium channels expressed in *Xenopus* oocytes from cloned subunits. *Neuron* 2:405–11
23. Chutkow WA, Simon MC, Le Beau MM, Burant CF. 1996. Cloning, tissue expression, and chromosomal localization of SUR2, the putative drug-binding subunit of cardiac, skeletal muscle, and vascular K_{ATP} channels. *Diabetes* 45:1439–45
24. Clement JP IV, Kunjilwar K, Gonzalez G, Schwanstecher M, Panten U, et al. 1997. Association and stoichiometry of K_{ATP} channel subunits. *Neuron* 18:827–38
25. Collins A, Germa MS, Jan YN, Jan LY, Zhao B. 1996. A strongly inwardly rectifying K^+ channel that is sensitive to ATP. *J. Neurosci.* 16:1–9
26. Cook DL, Hales CN. 1984. Intracellular ATP directly blocks K^+ channels in pancreatic β-cells. *Nature* 311:271–73
27. Cook DL, Satin LS, Ashford MLJ, Hales CN. 1988. ATP-sensitive K^+ channels in pancreatic β-cells. *Diabetes* 37:495–98
28. Dascal N, Lim NF, Schriebmayer W, Wang W, Davidson N, Lester HA. 1993. Expression of an atrial G-protein-activated potassium channel in *Xenopus* oocytes. *Proc. Natl. Acad. Sci. USA* 90: 6596–600
29. Doupnik CA, Davidson N, Lester HA. 1995. The inward rectifier potassium channel family. *Curr. Opin. Neurobiol.* 5:268–77

29a. Drain P, Li L, Wang J. 1998. K_{ATP} channel inhibition by ATP requires distinct functional domains of the cytoplasmic C terminus of the pore-forming subunit. *Proc. Natl. Acad. Sci. USA.* 95:13953–58

30. Dunne MJ, Kane C, Shepherd RM, Sanchez JA, James RFL, et al. 1997. Familial persistent hyperinsulinemic hypoglycemia of infancy and mutations in the sulfonylurea receptor. *N. Engl. J. Med.* 336:703–6
31. Findly I, Dunne MJ, Petersen OH. 1985. ATP-sensitive inward rectifier and voltage and calcium activated K^+ channels in cultured pancreatic islet cells. *J. Membr. Biol.* 88:165–72
32. Gaines KL, Hamilton S, Boyd AE III. 1988. Characterization of the sulfonylurea receptor on beta cell membranes. *J. Biol. Chem.* 263:2589–92
33. Garlid KD. 1996. Cation transport in mitochondria—the potassium cycle. *Biochem. Biophys. Acta* 1275:123–26
34. Glaser B, Chiu KC, Anker R, Nestorowiz A, Landau H, et al. 1994. Familial hyperinsulinism maps to chromosome 11p14–15. 1, 30 cM centromeric to the insulin gene. *Nat. Genet.* 7:185–88
35. Gribble FM, Ashfield R, Ämmälä C, Ashcroft FM. 1997. Properties of cloned ATP-sensitive K^+ currents expressed in *Xenopus* oocytes. *J. Physiol.* 498:87–98
36. Gribble FM, Tucker SJ, Ashcroft FM.

1997. The essential role of the Walker A motifs of SUR1 in K-ATP channel activation by Mg-ADP and diazoxide. *J.* 16:1145–52

36a. Gribble FM, Tucker SJ, Seino S, Ashcroft FM. 1998. Tissue specificity of sulfonylureas. Studies on cloned cardiac and β-cell KATP channels. *Diabetes* 47: 1412–18

37. Hansen L, Echwald SM, Hansen T, Urhammer SA, Clausen JO, et al. 1997. Amino acid polymorphisms in the ATP-regulatable inward rectifier Kir6.2 and their relationships to glucose- and tolbutamide-induced insulin secretion, the insulin sensitivity index, and NIDDM. *Diabetes* 46:508–12

38. Hansen T, Echwald SM, Hansen L, Moller AM, Almind K, et al. 1998. Decreased tolbutamide-stimulated insulin secretion in healthy subjects with sequence variants in the high-affinity sulfonylurea receptor gene. *Diabetes* 47:598–605

39. Hardy SP, Goodfellow HR, Valverde AM, Gill DR, Sepulveda FV, et al. 1995. Protein kinase C-mediated phosphorylation of the human multidrug resistance P-glycoprotein regulates cell volume-activated chloride channels. *EMBO J.* 14: 68–75

40. Heginbotham L, Abramson T, Mackinnon R. 1992. A functional connection between the pores of distantly related ion channels as revealed by mutant K^+ channels. *Science* 258:1152–55

41. Henquin JC. 1980. Tolbutamide stimulation and inhibition of insulin release: studies of the underlying ionic mechanisms in isolated rat islets. *Diabetologia* 18:151–60

42. Hernandez-Sanchez C, Wood TL, Leroith D. 1997. Developmental and tissue-specific sulfonylurea receptor gene expression. *Endocrinology* 138:705–11

42a. Heron L, Virsolvy A, Peyrollier K, Gribble FM, Cam AL, et al. 1998. Human α-endosulfine, a possible regulator of a sulfonylurea-sensitive K_{ATP} channel: molecular cloning, expression, and biological properties. *Proc. Natl. Acad. Sci. USA* 95:8387–91

43. Higgins CF. 1992. ABC transporters: from microorganisms to man. *Annu. Rev. Cell Biol.* 8:67–113

44. Higgins CF. 1995. The ABC of channel regulation. *Cell* 82:693–96

45. Ho K, Nichols CG, Lederer WJ, Lytton J, Vasselev PM, et al. 1993. Cloning and expression of an inwardly rectifying ATP-regulated potassium channel. *Nature* 362:31–38

46. Hoshi T, Zagotta WN, Aldrich RW. 1990. Biophysical and molecular mechanisms of Shaker potassium channel inactivation. *Science* 250:533–38

47. Hunter M, Giebisch G. 1988. Calcium-activated K-channels of *Amphiuma* early distal tubule: inhibition by ATP. *Pflügers Arch.* 412:331–33

48. Inagaki N, Gonoi T, Clement JP IV, Namba N, Inazawa J, et al. 1995. Reconstitution of IKATP: an inward rectifier subunit plus the sulfonylurea receptor. *Science* 270:1166–70

49. Inagaki N, Gonoi T, Clement JP IV, Wang C-Z, Aguilar-Bryan L, et al. 1996. A family of sulfonylurea receptors determines the pharmacological properties of ATP-sensitive K^+ channels. *Neuron* 16:1011–17

50. Inagaki N, Gonoi T, Seino S. 1997. Subunit stoichiometry of the pancreatic β-cell ATP-sensitive K^+ channel. *FEBS Lett.* 409:232–36

51. Inagaki N, Inazawa J, Seino S. 1995. cDNA sequence, gene structure, and chromosomal localization of the human ATP-sensitive potassium channel, uK_{ATP}-1, gene (KCNJ8). *Genomics* 30:102–4

52. Inagaki N, Tsuura Y, Namba N, Masuda K, Gonoi T, et al. 1995. Cloning and functional characterization of a novel ATP-sensitive potassium channel ubiquitously expressed in rat tissues, including pancreatic islets, pituitary, skeletal muscle, and heart. *J. Biol. Chem.* 270:5691–94

53. Inoue H, Ferrer J, Warren-Terry M, Zhang Y, Millns H, et al. 1997. Sequence variants in the pancreatic islet β-cell inwardly rectifying K^+ channel Kir6.2 (Bir) gene: identification and lack of role in Caucasian patients with NIDDM. *Diabetes* 46:502–7

54. Inoue I, Nagase H, Kishi K, Higuti T. 1991. ATP-sensitive K^+ channel in the mitochondrial inner membrane. *Nature* 352:244–47

55. Isocoff EY, Jan YN, Jan LY. 1990. Evidence for the formation of heteromultimeric potassium channels in *Xenopus* oocytes. *Nature* 345:530–34

56. Isomoto S, Kondo C, Yamada M, Matsumoto S, Higashiguchi O, et al. 1996. A novel sulfonylurea receptor forms with BIR (Kir6.2) a smooth muscle type ATP-sensitive K^+ channel. *J. Biol. Chem.* 271:24321–24

57. Iwasaki N, Kawamura M, Yamagata K, Cox NJ, Karibe S, et al. 1996. Identification of microsatellite markers near the human genes encoding the β-cell ATP-sensitive K^+ channel and linkage studies

with NIDDM in Japanese. *Diabetes* 45: 267–69
58. Jan LY, Jan Y. 1994. Potassium channels and their evolving gates. *Nature* 371:119–22
59. Jan LY, Jan Y. 1997. Cloned potassium channels from eukaryotes and prokaryotes. *Annu. Rev. Neurosci.* 20:91–123
60. Kane C, Shepherd RM, Squires PE, Johnson PRV, James RFL, et al. 1996. Loss of functional K_{ATP} channels in pancreatic β-cells causes persistent hyperinsulinemic hypoglycemia of infancy. *Nat. Med.* 2:1344–47
61. Karschin C, Ecke C, Ashcroft FM, Karschin A. 1997. Overlapping distribution of K_{ATP} channel-forming Kir6.2 subunit and the sulfonylurea receptor SUR1 in rodent brain. *FEBS Lett.* 401:59–64
62. Kerr ID, Sansom MSP. 1995. Cation selectivity in ion channels. *Nature* 373:112
63. Kofuji PK, Davidson N, Lester HA. 1995. Evidence that neuronal G-protein-gated inwardly rectifying K^+ channels are activated by $G\beta\gamma$ subunits and function as heteromultimers. *Proc. Natl. Acad. Sci. USA* 92:6542–46
64. Kramer W, Muller G, Girbig F, Gutjahr U, Kowalewski S, et al. 1995. The molecular interaction of sulfonylureas with β-cell ATP-sensitive K^+-channels. *Diabetes Res. Clin. Pract.* 28:67–80
65. Kramer W, Oekonomopulos R, Punter J, Summ H-D. 1988. Direct photoaffinity labeling of the putative sulfonylurea receptor in rat β-cell tumor membranes by $[^3H]$glibenclamide. *FEBS Lett.* 229:355–59
66. Krapivinsky G, Gordon EA, Wickman K, Velimirovic B, Krapivinsky L, et al. 1995. The G-protein-gated atrial K^+ channel IKACh is a heteromultimer of two inwardly rectifying K^+ channel proteins. *Nature* 374:135–41
67. Krapivinsky G, Medina I, Eng L, Krapivinsky L, Yang Y, Clapham DE. 1998. A novel inward rectifier K^+ channel with unique pore properties. *Neuron* 20:995–1005
68. Kubo Y, Baldwin T, Jan YN, Jan LY. 1993. Primary structure and functional expression of a mouse inward rectifier potassium channel. *Nature* 362:127–133
69. Kubo Y, Reuveny E, Slesinger PA, Jan YN, Jan LY. 1993. Primary structure and functional expression of a rat G-protein-coupled muscarinic potassium channel. *Nature* 364:802–6
70. Kurachi Y. 1995. G protein regulation of cardiac muscarinic potassium channel. *Am. J. Physiol.* 269:C821–30
71. Leonhardt N, Martin E, Vavasseur A, Forestier C. 1997. Evidence for the existence of a sulfonylurea-receptor-like protein in plants: modulation of stomatal movements and guard cell potassium channels by sulfonylureas and potassium channel openers. *Proc. Natl. Acad. Sci. USA* 94:14156–61
72. Li L, Wang J, Drain P. 1998. ATP-dependent inhibition gating of a mouse β-cell K_{ATP} channel requires two distinct segments of the cytoplasmic C-terminal domain of the pore-forming subunit. *Biophys. J.* 74:A241
73. Liman ER, Tytgat J, Hess P. 1992. Subunit stoichiometry of a mammalian K^+ channel determined by construction of multimeric cDNAs. *Neuron* 9:861–71
74. Lorenz E, Alekseev AE, Krapivinsky GB, Carrasco AJ, Clapham DE, et al. 1998. Evidence for direct physical association between a K^+ channel (Kir6.2) and an ATP-binding cassette protein (SUR1) which affects cellular distribution and kinetic behavior of an ATP-sensitive K^+ channel. *Mol. Cell. Biol.* 18:1652–59
75. Lu C, Halvorsen SW. 1997. Channel activators regulate ATP-sensitive potassium channel (Kir6.1) expression in chick cardiomyocytes. *FEBS Lett.* 412:121–25
76. Luckie DB, Krouse ME, Harper KL, Law TC, Wine JJ, et al. 1994. MDR1/P-glycoprotein enhances swelling-activated K^+ and Cl^- currents in NIH/3T3 cells. *Am. J. Physiol.* 267:C650–58
77. Makhina EN, Nichols CG. 1998. Independent trafficking of K_{ATP} channel subunits to the plasma membrane. *J. Biol. Chem.* 273:3369–75
78. McNicholas CM, Guggino WB, Schwiebert EM, Hebert SC, Giebisch G, et al. 1996. Sensitivity of a renal K^+ channel (ROMK2) to the inhibitory sulfonylurea compound glibenclamide is enhanced by coexpression with the ATP-binding cassette transporter cystic fibrosis transmembrane regulator. *Proc. Natl. Acad. Sci. USA* 93:8083–88
79. McNicholas CM, Yang Y, Giebisch G, Hebert SC. 1996. Molecular site for nucleotide binding on an ATP-sensitive renal K^+ channel (ROMK2). *Am. J. Physiol.* 271:F275–85
80. Miki T, Nagashima K, Tashiro F, Kotake K, Yoshitomi H, et al. 1998. Defective insulin secretion and enhanced insulin action in K_{ATP} channel–deficient mice. *Proc. Natl. Acad. Sci. USA* 95:10402–6
81. Miki T, Tashiro F, Iwanaga T, Nagashima K, Yoshitomi H, et al. 1997. Abnormali-

ties of pancreatic islets by targeted expression of a dominant-negative K_{ATP} channel. *Proc. Natl. Acad. Sci. USA* 94:11969–73

82. Misler S, Giebisch G. 1992. ATP-sensitive potassium channels in physiology, pathophysiology, and pharmacology. *Curr. Opin. Nephrol. Hypertens.* 1:21–33
83. Nelson DA, Aguilar-Bryan L, Bryan J. 1992. Specificity of photolabeling of β-cell membrane proteins with an ^{125}I-labeled glyburide analog. *J. Biol. Chem.* 267:14928–33
84. Nestorowicz A, Inagaki N, Gonoi T, Schoor KP, Wilson BA, et al. 1997. A nonsense mutation in the inward rectifier potassium channel gene, Kir6.2, is associated with familial hyperinsulinism. *Diabetes* 46:1743–48
85. Nestorowicz A, Wilson BA, Schoor KP, Inoue H, Glaser B, et al. 1996. Mutations in the sulfonylurea receptor gene are associated with familial hyperinsulinism in Ashkenazi Jews. *Hum. Mol. Genet.* 5:1813–22
86. Nichols CG, Lopatin AN. 1997. Inward rectifier potassium channels. *Annu. Rev. Physiol.* 59:171–91
87. Nichols CG, Shyng S-L, Nestorowicz A, Glaser B, Clement CG IV, et al. 1996. Adenosine diphosphate as an intracellular regulator of insulin secretion. *Science* 272:1785–87
88. Noma A. 1983. ATP-regulated K^+ channels in cardiac muscle. *Nature* 305:147–48
89. North RA. 1995. *Handbook of Receptors and Channels Series. Ligand- and Voltage-Gated Ion Channels.* Boca Raton, FL: CRC Press
90. Okuyama Y, Yamada M, Kondo C, Satoh E, Isomoto S, et al. 1998. The effects of nucleotides and potassium openers on the SUR2A/Kir6.2 complex K^+ channel expressed in a mammalian cell line, HEK239T cells. *Pflügers Arch.* 435:595–603
91. Ozanne SE, Guest PC, Hutton JC, Hales CN. 1995. Intracellular localization and molecular heterogeneity of the sulphonylurea receptor in insulin-secreting cells. *Diabetologia* 38:277–82
92. Permutt MA, Nestorowicz A, Glaser B. 1997. Familial hyperinsulinism: an inherited disorder of spontaneous hypoglycemia in neonates and infants. *Diabetes Rev.* 4:347–55
93. Proks P, Ashcroft FM. 1997. Phentolamine block of K_{ATP} channels is mediated by Kir6.2. *Proc. Natl. Acad. Sci. USA* 94:11716–2091
94. Quayle JM, Nelson MT, Standen NB. 1997. ATP-sensitive and inwardly rectifying potassium channels in smooth muscle. *Physiol. Rev.* 77:1166–1215
95. Ribalet B, Ciani S. 1987. Regulation by cell metabolism and adenine nucleotides of a K channel in insulin-secreting β cell (RINm5F). *Proc. Natl. Acad. Sci. USA* 84:1721–25
96. Rorsman P, Trube G. 1985. Glucose dependent K^+-channels in pancreatic β-cells are regulated by intracellular ATP. *Pflügers Arch.* 405:305–9
97. Ruppersberg JP, Schorter KH, Sakmann B, Stocker M, Sewing S, et al. 1990. Heteromultimeric channels formed by rat brain potassium-channel proteins. *Nature* 345:535–37
98. Sakura H, Ämmälä C, Smith PA, Gribble FM, Ashcroft FM. 1995. Cloning and functional expression of the cDNA encoding a novel ATP-sensitive potassium channel subunit expressed in pancreatic β-cells, brain, heart and skeletal muscle. *FEBS Lett.* 377:338–44
99. Sakura H, Wat N, Horton V, Milins H, Turner RC, et al. 1996. Sequence variations in the human Kir6.2 gene, a subunit of the beta-cell ATP-sensitive K^+ channel: no association with NIDDM in white Caucasian subjects or evidence of abnormal function when expressed in vitro. *Diabetologia* 39:1233–36
100. Sanchez JA, Gonoi T, Inagaki N, Katada T, Seino S. 1998. Modulation of reconstituted ATP-sensitive K^+ channels by GTP-binding proteins. *J. Physiol.* 507:315–24
101. Schmid-Antomarchi H, Weille JD, Fosset M, Lazdunski M. 1987. The receptor for antidiabetic sulfonylureas controls the activity of the ATP-modulated K^+ channel in insulin-secreting cells. *J. Biol. Chem.* 262:15840–44
102. Schwanstecher M, Loser S, Chudziak F, Panten U. 1994. Identification of a 38-kDa high affinity sulfonylurea-binding peptide in insulin-secreting cells and cerebral cortex. *J. Biol. Chem.* 269:17768–71
103. Seino S, Inagaki N, Namba N, Gonoi T. 1996. Molecular biology of the β-cell ATP-sensitive K^+ channel. *Diabetes Rev.* 4:177–90
104. Shyng S-L, Ferrigni T, Nichols CG. 1997. Control of rectification and gating of cloned K_{ATP} channels by the Kir6.2 subunit. *J. Gen. Physiol.* 110:141–53
105. Shyng S-L, Ferrigni T, Nichols CG. 1997. Regulation of K_{ATP} channel activity by diazoxide and MgADP distinct functions of the two nucleotide binding folds of

the sulfonylurea receptor. *J. Gen. Physiol.* 110:643–54
106. Shyng S-L, Nichols CG. 1997. Octameric stoichiometry of the K_{ATP} channel complex. *J. Gen. Physiol.* 110:655–64
107. Spruce AE, Standen NB, Stanfield PR. 1985. Voltage-dependent ATP-sensitive potassium channels of skeletal muscle membrane. *Nature* 316:736–38
108. Standen NB, Quayle JM, Davies NW, Brayden JE, Huang Y, et al. 1989. Hyperpolarizing vasodilators activate ATP-sensitive K^+ channels in arterial smooth muscle. *Science* 245:177–80
109. Sturgess NC, Ashford NLJ, Cook DL, Hales CN. 1985. The sulphonylurea receptor may be an ATP-sensitive potassium channel. *Lancet* 8453:474–75
110. Stutts MJ, Canessa CM, Olsen JC, Hamrick M, Cohn JA, et al. 1995. CFTR as a cAMP-dependent regulator of sodium channels. *Science* 269:847–50
111. Suzuki M, Fujikura K, Inagaki N, Seino S, Takata K, et al. 1997. Localization of the ATP-sensitive K^+ channel subunit Kir6.2 in mouse pancreas. *Diabetes* 46:1440–44
112. Suzuki M, Kotake K, Fujikura K, Inagaki N, Suzuki T, et al. 1997. Kir6.1: a possible subunit of ATP-sensitive K^+ channels in mitochondria. *Biochem. Biophys. Res. Commun.* 241:693–97
113. Szewezyk A, Wojcik G, Lobanov NA, Nalecz MJ. 1997. The mitochondrial sulfonylurea receptor: identification and characterization. *Biochem. Biophys. Res. Commun.* 230:611–15
114. Terzic A, Jahangir A, Kurachi Y. 1995. Cardiac ATP-sensitive K^+ channels: regulation by intracellular nucleotides and K^+ channel-opening drugs. *Am. J. Physiol.* 269:C525–45
115. Thomas PM, Cote GJ, Wohllk N, Haddad B, Mathew PM, et al. 1995. Mutations in the sulfonylurea receptor gene in familial persistent hyperinsulinemic hypoglycemia of infancy. *Science* 268:426–29
116. Thomas PM, Wohllk N, Huang E, Kuhnle U, Rabl W, et al. 1996. Inactivation of the first nucleotide-binding fold of the sulfonylurea receptor, and familial persistent hyperinsulinemic hypoglycemia of infancy. *Am. J. Hum. Genet.* 59:510–18
117. Trapp S, Tucker SJ, Ashcroft FM. 1997. Activation and inhibition of K-ATP currents by guanine nucleotides is mediated by different channel subunits. *Proc. Natl. Acad. Sci. USA* 94:8872–77
118. Trube G, Hescheler J. 1984. Inward-rectifying channels in isolated patches of the heart cell membrane: ATP-dependence and comparison with cell-attached patches. *Pflügers Arch.* 401:178–84
119. Trube G, Rorsman P, Ohno S. 1986. Opposite effects of tolbutamide and diazoxide in the ATP-dependent K^+ channel in mouse pancreatic β-cells. *Pflügers Arch.* 407:493–99
120. Tucker SJ, Ashcroft FM. 1998. A touching case of channel regulation: the ATP-sensitive K^+ channel. *Curr. Opin. Neurobiol.* 8:316–320
121. Tucker SJ, Gribble FM, Proks P, Trapp S, Ryder TJ, et al. 1998. Molecular determinants of K_{ATP} channel inhibition by ATP. *EMBO J.* 17:3290–96
122. Tucker SJ, Gribble FM, Zhao C, Trapp S, Ashcroft FM. 1997. Truncation of Kir6.2 produces ATP-sensitive K^+ channels in the absence of the sulphonylurea receptor. *Nature* 387:179–83
123. Tusnády GE, Bakos E, Varadi A, Sarkadi B. 1997. Membrane topology distinguishes a subfamily of the ATP-binding cassette (ABC) transporters. *FEBS Lett.* 402:1–3
124. Ueda K, Inagaki N, Seino S. 1997. Mg-ADP antagonism to Mg^{2+}-independent ATP binding of the sulfonylurea receptor SUR1. *J. Biol. Chem.* 272:22983–86
125. Virsolvy-Vergine A, Leray H, Kuroki S, Lupo B, Dufour M, et al. 1992. Endosulfine, an endogenous peptidic ligand for the sulfonylurea receptor: purification and partial characterization from ovine brain. *Proc. Natl. Acad. Sci. USA* 89: 6629–33
126. Vivaudou MB, Arnoult C, Villaz M. 1991. Skeletal muscle ATP-sensitive K^+ channels recorded from sarcolemmal blebs of split fibers: ATP inhibition is reduced by magnesium and ADP. *J. Membr. Biol.* 122:165–75
127. Walker JE, Saraste M, Runswick MJ, Gay N. 1982. Distantly related sequences in the α- and β-subunits of ATP synthase, myosin, kinases and other ATP-requiring enzymes and a common nucleotide binding fold. *EMBO J.* 1:945–51
128. Weik R, Neumcke B. 1990. Effects of potassium channel openers on single potassium channels in mouse skeletal muscle. *Naunyn-Schmied Arch. Pharmacol.* 342:258–63
129. Wickman K, Clapham DE. 1995. Ion channel regulation by G proteins. *Physiol. Rev.* 75:865–85
130. Woll KH, Lönnendonker U, Neumcke B. 1989. ATP-sensitive potassium channels in adult mouse skeletal muscle: different modes of blockage by internal

cations, ATP and tolbutamide. *Pflügers Arch.* 414:622–28

131. Yamada M, Isomoto S, Matsumoto S, Kondo C, Shindo T, et al. 1997. Sulphonylurea receptor 2B and Kir6.1 form a sulphonylurea-sensitive but ATP-insensitive K^+ channel. *J. Physiol.* 499:715–20
132. Yang J, Jan YN, Jan LY. 1995. Determination of the subunit stoichiometry of an inwardly rectifying potassium channel. *Neuron* 15:1441–47
133. Zhang H-L, Bolton TB. 1996. Two types of ATP-sensitive potassium channels in rat portal vein smooth muscle cells. *Br. J. Pharmacol.* 118:105–14

Annu. Rev. Physiol. 1999. 61:363–89

ADRENOMEDULLIN AND THE CONTROL OF FLUID AND ELECTROLYTE HOMEOSTASIS

Willis K. Samson
Department of Physiology, University of North Dakota, Grand Forks, North Dakota 58202; e-mail: wsamson@mail.med.und.nodak.edu

KEY WORDS: preproadrenomedullin, proadrenomedullin N-terminal 20 peptide, vasoactive hormones, natriuresis/diuresis, renin-angiotensin system, cardiovascular regulation

ABSTRACT

Two potent hypotensive peptides, adrenomedullin (AM) and proadrenomedullin N-terminal 20 peptide (PAMP), are encoded by the adrenomedullin gene. AM stimulates nitric oxide production by endothelial cells, whereas PAMP acts presynaptically to inhibit adrenergic nerves that innervate blood vessels. Complementary, but mechanistically unique, actions also occur in the anterior pituitary gland where both peptides inhibit adrenocorticotropin release. In the adrenal gland both AM and PAMP inhibit potassium and angiotensin II-stimulated aldosterone secretion. Natriuretic and diuretic actions of AM reflect unique actions of the peptide on renal blood flow and tubular function. In the brain AM inhibits water intake and, in a physiologically relevant manner, salt appetite. Both AM and PAMP act in the brain to elevate sympathetic tone, effects that mirror the positive inotropic action of AM in the heart. Cardioprotective actions in the brain and heart may be important counter-regulatory actions that buffer the extreme hypotensive actions of the peptides when released in sepsis. Thus the biologic actions of the proadrenomedullin-derived peptides seem well coordinated to contribute to the physiologic regulation of volume and electrolyte homeostasis.

0066-4278/99/0315-0363$08.00

BIOCHEMISTRY AND MOLECULAR BIOLOGY OF ADRENOMEDULLIN

One of the major advances in physiology over the past decade has been the realization of the importance of the vasculature as an endocrine tissue. Just as significant has been the development of an understanding of the importance of local, paracrine or autocrine actions of hormones, independent of their circulating effects. In large part, this expansion of insight into the mechanisms of integrative physiology has been driven by the discovery beginning in 1980s of several major families of vasoactive hormones (1). Now lessons learned from the elucidation of the pharmacologic and physiologic effects of the natriuretic peptides and the endothelins are being extended in the characterization of the actions of another family of vasoactive hormones described, the preproadrenomedullin-derived peptides. In the five years since their initial discovery, these peptides have been demonstrated to exert powerful pharmacologic effects on fluid and electrolyte homeostasis and cardiovascular function, some with apparent physiologic relevance.

Discovery and Gene Cloning

While screening extracts of a pheochromocytoma for novel bioactive peptides, a group headed by Eto (2) (1993), identified a 52-amino acid peptide that stimulated adenylyl cyclase activity in a platelet bioassay. The peptide, named adrenomedullin (AM), also lowered blood pressure following intravenous infusion in rats. These two actions of AM were similar to those of its structural homolog calcitonin gene-related peptide (CGRP). Until recently (see below), confusion over these shared biologic activities and close structural homology raised doubt about the physiologic relevance of AM; however, unique AM receptors exist (3, 4) and many of the actions of AM are not recapitulated by CGRP.

Since a pheochromocytoma was the source for sequence identification, the AM gene was cloned from a cDNA library from the same tissue (5). Surpisingly, two vasoactive hormones are encoded by the precursor 185-amino acid prohormone (Figure 1). In the N-terminal portion, the 20-amino acid proadrenomedullin N-terminal 20 peptide (PAMP) is located adjacent to a 21-amino acid signal peptide. The signal peptide is removed by cleavage between the threonine in position 21 and the alanine in position 22, resulting in formation of a 164-amino acid prohormone. Subsequent cleavage between the lysine at position 43, and arginine at position 44, liberates PAMP. The final post-translational modification of the prohormone in the human involves enzymatic cleavage between positions 93 and 94 (lysine-arginine) and 148 and 149 (lysine-lysine), resulting in the formation of a 52-amino acid circulating form of AM.

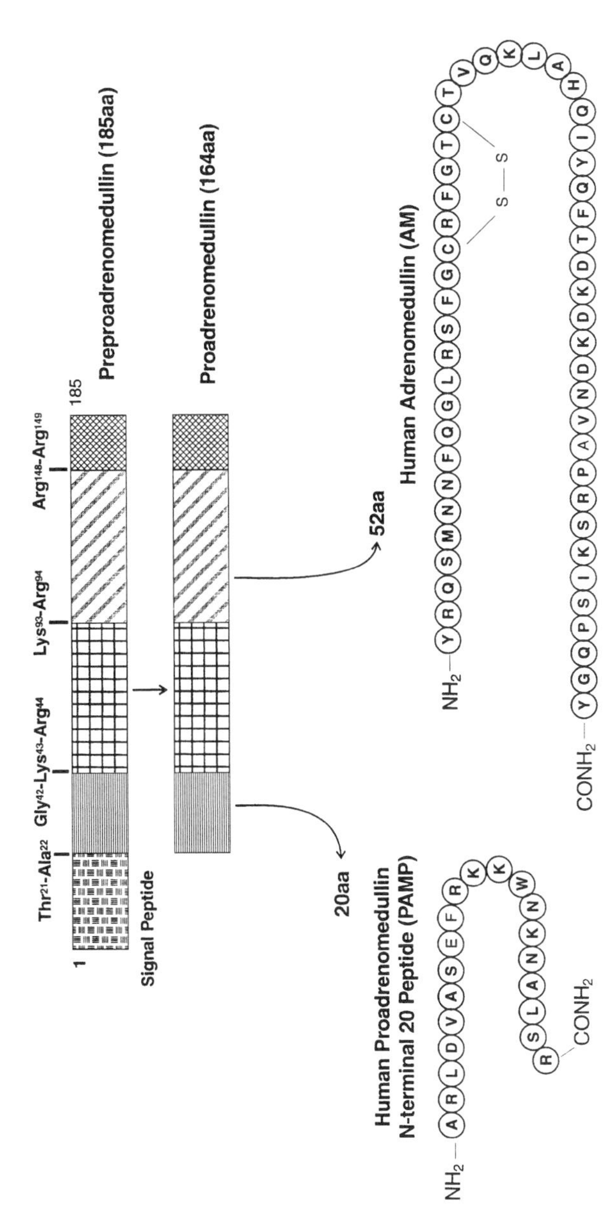

Figure 1 Post-translational processing of the human preproadrenomedullin gene product.

To date, with the exception of shortened forms of PAMP and AM, no other post-translational product of the preproAM gene is known to possess biologic activity.

The human AM gene, located on chromosome 11, consists of four exons and three introns (6), and contains upstream activator protein-2 (AP-2) and cAMP-regulated enhancer sequences. Among species the coding sequence and the level of peptide homology are similar (7). Rat AM differs from human in only six positions and is 50 amino acids in length. Human and rat PAMP are 20 amino acids in length and differ in three positions. Human preproadrenomedullin-derived peptides are biologically active in the rat.

Sites of Production

Originally identified in pheochromocytoma and normal adrenal medulla (2), AM gene products have been detected in numerous tissues including adrenal cortex, kidney, lung, heart, spleen, small intestine, salivary gland, and brain (8–12). The most abundant transcription is observed (13) in endothelial cells (ECs), and therefore ECs and vascular smooth muscle cells (VSMCs) have been utilized for transcriptional regulation studies (14–16). An even broader distribution of preproadrenomedullin-derived peptide production is suggested by radioimmunoassay and immunohistochemical studies, but some of the tissue localization [human (8–10, 14, 17–19), rat (10, 13, 14, 16, 20, 21), pig (10), dog (22)] may be due to blood vessels in the organ analyzed (Table 1).

Table 1 Tissue localization of AM-like immunoreactivity[a]

Tissue/organ	Man	Rat	Pig	Dog
Adrenal medulla	+	+	+	—
Blood vessels	+	+	—	+
Kidney	+	+	—	+
Anterior pituitary	+	+	+	—
Hypothalamus	+	+	—	—
Heart	+	+	—	—
Lung	+	+	—	+
Thyroid	+	+	—	—
Submandibular gland	—	+	—	—
Liver	+	+	—	—
Pancreas	+	+	+	—
Stomach	+	+	+	—
Intestine	+	+	+	—
Testis	—	+	—	—
Choroid plexus	+	+	+	—

[a]See text for references.

Table 2 Human pathologies displaying increased circulating levels or increased tissue production of adrenomedullin[a]

Essential hypertension (23, 31, 32)	Liver disease with ascites (37, 38)
Pulmonary hypertension (33, 34)	Renal failure (25, 31, 37)
Heart failure (18)	Thyrotoxicosis (39)
Hypertrophic obstructive cardiomyopathy (35)	Acute asthma (40)
Myocardial infarction (36)	Septic shock (41, 42)

[a]References are indicated in parentheses.

Although the factors appear to have local paracrine or autocrine actions, within the tissue of origin, AM and PAMP also circulate in plasma, and intravenous administration of exogenous peptide elicits significant pharmacologic effects. Thus these peptides may, in certain circumstances, function as circulating hormones. In humans, AM and PAMP circulate in the low pg/ml range (23–25). The plasma half-life of AM is estimated to be approximately 22 min, the metabolic clearance rate 27.4 ml/kg/min, and the volume of distribution is just under 900 ml/kg (26). Similar plasma levels have been reported in experimental animals. It is not known whether plasma levels reflect tissue spillover into the circulation or physiologic secretion, but the peptides are released from organ culture and from cell preparations (20, 27–29). However, arterio-venous concentration gradients across organ systems have not been demonstrated (30). Thus the elevated plasma levels of AM observed in human disease states (18, 23, 25, 31, 32–42) (Table 2) may merely reflect tissue damage and not physiologic compensatory mechanisms, with one exception. That exception is sepsis, in which the plasma levels of AM not only correlate with hypotension (41) but also predict survival rates (42). As described below, proinflammatory cytokines stimulate AM gene transcription and hormone release (16). Thus in septic shock, AM may, in part, be a chemical mediator of the pathology, although additional cardiac and neural actions exerted by the high circulating levels of the peptide may protect against cardiovascular collapse (35, 43, 44).

Control of Transcription

Physical factors such as volume overload (21, 45) and rapid ventricular pacing (46) can activate AM gene transcription, but by far the best characterized activators are cytokines and growth factors. In cultured VSMCs, lipopolysaccharide (LPS), interleukin-1 (IL-1), and tumor necrosis factor (TNF) alpha stimulate AM gene transcription (16). This is most likely mediated via induction of the transcription factor, nuclear factor for interleukin-6 expression (NF-IL6) (47). TNF alpha and IL-1 also stimulate AM synthesis in cultured mesangial cells

(16). Intravenous administration of LPS lowers blood pressure and elevates plasma levels of AM (48), analogous to elevations in hormone levels observed in sepsis in humans (41, 42). In rats, LPS administration elevates AM gene expression in aorta, lung, adrenal gland, skeletal and cardiac muscle, ileum/jejunum, brain, kidney, and submaxillary gland (48). Thus the global, vasodilatory effect of endotoxins may be due to recruitment of locally produced AM.

Induction of AP-2, secondary to activation of phospholipase C and protein kinase C, may be the mechanism by which growth factors such as fibroblast growth factor and platelet- and epidermal-derived growth factors stimulate transcription of the AM gene (47) in VSMCs. In neonatal cardiomyocytes, the promitogenic actions of angiotensin II and fetal bovine serum are accompanied by stimulations of AM gene transcription (49). Interferon gamma and IL-1 beta increase AM gene transcription in glial cell tumors (50) and astrocytes (51). Other stimulators of AM gene transcription include retinoic acid, mineralo- and glucocorticoids, and thyroid hormones (14). The effects of the thyroid hormones in culture may be reflected in vivo by the elevated circulating levels of AM in thyrotoxicosis (39). Transcription of the AM gene is inhibited in cultured VSMCs by cAMP and transforming growth factor beta (14) and in glioma cells by TNF alpha (50).

CELLULAR BIOLOGY OF ADRENOMEDULLIN

The pharmacologic actions of AM initially were thought to be mediated through the CGRP receptor because the two peptides share significant structural homology and because the CGRP antagonist, $CGRP_{8\text{-}37}$ can block some actions of AM.

Receptors

The vasorelaxant effect of AM in cerebral arterioles (52–54) and mesenteric arteries (55, 56) is blocked by the CGRP antagonist. On the other hand, the blood pressure lowering effect of infused AM is not blocked by $CGRP_{8\text{-}37}$ (57–59), nor is its action to increase renal blood flow in isolated or in situ kidney preparations blocked (58, 60). The concept that only some of the biologic actions of AM are expressed via the CGRP receptor was confirmed with demonstration of the ability of the $CGRP_1$ receptor subtype to bind AM, with low affinity (61). In contrast, the AM receptor (3) apparently does not bind CGRP (62). The AM receptor is coupled, via a cholera-toxin sensitive G protein, to adenylyl cyclase and phospholipase C (63). A second, non-adenylyl cyclase–linked subtype of AM receptor may be present in anterior pituitary cells (64), in which the biologic action of AM, inhibition of basal and stimulated hormone secretion, is not associated with an activation of adenylyl cyclase. Little is known of the identity of the PAMP receptor(s), but PAMP binds specifically to a 90-kDa protein (65).

Mechanisms of Action

While originally thought to signal solely via activation of adenylyl cyclase, AM receptors are also linked to ion channels and to a variety of second messenger systems through direct effects on G protein–coupled enzymes. As with other vasoactive hormones, the phenotype of the receptive cell determines the second messenger pathway activated by hormone binding (Figure 2). In bovine aortic endothelial cells (63), AM activates adenylyl cyclase and phospholipase C via a cholera toxin–sensitive G protein mechanism. Cytosolic calcium concentrations rise initially as a result of IP_3 generation and are maintained by opening of a calcium channel in the cell membrane. These increased cytosolic calcium levels may then activate nitric oxide synthase (NOS); a direct G protein–mediated pathway for NOS activation may also exist (63).

In other tissues mobilization of intracellular and extracellular calcium ions does not appear to rely upon activation of adenylyl cyclase. The fact that inhibition of protein kinase A failed to block the positive inotropic effect of AM in isolated rat hearts (66) suggests that the procontractile action of AM is the result of cAMP-independent calcium mobilization, probably via protein kinase C activation, since staurosporine and ryanodine block the contractile response. Furthermore, depletion of intracellular calcium stores with thapsigargin attenuates the early phase of tension development, and the L-type calcium channel blocker diltiazem reduces the sustained increase in tension development caused by AM. Thus AM appears to exert positive inotropic effects in heart via mobilization of both intracellular and extracellular calcium ions.

Additional, cAMP-dependent and -independent actions of AM have been identified. Inhibition of platelet-derived growth factor-stimulated mesangial cell proliferation appears to be due to an action of AM to inhibit the mitogen-activated protein kinase (MAPK) pathway, perhaps because of phosphorylation of the Raf-1 protein kinase (67). Not all of the actions of AM are antimitogenic, however. In vascular smooth muscle cells, AM stimulates tyrosine phosphorylation and cell proliferation via a cAMP-independent mechanism (68). Genistein and ST638 block the proliferative effect, linking the activation of protein tyrosine kinase(s) to this mitogenic action. Cell proliferation in this model also depends on MAPK activation because the effect is blocked by PD98059, a potent MAPK inhibitor. A similar mechanism may underlie the ability of AM to inhibit basal- and corticotropin-releasing hormone (CRH)-stimulated adrenocorticotropin (ACTH) release (64).

Some of the vasodilatory effects of AM may be due to interaction with potassium channels. In coronary artery, AM interacts with the adenosine receptor,

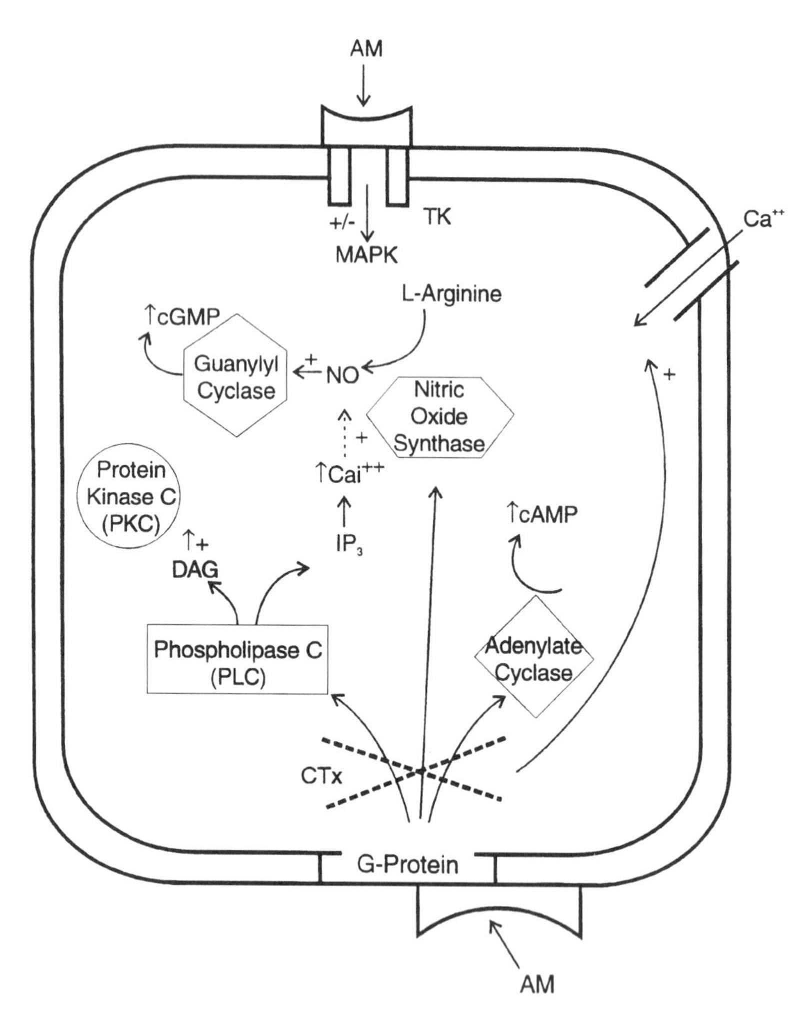

Figure 2 Schematic representation of the cellular signaling mechanisms for adrenomedullin (AM). NO, nitric oxide; cGMP, cyclic guanosine monophosphate; cAMP, cyclic adenosine monophosphate; IP_3, inositol triphosphate; DAG, diacyl glycerol; CTx, cholera toxin; TK, tyrosine kinase; MAPK, mitogen-activated protein kinase; Cai^{++}, cytosolic calcium.

which results in activation of ATP-sensitive potassium channels (69). Glibenclamide, an inhibitor of ATP-sensitive potassium channels, and iberiotoxin, an inhibitor of calcium-dependent potassium channels, both block the ability of AM to dilate rat cerebral arterioles. On the other hand, glibenclamide does not block the vasodilatory effect of AM in canine retinal arteries (70), and the peripheral hypotensive effects of AM in cat and rat are not antagonized by the ATP-sensitive potassium channel blocker U-37883A (71).

The hypotensive effect of PAMP appears to be mediated primarily by a presynaptic effect on sympathetic terminals that innervate the vasculature (72). Norepinephrine overflow induced by periarterial nerve stimulation is inhibited by PAMP, and this inhibition is not blocked by $CRGP_{8\text{-}37}$, yohimbine, or hexamethonium, thus suggesting a direct effect of the peptide on membrane polarization. The inhibitory effect is attenuated in the rat treated with pertussis toxin, indicating a G protein–signaling mechanism. Within the adrenal medulla, PAMP exerts an autocrine effect to inhibit catecholamine release by attenuating carbachol-induced epinephrine release (20). Although the exact mechanism is unclear, PAMP reduces the ability of carbachol to stimulate sodium and calcium influx in these cells and further reduces the response of tyrosine hydroxylase to nicotinic stimulation. In PC-12 cells, which are derived from pheochromocytoma, PAMP inhibits voltage-gated (N-type) calcium channels via a pertussis toxin-sensitive mechanism (73). Pertussis toxin also blocks the ability of PAMP to open inwardly rectifying potassium channels in these cells (Figure 3). Preliminary evidence in the author's laboratory indicates involvement of a potassium channel in the inhibition of adrenocorticotropin release by PAMP as well (74).

INTEGRATIVE PHYSIOLOGY OF ADRENOMEDULLIN

Two hallmark actions of adrenomedullin, hypotension and diuresis/natriuresis, suggest that the preproadrenomedullin-derived peptides play a role in the physiologic regulation of fluid and electrolyte homeostasis. Multiple pharmacologic studies of both AM and PAMP support such roles; however, to date only one experimental paradigm, salt appetite (75), has revealed a physiologically relevant action of AM. It is known that AM and PAMP can exert multiple pharmacologic effects in a variety of tissues all contributing to homeostatic mechanisms regulating plasma volume and composition. To date, only limited and relatively weak peptide antagonists for AM are available, and limited studies have been done with an overexpression model (76, 77). It has been established, however, that AM exerts physiologically relevant control over salt and water intake (75, 78) and possibly on the output of salt and water as well. A role for

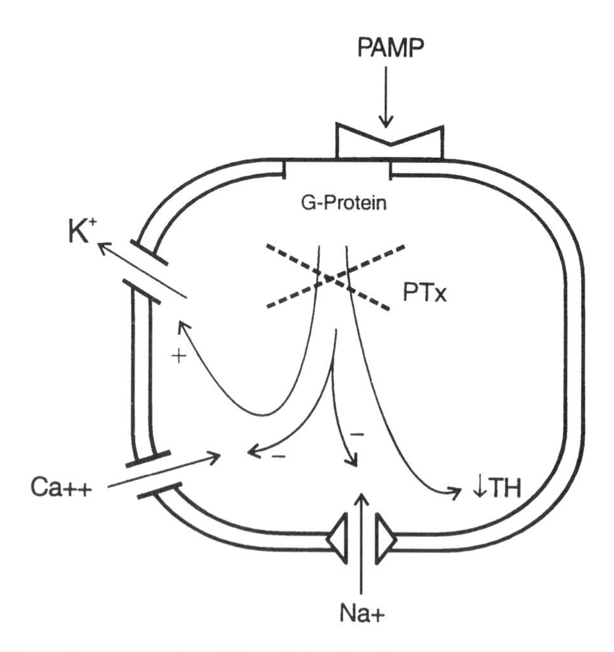

Figure 3 Schematic representation of the cellular signaling mechanisms for proadrenomedullin N-terminal 20 peptide (PAMP). PTx, pertussis toxin; TH, tyrosine hydroxylase; K^+, potassium ion; Ca^{++}, calcium ion; Na^+, sodium ion.

AM or PAMP in the day-to-day regulation of cardiovascular function has not established but may be significant (79).

Renal Actions

The initial studies of the effects of AM on renal function employed direct intrarenal arterial infusion in anesthetized dogs (80). Renal blood flow (RBF), urine flow, and urinary sodium excretion increased in a dose-related fashion, without changes in heart rate or mean arterial blood pressure, indicating direct renovascular and tubular effects. In subsequent studies it was found that the effects of AM on RBF were mediated by nitric oxide (81). In the anesthetized rat, intrarenal AM infusion increases RBF, arterial conductance, glomerular filtration (GFR), urine flow, and sodium excretion (58, 82, 83), effects that are not blocked by the CGRP antagonist (82). When AM was infused peripherally in the anesthetized rat, even in the face of significant decreases in mean arterial pressure, the increases in RBF and urine flow were maintained (83). Those increases in RBF, GFR and urine flow were correlated with increased NO release within the kidney (84).

However, it is unlikely that circulating levels of AM physiologically regulate renal function because the threshold for renal actions in rats and humans

(22, 85) exceeds that for the vascular actions of the peptide. Instead, it is believed that AM exerts local, paracrine, or autocrine effects. Renal artery smooth muscle cells express AM mRNA, and AM can decrease the tension and calcium mobilization in these cells following exposure to phenylephrine (86). In the dog, AM-like immunoreactivity is present in glomeruli, cortical distal tubules, and medullary collecting duct cells (22). A role for endogenous, locally produced AM in renal function is supported by glomerular and tubular localization, and by the finding that intrarenal infusion of AM in dogs increases GFR and fractional sodium excretion, while decreasing distal tubular sodium reabsorption (22, 87). Evidence for a paracrine effect of AM in kidney was obtained by Owada and colleagues who showed that AM mRNA is localized in glomerulus, cortical collecting ducts, and outer medullary and inner medullary collecting ducts (88). In microdissected nephron segments, cAMP accumulation was stimulated by AM only in those segments where AM mRNA is present. Furthermore, the glomerular production of AM was accompanied by significant stimulation of adenylyl cyclase activity by the peptides. The localization of AM mRNA in inner medullary collecting duct correlated with the capacity of AM to increase water permeability in the tissue. These findings support the hypothesis that locally generated AM plays an important role in the regulation of GFR and the tubular handling of sodium and water.

In addition to its potential role in altering mesangial cell (MC) contraction, AM can block mitogen-stimulated MC proliferation. Activation of MAPK and of cell proliferation by platelet-derived growth factor (PDGF) is also inhibited by pretreatment of cells with AM (67), probably due to the stimulation by AM of a mitogen-activated protein kinase phosphatase (89) and subsequent stimulation of cAMP accumulation and PKA activity (67). In addition, the stimulation by PDGF of the production of endothelin-1, a known MC mitogen, is inhibited by AM (90). A role for endogenous AM in the protection against immuno-inflammatory injury of the glomeruli has also been proposed as a consequence of the demonstration that TNF alpha and IL-1 beta stimulate MC production of AM and that, via a PKA-dependent mechanism, AM inhibits the generation of reactive oxygen metabolites in both MCs and macrophages (91). AM inhibits MC proliferation via a MAPK-dependent mechanism (91). Thus AM in MCs may play an important role, one that would be difficult to demonstrate in whole-animal studies.

Adrenomedullin may also control endocrine function of the kidney. In whole-animal studies, the ability of AM to elevate circulating levels of renin was thought to be secondary to the hypotensive action of the peptide, but studies employing isolated, perfused rat kidneys and cultured mouse juxtaglomerular cells demonstrate (92) that AM can stimulate renin secretion directly via a cAMP-dependent mechanism.

Regardless of whether these pharmacologic effects on renal function are physiologically relevant, they may have therapeutic significance. In an ovine model of congestive heart failure (CHF), intravenous administration of AM improves cardiac performance and increases urinary sodium excretion, while maintaining urine output even in the face of a significant fall in mean arterial pressure (79). Thus AM may be useful clinically for the reduction of cardiac pre- and afterload and for the re-establishment of a normal vascular volume.

Adrenal Actions

Binding sites for both AM and PAMP are present in outer cortex and medulla of the human adrenal gland (93). In cortex, AM binding can be displaced by the CGRP antagonist, but PAMP binding is not displaced by $CGRP_{8\text{-}37}$. The stimulation of aldosterone release from dispersed human adrenal cells by angiotensin II and potassium is significantly inhibited by both peptides. The effects of AM are less potent than those of PAMP, and AM's actions are antagonized by $CGRP_{8\text{-}37}$ (94, 95). As in human cells, AM inhibits AII- and potassium-stimulated, but not basal- or ACTH-stimulated, aldosterone release from rat adrenal cells in culture, an effect mirrored by agents that elevate cellular levels of cAMP (96). Inhibition of aldosterone action by AM has been demonstrated in two rat models of sodium dishomeostasis (97). Thus in vitro actions of AM on mineralocorticoid secretion can also occur in vivo. Direct effects of AM on ACTH-stimulated glucocorticoid secretion were not observed (98) in cultured cells, but intravenous AM infusion lowers circulating cortisol levels and ACTH in sheep (99). AM and PAMP also have direct effects on ACTH secretion from dispersed pituitary cells in vitro (64, 74).

In cultured bovine adrenal medullary cells, carbachol releases both catecholamines and PAMP in a molar ratio equal to that present in the cells (20). Addition of exogenous PAMP to cultured medullary cells inhibits carbachol-induced sodium influx, thereby decreasing calcium influx through voltage-dependent calcium channels and ultimately decreasing catecholamine release. Tyrosine hydroxylase activity is also reduced in the presence of PAMP, indicating that the peptide alters production and release of catecholamines. In PC-12 cells, PAMP reduces tyrosine hydrolyase mRNA levels and norepinephrine overflow and inhibits cell growth via a pertussis toxin–sensitive mechanism (100). Pertussis toxin–sensitive mechanisms also underlie the inhibition by PAMP of voltage-gated calcium currents and inhibition of the hyperpolarization caused by activation of an inwardly rectifying potassium current in these cells (73). Thus PAMP acts within the adrenal medulla, as in the peripheral vasculature, to reduce catecholamine release in response to sympathetic activation. These actions, together with the demonstrated abilities of AM to desensitize the baroreceptor reflex and relax vascular smooth muscle, reveal the broad potential for the preproadrenomedullin-derived peptides to contribute to the physiologic regulation of cardiovascular homeostasis.

Cardiovascular Actions

In cat, rat, rabbit, sheep and humans, intravenous infusion of AM causes prolonged hypotension (38, 43, 59, 85, 99, 101–106), largely through the generation of NO in the vasculature (81, 84, 101). In canine arteries, AM-induced relaxation occurs in the absence and in the presence of the endothelium (107) and is accompanied by an increase in cAMP accumulation. Furthermore, the effect of AM in these arteries is blocked by the CGRP antagonist. In canine veins, however, the relaxant effect is endothelium dependent but independent of cyclic nucleotide generation, NO production, indomethacin-sensitive prostanoids, TEA-sensitive hyperpolarizing factors, and oxygen free radical generation (107). The effect in veins is not blocked by the CGRP antagonist.

There is marked individuality in these responses among species. In the systemic vascular beds of the rat and cat (71), AM and PAMP are vasodilatory, and the effect of AM can be blocked by $CGRP_{8\text{-}37}$. In rat pulmonary and hindlimb vasculature the vasodilatory effect of AM, but not PAMP, is blocked by pretreatment with the false substrate for nitric oxide, N^G-nitro-L-arginine methyl ester (L-NAME). On the other hand, in the cat the vasodilatory action of AM is not blocked by false substrates for NOS, and the fact that the duration of vasodilation is prolonged in the presence of the type V cAMP phosphodiesterase inhibitor, rolipram, suggests that it is cAMP mediated (71, 108). The effect in the cat may be unique (indeed, the cat may be a unique species) because, unlike the response in the rat (71), the effect of PAMP does not appear to depend upon the presence of sympathetic innervation of the blood vessel (109).

In addition to influencing the contractile state of the blood vessels, AM may prevent pathologic vascular remodeling. In rat VSMCs, enhancement in thymidine incorporation and cell number by fetal calf serum is inhibited by AM (110). In cultured human coronary artery cells, angiotensin II (AII) -stimulated cell migration is inhibited by AM (111), suggesting a role for locally produced peptide in restraining the intimal thickening of coronary atherosclerosis. Tumor necrosis factor alpha, IL-1 beta, and lysophosphatidylcholine (lyso-PC) (a major component of low-density lipoproteins) stimulate oxidative stress and the generation of oxygen radicals. In turn, oxygen radicals stimulate AM release (112). Similarily, shear stress elevates AM production and release (17). The release of AM in response to oxidative and shear stress may mediate the promotion of vasodilation and inhibition cell growth by endothelial cells (113). In fact lyso-PC stimulates migration of human coronary artery smooth muscle cells, probably by stimulating local production and release of basic fibroblast growth factor (112). These effects of lyso-PC are blocked by AM in parallel with cAMP accumulation in those cells. Thus oxidized LDL may stimulate coronary atherosclerosis, and locally generated AM may be an endogenous protective factor that restrains the migration of coronary smooth muscle cells during oxidative stress.

Although AM is antimitogenic in most cells (110, 112), promitogenic actions have been described (68). AM stimulates DNA synthesis and cell proliferation in quiescent rat VSMCs. The effect, which is blocked by the CGRP antagonist, is not mediated via activation of adenylyl cyclase or by changes in intracellular calcium levels. Instead, this action of AM is mediated via increased MAPK activity secondary to enhanced tyrosine phosphorylation, because PTK inhibitors such as genistein and ST638 block the increases in MAPK activity and in cell proliferation (68). This apparent paradox of anti- and promitogenic actions may be dependent on cell type or alternatively reflect the stage in cell cycle encountered by AM under the varying experimental conditions. Another action of AM in EC is suppression of apoptosis (114), perhaps contributing in vivo to the inhibition of pathologic vascular remodeling.

Tumor necrosis factor, IL-1, and lipopolysaccharide stimulate AM production and secretion from ECs and VSMCs and enhance AM secretion by macrophages and monocytes (16, 115), which possibly explains the fact plasma AM levels are elevated almost 50-fold in septic shock. The fact that circulating levels of AM correlate well with TNF alpha levels again indicates that endogenous AM is recruited during sepsis. In septic shock, plasma levels of AM correlate inversely with mean arterial and diastolic blood pressures (41). In fact, plasma AM levels correlate positively with severity of the illness and predict survival in these patients (41, 42). This protective effect of AM is mirrored in transgenic animals in which AM is expressed (77). In addition to having lower mean arterial blood pressure than their wild-type litter mates, mice that over express AM have enhanced hypertensive response to false substrates for NOS, the survival rate following LPS administration is enhanced, and less hemorrhagic liver damage is observed. These findings suggest that AM may have a therapeutic use in treatment of shock.

Transcription of the AM gene in heart is enhanced by hormonal (49, 116), genetic (117), and physical (21, 45, 46) factors. As in other tissues, AM may act in heart to inhibit cell growth and hypertrophy (49). In cardiac myocytes, AM inhibits AII-stimulated protein synthesis (118), increases immediate early gene expression (49), and down regulates ANP gene expression, while stimulating cAMP accumulation (119). Both myocyte and non-myocyte cells produce AM, and AM gene transcription is stimulated by IL-1 beta (120). Pressure overload elevates left ventricular content of AM mRNA and protein (66) in isolated, perfused rat hearts and in pressure overloaded rat hearts in vivo (21). AM mRNA levels in canine ventricle also increase in vivo during rapid ventricular pacing (46). Circulating levels of AM are elevated in human models of cardiac overload (18, 35), and in pressure overload in sheep, intravenous infusions of AM decrease total peripheral resistance, mean arterial pressure, and left atrial pressure. Cardiac output increased, as did urinary sodium excretion and flow, while plasma aldosterone levels fell. In humans with heart failure (85), AM infusion decreased systolic and diastolic blood pressure, increased heart rate, increased renin levels, and decreased plasma aldosterone levels.

Infusion of AM into sheep causes hypotension, tachycardia, increased cardiac output, and increased force of cardiac contractility (99, 104). The increased heart rate is not secondary to the hypotension, because increased cardiac contractility is also observed when pressure is maintained constant (104). In addition, the sympathetic response to a fall in blood pressure caused by AM infusion is less than that induced by sodium nitroprusside, suggesting that AM dampens the baroreceptor reflex (102). Direct cardiac effects of AM have been demonstrated in isolated heart preparations and during pharmacologic blockade in conscious sheep. Ruskoaho and co-workers (66, 121) have shown that AM exerts positive inotropic effects in isolated rat hearts that are not blocked by $CGRP_{8\text{-}37}$ or the cAMP-dependent protein kinase inhibitor H-89. The development of tension was reduced by pretreatment with ryanodine or thapsigargin, indicating mobilization of calcium from the sarcoplasmic reticulum during the initial contractile phase. The plateau phase of contraction was reduced by staurosporine and diltiazem pretreatment, indicating that the sustained phase of contraction depends upon protein kinase C activation and opening of L-type calcium channels. In conscious sheep the positive inotropic effects of AM are still present during alpha and beta adrenergic blockade and are enhanced under muscarinic blockade. The direct, cardiostimulatory effects of AM may be protective, preventing vascular collapse during the severe hypotension that often accompanies septic shock. In that condition, plasma levels of AM remain elevated until the inflammatory stimulus has resolved (41, 42), and in the transgenic animal that over expresses AM, elevated plasma levels of AM predict survival outcome (77).

Other Peripheral Effects

In addition to pulmonary vasodilation, AM inhibits bronchoconstriction in response to acetylcholine and histamine (122), suggesting a physiologic role for the elevated plasma levels of the peptide observed in acute asthma attacks (40). The vasodilatory effects of AM may also serve to protect the pulmonary circulation of patients with pulmonary hypertension (33, 34). Finally, endogenous AM may play an anti-inflammatory role in lung. Neutrophil chemoattractant release from cytokine-challenged alveolar macrophages is inhibited by AM (123).

Some, but not all, immunohistochemical localization studies have demonstrated AM in pancreas (11, 25, 124). Locally produced or circulating AM might modulate insulin secretion because the peptide stimulates insulin release in the presence of 3.3 nmol/L glucose and potentiates the insulin response to 8.3 nmol/L glucose (124). Increased plasma AM levels have been observed in a number of malignancies, and AM stimulates increased thymidine incorporation and cell proliferation in cultured fetal rat osteoblasts and mouse calvaria, suggesting that, like its structural homolog amylin, AM may regulate bone formation osteoporosis (125).

Pituitary Actions

The anterior pituitary gland of numerous species (11, 25), including humans (25, 126), contains immunoreactive AM, and AM mRNA is present in human anterior pituitary gland (126). Because the magnocellular paraventricular and supraoptic nuclei of the hypothalamus contain abundant AM-like immunoreactivity, it is assumed that significant amounts of AM are also present in the posterior lobe of the pituitary (9, 12). Within the anterior lobe, PAMP immunoreactivity is present in gonadotrophs (127). AM binds to pituitary membranes, but this binding may not be specific since both amylin and CGRP can displace AM from these sites (62). In vivo and in vitro studies suggest that AM and PAMP receptors are expressed in the corticotrophs. Intravenous but not intracerebroventricular administration of AM to conscious sheep lowers circulating levels of ACTH (99). This lowering occurs even in the face of the peripheral hypotension, suggesting a direct pituitary site of action. In dispersed rat anterior pituitary cells in culture, AM inhibits basal and corticotropin-releasing hormone (CRH)-stimulated ACTH secretion, in a dose-related fashion (64). The effect is specific for the corticotroph because the release of luteinizing hormone and growth hormone is unaffected. The ACTH-inhibiting action of AM is not mediated via interaction with the cloned AM receptor (3) since the peptide does not significantly alter basal or CRH-stimulated cAMP accumulation (64). Additionally, AM does not alter the activity of guanylyl cyclase or NOS, and its action is not blocked by $CGRP_{8-37}$.

The rat pituitary gland contains ~1.12 pmol AM/mg wet weight (11), and the human gland contains tenfold higher amounts of peptide (126). The doses of AM that effectively inhibit basal ACTH secretion (10-100 pM, or 57.3-573 pg/ml) approximate the range of peptide levels in the rat anterior pituitary gland (50-100 pg/gland). This suggests that endogenous, locally produced AM has a role in the regulation of corticotroph function.

We have also demonstrated that PAMP influences corticotroph function (74). The inhibitory effect of PAMP on ACTH secretion is similar to that of AM in terms of effective dose and action on basal hormone secretion but differs in that PAMP does not abrogate CRH-stimulated ACTH secretion. In the case of PAMP, the inhibitory effect is reversed by glibenclamide, suggesting an action of the peptide on ATP-sensitive potassium channels. Thus AM and PAMP may exert complementary actions in the pituitary gland, as they do in the periphery, via parallel signaling mechanisms. Additionally, the pituitary actions of AM and PAMP appear to integrate with the major peripheral actions of the two hormones to modulate fluid and electrolyte homeostasis.

One might predict that the diuretic action of AM in kidney would be matched by a hypothalamic or direct posterior pituitary effect to inhibit vasopressin (AVP) release. Indeed, magnocellular neurons of the paraventricular and supraoptic nuclei that project to the neural lobe contain substantial amounts of AM (9, 12). However, in normal sheep, intracerebroventricular (icv) injection of AM does not significantly alter AVP secretion (99). But when plasma levels of AVP are experimentally elevated, an inhibitory effect of AM or AVP secretion can be observed. Indeed, in hypovolemic or hypernatremic rats (128), icv administration of AM significantly lowers the experimentally elevated plasma levels of AM. It remains to be seen whether this central effect of AM can be demonstrated in other species and whether this effect has physiologic relevance. An inhibitory effect of the peptide under conditions in which the physiology would predict a stimulatory action is difficult to reconcile. It may be that only under conditions of elevated secretion of AVP in the brain is it possible to detect a physiologically relevant action of AM on AVP release. Indeed, an inhibitory effect of AM on AVP release would make physiologic sense under conditions of volume excess, since in the periphery, the peptide acts to dilate the vasculature, producing central venous pressure, and to inhibit sodium (and therefore water) reabsorption via direct renal action.

Central Nervous System Actions

For many vasoactive peptides, central nervous system (CNS) actions complement or parallel their peripheral effects (1). For example, atrial natriuretic peptide exerts natriuretic and diuretic effects in kidney and acts within the CNS to inhibit AVP release, water drinking, and salt appetite (129–131). Thus when it became apparent that the AM gene is transcribed in the brain (5), it was predicted that CNS actions of AM and PAMP might complement their effects in the periphery. Indeed, the natriuretic and diuretic effects of AM in kidney are matched by CNS actions to inhibit water drinking (78) and salt appetite (75) under circumstances in which food intake is not significantly altered. The CNS action of AM on salt appetite and water drinking is the first biologic effect of the peptide shown to be physiologically relevant. While exogenous peptide inhibits these behaviors, neutralization of endogenously produced AM by anti-AM antibodies administered into the brain (i.e. passive immuno-neutralization) results in exaggerated salt and water intake (75). These effects of AM on appetite are not shared by PAMP, which is not surprising because PAMP does not exert natriuretic or diuretic actions.

As in the periphery, AM exerts profound effects on the vasculature of the brain. Increases in cerebral blood flow after the administration of AM are blocked by the CGRP antagonist (54), suggesting that the effects may not be unique for AM. Nevertheless, these effects may be physiologically relevant. Central administration of AM blocks the decrease in cerebral blood flow that normally follows middle cerebral artery occlusion in spontaneously hypertensive rats (132). AM also increases total cerebral blood flow in this model. Thus AM may act to prevent ischemic brain damage by increasing collateral blood flow or by antagonizing the effects of procontractile factors in the cerebral vasculature.

The AM gene is transcribed in glia (50), AM binding sites are present on these cells (133), and addition of the peptide to glial cells increases cAMP accumulation (134). AM may also have antimitogenic actions in normal and hybrid glioma cells (133). Thus, as in the periphery, the peptide may exert antigrowth effects that protect against proliferative stimuli. However, it has also been suggested that AM may exert mitogenic effects in C6 glioma cell cultures (135).

The hypotensive actions of AM and PAMP in the periphery are not mirrored by similar effects in the brain. In fact, both peptides exert significant, dose-related hypertensive actions when administered in the cerebral ventricles (44). The central hypertensive action of AM was demonstrated in rats anesthetized with urethane (136) and not confirmed in animals anesthetized with inactin (78). Direct effects of AM on neuronal firing rates of cardiovascular regulatory neurons were observed (137) in slice preparations of area postrema, and application of AM to the area postrema caused significant effects in animals anesthetized with urethane (138). Studies were then carried out in conscious, freely moving rats in order to avoid the complications of anesthesia.

Administration of AM into either the lateral or fourth cerebral ventricle elevates blood pressure in conscious, unrestrained rats (44). The effect is dose related and not blocked by the CGRP antagonist, which is not surprising since CGRP at similar doses does not alter blood pressure in these rats. Interestingly, the administration of PAMP, at similar doses, into the lateral cerebroventricle also elevates blood pressure (44). The exact site of action of AM and PAMP in brain is not known; however, the rapidity of the effect following lateral ventricle administration of peptide suggests a hypothalamic action, perhaps in the paraventricular nucleus (44).

The time course of blood pressure elevations with centrally administered AM and PAMP is similar to that seen following administration of AII (44), suggesting that the mechanisms underlying the hypertensive actions of these peptides in brain might be similar. Like the actions of AII, the hypertensive actions of both AM and PAMP in the CNS can be blocked by pretreatment of the animals with phentolamine (44). Thus AM and PAMP, similar to AII, act within brain to stimulate sympathetic nervous system function. A sympathetic nervous system mechanism may also explain the fact that the central administration of AM inhibits gastric emptying (139).

These similarities in mechanisms of action and duration of effects further suggest that preproadrenomedullin-derived peptides recruit endogenous AII within brain or at least interact with neuronal systems converging on angiotensinergic neurons in brain. This appears to be the case because pretreatment with the angiotensin receptor blocker saralasin, administered into the lateral cerebral ventricle, prevents the hypertensive action of centrally administered AII and that of PAMP (44). AM and PAMP probably act within brain on neuronal systems that converge on cells receptive to endogenous AII, most likely upstream of the AII-expressing neurons themselves. These central hypertensive actions of AM and PAMP may be cardioprotective, either counterbalancing their volume unloading effects in the periphery or acting to protect against circulatory collapse in conditions such as septic shock when circulating levels of AM are extremely elevated. Alternatively, centrally produced AM and PAMP may be part of a neuronal system that responds to all decreases in vascular volume, recruited in hypotensive crises to maintain vascular competence and adequate perfusion pressures to vital organs. Thus the CNS cardioprotective actions may be analogous to the positive inotropic effects of AM in the heart. Future studies must determine the mechanisms by which transcription of the AM gene is regulated in the brain and the stimuli that control peptide release. Similarly, the physiologic relevance of these CNS hypertensive actions must be addressed, perhaps by passive immunoneutralization or antisense approaches, before the role of these effects in the day-to-day regulation of cardiovascular homeostasis is established.

SUMMARY

The adrenomedullin gene encodes two biologically active peptides that exert multiple pharmacologic effects on fluid and electrolyte homeostasis (Figure 4). Diuretic and natriuretic effects of AM in the kidney are complemented by actions in the brain to inhibit water drinking, salt appetite, and vasopressin secretion. In the pituitary gland, AM and PAMP inhibit ACTH secretion, and aldosterone release from adrenal gland is also inhibited by both peptides. These actions, together with potent hypotensive effects in the periphery, make AM and PAMP candidates for physiologic regulators of vascular volume and electrolyte homeostasis. Equally intriguing are the potential antimitogenic effects of AM,

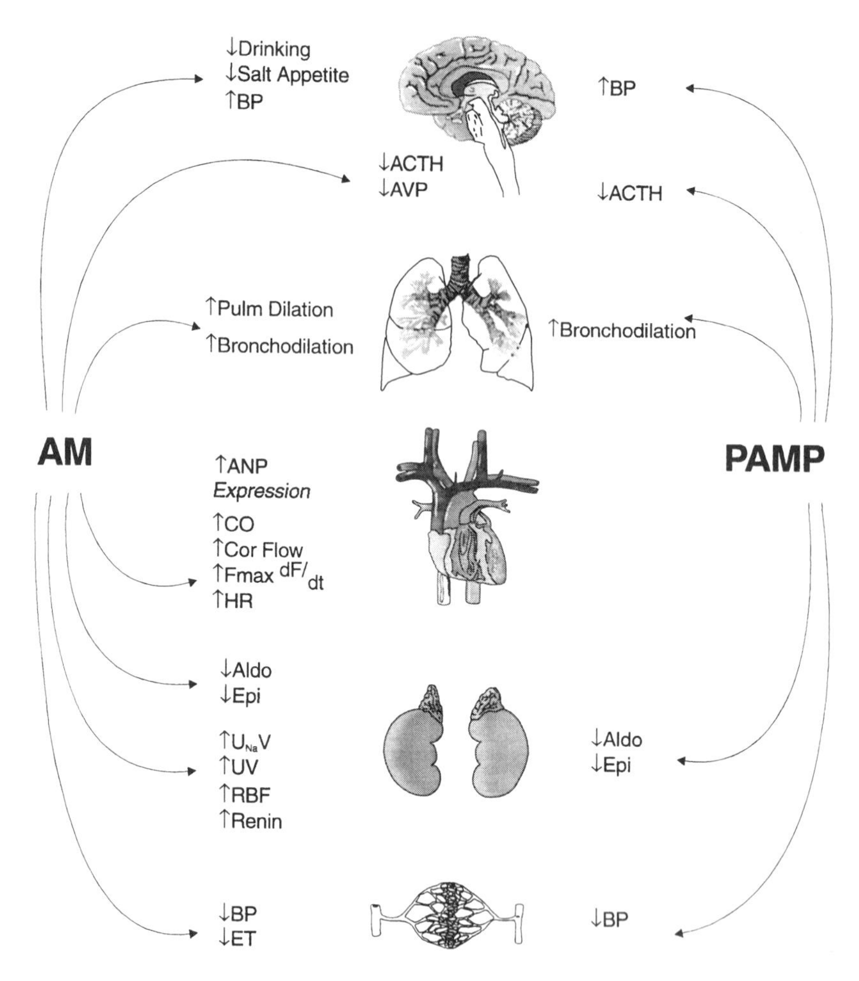

Figure 4 Multiple pharmacologic actions of adrenomedullin (AM) and proadrenomedullin N-terminal 20 peptide (PAMP). BP, blood pressure; ACTH, adrenocorticotropin; Aldo, aldosterone; Epi, epinephrine; ANP, atrial natriuretic peptide; CO, cardiac output; Fmax $^{dF}/_{dt}$, maximal coronary blood flow; HR, heart rate; $U_{na}V$, urinary sodium excretion; UV, urine volume; RBF, renal blood flow.

perhaps providing protection against proliferative vascular and kidney disease. Therapeutic strategies can be envisioned in which the peptides may provide protective advantage in congestive heart failure, sepsis, and ischemic brain injury. At least one pharmacologic action of AM, the inhibition of salt appetite, has been demonstrated to be physiologically relevant, and the protective effects of AM in the heart and perhaps of PAMP in both the heart and brain promise insight into mechanisms of protection against cardiovascular collapse. Clearly, the interaction of these peptides with other vasoactive hormones and their effects in multiple tissue systems suggest that the peptides have roles in the physiologic maintenance of fluid and electrolyte homeostasis.

ACKNOWLEDGMENTS

Studies in the author's laboratory on the physiology and pharmacology of the proadrenomedullin-derived peptides are supported by the Max Baer Heart Fund, Fraternal Order of Eagles.

Literature Cited

1. Samson WK. 1997. Cardiovascular hormones. In *Endocrinology, Basic and Clinical Principles*, ed. PM Conn, S Melmed, 361–76. Totowa, NJ: Humana. 448 pp.
2. Kitamura K, Kangawa K, Kawamoto M, Ichiki Y, Nakamura S, et al. 1993. Adrenomedullin: a novel hypotensive peptide isolated from human pheochromocytoma. *Biochem. Biophys. Res. Commun.* 192:553–60
3. Kapas S, Catt KJ, Clark AJL. 1995. Cloning and expression of cDNA encoding a rat adrenomedullin receptor. *J. Biol. Chem.* 270:25344–47
4. Smith DG, Owji AA, Coppock HA, Taylor GM, Ghatei MA, Bloom SR. 1998. *Characterization of adrenomedullin receptor binding*. Presented at 1st Intl. Symp. AM and PAMP, Osaka, Japan
5. Kitamura K, Sakata J, Kangawa K, Kojima H, Matsuo H, Eto T. 1993. Cloning and characterization of cDNA encoding a precursor for human adrenomedullin. *Biochem. Biophys. Res. Commun.* 194:720–25
6. Ishimitsu T, Kojima M, Hino J, Matsuoka H, Kitamura K, et al. 1994. Genomic structure of human adrenomedullin gene. *Biochem. Biophys. Res. Commun.* 203:631–39
7. Sakata J, Shimokubo T, Kitamura K, Nakamura S, Kangawa K, et al. 1994. Molecular cloning and biological activities of rat adrenomedullin, a hypotensive peptide. *Biochem. Biophys. Res. Commun.* 195:921–27
8. Ichiki Y, Kitamura K, Kangawa K, Kawamoto M, Matsuo H, Eto T. 1994. Distribution and characterization of immunoreactive adrenomedullin in human tissue and plasma. *FEBS Lett.* 338:6–10
9. Satoh F, Takahashi K, Murakami O, Totsune K, Sone M, et al. 1996. Immunocytochemical localization of adrenomedullin-like immunoreactivity in the human hypothalamus and adrenal gland. *Neurosci. Lett.* 203:207–10
10. Washimine H, Asada Y, Kitamura K, Ichiki Y, Hara S, et al. 1995. Immunohistochemical identification of adrenomedullin in human, rat, and porcine tissue. *Histochem. Cell. Biol.* 103:251–54
11. Sakata J, Shimokubo T, Kitamura K, Nakamura S, Kangawa K, et al. 1994. Distribution and characterization of immunoreactive rat adrenomedullin in tissue and plasma. *FEBS Lett.* 352:105–8
12. Ueta Y, Kitamura K, Isse T, Shibuya I,

Kabashima N, et al. 1995. Adrenomedullin-immunoreactive neurons in the paraventricular and supraoptic nuclei of the rat. *Neurosci. Lett.* 202:37–40
13. Sugo S, Minamino N, Kangawa K, Miyamoto K, Kitamura K, et al. 1994. Endothelial cells actively synthesize and secrete adrenomedullin. *Biochem. Biophys. Res. Commun.* 201:1160–66
14. Minamino N, Shoji H, Sugo S, Kangawa K, Matsuo H. 1995. Adrenocortical steroids, thyroid hormones and retinoic acid augment the production of adrenomedullin in vascular smooth muscle cells. *Biochem. Biophys. Res. Commun.* 211:686–93
15. Sugo S, Minamino N, Shoji H, Kangawa K, Matsuo H. 1995. Effects of vasoactive substances and cAMP related compounds on adrenomedullin production in cultured vascular smooth muscle cells. *FEBS Lett. Lett.* 369:311–14
16. Sugo S, Minamino N, Shoji H, Kangawa K, Kitamura K, et al. 1995. Interleukin-1, tumor necrosis factor and lipopolysaccharide additively stimulate production of adrenomedullin in vascular smooth muscle cells. *Biochem. Biophys. Res. Commun.* 207:25–32
17. Chun TH, Itoh H, Ogawa Y, Tamura N, Takaya K, et al. 1997. Shear stress augments expression of C-type natriuretic peptide and adrenomedullin. *Hypertension* 29:1296–1302
18. Jougasaki M, Wei CM, Mckinley LJ, Burnett JC. 1995. Elevation of circulating and ventricular adrenomedullin in human congestive heart failure. *Circulation* 92:286–89
19. Satoh F, Takahashi K, Murakami O, Totsune K, Sone M, et al. 1995. Adrenomedullin in human brain, adrenal glands and tumor tissues of pheochromocytoma, ganglioneuroblastoma and neuroblastoma. *J. Clin. Endocrinol. Metab.* 80:1750–52
20. Katoh F, Kitamura K, Niina H, Yamamoto R, Washimine H, et al. 1995. Proadrenomedullin N-terminal 20 peptide (PAMP), an endogenous anticholinergic peptide: its exocytotic secretion and inhibition of catecholamine secretion in adrenal medulla. *J. Neurochem.* 64:459–61
21. Romppanen H, Marttila M, Magga J, Vuolteenaho O, Kinnunen P. 1997. Adrenomedullin gene expression in the rat heart is stimulated by acute pressure overload: blunted effect in experimental hypertension. *Endocrinology* 138:2636–39
22. Jougasaki M, Wei CM, Aarhus LL, Heublein DM, Sandberg SM, Burnett JC. 1995. Renal localization and actions of adrenomedullin: a natriuretic peptide. *Am. J. Physiol.* 268:F657–63
23. Kitamura K, Ichiki Y, Tanaka M, Kawamoto M, Emura J, et al. 1994. Immunoreactive adrenomedullin in human plasma. *FEBS Lett.* 341:288–90
24. Sato K, Hirata Y, Imai T, Iwashina M, Marumo F. 1995. Characterization of immunoreactive adrenomedullin in human plasma and urine. *Life Sci.* 57:189–94
25. Washimine H, Yamamoto Y, Kitamura K, Tanaka M, Ichiki Y, et al. 1995. Plasma concentrations of human adrenomedullin in patients on hemodialysis. *Clin. Nephrol.* 44:389–93
26. Meeran K, O'Shea D, Upton PD, Small CJ, Ghatei MA, et al. 1997. Circulating adrenomedullin does not regulate systemic blood pressure but increases plasma prolactin after intravenous infusion in humans: a pharmacokinetic study. *J. Clin. Endocrinol. Metab.* 82:95–100
27. Isumi Y, Shoji H, Sugo S, Tochimoto T, Yoshioka M, et al. 1998. Regulation of adrenomedullin production in rat endothelial cells. *Endocrinology* 139:838–46
28. Katoh F, Niina H, Kitamura K, Ichiki Y, Yamamoto Y, et al. 1994. Calcium-dependent cosecretion of adrenomedullin and catecholamines mediated by nicotinic receptors in bovine adrenal medullary cells. *FEBS Lett.* 348:61–64
29. Sato K, Imai T, Iwashima M, Marumo F, Hirata Y. 1998. Secretion of adrenomedullin by renal tubular cell lines. *Nephron* 78:9–14
30. Nishikimi T, Kitamura K, Saito Y, Shimada K, Ishimitsu T, et al. 1994. Clinical studies on the sites of production and clearance of circulating adrenomedullin in human subjects. *Hypertension* 24:600–4
31. Ishimitsu T, Nishikimi T, Saito Y, Kitamura K, Eto T, et al. 1994. Plasma levels of adrenomedullin, a newly identified hypotensive peptide, in patients with hypertension and renal failure. *J. Clin. Invest.* 94:2158–61
32. Kohno M, Hanehira T, Kano H, Horio T, Yokokawa K, et al. 1996. Plasma adrenomedullin concentrations in essential hypertension. *Hypertension* 27:102–7
33. Shimokubo T, Sakata J, Kitamura K, Kangawa K, Matsuo H, Eto T. 1995. Augmented adrenomedullin concentrations in right ventricle and plasma of

experimental pulmonary hypertension. *Life Sci.* 57:1771–79
34. Nisikimi T, Nagata S, Sasaki T, Tomimoto S, Matsuoka H, et al. 1997. Plasma concentrations of adrenomedullin correlate with the extent of pulmonary hypertension in patients with mitral stenosis. *Heart* 78:390–95
35. Hamada M, Shigematsu Y, Kawakami H, Minamino N, Kangawa K, et al. Increased plasma levels of adrenomedullin in patients with hypertrophic cardiomyopathy: its relation to endothelin-1, natriuretic peptide, and noradrenaline. *Clin. Sci. Colch.* 94:21–28
36. Miyao Y, Nishikimi T, Goto Y, Miyazaki S, Daikoku S, et al. 1998. Increased plasma adrenomedullin levels in patients with acute myocardial infarction in proportion to the clinical severity. *Heart* 79:39–44
37. Cheung B, Leung R. 1997. Elevated plasma levels of human adrenomedullin in cardiovascular, respiratory, hepatic and renal disorders. *Clin. Sci.* 92:59–62
38. Guevara M, Gines P, Jimenez W, Sort P, Fernandez-Esparrach G, et al. 1998. Increased adrenomedullin levels in cirrhosis: relationship with hemodynamic abnormalities and vasoconstrictor systems. *Gastroenterology* 114:336–43
39. Taniyama M, Kitamura K, Ban Y, Sigita E, Ito K, Katagiri T. 1997. Elevation of circulating proadrenomedullin N-20 terminal peptide in thyrotoxicosis. *Clin. Endocrinol.* 46:271–74
40. Kohno M, Hanehira T, Hirata K, Kawaguchi T, Okishio K, et al. 1996. An accelerated increase of plasma adrenomedullin in acute asthma. *Metabolism* 45:1323–25
41. Hirata Y, Mitaka C, Sato K, Nagura T, Tsunoda Y, et al. 1996. Increased circulating adrenomedullin, a novel vasodilatory peptide, in sepsis. *J. Clin. Endocrinol. Metab.* 81:1449–53
42. Nishio K, Akai Y, Murao Y, Doi N, Ueda S. 1997. Increased plasma concentration of adrenomedullin correlates with relaxation of vascular tone in patients with septic shock. *Crit. Care Med.* 25:953–57
43. Parkes DG, May CN. 1997. Direct cardiac and vascular actions of adrenomedullin in conscious sheep. *Br. J. Pharmacol.* 120: 1179–85
44. Samson WK, Murphy TC, Resch ZT. 1998. Central mechanisms for the hypertensive effects of preproadrenomedullin derived peptides in conscious rats. *Am. J. Physiol.* 274:R1505–9
45. Nishikimi T, Horio T, Sasaki T, Yoshihara F, Takishita S, et al. 1997. Cardiac production and secretion of adrenomedullin are increased in heart failure. *Hypertension* 30:1369–75
46. Jougasaki M, Stevens L, Borgeson DD, Luchner A, Redfield MM, Burnett JC. 1997. Adrenomedullin in experimental congestive heart failure: cardiorenal activation. *Am. J. Physiol.* 273:R1392–99
47. Ishimitsu T, Miyata A, Matsuoka H, Kangawa K. 1998. Transcriptional regulation of human adrenomedullin gene in vascular endothelial cells. *Biochem. Biophys. Res. Commun.* 243:463–70
48. Shoji H, Minamino N, Kangawa K, Matsuo H. 1995. Endotoxin markedly elevates plasma concentration and gene transcription of adrenomedullin in rat. *Biochem. Biophys. Res. Commun.* 215: 531–37
49. Tsuruda T, Kato J, Kitamura K, Kuwasako K, Imamura T, et al. 1998. Adrenomedullin: a possible autocrine or paracrine inhibitor of hypertrophy of cardiomyocytes. *Hypertension* 31:505–10
50. Takahashi K, Satoh F, Hara E, Sone M, Murakami O, et al. 1997. Production and secretion of adrenomedullin from glial cell tumors and its effects on cAMP production. *Peptides* 18:1117–24
51. Kuchinke W, Hart RP, Jonakait GM. 1995. Identification of mRNAs regulated by interferon-gamma in cultured rat astrocytes by PCR differential display. *Neuroimmunomodulation* 2:347–55
52. Baskaya M, Suzuki Y, Anzai M, Seki Y, Saito K, et al. 1995. Effects of adrenomedullin, calcitonin gene-related peptide, and amylin on cerebral circulation in dogs. *J. Cereb. Blood Flow Metab.* 15:827–34
53. Mori T, Takayasu M, Suzuki Y, Shibuya M, Yoshida J, Hidaka H. 1997. Effects of adrenomedullin on rat cerebral arterioles. *Eur. J. Pharmacol.* 330:195–98
54. Lang MG, Paterno R, Faraci FM, Heistad DD. 1997. Mechanisms of adrenomedullin induced dilatation of cerebral arterioles. *Stroke* 28:181–85
55. Berthiaume N, Claing A, Lippton H, Cadieux A, D'Orleans-Juste P. 1995. Rat adrenomedullin induces selective arterial vasodilation via CGRP1 receptors in the double perfused mesenteric bed of the rat. *Can. J. Physiol. Pharmacol.* 73:1080–83
56. Nuki C, Kawasaki H, Kitamura K, Takenaga M, Kangawa K. 1993. Vasodilator effect of adrenomedullin and calcitonin gene related peptide receptors in rat mesenteric vascular beds. *Biochem.*

Biophys. Res. Commun. 196:245–51
57. Nandha KA, Taylor GM, Smith DM, Owji AA, Byfield PG, et al. 1995. Specific binding sites and hypotension in the rat systemic vascular bed. *Regul. Pept.* 62: 145–51
58. Haynes JM, Cooper ME. 1995. Adrenomedullin and calcitonin gene related peptide in the rat isolated kidney and the anesthetized rat: in vitro and in vivo effects. *Eur. J. Pharmacol.* 280: 91–94
59. Hjelmqvist H, Keil R, Mathai M, Hubschle T, Gertsberger R. 1997. Vasodilation and glomerular binding of adrenomedullin in rabbit kidney are not CGRP receptor mediated. *Am. J. Physiol.* 273:R716–24
60. Gardiner SM, Kemp PA, March JE, Bennett T. 1995. Regional hemodynamic effects of human and rat adrenomedullin in conscious rats. *Br. J. Pharmacol.* 114: 584–91
61. Aiyar H, Rand K, Elshourbagy NA, Zeng Z, Adamou JE, et al. 1996. A cDNA encoding the calcitonin gene-related peptide type 1 receptor. *J. Biol. Chem.* 271: 11325–29
62. Owji AA, Smith DM, Coppock HA, Morgan DGA, Bhogal R, et al. 1995. An abundant and specific binding site for the novel vasodilator adrenomedullin in the rat. *Endocrinology* 136:2127–34
63. Shimekake Y, Nagata K, Ohta S, Kambayashi Y, Teraoka H, et al. 1995. Adrenomedullin stimulates two signal transduction pathways, cAMP accumulation, and calcium mobilization, in bovine aortic endothelial cells. *J. Biol. Chem.* 270:4412–17
64. Samson WK, Murphy TC, Schell DA. 1995. A novel vasoactive peptide, adrenomedullin, inhibits pituitary adrenocorticotropin release. *Endocrinology* 136: 2349–52
65. Iwasaki H, Hirata Y, Iwashina M, Sato K, Marumo F. 1996. Specific binding for proadrenomedullin N-terminal 20 peptide (PAMP) in the rat. *Endocrinology* 137:3045–50
66. Ruskoaho H, Szokodi I, Kinnunen P, Romppanen H, Tavi P. 1998. *Cardiac synthesis and effects of adrenomedullin.* Presented at 1st Intl. Symp. AM and PAMP, Osaka, Japan
67. Chini EN, Choi E, Grande JP, Burnett JC, Douse TP. 1995. Adrenomedullin suppresses mitogenesis in rat mesangial cells via cAMP pathway. *Biochem. Biophys. Res. Commun.* 215:868–73
68. Hirata Y, Iwasaki H, Eguchi S. 1998. *Role of adrenomedullin as a growth factor and its signal transduction in vascular smooth muscle cells.* Presented at 1st Intl. Symp. AM and PAMP, Osaka, Japan
69. Sabates BL, Pigott JD, Choe EU, Cruz MP, Lippton HL, et al. 1997. Adrenomedullin mediates coronary vasodilation through adenosine receptors and K_{ATP} channels. *J. Surg. Res.* 67:163–68
70. Okamura T, Ayajiki K, Kangawa K, Toda N. 1997. Mechanism of adrenomedullin-induced relaxation in isolated canine retinal arteries. *Invest. Ophthalmol. Vis. Sci.* 38:56–61
71. Kadowitz PJ, Bivalacqua TJ, McNamara DB, Champion HC. 1998. *Analysis of pulmonary and peripheral responses to adrenomedullin and proadrenomedullin N-terminal 20 peptide inthe cat and rat.* Presented at 1st Intl. Symp. AM and PAMP, Osaka, Japan
72. Shimosawa T, Ito Y, Ando K, Kitamura K, Kangawa K, Fujita T. 1995. Proadrenomedullin NH_2-terminal 20 peptide, a new product of the adrenomedullin gene, inhibits norepinephrine overflow from nerve endings. *J. Clin. Invest.* 96:1672–76
73. Takano K, Yamashita N, Fujita T. 1996. Proadrenomedullin N-terminal 20 peptide inhibits the voltage-gated calcium channel current through a pertussis toxin-sensitive G protein in rat pheochromocytoma-derived PC12 cells. *J. Clin. Invest.* 98:14–17
74. Samson WK, Murphy TC, Resch ZT. 1998. Proadrenomedullin N-20 terminal peptide inhibits basal adrenocorticotropin release in vitro. *Endocrine.* In press
75. Samson WK, Murphy TC. 1996. Adrenomedullin inhibits salt appetite. *Endocrinology* 138:613–16
76. Chao J, Jin L, Chao L. 1997. Adrenomedullin gene delivery reduces blood pressure in spontaneously hypertensive rats. *Hypertens. Res.* 20:269–77
77. Kurihara H, Shindo T, Maemura K, Kurihara Y, Kuwaki T, et al. 1998. *Transgenic mice overexpressing adrenomedullin in vasculature.* Presented at 1st Intl. Symp. on AM and PAMP, Osaka, Japan
78. Murphy TC, Samson WK. 1995. The novel vasoactive hormone, adrenomedullin, inhibits water drinking in the rat. *Endocrinology* 136:2459–63
79. Rademaker MT, Charles CJ, Lewis LK, Yandle TG, Cooper GJ, et al. 1997. Beneficial hemodynamic and renal effects of adrenomedullin in an ovine model of heart failure. *Circulation* 96:1983–90
80. Ebara T, Mura K, Okumura M, Matsuura T, Kim S, et al. 1994. Effect of

adrenomedullin on renal hemodynamics and functions in dogs. *Eur. J. Pharmacol.* 263:69–73
81. Miura K, Ebara T, Okumura M, Matsuura T, Kim S, et al. 1995. Attenuation of adrenomedullin-induced renal vasodilation by NG-nitro-L-arginine but not glibenclamide. *Br. J. Pharmacol.* 115: 917–24
82. Elhawary AM, Poon J, Pang CC. 1995. Effects of calcitonin gene related peptide antagonists on renal actions of adrenomedullin. *Br. J. Pharmacol.* 115: 1133–40
83. Vari RC, Adkins SD, Samson WK. 1995. Renal effects of adrenomedullin in the rat. *Proc. Soc. Exp. Biol. Med.* 211:178–83
84. Hirata Y, Hayakawa H, Suzuki Y, Suzuki Y, Ikenouchi H, et al. 1995. Mechanisms of adrenomedullin-induced vasodilation in the rat kidney. *Hypertension* 25:790–95
85. Lainchbury JG, Cooper GJ, Coy DH, Jiang NY, Lewis LK, et al. 1997. Adrenomedullin: a hypotensive hormone in man. *Clin. Sci.* 92:467–72
86. Seguchi H, Nishimura J, Kobayashi S, Kumazawa J, Kanaide H. 1995. Autocrine regulation of the renal arterial tone by adrenomedullin. *Biochem. Biophys. Res. Commun.* 215:619–25
87. Jougasaki M, Aarhus LL, Heublein DM, Sandberg SM, Burnett JC. 1997. Role of prostaglandins and renal nerves in the renal actions of adrenomedullin. *Am. J. Physiol.* 272:F260–66
88. Owada A, Nonoguchi H, Terada Y, Marumo F, Tomita K. 1997. Microlocalization and effects of adrenomedullin in nephron segments and in mesangial cells of the rat. *Am. J. Physiol.* 272:F691–97
89. Togawa M, Haneda M, Araki S, Sugimoto T, Isono M, et al. 1997. Beraprost sodium, an analogue of prostacyclin, induces the expression of mitogen-activated protein kinase phosphatase and inhibits the proliferation of cultured mesangial cells. *Eur. J. Pharmacol.* 336:291–94
90. Kohno M, Yasunari Y, Yokokawa K, Horio T, Ikeda M, et al. 1996. Interaction of adrenomedullin and platelet-derived growth factor on the production of endothelin. *Hypertension* 27:663–67
91. Chini EN, Chini CC, Bolliger C, Jougasaki M, Grande JP, et al. 1997. Cytoprotective effects of adrenomedullin in glomerular cell injury: central role of cAMP signaling pathway. *Kidney Int.* 52:917–25
92. Jensen BL, Kramer BK, Kurtz A. 1997. Adrenomedullin stimulates renin release and renin mRNA in mouse juxtaglomerular granular cells. *Hypertension* 29:1148–55
93. Nussdorfer GG, Rossi GP, Mazzochi G. 1997. Role of adrenomedullin and related peptides in the regulation of the hypothalamo-pituitary-adrenal axis. *Peptides* 18:1079–89
94. Andreis PG, Neri G, Prayer-Galetti T, Rossi GP, Gottardo, et al. 1997. Effects of adrenomedullin on the human adrenal glands: an in vitro study. *J. Clin. Endocrinol. Metab.* 82:1167–70
95. Andreis PG, Mazzocchi G, Rebuffat P, Nussdorfer GG. 1997. Effects of adrenomedullin and proadrenomedullin N-terminal 20 peptide on rat zona glomerulosa cells. *Life Sci.* 60:1693–97
96. Yamaguchi T, Baba K, Doi Y, Yano K. 1995. Effect of adrenomedullin on aldosterone secretion by dispersed rat adrenal zona glomerulosa cells. *Life Sci.* 56:379–87
97. Yamaguchi T, Baba K, Doi Y, Yano K, Kitamura K, Eto T. 1996. Inhibition of aldosterone production by adrenomedullin, a hypotensive peptide, in the rat. *Hypertension* 28:308–14
98. Mazzocchi G, Rebuffat P, Gottardo G, Nussdorfer GG. 1996. Adrenomedullin and calcitonin gene-related peptide inhibit aldosterone secretion in rats, acting via a common receptor. *Life Sci.* 58:839–44
99. Parkes DG, May CN. 1995. ACTH-suppressive and vasodilator actions of AM in conscious sheep. *J. Neuroendocrinol.* 7:923–29
100. Kobayashi H, Yamamoto R, Niina H, Katoh F, Kuwasako K, et al. 1998. *Adrenomedullin and PAMP in adrenal chromaffin cells.* Presented at 1st Intl. Symp. AM and PAMP, Osaka, Japan
101. Feng CJ, Kang B, Kaye AD, Kadowitz PJ, Nossman BD. 1994. L-NAME modulates responses to adrenomedullin in the hindquarters vascular bed of the rat. *Life Sci.* 55:433–38
102. Fukuhara M, Tsuchihashi T, Abe I, Fujishima M. 1995. Cardiovascular and neurohumoral effects of intravenous adrenomedullin in conscious rabbits. *Am. J. Physiol.* 269:R1289–93
103. Nakamura M, Yoshida H, Makita S, Arakawa N, Niinuma H, Hiramori K. 1997. Potent and long-lasting vasodilatory effects of adrenomedullin in humans. Comparisons between normal subjects and patients with chronic heart failure. *Circulation* 95:1214–21

104. Parkes DG. 1995. Cardiovascular actions of adrenomedullin in conscious sheep. *Am. J. Physiol.* 268:H2574–78
105. Shirai M, Shimouchi A, Ikeda S, Ninomiya I, Sunagawa K, et al. 1997. Vasodilator effects of adrenomedullin on small pulmonary arteries and veins in anesthetized cats. *Br. J. Pharmacol.* 121:679–86
106. Champion HC, Akers DL, Santiago JA, Lambert DG, McNamara DB, Kadowitz PJ. 1997. Analysis of responses to human adrenomedullin and calcitonin gene-related peptides in the hindlimb vascular bed of the cat. *Mol. Cell. Biochem.* 176:5–11
107. Barber DA, Park YS, Burnett JC, Miller VM. 1997. Adrenomedullin-mediated relaxations in veins are endothelium-dependent and distinct from arteries. *J. Cardiovasc. Pharmacol.* 30:695–701
108. Champion HC, Lambert DG, McWilliams SM, Shah MK, Murphy WA, et al. 1997. Comparison of responses to rat and human adrenomedullin in the hindlimb vascular bed of the cat. *Regul. Pept.* 70:161–65
109. Champion HC, Murphy WA, Coy DH, Kadowitz PJ. 1997. Proadrenomedullin NH_2-terminal 20 peptide has direct vasodilator activity in the cat. *Am. J. Physiol.* 272:R1047–54
110. Kano H, Kohno M, Yasunari K, Yokokawa K, Horio T, et al. 1996. Adrenomedullin as a novel antiproliferative factor in vascular smooth muscle cells. *J. Hypertension* 14:209–13
111. Kohno M, Yokokawa K, Kano H, Yasunari K, Minami M, et al. 1997. Adrenomedullin is a potent inhibitor of angiotensin II induced migration of human coronary artery smooth muscle cells. *Hypertension* 29:1309–13
112. Kohno M, Yasunari K, Yokokawa K, Minami M, Kano H, et al. 1998. *Interaction of adrenomedullin and lysophosphatidylcholine, a major phospholipid component of atherogenic lipoproteins, on human coronary artery smooth muscle cell migration.* Presented at 1st Intl. Symp. AM and PAMP, Osaka, Japan
113. Itoh H, Nakao K. 1998. *Adrenomedullin and vascular stress response.* Presented at 1st Intl. Symp. AM and PAMP, Osaka, Japan
114. Kato H, Shichiri M, Marumo F, Hirata Y. 1997. Adrenomedullin as an autocrine/paracrine survival factor for rat endothelial cells. *Endocrinology* 138: 2615–20
115. Minamino N, Isumi Y, Kubo A, Katafuchi T, Tomoda Y, et al. 1998. *Production of adrenomedullin in vascular cells, fibroblasts and macrophages.* Presented at 1st Intl. Symp. AM and PAMP, Osaka, Japan
116. Nishimori T, Tsujino M, Sato K, Imai T, Marumo F, Hirata Y. 1997. Dexamethasone-induced up-regulation of adrenomedullin and atrial natriuretic peptide genes in cultured rat ventricular myocytes. *J. Mol. Cell. Cardiol.* 29:2125–30
117. Inatsu H, Sakata J, Shimokubo T, Kitani M, Nishizoni M, et al. 1996. Distribution and characterization of rat immunoreactive proadrenomedullin N-terminal 20 peptide (PAMP) and the augmented cardiac PAMP in spontaneously hypertensive rat. *Biochem. Mol. Biol. Int.* 38:365–72
118. Sato A, Autelitano DJ. 1995. Adrenomedullin induces expression of c-fos and AP-1 activity in rat vascular smooth muscle cells and cardiomyocytes. *Biochem. Biophys. Res. Commun.* 217:211–16
119. Sato A, Canny BJ, Autelitano DJ. 1997. Adrenomedullin stimulates cAMP accumulation and inhibits atrial natriuretic peptide gene expression in cardiomyocyte. *Biochem. Biophys. Res. Commun.* 230:311–14
120. Nishikimi T, Horio T, Yoshihara N, Nagaya N, Matuo M, Kangawa K. 1998. *Adrenomedullin in failing heart.* Presented at 1st Intl. Symp. AM and PAMP, Osaka, Japan
121. Szokodi I, Kinnunen P, Ruskoaho H. 1996. Inotropic effect of AM in the isolated perfused rat heart. *Acta Physiol. Scand.* 156:151–52
122. Yang BC, Lippton H, Gumusel B, Hyman A, Mehta JL. 1996. Adrenomedullin dilates rat pulmonary artery rings during hypoxia: role of nitric oxide and vasodilator prostaglandins. *J. Cardiovasc. Pharmacol.* 28:458–62
123. Kamoi H, Kanazawa K, Hirata K, Kurihara N, Yano Y, Otani S. 1995. Adrenomedullin inhibits the secretion of cytokine induced neutrophil chemoattractant, a member of the interleukin-8 family, from rat alveolar macrophages. *Biochem. Biophys. Res. Commun.* 211:1031–35
124. Mulder H, Ahren B, Karlsson S, Sundler F. 1996. Adrenomedullin: localization in the gastrointestinal tract and effects on insulin secretion. *Regul. Pept.* 62:107–12
125. Cornish J, Callon KE, Coy DH, Jiang NY, Xiao L, et al. 1997. Adrenomedullin is a potent stimulator of osteoblastic activity in vitro and in vivo. *Am. J. Physiol.* 273:E1113–20
126. Takahashi K, Satoh F, Sone M, Murakami

O, Sasano H, et al. 1997. Expression of adrenomedullin mRNA in human brain and pituitary. *Peptides* 18:1051–53
127. Montuenga LM, Burrell M, Garayoa M, Garcia D, Martinez A, et al. 1998. *Expression of proadrenomedullin N-terminal 20 peptide in mammalian pituitary*. Presented at 1st Intl. Symp. AM and PAMP, Osaka, Japan
128. Yokoi H, Arima T, Kondo K, Iwasaki Y, Oiso Y. 1996. Intracerebroventricular injection of adrenomedullin inhibits vasopressin release in conscious rats. *Neurosci. Lett.* 216:65–67
129. Samson WK. 1985. Atrial natriuretic factor inhibits dehydration and hemorrhage-induced vasopressin release. *Neuroendocrinology* 40:277–79
130. Antunes-Rodrigues J, McCann SM, Rogers LC, Samson WK. 1985. Atrial natriuretic factor inhibits dehydration- and angiotensin II-induced water intake in the conscious, unrestrained rat. *Proc. Natl. Acad. Sci. USA* 82:8720–23
131. Antunes-Rodrigues J, McCann SM, Samson WK. 1986. Central administration of atrial natriuretic factor inhibits saline preference in the rat. *Endocrinology* 118: 1726–28
132. Dogan A, Suzuki Y, Koketsu N, Osuka K, Saito K, et al. 1997. Intravenous infusion of adrenomedullin and increase in regional cerebral blood flow and prevention of ischemic brain injury after middle cerebral artery occlusion in rats. *J. Cereb. Blood Flow Metab.* 17:19–25
133. Zimmerman U, Fischer JA, Frei K, Fischer AH, Reinscheid RK, Muff R. 1996. Identification of adrenomedullin receptors in cultured rat astrocytes and in neuroblastoma x glioma hybrid cells (NG108-15). *Brain Res.* 724:238–45
134. Yeung VT, Ho SK, Nicholls MG, Cockram CS. 1996. Adrenomedullin, a novel vasoactive hormone, binds to mouse astrocytes and stimulates cyclic AMP production. *J. Neurosci Res.* 46:330–35
135. Moody TW, Miller MJ, Martinez A, Unsworth E, Cuttitta F. 1997. Adrenomedullin binds with high affinity, elevates cAMP, and stimulates c-fos mRNA in C6 glioma cells. *Peptides* 18:1111–15
136. Takahashi H, Watanabe T, Nishimura M, Nakanishi T, Sakamoto M, et al. 1994. Centrally induced vasopressor and sympathetic responses to a novel endogenous peptide, adrenomedullin, in anesthetized rats. *Am. J. Hypertension* 7:478–82
137. Allen MA, Ferguson AV. 1996. In vitro recordings from area postrema neurons demonstrate responsiveness to adrenomedullin. *Am. J. Physiol.* 270:R920–92
138. Allen MA, Smith PA, Ferguson AV. 1997. Adrenomedullin microinjection into the area postrema increases blood pressure. *Am. J. Physiol.* 272:R1698–1703
139. Martinez V, Cuttitta F, Tache Y. 1997. Central action of adrenomedullin to inhibit gastric emptying in rats. *Endocrinology* 138:3749–55

Annu. Rev. Physiol. 1999. 61:391–415

PATHOPHYSIOLOGY OF ENDOTHELIN IN THE CARDIOVASCULAR SYSTEM

Takashi Miyauchi
Cardiovascular Division, Department of Internal Medicine, Institute of Clinical Medicine, University of Tsukuba, Tsukuba, Ibaraki 305-8575, Japan;
e-mail: t-miyauc@md.tsukuba.ac.jp

Tomoh Masaki
National Cardiovascular Center Research Institute, 5-7-1 Fujishirodai, Suita, Osaka 565-8565, Japan; e-mail: masaki@ri.ncvc.go.jp

KEY WORDS: endothelin receptor, signal transduction, receptor antagonist, pharmacology, heart failure

ABSTRACT

In this article, we review the basic pharmacological and biochemical features of endothelin and the pathophysiological roles of endothelin in cardiovascular diseases. Development of receptor antagonists has accelerated the pace of investigations into the pathophysiological roles of endogenous endothelin-1 in various diseases, e.g. chronic heart failure, renal diseases, hypertension, cerebral vasospasm, and pulmonary hypertension. In chronic heart failure, the expression of endothelin-1 and its receptors in cardiomyocytes is increased, and treatment with an endothelin receptor antagonist improves survival and cardiac function. Endothelin receptor antagonists also improve other cardiovascular diseases. These results suggest that the interference with endothelin pathway either by receptor blockade or by inhibition of endothelin converting enzyme may provide novel therapeutic drugs strategies for multiple disease states.

INTRODUCTION

Endothelin-1, a 21-amino acid peptide, was identified in 1988 as a potent vasoconstrictor and pressor substance in the supernatant of cultured porcine aortic

0066-4278/99/0315-0391$08.00

endothelial cells (1). This peptide has a molecular weight of 2492, free amino and carboxyl termini, and two intramolecular disulfide bonds. Endothelin-1 is present in many mammalian species, including humans. Two addition human endothelin isopeptides, endothelin-2 and endothelin-3 (2), are encoded by separate genes. These isoforms of endothelin show a high degree of primary amino acid sequence identity; all are 21–amino acid polypeptides that contain two intramolecular disulfide bonds. The three endothelins also have structural and functional similarities to the sarafotoxins, a family of isopeptides isolated from the venom of the snake *Atractaspis engaddensis*, which suggests a possible common evolutionary origin (3).

Although vascular endothelial cells are the major source of endothelin-1, the genes that encode the three endothelin isopeptides are expressed in a wide variety of cell types, including cardiac myocytes, vascular smooth muscle, renal tubular epithelium, glomerular mesangium, glia, the pituitary, macrophages, mast cells, etc, which suggests that the peptides may participate in complex regulatory mechanisms in various organs (2, 4). Furthermore, the endothelin have a variety of pharmacological actions both in the cardiovascular system and in other tissues. The pharmacological responses can be divided into two groups (5), and two receptors subtypes, ET_A and ET_B receptors (6, 7), mediate the effects of the endothelins (5). The discovery of the endothelin receptors stimulated the development of endothelin receptor antagonists and accelerated investigation of the physiological and/or pathophysiological roles of the endothelins. Development of endothelin-deficient (8) and endothelin-receptor–deficient (9) mice by means of gene targeting has provided additional unanticipated information about the effects of these peptides, i.e. demonstrating crucial roles in normal embryonic development. Endothelin-1–deficient mice have craniofacial and cardiac abnormities and die of respiratory failure soon after birth (8). In contrast, mice deficient in the ET_B receptor exhibit aganglionic megacolon (associated with coat color spotting), which resembles Hirschsprung's disease in humans (10).

In this article, we review briefly the molecular features of endothelin biosynthesis, endothelin-1 receptor interaction, and intracellular biochemical events that follow receptor activation and then describe the pathophysiological role of endothelin. Development of potent endothelin receptor agonists and antagonists has provided evidence for the involvement of endothelins in the etiology and pathology of cardiovascular diseases, including chronic heart failure, hypertension, cerebral vasospasm, and pulmonary hypertension.

SYNTHESIS OF ENDOTHELIN AND ITS REGULATION

The human endothelin-1 gene contains five exons that encode preproendothelin-1. Several regulatory elements are found in the 5′ region of the endothelin-1 gene: motifs of the consensus binding sequence for the transcription factor nuclear factor-1 (11), four copies of the hexanucleotide CTGGGA, the acute phase reaction regulatory element, and sequences highly homologous to the octanucleotide consensus AP-1/Jun-binding site (2, 12). The presence of an AP-1/Jun-binding site in the 5′-flanking region could explain the rapid induction of endothelin-1 mRNA following treatment of endothelial cells with phorbol ester.

Expression of endothelin-1 mRNA is increased after treatment of endothelial cells with growth factors and cytokines such as thrombin (13), transforming growth factor β (14), tumor necrosis factor α (15), immunoglobulin 1 (16), and insulin, or with vasoactive substances (17, 18) such as norepinephrine, angiotensin II, vasopressin, and bradykinin (Figure 1). Although no SSRE (shear stress responsive element) was detected in the endothelin-1 gene, endothelin mRNA expression and endothelin production in endothelial cells are regulated by fluid shear stress: High shear stress (25 dynes/cm^2) decreases mRNA levels (19, 20), whereas low shear stress (5 dynes/cm^2) increases endothelin-1 mRNA expression (21). Pulsatile stretch also causes enhanced production of endothelin-1 in endothelial cells (22). Shear stress appears to regulate endothelin-1 gene transcription via an upstream *cis* element (23). In contrast, the expression of endothelin-1 mRNA is inhibited by endothelium-derived relaxing factor (nitric oxide), prostacyclin, and atrial natriuretic peptide, presumably via cGMP-mediated inhibition of phosphatidylinositide metabolism (24). Heparin also decreases endothelin-1 mRNA expression via inhibition of protein kinase C (25). These characteristics of the endothelin-1 gene are similar to those of so-called early response genes.

Sequence analysis of the endothelin-1 cDNA revealed a single copy gene that encodes for a precursor, preproendothelin-1 (Figure 1). Human preproendothelin-1 is a 212-amino acid protein proteolytically cleaved, as in the case of many bioactive peptides, at paired dibasic amino acids (Figure 1). This protease is a furin-like enzyme, and the cleavage of the precursor by this protease results in the formation of a 38–amino acid residue intermediate peptide, termed big endothelin-1 (26). Big endothelin-1 is subsequently cleaved at Trp21-Val22 by another endopeptidase, termed endothelin converting enzyme (ECE), which appears to be specific for endothelin (1) and which does not act on the precursor without cleavage of Arg92 (Figure 1). In vascular endothelial cells, endothelin-1 is secreted via the constitutive pathway, and the rate-limiting step of its biosynthesis is thought to be at the level of transcription (1). Endothelin-1 gene expression in vascular endothelial cells is regulated by a variety of chemical stimuli, as described above. The conversion of big endothelin-1 to endothelin-1 is essential for biological activity, because the pressor action of big endothelin-1 is almost completely inhibited by a relatively large dose of phosphoramidon, an inhibitor of ECE (27, 28).

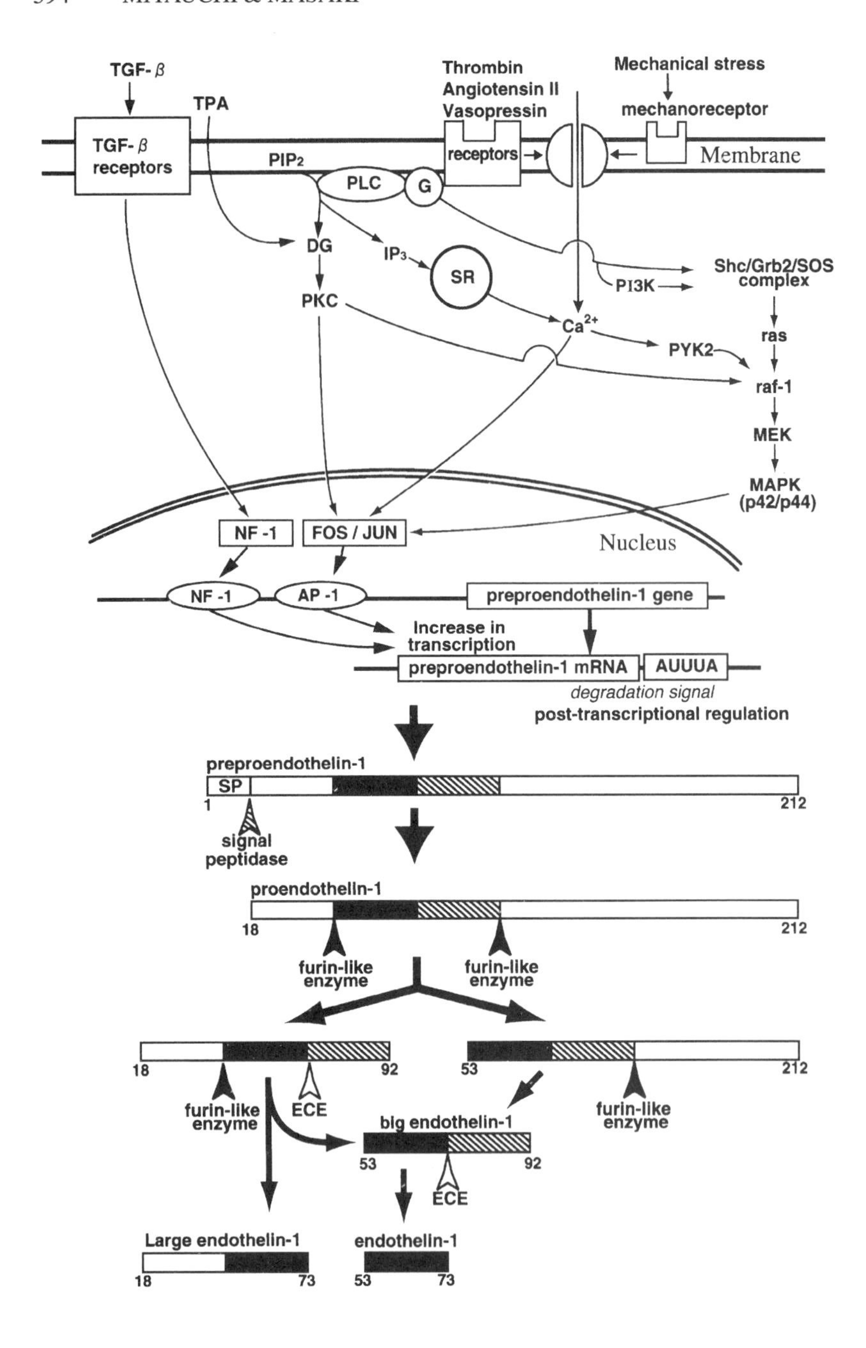
TGF-β
TPA
Thrombin
Angiotensin II
Vasopressin
Mechanical stress
mechanoreceptor
TGF-β receptors
PIP2
PLC
G
receptors
Membrane
DG
IP3
SR
Shc/Grb2/SOS complex
PI3K
PKC
Ca2+
ras
PYK2
raf-1
MEK
MAPK (p42/p44)
NF-1
FOS / JUN
Nucleus
NF-1
AP-1
preproendothelin-1 gene
Increase in transcription
preproendothelin-1 mRNA
AUUUA
degradation signal
post-transcriptional regulation
preproendothelin-1
SP
1
212
signal peptidase
proendothelin-1
18
212
furin-like enzyme
furin-like enzyme
18
92
53
212
furin-like enzyme
ECE
big endothelin-1
furin-like enzyme
53
92
ECE
Large endothelin-1
endothelin-1
18
73
53
73

ECE was initially purified from rat lung (29), and ECE cDNA was cloned from rat lung and from bovine adrenal cortex cDNA libraries (30). The ECE gene encodes a metalloprotease enzyme that contains a single membrane-spanning sequence with an N-terminal cytoplasmic tail and extracellular C-terminal amino acid residues that contain the catalytic domain. A highly conserved consensus sequence of a zinc-binding motif, HEXXH, is shared by many metalloproteases. Northern blot analysis demonstrated a ubiquitous distribution of mRNA for this enzyme, with the highest expression in endothelium, lung, ovary, testis, and adrenal medulla. The rat and bovine enzymes possess more than 90% primary amino acid homology and are termed ECE-1. They appear to be associated with the plasma membrane and Golgi complex and to process big endothelin-1 more efficiently than either big endothelin-2 or big endothelin-3.

ECE-2 was cloned from bovine endothelial cell cDNA libraries (31). ECE-2 is sensitive to phosphoramidon and converts big endothelin-1 more efficiently does than big endothelin-2 or big endothelin-3 but differs from ECE-1 in several ways. Interestingly, neural tissues such as cerebral cortex, cerebellum, and adrenal medulla have the highest expression of ECE-2 mRNA.

ENDOTHELIN RECEPTORS AND SIGNAL TRANSDUCTION

As described above, endothelin-induced responses may be divided into two groups. In the first group of responses, which includes vasoconstriction, bronchoconstriction, uterine smooth muscle contraction, and stimulation of aldosterone secretion, endothelin-1 and -2 are more potent agonists than endothelin-3. In the second group, which includes endothelium-dependent vasorelaxation and inhibition of ex vivo platelet aggregation, the three isopeptides have almost

←

Figure 1 The synthesis and processing of endothelin-1. (*Upper*) Possible regulatory mechanisms of gene expression of preproendothelin-1. (*Lower*) The processing pathway of endothelin-1. Endothelin-converting enzyme (ECE) does not cleave the Trp-Val bond without cleavage of Arg92, so that endothelin-1 is not produced directly from preproendothelin-1 (53–212). The three major forms of endothelin-1–related peptide in plasma are large endothelin-1, big endothelin-1, and endothelin-1, respectively. Among them, only endothelin-1 is biologically active. G, GTP-binding protein; PLC, phospholipase C; DG, 1,1-diacylglycerol; PKC, protein kinase C; TGF-β, transforming growth factor β; TPA, 12-*O*-tetradecanoylphorbol 13-acetate; IP_3, inositol-1,4,5-triphosphate; P13K, phosphatidilinositol-3 kinase; PYK2, proline-rich tyrosine kinase 2; Shc, Sh2-containing protein; Grb2, growth factor receptor bound 2; SOS, son of sevenless; MAPK, mitogen-activated protein kinase; MEK, MAPK/ERK (extracellular signal-regulated protein kinase) kinase; AP-1 and NF-1, transcription factors; SP, signal peptide.

equal potency. These observations suggest that at least two distinct ET receptors mediate these distinct pharmacological responses.

Two cDNAs that encode endothelin receptors were cloned from rat (6) and bovine (7) lungs, and another endothelin receptor cDNA was cloned from rats (32), pigs (33), and humans (34, 35). Those receptors can be classified into twogroups, according to the relative binding affinities of the three endothelin isopeptides for the receptors. The order of affinity of endothelins for the first receptor type, designated ET_A, is endothelin-1 > endothelin-2 > endothelin-3. The second receptor type, designated ET_B, shows equipotent affinity for all three endothelins (36).

Exposure of cultured smooth muscle cells (37), Swiss 3T3 cells (38), and glomerular mesangial cells (39) to endothelin-1 for a long time causes a marked decrease in [^{125}I]endothelin-1 binding sites, indicating down-regulation of endothelin receptors. As observed with other vasoconstrictor substances, internalization of the endothelin receptor complex is believed to be the mechanism for down-regulation (40). After internalization, the ligand-receptor complex is thought to be sequestered into lysosomes, where the acidic environment promotes ligand dissociation (37).

In a rat osteosarcoma cell line (ROS 17/2 cells), homologous down-regulation of the ET_B receptor mRNA is rapid (within several hours of exposure to endothelin-1) (41). The up-regulation of ET_B receptor has also been reported. In rat cardiomyocytes, the up-regulation of ET_B receptor mRNA induced by angiotensin II (AII) is probably mediated by stimulation of the AT1 (42). In vascular smooth muscle cells, ET_A receptor mRNA is up-regulated by cAMP (43) and down-regulated by dexamethasone (44).

Both ET_A and ET_B receptors may be coupled to phospholipase C (PLC) via a GTP-binding protein (45, 46). Activation of PLC causes phosphatidylinositol hydrolysis, rapid formation of 1,4,5-inositol triphosphate (IP_3), and accumulation of 1,2-diacylglycerol (DG). IP_3 stimulates the release of Ca^{2+} from intracellular stores, including endoplasmic reticulum. The application of endothelin-1 to arterial smooth muscle cells causes a rapid transient increase in intracellular Ca^{2+} concentration ($[Ca^{2+}]_i$) and a subsequent sustained increase in $[Ca^{2+}]_i$ (47). The initial transient $[Ca^{2+}]_i$ response is not dependent on the presence of external Ca^{2+} and is the result of IP_3-induced mobilization of Ca^{2+} from intracellular stores. In contrast, the sustained increase of $[Ca^{2+}]_i$ appears to be due to an influx of extracellular Ca^{2+} through either dihydropyridine-sensitive voltage-dependent L-type Ca^{2+} channels (48, 49) or receptor-operated (nonselective) cation channels that are insensitive to dihydropyridine (50). In addition to the increase in $[Ca^{2+}]_i$, endothelin receptor activation causes activation of phospholipase A_2 (40) and D (51) and changes in arachidonic acid metabolism. The activation of phospholipase D appears to contribute to sustained DG accumulation, which may lead to prolonged activation of protein kinase C (PKC) (52). In vascular smooth muscle and cardiac muscle, a change in intracellular pH (alkalinization) is also induced via stimulation of Na^+-H^+ exchange, which seems to be a consequence of PKC activation (53).

Endothelin-1 is a potent mitogen in cultured vascular smooth muscle cells (54), cardiac myocytes (55), glomerular mesangium (56), and other cells and induces the expression of several proto-oncogenes (c-*fos*, c-*myc*, c-*jun*) (57). A variety of mitogenic stimuli activate the intracellular kinase cascade, including the sequential activation of raf-1, mitogen-activated protein kinase (MAPK), MAPK kinase, and S6 kinase II. It is generally accepted that ET_A receptor mediates the regulation of cell growth. The ET_B receptor mediates some growth responses as well as growth inhibitory effects associated with apoptosis (58). The activation of ET receptors by endothelin-1 enhances MAPK activation (59). MAPK activation secondary to stimulation of the receptor, which belongs to the G protein–linked rhodopsin type of receptor superfamily, may be mediated not only through the PKC-dependent pathway but also through the PKC-independent, phosphatidylinositol-3-OH kinase (PI3K) dependent, PTX-sensitive pathway (60). As mentioned above, endothelin receptors are coupled to PLC and thereby activate classical PKC in various types of cells. Indeed, ET-1–augmented MAPK activation is inhibited by PKC down-regulation (61, 62) and by wortmannin (60). In addition, the tyrosine kinase pathway is also activated, accompanied by Shc-Grb2 complex formation (63).

ENDOTHELIN RECEPTOR ANTAGONISTS

Peptide Antagonists

A useful tool for the study of endothelin is the cyclic pentapeptide, BE-18257B, isolated from the fermentation products of *Streptomyces misakiensis* (64). Modification of BE-18257B resulted in the formation of another cyclic pentapeptide, BQ-123 (Banyu), which has higher affinity for ET_A receptor (65). Because of its competitive and selective nature, high potency, and aqueous solubility (66), BQ123 has been widely used both for in vitro pharmacological and biochemical studies and for the investigation of the physiological and/or pathophysiological roles of endogenous endothelin. A synthetic cyclic hexapeptide, TAK-044 (Takeda), exhibits antagonistic activity against both ET_A and ET_B receptors (67).

Subsequent structure-activity studies led to the development of a series of potent ET_A receptor–selective linear tripeptide antagonists: FR139317 (Fujisawa) (68), PD151242 (Parke-Davis) (69), and TTA-386 (Takeda) (70). Further modifications have resulted in the production of ET_B receptor–selective agonists BQ-3020 (Banyu) and IRL 1620 (71) (Ciba-Geigy), and of ET_B receptor–selective antagonist BQ-788 (Banyu) (72). IRL 2500 (Ciba-Geigy) (73), another linear triptide, is a selective antagonist for the ET_B receptor. These agonists and antagonists have been used in a wide variety of pharmacological and biochemical studies of endothelin physiology.

Orally Active Nonpeptide Antagonists

The first nonpeptide endothelin receptor antagonist for oral administration was Ro 46-2005 (Hoffmann-La Roche), which inhibits the binding of [^{125}I]endothelin-1 to human vascular smooth muscle cells (ET_A receptors) and to rat aortic endothelial cells (ET_B receptors), with 50% inhibitory concentration values of 220 and 1000 nM, respectively (74). Subsequent studies led to the discovery of Ro 47-0203, bosentan (Hoffmann-La Roche), a far more potent and more ET_A receptor–selective antagonist, with K_i values (affinity) of 6.5 and 343 nM for ET_A and ET_B receptors, respectively (75). When administered either orally or intravenously, Ro 47-0203 inhibits both the initial transient depressor (ET_B receptors mediated) response and the prolonged pressor (ET_A receptors mediated) response induced by intravenous endothelin-1. The use of ^{1}H-labeled nuclear magnetic resonance–derived conformational models of endothelin-1 led to the identification of SK&F 66861 (SmithKline Beecham) (76). Comparison of the three-dimensional structure of this compound to low-energy ^{1}H-labeled nuclear magnetic resonance–based conformations of endothelin-1 suggested that the 1- and 3-phenyl groups of SK&F 66861 are mimics of a combination of two of the aromatic side chains of Try13, Phe14, and Trp21 in endothelin-1. As the result of additional three-dimensional peptidomimetic simulations, a potent and highly specific nonpeptide endothelin receptor antagonist, SB 209670 (SmithKline Beecham), has been synthesized with K_i values inhibiting [^{125}I]endothelin binding to human endothelin receptor subtypes ET_A and ET_B of 0.2 and 18 nM, respectively (77).

Additional nonpeptide and orally active endothelin receptor antagonists include PD 156707 (Parke-Davis, K_i = 0.17 and 133.8 nM for ET_A and ET_B receptors, respectively) (78), L-754,142 (Merck, K_i = 0.062 and 2.25 nM for ET_A and ET_B receptors, respectively) (79, 80), T-0115 (Tanabe, K_i = 0.049 and 17 nM for ET_A and ET_B receptors, respectively) (81), T-0201 (Tanabe, K_i = 0.015 and 41 nM for ET_A and ET_B receptors, respectively) (82), and J-104121 (Banyu, K_i = 1.2 and 200 nM for ET_A and ET_B receptors, respectively) (83). Orally active nonpeptide antagonists of endothelin receptors include PD155080 (Parke-Davis) (84, 85), L-751,281 (Merck), and BMS-182874 (Bristol-Myers Squibb). These and other antagonists of endothelin receptors are under extensive investigation and are expected to be marketed in the near future.

PHYSIOLOGICAL SIGNIFICANCE OF ENDOTHELIN IN CARDIOVASCULAR SYSTEM

Despite numerous studies of endothelin function, the physiological significance of endothelin in cardiovascular systems is unclear. Because the plasma concentration is very low, endothelin is not a circulating hormone, but it may be a paracrine/autocrine mediator. The endothelin-1 that is released from vascular beds presumably acts on the underlying smooth muscles to increase peripheral vascular resistance. This concept is supported by the fact that in normal subjects, concentration of ET in venous plasma is slightly higher than in arterial blood. In addition, studies of the effects of BQ-123 on human forearm blood flow suggest that endogenous endothelin-1 plays a role in maintenance of basal tone.

In isolated cardiac muscle, endothelin-1 induces contraction and exerts a potent positive inotropic action. Endothelin-1 is also reported to induce positive chronotropic action via ET_B receptors and negative chronotropic action via ET_A receptors. In the initial work, bolus intravenous administration of endothelin-1 caused a transient depression of blood pressure followed by pressor responses. The initial depressor response is due to the relaxing factor released from endothelium and the subsequent pressor response is due to the direct action of endothelin-1 on smooth muscle.

In addition to controlling vascular tone and contraction of myocytes, the endothelium/endocardium also modulates the growth properties of the underlying vascular smooth muscle and the hypertrophy of cardiac myocyte by releasing vasoactive factors.

PATHOPHYSIOLOGY OF ENDOTHELIN

Chronic Heart Failure

In many countries, chronic heart failure (CHF) is a leading cause of death in humans (86). The Framingham Study found that coronary artery disease accounted for CHF in 59% of male patients (87). Once the diagnosis of heart failure was made in men, the five-year survival rate was only 25% (88). Occlusion of the coronary artery causes acute myocardial infarction, and survivors of acute myocardial infarction are at risk for development of CHF (89, 90).

Plasma endothelin-1 levels are elevated in both humans (91–93) and experimental animal models with CHF (94, 95) and in patients with acute myocardial infarction (96). Furthermore, the production of endothelin-1 is markedly increased in the surviving myocardium of rats with CHF 3 weeks after myocardial infarction (97), and it is produced by cardiac myocytes as well as by vascular endothelial cells (1, 98, 99). Locally produced endothelin-1 may act on the myocytes in an autocrine and/or paracrine manner. Because it greatly increases the contractility of vascular smooth muscle and cardiac muscle (1, 98, 100), the endothelin-1 enhances contractile response of cardiomyocytes. In addition to these immediate beneficial effects, endothelin-1 exerts long-term effects by inducing myocardial hypertrophy (98,100–103) and causing cellular injury in cardiac myocytes (104, 105). Acute application of an endothelin receptor antagonist decreases myocardial contractility in these rats but not in normal rats, which suggests that myocardial endothelin-1 enhances contractility in the failing heart (97). Therefore, up-regulation of endothelin pathways may be beneficial in providing short-term inotropic support for the failing myocardium in which β-adrenergic responsiveness is frequently attenuated. However, in the long term, it is unclear whether up-regulation of the myocardial endothelin system in CHF is beneficial or harmful. Prolonged stimulation by an up-regulated endothelin system may have maladaptive effects on myocardial structure and function, thereby leading to fatal events. In fact, the up-regulated myocardial endothelin system may aggravate the progression of CHF because long-term (12 weeks) treatment with an endothelin receptor antagonist improves the survival rate of rats with CHF (106). This beneficial effect is accompanied by amelioration of left ventricular dysfunction and improvement in ventricular remodeling (an increase in the ventricular mass of the surviving myocardium and cavity enlargement of the ventricle). These findings suggest that the up-regulated myocardial endothelin system is a potential target for therapeutic intervention in CHF.

The mechanisms for the beneficial effects of an endothelin antagonist in CHF are as follows: First, endothelin-1 has direct toxic effects on cardiac myocytes (104, 105), and an increase in the production of endothelin-1 in the heart of rats with CHF may lead to myocardial injury and contribute to the progression of CHF. Therefore, an endothelin antagonist may protect against the direct cardiotoxic effects of endothelin-1. Second, endothelin-1 has potent hypertrophic effects on cardiac myocytes (102, 103), and up-regulated endothelin-1 system in the heart may contribute to excessive hypertrophy of the myocardium in rats with CHF; thus, an endothelin antagonist may prevent the progression of hypertrophy of the myocardium. Because excessive hypertrophy in the failing heart may be maladaptive, the results are in good agreement with this hypothesis. Third, long-term inotropic (increased myocardial contractility) action by endothelin-1 in rats with CHF may contribute to the progression of CHF. This assumption is in agreement with the fact that in humans, long-term inotropic stimulation of the failing heart by β-adrenergic agonists and phosphodiesterase inhibitors is harmful because it enhances myocardial energy utilization, and the chronic administration of these agents increases long-term mortality in patients with CHF (107, 108). Therefore, it is likely that the reduction in myocardial contractility induced by an endothelin antagonist in rats with CHF (97) decreases myocardial energy utilization, thereby improving the metabolic status of the myocardium. Fourth, endothelin-1 induces ventricular arrhythmias (109), and inhibition of endothelin-1–induced arrhythmias by an endothelin antagonist might cause favorable effects. ET_A receptors are believed to be involved in the mediation of these actions of endothelin-1. Indeed, our data show that chronic treatment with ET_A receptor antagonist BQ-123 greatly improved the survival rate, ameliorated the left ventricular dysfunction, and prevented harmful ventricular remodeling in rats with CHF (106).

As described above, the production of endothelin-1 in vascular endothelial cells in culture is enhanced by angiotensin II (110), vasopressin (110), and norepinephrine (1) and by mechanical factors such as shear stress (21) and endothelial stretching (111). In cultured ventricular myocytes, the expression of preproendothelin-1 mRNA is increased by angiotensin II (112). Therefore, the production of endothelin-1 in the intact heart is probably regulated by several stimuli. We have shown that the production of endothelin-1 is increased in the hypertrophic heart caused by hemodynamic pressure overload due to either aortic banding (113) or pulmonary hypertension (101). In rats with CHF, endothelin-1 production in the heart is also increased (97, 106).

The mechanism for increased production of endothelin-1 in the failing heart is now understood. The expression of the c-*jun* proto-oncogene is increased in the failing heart of rats with myocardial infarction (114), and the 5′-flanking region of the preproendothelin-1 gene has three octanucleotide sequences that conform with a consensus of AP-1/Jun-binding elements. Phorbol ester, an activator of protein kinase C, which is a necessary upstream prerequisite for the regulation of the AP-1/Jun-binding elements, actually activates preproendothelin-1 mRNA expression in cultured endothelial cells (12, 115). Therefore, preproendothelin-1 mRNA expression in the failing heart may be enhanced via the expression of *trans*-acting transcription factors such as AP-1 and c-*jun*. It is of interest in this regard that expression of preproendothelin-1 mRNA in the kidney does not change with CHF (97, 106). Tissue-specific enhancement of the expression of preproendothelin-1 mRNA may occur in the heart of rats with CHF. It is likely that the heart is one of the sources of elevated plasma endothelin-1 in rats with CHF because plasma endothelin-1 level correlates positively with left ventricular (LV) endodiastolic pressure (EDP) and negatively with LV+dP/dt max. Furthermore, plasma endothelin-1 levels correlate with infarct size in rats with CHF. In patients with CHF, plasma endothelin-1 levels correlate with the severity of heart failure (91). Taken together, plasma endothelin-1 concentrations appear to reflect the severity of cardiac damage in CHF.

Endothelin-1 binding sites on cultured cardiocytes are down-regulated by pretreatment with endothelin-1 (116), and the level of ET_B receptor mRNA is down-regulated by endothelin-1 secondary to enhanced turnover of the mRNA molecules (41). Accordingly, it was anticipated that agonist-induced endothelin receptor down-regulation played a role in cardiac function. However, endothelin-1 binding sites in the heart were unexpectedly increased in the hearts of rats with CHF (97, 106). Although the precise mechanism of the increase is unclear, these results (97, 106) suggest that endothelin receptor–mediated signal transduction in the heart is potentiated in rats with CHF.

In CHF, as myocardial performance deteriorates, systemic neurohumoral reflexes function to maintain cardiac output, organ perfusion, and circulatory homeostasis. The renin-angiotensin axis, vasopressin, and the sympathetic nervous system are activated. These adaptive responses have the unfortunate effect of augmenting peripheral vascular tone, which increase afterload in the failing heart. These neurohumoral factors also enhance endothelin-1 production in endothelial cells. In patients with CHF, a condition frequently associated with high plasma endothelin-1 levels (91–93), acute intravenous infusion of the endothelin receptor antagonist bosentan reduces mean arterial, pulmonary arterial, right atrial, and pulmonary artery wedge pressures, decreases systemic and pulmonary vascular resistance, and increases stroke volume and cardiac output (117). These findings indicate that endothelin-1 contributes to the maintenance of vascular tone in such patients. Additionally, the plasma levels of endothelin-1 in patients with CHF correlate strongly with pulmonary artery pressure and pulmonary vascular resistance (118). Therefore, endothelin receptor antagonists may cause vasodilation in both the systemic circulation and the pulmonary circulation. In this regard, Spinale et al reported treatment with the ET_A receptor antagonist PD156707 for 3 weeks improved both global LV function and isolated myocyte function in rabbits with CHF resulting from chronic rapid ventricular pacing (119). This regimen improved LV fractional shortening and reduced the dimension of the end-diastolic LV (119).

Interestingly, in patients with acute myocardial infarction, which often leads to CHF, the higher the plasma level of endothelin-1, the higher the long-term mortality (120). Plasma levels of big endothelin-1, which is inactive until it is converted to endothelin-1, may also predict mortality in patients with moderate and severe CHF more accurately than hemodynamic variables (such as LV ejection fraction and atrial natriuretic factor levels) (121). Furthermore, Krum et al reported that changes in endothelin-1 levels in patients with CHF receiving a β-blocker vasodilator (carvedilol) provide a sensitive and noninvasive assessment of changes in disease status after drug therapy (122). Taken together, endothelin-1 appears to aggravate CHF in humans.

RENAL DISEASES

In acute renal failure reductions in renal blood flow may worsen renal tubular dysfunction (123). Endothelin-1 can reduce renal blood flow and glomerular filtration rate by acting as a potent renal vasoconstrictor (124). Accumulating evidence suggests that endothelin-1 plays a role in the pathogenesis of acute renal failure after renal ischemia, i.e. plasma levels of endothelin-1 are increased in patients with acute renal failure (125), and kidney levels of endothelin-1 are elevated after ischemic injury (126). Administration of an antibody to endothelin-1 before renal artery clamping in rats prevents the increase in periglomerular arteriolar resistance and the reduction in single nephron glomerular filtration rate that occurs for up to 48 h following clamping (127). The histological changes that accompany proximal renal tubular necrosis are also prevented by endothelin-1 antibody in the rat renal ischemia model (126, 128). An inhibitor of ECE-1, phosphoramidon, also protected against ischemia-induced acute renal failure in animals (129).

Additional evidence that endothelin-1 may play a pathogenic role in the development and/or maintenance of acute renal failure has been obtained from studies with endothelin receptor antagonists. BQ-123 attenuates the renal functional impairment, tubular degenerative changes, and mitochondrial calcium accumulation when administered to rats prior to bilateral renal artery occlusion insult (130). The administration of BQ-123 24 h after the onset of ischemia also reverses renal damage in rats with acute renal failure, clearly indicating a role in the treatment of established acute renal failure (131).

A potent immunosuppressive agent, cyclosporin, has been used to prevent allograft rejection and to suppress other immunological injuries. Nephrotoxicity is a major side effect of cyclosporin and is characterized by renal vasoconstriction with peritubular capillary congestion and tubular toxicity (132). Endothelin-1 was suspected to be implicated in the cyclosporin nephrotoxicity (133, 134), and the administration of cyclosporin to rats caused an increase in plasma endothelin-1 levels with concomitant renal vasoconstriction and impaired renal function (135, 136). Cyclosporin also increases renal endothelin receptor density and excretion of endothelin in urine (137, 138). Further, both endothelin receptor antagonists (BQ-123, PED-3512) and anti–endothelin-1 antiserum can prevent the renal hemodynamic alterations induced by cyclosporin in rats (139, 140).

The exact role of endothelin-1 in chronic renal failure is unclear (141), but a selective ET_A antagonist, FR139317, reduced protein excretion, improved glomerular injury, inhibited renal c-*fos* proto-oncogene expression, and prevented deterioration of renal function when administered daily for up to 60 days in rats in whom renal failure was reduced by reduction in renal mass

(141). Thus endothelin receptor antagonists may also be useful in the treatment of chronic renal failure.

Hypertension

Endothelin-1 causes potent vasoconstriction and prolonged elevation of blood pressure (1). Thus, endogenous endothelin-1 has been assumed to modulate vascular tone and regional blood flow as a circulating hormone or to exert its actions locally within the vascular wall in an autocrine or paracrine fashion. Intravenous infusion of the ET_A/ET_B antagonist TAK-044 decreases systemic blood pressure and total peripheral resistance in healthy men, which suggests that endogenous endothelin-1 may contribute to maintenance of peripheral vascular tone and blood pressure (142). Endothelin-1 is also thought to cause vascular wall thickening because of its potent proliferative effects (143). These activities of endothelin-1 may occur throughout the evolution of hypertension.

A significant correlation between the concentration of immunoreactive endothelin-1 in vascular tissue and the level of systemic blood pressure has been demonstrated in rats with deoxycorticosterone acetate (DOCA)-salt–induced hypertension (144) and in rats with hyperinsulinemic hypertension (145). Furthermore, in DOCA-salt–induced hypertension, the elevated blood pressure is markedly reduced by ET_A receptor antagonists, BQ-123 (146) and FR-139317 (147) and by the endothelin-converting enzyme inhibitor, phosphoramidon (148). In hyperinsulinemic hypertensive rats in which higher mesenteric endothelin-1 content appears to be the result of increased plasma insulin, chronic ET_A/ET_B receptor blockade by bosentan causes a sustained decrease in systemic blood pressure without affecting the elevated plasma insulin level or mesenteric endothelin-1 content (145).

Although the effects of endothelin receptor antagonists in spontaneously hypertensive rats (SHR) are inconsistent (149–151), the nonpeptide antagonist SB209670 exerts long-lasting hypotensive effects in this model of hypertension (77). The nonpeptide antagonists also lower blood pressure in squirrel monkeys with sodium-depletion–induced hypertension (74), in dogs with renal hypertension (152), and in rats with transgenic [(mRen-2)27] hypertension (153). In (mRen-2)27 hypertensive rats, in which the fulminant hypertension is assumed to be the result of overproduction of angiotensin II (154), SB209670 causes a sustained decrease in systemic blood pressure to a degree similar to that caused by losartan, an angiotensin II receptor (AT_1R) antagonist. The effects of SB209670 and losartan are additive, which suggests that overproduction of endothelin-1 presumably induced by angiotensin II may be involved in the pathogenesis of hypertension.

Adult ET_B-deficient mice and rats exhibit significantly elevated blood pressure under baseline conditions (155). In these mice, the hypertension is shown to be salt sentitive and resistant to ET_A blockade (155), strongly implicating the ET_B receptor function as a physiological natriuretic receptor in the kidney. Indeed, studies of the isolated perfused kidney have shown that endothelin-1 increases sodium excretion.

The relationship between the plasma levels of endothelin-1 and severity of hypertension are inconsistent in humans (156). The report by Krum et al (157) that bosentan lowers blood pressure in patients with essential hypertension (157) suggests that endothelin may contribute to elevated blood pressure in such patients.

Cerebral Vasospasm

Cerebral vasospasm after subarachnoid hemorrhage (SAH) is characterized by persistent contraction of arterial smooth muscle followed by organic changes in the vessel wall (158). Because of the potent and long-lasting constrictor action on cerebral arteries (159, 160), much of the interest surrounding endothelin-1 in the central nervous system evolves around its putative role in cerebral vasospasm. Levels of endothelin-1 in plasma and/or cerebrospinal fluid are elevated in patients with cerebral artery spasm (161–164). The inhibition of mRNA transcription by actinomycin D greatly ameliorates the development of chronic cerebral vasospasm in dogs (165), which implies that one or more peptides may be involved in the pathogenesis. Furthermore, ET_A receptor expression may be increased after SAH in dogs (166), and cerebral vessels may be sensitized to the effects of endothelin-1 after SAH (167). In addition to this indirect evidence, cerebral vasospasm in dogs (mostly double-hemorrhage model) can be ameliorated by intracisternal administration of FR139317 (168) or phosphoramidon (169), continuous intrathecal infusion of BQ-123 (166, 170), intracisternal administration of SB 209670 (171), or intravenous administration of bosentan (172).

Pulmonary Hypertension

Pulmonary hypertension is characterized by an increase in pulmonary vascular tone, vasoreactivity, and enhanced proliferation of pulmonary vascular smooth muscle cells, resulting in increased pulmonary vascular resistance and gradual onset of right ventricular hypertrophy (173). Pulmonary hypertension is associated with increased plasma endothelin levels (174), and the plasma concentration of endothelin-1 correlates with disease severity (175–177). Furthermore, in young patients with pulmonary hypertension secondary to congenital heart disease, the elevated plasma levels of endothelin-1 dramatically decrease following successful surgical repair (178). In patients with pulmonary hypertension from a variety of causes [plexogenic (primary) pulmonary arteriopathy, reactive (secondary) pulmonary hypertension due to heart failure, and pulmonary arteriopathy], expression of endothelin-1 mRNA and of endothelin-1–like immunoreactivity in pulmonary vascular endothelial cells is increased (179). These findings suggest that local production of endothelin-1 may contribute to the vascular abnormalities associated with this disorder. Similar observations have been made in patients with cryptogenic fibrosing alveolitis associated with pulmonary hypertension (180).

In rats with idiopathic pulmonary hypertension, endothelin-1 mRNA expression is increased (181), and smooth muscle cells cultured from pulmonary arteries of these rats overexpress endothelin-1 mRNA and produce more endothelin-1 peptide (182). The overproduced endothelin-1 contributes to the accelerated growth of pulmonary artery smooth muscle cells (182). In monocrotaline-induced pulmonary hypertension in rats, plasma endothelin-1 levels increase progressively before the development of pulmonary hypertension (101). Infusion of BQ-123 reduces progression of pulmonary hypertension and right ventricular hypertrophy and prevents thickening of the pulmonary artery (101). Losartan was not efficacious in this model of pulmonary hypertension (183). The infusion of another selective ET_A receptor antagonist, FR139317, decreases pulmonary artery pressure in beagle dogs with dehydromonocrotaline-induced pulmonary hypertension (184), and bosentan prevents the development of pulmonary hypertension in hypoxic rats (185). Furthermore, continuous infusion of BQ-123 by an osmotic minipump for a 2-week period in rats with chronic heart failure and severe pulmonary hypertension (permanent coronary artery ligation) markedly reduces right ventricular systolic pressure, a parameter of pulmonary arterial pressure, and central venous pressure, a parameter of systemic congestion, without significantly affecting left ventricular function (186).

CONCLUSIONS

In addition to its potent cardiovascular actions, endothelin-1 causes contraction of nonvascular smooth muscle (intestinal, tracheal, broncheal, mesangial, bladder, uterine, and prostatic smooth muscle); stimulation of the release of neuropeptides, pituitary hormones, and atrial natriuretic peptide; biosynthesis of aldosterone; modulation of neurotransmitter release; and increase of bone resorption. Furthermore, endothelin-1 has mitogenic properties, causing proliferation and hypertrophy of vascular smooth muscle, cardiac myocytes, mesangium, bronchial smooth muscle, and fibroblasts. Endothelin-1 also induces the expression of several proto-oncogenes (c-*fos*, c-*jun*, c-*myc*, etc). These actions are of potential significance in chronic congestive heart failure, renal disease, hypertension, cerebral vasospasm, and pulmonary hypertension, conditions commonly associated with increased expression of endothelin-1. The endothelin receptor antagonists, as well as animals in which the endothelin gene has been manipulated, are promising tools for revealing the exact pathophysiological roles of each of the endothelin family peptide and receptor subtypes and may make it possible to develop novel therapeutic agents for use in human disease.

Literature Cited

1. Yanagisawa M, Kurihara H, Kimura S, Tomobe Y, Kobayashi M, et al. 1988. A novel potent vasoconstrictor peptide produced by vascular endothelial cells. *Nature* 332:411–15
2. Inoue A, Yanagisawa M, Kimura S, Kasuya Y, Miyauchi T, et al. 1989. The human endothelin family: three structurally and pharmacologically distinct isopeptides predicted by three separate genes. *Proc. Natl. Acad. Sci. USA* 86:2863–67
3. Takasaki C, Tamiya N, Bdolah A, Wollberg Z, Kochva E. 1988. Sarafotoxins S6: several isotoxins from *Atractaspis engaddensis* (burrowing asp) venom that affect the heart. *Toxicon* 26:543–48
4. Sakurai T, Yanagisawa M, Inoue A, Ryan US, Kimura S, et al. 1991. cDNA cloning, sequence analysis and tissue distribution of rat preproendothelin-1 mRNA. *Biochem. Biophys. Res. Commun.* 175:44–47
5. Masaki T, Vane JR, Vanhoutte PM. 1994. International union of pharmacology nomenclature of endothelin receptors. *Pharmacol. Rev.* 46:137–42
6. Arai H, Hori S, Aramori I, Aramori I, Ohkub H, Nakanishi S. 1990. Cloning and expression of a cDNA encoding an endothelin receptor. *Nature* 348:730–32
7. Sakurai T, Yanagisawa M, Takuwa Y, Miyazaki H, Kimura S, et al. 1990. Cloning of a cDNA encoding a non isopeptide selective subtype of the endothelin receptor. *Nature* 348:732–35
8. Kurihara Y, Kurihara H, Suzuki H, Kodama T, Maemura K, et al. 1994. Elevated blood pressure and craniofacial abnormalities in mice deficient in endothelin-1. *Nature* 368:703–10
9. Hosoda K, Hammer RE, Giad A, Richardson JA, Baynash AG, et al. 1994. Targeted and natural (piebald-lethal) mutations of endothelin-B receptor gene produce megacolon associated with spotted coat color in mice. *Cell* 79:1267–76
10. Puffenberger EG, Hosoda K, Washington SS, Nakao K, deWit D, et al. 1994. A missense mutation of the endothelin-B-receptor gene in multigenic Hirschsprung's disease. *Cell* 79:1257–66
11. Gronostajski RM. 1987. Site specific DNA binding of nuclear factor 1: effect of spacer region. *Nucleic Acids Res.* 15:5545–59
12. Inoue A, Yanagisawa M, Takuwa Y, Mitsui Y, Kobayashi M, Masaki T. 1989. The human preproendothelin-1 gene: complete nucleotide sequence and regulation of expression. *J. Biol. Chem.* 264:14954–59
13. Emori T, Hirata Y, Imai T, Ohta K, Kanno K, et al. 1992. Cellular mechanisms of thrombin on endothelin-1 biosynthesis and release in bovine endothelial cell. *Biochem. Pharmacol.* 44:2409–11
14. Kurihara H, Yoshizumi M, Sugiyama T, Takaku F, Yanagisawa M, et al. 1989. Transforming growth factor beta stimulates the expression of endothelin mRNA from vascular endothelial cells. *Biochem. Biophys. Res. Commun.* 159:1435–40
15. Marsden PA, Brenner BM. 1992. Transcriptional regulation of the endothelin gene by TNF alpha. *Am. J. Physiol.* 262: C854–61
16. Maemura K, Kurihara H, Morita T, Hayashi Y, Yazaki Y. 1992. Production of endothelin-1 in vascular endothelial cells is regulated by factors associated with vascular injury. *Gerontorogy* 38 (Suppl. 1):29–35
17. Marsden PA, Dorfman DM, Collins T, Brenner BM, Orkin SH, Ballermann BJ. 1991. Regulated expression of endothelin-1 in glomerular capillary endothelial cells. *Am. J. Physiol.* 261:F117–25
18. Imai T, Hirata Y, Emori T, Yanagisawa M, Masaki T, Marumo F. 1992. Induction of endothelin-1 gene by angiotensin and vasopressin in endothelial cells. *Hypertension* 19:753–57

19. Sharefki JB, Diamond SL, Eskin SG, McIntire LV, Fenbach CW. 1991. Fluid flow decreases preproendothelin mRNA levels and suppresses endothelin-1 peptide release in cultured human endothelial cells. *J. Vasc. Surg.* 14:1–9
20. Malek A, Izumo S. 1992. Physiological fluid shear stress causes downregulation of endothelin-1 mRNA in bovine aortic endothelium. *Am. J. Physiol.* 263:C389–96
21. Yoshizumi M, Kurihara H, Sugiyama T, Takaku F, Yanagisawa M, et al. 1989. Hemodynamic shear stress stimulates endothelin production by cultured endothelial cells. *Biochem. Biophys. Res. Commun.* 161:859–64
22. Sumpio BE, Widmann MD. 1990. Enhanced production of endothelium-derived contracting factor by endothelial cells subjected to pulsatile stretch. *Surgery* 108:277–81
23. Malek AM, Greene AL, Izumo S. 1993. Regulation of endothelin-1 gene by fluid shear stress is transcriptionally mediated and independent of protein kinase C and cAMP. *Proc. Natl. Acad. Sci. USA* 90:5999–6003
24. Emori T, Hirata Y, Imai T, Eguchi S, Kanno K, Marumo F. 1993. Cellular mechanism of natriuretic peptides-induced inhibition of endothelin-1 biosynthesis in rat endothelial cells. *Endocrinology* 133:2474–80
25. Imai T, Hirata Y, Emori T, Marumo F. 1993. Heparin has an inhibitory effect on endothelin-1 synthesis and release by endothelial cells. *Hypertension* 21:353–58
26. Kido T, Sawamura T, Hoshikawa H, D'Orleans-Juste P, Denault JB, et al. 1997. Processing of proendothelin-1 at the C-terminus of big endothelin-1 is essential for proteolysis by endothelin-converting enzyme-1 in vivo. *Eur. J. Biochem.* 244:520–26
27. Matsumura Y, Hisaki K, Takaoka M, Morimoto S. 1990. Phosphoramidon, a metalloprotase inhibitor, suppresses the hypertensive effect of big endothelin-1. *Eur. J. Pharmacol.* 185:103–6
28. Gardiner SM, Compton AM, Kemp PA, Bennett T. 1991. The effects of phosphoramidon on the regional haemodynamic responses to human proendothelin (1–38) in conscious rats. *Br. J. Pharmacol.* 103:2009–15
29. Takahashi T, Matsushita Y, Iijima Y, Tanzawa K. 1993. Purification and characterization of endothelin-converting enzyme from rat lung. *J. Biol. Chem.* 268:21394–98
30. Shimada K, Takahashi M, Tanzawa K. 1994. Cloning and functional expression of endothelin-converting enzyme from rat endothelial cells. *J. Biol. Chem.* 269:18275–78
31. Emoto N, Yanagisawa M. 1995. Endothelin-converting enzyme-2 is a membrane-bound, phosphoramidon-sensitive metalloprotease with acidic pH optimum. *J. Biol. Chem.* 279:16262–68
32. Lin HY, Kaji EH, Winkel GK, Ives HE, Lodish HF. 1991. Cloning and functional expression of a vascular smooth muscle endothelin receptor. *Proc. Natl. Acad. Sci. USA* 88:3185–89
33. Elshourbagy NA, Lee JA, Korman DR, Nuthalaganti P, Sylvester DR, et al. 1992. Molecular cloning of the major endothelin receptor subtype in porcine cerebellum. *Mol. Pharmacol.* 41:465–73
34. Hosoda K, Nakao K, Tamura N, Arai H, Ogawa Y, et al. 1992. Organization, structure, chromosomal assignment, and expression of the gene encoding the human endothelin A receptor. *J. Biol. Chem.* 267:18797–804
35. Sakamoto A, Yanagisawa M, Sakurai T, Takuwa Y, Yanagisawa H, Masaki T. 1991. Cloning and functional expression of human cDNA for ET_B endothelin receptor. *Biochem. Biophys. Res. Commun.* 178:656–63
36. Sakurai T, Yanagisawa M, Masaki T. 1992. Molecular characterization of endothelin receptors. *Trends Pharmacol. Sci.* 13:103–8
37. Hirata Y, Yoshimi H, Takaichi S, Yanagisawa M, Masaki T. 1988. Binding and receptor down regulation of a novel vasoconstrictor endothelin in cultured rat vascular smooth muscle cells. *FEBS Lett.* 239:13–17
38. Devesly P, Phillips PE, Johns A, Rubanyi GM, Parker-Botelho LH. 1990. Receptor kinetics differ for endothelin 1 and endothelin 2 binding to Swiss 3T3 fibroblasts. *Biochem. Biophys. Res. Commun.* 172:126–34
39. Thomas CP, Baldi E, Simonson MS, Kester M, Dunn MJ. 1991. Endothelin receptors and coupled GTP binding proteins in glomerular mesangial cells. *J. Cardiovasc. Pharmacol.* 17(Suppl. 7):S79–84
40. Resink TJ, Scott-Burden T, Buhler FR. 1990. Activation of multiple signal transduction pathways by endothelin in cultured human vascular smooth muscle cells. *Eur. J. Biochem.* 189:415–21
41. Sakurai T, Morimoto Y, Kasuya Y, Takuwa Y, Nakauchi H, et al. 1992.

Level of ET_B receptor mRNA is down-regulated by endothelin through decreasing the intracellular stability of mRNA molecules. *Biochem. Biophys. Res. Commun.* 186:342–47
42. Kanno K, Hirata Y, Tsujino M, Imai T, Shichiri M, et al. 1993. Up-regulation of ET_B receptor subtype mRNA by angiotensin II in rat cardiomyocytes. *Biochem. Biophys. Res. Commun.* 194: 1282–87
43. Nishimura J, Chen X, Jahan H, Shikasho T, Kobayashi S, Kanaide H. 1992. cAMP induces up-regulation of ET_A receptor mRNA and increases responsiveness to endothelin-1 of rat aortic smooth muscle cells in primary culture. *Biochem. Biophys. Res. Commun.* 188:719–26
44. Nambi P, Pullen M, Wu HL, Nuthulaganti P, Elshourbagy N, Kumar C. 1992. Dexamethasone down-regulates the expression of endothelin receptors in vascular smooth muscle cells. *J. Biol. Chem.* 267: 19555–59
45. Badr KF, Murray JJ, Breyer MD, Takahashi K, Inagami T, Harris RC. 1989. Mesangial cell, glomerular and renal vascular responses to endothelin in the rat kidney. Elucidation of signal transduction pathways. *J. Clin. Invest.* 83:336–42
46. Takuwa Y, Kasuya Y, Takuwa N, Kudo M, Yanagisawa M, et al. 1990. Endothelin receptor is coupled to phospholipase C via a pertussis toxin insensitive guanine nucleotide binding regulatory protein in vascular smooth muscle cells. *J. Clin. Invest.* 85:653–58
47. Simonson MS, Dunn MJ. 1990. Cellular signaling by peptides of the endothelin gene family. *FASEB J.* 4:2989–3000
48. Silberberg SD, Poder TC, Lacerda A. 1989. Endothelin increases single channel calcium currents in coronary arterial smooth muscle cells. *FEBS Lett.* 247:68–72
49. Goto K, Kasuya Y, Matsuki N, Takuwa Y, Kurihara H, et al. 1989. Endothelin activates the dihydropyridine sensitive, voltage dependent Ca^{2+} channel in vascular smooth muscle. *Proc. Natl. Acad. Sci. USA* 86:3915–18
50. Iwamuro Y, Miwa S, Minowa T, Enoki T, Zhang XF, et al 1998. Activation of two types of Ca^{2+}-permeable nonselective cation channels by endothelin-1 in A7r5 cells. *Br. J. Pharmacol.* 124:1541–49
51. Liu Y, Geisburhler B, Jones AW. 1992. Activation of multiple mechanisms including phopholipase D by endothelin-1 in rat aorta. *Am. J. Physiol.* 262:C941–46
52. Griendling KK, Tsuda T, Alexander RW. 1989. Endothelin stimulates diacylglycerol accumulation and activates protein kinase C in cultured vascular smooth muscle cells. *J. Biol. Chem.* 264:8237–40
53. Lonchampt MO, Pinelis S, Goulin J, Chabrier PE, Braquet P. 1991. Proliferation and Na^+/H^+ exchange activation by endothelin in vascular smooth muscle cells. *Am. J. Hypertens.* 4:776–79
54. Chua BH, Krebs CJ, Chua CC, Diglio CA. 1992. Endothelin stimulates protein synthesis in smooth muscle cells. *Am. J. Physiol.* 262:E412–16
55. Bogoyevitch MA, Glennon PE, Sugden PH. 1993. Endothelin 1, phorbol esters and phenylephirine stimulate MAP kinase activities in ventricular cardiomyocytes. *FEBS Lett.* 317:271–75
56. Simonson MS, John JM, Dunn MJ. 1992. Differential regulation of *fos* and *jun* gene expression and AP 1 *cis* element activity by endothelin isopeptides. Possible implication for mitogenic signaling by endothelin. *J. Biol. Chem.* 267:8643–49
57. Simonson MS. 1993. Endothelins: multifunctional renal peptides. *Physiol. Rev.* 73:375–411
58. Okazawa M, Shiraki T, Ninomiya H, Kobayashi S, Masaki T. 1998. Endothelin-induced apoptosis of A 375 human melanoma cells. *J. Biol. Chem.* 273: 12584–92
59. Wang Y, Rose PM, Webb ML, Dunn MJ. 1994. Endothelins stimulate mitogen-activated protein kinase cascade through either ET_A or ET_B. *Am. J. Physiol.* 267: C1130–35
60. Sugawara F, Ninomiya H, Okamoto Y, Miwa S, Mazda O, et al. 1996. Endothelin-1-induced mitogenic responses of Chinese hamster ovary cells expressing human endothelin A: the role of a Wortmannin-sensitive signaling pathway. *Mol. Pharmacol.* 49:447–57
61. Cazaubon S, Parker PJ, Strosberg AD, Couraud P-O. 1993. Endothlins stimulate tyrosine phosphorylation and activity of p42/mitogen-activated protein kinase in astrocytes. *Biochem. J.* 293:381–86
62. Wang Y, Simonson MS, Pouysségur J, Dunn MJ. 1992. Endothelin rapidly stimulates mitogen-activated protein kinase activity in rat mesangial cells. *Biochem. J.* 287:589–94
63. Cazaubon SM, Ramos-Morales F, Fischer S, Schweighoffer F, Strosberg AD, Couraud P-O. 1994. Endothelin induces tyrosine phosphorylation and GRB2 association of Shc in astrocytes. *J. Biol. Chem.* 269:24805–9

64. Ihara M, Fukuroda T, Saeki T, Nishikibe M, Kojiri K, et al. 1991. An endothelin receptor (ET_A) antagonist isolated from *Streptomyces misakiensis*. *Biochem. Biophys. Res. Commun.* 178:132–37
65. Ihara M, Noguchi K, Saeki T, Fukuroda M, Tsuchida S, et al. 1992. Biological profiles of highly potent novel endothelin antagonists selective for the ET_A receptor. *Life Sci.* 50:247–55
66. Ishikawa K, Fukami T, Nagase T, Fujita K, Hayama T, et al. 1992. Cyclic pentapeptide endothelin antagonist with high ET_A selectivity. *J. Med. Chem.* 35:2139–42
67. Ikeda S, Awane Y, Kusumoto K, Wakimasu M, Watanabe T, Fujino M. 1994. A new endothelin receptor antagonist, TAK-044, shows long-lasting inhibition of both ET_A- and ET_B-mediated blood pressure responses in rats. *J. Pharmacol. Exp. Ther.* 270:728–33
68. Aramori I, Nirei H, Shoubo M, Sogabe K, Nakamura K, et al. 1993. Subtype selectivity of a novel endothelin antagonist, FR 139317, for the two endothelin receptors in transfected Chinese hamster ovary cells. *Mol. Pharmacol.* 43:127–31
69. Davenport AP, Kuc RE, Fitzgerald F, Maguire JJ, Berryman K, Doherty AM. 1994. [^{125}I]-PD151241: a selective radioligand for human ET_A receptors. *Br. J. Pharmacol.* 111:4–6
70. Kitada C, Ohtaki T, Masuda Y, Masuo Y, Nomura H, et al. 1993. Design and synthesis of ET_A receptor antagonists and study of ET_A receptor distribution. *J. Cardiovasc. Pharmacol.* 22(Suppl. 8):S128–31
71. James AF, Urade Y, Webb RL, Karaki H, Umemura I, et al. 1993. IRL 1620, succinyl-[Glu9, Ala11,15]-endothelin-1(8–21), a highly specific agonist of the ET_B receptor. *Cardiovasc. Drug. Rev.* 11:253–70
72. Ishikawa K, Ihara M, Noguchi K, Mase T, Mino N, et al. 1994. Biochemical and pharmacological profile of a potent and selective endothelin B-receptor antagonists, BQ-788. *Proc. Natl. Acad. Sci. USA* 91:4892–96
73. Webb RL, Navarrete AE, Ksander GM. 1995. Effects of the ET_B-selective antagonist IRL 2500 in conscious spontaneously hypertensive and Wistar-Kyoto rats. *J. Cardiovasc. Pharmacol.* 26(Suppl. 3):S389–92
74. Clozel M, Breu V, Burri K, Cassal JM, Fischli W, et al. 1993. Pathophysiological role of endothelin revealed by the first orally active endothelin receptor antagonist. *Nature* 365:759–61
75. Clozel M, Breu V, Gray GA, Kalina B, Loffler BM, et al. 1994. Pharmacological characterization of bosentan, a new potent orally active nonpeptide endothelin antagonist. *J. Pharmacol. Exp. Ther.* 270:228–35
76. Elliott JD, Lago MA, Cousins RD, Gao A, Leber JD, et al. 1994. 1,3-Diarylindan-2-carboxylic acids, potent and selective non-peptide endothelin receptor antagonists. *J. Med. Chem.* 37:1553–57
77. Ohlstein EH, Nambi P, Douglas SA, Edwards RM, Gellai M, Lago A. 1994. SB 209670, a rationally designed potent nonpeptide endothelin receptor antagonist. *Proc. Natl. Acad. Sci. USA* 91:8052–56
78. Reynolds EE, Keise JA, Haleen SJ, Walker DM, Olszewski B, et al. 1995. Pharmacological characterization of PD 156707, an orally active ET_A receptor antagonist. *J. Pharmacol. Exp. Ther.* 273:1410–17
79. Williams, DL Jr, Murphy KL, Nolan NA, O'Brien JA, Pettibone JA, et al. 1995. Pharmacology of L-754,142, a highly potent, orally active, nonpeptidyl endothelin antagonist. *J. Pharmacol. Exp. Ther.* 275:1518–26
80. Krause SM, Walsh TF, Greenlee WJ, Ranaei R, Kivlighn SD. 1995. Renal protection by endothelin antagonist, L-754,142, following aortic cross-clamping in the dog. *Circulation* 92(Suppl. 1):1065 (Abstr.)
81. Yamauchi R, Hoshino T, Ban Y, Kikkawa K, Murata S, et al. 1996. Effects of T-0115, a novel orally active endothelin antagonist, on monocrotaline-induced pulmonary hypertension in rats. *Jpn. J. Pharmacol.* 70(Suppl. I):236 (Abstr.)
82. Hoshino T, Yamauchi R, Kikkawa K, Yabana H, Murata S. 1998. Pharmacological profile of T-0201, a highly potent and orally active endothelin receptor antagonist. *J. Pharmacol. Exp. Ther.* 286:643–49
83. Nishikibe M, Ishikawa K, Fukuroda T, Ohta H, Kanoh T, et al. 1998. Pharmacology of J-104132, a potent, orally-active, mixed ET_A/ET_B endothelin receptor antagonist. *Naunyn Schmiedebergs Arch. Pharmacol.* 358(Suppl. 2):511 (Abstr.)
84. Doherty AM, Patt WC, Repine J, Edmunds JJ, Berryman KA, et al. 1995. Structure-activity relationships of a novel series of orally active nonpeptide ET_A and ET_A/B endothelin receptor-selective antagonists. *J. Cardiovasc. Pharmacol.* 26(Suppl. 3):S358–61
85. Maguire JJ, Kuc RE, Doherty AM, Davenport AP. 1995. Potency of PD155080,

an orally active ET_A receptor antagonist, determined for human endothelin receptors. *J. Cardiovasc. Pharmacol.* 26(Suppl. 3):S362–64
86. Smith TW, Braunwald E, Kelly RA. 1992. In *Heart Disease*, ed. E Braunwald, pp. 464–519. Philadelphia, PA: Saunders
87. Ho KK, Pinsky JL, Kannel WB, Levy D. 1993. The epidemiology of heart failure: the Framingham Study. *J. Am. Coll. Cardiol.* 22:6–13A
88. Ho KK, Anderson KM, Kannel WB, Grossman W, Levy D. 1993. Survival after the onset of congestive heart failure in Framingham Heart Study subjects. *Circulation* 88:107–15
89. Pfeffer MA. 1995. Left ventricular remodeling after acute myocardial infarction. *Annu. Rev. Med.* 46:455–66
90. Kannel WB, Sorlie P, McNamara PM. 1979. Prognosis after initial myocardial infarction: Framingham study. *Am. J. Cardiol.* 44:53–59
91. Hiroe M, Hirata Y, Fujita N, Umezawa S, Ito H, et al. 1991. Plasma endothelin-1 levels in idiopathic dilated cardiomyopathy. *Am. J. Cardiol.* 68:1114–15
92. McMurray JJ, Ray SG, Abdullah IA, Dargie HJ, Morton JJ. 1992. Plasma endothelin in chronic heart failure. *Circulation* 85:1374–79
93. Stewart DJ, Cernacek P, Costello KB, Rouleau JL. 1992. Elevated endothelin-1 in heart failure and loss of normal response to postural change. *Circulation* 85:510–17
94. Margulies KB, Hildebrand FL Jr, Lerman A, Perrella MA, Burnett JC Jr. 1990. Increased endothelin-1 in experimental heart failure. *Circulation* 82:2226–30
95. Underwood RD, Aarhus LL, Heublein DM, Burnett JC Jr. 1992. Endothelin in thoracic inferior vena caval constriction model of heart failure. *Am. J. Physiol.* 263:H951–55
96. Miyauchi T, Yanagisawa M, Tomizawa T, Sugishita Y, Suzuki N, et al. 1989. Increased plasma concentrations of endothelin-1 and big endothelin-1 in acute myocardial infarction. *Lancet* 2:53–54
97. Sakai S, Miyauchi T, Sakurai T, Kasuya Y, Ihara M, et al. 1996. Endogenous endothelin-1 participates in the maintenance of cardiac function in rats with congestive heart failure. Marked increase in endothelin-1 production in the failing heart. *Circulation* 93:1214–22
98. Rubanyi GM, Polokoff MA. 1994. Endothelins: molecular biology, biochemistry, pharmacology, physiology, and pathology. *Pharmacol. Rev.* 45:325–415
99. Suzuki T, Kumazaki T, Mitsui Y. 1993. Endothelin-1 is produced and secreted by neonatal rat cardiac myocytes in vitro. *Biochem. Biophys. Res. Commun.* 193:823–30
100. Goto K, Warner TD. 1995. Endothelin versatility. *Nature* 375:539–40
101. Miyauchi T, Yorikane R, Sakai S, Sakurai T, Okada M, et al. 1993. Contribution of endogenous endothelin-1 to the progression of cardiopulmonary alterations in rats with monocrotaline-induced pulmonary hypertension. *Circ. Res.* 73:887–97
102. Ito H, Hiroe M, Hirata Y, Fujisaka H, Adachi S, et al. 1994. Endothelin ET_A receptor antagonist blocks cardiac hypertrophy provoked by hemodynamic overload. *Circulation* 89:2198–203
103. Shubeita HE, McDonough PM, Harris AN, Knowlton KU, Glembotski CC, et al. 1990. Endothelin induction of inositol phospholipid hydrolysis, sarcomere assembly, and cardiac gene expression in ventricular myocytes. A paracrine mechanism for myocardial cell hypertrophy. *J. Biol. Chem.* 265:20555–562
104. Stawski G, Olsen UB, Grande P. 1991. Cytotoxic effect of endothelin-1 during 'stimulated' ischaemia in cultured myocytes. *Eur. J. Pharmacol.* 201:123–24
105. Prasad MR. 1991. Endothelin stimulates degradation of phospholipids in isolated rat hearts. *Biochem. Biophys. Res. Commun.* 174:952–57
106. Sakai S, Miyauchi T, Kobayashi M, Yamaguchi I, Goto K, Sugishita Y. 1996. Inhibition of myocardial endothelin pathway improves long-term survival in heart failure. *Nature* 384:353–55
107. Packer M, Carver JR, Rodeheffer RJ, Ivanhoe RJ, DiBianco R, et al for The PROMISE Study Research Group. 1991. Effect of oral milrinone on mortality in severe chronic heart failure. *N. Engl. J. Med.* 325:1468–75
108. Katz AM. 1986. Potential deleterious effects of inotropic agents in the therapy of chronic heart failure. *Circulation* 73:III184–88
109. Yorikane R, Koike H. 1990. The arrhythmogenic action of endothelin in rats. *Jpn. J. Pharmacol.* 53:259–63
110. Emori T, Hirata Y, Ohta K, Shichiri M, Marumo F. 1989. Secretory mechanism of immunoreactive endothelin in cultured bovine endothelial cells. *Biochem. Biophys. Res. Commun.* 160:93–100
111. Sumpio BE, Widmann MD. 1990. Enhanced production of endothelium-derived contracting factor by endothelial

cells subjected to pulsatile stretch. *Surgery* 108:277–81
112. Ito H, Hirata Y, Adachi S, Tanaka M, Tsujino M, et al. 1993. Endothelin-1 is an autocrine/paracrine factor in the mechanism of angiotensin II-induced hypertrophy in cultured rat cardiomyocytes. *J. Clin. Invest.* 92:398–403
113. Yorikane R, Sakai S, Miyauchi T, Sakurai T, Sugishita Y, Goto K. 1993. Increased production of endothelin-1 in the hypertrophied rat heart due to pressure overload. *FEBS Lett.* 332:31–34
114. Reiss K, Capasso JM, Huang H, Meggs LG, Li P, Anversa P. 1993. ANG II receptors, c-myc, and c-jun in myocytes after myocardial infarction and ventricular failure. *Am. J. Physiol.* 264:H760–69
115. Yanagisawa M, Inoue A, Takuwa Y, Mitsui Y, Kobayashi M, Masaki T. 1989. The human preproendothelin-1 gene: possible regulation by endothelial phosphoinositide turnover signaling. *J. Cardiovasc. Pharmacol.* 13(Suppl. 5):S13–17
116. Hirata Y, Fukuda Y, Yoshimi H, Emori T, Shichiri M, Marumo F. 1989. Specific receptor for endothelin in cultured rat cardiocytes. *Biochem. Biophys. Res. Commun.* 160:1438–44
117. Kiowski W, Sutsch G, Hunziker P, Muller P, Kim J, et al. 1995. Evidence for endothelin-1-mediated vasoconstriction in severe chronic heart failure. *Lancet* 346:732–36
118. Cody RJ, Haas GJ, Binkley PF, Capers Q, Kelly R. 1992. Plasma endothelin correlates with the extent of pulmonary hypertension in patients with chronic congestive heart failure. *Circulation* 85:504–9
119. Spinale FG, Walker JD, Mukherjee R, Inannini JP, Keever AT, Gallagher KP. 1997. Concomitant endothelin receptor subtype-A blockade during the progression of pacing-induced congestive heart failure in rabbits. *Circulation* 95:1918–29
120. Omland T, Lie RT, Aakvaag A, Arsland T, Dickstein K. 1994. Plasma endothelin determination as a prognostic indicator of 1-year mortality after acute myocardial infarction. *Circulation* 89:1573–79
121. Pacher R, Stanek B, Hulsmann M, Koller Sj, Berger R, et al. 1996. Prognostic impact of big endothelin-1 plasma concentrations compared with invasive hemodynamic evaluation in severe heart failure. *J. Am. Coll. Cardiol.* 27:633–41
122. Krum H, Gu A, Wilshire CM, Sackner BJ, Goldsmith R, et al. 1996. Changes in plasma endothelin-1 levels reflect clinical response to beta-blockade in chronic heart failure. *Am. Heart J.* 131:337–41
123. Brezis M, Epstein FH. 1993. Cellular mechanisms of acute ischemic injury in the kidney. *Annu. Rev. Med.* 44:27–37
124. Nord EP. 1993. Renal actions of endothelin. *Kidney Int.* 44:451–63
125. Tomita K, Ujiie K, Nakanishi T, Tomura S, Matsuda K, et al. 1989. Plasma endothelin levels in patients with acute renal failure. *N. Engl. J. Med.* 321:1127
126. Shibouta Y, Suzuki N, Shino A, Matsumoto H, Terashita Z-I, et al. 1990. Pathophysiological role of endothelin in acute renal failure. *Life Sci.* 46:1611–18
127. Kon V, Yoshioka T, Fogo A, Ichikawa I. 1989. Glomerular actions of endothelin in vivo. *J. Clin. Invest.* 83:1762–67
128. Lopez-Farre A, Gomez-Garre D, Bernabeu F, Lopez-Novoa M. 1991. A role for endothelin in the maintenance of post-ischemic renal failure in the rat. *J. Physiol.* 444:513–22
129. Vemulapalli S, Chiu PJS, Chintala M, Bernardino V. 1993. Attenuation of ischemic acute renal failure by phosphoramidon in rats. *Pharmacology* 47:188–90
130. Mino N, Kobayashi M, Nakajima A, Amano H, Shimamoto K, et al. 1992. Protective effect of a selective endothelin receptor antagonist, BQ-123, in ishemic acute renal failure in rats. *Eur. J. Pharmacol.* 221:77–83
131. Gellai M, Jugus M, Fletcher T, DeWolf R, Nambi P. 1994. Reversal of postischemic acute renal failure with a selective endothelin A receptor antagonist in the rat. *J. Clin. Invest.* 93:900–6
132. Kopp J, Klotmann PE. 1990. Cellular and molecular mechanisms of cyclosporin nephrotoxicity. *J. Am. Soc. Nephrol.* 1:162–70
133. Kon V, Sugiura M, Inagami T, Harvie BR, Ichikawa I, Hoover RL. 1990. Role of endothelin in cyclosporin induced glomerular dysfunction. *Kidney Int.* 37:1487–91
134. Kon V, Badr KF. 1991. Biological actions and pathophysiological significance of endothelin in the kidney. *Kidney Int.* 40:1–12
135. Kon V, Awazu M. 1992. Endothelin and cyclosporin nephrotoxicity. *Ren. Fail.* 14:345–50
136. Perico N, Dadan J, Remuzzi G. 1990. Endothelin mediates the renal vasoconstriction induced by cyclosporin in the rat. *J. Am. Soc. Nephrol.* 1:76–83
137. Awazu M, Sugiura M, Inagami T, Ichikawa I, Kon V. 1990. Cyclosporin promotes glomerular endothelin binding in vivo. *J. Am. Soc. Nephrol.* 1:1253–58

138. Brooks DP, Ohlstein EH, Contino LC, Storer B, Pullen M, et al. 1991. Effect of nifedipine on cyclosporin A-induced nephrotoxicity, urinary endothelin excretion and renal endothelin receptor number. *Eur. J. Pharmacol.* 194:115–17
139. Fogo F, Hellings SE, Inagami T, Kon V. 1992. Endothelin receptor antagonism is protective in in vivo acute cyclosporin toxicity. *Kidney Int.* 42:770–74
140. Bloom ITM, Bertley FR, Garrison RN. 1993. Acute cyclosporine-induced renal vasoconstriction is mediated by endothelin-1. *Surgery* 114:480–88
141. Takahashi K, Totsune K, Mouri T. 1994. Endothelin in chronic renal failure. *Nephron* 66:373–79
142. Haynes WG, Ferro CJ, O'Kane KPJ, Somerville D, Lomax CC, Webb DJ. 1996. Systemic endothelin receptor blockade decreases peripheral vascular resistance and blood pressure in humans. *Circulation* 93:1860–70
143. Hirata Y, Takagi N, Fukuda Y, Marumo F. 1989. Endothelin is a potent mitogen for rat vascular smooth muscle cells. *Atherosclerosis* 78:225–28
144. Fujita K, Matsumura Y, Kita S, Miyazaki Y, Hisaki K, et al. 1995. Role of endothelin-1 and the ET_A receptor in the maintenance of deoxycorticosterone acetate-salt-induced hypertension. *Br. J. Pharmacol.* 114:925–30
145. Verma S, Bhanot S, Mcneill LH. 1995. Effect of chronic endothelin blockade in hyperinsulinemic hypertensive rats. *Am. J. Physiol.* 269:H2017–21
146. Warner TD, Allcock GH, Vane JR. 1994. Reversal of established responses to endothelin-1 in vivo and in vitro by the endothelin receptor antagonists, BQ123 and PD145065. *Br. J. Pharmacol.* 112:207–13
147. Matsumura Y, Fujita K, Miyazaki Y, Takaoka M, Morimoto S. 1995. Involvement of endothelin-1 in deoxycorticosterone acetate-salt-induced hypertension and cardiovascular hypertrophy. *J. Cardiovasc. Pharmacol.* 26(Suppl. 3):S456–58
148. Vemulapalli S, Watkins RW, Brown A, Cook J, Bernardino V, Chiu PJ. 1993. Disparate effects of phosphoramidon on blood pressure in SHR and DOCA-salt hypertensive rats. *Life Sci.* 53:783–93
149. Nishikibe M, Tsuchida S, Okada M, Fukuroda T, Shimamoto K, Yano M. 1993. Antihypertensive effects of a newly synthesized endothelin antagonist, BQ-123, in a genetic hypertensive model. *Life Sci.* 52:717–24
150. Sogabe K, Nirei H, Shoubo M, Nomoto A, Ao S, et al. 1993. Pharmacological profile of FR 139317, a novel endothelin ET_A receptor antagonist. *J. Pharmacol. Exp. Ther.* 264:1040–46
151. Ohlstein EH, Douglas SA, Ezekiel M, Gellai M. 1993. Antihypertensive effects of the endothelin antagonist BQ-123 in conscious spontaneously hypertensive rats. *J. Cardiovasc. Pharmacol.* 22(Suppl. 8):S321–24
152. Donckier J, Stoleru L, Hayashida W, Van-Mechelen H, Selvais P, et al. 1995. Role of endogenous endothelin-1 in experimental renal hypertension in dogs. *Circulation* 92:106–13
153. Gardiner SM, March JE, Kemp PA, Mullins JJ, Bennett T. 1995. Haemodynamic effects of losartan and the endothelin antagonist, SB209670, in conscious, transgenic ((mRen-2) 27), hypertensive rats. *Br. J. Pharmacol.* 116:2237–44
154. Mullins JJ, Peters J, Ganten D. 1990. Fluminent hypertension in transgenic rats harbouring the mouse Ren-2 gene. *Nature* 344:541–44
155. Webb DJ, Monge JC, Rabelink TJ, Yanagisawa M. 1998. Endothelin: new discoveries and rapid progress in the clinic. *Trends Pharmacol. Sci.* 19:5–8
156. Battistini B, D'Orleans-Juste P, Sirois P. 1993. Biology of diseases, endothelin: circulating plasma levels and presence in other biological fluids. *Lab. Invest.* 6:600–28
157. Krum H, Viskoper RJ, Lacourciere Y, Budde M, Charlon V. 1998. The effect of an endothelin-receptor antagonist, bosentan, on blood pressure in patients with essential hypertension. *N. Engl. J. Med.* 338:784–90
158. Findlay JM, Weir BKA, Kanamaru K, Epinosal F. 1989. Arterial wall changes in cerebral vasospasm. *Neurosurgery* 25: 736–46
159. Asano T, Ikegaki I, Suzuki S, Shibuya M. 1989. Endothelin and the production of cerebral vasospasm in dogs. *Biochem. Biophys. Res. Commun.* 159:1345–13
160. Mima T, Yanagisawa M, Shigeno T, Saito A, Goto K, et al. 1989. Endothelin acts in feline and canine cerebral arteries from the adventitial side. *Stroke* 20:1553–56
161. Masaoka H, Suzuki R, Hirata Y, Emori T, Marumo F, Hirakawa K. 1990. Raised plasma endothelin in aneurysmal subarachnoid haemorrhage. *Lancet* 2:1402
162. Fujimori A, Yanagisawa M, Saito A, Goto K, Masaki T, et al. 1990. Endothelin in plasma and cerebrospinal fluid of patients

with subarachnoid hemorrhage. *Lancet* 336:633
163. Suzuki H, Sato S, Suzuki Y, Oka M, Tsuchiya T, et al. 1990. Endothelin immunoreactivity in cerebrospinal fluid of patients with subarachnoid haemorrhage. *Ann. Med.* 22:233–36
164. Kraus GE, Bucholz RD, Yook KW, Kneupfer MM, Smith KR. 1991. Cerebrospinal fluid endothelin-1 and endothelin-3 levels in normal and neurosurgical patients: a clinical study and literature review. *Surg. Neurol.* 35:20–29
165. Shigeno T, Mima Y, Yanagisawa M, Saito A, Goto K, et al. 1991. Prevention of cerebral vasospasm by actinomysin D. *J. Neurosurg.* 74:940–43
166. Itoh S, Sakaki T, Asai A, Kuchino Y. 1994. Prevention of delayed vasospasm by an endothelin ET_A receptor antagonist, BQ-123: change of ET_A receptor mRNA expression in a canine subrachnoid hemorrhage model. *J. Neurosurg.* 81:759–64
167. Alabadi JA, Salom JB, Torregross G, Miranda FJ, Jover T, Alborch E. 1993. Changes in the cerebrovascular effects of endothelin-1 and nicardipine after experimental subarachnoid hemorrhage. *Neurosurgery* 33:707–15
168. Nirei H, Hamada K, Shoubo M, Sogabe K, Notsu Y, Ono T. 1993. An endothelin ET_A receptor antagonist, FR139317, ameliorates cerebral vasospasm in dogs. *Life Sci.* 49:1869–74
169. Matsumura Y, Ikegawa R, Suzuki Y, Takaoka M, Uchida T, et al. 1991. Phosphoramidon prevents cerebral vasospasm following subarachinoid hemorrhage in dogs: the relationship to endothelin-1 levels in the cerebrospinal fluid. *Life Sci.* 49:841–48
170. Hirose H, Ide K, Sakaki T, Takahashi R, Kobayashi M, et al. 1995. The role of endothelin and nitric oxide in modulation of normal and spastic cerebral vascular tone in the dog. *Eur. J. Pharmacol.* 277:77–87
171. Willette RN, Zhang H, Mitchell MP, Sauermelch CF, Ohlstein EH, Sulpizio AC. 1994. Nonpeptide endothelin antagonist: cerebrovascular characterization and effects on delayed cerebral vasospasm. *Stroke* 25:2450–56
172. Shigeno T, Clozel M, Sakai S, Saito A, Goto K. 1995. The effect of bosentan, a new potent endothelin receptor antagonist, on the pathogenesis of cerebral vasospasm. *Neurosurgery* 37:87–91
173. Heath D, Smith P, Gosney J, Mulcahy D, Fox K, et al. 1987. The pathology of the early and late stages of primary-pulmonary hypertensin. *Br. Heart J.* 58: 204–13
174. Cernacek P, Stewart DJ. 1989. Immunoreactive endothelin in human plasma: marked elevations in patients in cardiogenic shock. *Biochem. Biophys. Res. Commun.* 161:562–67
175. Yoshibayashi M, Nishioka K, Nakao K, Saito Y, Matusmura M, et al. 1991. Plasma endothelin concentrations in patients with pulmonary hypertension associated with congenital heart defects: evidence for increased production of endothelin in pulmonary *Circulation* 84:2280–85
176. Cacoub P, Dorent R, Maistre G, Nataf P, Carayon A, et al. 1993. Endothelin-1 in primary pulmonary hypertension and the Eisenmenger syndrome. *Am. J. Cardiol.* 71:448–50
177. Ishikawa S, Miyauchi T, Ueno H, Ushinohama H, Sagawa K, et al. 1995. Influence of pulmonary blood pressure and flow on endothelin-1 production in humans. *J. Cardiovasc. Pharmacol.* 26:429–33
178. Ishikawa S, Miyauchi T, Sakai S, Ushinohama H, Sagawa K, et al. 1995. Elevated levels of plasma endothelin-1 in young patients with pulmonary hypertension caused by congenital heart disease are decreased after successful surgical repair. *J. Thorac. Cardiovasc. Surg.* 110:271–73
179. Giaid A, Yanagisawa M, Langleben D, Michel RP, Levy R, et al. 1993. Expression of endothelin-1 in the lungs of patients with pulmonary hypertension. *N. Engl. J. Med.* 328:1732–39
180. Giaid A, Michel RP, Stewart DJ, Sheppard M, Corrin B, Hamid Q. 1993. Expression of endothelin-1 in lungs of patients with crystogenic fibrosing alveolitis. *Lancet* 341:1550–54
181. Stelzner TJ, O'Brien RF, Sato K, Webb S, Zamora MR, et al. 1992. Increased endothelin-1 expression in rats with pulmonary hypertension. *Am. J. Physiol.* 262:L614–20
182. Zamora MR, Stelzner TJ, Webb S, Panos RJ, Ruff LJ, Dempsey EC. 1996. Overexpression of endothelin-1 and enhanced growth of pulmonary artery smooth muscle cell from fawn-fooded rats. *Am. J. Physiol.* 270:L101–9
183. Cassis LA, Rippetoe PA, Soltis EE, Painter DJ, Fitz R, Gillespie MN. 1992. Angiotensin II and monocrotaline-induced pulmonary hypertension: effect of losartan (DuP753), a nonpeptide angiotensin type I receptor antagonist. *J. Pharmacol. Exp. Ther.* 262:1168–72
184. Okada M, Yamashita C, Okada M,

Okada K. 1995. Role of endothelin-1 in beagles with dehydromonocrotaline-induced pulmonary hypertension. *Circulation* 92:114–19
185. Eddahibi S, Raffenstin B, Clozel M, Levame M, Adnot S. 1995. Protection from pulmonary hypertension with an orally active endothelin receptor antagonist in hypoxic rats. *Am. J. Physiol.* 268:H828–35
186. Sakai S, Miyauchi T, Sakurai T, Yamaguchi I, Kobayashi M, et al. 1996. Pulmonary hypertension caused by congestive heart failure is markedly ameliorated by chronic application of an endothelin receptor antagonist: increased expression of endothelin-1 mRNA and endothelin-1-like immunoreactivity in the lung in congestive heart failure in rats. *J. Am. Coll. Cardiol.* 28:1580–88

Annu. Rev. Physiol. 1999. 61:417–33

GENE INTERACTIONS IN GONADAL DEVELOPMENT

Keith L. Parker,[1] *Andreas Schedl,*[2] *and Bernard P. Schimmer*[3]
[1]Departments of Internal Medicine and Pharmacology, University of Texas Southwestern Medical Center, Dallas, Texas 75235; [2]Max-Delbrück-Centrum for Molecular Medicine, Robert-Rössle-Str.10, 13125 Berlin, Germany; [3]The Banting and Best Department of Medical Research, University of Toronto, Toronto, Canada M5G 1L6; e-mail: kparke@mednet.swmed.edu; bernard.schimmer@utoronto.ca; aschedl@mdc-berlin.de

KEY WORDS: sex determination, *SF-1*, *WT1*, *DAX-1*

ABSTRACT

The acquisition of a sexually dimorphic phenotype is a critical event in mammalian development. Although the maturation of sexual function and reproduction occurs after birth, essentially all of the critical developmental steps take place during embryogenesis. Temporally, these steps can be divided into two different phases: sex determination, the initial event that determines whether the gonads will develop as testes or ovaries; and sexual differentiation, the subsequent events that ultimately produce either the male or the female sexual phenotype. A basic tenet of sexual development in mammals is that genetic sex—determined by the presence or absence of the Y chromosome—directs the embryonic gonads to differentiate into either testes or ovaries. Thereafter, hormones produced by the testes direct the developmental program leading to male sexual differentiation. In the absence of testicular hormones, the pathway of sexual differentiation is female. This chapter reviews the anatomic and cellular changes that constitute sexual differentiation and discusses *SRY* and other genes, including *SF-1*, *WT1*, *DAX-1*, and *SOX9*, that play key developmental roles in this process. Dose-dependent interactions among these genes are critical for sex determination and differentiation.

0066-4278/99/0315-0417$08.00

ANATOMY AND CELL BIOLOGY OF SEXUAL DIFFERENTIATION

During the indifferent phase of sexual development, the ovaries and testes cannot be distinguished histologically and therefore are termed bipotential or indifferent gonads. As shown in Figure 1, these bipotential gonads arise from the urogenital ridge, a structure derived from the intermediate mesoderm, which contains cell precursors that help form the mesonephros, adrenal cortex, gonads, and kidneys. After sex determination, the testes and ovaries become histologically distinct as the testes organize into two distinct compartments: the testicular cords—precursors of the seminiferous tubules—and the interstitial region. The testicular cords contain fetal Sertoli cells and primordial germ cells, which originate outside the urogenital ridge and migrate into the indifferent gonad. The interstitial region surrounds the testicular cords and contains the steroidogenic Leydig cells and the peritubular myoid cells. In contrast, the ovaries have an amorphous, ground-glass appearance and exhibit little structural differentiation until late in gestation.

The urogenital tracts also are initially indistinguishable in male and female embryos. During the indifferent stage, both male and female embryos have two sets of paired ducts: the Müllerian ducts and the Wolffian (mesonephric) ducts. Under the influence of the Y chromosome in males, testes develop and produce specific hormones that trigger male sexual differentiation. The critical hormonal mediators of male sexual differentiation are the testicular androgens, produced by the Leydig cells in the interstitial region, and the glycoprotein hormone, Müllerian inhibiting substance (MIS) (also called anti-Müllerian hormone), produced by the Sertoli cells within the testicular cords (1, 2). Under the influence of the testicular androgens, the Wolffian ducts differentiate into the seminal vesicles, epididymis, vas deferens, and ejaculatory ducts; the Müllerian ducts degenerate under the influence of MIS. In the absence of the testicular hormones, the Wolffian ducts regress and the Müllerian ducts form the oviducts, Fallopian tubes, uterus, and upper vagina. The external genitalia also develop from structures that initially are common to both sexes: the genital tubercle, urethral folds, urethral groove, and genital swellings. As in the case of the urogenital tract, testicular androgens masculinize the external genitalia.

GENETICS OF SEX DETERMINATION

As a model system to characterize developmental decisions that occur during embryogenesis, sex determination is relevant to other aspects of developmental biology. Much of the understanding of sex determination has derived from cytogenetic studies linking specific chromosomal defects to abnormalities of sexual

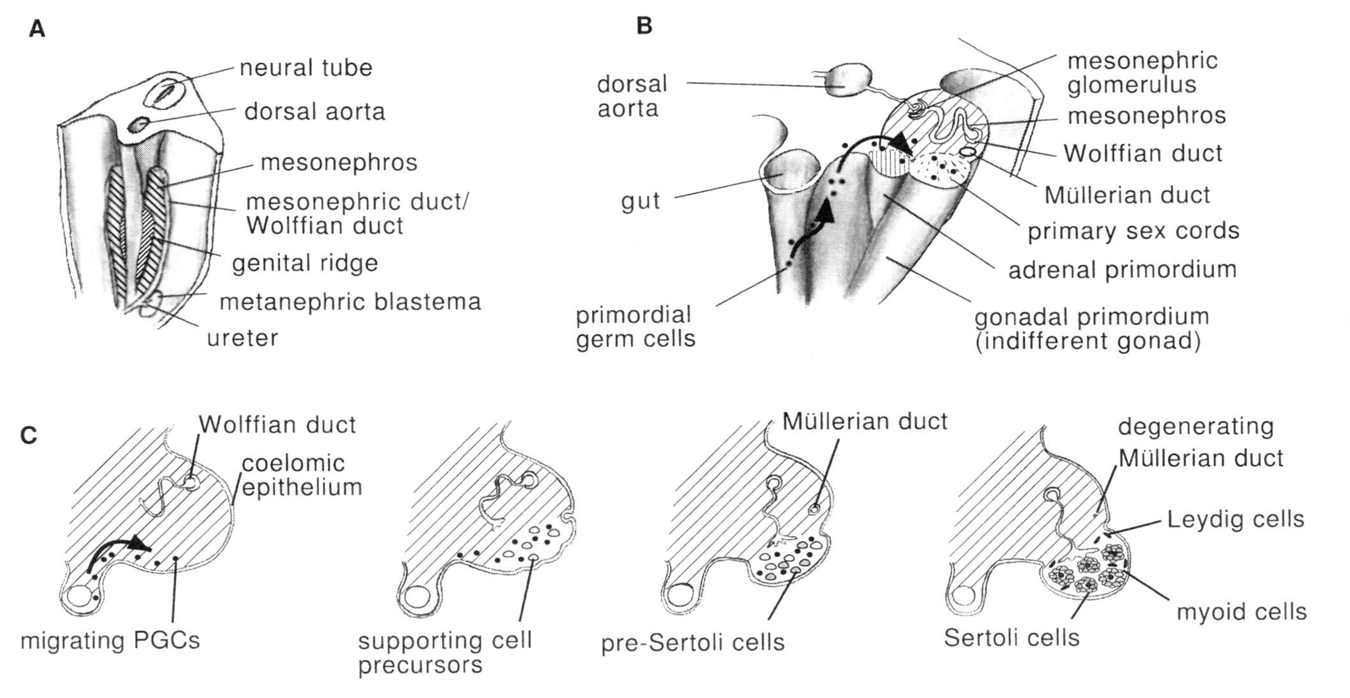

Figure 1 Events in gonadal development. (*A*) Diagram of the relative locations of the structures in the urogenital ridge. The gonads and mesonephros arise as paired structures. The kidney arises from inductive interactions between the ureteric bud and the metanephric blastema. (*B*) Diagram of the relative location of structures at the bipotential gonad stage. The primordial germ cells migrate into the gonads from the hindgut. (*C*) Schematic diagram of the sequential changes in the histologic organization of the testis as sex determination and differentiation occur. The Müllerian duct forms by invagination of the coelomic epithelium in the mesonephros. Following the expression of *SRY*, the supporting cells organize into testicular cords—precursors of the seminiferous tubules—containing Sertoli cells and primordial germ cells. The interstitial region around these cords contains the steroidogenic Leydig cells.

phenotype. In addition, molecular genetic analyses have identified specific mediators that regulate the process. Based on studies of *Drosophila* (reviewed in 3), sex determination in mammals was thought to depend on the ratio of X chromosomes to autosomes. The demonstration that XO individuals are phenotypically female and XXY individuals are phenotypically male, however, revealed the critical role of the Y chromosome in mammalian sex determination (4–6) and led to the concept that the Y chromosome encodes a specific product that mediates male sex determination. Further insights into the molecular basis of sex determination came from studies of individuals with primary sex reversal, a series of genetic disorders in which gonads and resulting sexual phenotype do not correlate with chromosomal sex. Cytogenetic studies of these patients revealed that a specific region of the Y chromosome correlated with testis formation and subsequent male sexual differentiation. This region was mapped to a small part of the Y chromosome, proximal to the pseudoautosomal region on the short arm, Yp (7). Positional cloning efforts ultimately led to the isolation of a gene from this region, designated *SRY* (sex-determining region-Y chromosome) (8), that met all the criteria predicted for a testis-determining factor (reviewed in 9, 10). The presence or absence of this gene correlated with the sex-reversal phenotype: *SRY* was detectable in most 46-XX subjects with a male phenotype and absent in a subset of 46-XY individuals with a female phenotype. More definitively, mutations that prevented expression of the *SRY* gene were identified in some sex-reversed 46-XY individuals (11, 12). Finally, introduction of mouse *SRY* as a transgene into XX mice induced testes formation and consequent male sexual differentiation (13).

The *SRY* gene encodes a DNA-binding motif, termed the high mobility group (HMG) box, which is found in a number of other proteins. *SRY* belongs to a subset of HMG box proteins that are expressed in a tissue-specific or developmentally regulated manner and that preferentially bind to specific DNA sequences (14). Other HMG box proteins of this subset have been isolated by virtue of their homology with *SRY*, and those with greater than 60% homology with the *SRY* HMG box are termed *SOX* genes (reviewed in 15). *SOX9*, one of these genes, also is involved in sex determination. Interestingly, almost all *SRY* mutations that cause sex reversal affect the HMG box, the only region tightly conserved through evolution, which supports an essential role for DNA binding in *SRY* action (16).

Multidimensional nuclear magnetic resonance spectroscopy analysis indicates that SRY interacts with DNA in its minor groove to induce a bend in the DNA double helix (17). Indeed, certain *SRY* mutations do not impair DNA binding but instead impair DNA bending—either by disordering the packing of the HMG box or by impairing direct contacts with DNA (18). These observations suggest that SRY, like other HMG box proteins (19), may regulate gene expression through "architectural" effects that convert promoter regions to a higher order of structure and facilitate the action of other transcriptional regulators.

Coupled with the documented role of SRY in activating the male developmental cascade, these findings suggest that SRY activates downstream genes, which then convert the bipotential gonad into a testis. Direct target genes of SRY, however, have not been isolated, and the mechanism by which it regulates gene transcription remains speculative. Some lines of evidence suggest that SRY does not activate a developmental cascade positively but rather represses a negative regulator that normally inhibits testicular development (20).

In summary, understanding the role of *SRY* in testicular development and hence in male sexual differentiation is incomplete. The timing and quantitative levels of *SRY* expression may be important for testes formation (21). Although SRY transcripts in the developing mouse testis correlate with the critical period of male sex determination, SRY protein has not been detected during this interval. In addition, most individuals with 46-XY sex reversal lack identifiable mutations in *SRY* coding sequences, and the same *SRY* mutation can have different effects when expressed on different genetic backgrounds (16). Thus, an important goal for further investigation is identifying the genes that act upstream and downstream of *SRY* in sex determination and differentiation.

OTHER GENES THAT PARTICIPATE IN GONADAL DEVELOPMENT

Steroidogenic Factor 1 (SF-1): An Essential Mediator of Endocrine Development

Mutations that impair genes essential for early events in gonadal development cause gonadal agenesis, thus impairing formation of both testes and ovaries. Such a role has been defined for steroidogenic factor 1 (SF-1) (reviewed in 22). SF-1 was identified initially as a transcription factor that regulates tissue-specific expression of the cytochrome P-450 steroid hydroxylases—enzymes that catalyze most of the reactions required for the synthesis of steroid hormones (23, 24). The subsequent isolation of a cDNA encoding SF-1 showed that this factor belongs to the nuclear hormone receptor family of transcription factors that mediate the actions of steroid hormones, thyroid hormone, vitamin D, and retinoids (25). In addition to the steroid hydroxylases, SF-1 also regulates adrenal and gonadal expression of many genes involved in steroidogenesis, including 3β-hydroxysteroid dehydrogenase, the ACTH receptor, and the steroidogenic acute regulatory protein (reviewed in 22). Analyses of reporter genes driven by the MIS promoter region in transfected Sertoli cells and transgenic mice suggest that SF-1 also regulates expression of the *MIS* gene (26–28). Thus, it appears that SF-1 controls the production of both hormones required for male phenotypic differentiation.

SF-1 is expressed in both male and female mouse embryos from the very earliest stages of gonadogenesis when the intermediate mesoderm condenses to form the urogenital ridge (29). With the onset of testicular differentiation, the levels of SF-1 transcripts increase in both functional compartments of the testes: the interstitial region (i.e. androgen-producing Leydig cells) and the testicular cords (i.e. MIS-synthesizing Sertoli cells). More striking, SF-1 transcripts in ovaries decrease coincident with sexual differentiation, which suggests that persistent SF-1 expression may impair female sexual differentiation. In addition to the gonads and adrenals, SF-1 transcripts also are detected in the anterior pituitary (30, 31) and hypothalamus (31, 32), which suggests that SF-1 regulates the endocrine axis at other levels.

Analyses of *SF-1* knockout mice confirmed essential roles of *SF-1* at all three levels of the hypothalamic-pituitary-steroidogenic organ axis. Most striking, these *SF-1* knockout mice lack adrenal glands and gonads because of programmed cell death in the primordial organs just as gonadal differentiation normally takes place (33, 34). As would be expected from the degeneration of testes before androgens and MIS are produced, *SF-1* knockout mice also exhibit male-to-female sex reversal of the internal and external urogenital tracts. These mice also have impaired expression of a number of markers of gonadotrops (30, 31), the cells in the anterior pituitary that regulate gonadal steroidogenesis, and they lack the ventromedial hypothalamic (VMH) nucleus (31, 32), a cell group in the medial hypothalamus linked to feeding and reproductive behaviors (35).

The early embryonic expression of *SF-1* in the gonads and its role as a transcription factor make it likely that *SF-1* is part of an ordered regulatory pathway that determines the expression of downstream genes required for gonadogenesis. In support of this, expression of SF-1 can direct pluripotential embryonic stem cells to differentiate, at least partly, down the steroidogenic pathway, activating expression of the cholesterol side-chain cleavage enzyme (36). These results suggest that other genes, in addition to *SF-1*, are required for full commitment to the steroidogenic lineage.

Mutations in *SF-1* have not yet been demonstrated in humans. The human *SF-1* gene shares extensive homology with its mouse counterpart (37, 38) and is expressed in many of the same sites (39), which suggests that *SF-1* in humans functions much as it does in mice. The human *SF-1* gene resides on chromosome 9q33 (40), and it is reasonable to speculate that patients will be found with abnormalities of gonadal development or sexual differentiation that map to this locus.

WT1: A Tumor Suppressor that Regulates Urogenital Development

WT1 was identified initially through its association with Wilms' tumors—embryonic kidney tumors that arise from abnormal proliferation of the metanephric blastema. Wilms' tumors occur almost exclusively during childhood and therefore represent a case of development gone awry (reviewed in 41). The genetics of Wilms' tumors are complex, involving at least four different genetic loci: chromosome 17q12-21 (42), chromosome 11p13, and two loci on chromosome 11p15 (43). Thus far, however, only one gene has been isolated whose mutation or deletion causes Wilms' tumors—the Wilms' tumor predisposition gene *WT1*. Patients with familial Wilms' tumors related to *WT1* usually inherit mutations or deletions of one *WT1* allele and subsequently undergo somatic loss of the second allele due to gross chromosomal events. Cloning of *WT1* was guided largely by heterozygous chromosomal deletions of human chromosome 11p13 that are associated with the WAGR syndrome, a disorder that includes Wilms' tumors, aniridia, genitourinary abnormalities, and mental retardation (44). Genitourinary abnormalities occur in only a subset of patients and are relatively mild, involving cryptorchidism and hypospadias in males and horseshoe kidneys in both sexes. The WAGR phenotype reflects the contiguous deletion of several genes, including *WT1* (45–47) and the transcription factor *PAX6* (48), which also is associated with aniridia in non-WAGR patients. Two other genes were subsequently identified within the WAGR region, both of which are expressed in the embryonic brain; deletion of these genes may contribute to the mental retardation associated with the WAGR syndrome (49, 50).

Sequence analysis of *WT1* identified four zinc fingers at the carboxyl terminus, the last three of which show high homology with the transcription factors Sp1 and Egr1. Consistent with a possible role as a transcription factor, WT1 interacts with specific DNA recognition sequences upstream of a large number of genes, including genes that encode growth factors and their receptors (reviewed in 51), generally repressing their transcription. Although repression of growth-stimulating genes provides a plausible explanation for tumor suppression, it is not clear that this role can fully explain the pleiotropic effects of *WT1*.

Alternative splicing (52) and alternative translation start sites (53) generate at least eight different isoforms of WT1, clearly indicating that *WT1* is a gene of considerable complexity. Besides differing somewhat in their DNA binding affinities (54), the various WT1 isoforms localize differently within the nucleus, determined mainly by the presence or absence of an alternative splice that introduces three amino acids [lysine-threonine-serine (KTS)] between zinc fingers 3 and 4. Isoforms lacking KTS (−KTS) show a diffuse nuclear staining pattern reminiscent of typical transcription factors, whereas isoforms containing

KTS (+KTS) are associated with spliceosomes. This suggests a role in RNA processing (55, 56). In support of this concept, WT1—particularly the +KTS isoforms—can bind RNA (57), and a putative RNA binding motif has been identified in the amino-terminal domain (58). Despite evidence for distinct functions of the different WT1 isoforms, the ratios of the various isoforms do not vary in different tissues where *WT1* is expressed.

Besides mediating tumor suppression, *WT1* plays essential roles in development of the urogenital tract. *WT1* is expressed very early during development of the urogenital ridge, and a specific expression pattern occurs in the developing kidneys and gonads (59). In the testes and ovaries, expression becomes restricted to the Sertoli and granulosa cells, respectively (60, 61). These cells support germ cell maturation, and *WT1* likely contributes to this function (62, 63). Mice homozygous for a *WT1* knockout allele lack kidneys and gonads (64) and show impaired adrenal development (A Schedl, unpublished result). As a result of gonadal degeneration before androgens and MIS are made, the internal and external genitalia develop along the female pathway. These results, coupled with the structural similarity of WT1 with other transcription factors, suggest that WT1 regulates target genes that are essential for gonadogenesis in both sexes.

Analyses of patients with mild genital abnormalities demonstrated that *WT1* also plays important developmental roles in humans (65). *WT1* mutations in these patients usually are heterozygous loss-of-function mutations. Because these mutations do not act as dominant negative inhibitors of WT1 function, this suggests that gene dosage of *WT1* is critical in humans. More interesting, mice heterozygous for the disrupted allele are phenotypically normal. Although this may reflect differences in the degree of impairment of *WT1*, mice may be less sensitive to reduced levels of WT1.

In addition to the classical Wilms' tumor and the WAGR syndrome, *WT1* mutations are associated with two other disorders in humans: Denys-Drash syndrome and Frasier syndrome. Denys-Drash syndrome is an autosomal dominant disorder consisting of gonadal and urogenital abnormalities in conjunction with diffuse mesangial sclerosis. The renal disease in Denys-Drash patients is severe, usually manifests in the first year of life, and causes end-stage renal disease by age 3. The gonadal abnormalities of these patients vary but generally are more severe than those associated with the WAGR syndrome, with streak gonads and sex-reversal of external and internal genitalia in 46-XY males at one extreme and varying degrees of pseudohermaphroditism in less-severely affected males. Wilms' tumors are common in Denys-Drash families. Denys-Drash syndrome almost always results from point mutations in the zinc finger region that abolish DNA binding; in view of the autosomal dominant inheritance of the disorder, these mutated proteins presumably inhibit function of wild-type

WT1 in a dominant negative fashion (66–68). In support of this model, WT1—at least in vitro—forms homodimers (69). Extrapolating from the *WT1* knockout mice, the degree of inhibition of WT1 action probably correlates with the impairment of genitourinary development, with the most severe mutations leading to early gonadal dysgenesis and female development of external and internal genitalia in males. Other factors affect the severity of the resulting phenotype, as demonstrated by individuals whose fathers—despite carrying the same *WT1* mutation as affected offspring—are phenotypically normal.

WT1 mutations also have been identified in patients with Frasier syndrome (70–72). Unlike Denys-Drash patients, these patients do not develop Wilms' tumors but have gonadal dysgenesis, male pseudohermaphroditism, and focal glomerular sclerosis. The glomerulopathy is less severe than that associated with Denys-Drash mutations; renal insufficiency is not evident until after age 4, and some renal function is preserved into adolescence or young adulthood. *WT1* mutations that cause Frasier syndrome cluster within intron 9 of the *WT1* gene and apparently interfere selectively with the synthesis of the +KTS isoforms. This finding suggests that the +KTS isoform is essential for gonadal development but plays no essential role in suppressing the development of Wilms' tumors. The same *WT1* mutations that cause Frasier syndrome in boys also may cause focal glomerular sclerosis in girls, who escape diagnosis because the urogenital tracts are normal. Recognition of the *WT1* mutations in these families may facilitate genetic counseling.

DAX-1: A Potential Mediator of Ovarian Development

46-XY sex reversal occurs in males who have a duplicated short arm of the human X chromosome and thus carry two copies of a 160-kb Xp locus. This phenomenon is termed dosage-sensitive sex reversal (73). Mutations or deletions of the same region of Xp in 46-XY males cause X-linked adrenal hypoplasia congenita (AHC), a disorder associated with ACTH-insensitive adrenal insufficiency due to impaired development of the definitive zone of the adrenal cortex—the site of postnatal steroidogenesis. Positional cloning of the AHC gene led to the isolation of a gene, designated *DAX-1* (dosage-sensitive sex reversal, adrenal hypoplasia congenita, X-linked) (74, 75). *DAX-1* encodes an atypical member of the nuclear hormone receptor family that retains the conserved ligand binding domain but lacks the typical zinc finger DNA-binding motif, which suggests that DAX-1 regulates gene expression through protein-protein interactions. AHC patients, if kept alive with adrenal steroids, later exhibit features of hypogonadotrophic hypogonadism due to a compound hypothalamic/pituitary defect. The combination of impaired adrenal development and hypogonadotrophic hypogonadism resembles the phenotype in *SF-1* knockout mice, which suggests that *DAX-1* and *SF-1* may act in the same developmental pathway. Moreover, both genes are expressed in many of the same sites, including the gonads, adrenal cortex, pituitary gonadotropes, and the VMH nucleus (76, 77). As discussed below, there is evidence in support of direct interactions between DAX-1 and SF-1.

INTERACTIONS AMONG TRANSCRIPTION FACTORS IN GONADAL DEVELOPMENT

Gonadal differentiation requires a complex series of events occurring in appropriate tissues at appropriate times of development. Although *SRY* is the dominant controller of male sex determination, considerable gaps remain in our understanding of how *SRY* mediates these critical events in development. As summarized in Figure 2, both X-linked genes (e.g. *DAX-1*) and autosomal genes (e.g. *SF-1*, *WT1*, and *SOX9*) also play critical roles in processes of sex determination and differentiation. An important goal for future studies is to define how these genes interact.

SF-1 and WT1

SF-1 appears to interact directly with other genes in gonadal and adrenal development. When analyzed in vitro with recombinantly expressed proteins or in

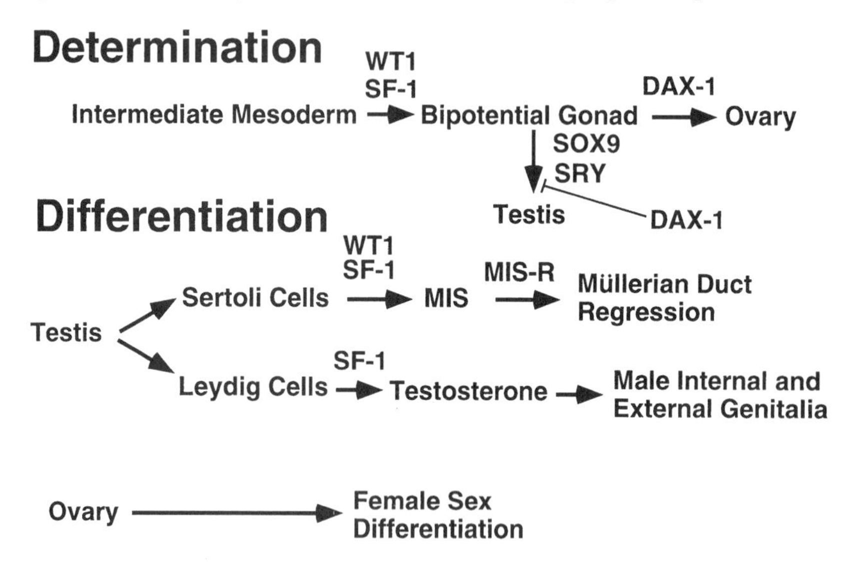

Figure 2 Summary of the molecular events in mammalian sex determination and differentiation. The positions of a number of genes believed to mediate key events in sex determination and differentiation are indicated, as discussed in the text. The proposed action of *DAX-1* in repressing testicular development also is indicated.

mammalian two-hybrid assays, WT1 and SF-1 proteins form heterodimers (78). The functional significance of this interaction is supported by the finding that cotransfection with WT1 augments SF-1–dependent transcriptional activation of the MIS promoter. This effect is most pronounced with the −KTS isoform of WT1, a puzzling result because studies of patients with Frasier syndrome implicate a role for the +KTS isoform in gonadogenesis. Cotransfection with WT1 increases the expression of reporter genes driven by the *SF-1* promoter, which suggests that *WT1* may act in part to regulate *SF-1* expression (D Lala, K Parker, unpublished observation). In these studies, the +KTS isoform induced promoter activity most potently, indicating a role for the +KTS isoform in testicular development that is more consistent with the finding of abnormal testes in patients with Frasier syndrome. *WT1* apparently is not essential for *SF-1* expression, as *WT1* knockout mice still have detectable SF-1 transcripts in the degenerating gonads (K Parker, J Kreidberg, unpublished observation). *WT1* may regulate *SF-1* activity by two mechanisms: facilitating SF-1–dependent activation of downstream genes such as MIS and increasing the levels of SF-1.

SF-1 and DAX-1

SF-1 and *DAX-1* also appear to interact directly, although the nature of the interactions differs considerably among studies. DAX-1 can form heterodimers with SF-1, thereby inhibiting SF-1–mediated transcriptional activation; mutations associated with adrenal hypoplasia congenita impair this interaction (79). *DAX-1* also may inhibit the expression of *SF-1*–dependent target genes by recruiting the corepressor N-Cor to their promoters (80). Finally, DAX-1 may interfere with *SF-1* action by binding to hairpin loops in the 5′-flanking region of *SF-1*–responsive genes, presumably blocking access of SF-1 to the promoters (81). In addition to these antagonistic models of *SF-1* and *DAX-1* action, a cooperative link between these two genes is suggested by reports that SF-1 can interact with promoter elements upstream of *DAX-1* to induce its expression (82, 83).

The functional consequences of these proposed interactions between *DAX-1* and *SF-1* presumably differ depending on the tissue. In certain sites (e.g. the adrenal cortex, gonadotropes, and VMH), *SF-1* and *DAX-1* may cooperate to activate the expression of target genes required for tissue-specific functions. Consistent with this hypothesis, the phenotypes of *SF-1* knockout mice and *DAX-1* patients are generally concordant in these sites. In gonads, in contrast, the actions of *SF-1* and *DAX-1* appear to be antagonistic. SF-1 levels in the ovaries decrease with time, whereas *SF-1* is required for testes development and male sexual differentiation. Thus, whereas *SF-1* is essential for normal male sexual differentiation, its expression may suppress ovarian development and female sexual differentiation. These findings lead to the possibility that a presumptive excess of *DAX-1*—in patients with dosage-sensitive sex reversal—would suppress *SF-1* function and favor ovarian development whereas the complete absence of *DAX-1* would not impede *SF-1* action and therefore would be compatible with normal testicular differentiation.

SUMMARY AND PERSPECTIVES

As outlined in Figure 2, a number of genes are now known to play critical roles in gonadal development and sexual determination/differentiation. Additional unidentified genes almost certainly contribute to these complex developmental pathways. For example, other chromosomal regions have been associated with 46-XY sex reversal in humans [e.g. monosomy of chromosome 9q24 (84), monosomy of the long arm of chromosome 10 (85)] and in mice (86, 87), implicating yet-to-be-defined genes at other loci that are essential for sex determination. One human gene includes a region homologous to a DNA-binding motif found in *doublesex*, a gene that plays key roles in sex determination and neuroblast differentiation in *Drosophila*. More intriguing, this gene (designated *DMT1*) is selectively expressed in the testis and maps to the same region of the distal short arm of chromosome 9 implicated in human 46-XY sex reversal (88). These findings suggest that this gene may be responsible for disorders of sexual differentiation associated with deletion of 9q24, and further, that there is a common evolutionary origin of at least some aspects of sexual regulation. Finally, analyses of gene function by targeted gene disruption have identified additional genes essential for early events in gonadal development, including the homeodomain proteins Lim1 (89) and Emx2 (90) and the polycomb-related protein M33 (91).

Gene dosage also plays a critical role in mammalian sex determination. As noted above, the ratio of autosomes to the X chromosome is the critical factor in *Drosophila*, and some insights have been obtained into the molecular mechanisms by which this "counting" takes place (92). Despite the apparent dominant action of *SRY*, the expression ratio of other genes also is crucial for gonadogenesis. Loss-of-function mutations of a single copy of the *WT1* gene can impair gonadogenesis, which suggests an important effect of gene dosage. This phenomenon—in which a loss-of-function mutation is dominant to the wild-type allele—is termed haploinsufficiency. Similar haploinsufficiency plays a role in disorders associated with the *SRY*-related *SOX9*. Mutations in SOX-9 cause campomelic dysplasia, an autosomal dominant disorder characterized by skeletal abnormalities (e.g. congenital bowing of long bones in association with brachydactyly, clinodactyly, and micrognathia), cardiac and renal abnormalities, and impaired testes development with resulting 46-XY sex reversal (93, 94). Again, the dominant nature of this disorder strongly implies that two functional copies of this autosomal gene are required for testicular development. Perhaps the most striking example of gene dosage effects in mammalian sex determination comes from studies with *DAX-1*. As discussed above, the *DAX-1* gene lies within a region of the X chromosome whose duplication is associated with 46-XY sex reversal, which suggests that an extra copy of *DAX-1* impedes the action of *SRY*. Direct evidence that *DAX-1* causes the sex reversal has been obtained in experiments in which overexpression of DAX-1 in gonadal cells impair testes development, either in XX mice carrying an *SRY* transgene or in XY mice with a relatively weak *SRY* allele (95). These findings support the concept that *DAX-1* is responsible for dosage-sensitive sex reversal and, again, highlight the importance of gene dosage in mammalian sex determination.

As suggested by this review, mammalian sexual determination may be more like sex determination in *Drosophila* and other metazoans than previously appreciated. Parallels in the influence of gene dosage and the involvement of homologous genes, such as *doublesex* (88), suggest that sexual determination among diverse life forms may have a common evolutionary origin.

Literature Cited

1. Jost A. 1953. Studies on sex differentiation in mammals. *Recent Prog. Horm. Res.* 8:379–418
2. Jost A, Vigier B, Prepin J, Perchellet J. 1973. Studies on sex differentiation in mammals. *Recent Prog. Horm. Res.* 29:1–41
3. Hodgkin J. 1992. Genetic sex determination mechanisms and evolution. *BioEssays* 14:253–61
4. Ford CE, Jones KW, Polani PE, Almeida JC, Briggs JH. 1959. A sex-chromosome anomaly in a case of gonadal dysgenesis (Turner's syndrome). *Lancet* 1:711–13
5. Jacobs PA, Strong JA. 1959. A case of human intersexuality having a possible XXY sex-determinating mechanism. *Nature* 183:302–3
6. Welshons WJ, Russell LB. 1959. The Y chromosome as the bearer of male determining factors. *Proc. Natl. Acad. Sci. USA* 45:560–66
7. Page DC, Mosher R, Simpson EM, Fisher EM, Mardon G, et al. 1987. The sex-determining region of the human Y chromosome encodes a finger protein. *Cell* 51:1091–104
8. Sinclair AH, Berta P, Palmer MS, Hawkins JR, Griffiths BL, et al. 1990. A gene from the sex-determining region encodes a protein with homology to a conserved DNA-binding motif. *Nature* 346:240–44
9. Goodfellow PN, Lovell-Badge R. 1993. SRY and sex determination in mammals. *Annu. Rev. Genet.* 27:71–92
10. Capel B. 1998 Sex in the 90s: SRY and the switch to the male pathway. *Annu. Rev. Physiol.* 60:497–523
11. Berta P, Hawkins JR, Sinclair AH, Taylor BL, Griffiths PN, et al. 1990. Genetic evidence equating SRY and the testis-determining factor. *Nature* 348:448–50
12. Jager RJ, Anvret M, Hall K, Scherer G. 1990. A human XY female with a frame shift mutation in the candidate testis-determining gene *SRY*. *Nature* 348:452–54
13. Koopman P, Gubbay J, Vivian N, Goodfellow P, Lovell-Badge R. 1991. Male development of chromosomally female mice transgenic for SRY. *Nature* 351:117–21
14. Laudet V, Stehelin D, Clevers H. 1993. Ancestry and diversity of the HMG box superfamily. *Nucleic Acids Res.* 21:2493–501
15. Pevny LH, Lovell-Badge R. 1997. Sox

genes find their feet. *Curr. Opin. Genet. Devel.* 7:338–44
16. Cameron FJ, Sinclair AH. 1997. Mutations in SRY and SOX9: Testis-determining genes. *Hum. Mutat.* 9:388–95
17. Werner MH, Huth JR, Gronenborn AM, Clore GM. 1995. Molecular basis of human 46X,Y sex reversal revealed from the three-dimensional solution structure of the human SRY-DNA complex. *Cell* 81:705–14
18. Pontiggia A, Rimini R, Harley VR, Goodfellow PN, Lovell-Badge R, Bianchi ME. 1994. Sex reversing mutations affecting the architecture of SRY-DNA complexes. *EMBO J.* 13:6115–24
19. Grosschedl R, Giese K, Pagel J. 1994. HMG domain proteins: architectural elements in the assembly of nucleoprotein structures. *Trends Genet.* 10:94–100
20. McElreavey K, Vilain E, Abbas N, Herskowitz I, Fellous M. 1993. A regulatory cascade hypothesis for mammalian sex determination: SRY represses a negative regulator of male development. *Proc. Natl. Acad. Sci. USA* 90:3368–72
21. Eicher EM, Washburn LL. 1986. Genetic control of primary sex determination in mice. *Annu. Rev. Genet.* 20:327–60
22. Parker KL, Schimmer BP. 1997. Steroidogenic factor 1: a key determinant of endocrine development and function. *Endocrine Rev.* 18:361–77
23. Lala DS, Rice DA, Parker KL. 1992. Steroidogenic factor I, a key regulator of steroidogenic enzyme expression, is the mouse homolog of fushi tarazu-factor I. *Mol. Endocrinol.* 6:1249–58
24. Honda S-I, Morohashi K-I, Nomura M, Takeya H, Kitajima M, Omura T. 1993. Ad4BP regulating steroidogenic P-450 gene is a member of steroid hormone receptor superfamily. *J. Biol. Chem.* 268:7494–502
25. Evans RM. 1988. The steroid and thyroid hormone receptor superfamily. *Science* 240:889–95
26. Shen W-H, Moore CCD, Ikeda Y, Parker KL, Ingraham HA. 1994. Nuclear receptor steroidogenic factor 1 regulates MIS gene expression: a link to the sex determination cascade. *Cell* 77:651–61
27. Hatano O, Takayama K, Imai T, Waterman MR, Takakusu T, et al. 1995. Sex-dependent expression of a transcription factor, Ad4BP, regulating steroidogenic P-450 genes in the gonads during prenatal and postnatal rat development. *Development* 120:2787–97
28. Giuili G, Shen WH, Ingraham HA. 1997. The nuclear receptor SF-1 mediates sexually dimorphic expression of Müllerian inhibiting substance, in vivo. *Development* 124:1799–807
29. Ikeda Y, Shen W-H, Ingraham HA, Parker KL. 1994. Developmental expression of mouse steroidogenic factor 1, an essential regulator of the steroid hydroxylases. *Mol. Endocrinol.* 8:654–62
30. Ingraham HA, Lala DS, Ikeda Y, Luo X, Shen W-H, et al. 1994. The nuclear receptor steroidogenic factor 1 acts at multiple levels of the reproductive axis. *Genes Dev.* 8:2302–12
31. Shinoda K, Lei H, Yoshii H, Nomura M, Nagano M, et al. 1995. Developmental defects of the ventromedial hypothalamic nucleus and pituitary gonadotroph in the Ftz-F1-disrupted mice. *Dev. Dyn.* 204:22–29
32. Ikeda Y, Luo X, Abbud R, Nilson JH, Parker KL. 1995. The nuclear receptor steroidogenic factor 1 is essential for the formation of the ventromedial hypothalamic nucleus. *Mol. Endocrinol.* 9:478–86
33. Luo X, Ikeda Y, Parker KL. 1994. A cell-specific nuclear receptor is essential for adrenal and gonadal development and for male sexual differentiation. *Cell* 77:481–90
34. Sadovsky Y, Crawford PA, Woodson KG, Polish JA, Clements MA, et al. 1995. Mice deficient in the orphan receptor steroidogenic factor 1 lack adrenal glands and gonads but express P450 side-chain-cleavage enzyme in the placenta and have normal embryonic serum levels of corticosteroids. *Proc. Natl. Acad. Sci. USA* 92:10939–43
35. Canteras NS, Simerly RB, Swanson LW. 1994. Organization of projections from the ventromedial hypothalamic nucleus of the hypothalamus: a *Phaseolus vulgaris*-leucoagglutinin study in the rat. *J. Comp. Neurol.* 348:41–79
36. Crawford PA, Sadovsky Y, Milbrandt J. 1997. Nuclear receptor steroidogenic factor 1 directs embryonic stem cells toward the steroidogenic lineage. *Mol. Cell. Biol.* 17:3997–4006
37. Oba K, Yanase T, Nomura M, Morohashi K, Takayanagi R, Nawata H. 1996. Structural characterization of human Ad4BP (SF-1) gene. *Biochem. Biophys. Res. Commun.* 226:261–67
38. Wong M, Ramayya MS, Chrousos GP, Driggers PH, Parker KL. 1996. Cloning and sequence analysis of the human gene encoding steroidogenic factor 1. *J. Mol. Endocrinol.* 17:139–47
39. Ramayya MS, Zhou J, Kino T, Segars JH, Bondy CA, Chrousos GP. 1997. Steroidogenic factor 1 messenger ribonucleic acid

expression in steroidogenic and nonsteroidogenic human tissues: Northern blot and in situ hybridization studies. *J. Clin. Endocrinol. Metab.* 82:1799–806

40. Taketo M, Parker KL, Howard TA, Tsukiyama T, Wong M, et al. 1995. Homologs of *Drosophila* fushi tarazu factor 1 map to mouse chromosome 2 and human chromosome 9q33. *Genomics* 25:565–67
41. Hastie ND. 1993. The genetics of Wilms' tumor—a case of disrupted development. *Annu. Rev. Genet.* 28:523–58
42. Rahman N, Arbour L, Tonin P, Renshaw J, Pelletier J, et al. 1996. Evidence for a familial Wilms' tumour gene (FWT1) on chromosome 17q12-q21. *Nat. Genet.* 13:461–63
43. Karnik P, Chen P, Paris M, Yeger H, Williams BRG. 1998. Loss of heterozygosity at chromosome 11p15 in Wilms' tumors: identification of two independent regions. *Oncogene* 17:237–40
44. Miller RW, Fraumeni JF, Manning MD. 1964. Association of Wilms' tumor with aniridia, hemihypertrophy and other congenital anomalies. *N. Engl. J. Med.* 270: 922–27
45. Call K, Glaser T, Ito C, Buckler AJ, Pelletier J, et al. 1990. Isolation and characterization of a zinc finger polypeptide gene at the human chromosome 11 Wilms' tumor locus. *Cell* 60:509–20
46. Gessler M, Poustka A, Cavenee W, Neve RL, Orkin SH, Bruns GA. 1990. Homozygous deletion in Wilms' tumours of a gene identified by chromosome jumping. *Nature* 343:774–78
47. Haber DA, Buckler AJ, Glaser T, Call KM, Pelletier J, et al. 1990. An internal deletion within an 11p13 zinc finger gene contributes to the development of Wilms' tumor. *Cell* 61:1257–69
48. Ton CC, Hirvonen H, Miwa H, Weil MM, Monaghan P, et al. 1991. Positional cloning and characterization of a paired box- and homeobox-containing gene from the aniridia region. *Cell* 67:1059–74
49. Schwartz F, Eisenman R, Knoll J, Gessler M, Bruns G. 1995. cDNA sequence, genomic organization, and evolutionary conservation of a novel gene from the WAGR region. *Genomics* 29:526–32
50. Kent J, Lee M, Schedl A, Boyle S, Fantes J, et al. 1997. The reticulocalbindin gene maps to the WAGR region in man and to the Small eye Harwell deletion in mouse. *Genomics* 42:260–67
51. Menke AL, van der Eb AJ, Jochemsen AG. 1998. The Wilms' tumor 1 gene: oncogene or tumor suppressor gene? *Int. Rev. Cytol.* 181:151–212
52. Haber DA, Sohn RL, Buckler AJ, Pelletier J, Call KM, Housman DE. 1991. Alternative splicing and genomic structure of the Wilms' tumor gene WT1. *Proc. Natl. Acad. Sci. USA* 88:9618–22
53. Bruening W, Pelletier J. 1996. A non-AUG translation initiation event generates novel WT1 isoforms. *J. Biol. Chem.* 271:8646–54
54. Bickmore WA, Oghene K, Little MH, Seawright A, van Heyningen V, Hastie ND. 1992. Modulation of DNA binding specificity by alternative splicing of the Wilms' tumour wt1 gene transcript. *Science* 257:235–37
55. Larsson SH, Charlieu JP, Miyagawa K, Engelkamp D, Rassoulzadegan M, et al. 1995. Subnuclear localization of WT1 in splicing or transcription factor domains is regulated by alternative splicing. *Cell* 81:391–401
56. Englert C, Vidal M, Maheswaran S, Ge Y, Ezzell R, et al. 1995. Truncated WT1 mutants alter the subnuclear localization of the wild-type protein. *Proc. Natl. Acad. Sci. USA* 92:11960–64
57. Caricasole A, Duarte A, Larsson SH, Hastie ND, Little M, et al. 1996. RNA binding by the Wilms' tumor suppressor zinc finger proteins. *Proc. Natl. Acad. Sci. USA* 93:7562–66
58. Kennedy D, Ramsdale T, Mattick J, Little M. 1996. An RNA recognition motif in Wilms' tumor protein (WT1) revealed by structural modelling. *Nat. Genet.* 12:329–32
59. Pritchard-Jones K, Fleming S, Davidson D, Bickmore W, Porteous D, et al. 1990. The candidate Wilms' tumor gene is involved in genitourinary development. *Nature* 346:194–97
60. Armstrong JF, Pritchard-Jones K, Bickmore WA, Hastie ND, Bard JBL. 1992. The expression of the Wilms' tumor gene, WT1, in the developing mammalian embryo. *Mech. Dev.* 40:85–97
61. Sharma PM, Yang X, Bowman M, Roberts B, Sukumar S. 1992. Molecular cloning of rat Wilms' tumor complementary DNA and study of messenger RNA expression in the urogenital system and the brain. *Cancer Res.* 52:6407–12
62. Hsueh SY, Kubo M, Chun SY, Haluska FG, Housman DE, Hsueh AJW. 1995. Wilms' tumor protein WT1 as an ovarian transcription factor: decreases in expression during follicle development and repression of inhibin-alpha gene promoter. *Mol. Endocrinol.* 9:1356–66
63. Del Rio Tsonis K, Covarrubias L, Kent J, Hastie ND, Tsonis PA. 1996. Regulation of

the Wilms' tumor gene during spermatogenesis. *Dev. Dyn.* 207:372–81
64. Kreidberg JA, Sariola H, Loring JM, Maeda M, Pelletier J, et al. 1993. WT-1 is required for early kidney development. *Cell* 74:679–91
65. Bruening W, Bardeesy N, Silverman BL, Cohn RA, Machin GA, et al. 1992. Germline intronic and exonic mutations in the Wilms' tumour gene (WT1) affecting urogenital development. *Nat. Genet.* 1:144–48
66. Pelletier J, Bruening W, Kashtan CE, Mauer SM, Manivel JC, et al. (1991) Germline mutations in the Wilms' tumor suppressor gene are associated with abnormal urogenital development in Denys-Drash syndrome. *Cell* 67:437–47
67. Hastie ND. 1993. Dominant negative mutations in the Wilms' tumour (WT1) gene cause Denys-Drash syndrome—proof that a tumour-suppressor gene plays a crucial role in normal genitourinary development. *Hum. Mol. Genet.* 1:293–95
68. Little MH, Williamson KA, Mannens M, Kelsey A, Gosden C, et al. 1993. Evidence that WT1 mutations in Denys-Drash syndrome patients may act in a dominant-negative fashion. *Hum. Mol. Genet.* 2:259–64
69. Moffet P, Bruening W, Nakgama H, Bardeesy N, Housman D, et al. 1995. Antagonism of WT1 activity by protein self-association. *Proc. Natl. Acad. Sci. USA* 92:11105–9
70. Barbaux S, Niaudet P, Gubler MC, Grunfeld JP, Jaubert F, et al. 1997. Donor splice-site mutations in WT1 are responsible for Frasier syndrome. *Nat. Genet.* 17:467–70
71. Klamt B, Koziell A, Poulat F, Wieacker P, Scambler P, et al. 1998. Frasier syndrome is caused by defective alternative splicing of WT1 leading to an altered ratio of WT1 +/−KTS splice isoforms. *Hum. Mol. Genet.* 7:709–14
72. Kikuchi H, Takata A, Akasaka Y, Fukuzawa R, Yoneyama H, et al. 1998. Do intronic mutations affecting splicing of WT1 exon 9 cause Frasier syndrome? *J. Med. Genet.* 35:45–48
73. Bardoni B, Zanaria E, Guioli S, Floridia G, Worley K, et al. 1994. A dosage sensitive locus at chromosome Xp21 is involved in male to female sex reversal. *Nat. Genet.* 7:497–501
74. Zanaria E, Muscatelli F, Bardoni B, Strom T, Guioli S, et al. 1994. An unusual member of the nuclear hormone receptor superfamily responsible for X-linked adrenal hypoplasia congenita. *Nature* 372:635–41
75. Muscatelli F, Strom TM, Walker AP, Zanaria E, Recan D, et al. 1994. Mutations in the DAX-1 gene give rise to both X-linked adrenal hypoplasia congenita and hypogonadotrophic hypogonadism. *Nature* 372:672–76
76. Swain A, Zanaria E, Hacker A, Lovell-Badge R, Camerino G. 1996. Mouse Dax-1 expression is consistent with a role in sex determination as well as in adrenal and hypothalamus function. *Nat. Genet.* 12:404–9
77. Ikeda Y, Swain A, Weber TJ, Hentges KE, Zanaria E, et al. 1996. Steroidogenic factor 1 and Dax-1 co-localize in multiple cell lineages: potential links in endocrine development. *Mol. Endocrinol.* 10:1261–72
78. Nachtigal MW, Hirokawa Y, Enjeart-VanHouten DL, Flanagan JN, Hammer GD, Ingraham HA. 1998. Wilms' tumor 1 and Dax-1 modulate the orphan nuclear receptor SF-1 in sex-specific gene expression. *Cell* 93:445–54
79. Ito M, Yu R, Jameson JL. 1997. DAX-1 inhibits SF-1-mediated transactivation via a carboxy-terminal domain that is deleted in adrenal hypoplasia congenita. *Mol. Cell. Biol.* 17:1476–83
80. Crawford PA, Dorn C, Sadovsky Y, Milbrandt J. 1998. Nuclear receptor DAX-1 recruits nuclear receptor corepressor N-Cor to steroidogenic factor 1. *Mol. Cell. Biol.* 18:2949–56
81. Zazopoulos E, Lalli E, Stocco DM, Sassone-Corsi P. 1997. DNA binding and transcriptional repression by DAX-1 blocks steroidogenesis. *Nature* 390:311–15
82. Burris TP, Guo W, Le T, McCabe ER. 1995. Identification of a putative steroidogenic factor-1 response element in the DAX-1 promoter. *Biochem. Biophys. Res. Commun.* 214:576–81
83. Yu RN, Ito M, Jameson JL. 1998. The murine Dax-1 promoter is stimulated by SF-1 (steroidogenic factor-1) and inhibited by COUP-TF (chicken ovalbumin upstream promoter-transcription factor) via a composite nuclear receptor regulatory element. *Mol. Endocrinol.* 12:1010–22
84. McDonald MT, Flejter W, Sheldon S, Putzi MJ, Gorski JL. 1997. XY sex reversal and gonadal dysgenesis due to 9p24 monosomy. *Am. J. Med. Genet.* 73:321–26
85. Wilkie AOM, Campbell FM, Daubeney P, et al. 1993. Complete and partial XY sex reversal associated with terminal deletion of 10q: report of 2 cases and literature review. *Am. J. Med. Gen.* 46:597–600
86. Washburn LL, Eicher EM. 1990. Normal

testis determination in the mouse depends on genetic interaction of locus on chromosome 17 and the Y chromosome. *Genetics* 123:173–79
87. Eicher EM, Washburn LL, Schork NJ, Lee B, Shown E, et al. 1997. Sex-determining genes on mouse autosomes identified by linkage analysis of C57BL/6J-YPOS sex reversal. *Nat. Genet.* 14:206–9
88. Raymond CS, Shamu CE, Shen MM, Seifert KJ, Hirsch B, et al. 1998. Evidence for evolutionary conservation of sex-determining genes. *Nature* 391:691–95
89. Shawlot W, Behringer R. 1995. Requirement for Lim1 in head organizer functions. *Nature* 374:425–30
90. Miyamoto N, Yoshida M, Kuratani S, Matsuo I, Aizawa S. 1997. Defects in urogenital development in mice lacking EMX2. *Development* 124:1653–64
91. Katohfukui Y, Tsuchiya R, Shiroishi T, Nakahara Y, Hashimoto N, et al. 1998. Male-to-female sex reversal in M33 mutant mice. *Nature* 393:688–86
92. Ryner LC, Swain A. 1995. Sex in the '90s. *Cell* 81:483–93
93. Wagner T, Wirth J, Meyer J, Zabel B, Held M, et al. 1994. Autosomal sex reversal and campomelic dysplasia are caused by mutations in and around the SRY-related gene SOX9. *Cell* 79:1111–20
94. Foster JW, Dominguez-Steglich MA, Guioli S, Kwok C, Weller P, et al. 1994. Campomelic dysplasia and autosomal sex reversal caused by mutations in an SRY-related gene. *Nature* 372:525–30
95. Swain A, Narvaez V, Burgoyne P, Camerino G, Lovell-Badge R. 1998. Dax1 antagonizes Sry action in mammalian sex determination. *Nature* 391: 761–67

Annu. Rev. Physiol. 1999. 61:435–56

SYNCHRONOUS ACTIVITY IN THE VISUAL SYSTEM

W. Martin Usrey and R. Clay Reid
Department of Neurobiology, Harvard Medical School, 220 Longwood Avenue, Boston, Massachusetts 02115; e-mail: Clay_Reid@hms.harvard.edu

KEY WORDS: vision, retina, LGN, thalamus, visual cortex, cerebral cortex

ABSTRACT

Synchronous activity among ensembles of neurons is a robust phenomenon observed in many regions of the brain. With the increased use of multielectrode recording techniques, synchronous firing of ensembles of neurons has been found at all levels in the mammalian visual pathway, from the retina to the extrastriate cortex. Here we distinguish three categories of synchrony in the visual system, (*a*) synchrony from anatomical divergence, (*b*) stimulus-dependent synchrony, and (*c*) emergent synchrony (oscillations). Although all three categories have been well documented, their functional significance remains uncertain. We discuss several lines of evidence both for and against a role for synchrony in visual processing: the perceptual consequences of synchronous activity, its ability to carry information, and the transmission of synchronous neural events to subsequent stages of processing.

INTRODUCTION

Synchronous neuronal activity is found in many forms in the mammalian visual system, from the sub-millisecond synchrony of several cells in the lateral geniculate nucleus (1), to the slower, coherent firing of large ensembles of neurons in the visual cortex (2, 3). In this review, we discuss a broad range of synchronous activity, which we have classified into three categories. The first category, synchrony from anatomical divergence, can include examples of the tightest synchrony, on the millisecond time scale. It is caused by strong, divergent input from a single source onto multiple targets. The second category, stimulus-dependent synchrony, includes forms that can be independent

0066-4278/99/0315-0435$08.00

of specific neural connections. Most simply, an external stimulus can excite a group of neurons in a time-locked fashion so that they all fire with a stereotyped time course. Finally, there is the category we call emergent synchrony, which includes phenomena that rely on the complex dynamics of the network as a whole. This category includes the oscillatory activity of ensembles of neurons in the visual cortex (reviewed in 2, 3).

At the outset, it is important to define what we mean by synchrony. The difference in spike timing between two neurons will never be exactly zero, thus synchrony must be defined in terms of an arbitrary upper bound on this difference. The distinction between synchrony and slower forms of correlated activity can be related to the distinction between a temporal code and a rate code. Although making this distinction is notoriously difficult, the debate can be recast in terms of either the interspike intervals of the presynaptic neurons or the time constants of integration by the postsynaptic neurons. In one formulation, "the interesting question is whether sensory neurons produce large numbers of spikes or small numbers of spikes in the time windows relevant for behavior and decision making." (4, p. 29). Here we make a similar distinction. We call correlated activity synchronous only when it occurs within a time window not much greater than the interspike interval or, alternatively, the integration time of postsynaptic neurons. A special case can be termed fast synchrony, when two neurons fire synchronous spikes at a scale significantly shorter than the interspike interval.

All three forms of synchrony considered in this review—anatomical, stimulus-dependent, and emergent—are present throughout the visual system, but their presence need not imply that they serve a function. It is entirely possible that neural synchrony is an epiphenomenon and is not necessary for normal visual processing. The strongest test of the importance of synchrony must be at the perceptual level: If synchrony is either disrupted or artificially induced, are there perceptual consequences? A slightly weaker test would be to determine whether synchronous activity can be transmitted to the next level. This could mean either the transmission of synchrony from one ensemble to the next, or the preferential response of postsynaptic targets to synchronous input. The distinction is important: In the one case, synchrony is merely reproduced faithfully but not selectively; in the other, it is read off. Finally, the potential importance of synchrony has been examined by asking whether synchronous activity might carry information about the stimulus that would be unavailable if the activity of individual neurons were considered separately. In this review, we examine the three forms of synchrony and then discuss their potential use at later stages of visual processing.

SYNCHRONY FROM ANATOMICAL DIVERGENCE: COMMON INPUT

It has frequently been suggested that action potentials in a single presynaptic neuron induce synchronous firing among multiple postsynaptic targets (5–7; see 8). One of the earliest examples of synchronous firing based on common input comes not from vision, but from studies in the spinal cord, where ensembles of intercostal motoneurons display extensive synchronous firing (9–12). Similarly, in the rabbit somatosensory cortex, synchronous activity has been found among suspected inhibitory neurons that receive divergent, monosynaptic input from neurons in the ventrobasal nucleus of the thalamus (13, 14).

In the visual system, synchrony based on common input has been found at several different levels of processing. Synchronous firing based on ascending common input has been described for neurons in the retina (15, 16) and the dorsal lateral geniculate nucleus (LGN) (1, 17, 18). Synchronous firing has also been described in the primary visual cortex (19–22), although its source is likely a mix of common input and reciprocal excitation that cannot be reliably distinguished. A more complex form of synchrony (or slower correlated activity) from anatomical divergence is induced by selectively activating a common presynaptic pool, such as the feedback connections from cortex to the LGN (23).

When there is divergent input from a common source onto several targets, the degree of synchronous firing evoked in the targets is dependent on both the number and the strength of common inputs. If an ensemble of postsynaptic neurons is driven strongly by only a few common inputs (for instance, input from retinal ganglion cells to geniculate neurons), then a large percentage of the ensemble's spikes should be synchronous. If an ensemble is weakly driven by many common inputs (for instance, input from geniculate cells to cortical simple cells), then synchrony should be weaker. These two cases are illustrated in Figure 1. In each example, two postsynaptic neurons receive half of their excitatory drive from a common presynaptic source. If the first pair of postsynaptic neurons (Figure 1*a*) receives its common input from only one presynaptic neuron that has 40% efficacy (40% of the input spikes evoke an output spike), then this pair of postsynaptic neurons will fire 8% of their spikes synchronously. The value 8% comes from the product of the following values $[0.5 \cdot 1 \cdot (40\%)^2]$: (0.5 of excitatory drive) $\cdot$ (1 common input) $\cdot$ $(40\%)^2$ of input spikes. Of the spikes from the common input, 40% evoke a spike in each of the output neurons, therefore, assuming independence, $(40\%)^2$ evoke synchronous spikes in both output neurons. If the second pair (Figure 1*b*) receives its common input from 10 uncorrelated presynaptic neurons, each of which has 4% efficacy, then only 0.8% of the spikes will be synchronous $[0.5 \cdot 10 \cdot (4\%)]$. In general,

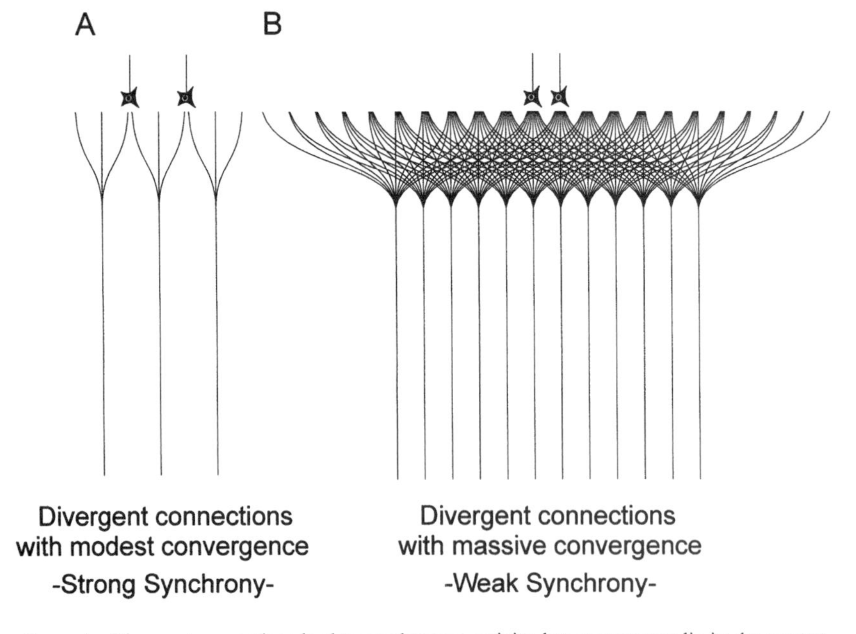

Figure 1 Divergent connections lead to synchronous activity, but convergence limits the amount of synchrony. In general, if two postsynaptic neurons are strongly driven by only a few common inputs (as in *A*), then they will fire many synchronous spikes (*Strong Synchrony*). In contrast, if a pair of neurons are weakly driven by many common inputs (as in *B*), then they will fire fewer synchronous spikes (*Weak Synchrony*).

given two neurons that have a pool of common presynaptic inputs of a given total strength, the degree of induced correlation between these two neurons will be inversely proportional to the number of neurons that provide this shared input. These arguments make two assumptions—that the presynaptic neurons are uncorrelated and that all presynaptic spikes are equally effective—neither of which is strictly true in the visual system (17, 18). Nevertheless, the general principle holds: While divergence will usually lead to synchrony, the degree of convergence strongly affects the magnitude of this synchrony.

In the following sections, we discuss synchrony resulting from common input for neurons in the retina, LGN, and visual cortex. Before describing the types of synchrony encountered in each of these structures, it is useful to quickly review how the firing patterns of multiple neurons are typically analyzed. The primary tool for examining the relationship between spike trains in two neurons is the cross-correlogram (6, 24, 25). In a cross-correlogram, all of the spikes occurring in cell *A* are considered to occur at time zero. Spikes occurring in cell *B* are then plotted relative to the firing of spikes in cell *A*. If there is a peak to the right of zero, then cell *B* tends to fire spikes at some latency after a spike in cell *A* (perhaps the result of a monosynaptic connection between cell *A* and cell *B*; see Figure 2, Ret A → LGN B, which appears later in text). If the cross-correlogram has a peak centered at time zero, then the two cells tend to fire spikes simultaneously (perhaps the result of common input; see Figure 2, LGN B—LGN C). Cross-correlograms can exhibit an enormous range of features, each of which is consistent with several interpretations. Given anatomical knowledge of the system, however, certain types of correlograms can be interpreted with relative certainty in terms of neural connections. As a prime example, cross-correlograms have been usefully applied to understanding the circuitry within the retina, between the retina and LGN, and between the LGN and visual cortex.

Intraretinal Synchrony

In the adult retina, synchronous spiking of neighboring ganglion cells has been described in the cat, rabbit, salamander, and goldfish (15, 16, 26–33). In cats and salamanders, ensembles of ganglion cells display three distinct types of synchronous firing that differ in their time course—slow, medium, and fast—and in their underlying circuitry. While slow synchrony (40–50 msec for cat; 50–100 msec for salamander) requires chemical synaptic transmission, both fast (<1 msec) and medium (2–10 msec for cat; 10–50 msec for salamander) synchrony appear to involve current passed through gap junctions (31, 33). Both slow and medium synchrony between retinal ganglion cells appear to result from common input. Slow synchrony is most likely due to noise in the visual transduction reactions of photoreceptors; it is slowest in the dark, where it is thought to reflect single quantal events, and somewhat faster in the light (15, 34). Slow synchrony can be established by the divergent connections of either the photoreceptors onto bipolar cells, or the bipolar cells onto ganglion cells. Medium synchrony (2–10 msec for cat; 10–50 msec for salamander) is thought to arise from amacrine cells that provide common input to ganglion cells (31, 33). Although amacrine cells provide predominantly inhibitory input to ganglion cells via chemical synapses, they also provide excitatory input via gap junctions (35–38). Because most amacrine cells generate graded potentials rather than action potentials, the synchronous responses they elicit in ganglion cells are slower than those resulting from gap junctions between ganglion cells (described below).

The fastest synchrony (<1 msec) displayed by nearby ganglion cells is not the result of common input from upstream sources, but most likely is the result of reciprocal excitation from other ganglion cells. For this reason, the cells tend to fire not truly synchronously, but one after the other. In the cat, cross-correlograms between these pairs of cells have two peaks, ~1 msec on either side of zero (15, 31; these correlations are faster in the salamander, 33). For two reasons, it is likely that excitation between ganglion cells is transmitted via gap junctions. First, antidromic activation of ganglion cells often triggers the firing of nearby ganglion cells (31). Second, fast synchrony persists in the presence of agents that block synaptic transmission (33).

The functional importance of retinal synchrony is not known. It has been shown that the receptive field of the synchronous activity of two ganglion cells is different from the receptive field of either neuron alone (16), and thus could potentially transmit distinct information to higher levels. Given the faithful transmission of activity from retina to LGN, it is likely that much of the synchrony (and therefore the information carried within it) is transmitted to the next level. Whether this synchrony is selectively transmitted, that is, whether it is read off, remains speculative.

What is certain, however, is that new forms of synchrony emerge at the level of the LGN. In the cat retina, fast synchrony is seen between only some pairs of Y cells (a class of large ganglion cells, less than 5% of the total). More importantly, in fast retinal synchrony there are always two correlogram peaks. In the principal layers of the LGN, there emerges a new form of fast synchrony between all cells, both X (the majority of cells, with smaller receptive fields) and Y. This synchrony is characterized by cross-correlograms with a single peak, centered at time zero, which is narrower (<1 msec) than the double peak seen in fast retinal synchrony (1).

Retinal Divergence and Geniculate Synchrony

Within the retina, feedforward connections are from non-spiking neurons (with the possible exception of some spiking amacrine cells); therefore, correlations based on divergence are slow. Action potentials in divergent retinal ganglion cell axons could, however, generate much faster synchrony among thalamic targets. In the cat, there is significant numerical divergence in the retinogeniculate pathway. The retina contains on the order of 100,000 X cells and 5000 Y cells (39, 40). The number of relay neurons in the principal laminae (A and A1) of the LGN is far greater: 240,000 X cells and 120,000 Y cells (reviewed in 41). Even if each relay neuron received input from only a single ganglion cell, there should be considerable divergence. Ultrastructural examination of a single ganglion-cell axon has directly demonstrated this divergence, as well as convergence. A single ganglion cell can contribute 100% of the retinal synapses onto some relay neurons, 30–50% of the retinal synapses onto others, and a very small number (~2%) of synapses onto yet other geniculate cells (42). Finally, dual recording studies from neurons in the retina and the LGN have identified divergent, monosynaptic connections from individual retinal ganglion cells onto multiple geniculate neurons (17, 18).

Divergent input leads to synchrony, but the degree of this synchrony depends on the strength of the connections (Figure 1). The feedforward connections from retina to LGN are very strong (17, 18, 43–46): on average, stronger than any others in the visual pathway (1, 22, 47–50). Individual geniculate neurons typically receive very strong input from a single retinal ganglion cell and often weaker input from only 1–3 other ganglion cells (42–44). Input from the dominant ganglion cell is so strong that the evoked excitatory post-synaptic potential (S-potential) can be measured with extracellular electrodes (51–53). This feature has allowed researchers to record simultaneously the action potentials and S-potentials of individual geniculate neurons (43, 51–56). Another method for examining the strength of connections between the retina and LGN involves simultaneous recordings from neurons in both structures. This method can be used to reveal the spike trains of strong retinal inputs to geniculate neurons (those that generate S-potentials), as well as the spike trains of weaker retinal inputs. Dual recording studies have found some retinal cells that contribute 100% of the spikes that drive an individual geniculate neuron, as well as weaker connections with as low as 1% contribution (17, 18, 43–46).

As a result of divergent, highly effective connections from the retina to LGN, Cleland (57) predicted that there should be small ensembles of geniculate neurons that fire many of their spikes synchronously. He further suggested that within these ensembles, there should be a range of correlation strengths between neurons, depending on the proximity of their receptive fields. This model has recently received experimental support (1, see 23, 58–60). When spike trains from neighboring geniculate neurons were recorded with separate electrodes, cross-correlation analysis revealed strong and narrow peaks (<1 msec) centered at time zero (1; Figure 2, LGN D—LGN E). Pairs of cells with extremely similar receptive fields were the most likely to display synchronous firing, which accounted for up to 40% of either neuron's spike train. Pairs with less well overlapped receptive fields were less likely to display synchronous firing; when they did, a lower percentage of their spikes were synchronous. Subsequently, geniculate synchrony has been directly shown to result from input from single ganglion cells. For the example shown in Figure 2, a single ganglion cell (Ret A) drove 84% of the synchronous spikes that occurred between two geniculate neurons (LGN B—LGN C; 17, 18).

Fast synchrony between pairs of geniculate neurons has also been examined for a possible role in the encoding of visual information (61). For a pair of synchronized geniculate neurons, the receptive field of synchronous spikes (bicellular receptive field; 62, see 16) is slightly but significantly different from the receptive fields of either individual neuron. This raises the question: Is there useful information in the receptive field of synchronous spikes? It turns out that if the synchronous spikes could be decoded as a distinct third channel, up to 40% more information about the stimulus could be conveyed than if synchrony were ignored. Further, the amount of increased information carried in synchronous

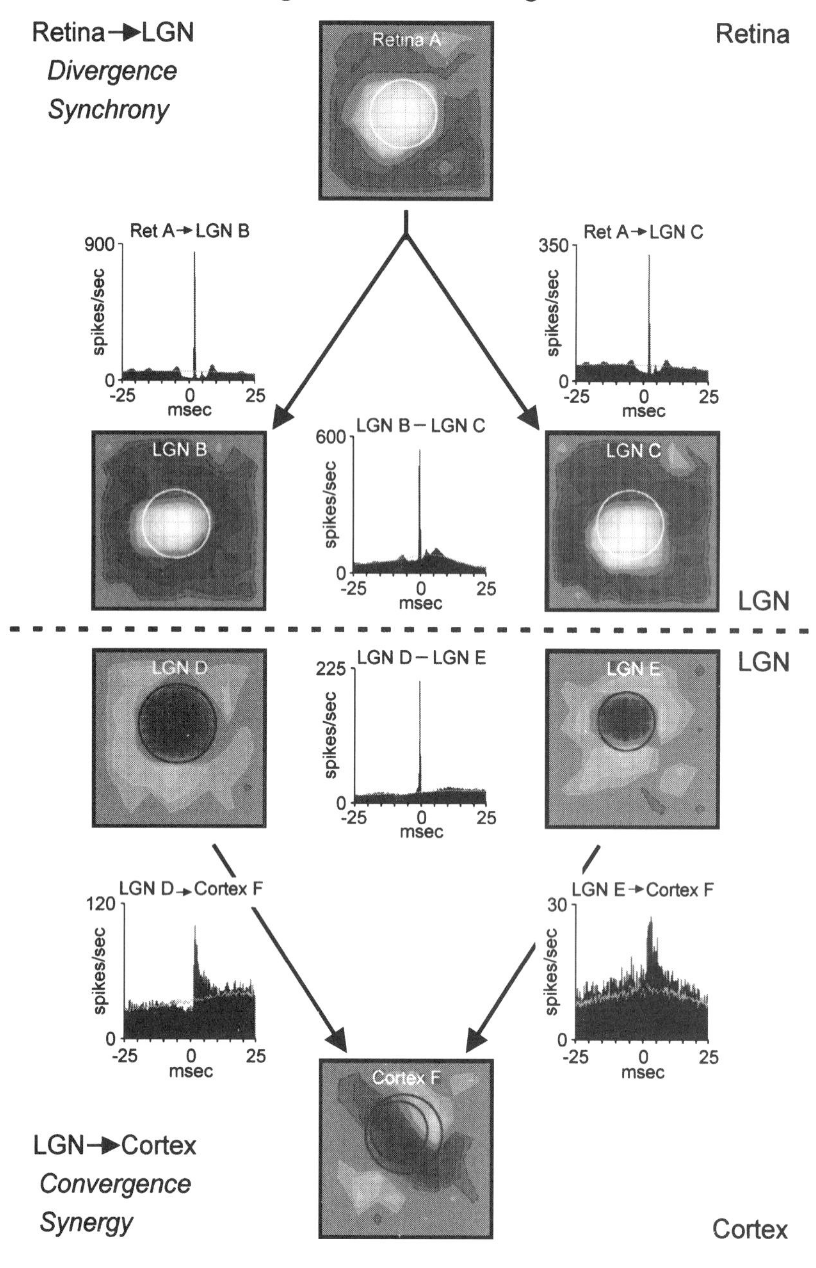
Divergence - Reconvergence
Retina→LGN
Divergence
Synchrony
Retina A
Retina
Ret A→LGN B
900
spikes/sec
0
-25
0
25
msec
Ret A→LGN C
350
spikes/sec
0
-25
0
25
msec
LGN B
LGN B – LGN C
600
spikes/sec
0
-25
0
25
msec
LGN C
LGN
LGN D
LGN D – LGN E
225
spikes/sec
0
-25
0
25
msec
LGN E
LGN
LGN D→Cortex F
120
spikes/sec
0
-25
0
25
msec
LGN E→Cortex F
30
spikes/sec
0
-25
0
25
msec
Cortex F
LGN→Cortex
Convergence
Synergy
Cortex

spikes appears to be dependent on the degree of synchrony itself: The greater the synchrony, the greater the gain in information (61).

Given the finding that fast geniculate synchrony carries information, two questions arise: What is the source of this information, and can it be used at subsequent levels of processing? The information present in synchronous geniculate spikes must result from information somehow embedded in the firing patterns of single retinal ganglion cells. Recent work has shown that more information is encoded in a retinal spike train, above a simple rate code, during periods of very high spike rate (63). This information may be used by the LGN via the following mechanism. When a single ganglion cell fires two closely spaced spikes, the second spike is much more likely than the first to elicit a geniculate spike—an effect referred to as paired-spike enhancement (18; so named because, unlike paired-pulse facilitation, the mechanism is entirely unknown). The enhanced efficacy of second retinal spikes is at a maximum at very short interspike intervals (~3–4 msec) and then declines gradually out to ~30 msec. Thus in the transition from low to high firing rates, spikes are differentially transmitted through the LGN. Further, paired-spike enhancement not only increases the likelihood of evoking spikes in individual target geniculate neurons, but also increases the number of synchronous spikes in multiple target neurons (18). Taken together, divergent retinal axons and paired-spike enhancement act not only to increase the number of synchronous spikes in the LGN, but also to ensure that certain retinal spikes (those with more information

Figure 2 Divergence and reconvergence in the retino-geniculo-cortical pathway of the cat. (*Upper half*) Divergence from a single retinal ganglion synchronizes two geniculate neurons. The three panels show receptive field maps of simultaneously recorded neurons (Retina A, LGN B, LGN C; each is an on-center Y cell; grid size: 0.6°). The *circles* shown over the receptive field centers correspond to the best fitting Gaussian of the retinal receptive-field center (radius: 2.5 σ_{ret}). The cross-correlograms between the retinal and geniculatpike trains (Ret A → LGN B; Ret A → LGN C) have strong and narrow monosynaptic peaks, displaced ~2.5 msec to the right of zero. The two geniculate neurons fired many of their spikes synchronously (correlogram: LGN B—LGN C). Of the synchronous spikes in the two geniculate cells, 84% were driven by retinal cell *A* (adapted from 17, 18). (*Lower half*) Geniculate neurons with synchronous activity provide convergent input to cortical simple cells. The two geniculate neurons (LGN D, LGN E) are both off-center, X cells (grid size: 0. 4°. Their receptive field centers are overlapped with each other as well as with the off-subregion of a simultaneously recorded simple cell (Cortex F). The geniculate neurons fired many of their spikes synchronously (correlogram: LGN D—LGN E), most likely the result of common retinal input. The cross-correlograms between the geniculate neurons and the simple cell (LGN D → Cortex F; LGN E → Cortex F) have monosynaptic peaks (typically slower and weaker than those for retinogeniculate connections). Analysis of the geniculate spikes trains showed that synchronous geniculate spikes were 70% more effective than non-synchronous spikes in driving cortical responses (adapted from 1).

during periods of high retinal firing) are more likely to be transformed into synchronous geniculate spikes.

The second question remains: Can the information in synchronous spikes be used at later stages? Recordings from two geniculate neurons and a postsynaptic layer-4 simple cell (see Figure 2: LGN D, LGN E, Cortex F) have shown that simultaneously arriving spikes are more effective than nonsimultaneous spikes at eliciting cortical action potentials (1). The efficacy of a geniculate spike (probability that a geniculate spike will lead to a cortical spike, above chance) is greatest when it occurs within a few msec of a spike from another geniculate cell (65). Efficacy then decreases rapidly with interspike intervals between 5–10 msec. More importantly, the influence of simultaneously (<1 msec, the time-scale of intrageniculate synchrony) arriving spikes is supralinear (1). That is, the efficacy of simultaneous spikes is greater than the sum of the efficacies of nonsimultaneous spikes. While the mechanisms that underlie synergistic interactions are unknown, they almost certainly include the postsynaptic membrane threshold—a nonlinearity that would favor the generation of spikes from simultaneous inputs.

The functional consequences of divergence from retina to LGN and reconvergence from LGN to visual cortex (Figure 2) can be summarized as follows: (*a*) Divergent and strong input from single ganglion cells to multiple geniculate neurons can induce strong and fast synchronous responses (1, 18). (*b*) Paired-spike enhancement increases the amount of geniculate synchrony during periods when retinal ganglion cells are firing rapidly or rapidly increasing their rate of firing (18, see 64). (*c*) Synchronous geniculate spikes contain more information than non-synchronous spikes (61). (*d*) Geniculate spikes that arrive simultaneously to cortical neurons are synergistic in eliciting cortical spikes (1). One potential reason for this complex scenario is that while the spike trains of retinal ganglion cells carry rich temporal information, cortical neurons—which receive many convergent inputs (41)—are not particularly suited to responding to the fine temporal structure of individual inputs (66). If, however, there is an intermediate stage in the thalamus—where high individual rates are translated into distributed, synchronized ensembles of neurons—then the same information may be relayed in a form more easily detected by cortical neurons.

Common Input and Intracortical Synchrony

Cross-correlation analysis has also been widely used in the study of cat primary visual cortex, primarily as a tool to assess connections between cortical neurons (19–22). Other than oscillatory firing seen under certain conditions (see below), any synchrony found in the cortex is an order of magnitude weaker than is found in either the retina or the LGN. This is most likely because neural connections in the cortex, both afferent and intrinsic, are more diffuse than those at earlier stages (41)—i.e. there is more convergence (see Figure 1*b*). For this reason, it is difficult to determine whether neural synchrony in the cortex is caused by common input or by reciprocal excitation.

It is likely that the situation in the primate is different. At any location in layer 4 of cat visual cortex, there is overlap of 360–540 X-axons and 300–540 Y-axons (41). In the macaque visual cortex, however, the magnocellular and parvocellular thalamic afferents stratify in different cortical sublaminae (4Cα 4Cβ). In both sublaminae, there is overlap of only 24 thalamic axons (67). It is thus likely that thalamo-recipient neurons receive far fewer convergent afferent inputs in the macaque than in the cat.

Although synchrony in layer 4 of primate visual cortex has not been studied directly, preliminary analysis of thalamocortical connections suggests that synchrony in layer 4 may be both fast and strong (65). A cross-correlogram between a magnocellular afferent and a layer-4 neuron, recorded simultaneously, is shown in Figure 3. Both the strength of the correlation (efficacy 8.6%, contribution 17.6%) and its time course (0.7 msec full width at half maximum) are reminiscent of those found in retinogeniculate correlations in the cat. Because there is considerable numerical divergence between the primate LGN and layer 4C (approximately 1:20 for the parvocellular projection, 1:100 for the magnocellular; 67–69), it is likely that many cortical cells are driven by

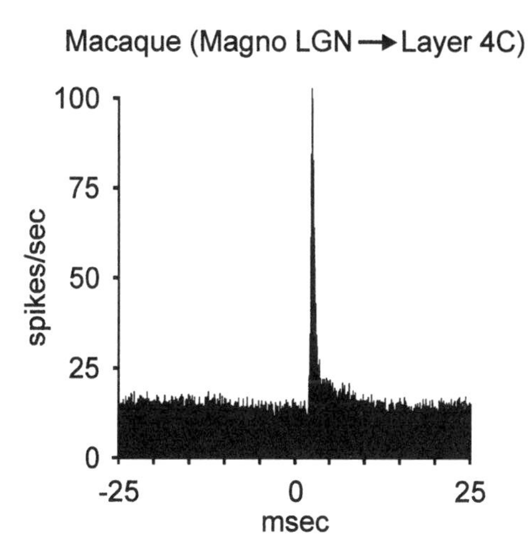

Figure 3 Cross-correlogram between a magnocellular neuron in the LGN and a neuron in layer 4C of macaque primary visual cortex (65). The narrow peak (0.7 msec full width at half maximum) displaced 2.4 msec to the right of zero indicates that the geniculate neuron provided monosynaptic input to the cortical cell. The monosynaptic input was strong; 17.6% of the cortical cell's spikes were triggered from a spike in the LGN cell. The strength of thalamocortical connections in the macaque, taken together with the anatomy of their projections—divergence with modest convergence—suggests that many neurons in layer 4C will receive strong common input and should therefore fire synchronous spikes (see text).

each thalamic afferent. Thus there should be ensembles of tightly correlated cells in layer 4C.

In the same manner that thalamic synchrony synergistically drives layer-4 neurons in the cat visual cortex, it is likely that synchrony in cortical layer 4 of the primate will be particularly effective in driving postsynaptic neurons in the cortex. Because of massive convergence of cortico-cortical connections, however, this form of synchronous firing is unlikely to be propagated to higher levels (66a).

Finally, it is an open question whether synchrony in the visual cortex can carry information about the stimulus. Ghose and colleagues have shown that the receptive field of the synchronous activity of two neurons is different from the receptive field of either neuron alone, but did not examine whether this difference could carry more information about the stimulus (62; but see 70, 71).

STIMULUS-DEPENDENT SYNCHRONY

The activity of neural populations can be synchronized by a visual stimulus in several ways. The truest form of stimulus-dependent synchrony is entirely independent of underlying neural connections, as in, for instance, the synchrony induced between the two retinas by a flash of light. There can also be a strongly stimulus-dependent component of certain types of synchrony from anatomical convergence (23) or of emergent synchrony (reviewed in 2, 3). Here, however, we consider only true stimulus-dependent synchrony of the first kind, in which a stimulus excites a neuron with a stereotyped time course. This type of synchrony—seen when an ensemble is time-locked to a stimulus—would require the faithful transmission of temporal information all the way from photoreceptors up to the neurons under study.

Most studies that use cross-correlation analysis have been concerned with characterizing neural connections; thus stimulus-dependent correlations have usually been treated as contamination to be avoided (6). Because of this historical bias in the literature of visual physiology in particular, fast stimulus-dependent synchrony has been largely ignored. This is in marked contrast to the literature of auditory physiology, in which both the precise time-locked neural responses to a stimulus and the subsequent detection of synchronous activity have been extensively studied (see E Covey & J Casseday, D Oertel, and L Trussell, this volume). In vision, however, there is a growing literature on the reproducibility of spike trains to a stereotyped input, which provides strong indirect evidence that visual stimuli can synchronize neurons on the time scale of several milliseconds. If neurons can respond to many repetitions of a stimulus with high temporal precision, then, assuming a homogeneous population, these neurons could also be synchronized at the same level of precision. As noted in the introduction to this review, temporal precision is usually defined with respect to the interspike interval. Temporal precision faster than the interspike interval has been demonstrated in the invertebrate visual system (72), the vertebrate retina (73–75), LGN (75, 76), and middle temporal (MT) cortical area in the primate (77, 78; but see 66a, 79). A similar form of synchrony, but with lower temporal precision, can be inferred from the work of Richmond, Optican, and colleagues, who studied the responses of visual neurons to instantaneously presented spatial stimuli. In these studies, a variable degree of temporal reproducibility was seen in neurons of the primate LGN (80; see 81), striate cortex (82), and extrastriate cortex (83).

Stimulus-evoked synchrony requires not only that individual responses have high temporal precision, but that the stimulus excites the population simultaneously, such as with an instantaneous onset, rather than asynchronously, such as with smooth motion. Although the argument can be made that stimulus-dependent synchrony of this sort depends on a stimulus with an unnatural time course, it has been suggested that when the eyes alight on a new scene at the end of a saccade, the retinal stimulus is very similar to an instantaneous presentation of a new pattern (82). Recently, it has been found that in freely-viewing animals, neurons in the visual cortex in fact respond with brief bursts of activity following each small saccade (84; see 85). These bursts of activity in single neurons, which certainly must correspond to highly synchronous activity in the ensemble, are very likely important in visual processing. The bursts might help prevent the fading of a static image, but they might also provide a "time-zero" signal for temporal coding mechanisms (86).

Although stimulus-dependent synchrony has received the least attention of the three forms discussed in this review, it is the one form of synchrony that we can be certain is reproduced from one level to the next (but see 87). The 2–10 msec precision seen in the reliability of spike trains of neurons in cortical area MT under some conditions (median precision ~6 msec; 78) (77, 78) suggests that synchronous activity can be transmitted reliably from one level to the next—from the retina to the LGN, the LGN to the primary visual cortex, and so on. Again, we have inferred the existence of synchrony and its transmission from studies of reproducible spike trains. These studies have been concerned primarily with issues of coding and information processing, but similar experimental protocols could prove very useful in explicitly studying the transmission of synchronous activity to successive levels of processing.

EMERGENT SYNCHRONY: COHERENT OSCILLATIONS

Coherent oscillations can be taken as a special case of synchrony, in which two (or more) neurons are oscillating at the same frequency with a small phase difference between them. This will result in an oscillatory correlogram whose peak is centered near time zero. Coherent oscillations of neuronal ensembles have been described in many studies of visual cortex (88, 89; reviewed in 2, 3). We call this synchrony emergent because, unlike synchrony caused directly by the activity of divergent inputs or by the responses to a flashed visual stimulus, coherent oscillations are thought to depend on complex interactions between membrane properties (90; see 91) and large ensembles of neurons. While neocortical oscillations were extensively studied first in the cat visual cortex (88, 89), synchrony based on coherent oscillations has been seen in cat sensorimotor cortex (92), rat somatosensory system (but at lower frequencies, 93), primate visual cortex (94–96), and primate motor cortex (97–100).

Within the visual pathway, coherent oscillations have been reported in the retina and LGN (58, 60, 101–104) but have been studied most intensively in the visual cortex. A recent study in the cat suggests that fast ($>\sim$50 Hz) subcortical oscillations can, in some cases, be transmitted to the visual cortex, but that slower oscillations ($<\sim$50 Hz) are cortical in origin (87). The amplitude of these slower intracortical correlations is variable, but it can in some cases be quite strong. The single-peaked correlograms seen in other forms of synchrony can be quantified in a simple manner—as the percentage of a neuron's spikes that are accounted for by the peak. Oscillatory correlograms can be quantified similarly—as the ratio between the oscillation amplitude and the baseline. In the cortex, a ratio of 0.50 is not uncommon; loosely speaking, this means that one half of the activity is coherent (although it does not follow that one half of the spikes are nearly synchronous).

Although many (but not all) groups find oscillatory activity in some visual cortical neurons, the importance of coherent oscillations in sensory processing is still a matter of debate. The most comprehensive view of the importance of oscillations has been proposed by Singer and colleagues (2, 3). Because these topics have been extensively reviewed, we discuss them only briefly. In outline, coherent oscillations have been proposed to bind a group of neurons into a coherent ensemble; that is, these oscillations make distant neurons stimulated by the same object fire together. Although this conjecture is far from proven, particularly in alert animals, it has been shown that when an extended stimulus excites many neurons simultaneously, the firing of these neurons can oscillate coherently. If this concerted activity defines an ensemble, then the ensemble itself may correspond to a distributed representation of a single percept. An attractive feature of this information-coding strategy is that ensembles can be dynamic; different extended stimuli will create different coherent groupings. Thus, in primary visual cortex, even entirely novel stimuli can be represented by the coherent activity of a particular ensemble.

In the absence of oscillatory activity, correlations between visual cortical neurons appear to be quite weak (usually on the order of 0.1% of total spikes;

19, 20). Presumably, the higher degree of synchrony seen in stimulus-evoked coherent oscillations stems from the tendency of weakly coupled oscillators to become entrained. Thus, if synchronization represents one strategy for combining the signals from a group of neurons so that they drive postsynaptic responses more strongly, then oscillatory activity might be an effective way of implementing this strategy. Below, we discuss whether this form of synchrony has perceptual consequences or whether it can be transmitted from one neural level to the next.

CONCLUSION: THE SIGNIFICANCE OF SYNCHRONOUS ACTIVITY

All three forms of synchrony described in this review—anatomical, stimulus-dependent and emergent—are prevalent throughout the visual system, but their significance is unclear. The most important question is whether synchrony is used at the perceptual level. This question has been posed in a number of recent psychophysical studies, with varied results. In all of these studies the general strategy was to use two or more sets of precisely timed stimuli to induce synchronous or asynchronous firing in populations of neurons, and then to assess whether these manipulations affected perceptual grouping of these populations. In some cases, there appeared to be a strong relation between stimulus-induced synchrony and high-order perceptual operations, such as figure/ground segregation; in other cases, synchrony appeared to be unimportant for perception (105–109). Television provides one example of a visual stimulus that can synchronize neurons at 60 Hz, as has been demonstrated in the cat LGN (110) and primate primary visual cortex (111). Despite likely behavioral consequences of watching television, there are no overt perceptual consequences of this synchrony.

Analysis of the neuronal, as opposed to perceptual, consequences of synchrony have centered around the transmission of synchronous activity to higher levels, in particular, on coincidence detection. The general issue of the precision of neurons in responding to temporal features has been a subject of considerable attention (4, 8, 112). The specific issue of coincidence detection has been analyzed in theoretical studies (113–116) as well as in several experimental systems. In the auditory system, it is clear that coincidence detection can be performed by neurons, such as in the nucleus laminaris of birds and the medial superior olive of mammals (see D Oertel, this volume). In vision, however, the ability of neurons (cortical neurons in particular) to act as coincidence detectors, or even to respond to precise temporal features, is disputed (reviewed in 66, 66a, 117–122). Evidence against coincidence detection by cortical neurons includes the large number of weak (and therefore weakly interacting) inputs (66, 66a) and the long membrane time constants (117). Arguments for the possibility of coincidence detection include the existence of active conductances in dendrites (114, 120; see 123) and the emerging view that the integration time of neurons (loosely defined as the mean delay between input and output) during normal activity is much faster than the classical membrane time constant (124).

A neuron's integration time is determined not by its passive membrane properties in the absence of synaptic input, but by its overall behavior in more natural settings. This behavior is determined by many factors such as the timing of presynaptic mechanisms (see B Sabatini & W Regehr, this volume), the overall level of synaptic conductances (that act to lower the membrane time constant; see, for example, 125, 125a–c), active dendritic conductances, and the somatic spiking mechanism. In the simplest example, transduction from synaptic inputs into spiking activity does not usually follow the entire time course of an excitatory postsynaptic potential, but instead only its rising phase (126; see 8). Further, neuronal integration times are far from constant but can be sped up in several ways. In particular, it has been shown that (*a*) the integration time of visual cortical neurons can be decreased dramatically by strong visual input that includes both low and high frequencies (127), (*b*) the transduction from injected current to spiking at high frequencies is enhanced by superimposing a slowly modulated current (see 128–130).

This discussion of integration times does not address directly the interaction between two or more inputs or coincidence detection. Only a few experiments have addressed this sort of interaction directly. One study analyzed the interaction between sinusoidal current and synaptic input on the spiking activity of cortical neurons (131). At certain frequencies, synaptic input will evoke spikes within only a very narrow window in the sinusoidal cycle, as short as 2–3 msec. A second study, which analyzed the interactions between two thalamic inputs to a single visual cortical neuron, demonstrated that synchronous input from two thalamic neurons is stronger than the sum of the two inputs arriving separately (1). It is unclear whether such a result would generalize to cortico-cortical connections, particularly since they are considerably less effective (19–22) than thalamocortical inputs (47–49). Although it is perhaps unlikely that pairwise, weak interactions of synchronous cortical inputs are synergistic, larger synchronous ensembles may be.

In summary, synchronous activity among ensembles of neurons is found at all levels in the mammalian visual pathway, from the retina to the extrastriate cortex. Because of the strong feedforward connections in the visual system—from retina to LGN and from LGN to visual cortex—coincidence detection is likely an important mechanism in the processing of synchronous inputs. Thus, the correlated activity of even a pair of neurons may serve an important functional role. Within the cortex, however, connections are weak and coincidence detection of pairs of inputs is unlikely. Read-off of larger synchronous ensembles, however, remains a possibility. For technical reasons, studies in vivo have lagged behind studies in vitro of the integration of synaptic input into postsynaptic responses. With the increasing use of multielectrode arrays to record simultaneously the activity of neuronal populations in vivo it is likely not only that we will unlock the rules that underlie the transmission of synchronous activity, but that we will develop a better understanding of the functional significance of synchrony.

ACKNOWLEDGMENTS

We thank Margaret Livingstone, John Reppas, Markus Meister, Iman Brivanlou, Bill Newsome, and Mike Shadlen for their insightful comments on this manuscript. This works is supported by National Institutes of Health grants F32 EY06604 and R01 EY10115 and the Harvard Mahoney Neuroscience Institute.

Literature Cited

1. Alonso JM, Usrey WM, Reid RC. 1996. Precisely correlated firing in cells of the lateral geniculate nucleus. *Nature* 383:815–19
2. Singer W, Gray CM. 1995. Visual feature integration and the temporal correlation hypothesis. *Annu. Rev. Neurosci.* 18:555–86
3. Engel AK, Roelfsema PR, Fries P, Brecht M, Singer W. 1997. Role of the temporal domain for response selection and perceptual binding. *Cereb. Cortex* 7:571–82
4. Rieke F, Warland D, de Ruyter van Steveninck R, Bialek W. 1997. *Spikes: Exploring the Neural Code.* Cambridge, MA: MIT Press
5. Moore GP, Segundo JP, Perkel DH, Levitan H. 1970. Statistical signs of synaptic interactions in neurones. *Biophys. J.* 10:876–900
6. Perkel DH, Gerstein GL, Moore GP. 1967. Neuronal spike trains and stochastic point processes. II. Simultaneous spike trains. *Biophys. J.* 7:419–40
7. Knox CK. 1974. Cross-correlation functions for a neuronal model. *Biophys. J.* 14:567–82
8. Abeles M. 1991. *Corticonics: Neural Circuits of the Cerebral Cortex.* Cambridge, UK: Cambridge Univ. Press
9. Sears TA, Stagg D. 1976. Short-term synchronization of intercostal motoneurone activity. *J. Physiol.* 263:357–81
10. Kirkwood PA, Sears TA. 1978. The synaptic connexions to intercostal motoneurones as revealed by the average common excitation potential. *J. Physiol.* 275:103–34
11. Kirkwood PA, Sears TA, Stagg D, Westgaard RH. 1982. The spatial distribution of synchronization of intercostal motoneurones in the cat. *J. Physiol.* 327:137–55
12. Kirkwood PA, Sears TA, Tuck DL, Westgaard RH. 1982. Variations in the time course of the synchronization of intercostal motoneurones in the cat. *J. Physiol.* 327:105–35
13. Swadlow HA. 1995. Influence of VPM afferents on putative inhibitory interneurons in S1 of the awake rabbit: evidence from cross-correlation, microstimulation, and latencies to peripheral sensory stimulation. *J. Neurophysiol.* 73:1584–99
14. Swadlow HA, Beloozerova I, Sirota M. 1998. Sharp, local synchrony among putative feed-forward inhibitory interneurons of rabbit somatosensory cortex. *J. Neurophysiol.* 79:567–82
15. Mastronarde DN. 1989. Correlated firing of retinal ganglion cells. *Trends Neurosci.* 12:75–80
16. Meister M, Lagnado L, Baylor DA. 1995. Concerted signaling by retinal ganglion cells. *Science* 270:1207–10
17. Reid RC, Usrey WM. 1996. The diver-

gence of retinal ganglion cells onto multiple geniculate neurons: implications for cortical processing. *Soc. Neurosci. Abst.* 22:1703
18. Usrey WM, Reppas JB, Reid RC. 1998. Paired-spike interactions and synaptic efficacy of retinal inputs to the thalamus. *Nature* 395:384–87
19. Toyama K, Kimura M, Tanaka K. 1981. Cross-correlation analysis of interneuronal connectivity in cat visual cortex. *J. Neurophysiol.* 46:191–214
20. Ts'o DY, Gilbert CD, Wiesel TN. 1986. Relationships between horizontal interactions and functional architecture in cat striate cortex as revealed by cross-correlation analysis. *J. Neurosci.* 6:1160–70
21. Nelson JI, Salin PA, Munk MH, Arzi M, Bullier J. 1992. Spatial and temporal coherence in cortico-cortical connections: a cross-correlation study in areas 17 and 18 in the cat. *Vis. Neurosci.* 9:21–37
22. Alonso J-M, Martinez L. 1999. Functional connectivity between simple cells and complex cells in cat visual cortex. *Nat. Neurosci.* 1:395–403
23. Sillito AM, Jones HE, Gerstein GL, West DC. 1994. Feature-linked synchronization of thalamic relay cell firing induced by feedback from the visual cortex. *Nature* 369:479–82
24. Gerstein GL, Perkel DH. 1969. Simultaneously recorded trains of action potentials: analysis and functional interpretation. *Science* 164:828–30
25. Bryant HL, Jr, Marcos AR, Segundo JP. 1973. Correlations of neuronal spike discharges produced by monosynaptic connections and by common inputs. *J. Neurophysiol.* 36:205–25
26. Rodieck RW. 1967. Maintained activity of cat retinal ganglion cells. *J. Neurophysiol.* 30:1043–71
27. Arnett DW. 1978. Statistical dependence between neighboring retinal ganglion cells in goldfish. *Exp. Brain Res.* 32:49–53
28. Johnsen JA, Levine MW. 1983. Correlation of activity in neighbouring goldfish ganglion cells: relationship between latency and lag. *J. Physiol.* 345:439–49
29. Arnett DW, Spraker TE. 1981. Cross-correlation analysis of the maintained discharge of rabbit retinal ganglion cells. *J. Physiol.* 317:29–47
30. Mastronarde DN. 1983. Correlated firing of cat retinal ganglion cells. I. Spontaneously active inputs to X- and Y-cells. *J. Neurophysiol.* 49:303–24
31. Mastronarde DN. 1983. Interactions between ganglion cells in cat retina. *J. Neurophysiol.* 49:350–65
32. Meister M. 1996. Multineuronal codes in retinal signaling. *Proc. Natl. Acad. Sci. USA* 93:609–14
33. Brivanlou IH, Warland DK, Meister M. 1998. Mechanisms of concerted firing among retinal ganglion cells. *Neuron* 20:527–39
34. Mastronarde DN. 1983. Correlated firing of cat retinal ganglion cells. II. Responses of X- and Y-cells to single quantal events. *J. Neurophysiol.* 49:325–49
35. Sakai HM, Naka K. 1990. Dissection of the neuron network in the catfish inner retina. IV. Bidirectional interactions between amacrine and ganglion cells. *J. Neurophysiol.* 63:105–19
36. Dacey DM, Brace S. 1992. A coupled network for parasol but not midget ganglion cells in the primate retina. *Vis. Neurosci.* 9:279–90
37. Vaney DI. 1994. Patterns of neuronal coupling in the retina. *Prog. Retin. Res.* 13:301–55
38. Xin D, Bloomfield SA. 1997. Tracer coupling pattern of amacrine and ganglion cells in the rabbit retina. *J. Comp. Neurol.* 383:512–28
39. Wässle H, Levick WR, Cleland BG. 1975. The distribution of the alpha type of ganglion cells in the cat's retina. *J. Comp. Neurol.* 159:419–38
40. Peichl L, Wässle H. 1979. Size, scatter and coverage of ganglion cell receptive field centres in the cat retina. *J. Physiol.* 291:117–41
41. Peters A, Payne BR. 1993. Numerical relationships between geniculocortical afferents and pyramidal cell modules in cat primary visual cortex. *Cereb. Cortex* 3:69–78
42. Hamos JE, Van Horn SC, Raczkowski D, Uhlrich DJ, Sherman SM. 1985. Synaptic connectivity of a local circuit neurone in lateral geniculate nucleus of the cat. *Nature* 317:618–21
43. Cleland BG, Dubin MW, Levick WR. 1971. Sustained and transient neurones in the cat's retina and lateral geniculate nucleus. *J. Physiol.* 217:473–96
44. Cleland BG, Dubin MW, Levick WR. 1971. Simultaneous recording of input and output of lateral geniculate neurones. *Nat. New Biol.* 231:191–92
45. Mastronarde DN. 1992. Nonlagged relay cells and interneurons in the cat lateral geniculate nucleus: receptive field properties and retinal inputs. *Vis. Neurosci.* 8:407–41

46. Cleland BG, Lee BB. 1985. A comparison of visual responses of cat lateral geniculate nucleus neurones with those of ganglion cells afferent to them. *J. Physiol.* 369:249–68
47. Tanaka K. 1983. Cross-correlation analysis of geniculostriate neuronal relationships in cats. *J. Neurophysiol.* 49:1303–18
48. Tanaka K. 1985. Organization of geniculate inputs to visual cortical cells in the cat. *Vision Res.* 25:357–64
49. Reid RC, Alonso JM. 1995. Specificity of monosynaptic connections from thalamus to visual cortex. *Nature* 378:281–84
50. Reid RC, Alonso JM. 1996. The processing and encoding of information in the visual cortex. *Curr. Opin. Neurobiol.* 6:475–80
51. Bishop PO, Burke W, Davis R. 1958. Synapse discharge by single fibre in mammalian visual system. *Nature* 128: 728–30
52. Bishop PO, Burke W, Davis R. 1962. The interpretation of the extracellular response of single lateral geniculate cells. *J. Physiol.* 162:451–72
53. Freygang J, WH. 1958. An analysis of extracellular potentials from single neurons in the lateral geniculate nucleus of the cat. *J. Gen. Physiol.* 41:543–64
54. Hubel DH, Wiesel TN. 1961. Integrative action in the cat's lateral geniculate body. *J. Physiol.* 155:385–98
55. Kaplan E, Shapley R. 1984. The origin of the S (slow) potential in the mammalian lateral geniculate nucleus. *Exp. Brain Res.* 55:111–16
56. Kaplan E, Purpura K, Shapley RM. 1987. Contrast affects the transmission of visual information through the mammalian lateral geniculate nucleus. *J. Physiol.* 391:267–88
57. Cleland BG. 1986. The dorsal lateral geniculate nucleus of the cat. In *Vis. Neurosci.*, ed. JD Pettigrew, KS Sanderson, WR Levick, pp. 111–20. London: Cambridge Univ. Press
58. Arnett DW. 1975. Correlation analysis of units recorded in the cat dorsal lateral geniculate nucleus. *Exp. Brain Res.* 24:111–30
59. Stevens JK, Gerstein GL. 1976. Interactions between cat lateral geniculate neurons. *J. Neurophysiol.* 39:239–56
60. Neuenschwander S, Singer W. 1996. Long-range synchronization of oscillatory light responses in the cat retina and lateral geniculate nucleus. *Nature* 379:728–32
61. Dan Y, Alonso JM, Usrey WM, Reid RC. 1998. Coding of visual information by precisely correlated spikes in the LGN. *Nat. Neurosci.* 1:501–7
62. Ghose GM, Ohzawa I, Freeman RD. 1994. Receptive-field maps of correlated discharge between pairs of neurons in the cat's visual cortex. *J. Neurophysiol.* 71:330–46
63. Smirnakis SM, Warland DK, Berry MJ, Meister M. 1996. Spike bursts in visual responses of retinal ganglion cells. *Soc. Neurosci. Abst.* 22:494
64. Mastronarde DN. 1987. Two classes of single-input X cells in cat lateral geniculate nucleus. II. Retinal inputs and the generation of receptive-field properties. *J. Neurophysiol.* 57:381–413
65. Usrey WM, Alonso J-M, Reppas JB, Reid RC. 1998. Time course of heterosynaptic and homosynaptic integration of thalamic inputs to cortical neurons in cat and monkey. *Soc. Neurosci. Abst.* 24: In press
66. Shadlen MN, Newsome WT. 1994. Noise, neural codes and cortical organization. *Curr. Opin. Neurobiol.* 4:569–79
66a. Shadlen MN, Newsome WT. 1998. The variable discharge of cortical neurons: implications for connectivity, computation, and information coding. *J. Neurosci.* 18:3870–96
67. Peters A, Payne BR, Budd J. 1994. A numerical analysis of the geniculocortical input to striate cortex in the monkey. *Cereb. Cortex* 4:215–29
68. O'Kusky J, Colonnier M. 1982. A laminar analysis of the number of neurons, glia, and synapses in the adult cortex (area 17) of adult macaque monkeys. *J. Comp. Neurol.* 210:278–90
69. Connolly M, Van Essen D. 1984. The representation of the visual field in parvicellular and magnocellular layers of the lateral geniculate nucleus in the macaque monkey. *J. Comp. Neurol.* 226:544–64
70. Riehle A, Grün S, Diesmann M, Aertsen A. 1997. Spike synchronization and rate modulation differentially involved in motor cortical function. *Science* 278:1950–53
71. deCharms RC, Merzenich MM. 1996. Primary cortical representation of sounds by the coordination of action-potential timing. *Nature* 381:610–13
71a. Covey E, Casseday JH. 1999. Timing in the auditory system of the bat. *Annu. Rev. Physiol.* 61: In press
71b. Oertel D. 1999. The role of timing in the

brainstem auditory nuclei of vertebrates. *Annu. Rev. Physiol.* 61: In press
71c. Trussell LG. 1999. Synaptic mechanisms for coding timing in auditory neurons. *Annu. Rev. Physiol.* 61: In press
72. de Ruyter van Steveninck RR, Lewen GD, Strong SP, Koberle R, Bialek W. 1997. Reproducibility and variability in neural spike trains. *Science* 275:1805–8
73. Berry MJ, Warland DK, Meister M. 1997. The structure and precision of retinal spike trains. *Proc. Natl. Acad. Sci. USA* 94:5411–16
74. Berry MJ, 2nd, Meister M. 1998. Refractoriness and neural precision. *J. Neurosci.* 18:2200–11
75. Reich DS, Victor JD, Knight BW, Ozaki T, Kaplan E. 1997. Response variability and timing precision of neuronal spike trains in vivo. *J. Neurophysiol.* 77:2836–41
76. Reinagel P, Reid RC. 1998. Visual stimulus statistics and the reliability of spike timing in the LGN. *Soc. Neurosci. Abst.* 24:139
77. Bair W, Koch C. 1996. Temporal precision of spike trains in extrastriate cortex of the behaving macaque monkey. *Neural Comput.* 8:1185–202
78. Buračas GT, Zador AM, DeWeese MR, Albright TD. 1998. Efficient discrimination of temporal patterns by motion-sensitive neurons in primate visual cortex. *Neuron* 20:959–69
79. Bair W, Koch C, Newsome W, Britten K. 1994. Power spectrum analysis of bursting cells in area MT in the behaving monkey. *J. Neurosci.* 14:2870–92
80. McClurkin JW, Gawne TJ, Richmond BJ, Optican LM, Robinson DL. 1991. Lateral geniculate neurons in behaving primates. I. Responses to two-dimensional stimuli. *J. Neurophysiol.* 66:777–93
81. Golomb D, Kleinfeld D, Reid RC, Shapley RM, Shraiman BI. 1994. On temporal codes and the spatiotemporal response of neurons in the lateral geniculate nucleus. *J. Neurophysiol.* 72:2990–3003
82. Richmond BJ, Optican LM, Spitzer H. 1990. Temporal encoding of two-dimensional patterns by single units in primate primary visual cortex. I. Stimulus-response relations. *J. Neurophysiol.* 64:351–69
83. Richmond BJ, Optican LM, Podell M, Spitzer H. 1987. Temporal encoding of two-dimensional patterns by single units in primate inferior temporal cortex. I. Response characteristics. *J. Neurophysiol.* 57:132–46
84. Martinez-Conde S, Macknik SL, Hubel DH. 1998. Correlation between eye movements and neural responses in area V–1 of the awake behaving monkey during visual fixation. *Soc. Neurosci. Abst.* 24:1981
85. Livingstone MS, Freeman DC, Hubel DH. 1996. Visual responses in V1 of freely viewing monkey. In *Cold Spring Harbor Symposia on Quantitative Biology*, Vol. LXI. Plainview, NY: Cold Spring Harbor Lab. Press
86. Gaarder K. 1968. Interpretive study of evoked responses elicted by gross saccadic eye movements. *Percept. Motor Skills* 27:683–703
87. Castelo-Branco M, Neuenschwander S, Singer W. 1998. Synchronization of visual responses between the cortex, lateral geniculate nucleus, and retina in the anesthetized cat. *J. Neurosci.* 18:6395–410
88. Eckhorn R et al. 1988. Coherent oscillations: a mechanism of feature linking in the visual cortex? Multiple electrode and correlation analyses in the cat. *Biol. Cybern.* 60:121–30
89. Gray CM, König P, Engel AK, Singer W. 1989. Oscillatory responses in cat visual cortex exhibit inter-columnar synchronization which reflects global stimulus properties. *Nature* 338:334–37
90. Gray CM, McCormick DA. 1996. Chattering cells: superficial pyramidal neurons contributing to the generation of synchronous oscillations in the visual cortex. *Science* 274:109–13
91. Jagadeesh B, Gray CM, Ferster D. 1992. Visually evoked oscillations of membrane potential in cells of cat visual cortex. *Science* 257:552–54
92. Roelfsema PR, Engel AK, König P, Singer W. 1997. Visuomotor integration is associated with zero time-lag synchronization among cortical areas. *Nature* 385:157–61
93. Nicolelis MA, Baccala LA, Lin RC, Chapin JK. 1995. Sensorimotor encoding by synchronous neural ensemble activity at multiple levels of the somatosensory system. *Science* 268:1353–58
94. Frien A, Eckhorn R, Bauer R, Woelbern T, Kehr H. 1994. Stimulus-specific fast oscillations at zero phase between visual areas V1 and V2 of awake monkey. *NeuroReport* 5:2273–77
95. Livingstone MS. 1996. Oscillatory firing and interneuronal correlations in squirrel monkey striate cortex. *J. Neurophysiol.* 75:2467–85

96. Kreiter AK, Singer W. 1996. Stimulus-dependent synchronization of neuronal responses in the visual cortex of the awake macaque monkey. *J. Neurosci.* 16:2381–96
97. Murthy VN, Fetz EE. 1992. Coherent 25- to 35-Hz oscillations in the sensorimotor cortex of awake behaving monkeys. *Proc. Natl. Acad. Sci. USA* 89:5670–74
98. Murthy VN, Fetz EE. 1996. Synchronization of neurons during local field potential oscillations in sensorimotor cortex of awake monkeys. *J. Neurophysiol.* 76:3968–82
99. Murthy VN, Fetz EE. 1996. Oscillatory activity in sensorimotor cortex of awake monkeys: synchronization of local field potentials and relation to behavior. *J. Neurophysiol.* 76:3949–67
100. Sanes JN, Donoghue JP. 1993. Oscillations in local field potentials of the primate motor cortex during voluntary movement. *Proc. Natl. Acad. Sci. USA* 90:4470–74
101. Doty RW, Kimura D. 1963. Oscillatory potentials in the visual system of cats and monkeys. *J. Physiol.* 168:205–18
102. Laufer M, Verzeano M. 1967. Periodic activity in the visual system of the cat. *Vision Res.* 7:215–29
103. Steriade M. 1968. The flash-evoked afterdischarge. *Brain Res.* 9:169–212
104. Ghose GM, Freeman RD. 1992. Oscillatory discharge in the visual system: Does it have a functional role? *J. Neurophysiol.* 68:1558–74
105. Fahle M, Koch C. 1995. Spatial displacement, but not temporal asynchrony, destroys figural binding. *Vision Res.* 35:491–94
106. Fahle M. 1993. Figure-ground discrimination from temporal information. *Proc. R. Soc. London Ser. B* 254:199–203
107. Leonards U, Singer W, Fahle M. 1996. The influence of temporal phase differences on texture segmentation. *Vision Res.* 36:2689–97
108. Kiper DC, Gegenfurtner KR, Movshon JA. 1996. Cortical oscillatory responses do not affect visual segmentation. *Vision Res.* 36:539–44
109. Alais D, Blake R, Lee S-H. 1998. Visual features that vary together over time group together over space. *Nat. Neurosci.* 1:160–64
110. Wollman DE, Palmer LA. 1995. Phase locking of neuronal responses to the vertical refresh of computer display monitors in cat lateral geniculate nucleus and striate cortex. *J. Neurosci. Meth.* 60:107–13
111. Mechler F, Shapley R, Hawken MJ, Ringach DL. 1996. Video refresh entrains neurons in monkey V1. *Soc. Neurosci. Abst.* 22:1704
112. Abeles M. 1982. *Local Cortical Circuits.* Berlin: Springer-Verlag
113. Murthy VN, Fetz EE. 1994. Effects of input synchrony on the firing rate of a three-conductance cortical neuron model. *Neural Comp.* 6:1111–26
114. Softky W. 1994. Sub-millisecond coincidence detection in active dendritic trees. *Neuroscience* 58:13–41
115. Abeles M. 1982. Role of the cortical neuron: integrator or coincidence detector? *Isr. J. Med. Sci.* 18:83–92
116. Lumer ED, Edelman GM, Tononi G. 1997. Neural dynamics in a model of the thalamocortical system. II. The role of neural synchrony tested through perturbations of spike timing. *Cereb. Cortex* 7:228–36
117. Douglas RJ, Martin KA. 1991. Opening the grey box. *Trends Neurosci.* 14:286–93
118. König P, Engel AK, Singer W. 1996. Integrator or coincidence detector? The role of the cortical neuron revisited. *Trends Neurosci.* 19:130–37
119. Softky WR, Koch C. 1993. The highly irregular firing of cortical cells is inconsistent with temporal integration of random EPSPs. *J. Neurosci.* 13:334–50
120. Softky WR. 1995. Simple codes versus efficient codes. *Curr. Opin. Neurobiol.* 5:239–47
121. Lisman JE. 1997. Bursts as a unit of neural information: making unreliable synapses reliable. *Trends Neurosci.* 20:38–43
122. Aertsen A, Arndt M. 1993. Response synchronization in the visual cortex. *Curr. Opin. Neurobiol.* 3:586–94
123. Hirsch JA, Alonso JM, Reid RC. 1995. Visually evoked calcium action potentials in cat striate cortex. *Nature* 378:612–16
124. Koch C, Rapp M, Segev I. 1996. A brief history of time (constants). *Cereb. Cortex* 6:93–101

124a. Sabatini BL, Regehr WG. 1999. Timing of synaptic transmission. *Annu. Rev. Physiol.* 61: In press

125. Bernander O, Douglas RJ, Martin KA, Koch C. 1991. Synaptic background activity influences spatiotemporal integration in single pyramidal cells. *Proc. Natl. Acad. Sci. USA* 88:11569–73

125a. Borg-Graham L, Monier C, Frégnac

Y. 1996. Voltage-clamp measurement of visually-evoked conductances with whole-cell patch recordings in primary visual cortex. *J. Physiol. Paris* 90:185–88

125b. Borg-Graham LJ, Monier C, Frégnac Y. 1998. Visual input evokes transient and strong shunting inhibition in visual cortical neurons. *Nature* 393:369–73

125c. Hirsch JA, Alonso JM, Reid RC, Martinez LM. 1998. Synaptic integration in striate cortical simple cells. *J. Neurosci.* 18:9517–28

126. Fetz EE, Gustafsson B. 1983. Relation between shapes of post-synaptic potentials and changes in firing probability of cat motoneurones. *J. Physiol.* 341:387–410

127. Reid RC, Victor JD, Shapley RM. 1992. Broadband temporal stimuli decrease the integration time of neurons in cat striate cortex. *Vis. Neurosci.* 9:39–45

128. Mainen ZF, Sejnowski TJ. 1995. Reliability of spike timing in neocortical neurons. *Science* 268:1503–6

129. Nowak LG, Sanchez-Vives MV, McCormick DA. 1997. Influence of low and high frequency inputs on spike timing in visual cortical neurons. *Cereb. Cortex* 7:487–501

130. Carandini M, Mechler F, Leonard CS, Movshon JA. 1996. Spike train encoding by regular-spiking cells of the visual cortex. *J. Neurophysiol.* 76:3425–41

131. Volgushev M, Chistiakova M, Singer W. 1998. Modification of discharge patterns of neocortical neurons by induced oscillations of the membrane potential. *Neuroscience* 83:15–25

Annu. Rev. Physiol. 1999. 61:457–76

TIMING IN THE AUDITORY SYSTEM OF THE BAT

Ellen Covey and John H. Casseday
Department of Psychology, Box 351525, University of Washington, Seattle, Washington 98195-1525, e-mail: ecovey@u.washington.edu

KEY WORDS: temporal patterns, echolocation, nuclei of the lateral lemniscus, inferior colliculus, neural computation

ABSTRACT

Echolocating bats use audition to guide much of their behavior. As in all vertebrates, their lower brainstem contains a number of parallel auditory pathways that provide excitatory or inhibitory outputs differing in their temporal discharge patterns and latencies. These pathways converge in the auditory midbrain, where many neurons are tuned to biologically important parameters of sound, including signal duration, frequency-modulated sweep direction, and the rate of periodic frequency or amplitude modulations. This tuning to biologically relevant temporal patterns of sound is created through the interplay of the time-delayed excitatory and inhibitory inputs to midbrain neurons. Because the tuning process requires integration over a relatively long time period, the rate at which midbrain auditory neurons respond corresponds to the cadence of sounds rather than their fine structure and may provide an output that is closely matched to the rate at which motor systems operate.

INTRODUCTION

Temporal Structure in Biological Sounds

The auditory world of animals is rich in temporal features that we identify as buzzes, hums, snaps, cracks, and the variety of sounds produced by the larynx or syrinx. Only occasionally does the staple sound of the auditory physiologist—a pure tone—emerge from this cacophony. All animals make sounds, either vocally or by some other body movement. These biological sounds are used to identify prey or predators and to communicate. What biologically important

0066-4278/99/0315-0457$08.00

sounds have in common is that their cadence follows the pace of body movements. They arise from movements of the vocal apparatus, footfalls, wingbeats, etc, and they come and go at a rate no faster than the speed at which the organs that produce them can move. Echolocating bats are no exception. Although the frequency range of their echolocation signals is very high, 20 to >100 kHz, the rate at which individual sounds are emitted is relatively slow, usually not more than 150/s. This review concerns the mechanisms for processing some basic temporal features of sound, such as sound onset, sound duration, intervals between sounds, direction of frequency sweeps, and rate of modulation of amplitude or frequency. Although these features do not completely describe natural sounds, they represent some of the elements of natural sounds; they are readily produced in the laboratory and can be quantitatively described. Our interest in many of these sounds arises from their similarity to echolocation sounds, and we propose that their use as stimuli for studying the operation of brainstem pathways in bats can yield general physiological principles applicable to mammalian hearing.

ECHOLOCATION The signals that bats use for echolocation have specific temporal and spectral patterns that correspond to specific stages and strategies of foraging behavior. The most common type of echolocation signal is a frequency-modulated (FM) sweep. Within a hunting sequence, the bat systematically alters its signal as it searches, approaches, and finally catches an insect (35, 43, 60). When the bat is searching for an insect, it emits a relatively long (10–20 ms), shallow FM sweep that changes only from ~28 to ~23 kHz. The repetition rate of this signal is about 3/s. When pursuing an insect, the bat emits short (<1 to 5 ms) FM sounds that are spectrally broad (~80 – ~20 kHz), and the repetition rate increases to as much as 150/s (63). Long-duration signals with narrow bandwidth are used to detect the presence of prey, while short-duration, broadband signals are used to determine the distance of targets based on the timing relationship between pulse and echo (43, 63).

In summary, the bat's vocalizations have specific temporal features that are potential sources of information for echolocation. These features include the duration of the pulses, the rate of frequency change within a pulse, and the interval between pulses. The echoes contain the same information as the pulses plus whatever modifications are imposed by the reflective environment. The time difference between pulse and echo is a potential cue for determining the distance of a reflective object. If, as is usually the case, the reflective environment has texture, then multiple reflections from varying depths of the surface will mix to produce interference patterns, thus changing the spectral and temporal structure of the echo (63). If the objects are dispersed enough in distance, multiple echoes will return, dispersed in time. Finally, even though the bat contracts its middle ear muscles during pulse emission, it cannot avoid hearing its vocalizations in addition to the echoes. Therefore, what the bat hears must be a complex temporal sequence in which pulses are interspersed with echoes modified by objects in the environment. Although we do not know precisely how the bat constructs its auditory world, it is clear that temporal cues provide considerable information that could be used for this purpose.

PASSIVE LISTENING The auditory system of bats is not only a specialized system for processing the ultrasonic sounds used for echolocation. Bats clearly must process many of the same kinds of sounds that other mammals do. For example, most bats have a rich repertoire of communication sounds with temporal properties quite different from those of echolocation sounds (36).

Some echolocating bats use passive hearing for hunting; these are the so-called gleaning bats, such as the pallid bat (20, 21) and the false vampire bat (40). These bats use echolocation for navigation, yet they hunt by listening to sounds generated by their prey.

This review concerns the neural apparatus used by echolocating bats to encode and process temporal information. Because cortical mechanisms have been reviewed extensively elsewhere (70), this review focuses primarily on the midbrain and the pathways leading to it.

OVERVIEW OF AUDITORY PATHWAYS

The processing of information contained in sounds begins in the cochlea and continues in the auditory structures of the lower brainstem. Certain parts of the auditory brainstem in bats and dolphins have obvious anatomical specializations that appear to play a role in analyzing the temporal structure of echolocation sounds (9, 10, 51, 62, 74, 84, 88). These specializations are mainly in the nuclei of the lateral lemniscus. The auditory system between the cochlea and the midbrain consists of multiple parallel pathways that provide multiple transformations of the cochlear signal. These transformations include changes from excitatory input to inhibitory output, changes in the temporal patterns of neural discharge, and the creation of delay lines. The lower brainstem pathways provide different patterns of input to the auditory midbrain, the inferior colliculus (IC), where integration at the cellular level produces yet other transformations.

The Lower Brainstem Auditory Pathways

The parallel pathways of the lower brainstem can be grouped into two broad classes, a binaural system that receives input from both ears and a monaural system that receives input only from the contralateral ear (Figure 1). The structure

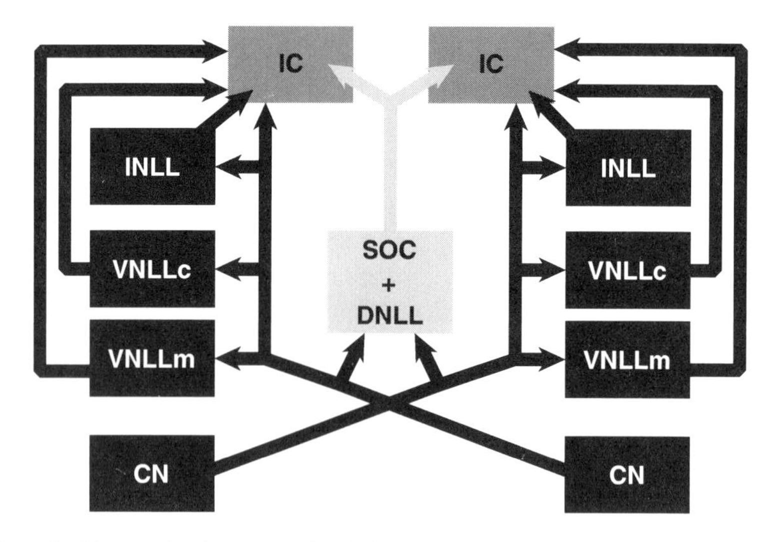

Figure 1 Diagram showing monaural and binaural auditory pathways in the brainstem of an echolocating bat. Each cochlear nucleus (CN) receives input from the ipsilateral ear via the auditory nerve. Binaural pathways: The CN projects bilaterally to the superior olivary complex (SOC); the SOC, in turn, projects bilaterally to the dorsal nucleus of the lateral lemniscus (DNLL) and the inferior colliculus (IC). The DNLL also projects bilaterally to the IC. Monaural pathways: The CN projects directly to the contralateral IC; in addition, it projects to the contralateral nuclei of the lateral lemniscus, including the multipolar cell region of the ventral nucleus (VNLLm), the columnar region of the ventral nucleus (VNLLc), and the intermediate nucleus (INLL), each of which in turn projects to the IC. Thus, the IC receives direct and indirect monaural inputs from the contralateral ear.

and function of the binaural pathways of the brainstem have been studied in sufficient detail to show that they perform the initial computations for sound localization (e.g. 24, 33, 37, 81). Here we focus on the monaural pathways because they are especially highly developed in echolocating bats (1) and seem to play an important role in the initial stages of processing temporal patterns of sound (9, 10, 11, 62, 84). Nevertheless, there is almost certainly interaction of monaural and binaural pathways, especially at the IC or higher (13), and their interaction may play a role in temporal processing.

The monaural system in echolocating bats includes direct pathways from the divisions of the cochlear nucleus to the midbrain and indirect pathways via the intermediate nucleus of the lateral lemniscus (INLL) and two divisions of the ventral nucleus of the lateral lemniscus (VNLL) (Figure 1). Of these nuclei, the most structurally distinct is the columnar division of the VNLL (VNLLc), a specialized group of cells that is most highly developed in echolocating bats and dolphins (9, 75, 88).

The Auditory Midbrain

The IC is the target of ten or more pathways, each of which is anatomically and functionally distinct (e.g. 2, 9, 11, 52, 58, 85–87). From this evidence it is reasonable to hypothesize that some of these pathways converge at the cellular level (73). Recent research reviewed here indicates that much of this integration results in tuning to temporal features of sound. The IC in bats, as in other mammals, is the major source of auditory input to the thalamocortical pathway (11). In addition, the IC of echolocating bats is a major source of input to areas involved in motor coordination, including the superior colliculus (12), an area responsible for orienting movements, and the pontine grey (61), a source of input to the cerebellum.

TIMING IN THE AUDITORY BRAINSTEM

The processing of signals in the brainstem auditory pathways seems to accomplish three transformations: a reversal in the sign of the neural signal from excitation to inhibition in some pathways, changes in the temporal pattern of neural discharge, and an increase in the range of latencies. All of these operations occur at all levels, starting at the cochlear nucleus. Consequently, there is a proliferation of response properties at all levels. Each neuron's repertoire of response properties provides clues about the type of processing it performs.

Neural Inhibition

Inhibition plays an important role in altering temporal response patterns. The recognized inhibitory neurotransmitters in the auditory brainstem are glycine and GABA (19, 23, 73, 75–77). The INLL and VNLL have many neurons that stain for glycine, indicating that a high proportion of these neurons provide inhibitory input to the IC. Neuropharmacological experiments to block inhibitory inputs to IC neurons show that both GABA and glycine affect their response properties (16, 34, 49, 53). Much of the inhibitory input from monaural pathways arises from the INLL and VNLL (75). To see how these inputs might participate in tuning IC neurons to temporal features of sound, we now examine the different temporal patterns of neural discharge in the monaural nuclei of the lateral lemniscus.

Discharge Patterns: Distribution of Information over Time

The basic temporal discharge patterns of neurons in the INLL and VNLL include onset and sustained responses. Neurons in the VNLLc have the most distinctive response properties. These cells have no spontaneous activity and respond with one and only one spike over an exceptionally broad range of sound frequencies (10, 72). For bursts of pure tones or noise, the timing of the spike is precisely correlated with the time of sound onset. Under constant stimulus conditions, the trial-to-trial variability of the spike time is only a few tens of microseconds; moreover, the spike times remain virtually constant over a wide range of stimulus amplitudes and frequencies. Constant latency responses of the type seen in the VNLLc are not present in the cochlear nucleus (31). For an echolocating animal such as a bat, constant latency neurons might be especially important for marking the time of an outgoing high-intensity biosonar signal. This information would be used at a higher level to measure target distance by calculating the difference between the time of the signal and time of its echo.

The fact that all auditory nerve fibers fire in a sustained manner raises the question of how transient responses arise. Although there is evidence that neurons' intrinsic properties could play a role (e.g. 39, 44), neural circuitry could also create transient responses, as has been demonstrated in a study of the medial superior olive of the mustached bat (26, 29). In this case, transient responses are created through convergence of two sustained inputs, one excitatory and one inhibitory, slightly offset in time. The result is a transient onset response if excitation leads and a transient offset response if inhibition leads. Transient responses in the VNLLc may be created in a similar manner. However, the mechanism for producing level-tolerant constant latency responses is not known.

The predominant response pattern in the INLL and in the multipolar cell division of the VNLL is a sustained discharge that continues at a relatively steady rate throughout the duration of a pure tone. Sustained responses provide a real-time measure of stimulus duration for discrete stimuli; for modulated stimuli, they could provide a real-time measure of the period during which the stimulus is within the neuron's amplitude-frequency area of sensitivity.

On the basis of the response types just described, the monaural pathways from the brainstem to the IC can be divided into two streams of processing, one of which transmits information about stimulus onset and the other of which transmits information about stimulus duration and intensity (Figure 2). In both of these streams of processing, neural activity corresponds to real-time features of the stimulus, such as onset, offset, duration, rate and depth of amplitude modulation, and rate of frequency modulation. As is shown below, combining excitatory and inhibitory inputs with these different patterns provides a means of creating tuning for simple temporal patterns of sound. However, for this mechanism to be effective, the inputs must also be offset from one another in time. This offset requires delay lines.

Delay Lines in the Nuclei of the Lateral Lemniscus and IC

When the first-spike latencies of neurons in the nuclei of the lateral lemniscus are compared with those in the cochlear nucleus and IC, it is clear that

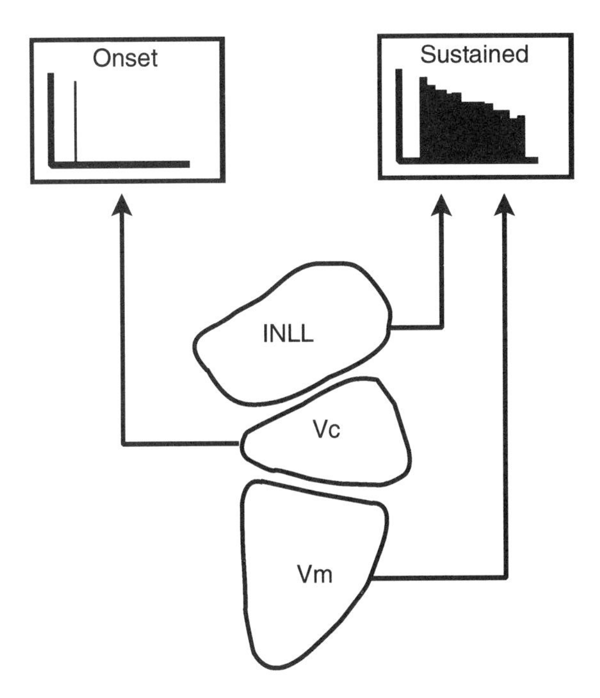

Figure 2 The monaural nuclei of the lateral lemniscus provide two functionally distinct streams of input to the inferior colliculus. The first stream (onset) originates in units that respond transiently with a single action potential and provide a precise timing marker for the onset of sound. These units respond to periodic frequency modulations, but poorly or not at all to periodic amplitude modulations. The second stream (sustained) originates in units that respond throughout the duration of a sound. These units respond well to periodic amplitude modulations and provide information about sound duration and intensity.

there is a large increase in latency at levels above the cochlear nucleus (31). In the cochlear nucleus, response latencies are short, ranging from approximately 1 to 6 ms. Although the major source of excitatory input to the nuclei of the lateral lemniscus is the cochlear nucleus, the range of latencies recorded at the nuclei of the lateral lemniscus is considerably greater than would be expected from synaptic delays alone—approximately 2 to 20 ms. Similarly, the latency range in the IC is about double that—approximately 3 to 40 ms. In the IC of the mustached bat, each isofrequency contour contains a systematic "map" of response latencies in which the longest latencies are dorsal and the shortest latencies are ventral (18, 31, 32, 49). Because the range of latencies in the IC cannot be entirely accounted for by synaptic delays across excitatory synapses, these increases in delay at each stage must be at least partly created through synaptic inhibition. Evidence for lengthening of latency through neural circuitry comes from several studies showing that blocking inhibitory neurotransmitters causes latencies to shorten (34, 49, 59).

CONVERGENCE AND INTEGRATION AT THE INFERIOR COLLICULUS

In the IC, many neurons are tuned to one or more temporal parameters of sound; these temporal parameters include sound duration, FM sweep direction, and modulation rate. Many IC neurons are selective in that they are tuned to a specific range within one of these parameters, and they respond poorly or not at all to sounds outside this parameter range. For example, some IC neurons respond only to FM sweeps and not to other types of stimuli, such as pure tones or noise. In addition to being selective for FM sweeps, these neurons may be tuned to a specific direction, rate, and depth of frequency change.

Tuning for Sound Duration

The duration of sound is a biologically important feature of signals as diverse as echolocation calls, animal communication sounds, music, and speech. However, unlike frequency, there is no peripheral mechanism for encoding sound duration into neural place. The first evidence of neural tuning to sound duration was seen in the auditory midbrain of frogs (42, 54). Duration tuning is not found at lower levels (7, 17, 30), suggesting that duration tuning first emerges at the level of the midbrain. In frogs, midbrain neurons are tuned to the same range of durations as the sound pulses of conspecific vocalizations (25).

For echolocation, neural tuning to the duration of sound would provide an additional filter beside those for frequency and intensity. Neurons in the IC of the big brown bat (6, 15, 50) and the pallid bat (20) are tuned to sound duration. In the big brown bat, somewhat more than 30% of IC neurons show an increase of 50% or more in the response to specific sound durations. The durations of the echolocation sounds used by this species of bat range from 1 to 10 ms or more and match the range of duration tuning of its IC neurons (15, 63).

Neurophysiological studies in which antagonists of GABA or glycine were applied to duration-tuned neurons in the IC of the big brown bat showed that blocking inhibitory input eliminated duration tuning (6). Antagonists of either inhibitory transmitter were effective in eliminating or greatly reducing duration tuning. This finding suggests that both GABAergic and glycinergic inputs contribute to duration tuning and that duration tuning is the result of several convergent excitatory and inhibitory inputs.

The results of intracellular recording from IC neurons suggest a model for the neural computation of sound duration (6, 13) (Figure 3). Inhibitory input arrives first and is sustained for the duration of the stimulus. The cell also

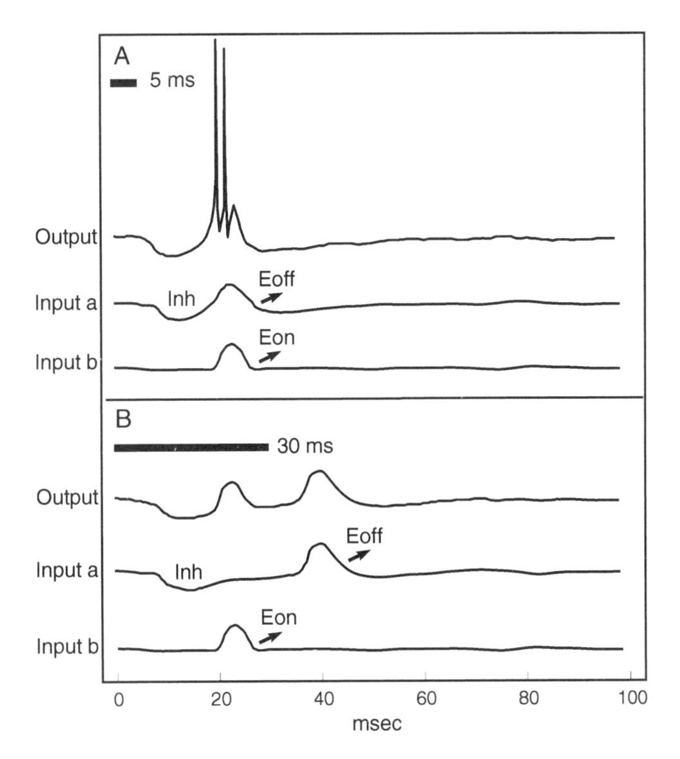

Figure 3 Model of the mechanism for duration tuning. This neuron receives sustained inhibitory input (*middle trace*) followed by a depolarization (Eoff) due to either an excitatory offset response or a rebound from inhibition. This offset depolarization by itself is subthreshold. The neuron receives a second transient excitatory input (*lower trace*) that causes depolarization (Eon) at a fixed latency relative to sound onset. If the sound is long enough, the onset excitation is partially cancelled by the inhibition, rendering it subthreshold. (*A*) In response to a 5-ms stimulus, the onset depolarization and offset depolarization coincide, allowing the cell to reach threshold and fire (*A*: *upper trace*). (*B*) In response to a 30-ms tone, the onset depolarization and offset depolarization do not coincide, so the neuron does not respond (*B*: *upper trace*) (from 15).

receives transient excitatory input correlated with stimulus onset, but it is rendered subthreshold by the sustained inhibitory input. At stimulus offset, there is either a second excitatory input or a "rebound" from inhibition; the resulting offset depolarization is insufficient to produce a spike on its own. However, when the duration of the sound is such that the onset excitation coincides with the offset depolarization, a spike occurs. Tuning to longer or shorter sounds can be created by having longer or shorter delays in the onset excitatory input. The range of latencies of neurons in the lateral lemniscus is adequate to account for most of the range of duration tuning observed. Intrinsic projections within the IC could account for the longest durations to which IC neurons are tuned.

Tuning for Frequency Sweeps

Neurons that respond only to downward FM sweeps and not to other test sounds such as pure tones, noise, or clicks have been found consistently in the IC of FM bats (2, 6, 20, 65–67). Recent results using bicuculline to antagonize the action of GABA indicate that GABAergic inhibition is involved in producing selectivity for FM direction in at least some IC neurons (22).

Suga (67, 68) used the term FM specialists to describe this class of neurons. Although there is evidence that neurons in the VNLLc may already be selective for FM sweep direction (75), they also respond to pure tones and noise. Thus, for neurons that respond exclusively to FM, it seems likely that this specialization is created in the IC.

Suga (67, 68) and Fuzessery (20) proposed several mechanisms that could create FM direction specialization in IC neurons. Some of these models share features of the model for duration tuning, in that they combine inhibitory and excitatory inputs. However, they do not combine features of different discharge patterns with different latencies. Some of the most likely mechanisms to account for FM sweep selectivity are shown in Figure 4.

The simplest way to create a neuron that responds selectively to downward FM sweeps would be to have subthreshold excitation from high frequencies arrive at the IC neuron with a longer latency than subthreshold excitation from low frequencies, so that the neuron would fire only if the timing relationship between high and low frequencies were such that the two responses coincided (Figure 4*A*). This type of arrangement could be created by having inputs from different frequency ranges but similar latencies distributed at different points along the dendritic tree (20, 75) or by having inputs with different latencies arriving at the same point.

→

Figure 4 Three hypothetical mechanisms for producing FM direction selectivity. In each panel, F1 represents higher frequencies and F2 represents lower frequencies in the FM sweep. R1 is the synaptic potential produced by F1, and R2 is the synaptic potential produced by F2. The *lower trace* represents the output of the neuron, as it would appear in extracellular recording. (*A*) R1 and R2 are both excitatory, but have different latencies. When F1 precedes F2, R1 and R2 coincide and bring the cell to threshold. When F2 precedes F1, R1 and R2 do not coincide and the cell does not respond. (*B*) R1 is excitatory and has a short latency; R2 is inhibitory and has a longer latency. When F1 precedes F2, R1 and R2 do not coincide, allowing R1 to elicit an action potential. When F2 precedes F1, R2 and R1 coincide; R2 cancels R1, and the neuron does not fire. (*C*) R1 is inhibitory, but with a rebound following hyperpolarization. R2 is excitatory, with a latency similar to that of R1. When F1 precedes F2, the rebound from R1 coincides with the excitation from R2, and the cell fires. When F2 precedes F1, the rebound and the excitation do not coincide, and the cell does not fire.

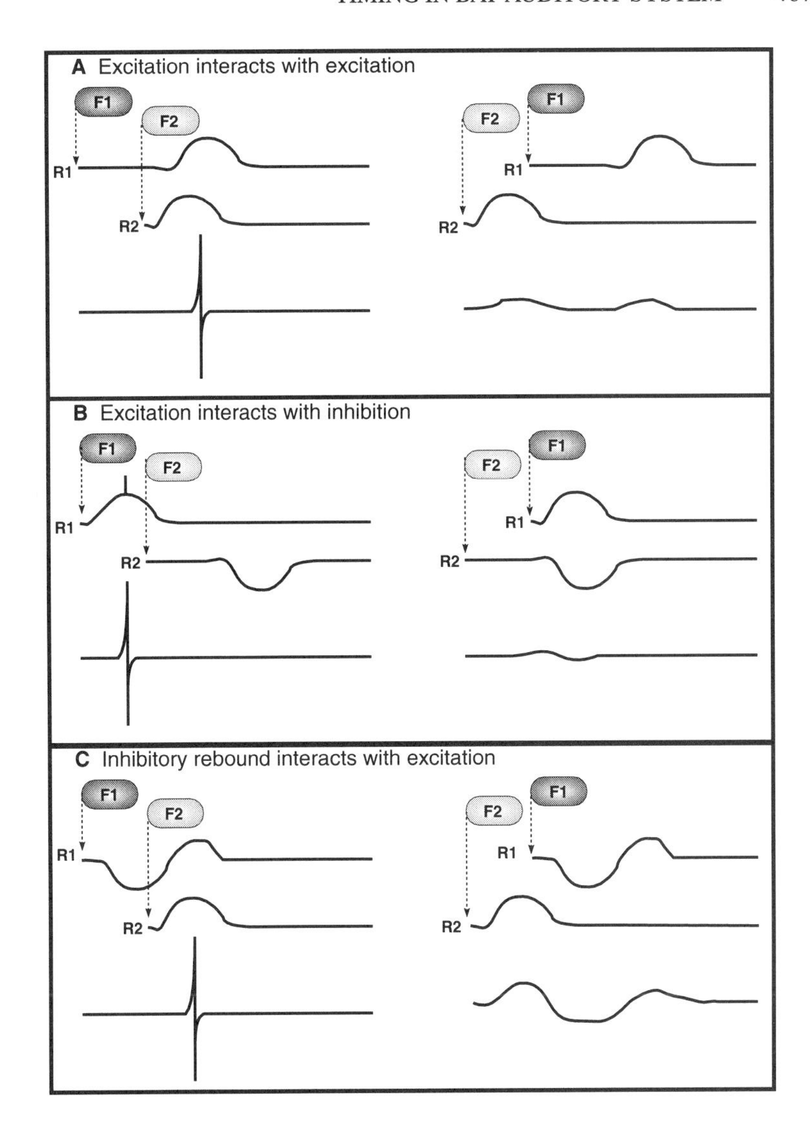

A second way to create FM tuning would be through an excitatory input from one frequency range and an inhibitory input from another frequency range (Figure 4*B*). This is the mechanism proposed by Suga (69) to account for FM specialized neurons. In that model, sound sweeping from an excitatory region to an inhibitory region of the frequency tuning curve would permit the cell to fire, whereas sound sweeping in the opposite direction would suppress the cell's response. This model could explain FM direction selectivity but would not account for the failure of FM specialists to respond to pure tones.

A third model (3, 15) (Figure 4*C*) combines excitatory and inhibitory inputs in a way similar to the mechanism for duration tuning described above. In this model, inhibition from a high-frequency input arrives first and is sustained for the period during which the FM sweep remains within the frequency response area of the input neuron. The inhibition is followed by a rebound as the sweep passes out of the input neuron's range of frequency tuning. Subthreshold excitation from low-frequency inputs is delayed relative to the inhibitory input, so that excitation is transient. The neuron would fire whenever the rebound from inhibition evoked by the higher frequency coincided in time with the excitatory input from the lower frequency. The neuron could not respond to upward FM sweeps because the timing of inhibitory rebound and excitation would not produce coincidence, nor would it respond to pure tones of low frequency because this excitatory input alone is too weak to initiate an action potential. The neuron would not respond to pure tones of high frequency because this excitatory input is normally counterbalanced by an inhibitory input with the same latency, temporal pattern, and frequency tuning characteristics. The latter assumption is supported by evidence that the thresholds of many IC neurons are normally elevated by inhibitory inputs with the same frequency tuning characteristics as the excitatory inputs (16, 34, 49, 53).

The attraction of this last model is that it incorporates the known biological features of the IC circuitry, including a combination of excitatory and inhibitory inputs with different latencies and discharge patterns. The dependence of the response on the timing of the excitatory and inhibitory inputs is consistent with the fact that many FM specialized neurons are tuned to the duration of the sweep and/or to the rate of the sweep (6, 15, 20). Moreover, the inhibitory component of the input provides "level tolerance," i.e. merely increasing sound level is not sufficient to initiate a spike. A purely excitatory model would not be level tolerant.

Tuning for Modulation Rate

Another temporal feature to which IC neurons are tuned is the rate of frequency or amplitude modulations, especially those that occur in communication sounds or echolocation sounds, as first shown in amphibians (25, 55–57). Most are tuned to rates that resemble the amplitude modulation rates of the mating calls of conspecifics. Grothe et al (28) showed that neurons in the medial superior olive (MSO) of the Mexican free-tailed bat respond to sinusoidally amplitude-modulated signals (SAM) with low-pass filter characteristics. Yang & Pollak (80) found that neurons in the dorsal nucleus of the lateral lemniscus (DNLL) also respond to SAM with low-pass filter characteristics; this might be expected, given that the DNLL receives a large input from the MSO (74, 87). The MSO and DNLL appear to be the only regions below the level of the IC to have low-pass responses to SAM. It has been proposed that the MSO in small mammals may be a temporal pattern processor that evolved in species too small to use binaural time differences as a cue for sound localization, in contrast to large mammals with good low-frequency hearing, in which the MSO appears to be specialized to process interaural time or phase differences (29, 48).

In the IC of the big brown bat, many units respond selectively to sinusoidally frequency-modulated (SFM) tones (5). These units do not respond to pure tones or noise, and if they do respond to single presentations of a frequency sweep, the response is weaker than the response to SFM. SFM-selective cells are tuned to low modulation rates, usually <100 Hz. It is possible that this type of cell is really specialized for a sequence of FM signals such as occurs in the final stages of insect pursuit, and that the modulation rate of the SFM stimulus simply resembles this natural sequence of sounds. In any case, these neurons are clearly tuned to very specific temporal patterns of sounds. The fact that some SFM specialists respond poorly or not at all to the first cycle of an SFM signal indicates that they probably do require a sequence of FM sweeps and further suggests a mechanism that could produce SFM specialization (Figure 5). This

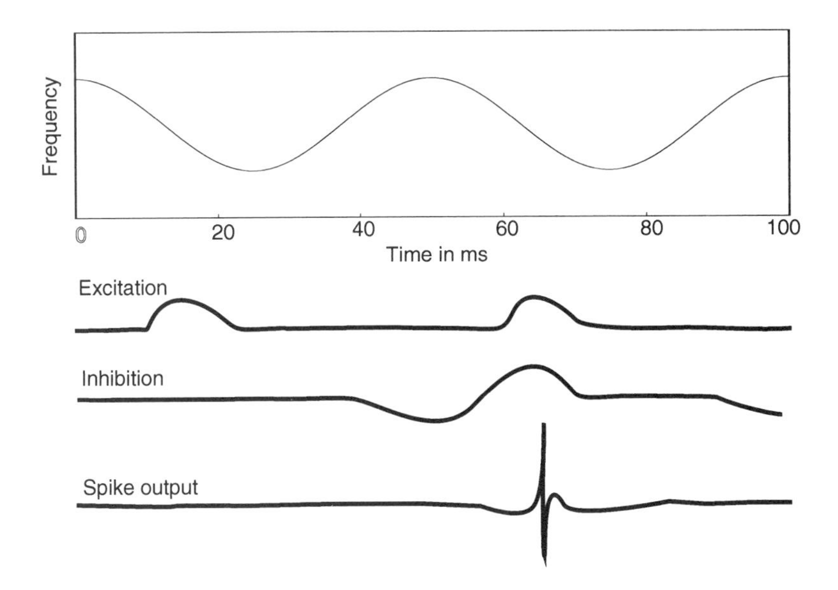

Figure 5 Hypothetical mechanism for producing selectivity for SFM stimuli. *Top*: Waveform of the modulating frequency. Excitation: excitatory postsynaptic potentials (EPSP) elicited by each downward phase of the SFM signal. Inhibition: inhibitory postsynaptic potential (IPSP) and rebound elicited by the upward phase of the SFM signal. Spike output: A spike results only when the rebound following the IPSP coincides with the EPSP (from Reference 5).

mechanism is a variation of the one shown in Figure 4*C* for FM sweep tuning, in that it requires coincidence between subthreshold excitation and a rebound from inhibition. In the case of SFM signals, the excitation would be provided by the downward FM component and the inhibition by the upward FM component. Because the first cycle always lacks one of the two inputs, the cell requires at least one cycle to become primed to respond.

The finding that many IC neurons respond selectively to low modulation rates (e.g. 8, 27) is consistent with another temporal response property, recovery time. When two sequential sounds are presented, many IC neurons respond poorly to the second sound over a relatively long range of interstimulus intervals (10 to >100 ms) (3, 38, 64; see 4 for a review of earlier findings on recovery times in bat IC neurons). Recovery times also appear to be controlled by GABAergic inhibition (38).

Delay Tuning

O'Neill & Suga (45) first described neurons that responded selectively to pairs of sounds separated by a specific time delay. They proposed that these delay-tuned neurons provided the information necessary for the bat to determine the distance of an object from which echoes were reflected. Although delay-tuned neurons were first described in the cortex, they have since been found in the medial geniculate complex (46, 47) and IC of echolocating bats (41, 78, 79). Delay-tuned neurons are also found in a region between the IC and superior colliculus (SC) in *Eptesicus* (14).

Suga proposed that a model composed of delay lines and coincidence detectors can account for the tuning of thalamic and cortical neurons to pulse-echo delays. In order for such a model to work, there needs to be at least a 20-ms range of latencies in the inputs. There is evidence that this latency range may be at least partly created in the IC through interaction of excitatory and inhibitory inputs. Blocking of inhibitory inputs decreases the response latency to sound for many neurons (34, 49), and whole-cell patch-clamp recordings from IC neurons (13) indicate that synaptic inhibition dominates the early part of the response, resulting in an early unresponsive period correlated with the onset of the stimulus. For some IC neurons, the threshold of the inhibitory input is higher than that of the excitatory input; as a result, the latency of response to low-intensity sounds is shorter than that to high-intensity sounds. This mismatch in the thresholds of excitatory and inhibitory inputs could be the basis for "paradoxical latency shift," first proposed by Sullivan (71) as a mechanism for producing delay tuning in cortical neurons. According to this hypothesis, the response to the bat's intense emitted vocalization would have a longer latency than the response to the faint echoes returning at a later time. As a result, the delayed response to the pulse would coincide with the response to the echo, resulting in coincidence of two excitatory inputs. The finding of paradoxical latency shift in IC neurons strengthens this hypothesis and suggests that the IC plays a key role in creating delay tuning of neurons at higher levels.

PRINCIPLES OF OPERATION OF THE INFERIOR COLLICULUS

It seems likely that the temporal processing mechanisms described in the previous sections are examples of general principles of the operation of the vertebrate midbrain (4). The first principle is that inhibitory and excitatory inputs, which themselves have different temporal properties, interact to produce filters for temporal features of sounds. The second principle is that the filters are mainly for biologically important sounds, especially sounds produced by other animals. At one level of analysis, these sounds consist of the very rapid frequency components, or fine structure of the sounds. Auditory nerve fibers can follow, or phase lock, to sounds up to about 3 kHz. Phase locking becomes degraded at levels above the superior olive, so it is likely that processing in the IC is not concerned with the rapid events related to the carrier waveform of sounds. At another level of analysis, biologically important sounds have a slower rate that is described in terms of either the sound envelope, the duration, the envelope modulation rate, or the frequency modulation. These temporal aspects of biologically important sounds are limited by the rate of movement of the skeletal and muscular elements that produce them during running, flying, or vocalizing. The rate of change of these sounds is slow relative to the rate at which neurons can fire action potentials. For example, the most rapidly produced echolocation sounds of the big brown bat have a repetition rate of about 150/s. Wing beat frequencies of flying insects that the bat hunts are much less. If it is the job of the IC to filter for these kinds of sounds, then its operation must become slower to accommodate the filtering. Duration tuning is a good example: In order to measure the duration of sound, the neurons that do so cannot respond until the end of the sound. Thus a byproduct of filtering for biologically important sounds is that inhibitory mechanisms reduce the rate of temporal operations in the IC to match the rate at which the sounds can be analyzed (4). The consequence of the processes that occur in the IC is a temporal window or multiple windows during which the neuron can or cannot fire.

An important component of the timing operations in the IC is cortical feedback. A recent study by Yan & Suga (78, 79) took advantage of the fact that the auditory cortex of the mustached bat has a topographical map of best delays. Thus, they could activate or inactivate specific delay areas in the cortex while recording best delays in the IC to show that the cortex has a sharpening effect on tuning in the IC. When cortical areas and IC areas were matched in terms of best delay, electrical stimulation of the cortex increased the responsiveness of IC neurons tuned to delays of two-tone sequences. However, when the cortical stimulating electrode was in an area that did not match the best delay of neurons at the recording electrode in the IC, cortical stimulation reduced the response of IC neurons. Furthermore, cortical stimulation systematically shifted best delays of IC neurons. Stimulation of cortical areas with long delays shortened delays of IC neurons, whereas stimulation of cortical areas with short delays lengthened delays of IC neurons. Inactivation of cortical areas had the opposite effect of electrical stimulation on delay tuning in the IC. Thus, the cortex serves to sharpen delay tuning by a facilitative mechanism for matched delays and a suppressive mechanism for unmatched delays. This matched facilitation with flanking suppression may be a general principle of corticofugal operation because it is found for other tuned parameters in the IC (82, 83).

SUMMARY AND CONCLUSIONS

In summary, the studies reviewed here indicate that inhibitory mechanisms are crucial for the integrative properties of the IC, especially those involving temporal processing. An initial set of transformations in the brainstem are important for setting up mechanisms for creating neural tuning to biologically important parameters of sound. The brainstem transformations include a change in sign from excitatory to inhibitory, changes in discharge pattern, and creation of delay lines. These transformations are segregated into separate pathways or streams of processing below the IC. Convergence of these pathways at the IC produces tuning for temporal features of sound including duration, the direction of frequency sweeps, modulation rate, and interstimulus interval. The auditory cortex exerts control over some of this processing by sharpening temporal filters. The bat's brainstem circuitry provides a good general model of neural mechanisms for the analysis of temporal patterns. The computational processes that occur in the IC result in a slowing of the rate of neural processing, bringing it more in line with the rate at which biological sounds are produced.

ACKNOWLEDGMENTS

This work was supported by National Institutes of Health research grants DC-00607 (EC) and DC-00287 (JHC) and by a National Science Foundation research grant IBN-9511362 (EC).

Literature Cited

1. Baron G. 1974. Differential phylogenetic development of the acoustic nuclei among chiroptera. *Brain Behav. Evol.* 9:7–40
2. Casseday JH, Covey E. 1992. Frequency tuning properties of neurons in the inferior colliculus of an FM bat. *J. Comp. Neurol.* 319:34–50
3. Casseday JH, Covey E. 1995. Mechanisms for analysis of auditory temporal patterns in the brainstem of echolocating bats. In *Neural Representation of Temporal Patterns*, ed. E Covey, H Hawkins, R Port, pp. 25–52. New York: Plenum
4. Casseday JH, Covey E. 1996. A neuroethological theory of the operation of the inferior colliculus. *Brain Behav. Evol.* 47:311–36
5. Casseday JH, Covey E, Grothe B. 1997. Neural selectivity and tuning for sinusoidal frequency modulations in the inferior colliculus of the big brown bat, *Eptesicus fuscus*. *J. Neurophysiol.* 77:1595–605
6. Casseday JH, Ehrlich D, Covey E. 1994. Neural tuning for sound duration: role of inhibitory mechanisms in the inferior colliculus. *Science* 264:847–50
7. Condon CJ, Chang SH, Feng AS. 1991. Processing of behaviorally relevant temporal parameters of acoustic stimuli by single neurons in the superior olivary nucleus of the leopard frog. *J. Comp. Physiol. A* 168: 709–25
8. Condon CJ, White KR, Feng AS. 1996. Neurons with different temporal firing patterns in the inferior colliculus of the little brown bat differentially process sinusoidal amplitude-modulated signals. *J. Comp. Physiol. A* 178:147–57
9. Covey E, Casseday JH. 1986. Connectional basis for frequency representation in the nuclei of the lateral lemniscus of the bat *Eptesicus fuscus*. *J. Neurosci.* 6:2926–40
10. Covey E, Casseday JH. 1991. The monaural nuclei of the lateral lemniscus in an echolocating bat: parallel pathways for analyzing temporal features of sound. *J. Neurosci.* 11:3456–70
11. Covey E, Casseday JH. 1995. The lower brainstem auditory pathways. In *Hearing by Bats, Springer Handbook of Auditory Research*, ed. A Popper, R Fay, 11:235–95. New York: Springer-Verlag
12. Covey E, Hall WC, Kobler JB. 1987. Subcortical connections of the superior colliculus in the mustache bat, *Pteronotus parnellii*. *J. Comp. Neurol.* 263:179–97
13. Covey E, Kauer JA, Casseday JH. 1996. Whole-cell patch-clamp recording reveals subthreshold sound-evoked postsynaptic currents in the inferior colliculus of awake bats. *J. Neurosci.* 16:3009–18
14. Dear SP, Suga N. 1995. Delay-tuned neurons in the midbrain of the big brown bat. *J. Neurophysiol.* 73:1084–100
15. Ehrlich D, Casseday JH, Covey E. 1997. Neural tuning to sound duration in the inferior colliculus of the big brown bat, *Eptesicus fuscus*. *J. Neurophysiol.* 77:2360–72
16. Faingold CL, Boersma Anderson CA, Caspary DM. 1991. Involvement of GABA in acoustically-evoked inhibition in inferior colliculus neurons. *Hear. Res.* 52:201–16
17. Feng AS, Hall JC, Gooler DM. 1990. Neural basis of sound pattern recognition in Anurans. *Prog. Neurobiol.* 34:313–29
18. Ferragamo MJ, Haresign T, Simmons JA. 1998. Frequency tuning, latencies, and responses to frequency-modulated sweeps in the inferior colliculus of the echolocating bat, *Eptesicus fuscus*. *J. Comp. Physiol. A* 182:65–79
19. Fubara BM, Casseday JH, Covey E, Schwartz-Bloom RD. 1996. Distribution of $GABA_A$, $GABA_B$, and glycine receptors in the central auditory system of the big brown bat, *Eptesicus fuscus*. *J. Comp. Neurol.* 369:83–92
20. Fuzessery ZM. 1994. Response selectivity for multiple dimensions of frequency sweeps in the pallid bat inferior colliculus. *J. Neurophysiol.* 72:1061–79
21. Fuzessery ZM. 1997. Acute sensitivity to interaural time differences in the inferior colliculus of a bat that relies on passive sound localization. *Hear. Res.* 109:46–62
22. Fuzessery ZM, Hall JC. 1996. Role of GABA in shaping frequency tuning and creating FM sweep selectivity in the inferior colliculus. *J. Neurophysiol.* 76:1059–73
23. Glendenning KK, Baker BN. 1988. Neuroanatomical distribution of receptors for three potential inhibitory neurotransmitters in the brainstem auditory nuclei of the cat. *J. Comp. Neurol.* 275:288–308
24. Goldberg JM, Brown PB. 1968. Functional organization of the dog superior olivary complex: an anatomical and electrophysiological study. *J. Neurophysiol.* 31:639–56
25. Gooler DM, Feng AS. 1992. Temporal coding in the frog auditory midbrain: the influence of duration and rise-fall time on the processing of complex amplitude-modulated stimuli. *J. Neurophysiol.* 67:1–22
26. Grothe B. 1994. Interaction of excitation

and inhibition in processing pure tone and amplitude-modulated stimuli in the medial superior olive of the mustached bat. *J. Neurophysiol.* 71:706–21
27. Grothe B, Covey E, Casseday JH. 1996. Spatial tuning of neurons in the inferior colliculus of the big brown bat: effects of sound level, stimulus type and multiple sound sources. *J. Comp. Physiol. A* 179: 89–102
28. Grothe B, Park TJ, Schuller G. 1997. Medial superior olive in the free-tailed bat: response to pure tones and amplitude-modulated tones. *J. Neurophysiol.* 77: 1553–65
29. Grothe B, Vater M, Casseday JH, Covey E. 1992. Monaural interaction of excitation and inhibition in the medial superior olive of the mustached bat: an adaptation for biosonar. *Proc. Natl. Acad. Sci. USA* 89:5108–12
30. Hall JC, Feng AS. 1991. Temporal processing in the dorsal medullary nucleus of the northern leopard frog (*Rana pipiens pipiens*). *J. Neurophysiol.* 66:955–73
31. Haplea S, Covey E, Casseday JH. 1994. Frequency tuning and response latencies at three levels in the brainstem of the echolocating bat, *Eptesicus fuscus*. *J. Comp. Physiol. A* 174:671–83
32. Hattori T, Suga N. 1997. The inferior colliculus of the mustached bat has the frequency-vs-latency coordinates. *J. Comp. Physiol. A* 180:271–84
33. Jeffress LA. 1948. A place theory of sound localization. *J. Comp. Physiol. Psychol.* 41: 35–39
34. Johnson BR. 1993. *GABAergic and glycinergic inhibition in the central nucleus of the inferior colliculus of the big brown bat.* PhD thesis. Duke Univ., Durham, NC
35. Kalko EKV, Schnitzler H-U. 1989. The echolocation and hunting behavior of Daubenton's bat, *Myotis daubentoni*. *Behav. Ecol. Sociobiol.* 24:225–38
36. Kanwal JS, Matsumura S, Ohlemiller K, Suga N. 1994. Anaylsis of acoustic elements and syntax in communication sounds emitted by mustached bats. *J. Acoust. Soc. Am.* 96:1229–54
37. Kuwada S, Yin TCT. 1987. Physiological studies of directional hearing. In *Directional Hearing*, ed. WA Yost, G Gourevitch, pp. 146–76. New York: Springer-Verlag
38. Lu Y, Jen PH, Zheng QY. 1997. GABAergic disinhibition changes the recovery cycle of bat inferior collicular neurons. *J. Comp. Physiol. A* 181:331–41
39. Manis PB. 1990. Membrane properties and discharge characteristics of guinea pig dorsal cochlear nucleus neurons studied in vitro. *J. Neurosci.* 10:2338–51
40. Marimuthu G, Neuweiler G. 1987. The use of acoustical cues for prey detection by the Indian false vampire bat, *Megaderma lyra*. *J. Comp. Physiol. A* 160:509–15
41. Mittmann DH, Wenstrup JJ. 1995. Combination-sensitive neurons in the inferior colliculus. *Hear. Res.* 90:185–91
42. Narins PM, Capranica RR. 1980. Neural adaptations for processing the two-note call of the Puerto Rican treefrog, *Eleutherodactylus coqui*. *Brain Behav. Evol.* 17:48–66
43. Neuweiler G. 1990. Auditory adaptations for prey capture in echolocating bats. *Physiol. Rev.* 70:615–41
44. Oertel D. 1991. The role of intrinsic neuronal properties in the encoding of auditory information in the cochlear nuclei. *Curr. Opin. Neurobiol.* 1:221–28
45. O'Neill WE, Suga N. 1982. Encoding of target range information and its representation in the auditory cortex of the mustached bat. *J. Neurosci.* 2:17–24
46. Olsen JF, Suga N. 1991a. Combination-sensitive neurons in the medial geniculate body of the mustached bat: encoding of relative velocity information. *J. Neurophysiol.* 65:1254–74
47. Olsen JF, Suga N. 1991b. Combination-sensitive neurons in the medial geniculate body of the mustached bat: encoding of target range information. *J. Neurophysiol.* 65:1275–96
48. Park TJ, Grothe B. 1996. From pattern recognition to sound localization: a by-product of growing larger during evolution. *Naturwissenschaften* 83:30–32
49. Park TJ, Pollak GD. 1993. GABA shapes a topographic organization of response latency in the mustached bat's inferior colliculus. *J. Neurophysiol.* 13:5172–87
50. Pinheiro AD, Wu M, Jen PHS. 1991. Encoding repetition rate and duration in the inferior colliculus of the big brown bat, *Eptesicus fuscus*. *J. Comp. Physiol. A* 169:69–85
51. Poljak S. 1926. Untersuchungen am Oktavussystem der Säugetiere und an den mit diesem koordinierten motorischen Apparaten des Hirnstammes. *J. Psychol. Neurol.* 32:170–231
52. Pollak GD, Casseday JH. 1989. The neural basis of echolocation in bats. In *Zoophysiology*, Vol. 25. Berlin: Springer-Verlag
53. Pollak GD, Park TJ. 1993. The effects of GABAergic inhibition on monaural response properties of neurons in the mustache bat's inferior colliculus. *Hear. Res.* 65:99–117

54. Potter HD. 1965. Patterns of acoustically evoked discharges of neurons in the mesencephalon of the bullfrog. *J. Neurophysiol.* 28:1155–84
55. Rose GJ. 1995. Representation of temporal patterns of signal amplitude in the anuran auditory system and electrosensory system. In *Neural Representation of Temporal Patterns*, ed. E Covey, HL Hawkins, RF Port, pp. 1–24. New York: Plenum
56. Rose GJ, Capranica RR. 1984. Processing amplitude-modulated sounds by the auditory midbrain of two species of toads: matched temporal filters. *J. Comp. Physiol. A* 154:211–19
57. Rose GJ, Capranica RR. 1985. Sensitivity to amplitude modulated sounds in the anuran auditory nervous system. *J. Neurophysiol.* 53:446–65
58. Ross LS, Pollak GD, Zook JM. 1988. Origin of ascending projections to an isofrequency region of the mustache bat's inferior colliculus. *J. Comp. Neurol.* 270: 488–505
59. Saitoh I, Suga N. 1995. Long delay lines for ranging are created by inhibition in the inferior colliculus of the mustached bat. *J. Neurophysiol.* 74:1–11
60. Schnitzler H-U, Kalko E, Miller L, Surlykke A. 1987. The echolocation and hunting behavior of the bat, *Pipistrellus kuhli*. *J. Comp. Physiol. A* 161:267–74
61. Schuller G, Covey E, Casseday JH. 1991. Auditory pontine grey: connections and response properties in the horseshoe bat. *Eur. J. Neurosci.* 3:648–62
62. Schweizer H. 1981. The connections of the inferior colliculus and the organization of the brainstem auditory system in the greater horseshoe bat (*Rhinolophus ferrumequinum*). *J. Comp. Neurol.* 201:25–49
63. Simmons JA. 1989. A view of the world through the bat's ear: the formation of acoustic images in echolocation. *Cognition* 33:155–99
64. Suga N. 1964. Recovery cycles and responses to frequency modulated tone pulses in auditory neurons of echolocating bats. *J. Physiol.* 175:50–80
65. Suga N. 1965. Analysis of frequency modulated sounds by neurons of echolocating bats. *J. Physiol.* 179:26–53
66. Suga N. 1968. Analysis of frequency modulated and complex sounds by single auditory neurons of bats. *J. Physiol.* 198:51–80
67. Suga N. 1969. Classification of inferior collicular neurons of bats in terms of responses to pure tones, FM sounds and noise bursts. *J. Physiol.* 200:555–74
68. Suga N. 1972. Analysis of information bearing elements in complex sounds by auditory neurons of bats. *Audiology* 11:58–72
69. Suga N. 1973. Feature extraction in the auditory system of bats. In *Basic Mechanisms in Hearing*, ed. AR Møller, pp. 675–712. New York: Academic
70. Suga N. 1994. Multi-function theory for cortical processing of auditory information: implications of single-unit and lesion data for future research. *J. Comp. Physiol. A* 175:135–44
71. Sullivan WE. 1982. Possible neural mechanisms of target distance coding in auditory system of the echolocating bat, *Myotis lucifugus*. *J. Neurophysiol.* 48:1033–47
72. Tougaard J, Casseday JH, Covey E. 1998. Arctiid moths and bat echolocation: broadband clicks interfere with neural responses to auditory stimuli in the nuclei of the lateral lemniscus of the big brown bat. *J. Comp. Physiol. A* 182:203–15
73. Vater M. 1995. Ultrastructural and immunocytochemical observations on the superior olivary complex of the mustached bat. *J. Comp. Neurol.* 358:155–80
74. Vater M, Casseday JH, Covey E. 1995. Convergence and divergence of ascending binaural and monaural pathways from the superior olives of the mustached bat. *J. Comp. Neurol.* 351:632–46
75. Vater M, Covey E, Casseday JH. 1997. The columnar region of the ventral nucleus of the lateral lemniscus in the big brown bat (*Eptesicus fuscus*): synaptic arrangements and structural correlates of feedforward inhibitory function. *Cell Tissue Res.* 289:223–33
76. Wenthold RJ, Huie D, Altschuler RA, Reeks KA. 1987. Glycine immunoreactivity localized in the cochlear nucleus and superior olivary complex. *Neuroscience* 22:897–912
77. Wenthold RJ, Zempel JM, Parakkal MH, Reeks KA, Altschuler RA. 1986. Immunocytochemical localization of GABA in the cochlear nucleus of the guinea pig. *Brain Res.* 380:7–18
78. Yan J, Suga N. 1996a. Corticofugal modulation of time-domain processing of biosonar information in bats. *Science* 273: 1100–3
79. Yan J, Suga N. 1996b. The midbrain creates and the thalamus sharpens echo-delay tuning for the cortical representation of target-distance information in the mustached bat. *Hear. Res.* 93:102–10
80. Yang L, Pollak GD. 1997. Differential response properties to amplitude modulated signals in the dorsal nucleus of the lateral lemniscus of the mustache bat and the roles of GABAergic inhibition. *J. Neurophysiol.* 77:324–40

81. Yin TCT, Chan JCK. 1990. Interaural time sensitivity in medial superior olive of cat. *J. Neurophysiol.* 64:465–88
82. Zhang Y, Suga N. 1997. Corticofugal amplification of subcortical responses to single tone stimuli in the mustached bat. *J. Neurophysiol.* 78:3489–92
83. Zhang Y, Suga N, Yan J. 1997. Corticofugal modulation of frequency processing in bat auditory system. *Nature* 387:900–3
84. Zook JM, Casseday JH. 1982a. Cytoarchitecture of auditory system in lower brainstem of the mustache bat, *Pteronotus parnellii*. *J. Comp. Neurol.* 207:1–13
85. Zook JM, Casseday JH. 1982b. Origin of ascending projections to inferior colliculus in the mustache bat, *Pteronotus parnellii*. *J. Comp. Neurol.* 207:14–28
86. Zook JM, Casseday JH. 1985. Projections from the cochlear nuclei in the mustache bat, *Pteronotus parnellii*. *J. Comp. Neurol.* 237:307–24
87. Zook JM, Casseday JH. 1987. Convergence of ascending pathways at the inferior colliculus of the mustache bat, *Pteronotus parnellii*. *J. Comp. Neurol.* 261:347–61
88. Zook JM, Jacobs MS, Glezer I, Morgane PJ. 1988. Some comparative aspects of auditory brainstem cytoarchitecture in echolocating mammals: speculations on the morphological basis of time-domain signal processing. In *Animal Sonar: Processes and Performance*, ed. PE Nachtigall, PWB Moore, pp. 311–16. New York: Plenum

Annu. Rev. Physiol. 1999. 61:477–96

SYNAPTIC MECHANISMS FOR CODING TIMING IN AUDITORY NEURONS

Laurence O. Trussell
Department of Physiology, University of Wisconsin, Madison, Wisconsin 53706;
e-mail: trussell@physiology.wisc.edu

KEY WORDS: glutamate receptors, potassium channels, synapses, plasticity

ABSTRACT

Neurons in the cochlear ganglion and auditory brain stem nuclei preserve the relative timing of action potentials passed through sequential synaptic levels. To accomplish this task, these neurons have unique morphological and biophysical specializations in axons, dendrites, and nerve terminals. At the membrane level, these adaptations include low-threshold, voltage-gated potassium channels and unusually rapid-acting transmitter-gated channels, which govern how quickly and reliably action potential threshold is reached during a synaptic response. Some nerve terminals are remarkably large and release large amounts of excitatory neurotransmitter. The high output of transmitter at these terminals can lead to synaptic depression, which may itself be regulated by presynaptic transmitter receptors. The way in which these different cellular mechanisms are employed varies in different cell types and circuits and reflects refinements suited to different aspects of acoustic processing.

THE TEMPORAL CODE IN AUDITION

In order to convey information about pitch, intensity, and location, the auditory system takes advantage of place, rate, and temporal codes. An anatomical map of acoustic frequency is generated in the cochlea by the tonotopic response of the hair cell epithelium (1). While the spatial pattern of activation of this array and the firing rate of its auditory nerve output encode information, the timing of action potentials is the lingua franca of auditory processing,

0066-4278/99/0315-0477$08.00

used by a wide variety of neurons to convey specific aspects of the acoustic environment.

The temporal code appears in different forms. Phase-locking occurs when the onset of an action potential appears reproducibly at a particular part of the cycle of the stimulating sound source (1a). While phase-locking is a typical feature of the response to low-frequency sound ($\lesssim$ 1–2 kHz), phase-locked firing of action potentials may also occur with respect to the cycle of amplitude modulation of a high-frequency carrier (2). In some cases, neurons are adapted to preserving the timing of action potentials with respect to action potentials in other circuits rather than to the sound cycle itself (3). For other neurons, the precision of action potential timing may be retained just in the earliest part of an acoustic response, such as when an onset must be encoded. Neural circuits, which use timing to extract the location and meaning of sounds, are discussed in this volume (3a).

Several principles are played out in the cellular adaptions that permit the conveyance of timing. The surety and consistent timing of the response are essential to transmitting the onset and frequency of an acoustic stimulus and to promote entrainment. As signals are passaged from synapse to axon to synapse, conduction and synaptic delays inevitably accumulate; the processing of temporal information, particularly when convergence is an issue, requires that these delays be highly uniform, despite the inherently probabilistic nature of ion channel gating and transmitter release. Uniform latencies are achieved in part by the large size of the excitatory synaptic potential (EPSP), which ensures that the variability or jitter in the timing of threshold crossing is kept short (4). The shape of the EPSP is fundamental to auditory timing circuits, since narrow EPSPs help minimize temporal summation and ensure a brief refractory period. In this review, we examine how the timing of action potentials can be preserved and transmitted through different synaptic levels in the auditory system, focusing on the mechanisms by which brief, well-timed EPSPs are generated and how their amplitude may be regulated.

SYNAPTIC MORPHOLOGY AND TIMING

In bushy cells of the mammalian ventral cochlear nucleus (VCN) and in their avian homologs of the nucleus magnocellularis (nMAG), as well as in principal cells of the mammalian medial nucleus of the trapezoid body (MNTB) and the ventral nucleus of the lateral lemniscus, somatic innervation by large calyceal or end-bulb terminals, which feature large numbers of functional synaptic release sites per axon terminal, facilitates reliable transmission (5–8). In spherical bushy cells, MNTB, and nMAG, a single stimulus liberates 100–200 transmitter quanta from each axon terminal, as indicated by quantal analysis (9–11). This bolus of transmitter generates an excitatory postsynaptic current (EPSC) more than 30 times larger than that needed to drive an action potential (4, 11). The resulting EPSP reaches threshold quickly and reliably, despite considerable use-dependent rundown (see below). Somatic innervation avoids the slowing of the onset that dendritic innervation would produce (12). However, despite the apparent adaptive significance of somatic innervation, the octopus cells of the VCN (13), the neurons of the mammalian medial superior olive (MSO) (14), their avian homolog the nucleus laminaris (NL) (15, 16), and to a lesser extent the lateral superior olive (LSO) (3) and the stellate cells of the VCN (17) combine dendrites and good timing, possibly because of biophysical specializations that compensate for cable effects. Moreover, in these dendritic cells and in the globular bushy cells of the VCN, convergence of many axonal inputs is favored over the presence of only a few massive synapses.

CONTROL OF EPSC DURATION

Synaptic Recordings

The duration of the EPSC is the starting point for controlling the time course of EPSPs in neurons (reviewed in reference 18). EPSPs in auditory neurons must be brief in order to accommodate rapid transmission and minimize temporal distortion through synaptic networks, and brief EPSPs can be achieved only by having short EPSCs. A short membrane time constant ($R_m C_m$), generally influenced by resting potassium conductances, is also important (see below); however, a large synaptic conductance will itself lower the membrane time constant (19), and so EPSPs may decay faster than the intrinsic membrane $R_m C_m$. It remains unclear if this plays a role in the auditory system.

Glutamate, or a related substance, and glutamate receptors mediate fast excitatory transmission in the cochlea and in brain stem auditory neurons. Hair cells and nerve terminals in the cochlear nuclei and trapezoid body exhibit glutamate-like immunoreactivity (20–22), and evoked release of glutamate can be demonstrated biochemically or by a bioassay (23, 24). While there remains some controversy about whether glutamate itself is the afferent transmitter (25), the role of glutamate receptors is clear. As discussed below, glutamate receptors have been localized to the subsynaptic membrane in the cochlea and cochlear nuclei by using immunohistochemical techniques. Recently, the development of a wide range of specific pharmacological reagents and their use on preparations maintained in vitro have permitted precise identification of receptor subtypes mediating transmission in particular cell types. Selective antagonists of α-amino-3-hydroxy-5-methyl-4-isoxazolepropionic acid (AMPA) receptors block fast excitatory synaptic transmission in rodent bushy cells (26), stellate cells (17, 26), fusiform cells (27), and octopus cells (13). Beyond the cochlear

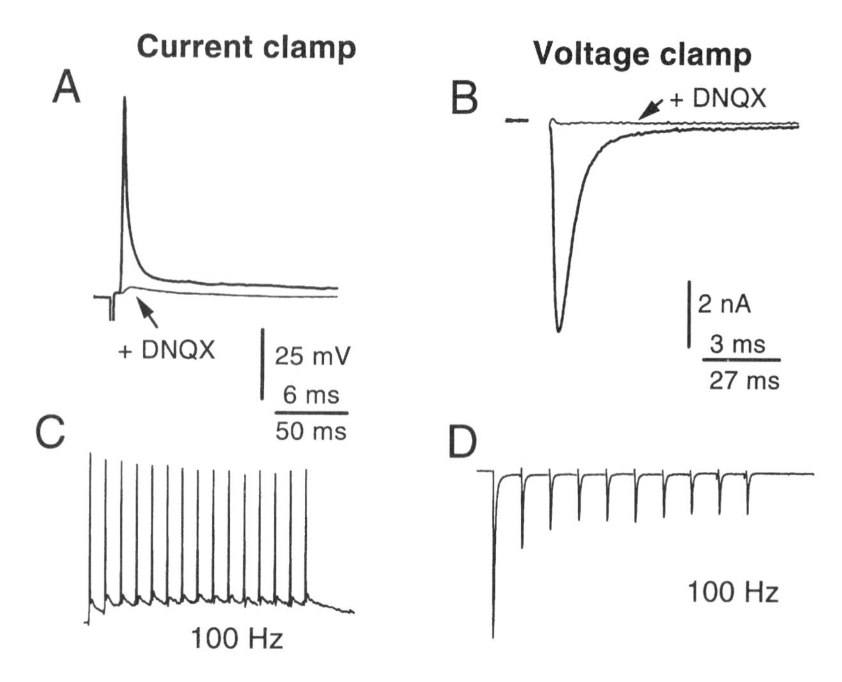

Figure 1 Pharmacology and frequency-dependent depression of synaptic events in nMAG. (*A*) Single, suprathreshold EPSPs ($V_{rest} = -65$ mV) are almost completely blocked by bath application of 30 μM DNQX. (*B*) Under voltage clamp, large inward EPSCs ($V_{hold} = -30$ mV) are also blocked by DNQX. (*C*) Postsynaptic action potentials entrain to 100-Hz synaptic stimuli. (*D*) The depression of the EPSC activated at this same rate is revealed under voltage clamp.

nucleus, block by AMPA antagonists has been observed in the rodent LSO (28) and MNTB (28–30). In chick brain stem or brain slice preparations, auditory-nerve evoked responses in nMAG are completely blocked by AMPA receptor antagonists (4, 11, 31), as illustrated in Figure 1*A* and *B*. Excitatory transmission in the avian NL is also blocked by these agents (32, 33).

Overall, it seems that *N*-methyl-D-aspartate (NMDA) receptors contribute little to the excitatory drive for those neurons that transmit well-timed signals. In the chick nMAG, NMDA receptors contribute only slightly to the EPSP (4), and by hatching age only 10% of the peak EPSC is produced by NMDA receptors (11); even this occurs only at positive membrane potentials where magnesium block of the NMDA receptor is minimized. However, during repetitive synaptic stimulation, NMDA receptors may contribute to a small plateau potential (4). In bushy cells of newborn rats, a small NMDA component is apparent, but it has nearly disappeared by the beginning of the third week after birth (26). NMDA receptor EPSCs have also been observed in the MNTB of rats up to

2 weeks of age (29); however, it remains possible that these also disappear as the neurons mature. In all of these cases, the NMDA receptor-mediated EPSCs do not have a notably different time course from their counterparts in other brain regions.

While the duration of synaptic currents varies in different cell types, the very fastest currents have been found only in neurons of the auditory system. Single quantal currents and miniature excitatory post-synaptic currents (mEPSCs) in chick nMAG decay with an exponential time constant of just under 0.5 ms at room temperature, declining to 0.18 ms at 31°C (11, 34). Given the bird brain temperature of 40–41°C and a Q_{10} for receptor kinetics of >2, it is likely that nMAG mEPSCs normally last less than 0.1 ms. Similar values have been reported for chick NL (35, 36) and nucleus angularis (NA) (35). In rodent bushy cells, mEPSCs decay with a time course identical to that in chick bushy cells (9, 35, 37), perhaps reflecting the high sequence homology of the genes encoding avian and rodent glutamate receptor subunit (38, 39). Figure 2 illustrates the remarkable speed in auditory synaptic kinetics by comparing mEPSCs recorded from a cell in the VCN and from a hippocampal neuron.

The time course of the EPSC represents the convergence of several factors. Isaacson & Walmsley (9) showed that the evoked EPSC in rat bushy cells could be described as the convolution of the time course of the mEPSC and the period over which quanta are released, the release time course. The latter represents a narrow, skewed function with a duration of less than 1 ms. Similar estimates were made by Borst & Sakmann (10) with rat MNTB. The duration of the EPSC is therefore longer than that of the mEPSC, with a dominant exponential

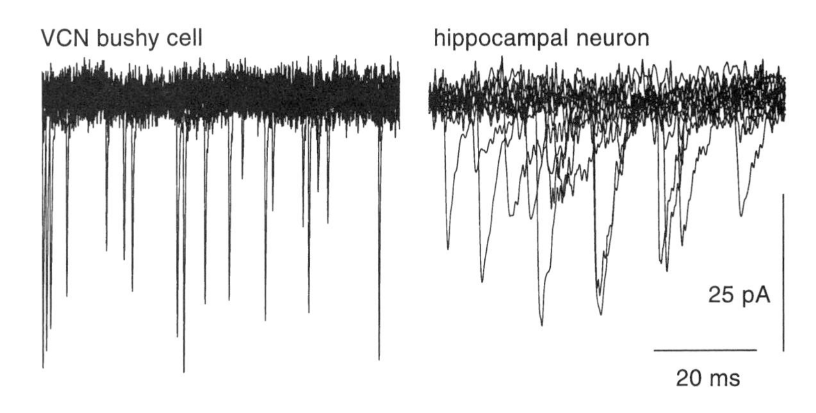

Figure 2 Comparison of randomly occurring mEPSCs (downward current deflections) recorded from a mouse VCN cell (identified histologically as a bushy cell) in a slice and from a cultured rat hippocampal cell. $V_{\text{hold}} = -70$ mV.

decay time of about 0.9 ms at room temperature. Although it is clear that a narrow release time course is necessary for auditory function, it is probably not unique to the auditory system. Although much broader release profiles have been observed in cultured hippocampal pyramidal neurons (40), the release time courses at excitatory and inhibitory contacts in the dentate gyrus are just as brief as in the calyceal auditory synapses (19).

In chick nMAG, while the major component of decay is essentially identical to that of mammals, the situation is more complex. First, at least two other, smaller components of decay are present, one of about 3 ms and one lasting several tens of milliseconds (41). Second, evidence indicates that in addition to mEPSC and release time course, transmitter clearance and desensitization help to shape the nMAG EPSC. Unlike in rat bushy cells (9), an increase in the quantal content broadens the EPSC, consistent with delayed clearance of transmitter (42). In the presence of drugs that block desensitization and prolong EPSCs, the effect of changing quantal content on EPSC duration is even more dramatic (34). The slowest component of the EPSC (41), whose amplitude is less than 1% of the peak current, is a consequence of transmitter pooling in the large synaptic cleft after glutamate release from many adjacent release sites.

Properties of AMPA Receptors

The brevity of EPSCs in auditory neurons reflects the intrinsic, biophysical properties of postsynaptic AMPA receptors (43). In outside-out patches from nMAG, the time course of current decay after a brief pulse of glutamate (which estimates the so-called channel deactivation time) and the duration of mEPSCs are virtually identical (41). This matching of synaptic and receptor kinetics is maintained over a range of membrane potentials that cause graded shifts in AMPA receptor gating kinetics (41, 44). The results imply that when one vesicle is released, it is the channel burst duration, rather than the receptor desensitization time course or the transmitter clearance rate, that determines the decay time of the postsynaptic response. Moreover, since the mEPSCs decay with a 0.5-ms time constant, the lifetime of the transmitter must be much briefer. Except for MNTB, in which deactivation is 0.9 ms (45), no other such measurements are yet available for mammalian auditory neurons. However, given the uniformly rapid mEPSC time courses among the cells described above, it seems likely that the kinetics of their AMPA receptors are also similar.

A broader survey of AMPA receptor kinetics in chick was made by Raman et al (35), focusing on the time course of desensitization to rapidly applied glutamate. The desensitization time constant was found to be similar in cells from nMAG, NA, NL, and cochlear ganglion. These values were all significantly shorter than the desensitization time constant of non-auditory neurons, including cerebellar Purkinje cells, granule cells, motor neurons, and cortical cells. While cerebellar granule cells and cortical interneurons have quite fast AMPA channel kinetics (19, 45, 46), decay times identical to those for auditory cells are found only in patches excised from rod photoreceptor cells (47).

Receptor Expression Studies

Various studies of the types of AMPA receptors expressed in auditory neurons form a suggestive, but still incomplete, picture of the molecular underpinnings of the rapid EPSC. AMPA receptors are pentameric complexes composed of subunits that are the product of up to four different genes, termed GluR1 through GluR4 or GluRA through GluRD. Each subunit is subject to alternative splicing (the flip/flop splice cassette) and RNA editing, which further determines channel kinetics and permeability (48). Expression studies, examining the biophysical properties of receptors composed of different receptor subunits, have shown that receptors whose subunits are dominated by "flop" splice variants (49, 50), and in particular those composed mostly of $GluR4_{flop}$ and which lack GluR2 (45, 50), have the most rapid channel kinetics. RNA editing at a site just N-terminal to the flip/flop cassette produces channels that recover faster from desensitization (51). Moreover, AMPA receptors with a paucity of GluR2 have higher calcium permeability along with sensitivity to block intracellularly by polyamines and extracellularly by components of the venom of certain spiders and wasps (52).

In situ hybridization has revealed expression of mRNA for GluR2 through GluR4, but very little GluR1, in rodent spiral ganglion (53, 54) and VCN (55, 56). Initial studies of protein distribution used antibodies to GluR1, GluR2/3 (nonselective), and GluR4; in general, they demonstrated a pattern consistent with the mRNA analysis (53, 57, 58). A recent study of expression at the ultrastructural level in rat end-bulbs of Held has reexamined this issue by using antibodies specific for GluR2, as well as those for GluR2/3 and GluR4, concluding that this synapse uses primarily GluR3- and GluR4-containing receptors for transmission (59). Using the GluR1, GluR2/3, and GluR4 antibody set in owl, Levin et al (60) found high expression of GluR2/3 and GluR4 and low expression of GluR1, in cells of the nMAG and NL, with heterogeneous expression of GluR4 in NA.

Geiger et al (45) have examined subunit expression by the method of reverse transcriptase polymerase chain reaction (RT-PCR) in a variety of cell types, including the MNTB. They found that MNTB expressed a high level of GluR4, moderate levels of GluR1 and GluR2, but only a low level of GluR3. Significantly, virtually all the subunits in MNTB were of the *flop* splice variant. The prevalence of $GluR4_{flop}$ is consistent with the rapid channel kinetics found in that study. It will be important to determine if the fast kinetic receptors found in bushy cells, nMAG cells, and cochlear ganglion cells also express the *flop* variant. However, the expectation that $GluR4_{flop}$ is a general mediator of rapid auditory transmission is tempered by the results of Angulo et al (61), who performed RT-PCR on a population of neocortical interneurons and found little correlation between AMPA channel kinetics and the splice variant.

Given the preponderance of GluR4 in fast auditory synapses, a central issue to address will be the mechanisms that cause GluR4 gene expression to be favored over other subunit genes, especially GluR1 and GluR2. One hypothesis is that since targets of the auditory nerve in general often express fast kinetic receptors in the cochlear nuclei, the auditory nerve itself may have control over postsynaptic subunit expression. In this regard, Rubio & Wenthold (62) found that fusiform cells of the dorsal cochlear nucleus (DCN), which are innervated by glutamatergic parallel fibers as well as by auditory nerve fibers, do express GluR4 but, remarkably, target it only to the dendrites that are contacted by the primary afferents. This results suggests not only that innervation plays an instructive role for gene expression but also that mechanisms for subcellular targeting of different GluR subunits are coordinated somehow by particular presynaptic neurons.

Calcium Flux during Transmission

The calcium permeability of AMPA receptors of auditory relay centers is an important issue for several reasons. Since auditory neurons are highly active, calcium loading of the cytoplasm by synaptic activity would constitute a severe metabolic challenge. Buildup of calcium may serve physiological functions, including activation of Ca^{2+}-sensitive ion channels and activation of second-messenger systems [although in some auditory neurons, calcium-activated channels are conspicuously absent (63)]. In principle, the presence of calcium-permeable transmitter-gated channels might serve to cause rapid control of extracellular [Ca^{2+}] in the synaptic cleft (64, 65). Circumstantial evidence is consistent with calcium loading of the cytosol. Neurons of the timing pathway in avians have high concentrations of the cytosolic calcium-binding proteins calretinin and calbindin (66–68). In mammals, neurons in the spiral ganglion, cochlear nuclei, superior olive, lemniscal nuclei, and inferior colliculus express high levels of a variety of calcium-binding proteins on a cell-type-specific basis (5, 69–72). Moreover, chick nMAG and NL cells express high levels of the sarcoplasmic/endoplasmic reticulum calcium uptake protein, SERCA (73), further suggesting that these cells have adaptations for coping with near-chronic influx of Ca^{2+}.

Several studies have indicated that in some cells of the auditory pathways, Ca^{2+} permeates AMPA receptor channels. Otis et al (65) measured inward current in nMAG generated by application of glutamate or stimulation of end-bulb synapses while in the presence of isotonic extracellular Ca^{2+} solutions, indicating that these AMPA receptors must pass Ca^{2+}. These authors determined a ratio of calcium versus cesium (P_{Ca}/P_{Cs}) of 1.2:3, depending on the assumptions made in estimating free calcium levels. As with low-GluR2-containing receptors, nMAG AMPA receptors exhibit block by intracellular polyamines (S Kriegler, J Lawrence & LO Trussell, unpublished observations). Zhou et al (74) also determined that the AMPA channel of nMAG and NL passes Ca^{2+} by taking advantage of the observation that Ca^{2+}-permeable AMPA receptors pass Co^{2+}, which can be precipitated intracellularly and therefore used as a histological assay of divalent-ion permeability. In mammals, the AMPA receptors of MNTB neurons, which also feature rapid channel kinetics, have a Ca^{2+} permeability close to that seen in chick (45). Whether the high calcium influx which must accompany acoustic signaling has any physiological role in central auditory timing neurons remains unknown.

POTASSIUM CURRENTS SHAPE THE SYNAPTIC RESPONSE

The response to transmitter is dependent on the complement of voltage-sensitive channels active during the synaptic potential. While some studies have focused on inward sodium and calcium currents in spiral ganglion and cochlear nuclear cells (75–79), we restrict our discussion here primarily to potassium currents, since these seem to play a prominent role in the ability of auditory neurons to relay spike timing.

The consequence of these outward currents is clear from the characteristic response profile of several cell types in the cochlear nucleus and olivary complex, in which outward rectification is so strong that prolonged depolarizing current steps generate only a single, short-latency action potential. This electrical behavior, shown in Figure 3*A*, is observed in spiral ganglion cells (77, 80, 81), bushy cells (26, 82, 83), octopus cells (13) and neurons of the MNTB (30, 84, 85) and MSO (86), and, in chick neurons of the nMAG (4, 63, 87) and NL (36, 87). The short time for onset of the increase in membrane conductance and outward current (4, 63, 79, 82, 88, 89) may provide a simple mechanism for ensuring that the latency to spike onset is brief. Very large EPSPs reach threshold quickly, before the onset of rectification. Smaller EPSPs take longer to attain an equivalent, near-threshold potential; during their rising phase, the ensuing rectification raises the threshold beyond their reach. Thus, the onset time of rectification makes certain that postsynaptic spikes, when they occur, always fire with a short latency.

Moreover, outward rectification near the resting potential shortens the membrane time constant so that synaptic potentials are brief (provided that the synaptic currents are also brief), and temporal summation of jittery subthreshold, converging inputs is minimized (83). Indeed, by this mechanism, jitter in

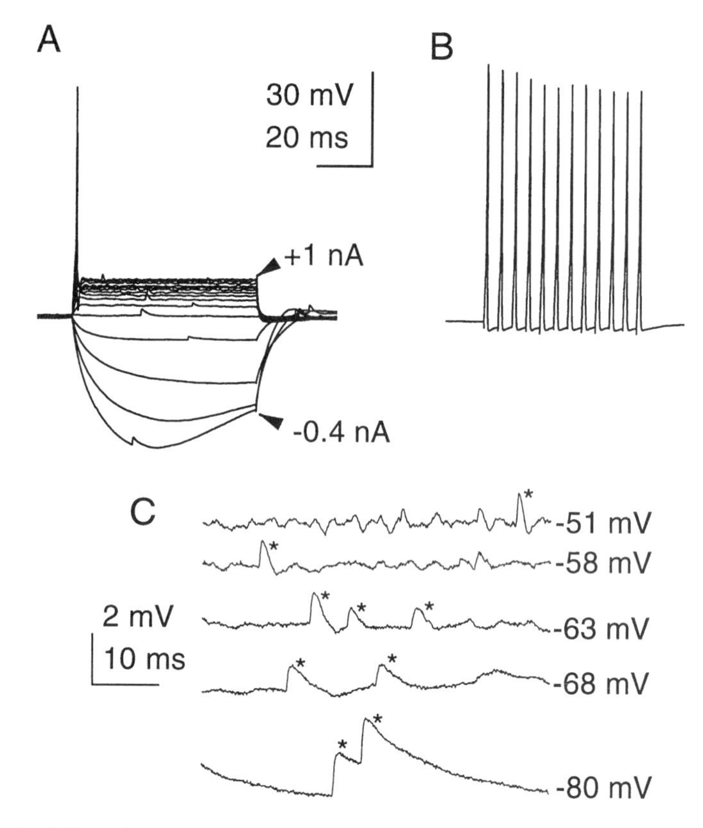

Figure 3 Effects of outward rectification on response properties of nMAG. (*A*) A set of voltage responses to inward and outward current stimuli ranging from −0.4 to 1 nA at 50-pA intervals. Note the decrease in membrane resistance upon depolarization and the single-spike response profile. (*B*) A series of brief 200-Hz, 1 nA-current pulses produces a train of well-timed postsynaptic action potentials. (*C*) mEPSPs (*) occurring during steps to different potentials reveal the effects of outward rectification on the time course of synaptic potentials. Note that at potentials just above rest (−68 mV), the mEPSPs often terminate with a slight oscillation, due to rapid activation and deactivation of the low-threshold outward current.

the timing of each presynaptic action potential may actually be subtracted if postsynaptic spiking requires precisely coincident EPSPs (90). After EPSPs reach threshold, a short membrane time constant allows the membrane to return quickly to a ready state for the next stimulus (18). Thus, when the cell in Figure 3*A* is driven by brief current pulses instead of one long current, it can fire well-timed spikes at a high rate (Figure 3*B*). Estimates of the half-time of decay of the response to current injection in nMAG at 31°C gave half-times of about 2.5 ms near the resting potential of −66 mV, declining to under 0.5 ms at −55 mV (4). The resulting effect on small synaptic currents is illustrated in Figure 3*C*, which shows mEPSPs (marked by asterisks) at different membrane potentials. Note that at the more positive potentials, activation and deactivation of rectification are so fast that each mEPSP terminates with an oscillation rather than a smooth exponential decline.

Voltage-clamp analysis of potassium currents that underlie outward rectification has been performed with rat bushy cells (82), chick nMAG (63, 79), and rat MNTB (89, 91). In these cases, profiles of depolarizing voltage steps from the resting potential activate primarily two outward currents with distinct voltage and pharmacological sensitivities. A high threshold current, which activates at potentials positive to −20 mV, is most sensitive to tetraethylammonium (TEA) (63, 79, 82, 88, 89, 91) and is weakly blocked by 4-aminopyridine (4-AP) (88). Dendrotoxin (DTX) and 4-AP, by contrast, are effective at blocking a conductance that activates only slightly depolarized to rest (63, 79, 82, 88, 89, 91). Spiral ganglion cells also exhibit a low-threshold outward current (75–77), but no pharmacological studies of these cells have been performed with 4-AP or DTX.

Current clamp recordings have illustrated the relative roles of high- and low-threshold currents in shaping the response properties of the neurons. The single-spike feature of the cells described above is altered profoundly by application of certain blockers of voltage-activated K^+ currents. Application of millimolar concentrations of 4-AP or 0.1 μM DTX allows these neurons to fire repetitive action potentials in response to single, prolonged currents steps (4, 30, 79, 85, 89). Most significantly, DTX promotes multiple postsynaptic spikes in response to single, brief synaptic stimuli, without any apparent effect on the duration of transmitter release (89). Application of TEA, by contrast, does not allow for repetitive firing (4, 79) but, like application of 4-AP, broadens action potentials (4, 63, 79, 91). Thus, while the high- and low-threshold currents are likely to play a role in repolarizing the action potential, the striking single-spike firing characteristic of auditory neurons involved in the fast relay of signals may be attributed to the activation of the low-threshold current.

Recent efforts have focused on the molecular identification of the high- and low-threshold potassium channels described above. One likely candidate for the low-threshold current is $K_V1.1$ or $K_V1.2$, since these channels have a relatively low activation threshold and are highly sensitive to DTX (92). Moreover, $K_V1.1/1.2$ is expressed in juxtaparanodal regions of axons in the brain stem and in cell bodies of the AVCN and MNTB (93, 94). Homomeric $K_V1.1/1.2$ channels have a higher threshold than the DTX-sensitive current in MNTB and nMAG (88, 89), suggesting that these cloned subunits alone cannot fully account for the channels observed in vivo.

$K_V3.1$ is a TEA-sensitive potassium channel that has been proposed to account for the high-threshold, TEA-sensitive channel in auditory timing and relay neurons (91, 95, 96). Wang et al (91) in particular have shown a close match in kinetics of current activation and sensitivity to TEA for expressed $K_V3.1$ and mouse MNTB TEA-sensitive current. Computer simulations of responses of neurons containing classical sodium channels and high- and low-threshold K^+ currents indicate that without the high threshold current, action potentials broaden and the responsiveness to trains of stimuli is degraded (91). Perney et al (95) have shown that the distribution of $K_V3.1$-immunoreactive cells is only partly consistent with a role in transmission of timing. High levels have been observed not only in bushy cells and MNTB but also in neurons not associated with fast relay of acoustic signals, such as DCN giant cells and granule cells. Most striking is the lack of $K_V3.1$ in the octopus cells, whose exceedingly fast and reliable EPSPs are well suited to precise relay of signal timing (13). It would seem that this channel and perhaps others not yet described are key players in fast spike repolarization, a necessary feature for the use of both temporal and rate coding in acoustic processing.

It remains unclear which subtypes of potassium currents are expressed in the membranes of presynaptic nerve terminals in the cochlear or olivary nuclei. Nerve terminal recordings in MNTB have shown that the terminals and associated axonal membrane support repetitive firing, unlike the cell bodies of the bushy cells that give rise to these axons (97). Single action potentials exhibit a pronounced after-depolarization in the nerve terminal in MNTB, also unlike the cell bodies in the VCN (98). It is intriguing that the terminals support a different pattern of firing than the cell body, from which excitation originates. These differences from the somatic response most probably reflect the lack of expression of low-threshold potassium currents in the synapse, an adaptation that may prevent shunting of the conducted action potential and facilitate its invasion throughout the fingers of the calyceal terminal.

I_H AND ITS POTENTIAL ROLES IN THE AUDITORY PERIPHERY AND BRAIN STEM

I_H is an inwardly rectifying, slowly activating and deactivating, mixed cation current, which is expressed in wide variety of neurons in the auditory pathway. I_H is also a prominent component of spiral ganglion cells in rodents, apparent either as a sag in the response to hyperpolarizing current steps or as a slow inward current during hyperpolarizing voltage steps (80, 99). This current is not apparent in voltage clamp recordings from chick cochlear ganglion (75). I_H is a prominent current in bushy cells (83, 100) and in cells of the MTNB (101), MSO (86), dorsal nucleus of the lateral lemniscus (102), and chicken nMAG

(4). Golding et al (13) showed that no depolarizing sag is apparent in octopus cells of the VCN; indeed, the input resistance of the cells is so low that it is practically impossible to measure membrane time constants to either depolarizing or hyperpolarizing current stimuli. However, they interpreted this leakiness to be due in part to a very large I_H active at rest, because bath application of 10 mM Cs^+ (but not TEA) markedly increased the input resistance and time constant, but only to hyperpolarizing current steps.

What is the function of this slow current in transmission of timing of brief signals? One possibility for some of the cells described above is that it helps define the resting membrane properties; in particular, that the membrane potential and input resistance may represent a balance between the depolarizing I_H and the hyperpolarizing low-threshold K^+ current. These resting values should have profound effects on the duration of synaptic potentials and action potential threshold in response to rapid depolarizing currents. Inasmuch as the low-threshold K^+ current is partially inactivated at potentials near rest (89), I_H may control the availability of the low-threshold current during a depolarization. Moreover, the voltage-dependence of I_H is modulated by protein kinases (80, 99, 101); such metabolic control may be a point of longer-term regulation in response to ongoing activity levels.

SHORT-TERM SYNAPTIC PLASTICITY

In response to stimuli delivered at rates of several hertz or higher, EPSCs in bushy cells and in cells of nMAG and MNTB exhibit pronounced synaptic depression (11, 34, 37, 103, 104). Examples of depression are shown in Figure 1*D* for an nMAG neuron. Note in Figure 1*C* that EPSC depression does not necessarily lead immediately to spike failure, since the safety factor for transmission is usually quite high. Several studies have focused on the cellular mechanisms of depression in these cells. von Gersdorff et al (105) concluded that depression seen with 10–20-Hz stimuli in MNTB was presynaptic, i.e., was due to a reduction in transmitter release. This conclusion is supported by recordings of presynaptic calcium current, which inactivates during repetitive stimulation, although not enough to account for depression of the EPSC (106). Trussell and colleagues have shown that in nMAG, depression observed with high-frequency stimuli may be due in part to AMPA receptor desensitization (34, 107), although the extent to which this may occur in mammals remains unclear. In any case, depression in response to high-frequency stimuli is characteristic of calyceal/end-bulb synapses studied under voltage clamp or current clamp (4, 98). By contrast, earlier current-clamp studies in VCN or MNTB with microelectrodes and recording at higher temperatures did not describe such pronounced depression (28, 108, 109). These differences may be attributed to the combined effects of nonlinear summation of EPSPs in current clamp and the pronounced reduction (but not elimination) of depression seen at physiological temperatures (104). Depression of EPSPs has also been observed in hair cells of the goldfish lateral line (110, 111); here, quantal analyses indicate that depression resulted largely from a reduction in the number of available release sites.

What is the role of depression in auditory processing? Use-dependent changes in synaptic strength in auditory neurons might determine the duration for which timing is transmitted effectively. The output of a neuron would initially reflect the information content of a single input, shifting to that of a group of convergent inputs. Such a shift in emphasis from single to many inputs would probably degrade the entrainment of a synaptic relay (i.e., reduce the one-for-one relation between input and output) but could still preserve or improve (90) phase-locking. Comparing firing rates in vivo with those that produce depression in vitro indicates that many auditory synapses may always be at least partially depressed. Spontaneous firing rates of auditory nerve and fibers in the trapezoid body vary from several hertz to nearly 200 Hz and can approach 500 Hz when driven by intense acoustic stimuli (112–115). By contrast, EPSCs in MNTB neurons are depressed by about 70% with stimuli at 5 Hz at room temperature (105), while EPSCs in nMAG are depressed by this amount at about 80 Hz at 36°C (104). Thus, depression is likely to occur during acoustic stimuli. Moreover, inasmuch as auditory nerve activity is relatively high in the absence of sound, mechanisms that induce depression may be potent determinants of synaptic strength even early in the response to sound.

MODULATION OF GLUTAMATE RELEASE BY PRESYNAPTIC RECEPTORS

Selective agonists of metabotropic glutamate receptors (mGluRs) markedly reduce the amplitude of EPSCs in MNTB by a presynaptic mechanism (103). Takahashi et al (116) have shown that these receptors are negatively coupled to calcium channels that elicit release at this synapse. It remains uncertain, however, whether synaptically released glutamate might feed back onto these receptors and contribute to depression. In their study of MNTB, von Gersdorff et al (105) found that antagonists of mGluRs only slightly altered depression to stimuli up to 10 Hz. Thus, these data question whether the transmitter can reach very far beyond the area near the active zone. Otis et al (107), in a study of nMAG synapses, found that when separate nerve terminals contacting the same cell body were sequentially activated, glutamate from one synapse did not apparently reach and desensitize the other nearby synapse. Moreover, block of glutamate transporters in nMAG markedly prolonged EPSCs (41). Thus, it may be that under most conditions, synaptically released glutamate is effectively taken up by glutamate transporters, preventing autoreceptor activation. However, further work should be done to explore possible functions of mGluRs. For example, it will be of interest to determine if synaptic activation of these autoreceptors can occur in response to higher-frequency stimuli or when a large number of synapses in a group of cells are activated in concert.

Both baclofen, an agonist at $GABA_B$ receptors, and GABA (γ-amino-butyric acid) itself (in the presence of $GABA_A$ receptor antagonists), markedly inhibit EPSCs in nMAG and MNTB through a presynaptic mechanism (104, 117). Brenowitz et al (104) explored the effects of combining repetitive stimulation with application of baclofen and found that EPSCs elicited at high rates were actually larger in the presence of baclofen. Additionally, high-frequency EPSPs in baclofen reached the spike threshold more reliably than in control solutions. This occurred because the strong frequency dependence of depression was removed by the action of baclofen. The mechanism of this effect is not clear, but the authors propose that reduction of release probability by $GABA_B$ receptors may prevent the depletion/desensitization that normally occurs during high-frequency activity. Because nMAG neurons receive GABAergic innervation from the superior olive (118), which is in turn innervated by the NA and NL, it may be that GABA serves to minimize depression in response to high-intensity sounds (104).

ACKNOWLEDGMENTS

I am grateful to my many laboratory colleagues over the years, in particular to Stephan Brenowitz and Su Zhang, who provided some of the data included in the figures in this review, and for support by the National Institute for Deafness and Communicative Disorders (grant DC02004) and the National Institute for Neurological Disorders and Stroke (grant NS28901). I also thank Donata Oertel and Indira Raman for comments on the manuscript.

Literature Cited

1. Fettiplace R, Fuchs P. 1999. Mechanism of hair cell tuning. *Annu. Rev. Physiol.* 61:809–34

1a. Geisler CD. 1998. *From Sound to Synapse. Physiology of the Mammalian Ear*. New York: Oxford University Press

2. Yin TC, Carney LH, Joris PX. 1990. Interaural time sensitivity in the inferior colliculus of the albino cat. *J. Comp. Neurol.* 295:438–48

3. Joris PX, Yin TCT. 1998. Envelope coding in the lateral superior olive. III. Comparison with afferent pathways. *J. Neurophysiol.* 79:253–69

3a. Oertel D. 1999. The role of timing in the auditory brain stem nuclei of vertebrates. *Annu. Rev. Physiol.* 61:497–519

4. Zhang S, Trussell LO. 1994. A characterization of excitatory postsynaptic potentials in the avian nucleus magnocellularis. *J. Neurophysiol.* 72:705–18

5. Adams JC. 1997. Projections from

octopus cells of the posteroventral cochlear nucleus to the ventral nucleus of the lateral lemniscus in cat and human. *Auditory Neurosci.* 34:335–350
6. Cant NB, Morest DK. 1979. The bushy cells in the anteroventral cochlear nucleus of the cat. A study with the electron microscope. *Neuroscience* 4:1925–45
7. Parks TN. 1981. Morphology of axosomatic endings in an avian cochlear nucleus: nucleus magnocellularis of the chicken. *J. Comp. Neurol.* 203:425–40
8. Lenn TR, Reese TS. 1966. The fine structure of nerve endings in the nucleus of the trapezoid body and the ventral cochlear nucleus. *Am. J. Anat.* 118:375–90
9. Isaacson JS, Walmsley B. 1995. Counting quanta: direct measurements of transmitter release at a central synapse. *Neuron* 15:875–84
10. Borst JG, Sakmann B. 1996. Calcium influx and transmitter release in a fast CNS synapse. *Nature* 383:431–34
11. Zhang S, Trussell LO. 1994. Voltage clamp analysis of excitatory synaptic transmission in the avian nucleus magnocellularis. *J. Physiol.* 480:123–36
12. Spruston N, Jaffe DB, Johnston D. 1994. Dendritic attenuation of synaptic potentials and currents: the role of passive membrane properties. *Trends Neurosci.* 17:161–66
13. Golding NL, Robertson D, Oertel D. 1995. Recordings from slices indicate that octopus cells of the cochlear nucleus detect coincident firing of auditory nerve fibers with temporal precision. *J. Neurosci.* 15:3138–53
14. Yin TC, Chan JC. 1990. Interaural time sensitivity in medial superior olive of cat. *J. Neurophysiol.* 64:465–88
15. Takahashi T, Moiseff A, Konishi M. 1984. Time and intensity cues are processed independently in the auditory system of the owl. *J. Neurosci.* 4:1781–16
16. Sullivan WE. 1985. Classification of response patterns in cochlear nucleus of barn owl: correlation with functional response properties. *J. Neurophysiol.* 53:201–16
17. Ferragamo MJ, Golding NL, Oertel D. 1998. Synaptic inputs to stellate cells in the ventral cochlear nucleus. *J. Neurophysiol.* 79:51–63
18. Trussell LO. 1997. Cellular mechanisms for preservation of timing in central auditory pathways. *Curr. Opin. Neurobiol.* 7:487–92
19. Geiger JR, Lubke J, Roth A, Frotscher M, Jonas P. 1997. Submillisecond AMPA receptor-mediated signaling at a principal neuron-interneuron synapse. *Neuron* 18:1009–23
20. Altschuler RA, Sheridan CE, Horn JW, Wenthold RJ. 1989. Immunocytochemical localization of glutamate immunoreactivity in the guinea pig cochlea. *Hear. Res.* 42:167–73
21. Hackney CM, Osen KK, Ottersen OP, Storm-Mathisen J, Manjaly G. 1996. Immunocytochemical evidence that glutamate is a neurotransmitter in the cochlear nerve: a quantitative study in the guinea-pig anteroventral cochlear nucleus. *Eur. J. Neurosci.* 8:79–91
22. Grandes P, Streit P. 1989. Glutamate-like immunoreactivity in calyces of Held. *J. Neurocytol.* 18:685–93
23. Kataoka Y, Ohmori H. 1996. Of known neurotransmitters, glutamate is the most likely to be released from chick cochlear hair cells. *J. Neurophysiol.* 76:1870–9
24. Puel JL. 1995. Chemical synaptic transmission in the cochlea. *Prog. Neurobiol.* 47:449–76
25. Sewell WF. 1997. Biochemistry and pharmacology of the auditory system. In *Encyclopedia of Acoustics*, ed. MJ Crocker, pp. 1401–8. New York: J Wiley & Sons
26. Isaacson JS, Walmsley B. 1995. Receptors underlying excitatory synaptic transmission in slices of the rat anteroventral cochlear nucleus. *J. Neurophysiol.* 73:964–73
27. Zhang S, Oertel D. 1994. Neuronal circuits associated with the output of the dorsal cochlear nucleus through fusiform cells. *J. Neurophysiol.* 71:914–30
28. Wu SH, Kelly JB. 1992. Synaptic pharmacology of the superior olivary complex studied in mouse brain slice. *J. Neurosci.* 12:3084–97
29. Forsythe ID, Barnes-Davies M. 1993. The binaural auditory pathway: excitatory amino acid receptors mediate dual timecourse excitatory postsynaptic currents in the rat medial nucleus of the trapezoid body. *Proc. R. Soc. London, Ser. B* 251:151–57
30. Banks MI, Smith PH. 1992. Intracellular recordings from neurobiotin-labeled cells in brain slices of the rat medial nucleus of the trapezoid body. *J. Neurosci.* 12:2819–37
31. Zhou N, Parks TN. 1992. Gamma-D-glutamylaminomethyl sulfonic acid (GAMS) distinguishes subtypes of glutamate receptor in the chick cochlear nucleus (nuc. magnocellularis). *Hear. Res.* 60:20–26
32. Funabiki K, Koyano K, Ohmori H. 1998. The role of GABAergic inputs for coin-

cidence detection in the neurones of nucleus laminaris of the chick. *J. Physiol.* 508:851–69
33. Zhou N, Parks TN. 1991. Pharmacology of excitatory amino acid neurotransmission in nucleus laminaris of the chick. *Hear. Res.* 52:195–200
34. Trussell LO, Zhang S, Raman IM. 1993. Desensitization of AMPA receptors upon multiquantal neurotransmitter release. *Neuron* 10:1185–96
35. Raman IM, Zhang S, Trussell LO. 1994. Pathway-specific variants of AMPA receptors and their contribution to neuronal signaling. *J. Neurosci.* 14:4998–5010
36. Reyes AD, Rubel EW, Spain WJ. 1996. In vitro analysis of optimal stimuli for phase-locking and time-delayed modulation of firing in avian nucleus laminaris neurons. *J. Neurosci.* 16:993–1007
37. Isaacson JS, Walmsley B. 1996. Amplitude and time course of spontaneous and evoked excitatory postsynaptic currents in bushy cells of the anteroventral cochlear nucleus. *J. Neurophysiol.* 76:1566–71
38. Ottiger HP, Gerfin-Moser A, Del Principe F, Dutly F, Streit P. 1995. Molecular cloning and differential expression patterns of avian glutamate receptor mRNAs. *J. Neurochem.* 64:2413–26
39. Ravindranathan A, Parks TN, Rao MS. 1996. Flip and flop isoforms of chick brain AMPA receptor subunits: cloning and analysis of expression patterns. *NeuroReport* 7:2707–11
40. Diamond JS, Jahr CE. 1995. Asynchronous release of synaptic vesicles determines the time course of the AMPA receptor-mediated EPSC. *Neuron* 15: 1097–1107
41. Otis TS, Wu YC, Trussell LO. 1996. Delayed clearance of transmitter and the role of glutamate transporters at synapses with multiple release sites. *J. Neurosci.* 16:1634–44
42. Otis TS, Trussell LO. 1996. Inhibition of transmitter release shortens the duration of the excitatory synaptic current at a calyceal synapse. *J. Neurophysiol.* 76: 3584–88
43. Raman IM, Trussell LO. 1992. The kinetics of the response to glutamate and kainate in neurons of the avian cochlear nucleus. *Neuron* 9:173–86
44. Raman IM, Trussell LO. 1995. Concentration-jump analysis of voltage-dependent conductances activated by glutamate and kainate in neurons of the avian cochlear nucleus. *Biophys. J.* 69:1868–79
45. Geiger JR, Melcher T, Koh DS, Sakmann B, Seeburg PH, et al. 1995. Relative abundance of subunit mRNAs determines gating and Ca^{2+} permeability of AMPA receptors in principal neurons and interneurons in rat CNS. *Neuron* 15:193–204
46. Silver RA, Colquhoun D, Cull-Candy SG, Edmonds B. 1996. Deactivation and desensitization of non-NMDA receptors in patches and the time course of EPSCs in rat cerebellar granule cells. *J. Physiol.* 493:167–73 (Erratum, 496:891, 1996)
47. Eliasof S, Jahr CE. 1997. Rapid AMPA receptor desensitization in catfish cone horizontal cells. *Visual Neurosci.* 14:13–8
48. Hollmann M, Heinemann S. 1994. Cloned glutamate receptors. *Annu. Rev. Neurosci.* 17:31–108
49. Lambolez B, Report N, Perrais D, Rossier J, Hestrin S. 1996. Correlation between kinetics and RNA splicing of alpha-amino-3-hydroxy-5-methylisoxazole-4-propionic acid receptors in neocortical neurons. *Proc. Natl. Acad. Sci. USA* 93:1797–1802
50. Mosbacher J, Schoepfer R, Monyer H, Burnashev N, Seeburg PH, et al. 1994. A molecular determinant for submillisecond desensitization in glutamate receptors. *Science* 266:1059–62
51. Lomeli H, Mosbacher J, Melcher T, Hoger T, Geiger JR, et al. 1994. Control of kinetic properties of AMPA receptor channels by nuclear RNA editing. *Science* 266:1709–13
52. Washburn MS, Numberger M, Zhang S, Dingledine R. 1997. Differential dependence on GluR2 expression of three characteristic features of AMPA receptors. *J. Neurosci.* 17:9393–9406
53. Matsubara A, Laake JH, Davanger S, Usami S, Ottersen OP. 1996. Organization of AMPA receptor subunits at a glutamate synapse: a quantitative immunogold analysis of hair cell synapses in the rat organ of Corti. *J. Neurosci.* 16:4457–67
54. Niedzielski AS, Wenthold RJ. 1995. Expression of AMPA, kainate, and NMDA receptor subunits in cochlear and vestibular ganglia. *J. Neurosci.* 15:2338–53
55. Hunter C, Petralia RS, Vu T, Wenthold RJ. 1993. Expression of AMPA-selective glutamate receptor subunits in morphologically defined neurons of the mammalian cochlear nucleus. *J. Neurosci.* 13:1932–46
56. Sato K, Kiyama H, Tohyama M. 1993. The differential expression patterns of messenger RNAs encoding non-*N*-methyl-D-aspartate glutamate receptor subunits (GluR1-4) in the rat brain. *Neuroscience* 52:515–39
57. Petralia RS, Wenthold RJ. 1992. Light

and electron immunocytochemical localization of AMPA-selective glutamate receptors in the rat brain. *J. Comp. Neurol.* 318:329–54
58. Kuriyama H, Jenkins O, Altschuler RA. 1994. Immunocytochemical localization of AMPA selective glutamate receptor subunits in the rat cochlea. *Hear. Res.* 80: 233–40
59. Wang YX, Wenthold RJ, Ottersen OP, Petralia RS. 1998. Endbulb synapses in the anteroventral cochlear nucleus express a specific subset of AMPA-type glutamate receptor subunits. *J. Neurosci.* 18:1148–60
60. Levin MD, Kubke MF, Schneider M, Wenthold R, Carr CE. 1997. Localization of AMPA-selective glutamate receptors in the auditory brain stem of the barn owl. *J. Comp. Neurol.* 378:239–53
61. Angulo MC, Lambolez B, Audinat E, Hestrin S, Rossier J. 1997. Subunit composition, kinetic, and permeation properties of AMPA receptors in single neocortical nonpyramidal cells. *J. Neurosci.* 17:6685–96
62. Rubio ME, Wenthold RJ. 1997. Glutamate receptors are selectively targeted to postsynaptic sites in neurons. *Neuron* 18:939–50
63. Reyes AD, Rubel EW, Spain WJ. 1994. Membrane properties underlying the firing of neurons in the avian cochlear nucleus. *J. Neurosci.* 14:5352–64
64. Jahr CE, Stevens CF. 1993. Calcium permeability of the *N*-methyl-D-aspartate receptor channel in hippocampal neurons in culture. *Proc. Natl. Acad. Sci. USA* 90:11573–77
65. Otis TS, Raman IM, Trussell LO. 1995. AMPA receptors with high Ca^{2+} permeability mediate synaptic transmission in the avian auditory pathway. *J. Physiol.* 482:309–15
66. Rogers JH. 1987. Calretinin: a gene for a novel calcium-binding protein expressed principally in neurons. *J. Cell Biol.* 105:1343–53 (Erratum, 110:1845, 1990)
67. Takahashi TT, Carr CE, Brecha N, Konishi M. 1987. Calcium binding protein-like immunoreactivity labels the terminal field of nucleus laminaris of the barn owl. *J. Neurosci.* 7:1843–56
68. Parks TN, Code RA, Taylor DA, Solum DA, Strauss KI, et al. 1997. Calretinin expression in the chick brain stem auditory nuclei develops and is maintained independently of cochlear nerve input. *J. Comp. Neurol.* 383:112–21
69. Berrebi AS, Spirou GA. 1998. PEP-19 immunoreactivity in the cochlear nucleus and superior olive of the cat. *Neuroscience* 83:535–54
70. Vater M, Braun K. 1994. Parvalbumin, calbindin D-28k, and calretinin immunoreactivity in the ascending auditory pathway of horseshoe bats. *J. Comp. Neurol.* 341:534–58
71. Dechesne CJ, Winsky L, Kim HN, Goping G, Vu TD, et al. 1991. Identification and ultrastructural localization of a calretinin-like calcium-binding protein (protein 10) in the guinea pig and rat inner ear. *Brain Res.* 560:139–48
72. Lohmann C, Friauf E. 1996. Distribution of the calcium-binding proteins parvalbumin and calretinin in the auditory brain stem of adult and developing rats. *J. Comp. Neurol.* 367:90–109
73. Campbell AM, Wuytack F, Fambrough DM. 1993. Differential distribution of the alternative forms of the sarcoplasmic/endoplasmic reticulum Ca(2+)-ATPase, SERCA2b and SERCA2a, in the avian brain. *Brain Res.* 605:67–76
74. Zhou N, Taylor DA, Parks TN. 1995. Cobalt-permeable non-NMDA receptors in developing chick brain stem auditory nuclei. *Neuroreport* 6:2273–76
75. Yamaguchi K, Ohmori H. 1990. Voltage-gated and chemically gated ionic channels in the cultured cochlear ganglion neurone of the chick. *J. Physiol.* 420:185–206
76. Santos-Sacchi J. 1993. Voltage-dependent ionic conductances of type I spiral ganglion cells from the guinea pig inner ear. *J. Neurosci.* 13:3599–3611
77. Lin X. 1977. Action potentials and underlying voltage-dependent currents studied in cultured spiral ganglion neurons of the postnatal gerbil. *Hear. Res.* 108:157–79
78. Moore EJ, Hall DB, Narahashi T. 1996. Sodium and potassium currents of type I spiral ganglion cells from rat. *Acta Otolaryngol* 116:552–60
79. Koyano K, Funabiki K, Ohmori H. 1996. Voltage-gated ionic currents and their roles in timing coding in auditory neurons of the nucleus magnocellularis of the chick. *Neurosci. Res.* 26:29–45
80. Chen C. 1997. Hyperpolarization-activated current (Ih) in primary auditory neurons. *Hear. Res.* 110:179–90
81. Mo ZL, Davis RL. 1997. Endogenous firing patterns of murine spiral ganglion neurons. *J. Neurophysiol.* 77:1294–1305
82. Manis PB, Marx SO. 1991. Outward currents in isolated ventral cochlear nucleus neurons. *J. Neurosci.* 11:2865–80
83. Oertel D. 1983. Synaptic responses and

electrical properties of cells in brain slices of the mouse anteroventral cochlear nucleus. *J. Neurosci.* 3:2043–53
84. Wu SH, Kelly JB. 1991. Physiological properties of neurons in the mouse superior olive: membrane characteristics and postsynaptic responses studied in vitro. *J. Neurophysiol.* 65:230–46
85. Forsythe ID, Barnes-Davies M. 1993. The binaural auditory pathway: membrane currents limiting multiple action potential generation in the rat medial nucleus of the trapezoid body. *Proc. R. Soc. London Ser. B* 251:143–50
86. Smith PH. 1995. Structural and functional differences distinguish principal from nonprincipal cells in the guinea pig MSO slice. *J. Neurophysiol.* 73:1653–67
87. Strohmann B, Schwarz DW, Puil E. 1995. Electrical resonances in central auditory neurons. *Acta Otolaryngol.* 115:168–72
88. Rathouz M, Trussell L. 1998. A characterization of outward currents in neurons of the nucleus magnocellularis. *J. Neurophysiol.* In press
89. Brew HM, Forsythe ID. 1995. Two voltage-dependent K^+ conductances with complementary functions in postsynaptic integration at a central auditory synapse. *J. Neurosci.* 15:8011–22
90. Joris PX, Carney LH, Smith PH, Yin TC. 1994. Enhancement of neural synchronization in the anteroventral cochlear nucleus. I. Responses to tones at the characteristic frequency. *J. Neurophysiol.* 71:1022–36
91. Wang LY, Gan L, Forsythe ID, Kaczmarek LK. 1998. Contribution of the $K_V3.1$ potassium channel to high-frequency firing in mouse auditory neurones. *J. Physiol.* 509:183–94
92. Grissmer S, Nguyen AN, Aiyar J, Hanson DC, Mather RJ, et al. 1994. Pharmacological characterization of five cloned voltage-gated K^+ channels, types $K_V1.1$, 1.2, 1.3, 1.5, and 3.1, stably expressed in mammalian cell lines. *Mol. Pharmacol.* 45:1227–34
93. Wang H, Kunkel DD, Martin TM, Schwartzkroin PA, Tempel BL. 1993. Heteromultimeric K^+ channels in terminal and juxtaparanodal regions of neurons. *Nature* 365:75–79
94. Wang H, Kunkel DD, Schwartzkroin PA, Tempel BL. 1994. Localization of $K_V1.1$ and $K_V1.2$, two K channel proteins, to synaptic terminals, somata, and dendrites in the mouse brain. *J. Neurosci.* 14:4588–99
95. Perney TM, Kaczmarek LK. 1997. Localization of a high threshold potassium channel in the rat cochlear nucleus. *J. Comp. Neurol.* 386:178–202
96. Kanemasa T, Gan L, Perney TM, Wang LY, Kaczmarek LK. 1995. Electrophysiological and pharmacological characterization of a mammalian Shaw channel expressed in NIH 3T3 fibroblasts. *J. Neurophysiol.* 74:207–17
97. Forsythe ID. 1994. Direct patch recording from identified presynaptic terminals mediating glutamatergic EPSCs in the rat CNS, in vitro. *J. Physiol.* 479:381–87
98. Borst JG, Helmchen F, Sakmann B. 1995. Pre- and postsynaptic whole-cell recordings in the medial nucleus of the trapezoid body of the rat. *J. Physiol.* 489:825–40
99. Mo ZL, Davis RL. 1997. Heterogeneous voltage dependence of inward rectifier currents in spiral ganglion neurons. *J. Neurophysiol.* 78:3019–27
100. Rusznak Z, Forsythe ID, Stanfield PR. 1996. Characterization of the hyperpolarization activated nonspecific cation current (Ih) of bushy neurones from the rat anteroventral cochlear nucleus studied in a thin brain slice preparation. *Neurobiology* 4:275–76
101. Banks MI, Pearce RA, Smith PH. 1993. Hyperpolarization-activated cation current (Ih) in neurons of the medial nucleus of the trapezoid body: voltage-clamp analysis and enhancement by norepinephrine and cAMP suggest a modulatory mechanism in the auditory brain stem. *J. Neurophysiol.* 70:1420–32
102. Fu XW, Brezden BL, Wu SH. 1997. Hyperpolarization-activated inward current in neurons of the rat's dorsal nucleus of the lateral lemniscus in vitro. *J. Neurophysiol.* 78:2235–45
103. Forsythe ID, Clements JD. 1990. Presynaptic glutamate receptors depress excitatory monosynaptic transmission between mouse hippocampal neurones. *J. Physiol.* 429:1–16
104. Brenowitz S, David J, Trussell L. 1998. Enhancement of synaptic efficacy by presynaptic GABA(B) receptors. *Neuron* 20:135–41
105. von Gersdorff H, Schneggenburger R, Weis S, Neher E. 1997. Presynaptic depression at a calyx synapse: the small contribution of metabotropic glutamate receptors. *J. Neurosci.* 17:8137–46
106. Forsythe ID, Tsujimoto T, Barnes-Davies M, Cuttle MF, Takahashi T. 1998. Inactivation of presynaptic calcium current contributes to synaptic depression at a fast central synapse. *Neuron* 20:797–807
107. Otis T, Zhang S, Trussell LO. 1996. Direct measurement of AMPA receptor desensi-

tization induced by glutamatergic synaptic transmission. *J. Neurosci.* 16:7496–7504
108. Oertel D. 1985. Use of brain slices in the study of the auditory system: spatial and temporal summation of synaptic inputs in cells in the anteroventral cochlear nucleus of the mouse. *J. Acoust. Soc. Am.* 78:328–33
109. Wu SH, Oertel D. 1987. Maturation of synapses and electrical properties of cells in the cochlear nuclei. *Hear. Res.* 30:99–110
110. Furukawa T, Matsuura S. 1978. Adaptive rundown of excitatory post-synaptic potentials at synapses between hair cells and eight nerve fibres in the goldfish. *J. Physiol.* 276:193–209
111. Furukawa T, Hayashida Y, Matsuura S. 1978. Quantal analysis of the size of excitatory post-synaptic potentials at synapses between hair cells and afferent nerve fibres in goldfish. *J. Physiol.* 276:211–26
112. Warchol ME, Dallos P. 1990. Neural coding in the chick cochlear nucleus. *J. Comp. Physiol. [A]* 166:721–34
113. Brownel WE. 1975. Organization of the cat trapezoid body and the discharge characteristics of its fibers. *Brain Res.* 94:413–33
114. Ruggero MA. 1992. Physiology and coding of sound in the auditory nerve. In *The Mammalian Auditory Pathway: Neurophysiology*, ed. AN Popper, RR Fay, pp. 34–93. New York: Springer-Verlag
115. Chen L, Trautwein PG, Shero M, Salvi RJ. 1996. Tuning, spontaneous activity and tonotopic map in chicken cochlear ganglion neurons following sound-induced hair cell loss and regeneration. *Hear. Res.* 98:152–64
116. Takahashi T, Forsythe ID, Tsujimoto T, Barnes-Davies M, Onodera K. 1996. Presynaptic calcium current modulation by a metabotropic glutamate receptor. *Science* 274:594–97
117. Takahashi T, Kajikawa Y, Tsujimoto T. 1998. G-protein-coupled modulation of presynaptic calcium currents and transmitter release by a $GABA_B$ receptor. *J. Neurosci.* 18:3138–46
118. Lachica EA, Rubsamen R, Rubel EW. 1994. GABAergic terminals in nucleus magnocellularis and laminaris originate from the superior olivary nucleus. *J. Comp. Neurol.* 348:403–18

Annu. Rev. Physiol. 1999. 61:497–519

THE ROLE OF TIMING IN THE BRAIN STEM AUDITORY NUCLEI OF VERTEBRATES

D. Oertel
Department of Physiology, University of Wisconsin, Madison, Wisconsin 53706;
e-mail: oertel@physiology.wisc.edu

KEY WORDS: hearing, phase-locking, auditory system, temporal coding

ABSTRACT

Vertebrate animals gain biologically important information from environmental sounds. Localization of sound sources enables animals to detect and respond appropriately to danger, and it allows predators to detect and localize prey. In many species, rapidly fluctuating sounds are also the basis of communication between conspecifics. This information is not provided directly by the output of the ear but requires processing of the temporal pattern of firing in the tonotopic array of auditory nerve fibers. The auditory nerve feeds information through several parallel ascending pathways. Anatomical and electrophysiological specializations for conveying precise timing, including calyceal synaptic terminals and matching axonal conduction times, are evident in several of the major ascending auditory pathways through the ventral cochlear nucleus and its nonmammalian homologues. One pathway that is shared by all higher vertebrates makes an ongoing comparison of interaural phase for the localization of sound in the azimuth. Another pathway is specifically associated with higher frequency hearing in mammals and is thought to make use of interaural intensity differences for localizing high-frequency sounds. Balancing excitation from one ear with inhibition from the other in rapidly fluctuating signals requires that the timing of these synaptic inputs be matched and constant for widely varying sound stimuli in this pathway. The monaural nuclei of the lateral lemniscus, whose roles are not understood (although they are ubiquitous in higher vertebrates), receive input from multiple pathways that encode timing with precision, some through calyceal endings.

0066-4278/99/0315-0497$08.00

INTRODUCTION

The picture of what is accomplished in the brain stem auditory nuclei as acoustic information ascends the auditory pathway is still fragmentary, but there is no doubt (*a*) that timing of firing of neurons carries information that is used both to localize and to interpret sound and (*b*) that neurons in the brain stem auditory nuclei are specialized for precisely timed electrical signaling. The importance of timing in auditory stimuli can be appreciated from our own experiences. Psychophysical studies show that interaural timing, or interaural phase, of low-frequency sounds (<4000 Hz) is an important cue for localizing sound in the horizontal plane. Detection of pitch in humans has also been shown to depend on a timing code of lower frequencies (e.g. 1). The timing of transients of complex sounds, on the other hand, is better resolved in the high frequencies. The features that distinguish consonants in human speech, for example, are rapid, broadband transients, features that become especially difficult to resolve with presbycusis, the most common pattern of hearing loss in humans.

In higher vertebrates, acoustic information at the lower frequencies is fed by hair cells to the auditory nerve cycle by cycle, causing postsynaptic excitation to be phase-locked and endowing postsynaptic cells with a temporal code of frequency. In reptiles phase-locked transmission reaches about 1000 Hz and in mammals about 4000 Hz; in barn owls it reaches 9000 Hz. Neurons in auditory pathways have anatomical and biophysical specializations that enable them to receive synaptic responses and fire action potentials with the precision, within 120 or 50 μs, that is necessary to convey phase in a 4000-Hz and 9000-Hz tone and that make possible the precise encoding of envelope in high-frequency sounds (see 1a). Many of the mechanisms that make possible this temporal precision are shared across classes of vertebrates as well as between neurons in these pathways. Terminals deliver neurotransmitter through large clusters of terminals, often through somatic calyceal endings, to unusually rapid neurotransmitter receptors; postsynaptic neurons have low-threshold potassium conductances, which make rapid electrical signaling possible. These features have been documented in animals as diverse as turtles and mammals and are found at multiple stages in the auditory pathways.

The general mechanisms whereby higher vertebrates hear seem to have evolved with the ancient reptiles. Although some fish and amphibians are sensitive to certain sounds, the inner ear structures that mediate hearing and the neuronal circuits in the brain stem vary, which suggests that specializations in these animals for detecting sound evolved separately from various parts of the octavolateralis system. In contrast, reptiles, birds, and mammals have a part of the inner ear (a basilar papilla or a cochlea) that is specialized for the transduction and resolution of sound frequency by a tonotopic array of tuned hair cells (see 1b).

The array of auditory nerve fibers conveys acoustic information synaptically to several distinct groups of neurons in the brain stem that serve as the beginnings of parallel pathways, which process different facets of auditory information. Each of these pathways encodes timing in a different way. The similarities in the organization of brain stem auditory nuclei in diverse animal classes are striking (Figure 1).

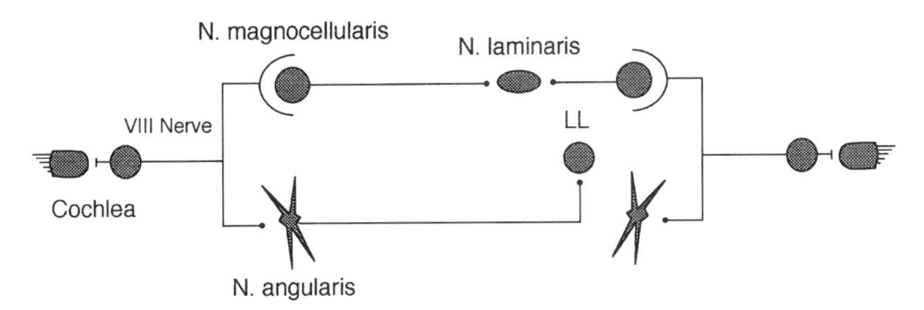

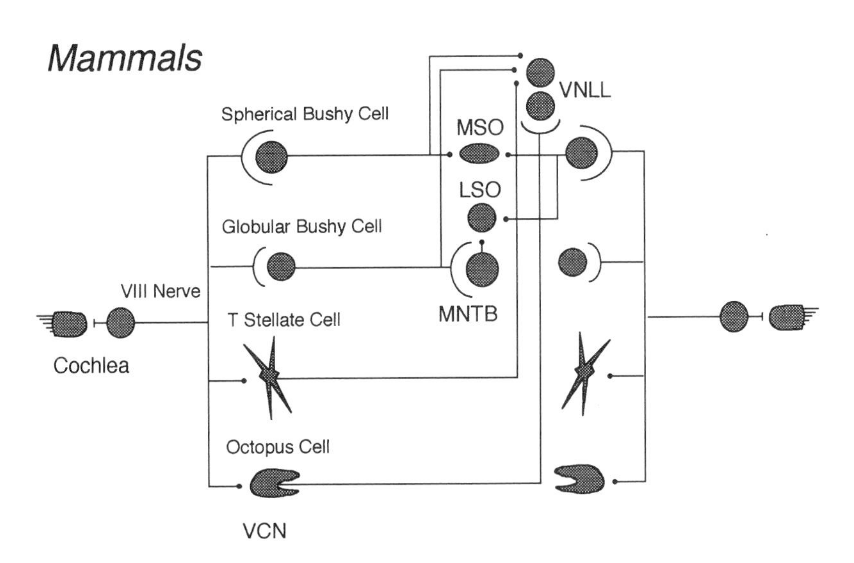

Figure 1 A schematic representation of the principal neuronal pathways that encode timing of sound in the brain stem. For simplicity, only one side of bilaterally symmetrical neuronal circuits is depicted. Calyceal terminals (*arcs*) are common features. Homology in animal classes is represented by common symbols. MSO, medial superior olive; LSO, lateral superior olive; MNTB, medial nucleus of the trapezoid body; VNLL, ventral nucleus of the lateral lemniscus; LL, lateral lemniscus; N., nucleus; VCN, ventral cochlear nucleus.

TIMING INFORMATION IN SOUND IS CAPTURED IN THE COCHLEA AND IS CONVEYED SYNAPTICALLY TO THE AUDITORY NERVE

Essential timing information for localization and for the interpretation of sound comes from the encoding of the onset and duration and from the preservation of phase in the transduction of sound. In turtles and birds, a systematic difference in the amplitude and kinetics of potassium conductances in the cochlear array of hair cells endows hair cells with electrical tuning that matches their tuning to sound, with characteristic frequencies varying between about 30 and 700 Hz (see 1b). Hair cells can be electrically tuned only to frequencies over which the hair cell membrane potential can follow cycle for cycle, giving tuning by this mechanism an upper limit. The fact that hair cells are electrically tuned necessarily means that neurotransmitter release onto neurons of the cochlear ganglion is in phase with the sound stimulus, cycle for cycle (phase-locked).

Timing information is preserved in the neurons of the cochlear ganglion whose axons are the auditory nerve, to the extent that the membrane voltage of those neurons can follow the rise and fall of synaptic activation. The rate at which synaptic excitation can follow the periodicity of sounds thus depends on the temporal resolution of neurotransmitter release from hair cells and on the filtering characteristics of the peripheral processes of cochlear ganglion cells on which the neurotransmitter acts. Recordings made from the afferent nerve endings beneath the hair cells of turtles and guinea pigs from what were likely to be auditory nerve fibers reveal rapidly rising and falling synaptic responses (2–4). In reptiles whose hearing range generally extends from about 0.1 to 5 kHz, the firing of auditory nerve fibers resolves phase at frequencies below about 1 kHz (5–7); phase resolution is lost in the synaptic transfer from the hair cell to cochlear ganglion cells at higher frequencies (8). The hearing range of birds ranges from about 0.1 to between 4 and 8 kHz; barn owls hear to 10 kHz, which is exceptional in birds (9). Tuning of hair cells arises in part, but not necessarily completely, from electrical tuning (see 1b). In most birds, phase-locking of auditory nerve fibers is well preserved to about 2 kHz and becomes undetectable at 4 or 5 kHz (10–13). The finding of phase-locking to 9000 Hz in the auditory nerve of barn owls indicates that hair cells and synaptic transmission between hair cells and auditory nerve fibers can follow sounds up to 9000 Hz, cycle for cycle (14, 15).

In reptiles and birds (as well as in mammals), the cochlea, the array of auditory nerve fibers, and to a large extent also the nuclei in the auditory pathway contain a roughly logarithmic representation of frequency. Frequency is encoded cycle for cycle in auditory nerve fibers over most of the hearing range of reptiles and birds; phase-locking occurs over all but the highest of the 5 or 6 octaves (7 octaves in barn owls).

The evolution of the mammalian middle and inner ear made possible the extension of the hearing range to higher frequencies (1b). Primates generally hear from about 0.05 to 20 kHz; the highest frequencies detected in mammals are found in insectivorous bats, which hear from about 2 to 120 kHz. Responses of auditory nerve fibers follow sounds cycle for cycle to frequencies between 3 and 5 kHz (16–18). Differences in the upper frequency limit for phase-locking between mammals are as large as an octave (19). At high frequencies, responses to tones in mammalian auditory nerve fibers consist of onset transients that are followed by tonic firing at a lower rate (20, 21). Although phase-locking carries important timing information in ongoing sound in cells that encode low frequencies, the envelope of natural broadband sounds is encoded with greater temporal resolution in cells that encode high frequencies (22).

It is interesting that psychophysical studies of humans show that many features of the processing of sound occur differently in the low- and high-frequency ranges. The localization of sounds in the azimuth, formant frequencies of vowels and the extraction of pitch, for example, depend mainly on sounds in the frequency range over which phase-locking occurs in mammals, below about 4000 Hz (23–25). On the other hand, monaural localization of sound, including the localization in elevation and the differentiation of consonants, depends most heavily on higher frequency sounds, 4000–20,000 Hz (21, 26, 27).

The orderly innervation of the cochlear nuclei by the array of tuned auditory nerve fibers generally provides the cochlear nuclei with a tonotopic representation of frequency. In reptiles and birds, one branch innervates nucleus magnocellularis and another innervates nucleus angularis. In mammals, the homologous region innervated by the auditory nerve is considered a single nucleus, the ventral cochlear nucleus (VCN), which contains several types of intermingled principal cells (28–34). (The dorsal cochlear nucleus has no homologue in reptiles and birds.) The branch of the auditory nerve fiber that innervates the nucleus magnocellularis in reptiles and birds and the anterior VCN in mammals usually has a large, specialized calyceal ending, also known as an end bulb, that more or less engulfs the cell body of the target. Calyceal endings have been found in turtles (35), lizards (36), birds (37–41), and mammals (33, 42–47). These endings are characterized by numerous release sites apposed to the target neuron (38, 45, 48). In cats, end bulbs on spherical bushy cells have been estimated to have between 500 and 2000 synaptic appositions (49).

Although the termination of auditory nerve fibers has common features in all higher vertebrates, the detailed innervation patterns vary not only from animal to animal but also among functionally different groups of auditory nerve fibers within individual animals (33, 34, 36, 40, 47, 49–53).

ROLE OF TIMING IN A PATHWAY FOR DETECTING INTERAURAL TIME DIFFERENCES IN LOW-FREQUENCY SOUNDS

Nucleus Magnocellularis Neurons in Reptiles and Birds, and Their Mammalian Homologues, Large Spherical Bushy Cells

Just as end bulbs are ubiquitous among the terminals of auditory nerve fibers in higher vertebrates, so are their targets, the bushy cells, and their nonmammalian homologues in the nucleus magnocellularis. These cells preserve and convey the timing information of auditory nerve fibers bilaterally to the nucleus laminaris in reptiles and birds or to its mammalian homologue, the medial superior olive (MSO).

Bushy cells and their nonmammalian homologues in reptiles and birds characteristically receive the majority of their synaptic input at the cell body through calyceal endings from few auditory nerve fibers. Their synaptic activation in vivo is rapid (54, 55), as it is in vitro (see 1a). Many of these neurons defy their mammalian homologues and have one or few sparsely branching dendrites, whereas others have no dendrites (35, 39, 53, 55–57). Similarly, large spherical bushy cells receive input from few (one to three) auditory nerve fibers through large end bulbs (33, 43, 52). In all higher vertebrates, the firing of bushy cells in response to sound reflects the firing in their auditory nerve inputs; these responses have thus been termed primary-like. Prepotentials that are thought to correspond to the firing of the calyceal auditory nerve ending can often be resolved in extracellularly recorded responses in the most anterior part of the VCN in which low frequencies are encoded (58–60). Not surprisingly, therefore, responses to tones of bushy cells and their homologues are sharply tuned and phase-locked at lower frequencies (15, 54, 59, 61, 62). Bushy cells do not serve exclusively as relays, however. The requirement of convergence of auditory nerve inputs increases the temporal precision of firing and enhances synchronization (27). Also, inhibition has been shown to influence the firing of units with prepotentials (63).

The projection patterns of neurons in the nucleus magnocellularis of birds and of the large spherical bushy cells produce delay lines in their targets, the nucleus laminaris in birds and the MSO in mammals. In chickens (64), barn owls (53, 65), and cats (66), it has been demonstrated that most of the axons of these neurons terminate in an isofrequency band within the ipsilateral target with collaterals that are of roughly equal length. Most terminate in an isofrequency band in the contralateral target with axon collaterals that vary systematically in length, being shortest medially and longest laterally. As a consequence of this projection pattern, neurons in the nucleus laminaris and in the MSO are activated as a systematic function of the location of sound in the horizontal plane. In cats, large spherical bushy cells also project to the lateral and ventral nucleus of the trapezoid body (LNTB and VNTB, respectively) and the ventral nucleus of the lateral lemniscus (VNLL) (66, 67).

The Nucleus Laminaris of Reptiles and Birds and Its Mammalian Homologue, the Medial Superior Olive

Neurons in the nucleus laminaris and in the MSO compare the timing of firing of bushy cells from the two ears. These comparisons are thought to be the basis of the ability of birds and mammals to use interaural time (or phase) differences to localize sound in the horizontal plane. In reptiles, the nucleus laminaris is indistinct (68, 69).

Both the nucleus laminaris in birds (57, 70) and the MSO in mammals (67, 71–73) are unicellular or multicellular sheets of cells, with each side of a sheet receiving input from one ear (67, 71, 74). In mammals, the frequencies represented in the MSO are skewed toward the low frequencies that show phase-locking (66, 75). The matching and orderly projections of bushy cells give one dimension of the sheet a tonotopic representation. The systematically varying lengths of bushy cell axons from the contralateral side produce a delay line in the nucleus laminaris of birds and in the MSO of mammals that results in a systematic representation of interaural time in the second dimension (64–66).

Electrophysiological studies in birds and mammals generally confirm that the nucleus laminaris and the MSO function as cross-correlators of phase-locked signals from the two ears (76–81). The view that neurons of the MSO serve as simple coincidence detectors of excitatory inputs from the two ears for localization of sound is overly simplistic, however. Most neurons in the MSO respond to monaural stimuli, indicating that coincidence from the two sides is not required for firing (81). Also, neurons in the MSO receive inhibitory inputs from the medial nucleus of the trapezoid body (MNTB) and LNTB in many mammals, including gerbils, cats, and bats, which may sharpen the temporal resolution of coincidence detection (73, 81–86).

Behavioral experiments support the conclusion that animals use interaural phase information from the nucleus laminaris and from the MSO to localize sounds in the horizontal plane. In barn owls, a map of space depends on the nucleus laminaris for azimuthal information (87). Even birds with small heads can localize surprisingly well in the horizontal plane, in part because the interaural canal allows the tympanic membrane to detect interaural pressure differences and enhance the detection of interaural time differences (88). The great tit, a small song bird with an interaural distance of 12 mm, for example, can resolve 20°, corresponding to an interaural time difference of 18 μs (89). Measurements of the upper frequency limit and the resolution of interaural phase for sound localization vary widely in mammals (9). In general, the size of the MSO is correlated to low-frequency hearing and to the temporal resolution of interaural phase differences (90–99). How temporal resolution is related to spatial resolution depends on the size of an animal's head. Animals with small heads need greater temporal resolution for equivalent spatial resolution. The MSO is small in animals with limited low-frequency hearing, such as mice, and in animals that do not use low-frequency hearing for localization, such as the naked mole rat (99). In the least weasel, on the other hand, which is roughly the size of a mouse and which has particularly acute localization, the MSO is large (94).

The nucleus laminaris in birds and the MSO in mammals generally project to the ipsilateral midbrain and to the ipsilateral lemniscal nuclei. The details of the projection pattern from the nucleus laminaris vary among groups of birds (69, 100), and in mammals, principal cells of the MSO generally project ipsilaterally to the dorsal nuclei of the lateral lemniscus (DNLL) and to the inferior colliculus (101–105). Among mammals there are also variations in projections. In moles, bats, and opossums, for example, the MSO projects bilaterally (85, 106–110).

ROLE OF TIMING IN A PATHWAY THAT DETECTS INTERAURAL INTENSITY DIFFERENCES IN HIGH-FREQUENCY SOUNDS

Globular Bushy Cells

In addition to the large spherical bushy cells, which are clearly homologous with cells of reptiles and birds in that they receive input and convey output to homologous structures, mammals have globular and small spherical bushy cells and targets in the MNTB and lateral superior olive (LSO) that do not have homologues in these animals. Although the characteristic frequencies of spherical and globular bushy cells overlap, the characteristic frequencies of spherical bushy cells are skewed to the low frequencies, whereas those of globular bushy cells are skewed to the high frequencies (33, 66, 111). Pathways through globular bushy cells can therefore be viewed as a specialization associated with high-frequency hearing.

Globular bushy cells receive converging input from more fibers through smaller end bulbs than do large spherical bushy cells (44, 45, 112). Estimates of the number of inputs to globular bushy cells vary between about 4, in mice (113), and 40, in cats (33). Globular bushy cells are sharply tuned (111, 114, 115). As a result of the convergence of auditory inputs, they show sharp onset transients that are followed by a break in firing that reflects the refractory period after the initial spike, "primary-like-with-notch" patterns (111, 116), and they show sharper phase-locking (27). At the cell body, rapid synaptic potentials have been observed to mediate responses to sound (114).

A characteristic feature of globular bushy cells is that, unlike spherical bushy cells, they have thick axons that contact neurons in the contralateral MNTB with large calyces (42, 111, 115, 117–123). Collaterals also terminate in periolivary nuclei, in the VNLL, and in the LSO (111, 121, 123).

Medial Nucleus of the Trapezoid Body

Neurons of the MNTB invert signals from bushy cells from excitation to inhibition while conveying them to the ipsilateral LSO quickly and with minimally varying latency. The consistent timing through this synapse makes possible the ongoing comparison of interaural intensity of rapidly fluctuating signals by the matching of excitation from the ipsilateral ear and inhibition from the contralateral ear in the LSO. Each MNTB cell receives input through only a single calyx (86, 111). As with other neurons with calyceal inputs, extracellularly recorded responses of MNTB cells are often preceded by prepotentials that probably reflect the action potential in the presynaptic terminal (86, 124, 125). Although responses of MNTB cells usually mirror those of their globular bushy cell inputs, they occasionally fail to show the sharp onset that is characteristic of their globular bushy cell inputs, indicating that these cells do not always behave as simple relays (86, 125, 126). Experiments in vitro confirm the finding that MNTB cells are specialized to convey signals with synaptic delays that vary minimally (126–136).

MNTB cells relay sharply timed inhibition to their targets. Intracellular labeling of single neurons has revealed the axonal arbor of MNTB cells to be extensive (86, 137). Immunocytochemical, ultrastructural, and electrophysiological evidence indicates that these neurons are inhibitory and glycinergic (73, 86, 128, 138–142). MNTB cells project to the LSO, MSO, VNLL, and among periolivary nuclei (86, 126, 137, 143, 144). In rodents, they have also been shown to project to the ipsilateral cochlear nucleus, where they terminate at globular bushy and stellate cells (145).

Lateral Superior Olive

The LSO has generally been considered the site where interaural intensity comparisons are made for azimuthal localization. Interaural level disparities of high-frequency sounds that reflect head-shadowing effects are important cues for localizing sounds in animals that hear frequencies high enough to produce head-shadowing. The finding that neurons in the LSO are sensitive to interaural level differences led to the suggestion that this pathway is involved in the localization of sound. This interpretation left open a question: Why should specializations that are associated with the encoding of timing be so prominent in this pathway?

Circuits of the MNTB-LSO and of the MSO can be viewed as related and complementary. Bushy cells provide the major input to both systems. These nuclei each represent the first major binaural interactions in parallel ascending auditory pathways. The tonotopy of the MSO is skewed toward the low frequencies, whereas the MNTB-LSO circuit is skewed toward the high frequencies (75, 146). The MSO is sensitive to interaural time differences, whereas the LSO is sensitive to interaural level differences. The MSO detects interaural temporal correlation, whereas the LSO detects interaural temporal decorrelation (147).

Neurons of the LSO detect the balance of sharply timed excitation from one ear and sharply timed inhibition from the other ear (128, 142, 146, 148–153). The timing of excitation and inhibition is roughly matched; inhibition from the contralateral ear can overcome even the earliest excitation from the ipsilateral ear in spite of the fact that inhibition arises through a pathway that has an additional synapse interposed (46, 52). As the relative timing of excitation and inhibition varies with the location of the sound source and with intensity, neurons in the LSO are sensitive not only to interaural level but also to interaural time (147, 149, 151, 154, 155). Joris & Yin (155) conclude that the close matching of the timing of inputs from the two ears is necessary for measuring rapid, ongoing interaural intensity fluctuations and that sensitivity to interaural timing arises secondarily.

The matching of timing of the excitatory and inhibitory inputs to the principal cells of the LSO is reflected in anatomical specializations. Separate groups of bushy cells mediate excitation and inhibition in cats (66, 156). Axons of spherical bushy cells that provide ipsilateral excitation are thin and would be expected to conduct more slowly than the large axons of globular bushy cells that innervate the MNTB and the axons of MNTB neurons themselves (66, 156, 157). Furthermore, the excitatory inputs are on dendrites whereas the inhibitory inputs are on the cell bodies of principal cells (158). In bats, too, separate populations of neurons innervate the LSO and the MNTB (159). Furthermore, the calyceal synaptic connection of globular bushy cells to MNTB neurons is particularly well suited to provide an inhibitory pathway whose conduction time is unchanging. Such a synapse has a constant and short latency (127–132, 134–136). Labeling of single neurons indicates that large spherical bushy cells (66) and globular bushy cells (111) do have small clusters of terminals in the LSO of cats and that globular bushy cells project both to the MNTB and to the LSO in rats (121). On the basis of track tracing studies (156, 159), however, these projections are minor ones. It is likely that small spherical bushy cells are a major source of excitation from the ipsilateral ear (66, 156).

The ability to use interaural intensity differences for localization in the azimuth is not strictly correlated with the presence of a large LSO. Hoofed animals, including cattle, horses, goats, and pigs, seem not to be able to make use of head-shadowing for localizing sounds in the azimuth (93, 97, 98). The LSO of domestic pigs, for example, is similar in size to that of cats, but pigs are unable to use interaural intensity cues in high frequencies to localize sound; they can, however, use interaural time differences in low-frequency sounds to localize sounds with great acuity (96). These results suggest that the role of the LSO may subserve functions beyond the localization of sound.

The principal cells of the LSO project to both ipsi- and contralateral inferior colliculi and to the DNLL (101, 102, 104, 105, 110, 143, 160). Many of the ipsilaterally projecting neurons are probably inhibitory and glycinergic (161), making the input from the LSO consistent with the responsivity of neurons of the inferior colliculus to contralateral inputs.

TIMING PATHWAYS THAT LEAD TO THE MONAURAL NUCLEI OF THE LATERAL LEMNISCUS

Stellate Cells

Stellate cells form a major, direct pathway from the cochlear nuclei to the contralateral midbrain. In all higher vertebrates, stellate cells also contribute to an indirect pathway to the midbrain through the periolivary and lateral lemniscal nuclei. The fact that stellate cells form a major ascending pathway across vertebrate classes suggests that the sharply tuned, tonic, consistent responses to tones of stellate cells carry essential acoustic information. This pathway, through "choppers," encodes the presence of energy in a narrow acoustic band with tonic firing; the firing of the population of stellate cells provides a representation of the spectral content of sounds. (The term chopping refers to the modes that arise in histograms of responses to tones from the regularity of firing, independent of periodicity in the sound stimulus.)

Midbrain-projecting stellate cells have been revealed in reptiles and birds. In turtles, the nucleus magnocellularis contains stellate cells that resemble stellate cells in birds and mammals, both in their morphology and in their projection to the midbrain (35). This class of cells has been studied more extensively in birds where midbrain projecting stellate cells lie in the nucleus angularis (162). The nucleus angularis holds neurons with consistently timed, tonic chopping responses to sound (163, 164). In barn owls, this nucleus has been shown to be essential for encoding the spectral cues for localizing sound sources in elevation (87). Because the nucleus angularis of owls and other birds could hold more than one group of neurons, the possibility remains that a subpopulation of neurons performs this task.

In mammals, midbrain-projecting stellate cells also have chopping responses (54, 165). Three features of these responses are noteworthy. The first is that resolution of chopping in tonically firing neurons requires that the first action potential in a response to a tone has consistent timing (116, 166–171), with a precision that is also reflected in synaptic responses from the auditory nerve in vitro (172–175). The second is that choppers encode the envelope of sound over a wide dynamic range (167, 170, 171, 176). How the enhancement of amplitude modulation over the auditory nerve inputs is produced is not entirely clear. Stellate cells in mice receive GABAergic input that may modulate their firing rates as a function of intensity from small neurons (Golgi cells) that surround the VCN (175, 177), a region in which the responses of neurons to sound have wide dynamic ranges (178). The third is that choppers effectively encode the envelope of sound energy (167, 171), a characteristic that is important for understanding speech (179). As a population, choppers provide a rate-representation of the spectrum of sound (170, 176).

How chopping responses are produced is not completely understood. It has been suggested that stellate cells integrate input from large numbers of auditory nerve fibers. However, stellate cells in mice have been shown to receive input from only a few (four to six) sharply timed auditory nerve fiber inputs (175). Activation of these inputs with trains of shocks produces entrained responses rather than chopping (172, 175), raising two questions: How are stellate cells prevented from encoding the timing of auditory nerve inputs after the initial action potential in response to sound, and how is their steady firing in response to tones produced from inputs that have strong onset transients? Excitatory interconnections between stellate cells produce prolonged excitation that presumably contributes to the shaping of responses to sound (175).

The axons of individual, chopping stellate cells have been labeled in cats (180). They were followed to the contralateral VNTB and VNLL and to the periolivary nuclei, but they faded before reaching the inferior colliculus. Track-tracing experiments support the conclusion that this group of stellate cells projects to the VNTB, LNTB, VNLL, and periolivary nuclei (67, 117, 122, 143, 181–188) and show that they also project to the contralateral inferior colliculus (101, 104–106, 188–193).

Octopus Cells

Octopus cells form a separate ascending pathway that encodes the coincident firing of large groups of auditory nerve fibers to the VNLL through calyceal end bulbs (194). In combining input from large groups of auditory nerve fibers, octopus cells lose tuning and encode the timing of sound stimuli; broadband transients and periodicity are encoded in sharply timed action potentials, which are conveyed through end bulbs to the VNLL. These cells are biophysically specialized to produce the briefest, most sharply timed synaptic responses recorded in the mouse cochlear nuclei (195).

It is not known whether nonmammalian species have octopus cells. Although they have not been recognized as mediating a separate parallel pathway through the brain stem, it is not clear that a thorough search for them has been made.

Octopus cells occupy the caudal VCN, where auditory nerve fibers converge as they pass to the dorsal cochlear nucleus in an area that is sharply delineated, at least in rodents (196). Their dendrites lie perpendicular to the path of auditory nerve fibers, enabling them to be innervated by fibers that span a wide range of characteristic frequencies. Octopus cells are prominent in all mammalian species examined, including humans (197), cats (28, 198), rats (199), opossums (106), mice (200), rabbits (201), chinchillas (202), guinea pigs (203), and bats (204).

In cats, octopus cells respond to onset transients with exceptional temporal precision (54, 116, 171, 205, 206). Their broad tuning and high thresholds to tones reflect the anatomical observation that octopus cells integrate input from large populations of auditory nerve fibers. Octopus cells can respond with one action potential at every cycle over the low frequencies up to about 800 or 900 Hz, revealing the extraordinary rates and temporal precision with which these cells can fire and convey phase-locking (116). These units also synchronize strongly with the fundamental frequency of a harmonic complex (206, 207). The timing of their firing generally reflects the pitch that humans perceive. Studies of octopus cells in slices from mice show that their biophysical properties account for the responses to sound recorded in vivo (195; see also 1a).

Octopus cells project to the contralateral VNLL and to the periolivary nuclei. The large axons of neurons with the characteristic onset responses have been shown by intracellular labeling and with histological labels to terminate with end bulbs in the VNLL and in periolivary nuclei (121, 180, 186, 187, 194). These results are supported by track-tracing studies (117, 122, 181, 208).

Ventral Nucleus of the Lateral Lemniscus

Lemniscal nuclei are ubiquitous in higher vertebrates, but the neuronal circuits and the biological functions associated with this group of nuclei are not understood in any species. Reptiles, birds, and mammals all have multiple nuclei, but it is not clear to what extent these nuclei are homologous (69). The mammalian VNLL is of special interest in the current context, however, because it is innervated by neurons that carry timing information by bushy, stellate, and octopus cells of the cochlear nuclei as well as by principal cells of the MNTB. Octopus cells terminate with end bulbs in a subregion of the VNLL, a region that is particularly strongly represented in humans (186, 194). End-bulb inputs have also been observed to be prominent in cats, rats, bats, and guinea pigs when label was deposited into the contralateral octopus cell area (121, 122, 180, 181, 186, 187, 194, 208). Reflecting their inputs, some cells in the VNLL respond to sounds with exceptionally well-timed responses (194, 209, 210). It is noteworthy that, in contrast with the other targets of some of the same bushy and stellate cells and of the MSO and LSO, the VNLL is innervated monaurally. Although the role of these nuclei in the processing of speech sounds is not understood, the monaural integration of acoustic timing information is interesting in light of the fact that the processing of speech is independent of binaural interactions.

It has long been recognized that the lemniscal nuclei form a major ascending auditory pathway in mammals (42, 71, 118). In contrast with the binaural DNLL, which receives its major afferent input from the LSO, MSO, and contralateral DNLL, the ventral nuclei receive input from the contralateral VCN and from the ipsilateral MNTB and are monaural (209, 211). Although the DNLL is clearly distinct from the VNLL and the intermediate nucleus of the lateral lemniscus (INLL), the border between the VNLL and INLL is indistinct in some species. In rats, for example, a single complex has a concentric tonotopic organization (212). Both regions receive inputs from the same sources but in differing proportions, and the VNLL itself has subdivisions with differing inputs (186). The VNLL receives input from anatomically identified globular bushy (111, 115, 121), spherical bushy (66), and octopus cells (186, 194). Anatomical (186, 194, 208, 213) and electrophysiological (210) evidence indicates that the separate pathways from the VCN appear to remain segregated to some degree in the VNLL. In echo-locating bats, lemniscal nuclei are exceptionally large (183, 204, 213).

In accordance with these anatomical results, neurons in the VNLL respond to sounds from the contralateral ear (209, 211). In bats, neurons in a hypertrophied region of the VNLL, the columnar area, respond with exceptionally sharp timing (209, 210). Recently it was reported that in cats, too, some neurons show sharp onset responses in a region of the VNLL that receives calyceal inputs from octopus cells (194). Other neurons in the VNLL respond to tones with less sharply timed onset responses or with tonic firing (194, 209, 210).

Neurons in the VNLL and INLL project largely to the ipsilateral inferior colliculus (101, 102, 104, 105, 182, 214). Some neurons in the VNLL also project directly to the medial geniculate body (214, 215).

SUMMARY

The timing of electrical signaling, conveyed with a precision within tens of microseconds in pathways from the cochlea to the midbrain, carries acoustic information in all higher vertebrates. As information is passed along the auditory pathway, several different facets of timing information are used and extracted along parallel pathways. There is strong evidence that birds and mammals detect interaural phase differences for localization of low-frequency sound in the horizontal plane in the nucleus laminaris and in the MSO, respectively. Timing information is also preserved and conveyed to the monaural VNLL. Mammals have an additional pathway through the MNTB and the LSO that is skewed toward the high frequencies, which is thought to enable mammals to use interaural intensity differences to localize sound in the horizontal plane, but this pathway probably has additional roles that are not understood. Although these pathways presumably also carry and extract information that allows speech patterns and other natural sounds to be interpreted, little is known about how or where this occurs.

ACKNOWLEDGMENTS

Most especially I thank Larry Trussell for sharing and helping with all aspects of preparing this manuscript. Discussions with Nell Cant, Catherine Carr, Michael Ferragamo, Robert Fettiplace, Rickye Heffner, and Brett Schofield were immensely helpful and fun. This work was supported by National Institutes of Health grant DC00176.

Literature Cited

1. Yost WA, Patterson R, Sheft S. 1996. A time domain description for the pitch strength of iterated rippled noise. *J. Acoust. Soc. Am.* 99:1066–78

1a. Trussell LO. 1998. Synaptic mechanisms for coding timing in auditory neurons. *Annu. Rev. Physiol.* 61:477–96

1b. Fettiplace R, Fuchs P. 1998. Mechanism of hair cell tuning. *Annu. Rev. Physiol.* 61: 809–34

2. Crawford AC, Fettiplace R. 1980. The frequency selectivity of auditory nerve fibres and hair cells in the cochlea of the turtle. *J. Physiol.* 306:79–125

3. Siegel JH, Dallos P. 1986. Spike activity recorded from the organ of Corti. *Hear. Res.* 22:245–48

4. Palmer AR, Russell IJ. 1986. Phase-locking in the cochlear nerve of the guinea-pig and its relation to the receptor potential of inner hair-cells. *Hear. Res.* 24:1–15

5. Rose C, Weiss TF. 1988. Frequency dependence of synchronization of cochlear nerve fibers in the alligator lizard: evidence for a cochlear origin of timing and non-timing neural pathways. *Hear. Res.* 33:151–65

6. Manley GA, Yates GK, Köppl C, Johnstone BM. 1990. Peripheral auditory processing in the bobtail lizard *Tiliqua rugosa*. IV. Phase locking of auditory-nerve fibres. *J. Comp. Physiol. A* 167:129–38

7. Manley GA. 1990. *Peripheral Hearing Mechanisms in Reptiles and Birds*. Berlin: Springer-Verlag

8. Weiss TF, Rose C. 1988. Stages of degradation of timing information in the cochlea: a comparison of hair-cell and nerve-fiber responses in the alligator lizard. *Hear. Res.* 33:167–74

9. Fay RR. 1988. *Hearing in Vertebrates: A Psychophysics Databook*. Winnetka, IL: Hill-Fay Assoc.

10. Sachs MB, Young ED, Lewis RH. 1974. Discharge patterns of single fibers in the pigeon auditory nerve. *Brain Res.* 70:431–47

11. Hill KG, Stange G, Mo J. 1989. Temporal synchronization in the primary auditory response in the pigeon. *Hear. Res.* 39:63–73

12. Salvi RJ, Saunders SS, Powers NL, Boettcher FA. 1992. Discharge patterns of cochlear ganglion neurons in the chicken. *J. Comp. Physiol. A* 170:227–41
13. Manley GA, Köppl C, Yates GK. 1997. Activity of primary auditory neurons in the cochlear ganglion of the emu *Dromaius novaehollandiae*: spontaneous discharge, frequency tuning, and phase locking. *J. Acoust. Soc. Am.* 101:1560–73
14. Sullivan WE, Konishi M. 1984. Segregation of stimulus phase and intensity coding in the cochlear nucleus of the barn owl. *J. Neurosci.* 4:1787–99
15. Köppl C. 1997. Phase locking to high frequencies in the auditory nerve and cochlear nucleus magnocellularis of the barn owl, *Tyto alba*. *J. Neurosci.* 17:3312–21
16. Rose JE, Brugge JF, Anderson DJ, Hind JE. 1967. Phase-locked response to low-frequency tones in single auditory nerve fibers of the squirrel monkey. *J. Neurophysiol.* 30:769–93
17. Johnson DH. 1980. The relationship between spike rate and synchrony in responses of auditory-nerve fibers to single tones. *J. Acoust. Soc. Am.* 68:1115–22
18. Ruggero MA, Rich NC. 1983. Chinchilla auditory-nerve responses to low-frequency tones. *J. Acoust. Soc. Am.* 73:2096–108
19. Weiss TF, Rose C. 1988. A comparison of synchronization filters in different auditory receptor organs. *Hear. Res.* 33:175–79
20. Liberman MC. 1978. Auditory-nerve response from cats raised in a low-noise chamber. *J. Acoust. Soc. Am.* 63:442–55
21. Rhode WS, Smith PH. 1985. Characteristics of tone-pip response patterns in relationship to spontaneous rate in cat auditory nerve fibers. *Hear. Res.* 18:159–68
22. Rhode WS, Greenberg S. 1994. Encoding of amplitude modulation in the cochlear nucleus of the cat. *J. Neurophysiol.* 71:1797–825
23. Moore BC. 1993. Frequency analysis and pitch perception. In *Human Psychophysics*, ed. WA Yost, AN Popper, RR Fay, pp. 56–115. New York: Springer-Verlag
24. Cariani PA, Delgutte B. 1996. Neural correlates of the pitch of complex tones. I. Pitch and pitch salience. *J. Neurophysiol.* 76:1698–716
25. Wightman FL, Kistler DJ. 1997. Factors affecting the relative salience of sound localization cues. In *Binaural and Spatial Hearing in Real and Virtual Environments*, ed. RH Gilkey, TR Anderson, pp. 1–23. Mahwah, NJ: Erlbaum Assoc.
26. Roffler SK, Butler RA. 1968. Factors that influence the localization of sound in the vertical plane. *J. Acoust. Soc. Am.* 43:1255–59
27. Joris PX, Smith PH, Yin TC. 1994. Enhancement of neural synchronization in the anteroventral cochlear nucleus. II. Responses in the tuning curve tail. *J. Neurophys.* 71:1037–51
28. Osen KK. 1969. Cytoarchitecture of the cochlear nuclei in the cat. *J. Comp. Neurol.* 136:453–84
29. Osen KK. 1970. Course and termination of the primary afferents in the cochlear nuclei of the cat. *Arch. Ital. Biol.* 108:21–51
30. Fekete DM, Rouiller EM, Liberman MC, Ryugo DK. 1984. The central projections of intracellularly labeled auditory nerve fibers in cats. *J. Comp. Neurol.* 229:432–50
31. Ryugo DK, Rouiller EM. 1988. Central projections of intracellularly labeled auditory nerve fibers in cats: morphometric correlations with physiological properties. *J. Comp. Neurol.* 271:130–42
32. Leake PA, Snyder RL. 1989. Topographic organization of the central projections of the spiral ganglion in cats. *J. Comp. Neurol.* 281:612–29
33. Liberman MC. 1991. Central projections of auditory-nerve fibers of differing spontaneous rate. I. Anteroventral cochlear nucleus. *J. Comp. Neurol.* 313:240–58
34. Liberman MC. 1993. Central projections of auditory nerve fibers of differing spontaneous rate. II: Posteroventral and dorsal cochlear nuclei. *J. Comp. Neurol.* 327:17–36
35. Browner RH, Marbey D. 1988. The nucleus magnocellularis in the red-eared turtle, *Chrysemys scripta elegans*: eighth nerve endings and neuronal types. *Hear. Res.* 33:257–71
36. Szpir MR, Sento S, Ryugo DK. 1990. Central projections of cochlear nerve fibers in the alligator lizard. *J. Comp. Neurol.* 295:530–47
37. Parks TN, Rubel EW. 1978. Organization and development of the brain stem auditory nuclei of the chicken: primary afferent projections. *J. Comp. Neurol.* 180:439–48
38. Parks TN. 1981. Morphology of axosomatic endings in an avian cochlear nucleus: nucleus magnocellularis of the chicken. *J. Comp. Neurol.* 203:425–40
39. Jhaveri S, Morest DK. 1982. Neuronal architecture in nucleus magnocellularis of the chicken auditory system with observations on nucleus laminaris: a light and

electron microscope study. *Neuroscience* 7:809–36
40. Köppl C. 1994. Auditory nerve terminals in the cochlear nucleus magnocellularis: differences between low and high frequencies. *J. Comp. Neurol.* 339:438–46
41. Carr CE, Boudreau RE. 1996. Development of the time coding pathways in the auditory brainstem of the barn owl. *J. Comp. Neurol.* 373:467–83
42. Held H. 1893. Die zentrale Gehoerleitung. *Arch. Anat. Physiol.* 201–48
43. Brawer JR, Morest DK. 1975. Relations between auditory nerve endings and cell types in the cat's anteroventral cochlear nucleus seen with the Golgi method and Nomarski optics. *J. Comp. Neurol.* 160:491–506
44. Tolbert LP, Morest DK. 1982. The neuronal architecture of the anteroventral cochlear nucleus of the cat in the region of the cochlear nerve root: Golgi and Nissl methods. *Neuroscience* 7:3013–30
45. Tolbert LP, Morest DK. 1982. The neuronal architecture of the anteroventral cochlear nucleus of the cat in the region of the cochlear nerve root: electron microscopy. *Neuroscience* 7:3053–67
46. Ryugo DK, Fekete DM. 1982. Morphology of primary axosomatic endings in the anteroventral cochlear nucleus of the cat: a study of the endbulbs of Held. *J. Comp. Neurol.* 210:239–57
47. Tsuji J, Liberman MC. 1997. Intracellular labeling of auditory nerve fibers in guinea pig: central and peripheral projections. *J. Comp. Neurol.* 381:188–202
48. Cant NB, Morest DK. 1979. The bushy cells in the anteroventral cochlear nucleus of the cat. A study with the electron microscope. *Neuroscience* 4:1925–45
49. Ryugo DK, Wu MM, Pongstaporn T. 1996. Activity-related features of synapse morphology: a study of endbulbs of Held. *J. Comp. Neurol.* 365:141–58
50. Leake PA, Snyder RL, Merzenich MM. 1992. Topographic organization of the cochlear spiral ganglion demonstrated by restricted lesions of the anteroventral cochlear nucleus. *J. Comp. Neurol.* 320:468–78
51. Rouiller EM, Cronin-Schreiber R, Fekete DM, Ryugo DK. 1986. The central projections of intracellularly labeled auditory nerve fibers in cats: an analysis of terminal morphology. *J. Comp. Neurol.* 249:261–78
52. Ryugo DK, Sento S. 1991. Synaptic connections of the auditory nerve in cats: relationship between endbulbs of Held and spherical bushy cells. *J. Comp. Neurol.* 305:35–48
53. Köppl C, Carr CE. 1997. Low-frequency pathway in the barn owl's auditory brainstem. *J. Comp. Neurol.* 378:265–82
54. Rhode WS, Oertel D, Smith PH. 1983. Physiological response properties of cells labeled intracellularly with horseradish peroxidase in cat ventral cochlear nucleus. *J. Comp. Neurol.* 213:448–63
55. Carr CE, Boudreau RE. 1993. Organization of the nucleus magnocellularis and the nucleus laminaris in the barn owl: encoding and measuring interaural time differences. *J. Comp. Neurol.* 334:337–55
56. Miller MR, Kasahara M. 1979. The cochlear nuclei of some turtles. *J. Comp. Neurol.* 185:221–35
57. Smith DJ, Rubel EW. 1979. Organization and development of brain stem auditory nuclei of the chicken: dendritic gradients in nucleus laminaris. *J. Comp. Neurol.* 186:213–39
58. Pfeiffer RR. 1966. Anteroventral cochlear nucleus: wave forms of extracellularly recorded spike potentials. *Science* 154:667–68
59. Bourk TR. 1976. *Electrical Responses of Neural Units in the Anteroventral Cochlear Nucleus of the Cat.* Boston: Mass. Inst. Technol.
60. Bourk TR, Mielcarz JP, Norris BE. 1981. Tonotopic organization of the anteroventral cochlear nucleus of the cat. *Hear. Res.* 4:215–41
61. Manley GA. 1974. Activity patterns of neurons in the peripheral auditory system of some reptiles. *Brain Behav. Evol.* 10:244–56
62. Manley GA. 1976. Auditory responses from the medulla of the monitor lizard *Varanus bengalensis*. *Brain Res.* 102: 329–24
63. Winter IM, Palmer AR. 1990. Responses of single units in the anteroventral cochlear nucleus of the guinea pig. *Hear. Res.* 44:161–78
64. Young SR, Rubel EW. 1983. Frequency-specific projections of individual neurons in chick brainstem auditory nuclei. *J. Neurosci.* 3:1373–78
65. Carr CE, Konishi M. 1990. A circuit for detection of interaural time differences in the brain stem of the barn owl. *J. Neurosci.* 10:3227–46
66. Smith PH, Joris PX, Yin TC. 1993. Projections of physiologically characterized spherical bushy cell axons from the cochlear nucleus of the cat: evidence for delay lines to the medial superior olive. *J. Comp. Neurol.* 331:245–60

67. Warr WB. 1966. Fiber degeneration following lesions in the anterior ventral cochlear nucleus of the cat. *Exp. Neurol.* 14:453–74
68. Kunzle H. 1986. Projections from the cochlear nuclear complex to rhombencephalic auditory centers and torus semicircularis in the turtle. *Brain Res.* 379:307–19
69. Carr CD, Code RA. 1998. The central auditory system of reptiles and birds. In *The Auditory System of Birds and Reptiles*, ed. R Dooling, AN Popper, RR Fay. New York: Springer-Verlag. In press
70. Rubel EW, Smith DJ, Miller LC. 1976. Organization and development of brain stem auditory nuclei of the chicken: ontogeny of *N. magnocellularis* and *N. laminaris*. *J. Comp. Neurol.* 166:469–89
71. Stotler WA. 1953. An experimental study of the cells and connections of the superior olivary complex of the cat. *J. Comp. Neurol.* 98:401–32
72. Scheibel ME, Scheibel AB. 1974. Neuropile organization in the superior olive of the cat. *Exp. Neurol.* 43:339–48
73. Smith PH. 1995. Structural and functional differences distinguish principal from nonprincipal cells in the guinea pig MSO slice. *J. Neurophysiol.* 73:1653–67
74. Parks TN, Rubel EW. 1975. Organization and development of brain stem auditory nuclei of the chicken: organization of projections from *N. magnocellularis* to *N. laminaris*. *J. Comp. Neurol.* 164:435–48
75. Guinan JJ Jr, Norris BE, Guinan S. 1972. Single auditory units in the superior olivary complex. II: Locations of unit categories and tonotopic organization. *Int. J. Neurosci.* 4:147–66
76. Goldberg JM, Brown PB. 1968. Functional organization of the dog superior olivary complex: an anatomical and electrophysiological study. *J. Neurophysiol.* 31:639–56
77. Moiseff A, Konishi M. 1983. Binaural characteristics of units in the owl's brainstem auditory pathway: precursors of restricted spatial receptive fields. *J. Neurosci.* 3:2553–62
78. Overholt EM, Rubel EW, Hyson RL. 1992. A circuit for coding interaural time differences in the chick brainstem. *J. Neurosci.* 12:1698–708
79. Joseph AW, Hyson RL. 1993. Coincidence detection by binaural neurons in the chick brain stem. *J. Neurophysiol* 69:1197–211
80. Reyes AD, Rubel EW, Spain WJ. 1996. In vitro analysis of optimal stimuli for phase-locking and time-delayed modulation of firing in avian nucleus laminaris neurons. *J. Neurosci.* 16:993–1007
81. Yin TCT, Chan JCK. 1990. Interaural time sensitivity in medial superior olive of cat. *J. Neurophysiol.* 64:465–88
82. Covey E, Vater M, Casseday JH. 1991. Binaural properties of single units in the superior olivary complex of the mustached bat. *J. Neurophysiol.* 66:1080–93
83. Grothe B, Sanes DH. 1993. Bilateral inhibition by glycinergic afferents in the medial superior olive. *J. Neurophysiol.* 69:1192–96
84. Grothe B, Sanes DH. 1994. Synaptic inhibition influences the temporal coding properties of medial superior olivary neurons: an in vitro study. *J. Neurosci.* 14:1701–9
85. Vater M, Casseday JH, Covey E. 1995. Convergence and divergence of ascending binaural and monaural pathways from the superior olives of the mustached bat. *J. Comp. Neurol.* 351:632–46
86. Smith PH, Joris PX, Yin TCT. 1998. Anatomy and physiology of principal cells of the medial nucleus of the trapezoid body. *J. Neurophysiol.* In press
87. Takahashi T, Moiseff A, Konishi M. 1984. Time and intensity cues are processed independently in the auditory system of the owl. *J. Neurosci.* 4:1781–86
88. Calford MB, Piddington RW. 1998. Avian interaural canal enhances interaural delay. *J. Comp. Physiol.* 162:503–10
89. Klump GM, Windt W, Curio E. 1986. The great tit's (*Parus major*) auditory resolution in azimuth. *J. Comp. Physiol.* 158:383–90
90. Moore JK, Moore RY. 1971. A comparative study of the superior olivary complex in the primate brain. *Folia Primatol.* 16:35–51
91. Masterton B, Thompson GC, Bechtold JK, RoBards MJ. 1975. Neuroanatomical basis of binaural phase-difference analysis for sound localization: a comparative study. *J. Comp. Physiol. Psychol.* 89:379–86
92. Houben D, Gourevitch G. 1979. Auditory lateralization in monkeys: an examination of two cues serving directional hearing. *J. Acoust. Soc. Am.* 66:1057–63
93. Heffner RS, Heffner HE. 1986. Localization of tones by horses: use of binaural cues and the role of the superior olivary complex. *Behav. Neurosci.* 100:93–103
94. Heffner RS, Heffner HE. 1987. Localization of noise, use of binaural cues, and a description of the superior olivary complex in the smallest carnivore, the least

weasel (*Mustela nivalis*). *Behav. Neurosci.* 101:701–8, 744–45

95. Heffner RS, Heffner HE. 1988. Sound localization acuity in the cat: effect of azimuth, signal duration, and test procedure. *Hear. Res.* 36:221–32
96. Heffner RS, Heffner HE. 1989. Sound localization, use of binaural cues and the superior olivary complex in pigs. *Brain Behav. Evol.* 33:248–58
97. Heffner RS, Heffner HE. 1990. Hearing in domestic pigs (*Sus scrofa*) and goats (*Capra hircus*). *Hear. Res.* 48:231–40
98. Heffner RS, Heffner HE. 1992. Hearing and sound localization in blind mole rats (*Spalax ehrenbergi*). *Hear. Res.* 62:206–16
99. Heffner RS, Heffner HE. 1993. Degenerate hearing and sound localization in naked mole rats (*Heterocephalus glaber*), with an overview of central auditory structures. *J. Comp. Neurol.* 331:418–33
100. Carr CD. 1992. Evolution of the central auditory system in reptiles and birds. In *The Evolutionary Biology of Hearing*, ed. DB Webster, RR Fay, AN Popper, pp. 511–43. New York: Springer-Verlag
101. Adams JC. 1979. Ascending projections to the inferior colliculus. *J. Comp. Neurol.* 183:519–38
102. Brunso-Bechtold JK, Thompson GC, Masterton RB. 1981. HRP study of the organization of auditory afferents ascending to central nucleus of inferior colliculus in cat. *J. Comp. Neurol.* 197:705–22
103. Henkel CK, Spangler KM. 1983. Organization of the efferent projections of the medial superior olivary nucleus in the cat as revealed by HRP and autoradiographic tracing methods. *J. Comp. Neurol.* 221:416–28
104. Ross LS, Pollak GD, Zook JM. 1988. Origin of ascending projections to an isofrequency region of the mustache bat's inferior colliculus. *J. Comp. Neurol.* 270:488–505
105. Ross LS, Pollak GD. 1989. Differential ascending projections to aural regions in the 60 kHz contour of the mustache bat's inferior colliculus. *J. Neurosci.* 9:2819–34
106. Willard FH, Martin GF. 1983. The auditory brainstem nuclei and some of their projections to the inferior colliculus in the North American opossum. *Neuroscience* 10:1203–32
107. Willard FH, Martin GF. 1984. Collateral innervation of the inferior colliculus in the North American opossum: a study using fluorescent markers in a double-labeling paradigm. *Brain Res.* 303:171–82
108. Grothe B, Schweizer H, Pollak GD, Schuller G, Rosemann C. 1994. Anatomy and projection patterns of the superior olivary complex in the Mexican free-tailed bat, *Tadarida brasiliensis* Mexicana. *J. Comp. Neurol.* 343:630–46
109. Kudo M, Nakamura Y, Moriizumi T, Tokuno H, Kitao Y. 1988. Bilateral projections from the medial superior olivary nucleus to the inferior colliculus in the mole (*Mogera robusta*). *Brain Res.* 463:352–56
110. Kudo M, Nakamura Y, Tokuno H, Kitao Y. 1990. Auditory brainstem in the mole (*Mogera*): nuclear configurations and the projections to the inferior colliculus. *J. Comp. Neurol.* 298:400–12
111. Smith PH, Joris PX, Carney LH, Yin TCT. 1991. Projections of physiologically characterized globular bushy cell axons from the cochlear nucleus of the cat. *J. Comp. Neurol.* 304:387–407
112. Tolbert LP, Morest DK, Yurgelun-Todd DA. 1982. The neuronal architecture of the anteroventral cochlear nucleus of the cat in the region of the cochlear nerve root: horseradish peroxidase labelling of identified cell types. *Neuroscience* 7:3031–52
113. Oertel D. 1985. Use of brain slices in the study of the auditory system: spatial and temporal summation of synaptic inputs in cells in the anteroventral cochlear nucleus of the mouse. *J. Acoust. Soc. Am.* 78:328–33
114. Smith PH, Rhode WS. 1987. Characterization of HRP-labeled globular bushy cells in the cat anteroventral cochlear nucleus. *J. Comp. Neurol.* 266:360–75
115. Spirou GA, Brownell WE, Zidanic M. 1990. Recordings from cat trapezoid body and HRP labeling of globular bushy cell axons. *J. Neurophysiol.* 63:1169–90
116. Rhode WS, Smith PH. 1986. Encoding timing and intensity in the ventral cochlear nucleus of the cat. *J. Neurophysiol.* 56:261–86
117. Warr WB. 1972. Fiber degeneration following lesions in the multipolar and globular cell areas in the ventral cochlear nucleus of the cat. *Brain Res.* 40:247–70
118. Cajal SR. 1909. *Histologie du Systeme Nerveux de l'Homme et des Vertebres.* Paris: Maloine
119. Lenn TR, Reese TS. 1966. The fine structure of nerve endings in the nucleus of the trapezoid body and the ventral cochlear nucleus. *Am. J. Anat.* 118:375–90
120. Glendenning KK, Hutson KA, Nudo RJ, Masterton RB. 1985. Acoustic chiasm. II: Anatomical basis of binaurality in lateral

superior olive of cat. *J. Comp. Neurol.* 232:261–85
121. Friauf E, Ostwald J. 1988. Divergent projections of physiologically characterized rat ventral cochlear nucleus neurons as shown by intra-axonal injection of horseradish peroxidase. *Exp. Brain Res.* 73:263–84
122. Vater M, Feng AS. 1990. Functional organization of ascending and descending connections of the cochlear nucleus of horseshoe bats. *J. Comp. Neurol.* 292: 373–95
123. Kuwabara N, DiCaprio RA, Zook JM. 1991. Afferents to the medial nucleus of the trapezoid body and their collateral projections. *J. Comp. Neurol.* 314:684–706
124. Guinan JJ Jr, Guinan SS, Norris BE. 1972. Single auditory units in the superior olivary complex. I: Responses to sounds and classifications based on physiological properties. *Int. J. Neurosci.* 4:101–20
125. Guinan JJ Jr, Li RY. 1990. Signal processing in brainstem auditory neurons which receive giant endings (calyces of Held) in the medial nucleus of the trapezoid body of the cat. *Hear. Res.* 49:321–34
126. Sommer I, Lingenhohl K, Friauf E. 1993. Principal cells of the rat medial nucleus of the trapezoid body: an intracellular in vivo study of their physiology and morphology. *Exp. Brain Res.* 95:223–39
127. Wu SH, Kelly JB. 1991. Physiological properties of neurons in the mouse superior olive: membrane characteristics and postsynaptic responses studied in vitro. *J. Neurophysiol.* 65:230–46
128. Wu SH, Kelly JB. 1993. Response of neurons in the lateral superior olive and medial nucleus of the trapezoid body to repetitive stimulation: intracellular and extracellular recordings from mouse brain slice. *Hear. Res.* 68:189–201
129. Wu SH, Kelly JB. 1995. Inhibition in the superior olivary complex: pharmacological evidence from mouse brain slice. *J. Neurophysiol.* 73:256–69
130. Banks MI, Smith PH. 1992. Intracellular recordings from neurobiotin-labeled cells in brain slices of the rat medial nucleus of the trapezoid body. *J. Neurosci.* 12:2819–37
131. Forsythe ID, Barnes-Davies M. 1993. The binaural auditory pathway: excitatory amino acid receptors mediate dual timecourse excitatory postsynaptic currents in the rat medial nucleus of the trapezoid body. *Proc. R. Soc. London Ser. B* 251:151–57
132. Forsythe ID, Barnes-Davies M. 1993. The binaural auditory pathway: membrane currents limiting multiple action potential generation in the rat medial nucleus of the trapezoid body. *Proc. R. Soc. London Ser. B* 251:143–50
133. Forsythe ID. 1994. Direct patch recording from identified presynaptic terminals mediating glutamatergic EPSCs in the rat CNS, in vitro. *J. Physiol.* 479:381–87
134. Borst JG, Helmchen F, Sakmann B. 1995. Pre- and postsynaptic whole-cell recordings in the medial nucleus of the trapezoid body of the rat. *J. Physiol.* 489:825–40
135. Brew HM, Forsythe ID. 1995. Two voltage-dependent K^+ conductances with complementary functions in postsynaptic integration at a central auditory synapse. *J. Neurosci.* 15:8011–22
136. Borst JG, Sakmann B. 1996. Calcium influx and transmitter release in a fast CNS synapse. *Nature* 383:431–34
137. Kuwabara N, Zook JM. 1992. Projections to the medial superior olive from the medial and lateral nuclei of the trapezoid body in rodents and bats. *J. Comp. Neurol.* 324:522–38
138. Zarbin MA, Wamsley JK, Kuhar MJ. 1981. Glycine receptor: light microscopic autoradiographic localization with [^{3}H]strychnine. *J. Neurosci.* 1:532–47
139. Wenthold RJ, Huie D, Altschuler RA, Reeks KA. 1987. Glycine immunoreactivity localized in the cochlear nucleus and superior olivary complex. *Neuroscience* 22:897–912
140. Helfert RH, Bonneau JM, Wenthold RJ, Altschuler RA. 1989. GABA and glycine immunoreactivity in the guinea pig superior olivary complex. *Brain Res.* 501:269–86
141. Adams JC, Mugnaini E. 1990. Immunocytochemical evidence for inhibitory and disinhibitory circuits in the superior olive. *Hear. Res.* 49:281–98
142. Sanes DH. 1990. An in vitro analysis of sound localization mechanisms in the gerbil lateral superior olive. *J. Neurosci.* 10:3494–506
143. Glendenning KK, Brunso-Bechtold JK, Thompson GC, Masterton RB. 1981. Ascending auditory afferents to the nuclei of the lateral lemniscus. *J. Comp. Neurol.* 197:673–703
144. Spangler KM, Warr WB, Henkel CK. 1985. The projections of principal cells of the medial nucleus of the trapezoid body in the cat. *J. Comp. Neurol.* 238:249–62
145. Schofield BR. 1994. Projections to the cochlear nuclei from principal cells in the

medial nucleus of the trapezoid body in guinea pigs. *J. Comp. Neurol.* 344:83–100
146. Tsuchitani C. 1977. Functional organization of lateral cell groups of cat superior olivary complex. *J. Neurophysiol.* 40:296–318
147. Joris PX. 1996. Envelope coding in the lateral superior olive. II. Characteristic delays and comparison with responses in the medial superior olive. *J. Neurophysiol.* 76:2137–56
148. Boudreau JC, Tsuchitani C. 1968. Binaural interaction in the cat superior olive S segment. *J. Neurophysiol.* 31:442–54
149. Tsuchitani C. 1988. The inhibition of cat lateral superior olive unit excitatory responses to binaural tone bursts. I. The transient chopper response. *J. Neurophysiol.* 59:164–83
150. Wu SH, Kelly JB. 1992. Binaural interaction in the lateral superior olive: time difference sensitivity studied in mouse brain slice. *J. Neurophysiol.* 68:1151–59
151. Park TJ, Grothe B, Pollak GD, Schuller G, Koch U. 1996. Neural delays shape selectivity to interaural intensity differences in the lateral superior olive. *J. Neurosci.* 16:6554–66
152. Park TJ, Monsivais P, Pollak GD. 1997. Processing of interaural intensity differences in the LSO: role of interaural threshold differences. *J. Neurophysiol.* 77:2863–78
153. Tsuchitani C. 1997. Input from the medial nucleus of trapezoid body to an interaural level detector. *Hear. Res.* 105:211–24
154. Joris PX, Yin TC. 1995. Envelope coding in the lateral superior olive. I. Sensitivity to interaural time differences. *J. Neurophysiol.* 73:1043–62; Errata. 1995. *J. Neurophysiol.* 73:1046
155. Joris PX, Yin TCT. 1998. Envelope coding in the lateral superior olive. III. Comparison with afferent pathways. *J. Neurophysiol.* 79:253–69
156. Cant NB, Casseday JH. 1986. Projections from the anteroventral cochlear nucleus to the lateral and medial superior olivary nuclei. *J. Comp. Neurol.* 247:457–76
157. Brownell WE. 1975. Organization of the cat trapezoid body and the discharge characteristics of its fibers. *Brain Res.* 94:413–33
158. Cant NB. 1984. The fine structure of the lateral superior olivary nucleus of the cat. *J. Comp. Neurol.* 227:63–77
159. Casseday JH, Covey E, Vater M. 1988. Connections of the superior olivary complex in the rufous horseshoe bat *Rhinolophus rouxi*. *J. Comp. Neurol.* 278:313–29
160. Glendenning KK, Masterton RB. 1983. Acoustic chiasm: efferent projections of the lateral superior olive. *J. Neurosci.* 3:1521–37
161. Saint Marie RL, Ostapoff EM, Morest DK, Wenthold RJ. 1989. Glycine-immunoreactive projection of the cat lateral superior olive: possible role in midbrain ear dominance. *J. Comp. Neurol.* 279:382–96
162. Takahashi TT, Konishi M. 1988. Projections of nucleus angularis and nucleus laminaris to the lateral lemniscal nuclear complex of the barn owl. *J. Comp. Neurol.* 274:212–38
163. Sullivan WE. 1985. Classification of response patterns in cochlear nucleus of barn owl: correlation with functional response properties. *J. Neurophysiol.* 53:201–16
164. Warchol ME, Dallos P. 1990. Neural coding in the chick cochlear nucleus. *J. Comp. Physiol. A* 166:721–34
165. Smith PH, Rhode WS. 1989. Structural and functional properties distinguish two types of multipolar cells in the ventral cochlear nucleus. *J. Comp. Neurol.* 282:595–616
166. Pfeiffer RR. 1966. Classification of response patterns of spike discharges for units in the cochlear nucleus: tone-burst stimulation. *Exp. Brain Res.* 1:220–35
167. Rhode WS. 1994. Temporal coding of 200% amplitude modulated signals in the ventral cochlear nucleus of cat. *Hear. Res.* 77:43–68
168. Young ED, Robert JM, Shofner WP. 1988. Regularity and latency of units in ventral cochlear nucleus: implications for unit classification and generation of response properties. *J. Neurophysiol.* 60:1–29
169. Blackburn CC, Sachs MB. 1989. Classification of unit types in the anteroventral cochlear nucleus: PST histograms and regularity analysis. *J. Neurophysiol.* 62:1303–29
170. Blackburn CC, Sachs MB. 1990. The representations of the steady-state vowel sound /e/ in the discharge patterns of cat anteroventral cochlear nucleus neurons. *J. Neurophysiol.* 63:1191–212
171. Frisina RD, Smith RL, Chamberlain SC. 1990. Encoding of amplitude modulation in the gerbil cochlear nucleus. I. A hierarchy of enhancement. *Hear. Res.* 44:99–122
172. Wu SH, Oertel D. 1987. Maturation of synapses and electrical properties. *Hear. Res.* 30:99–110
173. Oertel D, Wu SH, Garb MW, Dizack C. 1990. Morphology and physiology of cells in slice preparations of the

posteroventral cochlear nucleus of mice. *J. Comp. Neurol.* 295:136–54

174. Raman IM, Zhang S, Trussell LO. 1994. Pathway-specific variants of AMPA receptors and their contribution to neuronal signaling. *J. Neurosci.* 14:4998–5010
175. Ferragamo M, Golding NL, Oertel D. 1998. Synaptic inputs to stellate cells in the ventral cochlear nucleus. *J. Neurophysiol.* 79:51–63
176. Keilson SE, Richards VM, Wyman BT, Young ED. 1997. The representation of concurrent vowels in the cat anesthetized ventral cochlear nucleus: evidence for a periodicity-tagged spectral representation. *J. Acoust. Soc. Am.* 102:1056–71
177. Ferragamo M, Golding NL, Gardner SM, Oertel D. 1998. Golgi cells in the superficial granule cell domain overlying the ventral cochlear nucleus: morphology and eletrophysiology in slices. *J. Comp. Neurol.* In press
178. Ghoshal S, Kim DO. 1996. Marginal shell of the anteroventral cochlear nucleus: intensity coding in single units of the unanesthetized, decerebrate cat. *Neurosci. Lett.* 205:71–74
179. Shannon RV, Zeng FG, Kamath V, Wygonski J, Ekelid M. 1995. Speech recognition with primarily temporal cues. *Science* 270:303–4
180. Smith PH, Joris PX, Banks MI, Yin TCT. 1993. Responses of cochlear nucleus cells and projections of their axons. See Ref. 216, pp. 349–60
181. Warr WB. 1969. Fiber degeneration following lesions in the posteroventral cochlear nucleus of the cat. *Exp. Neurol.* 23:140–55
182. Kudo M. 1981. Projections of the nuclei of the lateral lemniscus in the cat: an autoradiographic study. *Brain Res.* 221:57–69
183. Zook JM, Casseday JH. 1985. Projections from the cochlear nuclei in the mustache bat, *Pteronotus parnellii*. *J. Comp. Neurol.* 237:307–24
184. Covey E, Casseday JH. 1986. Connectional basis for frequency representation in the nuclei of the lateral lemniscus of the bat *Eptesicus fuscus*. *J. Neurosci.* 6:2926–40
185. Zook JM, Casseday JH. 1987. Convergence of ascending pathways at the inferior colliculus of the mustache bat, *Pteronotus parnellii*. *J. Comp. Neurol.* 261:347–61
186. Schofield BR, Cant NB. 1997. Ventral nucleus of the lateral lemniscus in guinea pigs: cytoarchitecture and inputs from the cochlear nucleus. *J. Comp. Neurol.* 379:363–85
187. Schofield BR. 1991. Superior paraolivary nucleus in the pigmented guinea pig: separate classes of neurons project to the inferior colliculus and the cochlear nucleus. *J. Comp. Neurol.* 312:68–76
188. Schofield BR, Cant NB. 1996. Projections from the ventral cochlear nucleus to the inferior colliculus and the contralateral cochlear nucleus in guinea pigs. *Hear. Res.* 102:1–14
189. Osen KK. 1972. Projection of the cochlear nuclei on the inferior colliculus in the cat. *J. Comp. Neurol.* 144:355–72
190. Ryugo DK, Willard FH, Fekete DM. 1981. Differential afferent projections to the inferior colliculus from the cochlear nucleus in the albino mouse. *Brain Res.* 210:342–49
191. Cant NB. 1982. Identification of cell types in the anteroventral cochlear nucleus that project to the inferior colliculus. *Neurosci. Lett.* 32:241–46
192. Adams JC. 1983. Multipolar cells in the ventral cochlear nucleus project to the dorsal cochlear nucleus and the inferior colliculus. *Neurosci. Lett.* 37:205–8
193. Oliver DL. 1987. Projections to the inferior colliculus from the anteroventral cochlear nucleus in the cat: possible substrates for binaural interaction. *J. Comp. Neurol.* 264:24–46
194. Adams JC. 1997. Projections from octopus cells of the posteroventral cochlear nucleus to the ventral nucleus of the lateral lemniscus in cat and human. *Aud. Neurosci.* 3:335–50
195. Golding NL, Robertson D, Oertel D. 1995. Recordings from slices indicate that octopus cells of the cochlear nucleus detect coincident firing of auditory nerve fibers with temporal precision. *J. Neurosci.* 15:3138–53
196. Wickesberg RE, Whitlon D, Oertel D. 1991. Tuberculoventral neurons project to the multipolar cell area but not to the octopus cell area of the posteroventral cochlear nucleus. *J. Comp. Neurol.* 313:457–68
197. Adams JC. 1986. Neuronal morphology in the human cochlear nucleus. *Arch. Otolaryngol. Head Neck Surg.* 112:1253–61
198. Brawer JR, Morest DK, Kane EC. 1974. The neuronal architecture of the cochlear nucleus of the cat. *J. Comp. Neurol.* 155:251–300
199. Harrison JM, Irving R. 1966. The organization of the posterior ventral cochlear nucleus in the rat. *J. Comp. Neurol.* 126:391–402

200. Willott JF, Bross LS. 1990. Morphology of the octopus cell area of the cochlear nucleus in young and aging C57BL/6J and CBA/J mice. *J. Comp. Neurol.* 300:61–81
201. Disterhoft JF, Perkins RE, Evans S. 1980. Neuronal morphology of the rabbit cochlear nucleus. *J. Comp. Neurol.* 192:687–702
202. Morest DK, Hutson KA, Kwok S. 1990. Cytoarchitectonic atlas of the cochlear nucleus of the chinchilla, *Chinchilla laniger. J. Comp. Neurol.* 300:230–48
203. Hackney CM, Osen KK, Kolston J. 1990. Anatomy of the cochlear nuclear complex of guinea pig. *Anat. Embryol.* 182:123–49
204. Zook JM, Casseday JH. 1982. Cytoarchitecture of auditory system in lower brainstem of the mustache bat, *Pteronotus parnellii. J. Comp. Neurol.* 207:1–13
205. Godfrey DA, Kiang NYS, Norris BE. 1975. Single unit activity in the posteroventral cochlear nucleus of the cat. *J. Comp. Neurol.* 162:247–68
206. Rhode WS. 1998. Neural encoding of single-formant stimuli in the ventral cochlear nucleus of the chinchilla. *Hear. Res.* 117:39–56
207. Rhode WS. 1995. Interspike intervals as a correlate of periodicity pitch in cat cochlear nucleus. *J. Acoust. Soc. Am.* 97:2414–29
208. Vater M, Covey E, Casseday JH. 1997. The columnar region of the ventral nucleus of the lateral lemniscus in the big brown bat (*Eptesicus fuscus*): synaptic arrangements and structural correlates of feedforward inhibitory function. *Cell Tissue Res.* 289:223–33
209. Covey E, Casseday JH. 1991. The monaural nuclei of the lateral lemniscus in an echolocating bat: parallel pathways for analyzing temporal features of sound. *J. Neurosci.* 11:3456–70
210. Covey E. 1993. The monaural nuclei of the lateral lemniscus: parallel pathways from the cochlear nucleus to the midbrain. See Ref. 216, pp. 321–34
211. Aitkin LM, Anderson DJ, Brugge JF. 1970. Tonotopic organization and discharge characteristics of single neurons in nuclei of the lateral lemniscus of the cat. *J. Neurophysiol.* 33:421–40
212. Merchan MA, Berbel P. 1996. Anatomy of the ventral nucleus of the lateral lemniscus in rats: a nucleus with a concentric laminar organization. *J. Comp. Neurol.* 372:245–63
213. Huffman RF, Covey E. 1995. Origin of ascending projections to the nuclei of the lateral lemniscus in the big brown bat, *Eptesicus fuscus. J. Comp. Neurol.* 357:532–45
214. Whitley JM, Henkel CK. 1984. Topographical organization of the inferior collicular projection and other connections of the ventral nucleus of the lateral lemniscus in the cat. *J. Comp. Neurol.* 229:257–70
215. Henkel CK. 1983. Evidence of subcollicular auditory projections to the medial geniculate nucleus in the cat: an autoradiographic and horseradish peroxidase study. *Brain Res.* 259:21–30
216. Merchan MA, Juiz JM, Godfrey DA, Mugnaini E. 1993. *The Mammalian Cochlear Nuclei, Organization and Function.* New York: Plenum

Annu. Rev. Physiol. 1999. 61:521–42

TIMING OF SYNAPTIC TRANSMISSION

B. L. Sabatini and W. G. Regehr
Department of Neurobiology, Harvard Medical School, Boston, Massachusetts 02115;
e-mail: wregehr@warren.med.harvard.edu

KEY WORDS: synaptic delay, conduction velocity, calcium channel activation, presynaptic waveform, EPSC

ABSTRACT

Many behaviors require rapid and precisely timed synaptic transmission. These include the determination of a sound's direction by detecting small interaural time differences and visual processing, which relies on synchronous activation of large populations of neurons. In addition, throughout the brain, concerted firing is required by Hebbian learning mechanisms, and local circuits are recruited rapidly by fast synaptic transmission. To achieve speed and precision, synapses must optimize the many steps between the firing of a presynaptic cell and the response of its postsynaptic targets. Until recently, the behavior of mammalian synapses at physiological temperatures was primarily extrapolated from studies at room temperature or from the properties of invertebrate synapses. Recent studies have revealed some of the specializations that make synapses fast and precise in the mammalian central nervous system at physiological temperatures.

INTRODUCTION

In this article, the factors that control the timing of a neuron's influence on its postsynaptic targets are dissected. An example of the influence a cell has on the firing properties of its postsynaptic target is found in the synapses between retinal and thalamic cells in the visual system of cats (1). This connection was examined by calculation of a cross-correlegram of the action potential trains of the two neurons (Figure 1). In this case, a retinal ganglion cell action potential precedes the firing of the thalamic neuron 38% of the time, reflecting a strong excitatory connection.

0066-4278/99/0315-0521$08.00

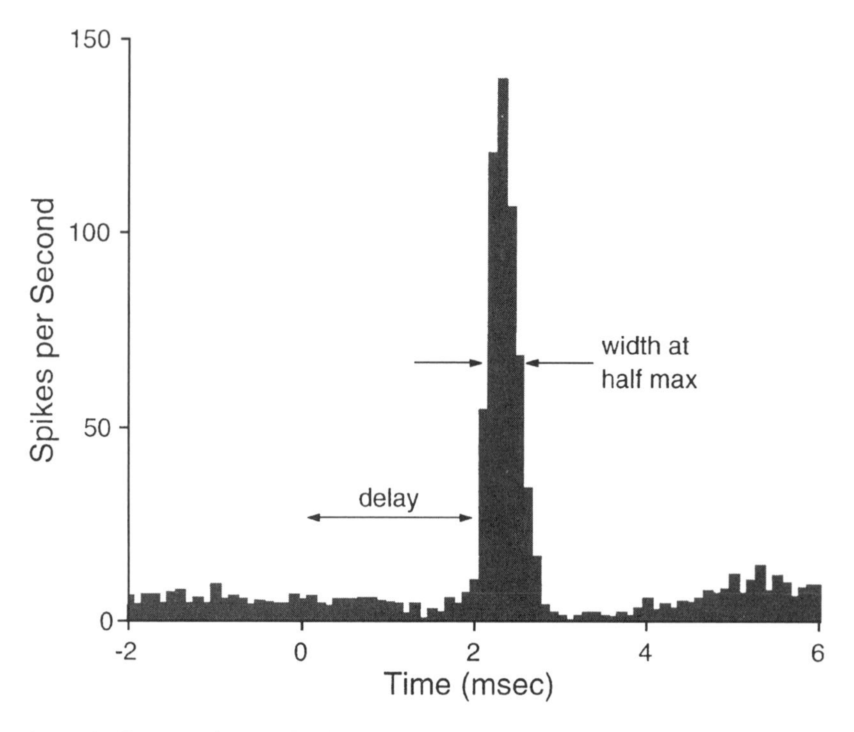

Figure 1 Cross-correlegram of action potential trains recorded simultaneously from a retinal ganglion cell and a neuron in the lateral geniculate nucleus. [Figure courtesy of M Usrey & RC Reid. See Reference 1 for details of methods and cross-correlation.]

This example illustrates two distinct aspects of timing: speed and precision. The speed of transmission, i.e. the delay between the firing of the retinal ganglion cell and the onset of firing in its target, is 2.1 ms. This delay is remarkably brief, particularly considering the fact that these two cells are separated by several centimeters. In addition, the duration of the influence on the firing of the postsynaptic cell is brief and precise, such that the thalamic cell fires in a window 400 μs in duration (width at half maximum).

To illustrate the distinction between precision and speed, two further examples are useful. First, consider the circuit in the barn owl responsible for sound localization. This circuit can resolve microsecond differences in the arrival times of sounds to each ear (2–4). This impressive capacity to preserve timing information is not correlated with speed, and the conduction delays in some of the axons in this circuit are long. Hence, this temporally precise circuit is not particularly fast. Although preservation of timing is most obvious in the auditory system (5–7), it is also important in other brain systems, including the cerebellum, hippocampus, and visual system (1, 8–11). Second, consider recurrent inhibition in local circuits. In area CA3 of the hippocampus, stimulation of a pyramidal cell can synaptically activate an inhibitory interneuron, leading it to fire an action potential and, in turn, inhibit its postsynaptic target. Remarkably, in this brain region, which is not noted for its speed, the total disynaptic delay is only 2.5 ms (12). This process is fast but need not be precise.

Here, we examine both the speed and precision of synaptic connections and determine what factors control the duration of the elevation of firing probability of the postsynaptic targets of a cell. We focus primarily on fast excitatory synapses in the mammalian brain. Many of the factors contributing to synaptic delays are highly temperature dependent (13–16), and we concentrate on physiological temperatures.

SEQUENCE OF EVENTS IN SYNAPTIC TRANSMISSION

The series of events by which neurons linked by fast excitatory synapses influence their postsynaptic targets (Figure 2) provides a framework for understanding cross-correlegrams such as that shown in Figure 1. After initiation near the soma (V_{soma}), an action potential propagates down an axon and, after a delay, reaches the presynaptic bouton. This delay depends on the length of the axon and the conduction velocity of the action potential. When the action potential invades the presynaptic terminal, it provides the depolarization (V_{pre}) required to open voltage-gated calcium channels. The time course of the presynaptic calcium current (I_{Ca}) is determined by a complex interaction between the presynaptic waveform and the properties of the voltage-gated calcium channels. Calcium entry increases the probability of vesicle fusion ($P_{release}$) such that, with a delay, neurotransmitter is released and activates postsynaptic receptors.

Each vesicle elicits a miniature excitatory postsynaptic current (mEPSC), and the summated effect of a number of released vesicles results in the EPSC. The synaptic current depolarizes the postsynaptic cell (V_{post}) and, if the cell reaches threshold, as in Figure 2, causes it to fire an action potential. Below we discuss each of these steps in detail.

Conduction Delay

In considering the time required for an action potential to propagate from the initial segment of the axon to the presynaptic terminal, the properties of myelinated and unmyelinated fibers must be considered separately (17–19). Local connections within a brain region are usually made via unmyelinated axons, and the conduction velocities of such fibers are typically less than 2 m/s (20, 21). Cells separated by greater distances are usually connected by axons that are

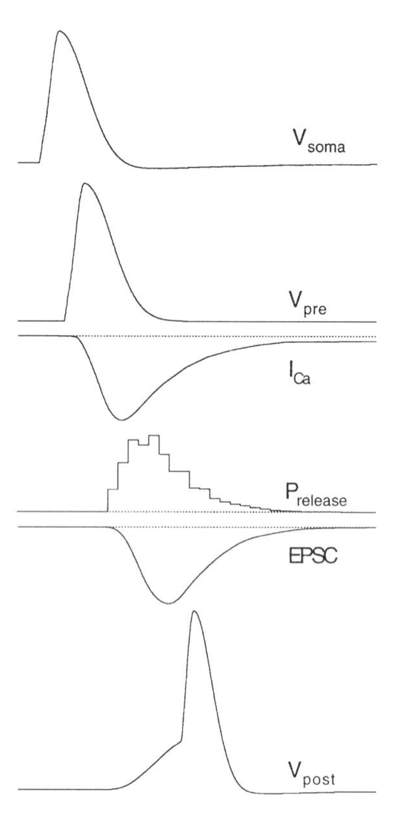

Figure 2 Schematic of events in fast excitatory synaptic transmission. Once an action potential is fired at the cell body (V_{soma}), it propagates into the presynaptic terminals (V_{pre}) and generates a calcium current (I_{Ca}). A rise in calcium concentration near the release site increases the probability of vesicle fusion ($P_{release}$). Released neurotransmitter generates an excitatory postsynaptic current (EPSC) that depolarizes the postsynaptic cell (V_{post}) and causes it to fire an action potential.

myelinated in order to increase the propagation speed of the action potential. Myelinated fibers display a wide range of conduction velocities, ranging from several to hundreds of meters per second (21). Internodal distances, the diameter of the axon, and a number of other factors control the conduction velocity (17–20, 22). As a myelinated fiber nears its targets, it loses its myelination, and the conduction velocity through this segment is substantially reduced, thereby increasing the conduction delay.

In many instances, the conduction delay is a significant fraction of the total delay between the firing of a cell and the influence it exerts on its postsynaptic target. This is the case for the cell pair in Figure 1, where the conduction velocity of 30–40 m/s (23) accounts for 0.5–0.75 ms of the delay between the firing of these cells. For connected neurons in close proximity to each other, conduction delays are brief. With a conduction velocity of 0.4 m/s, an axon of 40 μm would have a conduction delay of 100 μs. Such short conduction delays contribute to the speed of disynaptic responses in local circuits.

In some brain areas, the conduction velocity of an axon is finely tuned to preserve timing information. In the auditory system, where axons serve as delay lines that precisely control spike arrival time, conduction velocities may be tightly controlled by regulating internodal distances (4, 24). Furthermore, in the projection from inferior olive to cerebellum, axonal conduction velocity is set to ensure the synchronous activation of Purkinje cells (8).

Presynaptic Waveform

The waveform of the action potential in presynaptic terminals is a crucial determinant of the strength and timing of synaptic transmission. Judging from recordings made in cell bodies, action potential width and amplitude vary considerably among different cell types. This is true even among cortical neurons, as illustrated by intracellular recordings. For example, in a class of cortical cells known as chattering cells, action potentials are, on average, 310 μs in duration (width at half maximum), whereas in regular spiking cortical pyramidal cells action potentials are 620 μs in duration (25). The shape of the action potential can also be use-dependent (26, 27) and can be modulated by chemical messengers (28, 29).

Differences in geometry and in the complement of ion channels will result in the waveforms in presynaptic boutons being different from those measured at the cell body. Broadly speaking, two classes of presynaptic boutons are important when considering what determines the action potential waveform (30, 31). First, at en passant synapses, the presynaptic boutons are part of the axon, like beads on a string. In this case, as the action potential propagates down the axon, it passes through the boutons, and the membrane voltage is described by the wave equation

$$\frac{\partial^2 V_\mathrm{m}}{\partial x^2} = \frac{1}{\theta^2}\frac{\partial^2 V_\mathrm{m}}{\partial t^2} \propto I_\mathrm{m},$$

where V_m is the membrane potential, θ is the conduction velocity, and I_m is the transmembrane current. Second, other presynaptic boutons are the terminal outpouchings of branches of the axon, and the action potential terminates when it invades the terminal. In this case, the action potential in the presynaptic terminal is similar to the nonpropagating action potential, which is described by the equation

$$\frac{dV_\mathrm{m}}{dt} \propto I_\mathrm{i},$$

where I_i is the ionic current.

The dependence of these equations on the geometry of the bouton, coupled with the observed variation in the waveform of somatic action potentials, suggests there is likely to be considerable variation in the shape of action potentials in presynaptic boutons. However, precise measurements of presynaptic waveforms is difficult, and there are very few recordings of presynaptic action potentials in the mammalian central nervous system (CNS) at physiological temperatures. For many preparations, the arrival of the presynaptic action potential can be detected with extracellular methods (13, 32); however, these do not provide precise information on the shape of the presynaptic waveform. Some of the first recordings of action potentials in presynaptic terminals were made at squid giant synapse. The large size of the presynaptic terminal allowed direct measurement of the presynaptic waveform with an intracellular electrode (33). In a few special cases it has been possible to take a similar approach to synapses in the mammalian brain under physiological conditions. For calyceal synapses, which have particularly large presynaptic terminals, it is possible to record presynaptic potentials (34). At the calyx of Held, in one of the few examples of an action potential recorded from a presynaptic terminal near physiological conditions (36°C), the action potential started from a resting potential of −80 mV, had a rapid rate of rise and a slower decay rate, and was 110 mV in amplitude with a half-width of 260 μs (35).

Presynaptic boutons associated with en passant synapses are typically small (<1 μm in diameter), and it is not feasible to monitor their membrane potential with intracellular electrophysiological techniques. However, presynaptic waveforms can be measured using voltage-sensitive dyes (14, 36–38). Potentiometric indicators, such as the styryl dyes, partition into the membrane and respond rapidly (less than 1-μs delay) to changes in membrane potential (39). By this method, the action potential waveform can be recorded from presynaptic structures in a synchronously activated axonal projection. In parallel fibers from cerebellar granule cells, presynaptic waveforms have a half-width of 350 μs at 34°C (14, 40). One limitation of this method is that only the action potential time course and not its amplitude can be measured. The magnitude of the action potential in the presynaptic boutons may be smaller at physiological temperatures than at room temperature. Reduction of amplitude with increased temperature has been found for other propagating action potentials (15, 41). At elevated temperatures, potassium channels activate more quickly, and they become so effective at repolarizing the action potential that they can reduce the amplitude of the action potential.

Time Course and Timing of Presynaptic Calcium Entry

Classic studies showed that the delay between action potential invasion and calcium entry is a major contributor to the total synaptic delay at the giant synapse

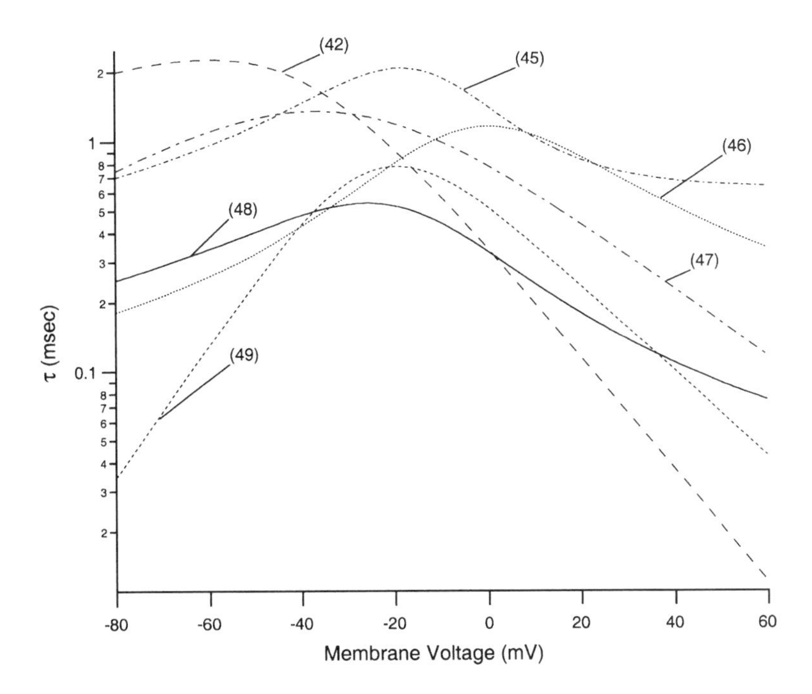

Figure 3 Calcium channel activation kinetics. Time constant of calcium channel opening and closing as a function of membrane voltage, as reported in the indicated studies. Each curve is calculated with equations that describe the fits to the observed channel activation (k_+) and deactivation (k_-) rates as a function of voltage. Numbers in parentheses correspond to references for each curve. The Hodgkin-Huxley time constant given by $\tau = (k_+ + k_-)^{-1}$ is plotted.

of squid (42–44). The timing and amplitude of calcium entry are determined by calcium channel kinetics and by the driving force for calcium influx. Each of these factors is explored separately below.

Surprisingly little is known about calcium channel kinetics at physiological temperatures in the CNS. Most studies of calcium channel opening kinetics have been done at room temperature, where reported rates of activation vary greatly (42, 45–52). Figure 3 shows the time constant of channel opening and closing as a function of voltage, as reported in several studies of calcium channel kinetics that were performed near room temperature (18–24°C). Calcium channel activation and deactivation rates are fastest at depolarized and hyperpolarized potentials and slowest near 0 mV. Activation time constants at depolarized potentials range from tens of microseconds to one millisecond. In two of the preparations in which vertebrate presynaptic calcium channels were studied in situ, the auditory hair cell and the calyceal synapse of Held, calcium channel kinetics are faster than those of channels from cell somas or invertebrates (49, 53). In addition to innate differences in the properties of calcium channels in each preparation (54–56), the variation in kinetics is due to the unusually high temperature dependence of calcium channel activation rates, with Q_{10} in the range of 6–12 (16, 57, 58). Because of this steep and variable temperature dependence, extrapolating calcium channel kinetics at mammalian physiological temperatures from room temperature data is imprecise at best. What is clear, however, is that at physiological temperatures, calcium channels are fast.

The second major determinant of the time course of calcium entry into the presynaptic cell is the driving force for calcium influx as set by the shape of the action potential. The Nernst reversal potential for calcium current with 2 mM external calcium and 50 nM internal calcium is 130 mV, and therefore, the driving force for calcium entry will typically be 200 mV at resting membrane potentials and 100 mV at the peak of the action potential. Thus, as the membrane repolarizes, the driving force for calcium influx nearly doubles. Interestingly, the reported reversal potential for current through calcium channels is usually in the range of 40–70 mV, depending on the internal solution and whether calcium or barium is used as a charge carrier (16, 46, 49, 51, 59). This discrepancy from the values predicted by the Nernst equation is usually attributed to either the presence of contaminating outward currents through other ion channels or the flow of monovalent cations through calcium channels (60). These changes in the reversal potential can have a large impact on the driving force for calcium entry at the peak of the action potential and, as shown in Figure 4, can alter the timing of the presynaptic calcium entry. As a further complication, the calcium reversal potential may change during the action potential because of the build up of calcium near open calcium channels (61–63).

Coupling of Presynaptic Waveform to Calcium Entry

The timing and magnitude of calcium entry is determined by the interplay between the presynaptic action potential and calcium channels. According to the classic view developed from studies of the giant synapse of squid, calcium influx occurs primarily during action potential repolarization (42, 44). Similar results have been found at other preparations (14, 49, 54, 55, 64–67) and have been explained with an analogy to calcium tail currents. As shown in Figure 5*A*, in a simulation of a voltage-clamped cell with calcium currents isolated, a step depolarization to the calcium reversal potential will generate a calcium current only on the return to negative potentials. During the step to the calcium reversal potential, calcium channels open, but there is no driving force for calcium influx. However, on stepping back to negative potentials, the driving force is suddenly large, and there is a transient calcium current, the tail current.

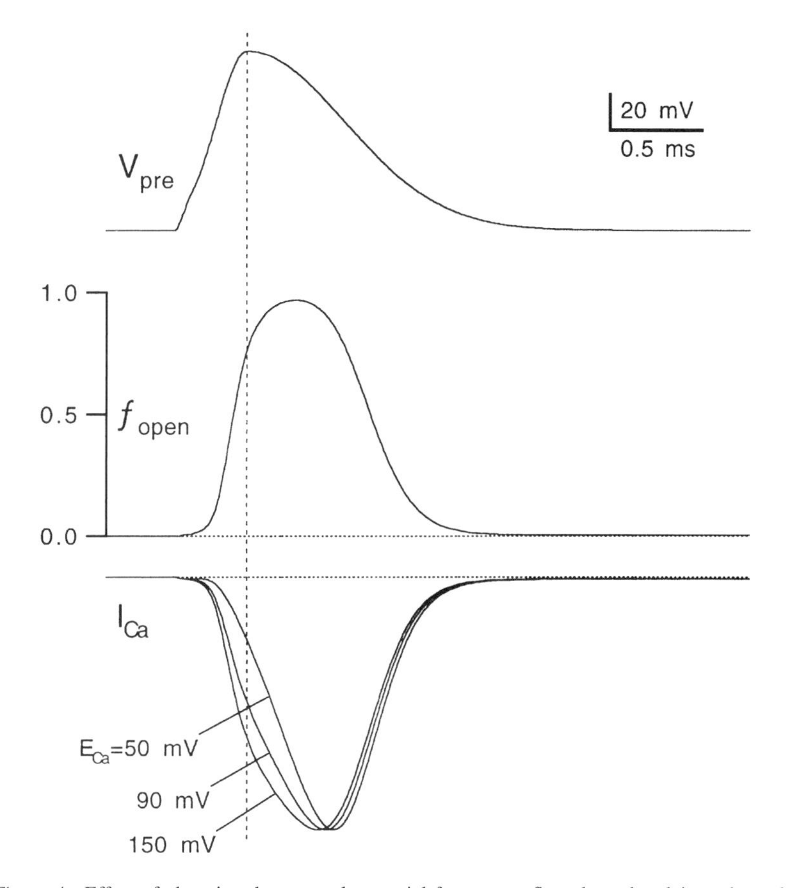

Figure 4 Effect of changing the reversal potential for current flow through calcium channels. Simulation of fraction of open calcium channels (*middle*) and current through channels with the indicated reversal potentials (*bottom*) in response to an action potential (*top*). The *dotted vertical line* is aligned to the peak of the action potential. The amplitudes of calcium currents have been normalized for comparison of time courses. Calcium currents were calculated as by Sabatini & Regehr (37), with rate constants of $k_{+} = 12\{1 + \exp[-0.072(V - 5)]\}^{-1}$ and $k_{-} = -0.16(V - 8.9)\{1 - \exp[0.2(V - 8.9)]\}^{-1}$.

Similarly, during an action potential, calcium channels begin to open as the cell depolarizes but, as their kinetics are slower than those of sodium channels, relatively few will open before the peak of the action potential (Figure 5*B*). By the peak of the action potential, a significant number of calcium channels will have opened, but the calcium current will be small because of the proximity of the membrane voltage to the calcium reversal potential. As the cell begins to repolarize, the driving force for calcium influx increases, and there will be a

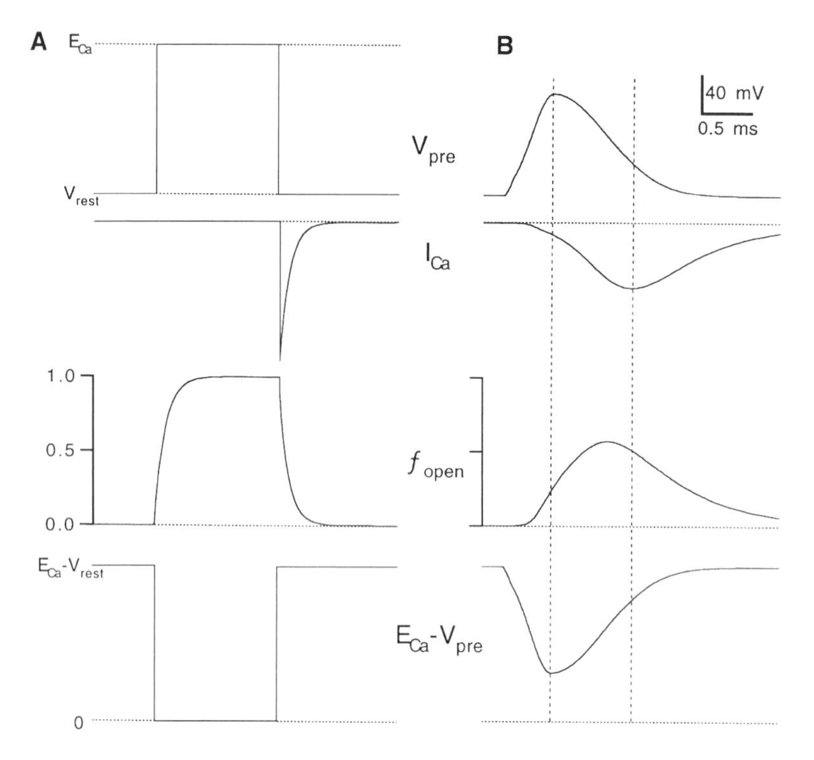

Figure 5 Generation of calcium tail currents. Simulation of calcium current (I_{Ca}) generated by a command voltage (V_{pre}) that is either (*A*) a voltage step to the calcium reversal potential or (*B*) an action potential. The fraction of open calcium channels (f_{open}) and the driving force for calcium influx ($E_{Ca} - V_{pre}$) are plotted below. The *dotted vertical lines* in *B* are aligned to the peaks of the action potential and calcium current. The channels have rate constants slowed by a factor of four relative to those in Figure 4.

period during which calcium channels are still open and the driving force for calcium entry is large. Once the membrane potential has returned to resting levels, the calcium channels close and calcium influx ends. According to this scheme, a major component of the synaptic delay is the time taken for the action potential to repolarize, and the calcium channel kinetics play only a minor role in determining the synaptic delay.

There have been few investigations of calcium channel activation by presynaptic waveforms in mammalian synapses at physiological temperatures. One such study was performed at the calyceal synapse of Held at 36°C (44). The calcium current evoked by an action potential had a half-width of 170 μs, thus providing an impulse-like signal to trigger vesicle release that may enhance the ability of this synapse to preserve timing information. Calcium entry lagged the action potential by 200–250 μs and was restricted to the falling phase of the action potential, which is consistent with the classical model of calcium entry.

Some mammalian synapses depart from this classical view at physiological temperatures (14, 40). Using optical methods to determine the time course of calcium entry revealed that rapid calcium channel opening leads to calcium influx during the depolarizing phase of the action potential in cerebellar granule cell presynaptic terminals at 34–38°C. There was a delay of just 90 μs between the start of the presynaptic action potential and the beginning of calcium entry. The calcium current in these presynaptic boutons was well approximated by a gaussian with a half-width of 340 μs at 34°C. Electrical recordings of calcium currents in Purkinje cells produced by action potential-like waveforms also show that at 35°C, calcium currents are rapid and significant calcium influx occurs before the peak of the action potential (68). Such timing of calcium entry may be representative of what occurs at many synapses in the CNS, where propagating action potentials and en passant synapses are common.

When the variability in the geometry of boutons, the waveforms of the presynaptic action potentials, and the properties of the calcium channels are considered, it is not surprising that the timing and duration of calcium entry should vary among preparations. The calcium current is always determined by a combination of calcium channel kinetics and the driving force for calcium entry. It is an oversimplification to attribute the timing of calcium influx solely to either of these factors. This is illustrated in Figure 5*B*, where the predominance of calcium entry during the falling phase of the action potential is a consequence of both continued calcium channel opening and increased driving force. At all temperatures, increased driving force during spike repolarization accentuates calcium influx during the downstroke of the action potential. However, at high temperatures, the speed of calcium channels and the properties of propagating action potentials allow for significant calcium entry before spike repolarization at some synapses.

The interplay between the waveform and the activation kinetics of calcium channels not only determines the time course of calcium influx, it also dictates what fraction of calcium channels open in response to an action potential, which has important implications for neurotransmitter release and synaptic modulation (37, 69–74). Figure 6 shows a simulation of calcium channel activation by action potentials of different durations for slow- and fast-activating calcium channels. These channels differ only in that the fast channels have rate constants four times faster than the slow channels. For the slow channels, only a small fraction of channels open in response to a single action potential, and as the action potential is broadened, more channels open and the current becomes larger and longer-lived. Similar experimental results have been found at squid

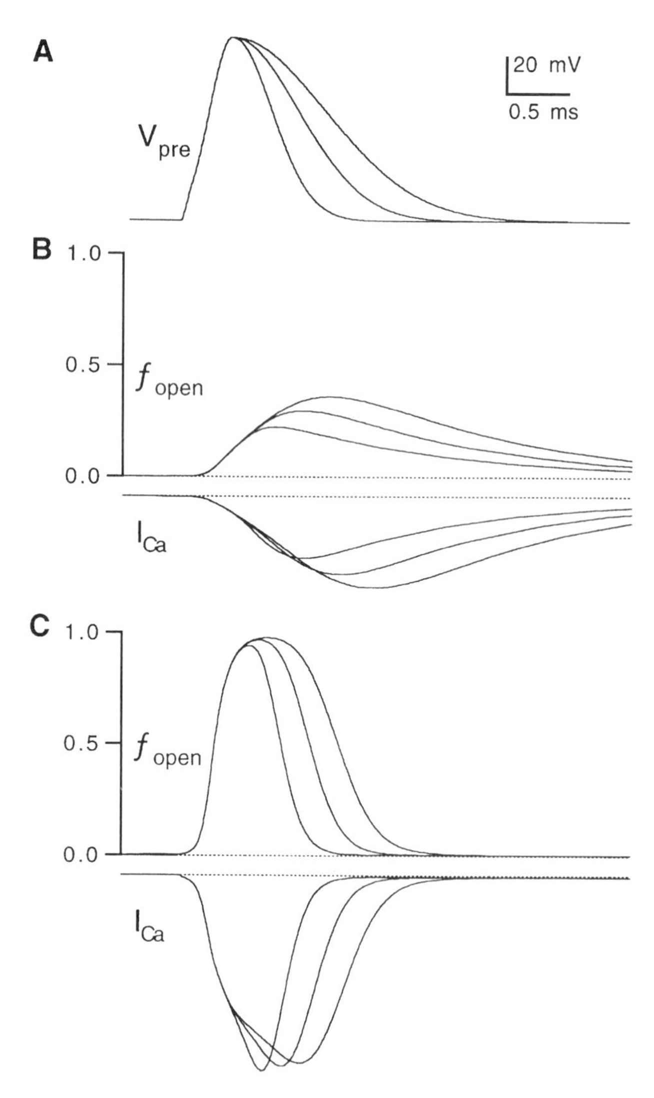

Figure 6 Effect of varying action potential duration on calcium influx. Simulation of calcium channel opening (*top*) and calcium current (*bottom*) for channels with (*B*) slow and (*C*) fast activation kinetics during (*A*) action potentials of varying durations. Channel rate constants are those of Figures 4 (fast channels) and 5 (slow channels).

giant synapse (47). In contrast, for the faster-activating channels, broadening the action potential does not increase the magnitude of the calcium current but merely prolongs it (37, 66, 75). This indicates that a single action potential opens the majority of calcium channels, as has been shown in cerebellar granule cell presynaptic boutons and at the synapse of Held at room temperature (37, 49). It remains to be seen what fraction of calcium channels open at mammalian physiological temperatures, where calcium channel kinetics are faster but action potentials are briefer.

Delay Between Calcium Transients and Postsynaptic Conductance Changes

A number of steps occur between calcium entry and the postsynaptic response: (*a*) Calcium must diffuse from the calcium channel to the release site, (*b*) the vesicle must fuse, (*c*) neurotransmitter must diffuse across the cleft, and (*d*) neurotransmitter must bind to and open ligand-gated ionotropic receptors. Several experimental findings suggest that the steps involving diffusion (*a* and *c*) do not contribute significantly to the delay between calcium entry and the postsynaptic response. First, the distances are small: Calcium channels associate directly with molecules involved with release (73, 76, 77), and the distance across the synaptic cleft is 100–200 Å. The delay introduced by diffusion can be estimated by using the equation for the characteristic time of diffusion, $\Delta t = x^2/2D$. With a diffusion coefficient, D, of 10^{-5} cm^2 sec^{-1}, the total delay introduced by diffusion is less than a few microseconds. Moreover, the observed temperature dependence of the delay between calcium entry and release of neurotransmitter is high ($Q_{10} = 3.4$) (14). This is inconsistent with diffusion, which is not very temperature sensitive ($Q_{10} < 1.2$), contributing significantly to the total delay (60).

Several powerful techniques are available to study the coupling of calcium to vesicle fusion (78). Caged calcium provides a means of directly controlling intracellular calcium levels to trigger release (79, 80). This technique bypasses the need to open voltage-gated calcium channels and avoids the complications introduced by spatiotemporal concentration gradients. It is also feasible to monitor neurotransmitter release without the need for a postsynaptic cell: Vesicle fusion can be detected by evanescent wave microscopy (81) or by measuring the changes in cell capacitance associated with vesicle fusion (82–85), and released neurotransmitter can be detected electrochemically (86–88). The combination of capacitance measurements and caged calcium has been particularly illuminating for bipolar neurons of goldfish, where the calcium dependence and precise timing of release has been determined (82, 89, 90). However, these techniques have not been applied to mammalian synapses at physiological temperatures.

Much of what we know about the timing of transmission was first demonstrated by Katz & Miledi at the frog neuromuscular junction. They found that following an action potential, miniature excitatory postsynaptic currents (mEPSCs) were observed in the postsynaptic cell starting 0.5 ms after stimulation and continuing for several milliseconds afterward (32). Similar evidence that release is asynchronous has been found at many types of synapses in the CNS (64, 91, 92). Studies of this sort also demonstrate the rapid response of ligand-gated channels to vesicle fusion. Each mEPSC reflects the response of a postsynaptic cell to the fusion of a single vesicle. Typically, the rise time of an mEPSC mediated by α-amino-3-hydroxy-S methyl-4-isoxazolepropian acid (AMPA) receptors is rapid and receptor kinetics are sufficiently fast that it is difficult to resolve any delay from the elevation in neurotransmitter levels to the response of an AMPA receptor (93–97). Thus, receptor kinetics are unlikely to make a significant contribution to the delay between calcium increases in the presynaptic cell and postsynaptic responses. The latency is likely to be dominated by the time needed to trigger vesicle fusion. In rats, this delay has been estimated to be approximately 60 μs at physiological temperatures for the granule cell to stellate cell synapses in the cerebellum (14, 40) and 150–200 μs at the calyx of Held [estimated from studies by Borst et al (35, 49)].

Receptor kinetics are, however, likely to make a significant contribution to the time course of the EPSC (93–97) because the falling phase of a mEPSC is often determined by the rate of receptor deactivation. At synapses where each vesicle contributes independently to the response of the postsynaptic cell, the time course of the EPSC is given by the convolution of the timing of vesicular release and an mEPSC (91, 92). This is illustrated in Figure 7*A*, which shows an average mEPSC, the probability distribution of vesicle fusion as a function of time, and the resulting time course of the evoked EPSC. The effect of asynchronous release is to broaden the evoked EPSC relative to the mEPSC. Thus, in considering how a presynaptic calcium signal is translated into a postsynaptic response, the dominant factors are the time course of the increase in probability of vesicle fusion and the shape of the mEPSC. Synapses must combine rapid increases in release probability with rapid mEPSCs to achieve rapid EPSCs.

It is instructive to consider these factors in the context of various types of contacts found within the CNS. The number of vesicles that fuse in response to an action potential depends on the probability of release and the number of release sites. Many neurons in the CNS are connected by single release sites and an action potential will trigger the release of either one vesicle or none, and there will be jitter in the timing of the resulting evoked EPSCs (98, 99) (Figure 7*B*). Other synapses are comprised of a small number of release sites so that few vesicles will fuse following an action potential, and consequently there will be variability in the number of mEPSCs contributing to the EPSC and in the timing

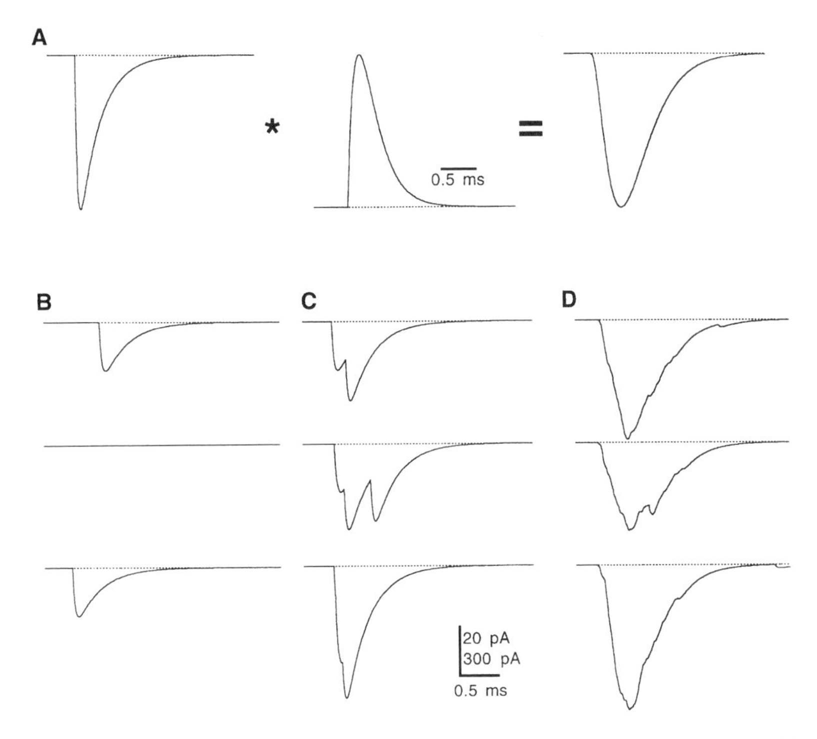

Figure 7 Effect of number of release sites on excitatory postsynaptic current (EPSC) variability. (*A*) At synapses where the contribution of each released vesicle to the EPSC is independent, the EPSC (*right*) is given by the convolution of the probability of release time course (*middle*) and the miniature (m) EPSC (*left*). In this example, the mEPSC has a time constant of decay of 300 μs, and the probability of release has an integrated release probability of 0.28 per site. EPSCs were calculated by convolving a mEPSC with the summed, randomly generated release distributions of (*B*) 1, (*C*) 5, or (*D*) 200 release sites each with the profiles depicted in (*A*). The vertical scale in *D* is 15 times the vertical scales of *B* and *C*.

of the EPSC (as shown in Figure 7*C*). Still other connections are comprised of hundreds of release sites and the EPSC observed in the postsynaptic cell is more stereotyped (64, 100), although there is some variability in the response (Figure 7*D*). Clearly, large suprathreshold synaptic inputs with little amplitude variability will be more effective at preserving timing information by eliciting reproducibly timed postsynaptic action potentials.

Many experiments have been conducted that provide information on the delay between action potential invasion and the response in the postsynaptic cell without distinguishing between the delays from action potential to calcium entry and calcium entry to postsynaptic response. At the mammalian neuromuscular junction, the total synaptic delay is 210 μs at 35°C (101). At 38°C, monosynaptic EPSPs in motorneurons show a delay of 300 μs (102). For calyceal synapses of Held in the medial nucleus of the trapezoid body, the delay is 400 μs at 36°C (35). At the granule cell to stellate cell synapse in the cerebellum of rats, the delay is 150 μs at 38°C and 300 μs at 33°C (14).

Properties of the Postsynaptic Cell and Spike Generation

The manner in which a synaptic connection shapes the firing pattern of its target is greatly influenced by the properties of the postsynaptic neuron. In the simplest case, where the cell is considered as a single compartment without active conductances near its rest potential, the depolarization of the postsynaptic cell will depend on its passive membrane properties. The resistance (R) and capacitance (C) act to low-pass filter the response of the postsynaptic cell with a time constant $\tau = RC$. The resistance of a neuron can be highly voltage dependent and thus the filtering properties of a neuron can be easily tuned (103). A number of studies suggest that some cells achieve the capacity to rapidly change membrane potential by virtue of having low resting resistances; this may be an important factor in the ability of a cell to distinguish closely timed synaptic inputs and act as a coincidence detector (9, 104). Action potential firing will occur when the membrane voltage crosses a threshold determined by the properties of the sodium current. This simple case is adequate to describe the influence of synaptic contacts that are located near the cell soma, as is often the case for synaptic contacts in the auditory system that are particularly good at preserving timing information.

The synaptic inputs of most neurons are distributed over large dendritic trees, whose complex morphological and electrical properties make spike initiation more difficult to understand (105–110). The passive properties of dendrites shape synaptic inputs such that inputs to distant dendritic regions are filtered, leading to an attenuated and delayed response at the soma (111, 112). The complement of ion channels present shapes the response of a neuron to synaptic activation. For example, outward rectification can prevent firing of more than one action potential, even in response to large synaptic inputs, and activation of calcium channels and noninactivating sodium channels can prolong the firing of the postsynaptic cell. Furthermore, dendrites can support action potentials (113, 114). Simulations based on realistic geometries and reasonable channel densities illustrate that, in principle, dendrites can serve a variety of functions, including coincidence detection (110) and can exhibit a great variety of behaviors. It is, however, extremely difficult to delineate the density and distribution of channels sufficiently to predict the manner in which a neuron with an extensive dendritic tree will respond to synaptic inputs.

Another approach is to study empirically the relative timing of synaptic activation and action potential initiation. For example, to determine how synaptic inputs shape the firing of cat motorneurons, the time courses of the EPSP and of the increase in firing probability were compared (115). For large synaptic inputs, the increase in firing rate lagged behind the start of the EPSP by 300–400 μs and was similar in time course to the first derivative of the EPSP. This is consistent with the neuron reproducibly reaching its firing threshold during the rising phase of the EPSP (116). The delay between the EPSP and the firing of the postsynaptic cell reflects both the propagation delay imposed by the dendrites and the time required for somatic voltage-gated sodium channels to initiate a spike. For smaller inputs, the increase in firing rate lags behind the start of the EPSP by 400–650 μs and has a time course intermediate to those of the EPSP and its derivative (108, 115, 117).

SUMMARY

A number of factors have been discussed that determine the time course of a neuron's influence on its postsynaptic targets. We focused our attention on mammalian synapses at physiological temperatures and considered each of the steps in synaptic transmission separately. In long projection neurons with myelinated axons, the propagation time of action potentials from the soma to the presynaptic terminals can contribute substantially to the synaptic delay, whereas in local recurrent connections conduction delays are brief. The waveform of the action potential varies greatly among different neurons and from soma to presynaptic terminal and plays a crucial role in determining the time course and magnitude of calcium entry. In different preparations, the delay from action potential invasion to calcium entry is determined either by the activation kinetics of calcium channels or by the timing of action potential repolarization. These differences result in large variations in the time course of calcium entry and in the speed of synaptic transmission. Following calcium entry, there is a brief delay to neurotransmitter release set by the time required for vesicle fusion. Lastly, the change in firing probability of the postsynaptic cell is determined by a complicated interaction between the spatial configuration of the synaptic inputs and the properties of somatic and dendritic conductances.

By keeping axons short, allowing calcium entry during the rising phase of an action potential, and by having rapid vesicle fusion, synaptic delays are reduced and local circuits can operate quickly. In contrast, precise synaptic timing is ensured by tight control of axonal conduction velocity, brief mEPSCs, and large suprathreshold synaptic inputs with minimal variability in amplitude. Further studies of the properties of mammalian synapses at physiological temperatures are needed to better understand the specializations that tailor synaptic timing to the needs of particular neuronal circuits.

ACKNOWLEDGMENTS

We thank Chinfei Chen, Matthew Friedman, Anatol Kreitzer, Henry Klapholtz, and Adam Carter for comments on the manuscript. This work was supported by National Institues of Health grant R01-NS32405–01, a McKnight Scholars Award, and a Klingenstein Fellowship Award in the Neurosciences to WR and by NEI training grant T32EY07110–06 and a Quan Fellowship to BS.

Literature Cited

1. Usrey WM, Reid RC. 1998. Synchronous activity in the visual system. *Annu. Rev. Physiol.* 61:000–00
2. Carr CE, Boudreau RE. 1996. Development of the time coding pathways in the auditory brainstem of the barn owl. *J. Comp. Neurol.* 373:467–83
3. Carr CE. 1993. Processing of temporal information in the brain. *Annu. Rev. Neurosci.* 16:223–43
4. Carr CE, Konishi M. 1990. A circuit for detection of interaural time differences in the brain stem of the barn owl. *J. Neurosci.* 10:3227–46
5. Trussell LO. 1998. Synaptic mechanisms for coding timing in auditory neurons. *Annu. Rev. Physiol.* 61:000–00
6. Oertel D. 1998. The role of timing in the brainstem auditory nuclei of vertebrates. *Annu. Rev. Physiol.* 61:000–00
7. Covey E, Casseday JH. 1998. Timing in the auditory system of bat. *Annu. Rev. Physiol.* 61:000–00
8. Sugihara L, Lang EJ, Llinas R. 1993. Uniform olivocerebellar conduction time underlies Purkinje cell complex spike synchronicity in the rat cerebellum. *J. Physiol.* 470:243–71
9. Geiger JR, Lubke J, Roth A, Frotscher M, Jonas P. 1997. Submillisecond AMPA receptor-mediated signaling at a principal neuron-interneuron synapse. *Neuron* 18:1009–23
10. Meek J. 1992. Why run parallel fibers parallel? Teleostean Purkinje cells as possible coincidence detectors, in a timing device subserving spatial coding of temporal differences. *Neuroscience* 48:249–83
11. Konig P, Engel AK, Singer W. 1996. Integrator or coincidence detector? The role of the cortical neuron revisited. *Trends Neurosci.* 19:130–37
12. Miles R. 1990. Synaptic excitation of inhibitory cells by single CA3 hippocampal cells of the guinea-pig in vitro. *J. Physiol.* 428:61–77
13. Katz B, Miledi R. 1965. The effect of temperature on the synaptic delay at the neuromuscular junction. *J. Physiol.* 181:656–70
14. Sabatini BL, Regehr WG. 1996. Timing of neurotransmission at fast synapses in the mammalian brain. *Nature* 384:170–72
15. Hodgkin AL, Katz B. 1949. The effect of temperature on the electrical activity of the giant axon of the squid. *J. Physiol.* 109:240–49
16. McAllister-Williams RH, Kelly JS. 1995. The temperature dependence of high-threshold calcium channel currents recorded from adult rat dorsal raphe neurones. *Neuropharmacology* 34:1479–90
17. Weiss TF. 1996. *Cellular Biophysics*, Vol 2. Cambridge, MA: MIT Press
18. Hodgkin AL. 1964. *The Conduction of the Nerve Impulse*. Cambridge, UK: Cambridge Univ. Press
19. Waxman SG. 1983. Action potential propagation and conduction velocity: new perspectives and questions. *Trends Neurosci.* 6:157–61
20. Eccles JC, Llinas R, Sasaki K. 1966. Parallel fiber stimulation and the responses induced thereby in the Purkinje cells of the cerebellum. *Exp. Brain Res.* 1:17–39
21. Boyd IA, Davey MR. 1968. *Composition of Peripheral Nerves*. Edinburgh, UK: Livingstone
22. Waxman SG. 1980. Determinants of conduction velocity in myelinated nerve fibers. *Muscle Nerve* 3:141–50
23. Bishop PO, Jeremy D, Lance JW. 1953. The optic nerve properties of a central tract. *J. Physiol.* 121:415–32
24. Smith PH, Joris PX, Yin TC. 1993.

Projections of physiologically characterized spherical bushy cell axons from the cochlear nucleus of the cat: evidence for delay lines to the medial superior olive. *J. Comp. Neurol.* 331:245–60
25. Gray CM, McCormick DA. 1996. Chattering cells: superficial pyramidal neurons contributing to the generation of synchronous oscillations in the visual cortex. *Science* 274:109–13
26. Jackson MB, Konnerth A, Augustine GJ. 1991. Action potential broadening and frequency-dependent facilitation of calcium signals in pituitary nerve terminals. *Proc. Natl. Acad. Sci. USA* 88:380–84
27. Gainer H, Wolfe SAJ, Obaid AL, Salzberg BM. 1986. Action potentials and frequency-dependent secretion in the mouse neurohypophysis. *Neuroendocrinology* 43:557–63
28. Mudge AW, Leeman SE, Fischbach GD. 1979. Enkephalin inhibits release of substance P from sensory neurons in culture and decreases action potential duration. *Proc. Natl. Acad. Sci. USA* 76:526–30
29. Byrne JH, Kandel ER. 1996. Presynaptic facilitation revisited: state and time dependence. *J. Neurosci.* 16:425–35
30. Plonsey R, Barr R. 1991. *Bioelectricity: A Quantitative Approach.* New York: Plenum. 305 pp.
31. Jack JJB, Noble D, Tsien RW. 1975. *Electric Current Flow in Excitable Cells.* Oxford, UK: Oxford Univ. Press. 518 pp.
32. Katz B, Miledi R. 1965. The measurement of synaptic delay, the time course of acetylcholine release at the neuromuscular junction. *Proc. R. Soc. London Ser. B* 161:496–503
33. Bullock TH, Hagiwara S. 1957. Intracellular recording from the giant synapse of squid. *J. Gen. Physiol.* 40:565–77
34. Martin AR, Pilar G. 1963. Dual mode of synaptic transmission at the avian ciliary ganglion. *J. Physiol.* 168:443–63
35. Borst JGG, Helmchen F, Sakmann B. 1995. Pre- and postsynaptic whole-cell recordings in the medial nucleus of the trapezoid body of the rat. *J. Physiol.* 489(3):825–40
36. Konnerth A, Obaid AL, Salzberg BM. 1987. Optical recording of electrical activity from parallel fibres and other cell types in skate cerebellar slices in vitro. *J. Physiol.* 393:681–702
37. Sabatini BL, Regehr WG. 1997. Control of neurotransmitter release by presynaptic waveform at the granule cell to Purkinje cell synapse. *J. Neurosci.* 17:3425–35
38. Salzberg BM. 1989. Optical recording of voltage changes in nerve terminals and in fine neuronal processes. *Annu. Rev. Physiol.* 51:507–26
39. Loew LM, Cohen LB, Salzberg BM, Obaid AL, Bezanilla F. 1985. Charge-shift probes of membrane potential. Characterization of aminostyrylpyridinium dyes on the squid giant axon. *Biophys. J.* 47:71–77
40. Sabatini BL, Regehr WG. 1998. Optical detection of presynaptic calcium currents. *Biophys. J.* 74:1549–63
41. Huxley AF. 1959. Ionic movements during nerve activity. *Ann. NY Acad. Sci.* 81: 221–46
42. Llinas R, Steinberg Z, Walton K. 1981. Presynaptic calcium currents in squid giant synapse. *Biophys. J.* 33:289–22
43. Llinas R, Steinberg IZ, Walton K. 1981. Relationship between presynaptic calcium current and postsynaptic potential in squid giant synapse. *Biophys. J.* 33:323–52
44. Llinas R, Sugimori M, Simon SM. 1982. Transmission by presynaptic spike-like depolarization at the squid giant synapse. *Proc. Natl. Acad. Sci. USA* 79:2415–19
45. Kay AR, Wong RKS. 1987. Calcium current activation kinetics in isolated pyramidal cells of the CA1 region of the mature guinea-pig hippocampus. *J. Physiol.* 392:603–16
46. Sala F. 1991. Activation kinetics of calcium currents in bull-frog sympathetic neurones. *J. Physiol.* 437:221–38
47. Augustine G. 1990. Regulation of transmitter release at the squid giant synapse by presynaptic delayed rectifier potassium current. *J. Physiol.* 431:343–64
48. Zidanic M, Fuchs PA. 1995. Kinetic analysis of barium currents in chick cochlear hair cells. *Biophys. J.* 68:1323–36
49. Borst JGG, Sakmann B. 1998. Calcium current during a single action potential in a large presynaptic terminal of the rat brainstem. *J. Physiol.* 506(1):143–57
50. Kostyuk PG, Shirokov RE. 1989. Deactivation kinetics of different components of calcium inward current in the membrane of mice sensory neurons. *J. Physiol.* 409:343–55
51. Yawo H, Momiyama A. 1993. Re-evaluation of calcium currents in pre- and postsynaptic neurones of the chick ciliary ganglion. *J. Physiol.* 460:153–72
52. Wright SN, Brodwick MS, Bittner GD. 1996. Presynaptic calcium currents at voltage-clamped excitor and inhibitor nerve terminals of crayfish. *J. Physiol.* 496(2):347–61
53. Hudspeth AJ, Lewis RS. 1988. Kinetic analysis of voltage- and ion-dependent

conductances in saccular hair cells of the bull-frog, *Rana catesbeiana*. *J. Physiol.* 400:237–74
54. McCobb DP, Beam KG. 1991. Action potential waveform voltage clamp commands reveal striking differences in calcium entry via low and high voltage-activated calcium channels. *Neuron* 7: 119–27
55. Scroggs RS, Fox AP. 1992. Multiple Ca^{2+} currents elicited by action potential waveforms in acutely isolated adult rat dorsal root ganglion cells. *J. Neurosci.* 12:1789–801
56. Lin Z, Haus S, Edgerton J, Lipscombe D. 1997. Identification of functionally distinct isoforms of the N-type Ca^{2+} channel in rat sympatheitc ganglia and brain. *Neuron* 18:153–66
57. van Lunteren E, Elmslie KS, Jones SW. 1993. Effects of temperature on calcium current of bullfrog sympathetic neurons. *J. Physiol.* 466:81–93
58. Taylor WR. 1988. Two-suction-electrode voltage-clamp analysis of the sustained calcium current in cat sensory neurones. *J. Physiol.* 407:405–32
59. Swandulla D, Armstrong CM. 1988. Fast-deactivating calcium channels in chick sensory neurons. *J. Gen. Physiol.* 92:197–218
60. Hille B. 1992. *Ionic Channels of Excitable Membranes*. Sunderland, MA: Sinauer. 2nd ed. 607 pp.
61. Fogelson AL, Zucker RS. 1985. Presynaptic calcium diffusion from various arrays of single channels. Implications for transmitter release and synaptic facilitation. *Biophys. J.* 48:1003–17
62. Simon SM, Llinas RR. 1985. Compartmentalization of the submembrane calcium activity during calcium influx and its significance in transmitter release. *Biophys. J.* 48:485–98
63. Chad JE, Eckert R. 1984. Calcium domains associated with individual channels can account for anomalous voltage relations of CA-dependent responses. *Biophys. J.* 45:993–99
64. Borst JGG, Sakmann B. 1996. Calcium influx and transmitter release in a fast CNS synapse. *Nature* 383:431–34
65. Yazejian B, DiGregorio DA, Vergara JL, Poage RE, Meriney SD, Grinnell AD. 1997. Direct measurements of presynaptic calcium and calcium-activated potassium currents regulating neurotransmitter release at cultured *Xenopus* nerve-muscle synapses. *J. Neurosci.* 17:2990–3001
66. Toth PT, Miller RJ. 1995. Calcium and sodium currents evoked by action potential waveforms in rat sympathetic neurones. *J. Physiol.* 485(1):43–57
67. Spencer AN, Przsiezniak J, Acosta-Urquidi J, Basarsky TA. 1989. Presynaptic spike broadening reduces junctional potential amplitude. *Nature* 340:636–38
68. McDonough SI, Mintz IM, Bean BP. 1997. Alteration of P-type calcium channel gating by the spider toxin omega-Aga-IVA. *Biophys. J.* 72:2117–28
69. Mintz IM, Sabatini BL, Regehr WG. 1995. Calcium control of transmitter release at a cerebellar synapse. *Neuron* 15: 675–88
70. Dittman JS, Regehr WG. 1996. Contributions of calcium-dependent and calcium-independent mechanisms to presynaptic inhibition at a cerebellar synapse. *J. Neurosci.* 16:1623–33
71. Wu LG, Saggau P. 1997. Presynaptic inhibition of elicited neurotransmitter release. *Trends Neurosci.* 20:204–12
72. Augustine GJ, Adler EM, Charlton MP. 1991. The calcium signal for transmitter secretion from presynaptic nerve terminals. In *Calcium Entry and Action at the Presynaptic Nerve Terminal*, ed. EF Stanley, MC Nowycky DJ Triggle, pp. 365–81. New York: NY Acad. Sci.
73. Stanley EF. 1997. The calcium channel and the organization of the presynaptic transmitter release face. *Trends Neurosci.* 20:404–9
74. Takahashi T, Momiyama A. 1993. Different types of calcium channels mediate central synaptic transmission. *Nature* 366:156–58
75. Wheeler DB, Randall A, Tsien RW. 1996. Changes in action potential duration alter reliance of excitatory synaptic transmission on multiple types of Ca^{2+} channels in rat hippocampus. *J. Neurosci.* 16:2226–37
76. Kim DK, Catterall WA. 1997. Ca^{2+}-dependent and -independent interactions of the isoforms of the alpha1A subunit of brain Ca^{2+} channels with presynaptic SNARE proteins. *Proc. Natl. Acad. Sci. USA* 94:14782–86
77. Bennett MK, Calakos N, Scheller RH. 1992. Syntaxin: a synaptic protein implicated in docking of synaptic vesicles at presynaptic active zones. *Science* 257:255–59
78. Angleson JK, Betz WJ. 1997. Monitoring secretion in real time: capacitance, amperometry and fluorescence compared. *Trends Neurosci.* 20:281–87
79. Zucker RS. 1993. The calcium concentration clamp: spikes and reversible

pulses using the photolabile chelator DM-nitrophen. *Cell Calcium* 14:87–100
80. Delaney KR, Zucker RS. 1990. Calcium released by photolysis of DM-nitrophen stimulates transmitter release at squid giant synapse. *J. Physiol.* 426:473–98
81. Lang T, Wacker I, Steyer J, Kaether C, Wunderlich I, et al. 1997. Ca^{2+}-triggered peptide secretion in single cells imaged with green fluorescent protein and evanescent-wave microscopy. *Neuron* 18: 857–63
82. Mennerick S, Matthews G. 1996. Ultrafast exocytosis elicited by calcium current in synaptic terminals of retinal bipolar neurons. *Neuron* 17:1241–49
83. Neher E, Marty A. 1982. Discrete changes of cell membrane capacitance observed under conditions of enhanced secretion in bovine adrenal chromaffin cells. *Proc. Natl. Acad. Sci. USA* 79:6712–16
84. Parsons TD, Coorssen JR, Horstmann H, Almers W. 1995. Docked granules, the exocytic burst, the need for ATP hydrolysis in endocrine cells. *Neuron* 15:1085–96
85. Henkel AW, Almers W. 1996. Fast steps in exocytosis and endocytosis studied by capacitance measurements in endocrine cells. *Cur. Opin. Neurobiol.* 6:350–57
86. Albillos A, Dernick G, Horstmann H, Almers W, Alvarez de Toledo G, Lindau M. 1997. The exocytotic event in chromaffin cells revealed by patch amperometry. *Nature* 389:509–12
87. Bruns D, Jahn R. 1995. Real-time measurement of transmitter release from single synaptic vesicles. *Nature* 377:62–65
88. Chow RH, von Ruden L, Neher E. 1992. Delay in vesicle fusion revealed by electrochemical monitoring of single secretory events in adrenal chromaffin cells. *Nature* 356:60–63
89. Heidelberger R. 1998. Adenosine triphosphate and the late steps in calcium-dependent exocytosis at a ribbon synapse. *J. Gen. Physiol.* 111:225–41
90. Heidelberger R, Heinemann C, Neher E, Matthews G. 1994. Calcium dependence of the rate of exocytosis in a synaptic terminal. *Nature* 371:513–15
91. Isaacson JS, Walmsley B. 1995. Counting quanta: direct measurements of transmitter release at a central synapse. *Neuron* 15:875–84
92. Diamond JS, Jahr CE. 1995. Asynchronous release of synaptic vesicles determines the time course of the AMPA receptor-mediated EPSC. *Neuron* 15:1097–107
93. Trussell LO, Fischbach GD. 1989. Glutamate receptor desensitization and its role in synaptic transmission. *Neuron* 3:209–18
94. Raman IM, Zhang S, Trussell LO. 1994. Pathway-specific variants of AMPA receptors and their contribution to neuronal signaling. *J. Neurosci.* 14:4998–5010
95. Hollmann M, Heinemann S. 1994. Cloned glutamate receptors. *Annu. Rev. Neurosci.* 17:31–108
96. Jonas P, Spruston N. 1994. Mechanisms shaping glutamate-mediated excitatory postsynaptic currents in the CNS. *Curr. Opin. Neurobiol.* 4:366–72
97. Edmonds B, Gibb AJ, Colquhoun D. 1995. Mechanisms of activation of glutamate receptors and the time course of excitatory synaptic currents. *Annu. Rev. Physiol.* 57:495–519
98. Dobrunz LE, Huang EP, Stevens CF. 1997. Very short-term plasticity in hippocampal synapses. *Proc. Natl. Acad. Sci. USA* 94:14843–47
99. Arancio O, Korn H, Gulyas A, Freund T, Miles R. 1994. Excitatory synaptic connections onto rat hippocampal inhibitory cells may involve a single transmitter release site. *J. Physiol.* 481:395–405
100. Eccles JC, Llinas R, Sasaki K. 1966. The excitatory synaptic action of climbing fibers on the Purkinje cells of the cerebellum. *J. Physiol.* 182:268–96
101. Hubbard JI, Schmidt RF. 1963. An electrophysiological investigation of mammalian motor nerve terminals. *J. Physiol.* 166:145–67
102. Eccles JC. 1964. *The Physiology of Synapses*. Berlin: Springer-Verlag. 316 pp.
103. Zhang S, Trussell LO. 1994. A characterization of excitatory postsynaptic potentials in the avian nucleus magnocellularis. *J. Neurophysiol.* 72:705–18
104. Trussell LO. 1997. Cellular mechanisms for preservation of timing in central auditory pathways. *Curr. Opin. Neurobiol.* 7:487–92
105. Regehr WG, Armstrong CM. 1994. Where does it all begin? *Curr. Biol.* 4: 436–39
106. Yuste R, Tank DW. 1996. Dendritic integration in mammalian neurons, a century after Cajal. *Neuron* 16(4)701—16
107. Llinas RR. 1988. The intrinsic electrophysiological properties of mammalian neurons: insights into central nervous system function. *Science* 242:1654–64
108. Abeles M. 1991. *Corticonics: Neural Circuits of the Cerebral Cortex*. Cambridge, UK: Cambridge Univ. Press
109. Koch C. 1996. A brief history of time

(constants). *Cereb. Cortex* 6:93–101
110. Softky W. 1994. Sub-millisecond coincidence detection in active dendritic trees. *Neuroscience* 58:13–41
111. Rall W, Burke RE, Holmes WR, Jack JJ, Redman SJ, Segev I. 1992. Matching dendritic neuron models to experimental data. *Physiol. Rev.* 72:S159–86
112. Rall W. 1964. Theoretical significance of dendritic trees for neuronal input-output relations. In *Neural Theory and Modelling*, ed. RF Reiss. Stanford, CA: Stanford Univ. Press
113. Miller JP, Rall W, Rinzel J. 1985. Synaptic amplification by active membrane in dendritic spines. *Brain Res.* 325:325–30
114. Booth V, Rinzel J. 1995. A minimal, compartmental model for a dendritic origin of bistability of motoneuron firing patterns. *J. Comput. Neurosci.* 2:299–312
115. Fetz EE, Gustafsson B. 1983. Relation between shapes of post-synaptic potentials and changes in firing probability of cat motoneurones. *J. Physiol.* 341:387–410
116. Knox CK. 1974. Cross-correlation functions for a neuronal model. *Biophys. J.* 14:567–82
117. Kirkwood PA, Sears TA. 1982. The effects of single afferent impulses on the probability of firing of external intercostal motoneurons in the cat. *J. Physiol.* 322:315–36

Annu. Rev. Physiol. 1999. 61:543–72

STRUCTURE, STRENGTH, FAILURE, AND REMODELING OF THE PULMONARY BLOOD-GAS BARRIER

J. B. West and O. Mathieu-Costello
Department of Medicine, University of California at San Diego, La Jolla, California 92093-0623; e-mail: jwest@ucsd.edu

KEY WORDS: pulmonary capillary, stress failure, type IV collagen, pulmonary edema, pulmonary hemorrhage, vascular injury, extracellular matrix, endothelial cells, epithelial cells

ABSTRACT

The pulmonary blood-gas barrier needs to satisfy two conflicting requirements. It must be extremely thin for efficient gas exchange, but also immensely strong to withstand the extremely high stresses in the capillary wall when capillary pressure rises during exercise. The strength of the blood-gas barrier on the thin side is attributable to the type IV collagen in the basement membranes. However, when the wall stresses rise to very high levels, ultrastructural changes in the barrier occur, a condition known as stress failure. Physiological conditions that alter the properties of the barrier include intense exercise in elite human athletes. Some animals, such as Thoroughbred racehorses, consistently break their alveolar capillaries during galloping, causing hemorrhage. Pathophysiological conditions causing stress failure include neurogenic pulmonary edema, high-altitude pulmonary edema, left heart failure, and overinflation of the lung. Remodeling of the capillary wall occurs in response to increased wall stress, a good example being the thickening of the capillary basement membrane in diseases such as mitral stenosis. The blood-gas barrier is able to maintain its extreme thinness with sufficient strength only through continual regulation of its wall structure. Recent experimental work suggests that rapid changes in gene expression for extracellular matrix proteins and growth factors occur in response to increases in

0066-4278/99/0315-0543$08.00

capillary wall stress. How the blood-gas barrier is regulated to be extremely thin but sufficiently strong is a central issue in lung biology.

STRUCTURE OF THE PULMONARY BLOOD-GAS BARRIER

Historical

In 1661, Marcello Malpighi (1628–1694) of Bologna wrote to his friend Giovanni Borelli (1608–1679), who was a professor of mathematics at Pisa and keenly interested in physiology. Malpighi had been using his new microscope to look at the frog lung, and after beginning disarmingly by referring to "a few little observations that might increase the things found out about the lungs," he blithely went on to announce the discovery of the alveoli and the pulmonary capillaries! In the first letter, after noting that the "substance of the lungs is commonly considered fleshy in as much as it must be opened to the blood, nor is it believed to be different from either the liver or the spleen," he went on to state, "However, more accurate observation and reasoning seemed to reveal a different nature for the substance, for by careful investigation I have discovered that the whole mass of the lung . . . is an aggregate of very fine thin membranes [*levissimis et tenuissimis membranis*] which, stretched and folded, form an almost infinite number of orbicular bladders." (1, p. 320, translation in 2). This was the first observation of the pulmonary blood-gas barrier (BGB).

As the light microscope was improved, additional information about the histology of the lung was obtained, but it was not possible to accurately describe the structure of the BGB because its dimensions are at the limit of the resolution of the light microscope. For example, in the early part of this century, there was debate on whether the barrier included an epithelial layer, and as late as 1929, the French pathologist Albert Policard (3) argued that the internal surface of the lung was "like the flesh of an open wound" (*la surface respiratoire est assimilable à une plaie à vif*), i.e. only the capillary endothelium intervened between the alveolar gas and capillary blood. However, when Frank Low made the first electron micrographs of the BGB, it immediately became clear that, on the thin side, the barrier consisted of the alveolar epithelium, the capillary endothelium, and the intervening extracellular matrix (ECM), which was composed of the basement membranes of the two cell layers (4). Modern electron micrographs show the ultrastructure of the BGB with great clarity.

Components of the Blood-Gas Barrier

From both anatomical and physiological points of view it is useful to divide the BGB into two parts, the thick side and the thin side. The thin side comprises about half of the surface area of the alveolar wall (5) and is the critical structure for pulmonary gas exchange. With a thickness of only 0.2–0.3 μm in the human lung (5), it provides a remarkably efficient structure for diffusive gas exchange.

The thick side of the BGB typically has a width of up to 1 μm or more and contains type I collagen fibers that are important in the scaffold support of the lung (6). The thick side also contains interstitial cells, such as fibroblasts and pericytes, and is probably important for fluid exchange across the pulmonary capillary. For example, in the early stages of interstitial edema of the lung, accumulations of fluid are seen in the thick side, which becomes distended. By contrast, the interstitium of the thin side, being composed of the two fused basement membranes of the endothelium and epithelium, appears to offer a high resistance to the ingress of fluid from the capillary, and substantial interstitial edema of the lung can occur with no change in the appearance of the thin side (7).

The structure of the extracellular matrix (ECM) is of particular interest because of its critical role in determining the strength of the BGB. The average thickness in μm of the interstitium of the BGB is only 0.175 ± 0.010 in rabbit, 0.318 ± 0.081 in dog, and 0.390 ± 0.02 in horse (8). However, these average values include both the thin and thick sides of the BGB, and on the thin side the thickness can be as little as 0.1 μm or less in all three species (8).

Four principal molecules are found in the ECM (9). Type IV collagen is the collagen of basement membranes and is synthesized by both epithelial and endothelial cells, and in smaller amounts by other mesenchymal cells. Type IV collagen has a triple-helix structure like that of other matrix collagens, but it is distinctive in that the C-terminal end has a NC1 globular domain that allows two of the approximately 400-nm-long molecules to join to form a doublet (Figure 1*a*). The other N terminus contains the 7S domain, which allows four doublet molecules to form a matrix configuration (Figure 1*d*) similar to chicken wire (10, 11). This arrangement apparently combines great strength with porosity. The 7S domain allows the collagen to link with integrins $\alpha1\beta1$ and $\alpha2\beta1$ (12). The most abundant form of type IV collagen in most tissues contains two $\alpha1$(IV) chains and one $\alpha2$(IV) chain. However, recent studies have shown that basement membranes contain type IV collagens encoded by at least six genes.

Collagens are some of the strongest soft tissues in the body. However, there have been few studies of the ultimate tensile strength of basement membrane. Fisher & Wakely (13) measured the ultimate tensile strength of basement membrane from the lens capsule of cat and gave a value of $1.7 \times 10^6\ \mathrm{N \cdot m^{-2}}$. This is not very different from the tensile strengths of cow ligamentum nuchae (which is mainly composed of type I collagen) and mouse collagen, which have values of 2×10^6 and $5 - 7 \times 10^6\ \mathrm{N \cdot m^{-2}}$, respectively (14). However, lens capsule basement membrane is about 15 μm thick (up to 150 times thicker than the

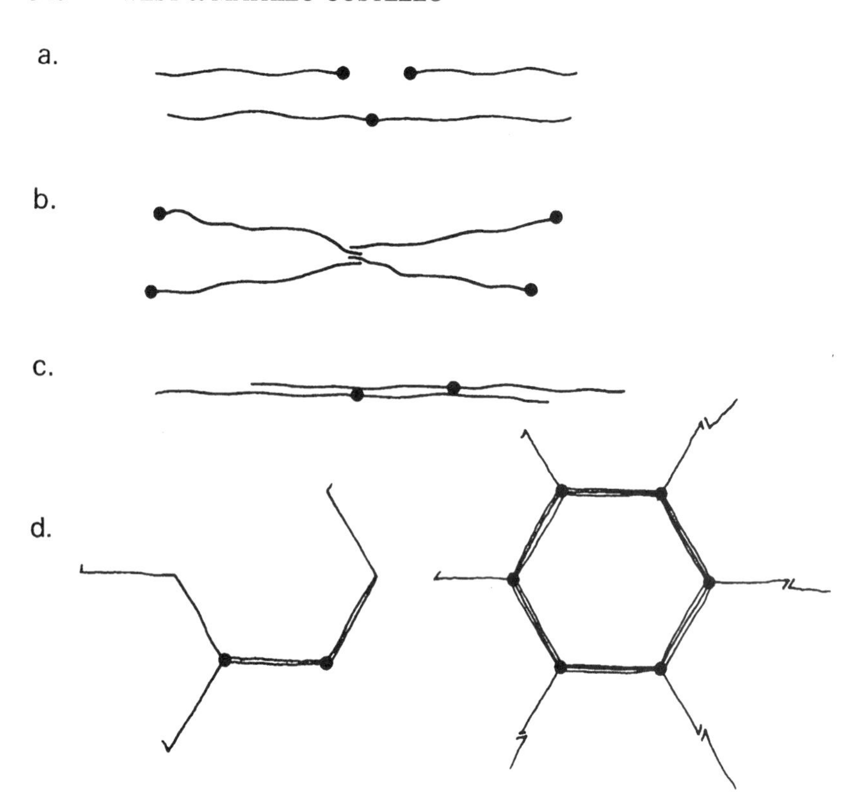

Figure 1 Assembly of type IV collagen molecules. (*a*) Single type IV collagen molecule is a rod-like structure with a globule at its C terminus. Two molecules combine to form a dimer. (*b*) The N terminus (7S domain) interacts with three other N termini. (*c*) Dimers form lateral associations. (*d*) Lattice structure is formed via the N terminus connections. Modified from (9).

basement membranes in the BGB), so there may be differences in molecular arrangement between the two.

Welling & Grantham (15) measured the elastic properties of basement membranes from isolated rabbit renal tubules by attaching the tubules to micropipettes and increasing the pressure within them while measuring their change of diameter. Although they were not able to determine the ultimate tensile strength because the tubules separated from the micropipettes at high pressures, they showed that a tubule with a diameter of 57 μm and wall thickness of 0.26 μm could withstand a transmural pressure of 42 cmH_2O (Table 1, Experiment 39 in Reference 15). Using the Laplace relationship, this means that the ultimate tensile strength exceeded 5×10^5 $N \cdot m^{-2}$, which is in reasonable agreement with the results of Fisher & Wakely (13).

Welling & Grantham (15) also obtained evidence that the elastic properties of the tubules were determined solely by their basement membrane. These tubules consist of only a single layer of epithelial cells and its basement membrane. When the layer of epithelial cells was removed with detergent, the relationship between transmural pressure and diameter of the tubule remained the same. Thus these results show that a single layer of epithelial cells does not contribute to the mechanical properties in extension. Additional evidence of the importance of basement membrane in determining mechanical properties of small structures comes from the work of Swayne et al (16). They showed that the distensibility of capillaries from frog mesentery was consistent with the Young's modulus of basement membrane.

There is additional indirect evidence that the basement membrane has an important role in the strength of capillaries. For example, Williamson et al (17) reported that the thickness of the basement membrane of systemic capillaries increased from the abdomen to the thigh to the calf in humans, consistent with the fact that the increased hydrostatic pressure requires stronger capillaries. The same investigators showed a progression from shoulder to leg in the giraffe. As discussed below, patients with long-standing pulmonary venous hypertension, —caused, for example, by mitral stenosis—develop marked thickening of the basement membranes of pulmonary capillaries (18).

There is evidence that molecules of type IV collagen have sites that allow bending of the molecules to occur. The triple-helical domain in the middle of the molecule has frequent interruptions. In human $\alpha 1$(IV) and $\alpha 2$(IV) polypeptide chains, there are about 25 irregularly spaced sites that impart flexibility to the whole molecule (19). Schwarz et al (20) refer to frequent interruptions of the central domain by non-triple-helical regions characterized by an imperfect Gly-Xaa-Yaa sequence repeat. Hofmann (21) described a 90-nm-long segment of high flexibility, near the 7S domain, which is very rich in non-triple-helical regions.

Changes in the shape of the molecules, or in their connections, might allow the lattice arrangement to distort when tensile stress is applied. An analogy would be chicken wire, which can lengthen in one direction if pulled. This extensibility of the type IV collagen sheet might explain some of the appearances seen when the transmural pressure of pulmonary capillaries is raised and disruptions occur in the alveolar epithelial and capillary endothelial cells (see below). Such appearances could possibly be explained by sliding of the cells over the basement membrane as it undergoes extension. Furthermore, this distortion of the basement membrane's lattice structure under tensile stress might explain why many of the cellular disruptions are rapidly reversible when the capillary transmural pressure is reduced and hoop stress in the capillary is therefore reduced (22).

There is evidence that the type IV collagen molecules are not uniformly distributed throughout the ECM on the thin side of the BGB. Electron micrographs show that the ECM has a central lamina densa with a lamina rara on either side (Figure 2*a*). The lamina rara externa is adjacent to the alveolar epithelial cell, and the lamina rara interna is adjacent to the capillary endothelial cell (23). Using anti-human type IV collagen antibody, Crouch and colleagues (9) showed that the distribution of type IV collagen in epithelial basement membrane and endothelial basement membrane of human lung is closely associated with the lamina densa. Thus it appears that the great strength of the thin part of the BGB comes from an extremely thin layer of type IV collagen, perhaps only 50 nm thick, which is sandwiched in the middle of the ECM (Figure 2*b*).

The thinness of the layer of type IV collagen implies that the molecules are arranged in a planar fashion along the lamina densa. Since each molecule is approximately 400 nm in length, and two of them join to form a doublet (Figure 1*a*), there is clearly not enough space to contain them in a layer only 50 nm thick unless the molecules are lined up along the lamina densa. Thus we can imagine the type IV collagen sheets as being like layers of chicken wire that are placed on a flat surface, thus providing great tensile strength in the plane

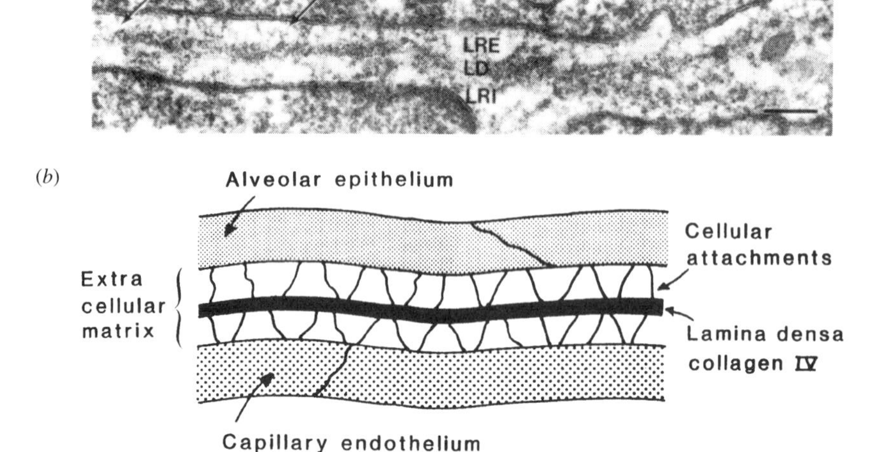

Figure 2 (*a*) Ultrastructure of the thin part of the BGB in rat with portions of alveolar epithelial cell (*top*) and capillary endothelial cell (*bottom*). Note that the ECM has a central lamina densa (LD) flanked by a lamina rara externa (LRE) and lamina rara interna (LRI). Bar, 0.1 μm. From (23). (*b*) Diagram of the thin part of the BGB. Most of the type IV collagen that is believed to be responsible for the strength of the BGB is located in the lamina densa. This is only about 50 nm thick, and is sandwiched in the middle of the ECM (91).

of the surface, but not at right angles to it. This arrangement is well suited to withstanding the loads associated with the large hoop stresses when the capillary transmural pressure is raised.

Other molecules in the ECM include laminins, of which at least seven types have now been identified, although it is not clear how many are found in the extracellular matrix of pulmonary capillaries (9). Laminin I is a cross-shaped molecule, and domains have been identified that allow various integrin binding sites (24). Laminins are important in linking the cells to their basement membranes. Perlecan is a globular core protein to which two or three long heparan sulfate glycosoaminoglycan side chains are attached at one end. Again, interactions between domains on the perlecan molecule and various integrins have been described (25). Entactin/nidogen is found extensively in basement membranes; the molecule consists of three globules linked by rod domains. The exact role of entactin/nidogen has not been established in basement membranes, but some studies indicate that it forms a tight complex with laminin (26). Other components of the ECM may include other types of collagen and fibronectin.

In summary, it is likely that type IV collagen is chiefly responsible for the great tensile strength of the ECM (Figure 2*b*) and that the other molecules play important roles in consolidating the structure of the ECM and its connections with overlying cells.

STRENGTH OF THE BLOOD-GAS BARRIER

It is remarkable that it is only recently that the great strength of the BGB has been appreciated. After all, it requires only a very simple calculation using the Laplace relationship to recognize that the hoop stress in the wall of a pulmonary capillary is enormous if the wall is only 0.2 μm thick, the capillary radius is about 3.5 μm, and the capillary transmural pressure is about 25 mmHg.

One of the reasons why the high wall stresses of pulmonary capillaries have not previously been recognized is the common misconception that pulmonary capillary pressure remains low during severe exercise. For example, the chapter on the pulmonary circulation in the current edition of the American Physiological Society's *Handbook of Physiology* includes the statement "The pulmonary wedge pressure is unaffected by mild exercise but may increase slightly as the intensity of the exercise increases" (27). Again, a popular current textbook of physiology states, "Because the left atrial pressure in a healthy person almost never rises above +6 mmHg even during the most strenuous exercise, the changes in left atrial pressure have virtually no effect on pulmonary circulatory function except when the left side of the heart fails." (28)

However, these are misconceptions. In a study of healthy volunteers who exercised on a bicycle ergometer at a mean oxygen consumption of $3.7 \, l \cdot min^{-1}$, mean pulmonary arterial wedge pressure increased from 3.4 mmHg to 21.1 mmHg during exercise (29). Concurrently, mean pulmonary arterial pressure increased from 13.2 mmHg at rest to 37.2 mmHg during exercise. Other studies have shown a similar pattern (30, 31). These findings imply that the pressure in the pulmonary capillaries rises substantially during exercise. Measurements by micropuncture of small pulmonary blood vessels in anesthetized cats have shown that capillary pressure is about halfway between arterial and venous pressure, and that much of the pressure drop in the pulmonary circulation occurs in the capillary bed (32). Furthermore, studies in dog lungs have shown that at high pulmonary blood flows, pulmonary capillary pressure is closer to arterial than venous pressure (33). Therefore, capillary pressure is at least equal to the average of arterial and venous pressures, and is probably more than this.

These findings mean that the pulmonary capillary pressure at mid-lung during heavy exercise in humans is about halfway between 37 and 21 mmHg, i.e. 29 mmHg. Since the capillaries at the bottom of the upright lung are some 10 cm lower, adding the hydrostatic gradient gives a capillary pressure at the bottom of the lung of about 36 mmHg (34). As indicated above, this is probably an underestimate, because at least some capillaries have a pressure closer to pulmonary arterial pressure. Pressures of this magnitude are sufficient to cause ultrastructural changes in the wall of pulmonary capillaries in animal preparations (see Failure of the Blood-Gas Barrier).

If we assume that pulmonary capillaries are thin-walled cylindrical tubes, wall stress can be calculated from the Laplace relationship $S = P \times r/t$ where S is the circumferential or hoop stress in the capillary wall, P is the capillary transmural pressure (difference in pressure between the inside and outside of the capillary), r is the capillary radius, and t is the wall thickness. As an example of the calculation of wall stress, we can use the capillary transmural pressure of 36 mmHg referred to above. The thickness of the wall is as small as 0.2 μm in some places (5). There are no good data on the radius of human pulmonary capillaries at high capillary pressures, but using the average for rabbits and dogs gives a value of 3.5 μm (8). Using these numbers, calculated wall stress is $(36 \times 1.36 \times 981 \times 3.5)/(0.2 \times 10)$, i.e. 8.4×10^4 N $\cdot$ m^{-2}.

However, as indicated above, the loads are probably borne by the type IV collagen that is mainly confined to the center of the ECM (Figure 2). Given that the ECM is about one-third of the thickness of the BGB (8), and assuming that the type IV collagen is concentrated in the middle third of the ECM (Figure 2*a*), the stress in the type IV collagen layer itself is calculated to be about 9×10^5 N $\cdot$ m^{-2}. As indicated above, the ultimate tensile strengths of basement membrane from cat lens capsule and renal tubules were measured as 1.7×10^6 N $\cdot$ m^{-2} and $>5 \times 10^5$ N $\cdot$ m^{-2} (13, 15). Thus, these admittedly rough calculations suggest that the stresses in the load-bearing elements of the pulmonary capillary wall are compatible with the ultimate tensile strength of type IV collagen.

These calculations have been carried out for the thin side of the BGB because, other things being equal, this is the side that would be expected to develop the highest hoop stresses for a given capillary transmural pressure. It would be of great interest to know the distribution of stresses in the various elements of the thick side of the BGB, but the heterogeneous nature of its structure makes this impossible in the present state of knowledge. However, note that in experimental animal preparations where stress failure of the pulmonary capillary is observed (see below), ultrastructural changes are observed on both the thin and thick sides of the BGB. Thus, although the thick side would be expected to have lower wall stresses based on a simple application of the Laplace relationship, the distribution of stresses on the thick side evidently exposes some elements to extremely high loads. This observation fits with general engineering principles that dictate that there is no point in overprotecting one part of a structure if another part is so weak that it is near failure.

So far we have been concentrating on the circumferential or hoop stresses caused by the capillary transmural pressure. In a thin-walled cylindrical tube, the corresponding longitudinal stress is half the hoop stress. Additional analysis (Figure 3) shows that pulmonary capillaries are exposed to three forces and that these probably interact (34). The first force is the circumferential tension given by $P \times r$. Using the values given above for the human lung during heavy exercise, the hoop tension is calculated to be $36 \times 1.36 \times 981 \times 3.5/10^4$, i.e. $17\ mN \cdot m^{-1}$. This is a relatively small tension, being of the same order of magnitude as the surface tension of the lung under normal inflation conditions.

The second force (Figure 3) is caused by the longitudinal tension in tissue elements of the alveolar wall associated with lung inflation. The tension of the tissue elements of the alveolar wall depends on lung volume. Neergaard (35) studied air- and liquid-filled pressure volume curves and concluded that the contribution to elastic lung recoil by tissue elements was negligible near functional residual capacity. In agreement with this, Gil et al (36) showed that in saline-filled lungs at normal volumes, the alveolar walls are undulated rather than straight. They therefore concluded that the tissue elements were not in a state of tension, and that the more linear appearance of the walls in air-filled lung was due to the surface tension of the alveolar lining layer.

On the other hand, it is generally agreed that at high lung volumes the tissue elements of the alveolar walls are in a state of tension, as evidenced by the fact that they are very straight and thin. In addition, the calculated tension in the alveolar walls based on the observed transpulmonary pressure far exceeds the surface tension of the alveolar lining layer (37). Since the alveolar wall is composed mostly of a string of pulmonary capillaries, it is reasonable to assume

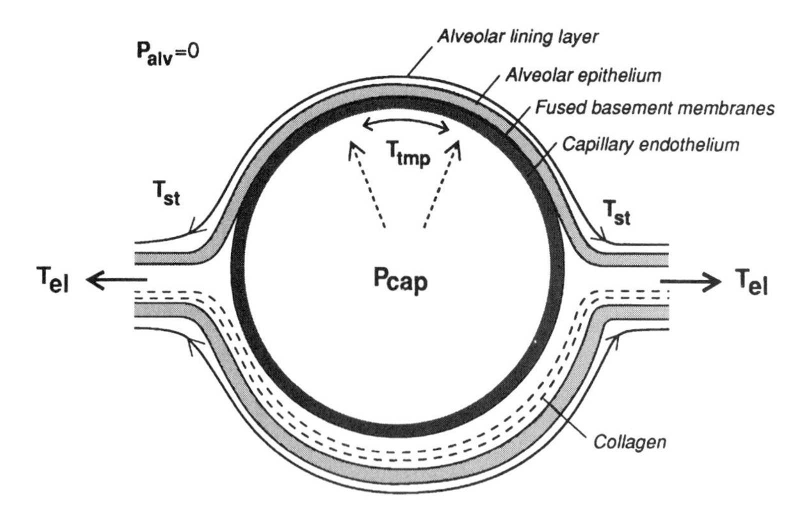

Figure 3 Three forces acting on the BGB. T_{tmp} is the circumferential or hoop tension caused by the capillary transmural pressure. T_{el} is the longitudinal tension in the alveolar wall elements associated with lung inflation; part of this is transmitted to the BGB. T_{st} is the surface tension of the alveolar lining layer; this apparently exerts an inward-acting force to support the capillary when the latter bulges into the alveolar space at high capillary transmural pressures. From (34).

that some of this longitudinal tension in the alveolar wall is transmitted to the walls of the capillaries. Certainly, as we shall see below, the frequency of the ultrastructural changes in the walls of the capillaries is greatly increased at high states of lung inflation (38).

The third force that can potentially act on the pulmonary capillaries is the surface tension of the alveolar lining layer (Figure 3). It is known that when the capillary transmural pressure is raised to high levels, the capillaries bulge prominently into the alveolar spaces (34, 39). This bulging means that the effect of surface tension in the alveolar lining layer is to support and strengthen the capillary walls, just as iron hoops strengthen a barrel of beer. The magnitude of the surface tension of the alveolar lining layer is dependent on lung volume. At low states of lung inflation, the surface tension may be as low as 1–10 $mN \cdot m^{-1}$. However, at high states of lung inflation, the surface tension rises to as much as 50 $mN \cdot m^{-1}$, and the equilibrium surface tension is believed to be about 20 $mN \cdot m^{-1}$ (40). Because, as shown above, the hoop tension in the wall of the capillary is calculated to be about 17 $mN \cdot m^{-1}$ under conditions of increased capillary transmural pressure, the surface tension of the alveolar lining layer, having a similar magnitude, would therefore provide substantial support. As shown below, studies in which the surface tension of the alveolar lining layer is essentially abolished by filling the lung with saline show that the pattern of ultrastructural changes is altered, confirming that surface tension does play a supportive role.

FAILURE OF THE BLOOD-GAS BARRIER

We have seen that in spite of its extreme thinness, the BGB is immensely strong. During exercise when the pulmonary capillary pressure rises, the wall stresses become extremely high, and indeed they approach the breaking stress of collagen. Under almost all physiological conditions, the BGB maintains its integrity; indeed, this is essential, because failure of the capillary wall would allow plasma or whole blood to enter the alveolar spaces, which would be catastrophic for gas exchange. As indicated below, the BGB seems to be just strong enough to withstand the maximal physiological stresses to which it is subjected.

However, under extreme physiological conditions, and in several pathophysiological conditions, disruptions of the BGB occur. This condition is referred to as stress failure because the structural alterations are the result of extremely high stresses. Stress failure is a general term used by structural engineers to refer to bending, distortion, or collapse of a structure such as a building or bridge when the loads are too great to be sustained.

About eight years ago, we began a study of the structural changes that occur in pulmonary capillaries when the transmural pressure is raised. Briefly, the chest of anesthetized rabbits was opened, cannulas were inserted into the pulmonary artery and left atrium, and the lung was perfused with the rabbit's own blood. After a short time, the blood was washed out with a saline/dextran mixture, and the lungs were fixed for electron microscopy with buffered glutaraldehyde, all perfusions being made at the same pressure. The compositions of the perfusates and fixatives were based on the work of Bachofen et al (41), who showed that these procedures accurately preserved the ultrastructure of the lung.

Preparations were made at perfusion pressures of either 20, 40, 60, or 80 cmH_2O. The pulmonary venous pressure was kept at 5 cmH_2O below the arterial pressure so that capillary pressure could be estimated within 2.5 cmH_2O. Since the alveolar pressure was kept at 5 cmH_2O, capillary transmural pressures were 12.5, 32.5, 52.5, and 72.5 $\pm$ 2.5 cmH_2O, corresponding to pressures of 9, 24, 39, and 53 mmHg.

An example of the ultrastructural changes in the capillary wall that occurred when the transmural pressure was raised to 39 mmHg is shown in Figure 4*a*. Note that there is disruption of the capillary endothelium, but its basement membrane is intact, as is the basement membrane of the alveolar epithelial layer and the epithelial layer itself. Close inspection of the two ends of the

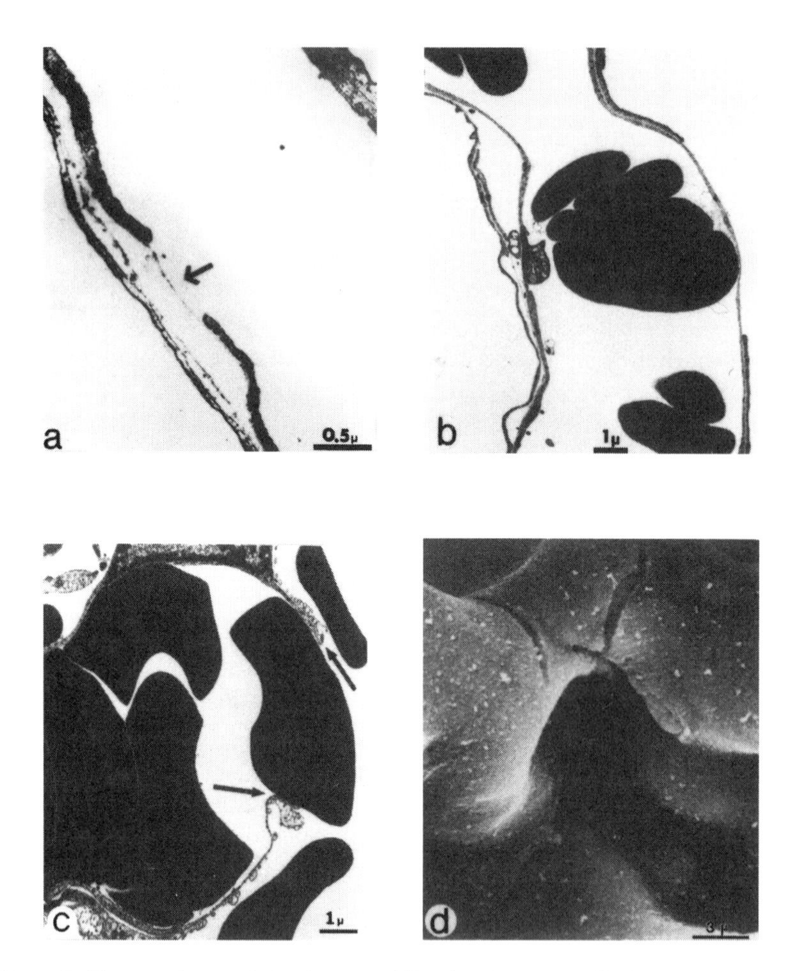

Figure 4 Electron micrograph showing stress failure in pulmonary capillaries. (*a*) Capillary endothelium is disrupted (*arrow*), but the alveolar epithelium and the two basement membranes are continuous. (*b*) Alveolar epithelial layer (*right*) and capillary endothelial layer (*left*) are disrupted. Note the platelet closely applied to the exposed endothelial basement membrane (*left*). (*c*) Disruption of all layers of the capillary wall, with a red cell apparently passing through the opening. (*d*) Scanning electron micrograph showing breaks in the alveolar epithelium. *a* and *b* are from (34); *c* is from (42); and *d* is from (43).

endothelial layer indicate that the structures are smoothly rounded, suggesting that the plasmalemmal layer is intact.

Figure 4*b* shows another example at the same capillary transmural pressure. On the right side, the alveolar epithelial layer is disrupted over a distance of several microns. The ends of the epithelial cells are clearly seen. Although not shown in this illustration, epithelial cell disruptions sometimes result in cellular fragments on the exposed basement membrane, but this appearance is not seen with disruption of capillary endothelial cells. On the left side of the capillary, the endothelial layer is disrupted and a platelet is closely applied to the exposed endothelial basement membrane. We also frequently see red blood cells in close proximity to the exposed basement membrane (42, Figures 3*a* and 3*d*). We know that the basement membrane is electrically charged and highly reactive and therefore tends to trap circulating cells. It is likely that the result is activation of platelets and leukocytes on the luminal side of the barrier, and macrophages on the alveolar gas side (see below).

Figure 4*c* shows disruption of all layers of the BGB at a capillary transmural pressure of 53 mmHg with a red cell apparently passing through the opening. This is a relatively uncommon appearance. In about half the instances, the capillary endothelial layer and/or the alveolar epithelial layer are disrupted but the basement membranes remain intact. This is what would be expected if the type IV collagen of the basement membranes is the strongest part of the BGB.

Figure 4*d* is a scanning electron micrograph (SEM) showing disruptions of the alveolar epithelial cells when the capillary pressure was 39 mmHg (43). SEM studies allow the shapes and positions of the breaks to be accurately determined. Over 90% of the breaks were elongated, with the remainder being roughly circular. Nearly 70% of the disruptions were oriented perpendicular to the capillary axis, which is not what would be expected if hoop stress were the only force operating. This suggests that the surface tension of the alveolar lining layer helps to protect the BGB against stress failure. The dimensions of the elongated breaks of the epithelium were approximately 4 μm (length) and 1 μm (width); the dimensions varied little with pressure, suggesting that once the disruption had occurred, the stresses were greatly relieved. It was striking that almost no breaks occurred at intercellular junctions, although many were seen within 1 μm of the junctions. This suggests that the junctions themselves have considerable mechanical strength, consistent with the highly organized intercellular junction of the type I alveolar epithelial cells. However, it may be that the consequent rigidity of these junctions makes the cell portion in the vicinity more vulnerable to mechanical failure.

We have no information on whether the endothelial disruptions occur at intercellular junctions. This might be expected because of previous claims that widening of the junctions between adjacent capillary endothelial cells can occur at high capillary pressures. For example, Schneeberger-Keeley & Karnowsky (44) reported that horseradish peroxidase could escape from the capillary lumen into the alveolar wall interstitium, apparently through interendothelial cell junctions, and Pietra et al (7) showed a similar finding with hemoglobin solution.

However, more recent studies clearly indicate that intracellular disruptions in endothelial cells can occur. Neal & Michel (45) raised the pressure in the microvessels of frog mesentery and made three-dimensional reconstructions of the electron micrographs. They found that over 80% of the breaks in the endothelium were transcellular rather than intercellular. Other features of this study fit closely with our own on rabbit pulmonary capillaries, which is remarkable given the very different environment of mesenteric capillaries. For example, Neal & Michel (45) found that frog mesenteric capillaries began to fail at a capillary pressure of about 30 cmH_2O, and as the pressure was raised, the frequency of breaks increased. This finding fits well with our own data, shown in Figure 5. Neal & Michel (45) also found that most of the breaks were reversible when the transmural pressure was decreased. Again, this fits well with our studies, as discussed below. The fact that approximately the same transmural

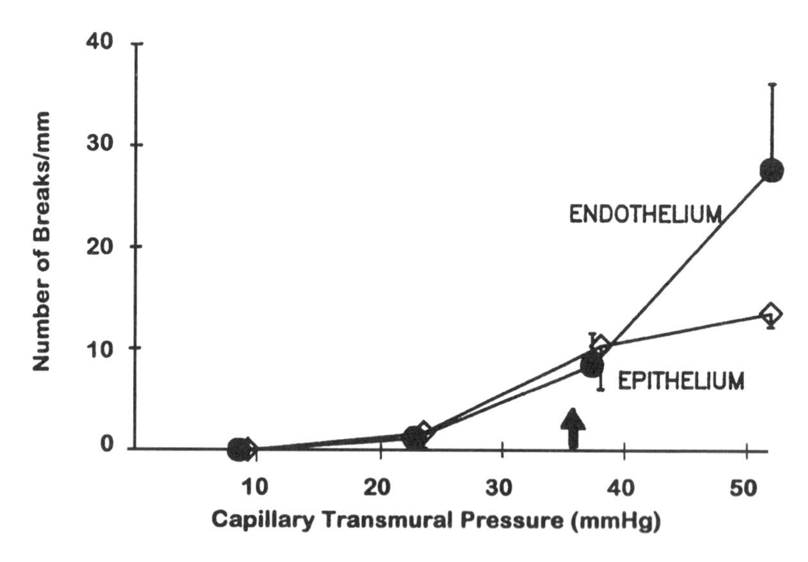

Figure 5 Number of breaks per millimeter of endothelial and epithelial boundary length plotted against capillary transmural pressure in rabbit preparation. Values are means ± SE. A few breaks occur at a pressure of about 24 mmHg, but these rapidly increase as the pressure is raised. The *arrow* indicates the pressure that is believed to exist in some capillaries of the human lung during maximal exercise (see text). Modified from (42).

pressures are necessary for stress failure in both preparations is consistent with the fact that the strength of the capillary is attributable to the basement membrane, and that the surrounding interstitial tissue in the mesentery, or the surrounding epithelial layer in the lung, confer little structural support.

Figure 5 shows that in the rabbit preparations, the first indications of stress failure were seen at a capillary transmural pressure of 24 mmHg. However, the number of breaks was much increased at a transmural pressure of 39 mmHg, and the frequency was even greater at 53 mmHg. The fact that some disruptions were seen at a capillary transmural pressure as low as 24 mmHg is striking in view of the evidence presented above that some capillaries of the human lung during severe exercise have a transmural pressure as high as 36 mmHg. Of course, we cannot assume that stress failure occurs at the same pressures in rabbit and human lung and as shown below, we know that there are species differences in the strength of pulmonary capillaries. Nevertheless, the fact that substantial ultrastructural changes occur in rabbit pulmonary capillaries at pressures that normally occur in human pulmonary capillaries during heavy exercise suggests that the capillaries are much more vulnerable than previously believed (see below).

An interesting finding in our studies is that most of the disruptions are rapidly reversible when the capillary transmural pressure is reduced. Using the rabbit preparation, Elliott et al (22) raised the capillary transmural pressure to 52.5 cmH_2O for 1 minute of blood perfusion and then reduced it to 12.5 cmH_2O for 3 minutes of saline/dextran perfusion followed by intravascular fixation at the same pressure. The results showed that the frequency of both endothelial and epithelial disruptions, and also the total fractional area of the breaks, were rapidly reduced when the pressure was lowered. For example, the number of endothelial breaks per millimeter decreased from 7.1 ± 2.1 to 2.4 ± 0.7, and the number of epithelial breaks per millimeter fell from 11.4 ± 3.7 to 3.4 ± 0.7. In other words, about 70% of both the endothelial and epithelial breaks closed within a few minutes. The study also showed that the breaks that closed were those that were initially small and also were associated with an intact basement membrane.

These results have implications for the micromechanics of stress failure (see below). They are also consistent with the observation that patients with high-altitude pulmonary edema, where we have good evidence that stress failure of pulmonary capillaries is the mechanism, typically recover very rapidly when brought to lower altitude, which reduces the pulmonary vascular pressures.

An intriguing question is what are the micromechanical events that give rise to the ultrastructural changes shown in Figure 4 and that can also explain the remarkably rapid reversibility of the disruptions. Electron micrographs such as that shown in Figure 4*a* suggest that the cells (in this case, endothelial cells) can move along their basement membrane when exposed to large tensile forces. Little is known about the rapidity with which attachments between the overlying cells and the basement membrane can break and make, but it is certainly accepted that cells migrate along basement membranes during development. Also, it is known that some interactions between cells can cycle on and off at very rapid rates. An example is the attachments between leukocytes and capillary endothelial cells that allow leukocytes to roll along an endothelial surface. Calculations show that the points of attachment between the leukocytes and the underlying endothelial cells must break and make many times a second. Therefore, it is not inconceivable that the attachments formed by integrins and other molecules between the overlying endothelial or epithelial cells and the basement membranes are able to break and make rapidly.

One possible mechanism for the patterns of cell disruption was noted in connection with Figure 1 and is shown in Figure 6. Because type IV collagen has bending sites, it seems possible that a meshwork of these molecules could elongate in the direction of applied tension, e.g. the hoop tension caused by a high capillary transmural pressure. This could result in elongation of the underlying basement membrane, but because the overlying cells, either endothelial or epithelial, would not be able to stretch in the same way, they would develop intracellular disruptions (Figure 6*b*). When the capillary transmural pressure is subsequently reduced, and therefore the hoop tension is relieved, the type IV co llagen meshwork would reassume its original configuration, and most of the disrupted cells would reunite.

Another question is, How does the cell wall reconstruct after an intracellular disruption without allowing the cellular contents to be spilled out? Presumably, the mechanism is the same one that allows the bilipid layer to reassume its

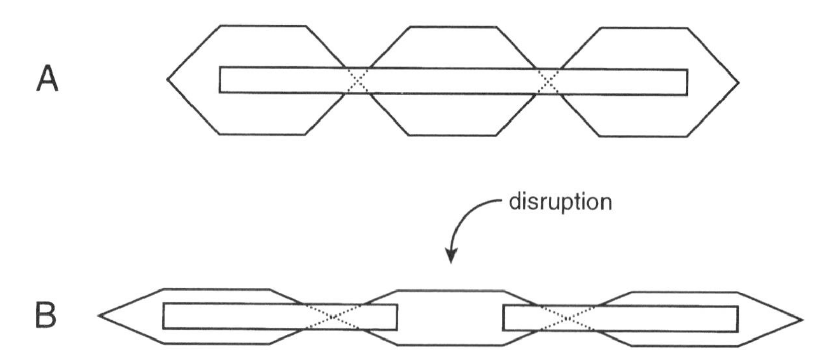

Figure 6 Diagram to indicate how distortion of the type IV collagen matrix (Figure 1) could cause disruptions in the capillary endothelial and alveolar epithelial layers. *A* shows the situation at a low capillary transmural pressure, and *B* at high pressure when the matrix is stretched.

usual configuration after the cell surface has been disrupted by an emerging pinocytotic vesicle. Bilipid layers have an intrinsic stability and tendency to reunite. As far as losing intracellular contents during disruption is concerned, it should be remembered that the cell is highly compartmentalized by the cytoskeleton and other organelles, and these presumably keep the intracellular contents intact while the bilipid layers rapidly reform.

In the discussion of the forces acting on the pulmonary capillary shown in Figure 3, it was pointed out that the surface tension of the alveolar lining layer would be expected to confer a protective effect on capillaries if they bulged into the alveolar spaces at high capillary transmural pressure, as demonstrated by Glazier et al (39). To explore this, Namba et al (46) abolished the gas-liquid surface tension of the alveoli by filling rabbit lungs with normal saline. The capillaries were then exposed to transmural pressures of 32.5 or 52.5 cmH_2O, and the lung fixed in the usual way. It was found that the frequency of breaks in the capillary endothelium was not significantly different between air and saline filling. However, after saline filling, a larger number of breaks were seen in the inner boundary of the epithelium. The results suggested that abolishing the surface tension of the alveolar lining layer removes support from parts of the BGB when the capillaries are exposed to high transmural pressures, but that not all portions of the barrier are subjected to the same forces.

Finally, a study was made of the pressures required to cause stress failure of pulmonary capillaries in different species (8, 47, 48). It was found that the capillaries were stronger in dog than in rabbit and in horse than in dog. This ordering corresponded to differences in capillary radius and thickness of the BGB as expected from the Laplace relationship.

DILEMMA OF THE BLOOD-GAS BARRIER

We have seen that the capillary transmural pressures in the human lung during severe exercise are high enough to cause ultrastructural changes in the pulmonary capillaries of rabbit, and also that the calculated wall stress of pulmonary capillaries under these conditions approaches the ultimate tensile strength of collagen. It is natural to ask why evolutionary processes have resulted in such a critical structure as the BGB being so close to mechanical failure during heavy exercise.

The answer is that the BGB has to satisfy two conflicting requirements. On the one hand, it has to be extremely thin for efficient gas exchange by diffusion. As indicated above, half of the gas-exchanging alveolar surface of the human lung has a thickness of 0.2–0.3 μm (5), and morphometric studies of rabbit, dog, and horse lung also show that all of these have some areas where the BGB is only about 0.2 μm thick (8). The importance of having the BGB so thin is emphasized by studies showing that at very high oxygen uptakes, the normal lung may exhibit diffusion limitation for oxygen. In other words, the diffusion rate through the BGB is not sufficiently fast for the blood to be fully oxygenated during its passage through the pulmonary capillary, and as a result, the PO_2 of end-capillary blood is below that of alveolar gas. This situation has been documented in some human athletes during heavy exercise (29, 49). Diffusion limitation is even more dramatic in the extremely aerobic racehorse, which develops marked arterial hypoxemia during galloping partly as a result of diffusion limitation (50). Thus in these situations, there would be a clear advantage in having a thinner BGB, and presumably there is continuous evolutionary pressure to keep the barrier as thin as possible.

At the same time, however, the BGB must be kept strong enough to prevent mechanical failure. As we shall see in the next section, failure of the barrier does occur in humans when the capillary wall stress is raised to abnormally high levels, and even some elite athletes at very high levels of exercise apparently change the permeability or integrity of the BGB. The most remarkable example of failure of the BGB under physiological conditions is seen in Thoroughbred racehorses, which all, when in training, break their pulmonary capillaries and bleed into their alveolar spaces.

Thus the BGB faces a dilemma in that it has to be extremely thin for gas exchange but just strong enough to maintain its integrity when the capillary pressure rises maximally during exercise. This means that the capillaries are the most vulnerable vessels in the pulmonary circulation. We believe that it also means that the structure of the BGB is being continually regulated in response to mechanical stresses.

PHYSIOLOGICAL CONDITIONS CAUSING STRESS FAILURE

The most dramatic example of stress failure of the BGB under physiological conditions is seen in Thoroughbred racehorses. There is evidence that all race-horses in training bleed into their lungs. For example, Whitwell & Greet (51) showed that tracheal washings from all thoroughbreds in training contained hemosiderin-laden macrophages.

We studied the ultrastructural appearances of Thoroughbred lungs after animals with known exercise-induced pulmonary hemorrhage (EIPH) had galloped on a treadmill at top speed (52). There was clear evidence of rupture of pulmonary capillaries including disruptions of capillary endothelial and alveolar epithelial layers, extensive collections of red blood cells in the alveolar wall interstitium, proteinaceous fluid and red blood cells in the alveolar spaces, interstitial edema, and fluid-filled protrusions of the endothelium into the capillary lumen. The appearances were consistent with the ultrastructural changes that we have previously seen in rabbit lungs at high capillary transmural pressures (Figure 4).

The reason why these animals break their capillaries is that they develop enormously high pulmonary vascular pressures during galloping. Left atrial pressures measured directly with an indwelling catheter can be as high as 70 mmHg, and the mean pulmonary artery pressure can be 120 mmHg (53–55). Therefore, the pulmonary capillary pressures approach 100 mmHg! The extraordinarily high left ventricular filling pressures are apparently necessary for the enormous cardiac outputs that allow the extraordinary aerobic performance of these animals, which have been selectively bred for more than 400 years. Thoroughbreds have enormous maximal oxygen consumptions of up to 180 $ml \cdot min^{-1} \cdot kg^{-1}$ (compare the elite human athlete at 60–80 $ml \cdot min^{-1} \cdot kg^{-1}$). The cardiac outputs of Thoroughbreds are as high as 750 $ml \cdot min^{-1} \cdot kg^{-1}$ compared with 500 $ml \cdot min^{-1} \cdot kg^{-1}$ in elite humans.

These remarkable findings in Thoroughbred racehorses after galloping prompt the question of whether elite human athletes ever have ultrastructural changes in their BGB during maximal exercise. There is now evidence that this is the case. Hopkins et al (56) studied 6 elite cyclists who had a history suggestive of lung bleeding. They performed a 4-km uphill sprint at maximal effort, which was sufficient to give a mean heart rate of 177 $beats \cdot min^{-1}$. Within an hour of finishing the exercise, the volunteers underwent bronchoalveolar lavage (BAL) using normal saline. The controls were normal sedentary subjects who did not exercise prior to BAL.

The athletes had higher ($p < 0.05$) concentrations of red blood cells (0.51×10^5 versus $0.01 \times 10^5 \cdot ml^{-1}$), total protein (128.0 versus 94.1 $\mu g \cdot ml^{-1}$), albumin (65.6 versus 53.0 $\mu g \cdot ml^{-1}$), and leukotriene B4 (LTB_4) (243 versus 0 $pg \cdot ml^{-1}$) in BAL fluid than control subjects. These results show that brief intense exercise in some athletes alters blood-gas barrier function, resulting in the higher concentrations of red blood cells and protein in BAL fluid.

The lack of activation of proinflammatory pathways (except LTB_4) in the air spaces was taken as support that the mechanism for altered BGB function was mechanical stress. The mechanism responsible for the increase in LTB_4 is not certain, but one possibility is activation of alveolar macrophages by the exposed alveolar basement membrane resulting from disruption of alveolar epithelial cells (compare Figure 4*b*). Alveolar macrophages are known to be rich in LTB_4. High concentrations of LTB_4 are also seen in BAL fluid removed from the rabbit lung preparation when the capillary transmural pressure is increased (57). For example, when the capillary transmural pressure was increased from

12.5 cmH_2O to 52.5 cmH_2O, the amount of LTB_4 in the BAL fluid increased from 6.0 to 49.5 μg ($p < 0.001$).

The hypothesis is that the structure of the BGB has evolved, or is regulated, so that only the absolute maximal wall stresses in pulmonary capillaries will result in ultrastructural changes. To test this, Hopkins et al (58) carried out a further study on a similar group of six elite cyclists who exercised at 77% of their $\dot{V}O_{2\,max}$ for one hour, and then underwent BAL. The controls were eight normal nonathletes who did not exercise before BAL. In contrast with the previous study described above, the concentrations of red blood cells, total protein, and LTB_4 in the BAL fluid of the exercising athletes were not increased compared with the control subjects. However, higher concentrations of surfactant apoprotein A and a higher surfactant apoprotein A-phospholipid ratio were observed in the athletes performing prolonged exercise, compared with both the controls and the athletes from the previous study. These results suggest that, in elite athletes, the integrity of the BGB is altered only at extreme levels of exercise.

PATHOPHYSIOLOGICAL CONDITIONS CAUSING STRESS FAILURE

There is now strong evidence that stress failure of pulmonary capillaries occurs in a number of pathophysiological settings including neurogenic pulmonary edema, high-altitude pulmonary edema, cardiovascular diseases that raise capillary pressure such as severe left ventricular failure and mitral stenosis, and diseases such as Goodpasture's syndrome where there are alterations in the type IV collagen. These conditions have been discussed elsewhere (59, 60), and limitations of space preclude including them here. However, one pathophysiological situation that should be mentioned is overinflation of the lung.

It has been known for many years that inflation of the lung to high volumes increases the permeability of pulmonary capillaries (61–66). This is a particularly serious practical problem in the intensive care unit when high levels of positive end-expiratory pressure (PEEP) are necessary to maintain viable levels of arterial PO_2. The mechanism for the increased permeability has been unclear, although Dreyfuss et al (62) and John et al (67) have documented ultrastructural evidence of damaged alveolar epithelium at high lung volumes.

Figure 3 implies that high states of lung inflation may exaggerate stress failure in pulmonary capillaries by adding a component from the longitudinal tension in the alveolar wall to the hoop tension caused by the capillary transmural pressure. Indeed, if the tension in the alveolar wall that was transmitted to the capillary wall was sufficiently high, ultrastructural changes might occur in the BGB irrespective of the level of the transmural pressure of the capillary. Studies were carried out in our rabbit preparation by increasing lung volume by raising the transpulmonary pressure from 5 to 20 cmH_2O (38). Capillary transmural pressure was maintained constant at 32.5 or 52.5 cmH_2O. We chose a transmural pressure of 32.5 cmH_2O for some of the measurements because, as Figure 5 shows, this is just sufficient to cause a few endothelial and epithelial disruptions at normal lung volumes.

Figure 7 shows that increasing lung volume from normal low values to high values resulted in a striking increase in the number of breaks per millimeter cell boundary layer length for both endothelium and epithelium at a fixed capillary transmural pressure of 32.5 cmH_2O. Consistent with Figure 5, there were few breaks in the endothelium or epithelium at a normal lung volume at this relatively

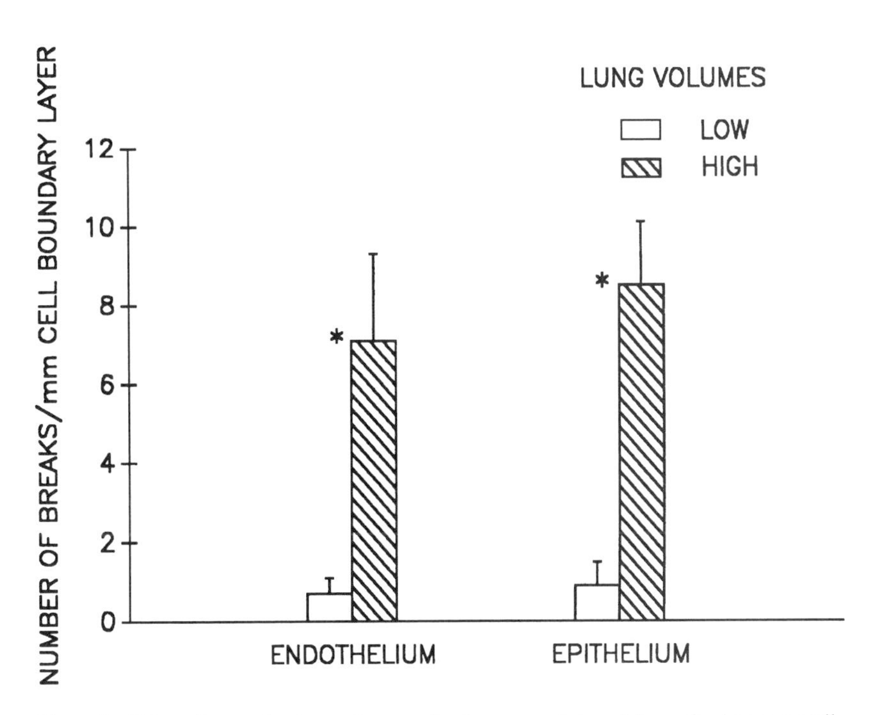

Figure 7 Effect of increasing lung volume on the frequency of stress failure of pulmonary capillaries. The transpulmonary pressure was 5 cmH_2O at the low (normal) volume and 20 cmH_2O at the high lung volume. In both instances, the capillary transmural pressure was maintained at 32.5 cmH_2O. Note the large increase in the frequency of stress failure when lung volume was increased. Modified from (38).

low capillary transmural pressure. However, when the transpulmonary pressure was increased to 20 cmH_2O, thus increasing lung volume close to total lung capacity, there was a striking increase in the number of breaks. Specifically, the number of endothelial breaks per millimeter cell lining increased from 0.7 ± 0.4 at the normal lung volume to 7.1 ± 2.2 at the high lung volume. The corresponding values for epithelium were 0.9 ± 0.6 and 8.5 ± 1.6 ($p < 0.05$). At the higher capillary transmural pressure of 52.5 cmH_2O, the same pattern of increases was seen, although here all the frequencies were higher.

An additional finding was that at high lung volumes the disruptions tended to be narrower, and fewer were oriented perpendicular to the axis of the pulmonary capillaries compared with the results at low lung volumes. A possible explanation is that at high states of lung inflation, the wall stress of the capillaries is increased in all directions because of uniform stretching of the alveolar wall, and therefore the support offered by the surface tension of the alveolar lining layer does not dominate, as it may do at low lung volumes.

REMODELING OF PULMONARY CAPILLARIES

There is extensive literature on pulmonary vascular remodeling, and the cellular and molecular mechanisms were recently reviewed (68). Only a brief summary of some of the work on pulmonary vascular remodeling is given here. Meyrick & Reid (69, 70) made rats hypoxic by exposing them to half the normal barometric pressure for 1 to 52 days, thus increasing pulmonary artery pressure through hypoxic pulmonary vasoconstriction. After 2 days they saw the appearance of new smooth muscle in small pulmonary arteries, and after 10 days there was a doubling of the thickness of the media and adventitia of the main pulmonary artery due to increased smooth muscle, collagen, elastin, and also edema. There was some recovery after 3 days of normoxia, and after 14–28 days, the thickness of the media was normal. However, some increase in collagen persisted up to 70 days.

The molecular biology of the responses of the larger pulmonary blood vessels to increased wall stress has been studied by several groups. Mecham et al (71) looked at the response of the pulmonary arteries of newborn calves to alveolar hypoxia. There was a two- to fourfold increase in elastin production in pulmonary arterial wall and medial smooth muscle cells. This was accompanied by a corresponding increase in elastin messenger RNA, consistent with regulation at the transcriptional level. Poiani et al (72) exposed rats to 10% oxygen for 1 to 14 days. Within 3 days of exposure, there was increased synthesis of collagen and elastin and an increase in mRNA for pro-α1(I) collagen.

A particularly interesting study was carried out by Tozzi et al (73), who placed rat main pulmonary artery rings in Krebs-Ringer bicarbonate and applied mechanical tension equivalent to a transmural pressure of 50 mmHg for 4 hours. They found increases in collagen synthesis (incorporation of ^{14}C proline), elastin synthesis (incorporation of ^{14}C valine), mRNA for pro-α1(I) collagen, and mRNA for proto-oncogene v-sis. The last may implicate platelet-derived growth factor (PDGF) or transforming growth factor-β (TGF-β) as the mediator. Tozzi et al (73) were also able to show that these changes were endothelium-dependent because they did not occur when the endothelium was removed from the arterial rings.

These changes are presumably the result of the increased transmural pressure, which raises hoop or circumferential stress. Another type of stress acting on endothelial cells is shear stress caused by high shear rates in the blood. There have been many studies of the molecular responses of endothelial cells to increased shear, partly because of the observation that the localization of atheroma appears to be related to the magnitude of the shear stress [for reviews, see Davies & Tripathi (74) and Nollert et al (75)]. A transcriptional shear stress–responsive element has been identified in the promoter region of several genes including PDGF-B chain and TGF-β1 by Resnick et al (76).

The mechanisms through which physical forces are converted to biological signals (mechanotransduction) are poorly understood but have been reviewed, e.g. by Watson (77). Putative mechanisms include distortion of the cell membrane with consequent stimulation of ion channels, and distortion of the cytoskeleton affecting the nucleus and thus alterations in transcription.

In contrast to the extensive literature on vascular remodeling in pulmonary arteries and veins, remodeling of pulmonary capillaries has been almost completely ignored. We know that it occurs because, as Figure 8 shows, marked thickening of the basement membranes of the capillary endothelial cells and alveolar epithelial cells occurs in the pulmonary capillaries of patients with mitral stenosis (18, 78, 79) and pulmonary veno-occlusive disease (80). In both conditions, capillary pressure is raised over long periods, and it is reasonable to assume that the thickening occurs in response to increased capillary wall stress. Careful inspection of electron micrographs of pulmonary capillaries in patients with mitral stenosis (e.g. Figure 8) suggests that most of the thickening of the basement membrane is associated with the capillary endothelial cell rather than the alveolar epithelial cell, implicating the endothelial cell as the main source. This might be relevant to the results of Tozzi et al (73) alluded to above, who showed that some aspects of vascular remodeling in pulmonary artery were endothelium dependent. Note, however, that removal of the endothelium made no difference to the mRNA levels for type I procollagen.

The fact that the increased basement membrane apparently comes from the endothelial cell does not necessarily mean that this cell is the primary sensor of the increased capillary transmural pressure through increased wall stress, i.e.

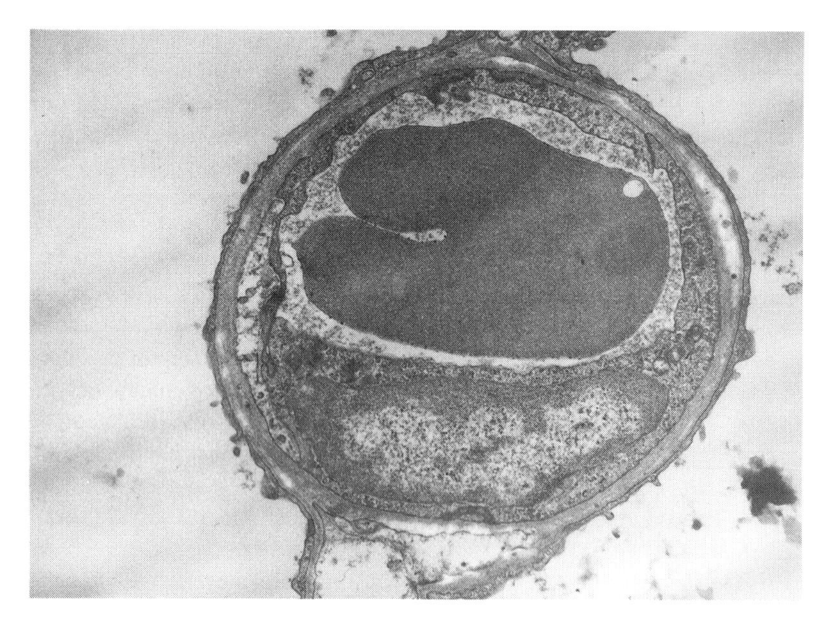

Figure 8 Electron micrograph of a pulmonary capillary from a young patient with mitral stenosis. Note thickening of the basement membranes of the capillary endothelial and alveolar epithelial cells, particularly the former. Courtesy of SG Haworth.

that the endothelial cell itself is the transducer. It is possible that some other cell in the parenchyma, e.g. an epithelial cell or fibroblast, responds to the increased tension and sends a signal to the endothelial cell. It is known that cultures of type II alveolar epithelial cells are very responsive to stretch, which causes a transient increase in cytosolic ionic calcium followed by a sustained stimulation of surfactant secretion for 15 to 30 minutes (81). It is also known that cultures of pulmonary fibroblasts respond to stretch with an increase in proliferation through an autocrine growth factor mechanism (82) involving PDGF-B (83).

Our hypothesis has been that pulmonary capillaries respond to increased wall stress by increasing the amount of ECM in the capillary wall. To test this, experiments were designed where capillary wall stress was raised and gene expression for ECM proteins—and the concentrations of the proteins themselves—were measured in peripheral lung tissue, which is primarily composed of lung parenchyma. There are two obvious ways of increasing capillary wall stress: (*a*) increase capillary transmural pressure and (*b*) greatly increase lung volume. We know that the latter method increases capillary wall stress because, as indicated above, it greatly increases the frequency of endothelial and epithelial disruptions (Figure 7).

The first method, that is increasing capillary transmural pressure, is complicated by the fact that it disturbs the Starling equilibrium and thus tends to cause severe edema. Therefore, our first experimental design was to greatly increase lung volume in one lung of anesthetized open-chest rabbits while ventilating the other lung at a normal volume (84). Additional control animals had both lungs at normal states of lung inflation. These experiments showed that high states of lung inflation over 4 hours resulted in increased gene expression for $\alpha 1$(III) and $\alpha 2$(IV) procollagens, fibronectin, basic fibroblast growth factor (bFGF), and transforming growth factor $\beta 1$ (TGF-$\beta 1$). By contrast, mRNA levels for $\alpha 1$(I) procollagen and vascular endothelial growth factor (VEGF) were unchanged (84).

An unexpected finding was that the changes in mRNA listed above were identical in both the overinflated lung (9 cmH_2O PEEP) and normally inflated lung (1 cmH_2O PEEP) of the rabbit preparation, in which one lung was overinflated and the other was normally inflated. This observation suggests that a generalized organ-specific response occurred after the localized (unilateral) application of mechanical force. The mechanism for this was not identified, but one possibility is that information was transferred via the circulation from the overinflated lung to the normally inflated lung. A precedent for this type of behavior comes from the transplantation studies of Hislop et al (85). These investigators transplanted an immature left lung into an adult rat and examined the morphological changes in both lungs. Normally, compensatory growth in the adult rat lung after pneumonectomy occurs through an increase in size of alveoli, rather than number (86). However, Hislop et al (85) found that the presence of the transplanted immature lung caused the contralateral adult lung to revert to an immature pattern of compensatory growth in that growth occurred through an increase in number rather than size of alveoli. Because all connections to the left lung were severed during transplantation, the investigators concluded that the immature lung must release blood-borne factors that influence growth in the mature lung.

In our second set of experiments, capillary transmural pressure was increased by raising the venous pressure in isolated perfused rat lungs (87). To avoid the occurrence of pulmonary edema, the venous pressure was increased cyclically to 28 cmH_2O for 15 s every minute for 4 h. This allowed fluid to leave the pulmonary capillaries when the venous pressure was raised, but to return to the capillary lumen when the pressure fell. Controls were similar lungs perfused at low pressure, and also unperfused lungs. This study showed significant increases in gene expression for $\alpha 1$(I) and $\alpha 1$(III) procollagens, fibronectin, laminin, and TGF-$\beta 1$ (87).

The two studies showed some differences, even though both were designed to increase capillary wall stress. For example, in the first study there were significant increases in mRNA for $\alpha 2$(IV) procollagen but not $\alpha 1$(I) procollagen, whereas in the second study there were significant increases in mRNA for $\alpha 1$(I) but not $\alpha 2$(IV) procollagen. This difference in results might be explained by the fact that both experimental techniques increase stress in structures other than capillary walls. For example, at high states of lung inflation, not only are stresses increased throughout the lung parenchyma, but also the larger blood vessels and airways are exposed to increased radial traction from the surrounding parenchyma. Again, when pulmonary venous pressure is raised as in the second experimental technique, the transmural pressures of the pulmonary veins and arteries are also increased. It may be that some of the increase in gene expression, e.g. for $\alpha 1$(I) procollagen, reflects the responses of larger blood vessels and airways rather than the structures in the alveolar walls themselves. Berg et al (84) made attempts to reduce this artifact as much as possible by collecting tissue from only the outer 3 or 4 millimeter of the lungs. However, although this tissue is chiefly composed of alveoli, it also contains some larger blood vessels and airways.

There is a third potential way of increasing capillary wall stress: alveolar hypoxia. This increases pulmonary artery pressure in rats within minutes as a result of pulmonary vasoconstriction, and if the vasoconstriction is uneven, some capillaries will be exposed to increased transmural pressures. Indeed, there is evidence that this is the mechanism for high-altitude pulmonary edema (88, 89). To investigate this, Madison strain Sprague-Dawley rats were exposed to 10% oxygen for 6 h or 3 days (short-term group) and 3 or 10 days (long-term group). Peripheral lung tissue was then collected, and mRNA levels for ECM proteins and growth factors were measured, as well as collagen content by hydroxyproline (90). It was found that levels of mRNA for $\alpha 2$(IV) procollagen increased 6-fold after 6 hours of hypoxia, and 7-fold after 3 days. The levels then decreased after 10 days of exposure. mRNA levels for PDGF-B doubled after 6 hours of hypoxia but returned to control values after 3 days. mRNA levels for $\alpha 1$(I) and $\alpha 1$(III) procollagens and fibronectin were increased after 3 days of hypoxia (7- to 12-fold, 1.6- to 8-fold, and 12-fold, respectively), then decreased toward control values after 10 days. By contrast, levels of VEGF mRNA and collagen content did not change. These results indicate that alveolar hypoxia causes vascular remodeling in peripheral lung tissue and are consistent with capillary remodeling in response to increased wall stress.

In summary, the pulmonary BGB has a dilemma that has only recently been fully appreciated. The conflicting requirements of being extremely thin for efficient gas exchange, but also being immensely strong to withstand the very high wall stresses that develop when capillary transmural pressure rises on exercise, mean that the BGB treads a knife edge. On the one hand, it cannot afford to be too thick because this would interfere with the gas exchange process of the lung, which is its primary function. On the other hand, the BGB cannot be excessively thin for diffusion because this will inevitably lead to weakness and therefore stress failure of pulmonary capillaries, leakage of fluid and blood into the alveolar spaces, and impairment of gas exchange. How the BGB maintains its extreme thinness, but just enough strength to withstand the maximal stresses to which it is exposed under physiological conditions, remains a central issue for lung biologists.

Literature Cited

1. Malpighi M. 1661. *Duae epistolae de pulmonibus*, Florence, Italy
2. Wilson LG. 1960. The transformation of ancient concepts of respiration in the Seventeenth Century. *ISIS* 51:161–72
3. Policard A. 1929. Les nouvelles idées sur la disposition de la surface respiratoire pulmonaire. *Presse Med.* 37:1293–95
4. Low FN. 1952. Electron microscopy of the rat lung. *Anat. Rec.* 113:437–43
5. Gehr P, Bachofen M, Weibel ER. 1978. The normal human lung: ultrastructure and morphometric estimation of diffusion capacity. *Respir. Physiol.* 32:121–40
6. Weibel ER. 1984. *The Pathway for Oxygen.* Cambridge, MA: Harvard Univ. Press
7. Pietra GG, Szidon JP, Leventhal MM, Fishman AP. 1969. Hemoglobin as a tracer in hemodynamic pulmonary edema. *Science* 166:1643–46
8. Birks EK, Mathieu-Costello O, Fu Z, Tyler WS, West JB. 1994. Comparative aspects of the strength of pulmonary capillaries in rabbit, dog and horse. *Respir. Physiol.* 97: 235–46
9. Crouch EC, Martin GR, Brody JS, Laurie GW. 1997. Basement membranes. In *The Lung: Scientific Foundations*, ed. RG Crystal, JB West, ER Weibel, PJ Barnes, pp. 769–91. Philadelphia, PA: Lippincott-Raven. 791 pp.
10. Timpl R, Wiedemann H, van Delden V, Furthmayr H, Kühn K. 1981. A network model for the organization of type IV collagen molecules in basement membranes. *Eur. J. Biochem.* 120:203–11
11. Yurchenco PD, Schittny JC. 1990. Molecular architecture of basement membranes. *FASEB J.* 4:1577–90
12. Kern A, Eble J, Golbik R, Kühn K. 1993. Interaction of type IV collagen with the isolated integrins $\alpha 1\beta 1$ and $\alpha 2\beta 1$. *Eur. J. Biochem.* 215:151–59
13. Fisher RF, Wakely J. 1976. The elastic constants and ultrastructural organization of a basement membrane (lens capsule). *Proc. R. Soc. London Ser. B* 193:335–58
14. Stromberg DD, Wiederhielm CA. 1969. Viscoelastic description of a collagenous tissue in simple elongation. *J. Appl. Physiol.* 26:857–62
15. Welling LW, Grantham JJ. 1972. Physical properties of isolated perfused renal tubules and tubular basement membranes. *J. Clin. Invest.* 51:1063–75
16. Swayne GT, Smaje LH, Bergel DH. 1989. Distensibility of single capillaries and venules in the rat and frog mesentery. *Int. J. Microcirc.: Clin. Exp.* 8:25–42
17. Williamson JR, Vogler NJ, Kilo C. 1971. Regional variations in the width of the basement membrane of muscle capillaries in man and giraffe. *Am. J. Pathol.* 63:359–70
18. Haworth SG, Hall SM, Patel M. 1988. Peripheral pulmonary vascular and airway abnormalities in adolescents with rheumatic mitral stenosis. *Int. J. Cardiol.* 18:405–16
19. Takami H, Burbelo PD, Fukuda K, Chang HS, Phillips SL, Yamada Y. 1994. Molecular organization and gene regulation of type IV collagen. *Contrib. Nephrol.* 107:36–46
20. Schwarz U, Schuppan D, Oberbaumer I, Glanville R, Deutzmann R, et al. 1986. Structure of mouse type IV collagen. Amino-acid sequence of the C-terminal 511-residue-long triple-helical segment of the alpha 2(IV) chain and its comparison with the alpha 1(IV) chain. *Eur. J. Biochem.* 157:49–56
21. Hofmann H, Voss T, Kuhn K, Engel J. 1984. Localization of flexible sites in thread-like molecules from electron micro-

graphs. Comparison of interstitial, basement membrane and intima collagens. *J. Mol. Biol.* 172:325–43
22. Elliott AR, Fu Z, Tsukimoto K, Prediletto R, Mathieu-Costello O, West JB. 1992. Short-term reversibility of ultrastructural changes in pulmonary capillaries caused by stress failure. *J. Appl. Physiol.* 73:1150–8
23. Vaccaro CA, Brody JS. 1981. Structural features of alveolar wall basement membrane in the adult rat lung. *J. Cell Biol.* 91: 427–37
24. Pfaff M, Timpl R, Brown JC. 1994. Binding of purified collagen receptors (a1b1, a2b1) and RGD-dependent integrins to laminins and laminin fragments. *Eur. J. Biochem.* 225:975–84
25. Chakravarti S, Horchar T, Jefferson B, Laurie GW, Hassell JR. 1995. Recombinant domain III of perlecan promotes cell attachment through its RGDS sequence. *J. Biol. Chem.* 270:404–9
26. Timpl R, Dziadek M, Fujiwara S, Nowack H, Wick G. 1983. Nidogen: a new self-aggregating basement membrane protein. *Eur. J. Biochem.* 137:455–65
27. Fishman AP. 1985. Pulmonary circulation. In *The Respiratory System*, Vol. 1, *Circulation and Nonrespiratory Functions*, ed. AP Fishman, p. 113. Bethesda, MD: Am. Physiol. Soc.
28. Guyton AC, Hall JE. 1996. *Textbook of Medical Physiology*, p. 495. Philadelphia: Saunders. 9th ed.
29. Wagner PD, Gale GE, Moon RE, Torre-Bueno JR, Stolp BW, Saltzman HA. 1986. Pulmonary gas exchange in humans exercising at sea level and simulated altitude. *J. Appl. Physiol.* 61:260–70
30. Groves BM, Reeves JT, Sutton JR, Wagner PD, Cymerman A, et al. 1987. Operation Everest II: elevated high-altitude pulmonary resistance unresponsive to oxygen. *J. Appl. Physiol.* 63:521–30
31. Ekelund LG, Holmgren A. 1967. Central hemodynamics during exercise. *Circ. Res.* 30:I33-43
32. Bhattacharya J, Nanjo S, Staub NC. 1982. Micropuncture measurement of lung microvascular pressure during 5-HT infusion. *J. Appl. Physiol.* 52:634–37
33. Younes M, Bshouty Z, Ali J. 1987. Longitudinal distribution of pulmonary vascular resistance with very high pulmonary blood flow. *J. Appl. Physiol.* 62:344–58
34. West JB, Tsukimoto K, Mathieu-Costello O, Prediletto R. 1991. Stress failure in pulmonary capillaries. *J. Appl. Physiol.* 70: 1731–42
35. Neergaard KV. 1929. Neue Auffassungen über einen Grundbegriff der Atemmechanik. Die Retraktionskraft der Lunge, abhängig von der Oberflächenspannung in den Alveolen. *Z.Ges. Exp. Med.* 66:373–94 (Engl. transl. *Translations in Respiratory Physiology*, ed. JB West. Stroudsburg, PA: Dowden, Hutchinson & Ross, 1975)
36. Gil J, Bachofen H, Gehr P, Weibel ER. 1979. Alveolar volume-surface area relation in air- and saline-filled lungs fixed by vascular perfusion. *J. Appl. Physiol.* 47: 990–1001
37. Bachofen H, Hildebrandt J, Bachofen M. 1970. Pressure-volume curves of air- and liquid-filled excised lungs—surface tension in situ. *J. Appl. Physiol.* 29:422–31
38. Fu Z, Costello ML, Tsukimoto K, Prediletto R, Elliott AR, et al. 1992. High lung volume increases stress failure in pulmonary capillaries. *J. Appl. Physiol.* 73: 123–33
39. Glazier JB, Hughes JM, Maloney JE, West JB. 1969. Measurements of capillary dimensions and blood volume in rapidly frozen lungs. *J. Appl. Physiol.* 26:65–76
40. Schürch S, Goerke J, Clements JA. 1978. Direct determination of volume- and time-dependence of alveolar surface tension in excised lungs. *Proc. Natl. Acad. Sci. USA* 75:3417–21
41. Bachofen H, Ammann A, Wangensteen D, Weibel ER. 1982. Perfusion fixation of lungs for structure-function analysis: credits and limitations. *J. Appl. Physiol.* 53: 528–33
42. Tsukimoto K, Mathieu-Costello O, Prediletto R, Elliott AR, West JB. 1991. Ultrastructural appearances of pulmonary capillaries at high transmural pressures. *J. Appl. Physiol.* 71:573–82
43. Costello ML, Mathieu-Costello O, West JB. 1992. Stress failure of alveolar epithelial cells studied by scanning electron microscopy. *Am. Rev. Respir. Dis.* 145:1446–55
44. Schneeberger-Keeley EE, Karnowsky MJ. 1968. The ultrastructural basis of alveolar-capillary membrane permeability to peroxidase used as a tracer. *J. Cell Biol.* 37:781–93
45. Neal CR, Michel CC. 1996. Openings in frog microvascular endothelium induced by high intravascular pressures. *J. Physiol.* 492:39–52
46. Namba Y, Kurdak SS, Fu Z, Mathieu-Costello O, West JB. 1995. Effect of reducing alveolar surface tension on stress failure in pulmonary capillaries. *J. Appl. Physiol.* 79:2114–21
47. Mathieu-Costello O, Willford DC, Fu Z, Garden RM, West JB. 1995. Pulmonary capillaries are more resistant to stress

failure in dog than in rabbit. *J. Appl. Physiol.* 79:908–17
48. Birks EK, Mathieu-Costello O, Fu Z, Tyler WS, West JB. 1997. Very high pressures are required to cause stress failure of pulmonary capillaries in Thoroughbred racehorses. *J. Appl. Physiol.* 82:1584–92
49. Dempsey JA, Hanson PG, Henderson KS. 1984. Exercise-induced alveolar hypoxemia in healthy human subjects at sea-level. *J. Physiol.* 355:161–75
50. Wagner PD, Gillespie JR, Landgren GL, Fedde MR, Jones BW, et al. 1989. Mechanism of exercise-induced hypoxemia in horses. *J. Appl. Physiol.* 66:1227–33
51. Whitwell KE, Greet TR. 1984. Collection and evaluation of tracheobronchial washes in the horse. *Equine Vet. J.* 16:499–508
52. West JB, Mathieu-Costello O, Jones JH, Birks EK, Logemann RB, et al. 1993. Stress failure of pulmonary capillaries in racehorses with exercise-induced pulmonary hemorrhage. *J. Appl. Physiol.* 75: 1097–109
53. Erickson BK, Erickson HH, Coffman JR. 1990. Pulmonary artery, aortic and oesophageal pressure changes during high intensity treadmill exercise in the horse: a possible relation to exercise-induced pulmonary haemorrhage. *Equine Vet. J. Suppl.* 9:47–52
54. Jones JH, Smith BL, Birks EK, Pascoe JR, Hughes TR. 1992. Left atrial and pulmonary arterial pressures in exercising horses. *FASEB J.* 6:A2020 (Abstr.)
55. Manohar M. 1993. Pulmonary artery wedge pressure increases with high-intensity exercise in horses. *Am. J. Vet. Res.* 54: 142–46
56. Hopkins SR, Schoene RB, Martin TR, Henderson WR, Spragg RG, West JB. 1997. Intense exercise impairs the integrity of the pulmonary blood-gas barrier in elite athletes. *Am. J. Resp. Crit. Care Med.* 155: 1090–94
57. Tsukimoto K, Yoshimura N, Ichioka M, Tojo N, Miyazato I, et al. 1994. Protein, cell, and LTB_4 concentrations of lung edema fluid produced by high capillary pressures in rabbit. *J. Appl. Physiol.* 76:321–27
58. Hopkins SR, Schoene RB, Henderson WR, Spragg RG, West JB. 1998. Sustained submaximal exercise does not alter the integrity of the lung blood-gas barrier in elite athletes. *J. Appl. Physiol.* 84:1185–89
59. West JB, Breen EC, Mathieu-Costello O. 1998. Strength, failure, and remodeling of the pulmonary blood-gas barrier. In *Pulmonary Edema*, ed. EK Weir, JT Reeves. Armonk, NY: Futura
60. West JB, Mathieu-Costello O. 1995. Vulnerability of pulmonary capillaries in heart disease. *Circulation* 92:622–31
61. Carlton DP, Cummings JJ, Scheerer RG, Poulain FR, Bland RD. 1990. Lung overexpansion increases pulmonary microvascular protein permeability in young lambs. *J. Appl. Physiol.* 69:577–83
62. Dreyfuss D, Basset G, Soler P, Saumon G. 1985. Intermittent positive-pressure hyperventilation with high inflation pressures produces pulmonary microvascular injury in rats. *Am. Rev. Respir. Dis.* 132:880–84
63. Dreyfuss D, Saumon G. 1991. Lung overinflation. Physiologic and anatomic alterations leading to pulmonary edema. In *Adult Respiratory Distress Syndrome*, ed. WM Zapol, F Lemaire, pp. 433–49. New York: Marcel Dekker. 449 pp.
64. Egan EA, Nelson RM, Olver RE. 1976. Lung inflation and alveolar permeability to non-electrolytes in the adult sheep in vivo. *J. Physiol.* 260:409–24
65. Kolobow T, Moretti MP, Fumagalli R, Mascheroni D, Prato P, et al. 1987. Severe impairment in lung function induced by high peak airway pressure during mechanical ventilation. *Am. Rev. Respir. Dis.* 135:312–15
66. Parker JC, Townsley MI, Rippe B, Taylor AE, Thigpen J. 1984. Increased microvascular permeability in dog lungs due to high peak airway pressures. *J. Appl. Physiol.* 57:1809–16
67. John E, McDevitt M, Wilborn W, Cassady G. 1982. Ultrastructure of the lung after ventilation. *Br. J. Exp. Path.* 63:401–7
68. Stenmark KR, Mecham RP. 1997. Cellular and molecular mechanisms of pulmonary vascular remodeling. *Annu. Rev. Physiol.* 59:89–144
69. Meyrick B, Reid L. 1978. The effect of continued hypoxia on rat pulmonary arterial circulation. An ultrastructural study. *Lab. Invest.* 38:188–200
70. Meyrick B, Reid L. 1980. Hypoxia-induced structural changes in the media and adventitia of the rat hilar pulmonary artery and their regression. *Am. J. Pathol.* 100:151–78
71. Mecham RP, Whitehouse LA, Wrenn DS, Parks WC, Griffin GL, et al. 1987. Smooth muscle-mediated connective tissue remodeling in pulmonary hypertension. *Science* 237:423–26
72. Poiani GJ, Tozzi CA, Yohn SE, Pierce RA, Belsky SA, et al. 1990. Collagen and elastin metabolism in hypertensive pulmonary arteries of rats. *Circ. Res.* 66:968–78
73. Tozzi CA, Poiani GJ, Harangozo AM, Boyd CD, Riley DJ. 1989. Pressure-

induced connective tissue synthesis in pulmonary artery segments is dependent on intact endothelium. *J. Clin. Invest.* 84: 1005–12
74. Davies PF, Tripathi SC. 1993. Mechanical stress mechanisms and the cell. An endothelial paradigm. *Circ. Res.* 72:239–45
75. Nollert MU, Panaro NJ, McIntire LV. 1992. Regulation of genetic expression in shear stress stimulated endothelial cells. *Ann. NY Acad. Sci.* 665:94–104
76. Resnick N, Collins T, Atkinson W, Bonthron DT, Dewey CF Jr, Gimbron MA Jr. 1993. Platelet-derived growth factor B chain promoter contains a cis-acting fluid shear-stress-responsive element. *Proc. Natl. Acad. Sci. USA* 90:4591–95
77. Watson PA. 1991. Function follows form: generation of intracellular signals by cell deformation. *FASEB J.* 5:2013–19
78. Kay JM, Edwards FR. 1973. Ultrastructure of the alveolar-capillary wall in mitral stenosis. *J. Path.* 111:239–45
79. Lee YS. 1979. Electron microscopic studies of the alveolar-capillary barrier in the patients of chronic pulmonary edema. *Jpn. Circ. J.* 43:945–54
80. Kay JM, De Sa DJ, Mancer JF. 1983. Ultrastructure of lung in pulmonary veno-occlusive disease. *Hum. Path.* 14:451–56
81. Wirtz HR, Dobbs LG. 1990. Calcium mobilization and exocytosis after one mechanical stretch of lung epithelial cells. *Science* 250:1266–69
82. Bishop JE, Mitchell JJ, Absher PM, Baldor L, Geller HA, et al. 1993. Cyclic mechanical deformation stimulates human lung fibroblast proliferation and autocrine growth factor activity. *Am. J. Respir. Cell Mol. Biol.* 9:126–33
83. Liu M, Liu J, Buch S, Tanswell AK, Post M. 1995. Antisense oligonucleotides for PDGF-B and its receptor inhibit mechanical strain-induced fetal lung cell growth. *Am. J. Physiol.* 269:L178–84
84. Berg JT, Fu Z, Breen EC, Tran H-C, Mathieu-Costello O, West JB. 1997. High lung inflation increases mRNA levels of ECM components and growth factors in lung parenchyma. *J. Appl. Physiol.* 83: 120–28
85. Hislop AA, Rinaldi M, Lee R, McGregor CG, Haworth SG. 1993. Growth of immature lung transplanted into an adult recipient. *Am. J. Physiol.* 264:L60–65
86. Buhain WJ, Brody JS. 1973. Compensatory growth of the lung following pneumonectomy. *J. Appl. Physiol.* 35:898–902
87. Parker JC, Breen EC, West JB. 1997. High vascular and airway pressures increase interstitial protein mRNA expression in isolated rat lungs. *J. Appl. Physiol.* 83:1697–705
88. Hultgren HN. 1969. High altitude pulmonary edema. In *Biomedicine of High Terrestrial Elevations*, ed. AH Hegnauer, pp. 131–41. New York: Springer-Verlag. 141 pp.
89. West JB, Colice GL, Lee YJ, Namba Y, Kurdak SS, et al. 1995. Pathogenesis of high-altitude pulmonary oedema: direct evidence of stress failure of pulmonary capillaries. *Eur. Resp. J.* 8:523–29
90. Berg JT, Breen EC, Fu Z, Mathieu-Costello O, West JB. 1998. Alveolar hypoxia causes increased gene expression of extracellular matrix proteins and PDGF-B in lung parenchyma. *Am. J. Resp. Crit. Care Med.* In press
91. West JB, Mathieu-Costello O. 1992. Strength of the pulmonary blood-gas barrier. *Respir. Physiol.* 88:141–48

Annu. Rev. Physiol. 1999. 61:573–92

EVOLUTION OF THE VERTEBRATE CARDIO-PULMONARY SYSTEM

C. G. Farmer
Department of Ecology and Evolutionary Biology, University of California at Irvine, Irvine, California 92697; e-mail: cfarmer@uci.edu

KEY WORDS: evolution, air-breathing fishes, myocardial hypoxia, ventricular septum, coronary circulation

ABSTRACT
Vertebrate lungs have long been thought to have evolved in fishes largely as an adaptation for life in hypoxic water. This view overlooks the possibility that lungs may have functioned to supply the heart with oxygen and may continue to serve this function in extant fishes. The myocardium of most vertebrates is avascular and obtains oxygen from luminal blood. Because oxygen-rich pulmonary blood mixes with oxygen-poor systemic blood before entering the heart of air-breathing fishes, lung ventilation may supply the myocardium with oxygen and expand aerobic exercise capabilities. Although sustained exercise in tetrapods is facilitated by septation of the heart and the formation of a dual pressure system, a divided cardio-pulmonary system may conflict with myocardial oxygenation because the right side of the heart is isolated from pulmonary oxygen. This may have contributed to the evolution of the coronary circulation.

INTRODUCTION

Early in the 19th century, biologists used the presence of a lung to distinguish amphibians and reptiles from fish; fish used gills for respiration, whereas terrestrial vertebrates used a membranous internal sac, a lung. Hence, when lungfish were discovered, they were considered to be gigantic amphibians. Yet so many other traits placed them firmly among fish that they were eventually assigned to a new and distinct subclass of fish called the Dipnoi. This mosaic of features is reflected in the name of the South American lungfish, *Lepidosiren paradoxa*. Species from two other genera are known from Africa (*Protopterus*) and

0066-4278/99/0315-0573$08.00

Australia (*Neoceratodus*). Initially, lungs were considered an adaptation that enabled these "amphibious" animals to breathe when venturing onto land, but because lungfish kept in captivity never left the water, it soon became evident that terrestrial journeys were more myth than reality. The selection pressure for the evolution of lungs was then deemed to be aquatic hypoxia (38). Lungs were thought to be an adaptation that enabled fish to obtain oxygen from air when it was scarce in water.

Over the next century, support for this idea grew. Numerous fossils of lungfish were unearthed in a red layer of sediment, known as the Old Red Sandstone, that was laid down during the Devonian, some 350–400 million years ago. Along with these fossils, remains of early amphibians and numerous traces of amphibian footprints were found, which revived the idea that lungs were important for terrestrial forays. In 1916, Barrell (1) proposed that the depositional environments of these fossils indicated a semi-arid flood plain subject to alternation of wet and dry seasons. As drought reduced the river systems to hypoxic pools, natural selection favored animals that could breathe air as well as migrate from smaller to larger water sources (1). The distribution of extant air-breathing fishes, which are generally said to live in hypoxic fresh water, further buttressed these ideas (16). Because warm water contains less oxygen than cold water, and because stagnant or poorly stirred environments (e.g. swamps, ponds) tend to be poorly oxygenated, tropical freshwater ecosystems were considered more probable settings for the origin of lungs than marine environments, which are stirred by tides and currents (for an alternate view, see 68).

In the past 50 years the fossil record of early fishes has become much better known, improving our understanding of their phylogeny, or genealogy. During the early evolution of bony fishes (Osteichthyes), two groups emerged—the ray-finned fishes (Actinopterygii) and the lobe-finned fishes (Sarcopterygii). Because extant members of both major radiations have lungs, it is probable that they were inherited from a common ancestor, thus dating the origin of lungs to at least as early as the Late Silurian, over 400 million years ago (Figure 1) (20). This poses a significant problem for the idea that lungs are an adaptation to aquatic hypoxia because the depositional environments of these early bony fishes are marine, yet marine environments are not widely hypoxic (9, 12, 18, 19, 83–85, 90). Another problem with the idea that lungs are an adaptation to hypoxic water is that the putative correlation between hypoxic freshwater habitats and the character of air-breathing has been based in part on speculation. Field data of aquatic oxygen content and the distribution of air-breathers are sometimes at odds with this speculation (54). For example, although early authors believed that the Australian lungfish inhabited hypoxic water (38), a study of the oxygen content throughout their habitat revealed that it is not hypoxic, even during periods of drought (37). The discovery of many marine air-breathing species

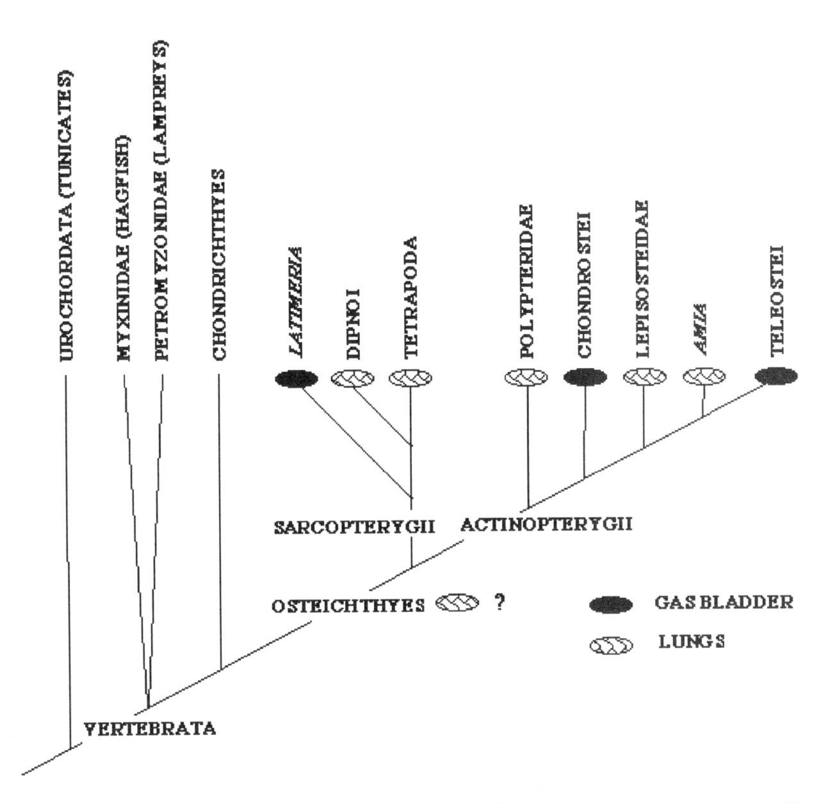

Figure 1 Hypothesis of the relationship of fishes showing the presence of lungs or a swim bladder (based in part on Lauder & Liem 1983) (57).

further erodes a correlation between warm, hypoxic freshwater habitats and the air-breathing habitus (35). Hence, in recent years it has become increasingly evident that numerous factors (e.g. buoyancy, hearing, etc) could have intertwined such that natural selection favored the evolution of air-breathing (34, 58).

One of these factors may have been the ability of lungs to supply the heart with oxygen. As vertebrates evolved from their protovertebrate ancestors, there was a shift in the primary site of gas exchange from the skin to the gills (30). Over the course of vertebrate evolution, this change, coupled with increases in body size and levels of activity, may have resulted in myocardial hypoxia.

LUNGS AS A SOURCE OF OXYGEN FOR THE HEART

Soft tissues do not fossilize readily. Consequently, our knowledge of the cardiorespiratory system of protovertebrates and early vertebrates comes primarily from comparing features found in extant cephalochordates with those of primitive vertebrates such as lampreys. The ancestors of vertebrates lived in the Cambrian, more than 500 million years ago. These animals were probably small, marine suspension feeders that relied upon the skin, rather than the gills, for gas exchange (30, 62). Ciliary tracts are used to obtain food in several chordate groups (ascidian tunicates, Amphioxus, and larval lampreys), suggesting that this feeding mode is representative of the protovertebrate pattern (Figure 1) (30, 62). In larval lampreys, the heart pumps blood through ciliated tracts in the pharynx, where thick strands of mucus trap food. This nutrient-rich blood flows to the tissues, including the skin, where carbon dioxide is unloaded and oxygen absorbed, and then returns to the heart (Figure 2*a*). The hearts of lampreys are distinct from mammalian hearts in that they do not contain a large lumen surrounded by a thick muscular wall. Instead, the heart is composed of an avascular, trabecular mesh of muscle cells (with a spongy appearance) that is encased by connective tissue, the epicardium. As the heart beats, blood flows to and fro through the spaces between the myocytes (referred to as sinusoidal channels or lacunae), and this blood supplies the muscle with oxygen. Ontogenetic studies and the phylogenetic distribution of avascular spongy myocardium indicate that it is the primitive condition for vertebrates (59). In larval lampreys, the heart is efferent to the gas exchanger, so this spongy myocardium is bathed in oxygen-rich blood.

As vertebrates evolved, gills lost their function as filter-feeding mechanisms and became the major site for gas exchange. When this happened, the spongy myocardium of the heart would have been bathed in oxygen-poor blood, as it is in extant gill-breathing fishes, because oxygen would have been unloaded to the other tissues of the body before entering the heart (Figure 2*b*). During the Ordovician and Silurian radiation, there arose both inactive (e.g. osteostracans and heterostracans) and highly active vertebrates (e.g. the bony fishes) (19, 62). In active animals, this circulatory design may have resulted in myocardial hypoxia and therefore may have been a selection pressure for the evolution of lungs and coronary circulation. Oxygen-rich blood from pulmonary respiration mixes with the oxygen-poor blood in the systemic venous return before entering the heart (Figure 2*c*). Therefore, pulmonary respiration could have functioned

→

Figure 2 Schematic of the cardiorespiratory design of (*a*) larval lamprey in which the heart contains an admixture of oxygen-rich and -poor blood; (*b*) gill-breathing fish in which the heart contains only oxygen-poor blood; (*c*) primitive air-breathing fish in which the heart contains an admixture of oxygen-rich and -poor blood; (*d*) *Protopterus*, the African lungfish that has nearly complete separation of oxygen-rich and -poor blood within the heart. Oxygen-poor blood, ■; admixture of oxygen-rich and -poor blood, ▩; oxygen-rich blood, ▭.

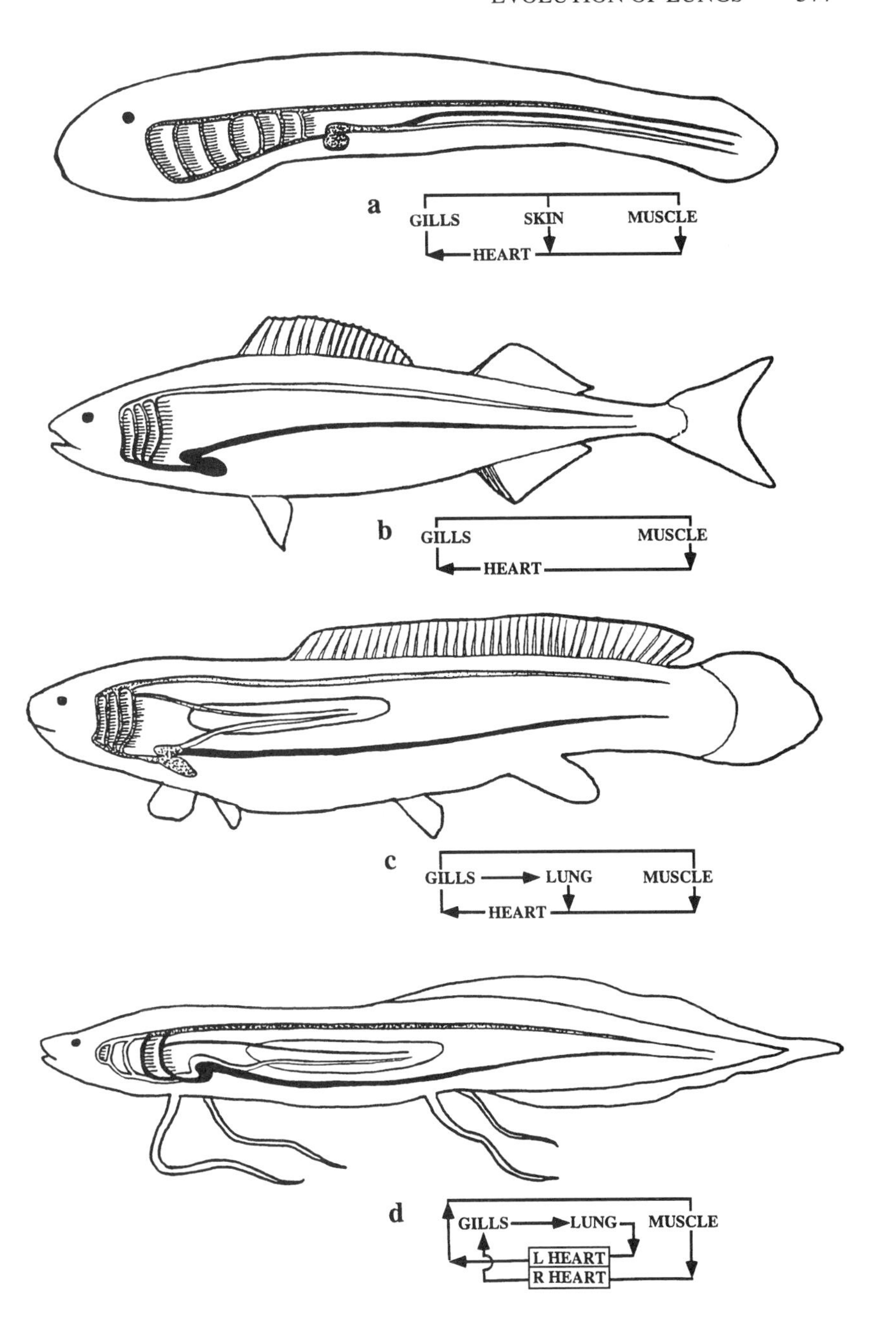
a
GILLS
SKIN
MUSCLE
HEART
b
GILLS
MUSCLE
HEART
c
GILLS
LUNG
MUSCLE
HEART
d
GILLS
LUNG
MUSCLE
L HEART
R HEART

ancestrally for myocardial oxygenation. This scenario for the evolution of lungs predicts that pulmonary respiration in extant fishes will continue to serve as a source of myocardial oxygen (24).

If pulmonary respiration is important for cardiac function, then it should be most useful during periods of activity. During exercise in fishes, when the work of the heart increases, the oxygen needs of the heart are elevated. But because working skeletal muscle extracts more oxygen from the blood than does resting muscle, the amount of oxygen in the blood entering the heart of gill-breathing fishes decreases (36, 50, 52). If the partial pressure of oxygen drops to a critical threshold, there will not be an adequate gradient to drive diffusion of oxygen throughout the ventricle (17). Hence, during exercise the supply of oxygen to the heart drops at the very time it is needed most. Although the myocardium of some vertebrates (e.g. turtles) is tolerant of hypoxia, this appears to be true at low work loads. At high work loads, myocardium has a primarily aerobic metabolism (13, 23, 27, 63, 76, 78). Because hypoxia directly inhibits myocardial function, an adequate supply of oxygen is essential for proper cardiac function during exercise (22, 32, 88).

Potentially exacerbating this decline in oxygen in the blood entering the heart is the acidosis that is routinely experienced by ectothermic animals during activity (5, 6). Acidosis inhibits myocardial power output, especially when combined with hypoxia (31, 33, 69). In addition, because acidosis decreases the affinity of hemoglobin for oxygen (the Bohr and Root effects), loading of oxygen in the gills becomes more difficult (6, 7). These factors may contribute to the lethal effects of intense exercise commonly observed in gill-breathing fishes, e.g. cod, dab, tench, salmon, bass, shad, haddock, and trout (6).

Although many gill-breathing fishes die from exhaustive exercise, the underlying cause of this mortality is unknown. A few electrocardiograms recorded from trout during periods of intense activity indicate that the heart stopped, leading Black (6) to suggest that the cause of death is circulatory failure, but Wood and colleagues disagree with this conclusion, asserting that trout die from a severe intracellular acidosis (95). However, exhaustive exercise in the bimodally breathing gar (*Lepisosteus*) produces a magnitude and pattern of blood acidosis similar to that observed in trout, but these fish survive as long as they have access to air (13a, 77). Furthermore, Black's data and hypothesis are consistent with electrocardiograms of resting fish subjected to severe environmental hypoxia, which indicate cardiac malfunction (e.g. increases in the p-r interval, inversion of the t wave) (70). Signs of cardiac malfunction (e.g. arrhythmia and decreases in pulse pressure concomitant with a reduced afterload) were observed when bowfin (*Amia*) swam in oxygen-rich water without access to air, but were not noted during exercise with access to aerial respiration (25). It is unresolved whether there is sufficient oxygen in the venous blood of active gill-breathing fishes to maintain maximum cardiac performance or if there is circulatory failure from intense activity. Air-breathing may circumvent osmoregulatory or other unknown problems faced by gill-breathing fishes. However, the well-established sensitivity of myocardium to hypoxia and acidosis at high workloads increases the probability that the spongy myocardium of gill-breathing fishes can be oxygen limited during exercise. Because pulmonary respiration can circumvent these problems, air-breathing ought to be induced by activity.

Indeed, breathing air when active is important for many fishes and, in some circumstances, activity is a stronger stimulus for air-breathing than is aquatic hypoxia. For example, when subjected to aquatic hypoxia, rates of air-breathing decrease in *Polypterus*, but activity strongly induces air-breathing (60). Activity induces air-breathing in other fishes as well, e.g. *Amia*, *Lepisosteus*, and *Neoceratodus*, in spite of ample oxygen in the water (26, 37, 48, 77). If lungs are functioning to supply the heart with oxygen, then air-breathing should be stimulated by chemoreceptors that sense the oxygen in the blood before it has passed through the gills, since this is the blood bathing the heart. On the other hand, if air-breathing is important solely to provide oxygen to the systemic system, then the drive to breathe ought to arise from chemoreceptors that sense the oxygen in the blood that has passed through the capillaries of the gills, since this is what flows to the systemic vasculature. In both *Lepisosteus* and *Amia*, chemoreceptors have been found that sense the oxygen in the blood afferent to the gills (64, 79). Hypoxia at this site triggers air-breathing and, in *Lepisosteus*, a bradycardia (64, 79). *Lepisosteus* also have external chemoreceptors that sense the oxygen in the water and cause a reduction in gill ventilation and an increase in air-breathing when in hypoxic water.

These observations on the use of pulmonary respiration in extant fishes are consistent with fossil evidence indicating that early bony fishes were active animals that may have inhabited oxygen-rich water.

The fossil remains of early fishes show locomotor and feeding features indicative of an active lifestyle. Furthermore, as previously mentioned, the depositional environments are largely, and many times wholly, marine. Denison states that "they (early Osteichthyes) must be reckoned among the best swimmers of their time. The crossopterygians had powerful jaws and well-developed, pointed marginal teeth, indicating that they were predacious." He also points out that, as far as the geologic evidence is concerned, all early fishes could have been marine (19). Thompson's studies of the ecology and morphology of the lobe-finned fishes indicate that many of the earliest bony fishes were the dominant predators of their time (84). Furthermore, many of the fossil lungfishes, the majority of the fossil coelacanths, many of the Rhipidistia, and even some of the early amphibians were completely marine (84). It appears that only a few genera, particularly in the late Devonian, were confined to freshwater habitats. Locomotor and feeding characters suggest that the lungfishes became specialized for a diet of plants and invertebrates, and the coelacanths became specialized for a more sedentary, stealthy approach to food, while the Rhipidistia (which contain the ancestors of tetrapods) remained active, cruising predators (84).

Why Don't All Fish Have Lungs?

If lungs are primitive and important in supplying oxygen to the heart, then why did the coelacanth, the Chondrostei, and the Teleostei convert the lung to a buoyancy device (Figure 1)? There are at least two circumstances that hinder aerial respiration in fishes, deep water habitats and aerial predation. Placement of food at progressively lower depths decreases air-breathing frequency (4, 55); trips to the surface for breaths of air may be too expensive for fishes occupying deep-water habitats. This may have contributed to the loss of lungs for gas exchange in the Chondrostei and the coelacanth, which occupy benthic and deep-water habitats (2, 29, 66).

A second factor that hinders breathing and that may bear on the loss of lungs in teleostean fishes is aerial predation. The fossil record indicates that the rise of teleosts is geologically contemporaneous with the origin of aerial vertebrate predators (pterosaurs and birds), many of whom ate fish (3). Some insight into the prehistoric impact predators may have had on their ecosystem is possible by the study of the historic impact of predators on extant ecosystems (21). Introduction of a new type of predator into an ecosystem can be devastating. For example, introduction of the brown tree snake (*Boiga irregularis*), which is native to Australia, to various Pacific islands has decimated or driven to extinction numerous species of birds and small mammals (73). Being totally naive to snakes, many of these birds seem to watch blithely as a snake approaches to eat them because they do not recognize the snake as a predator. For many millions of years, the predators of fish were other aquatic animals. Hence, fish were probably initially very naive to flying vertebrates, and it is possible that the evolution of flight had a significant impact on the aquatic ecosystem.

There are three lines of evidence from extant air-breathing fishes that indicate aerial predation is, and has been, a significant selection pressure. First, air-breathers show a strong diving reflex when they perceive a threat from the air. For example, placement of a stuffed heron over a tank of *Lepisosteus* caused the air-breathing interval to increase by 118% (80). Second, a large number of air-breathing fishes are nocturnal or crepuscular, a period when they are at less risk of aerial predation (e.g. *Neoceratodus forsteri, Lepidosiren* sp., *Lepisosteus* sp., *Amia calva, N. Notopterus, N. chitala, N. boreensis, Gymnarchus niloticus, Aspredinidae, Clarias lazera, Clarias batrachus, Callichthys, Hoplosternum, Brochis, Hypostomus, Ancistrus, Gymnotus, Electrophorus electricus,*

Loricaria) (34 and references therein; 84). Third, air-breathers tend to exhibit synchronous air-breathing behavior. In other words, they school, and when one fish surfaces to breathe they all do, reducing their risk of aerial predation (e.g. *Polypterus* sp., *Lepisosteus* sp., *Arapaima gigas, Heterotis niloticus, Megalops atlanticus, N. notopterus, N. chitala, Piabucina, Clarias batrachus, Hoplosternum thoracatum, Corydoras aeneus, Heteropneustes fossilis, Ancistrus spinosus, Hypostomus plecostomus, Colisa, Hoplerythrinus*) (34).

Specialists for Aquatic Hypoxia

Although the cardio-pulmonary system of the lungfish (Dipnoi) has received a great deal of attention from physiologists, this system is unusual and contrasts with the cardiopulmonary system of other lung-breathing fishes. Typically, fish hearts are composed of a series of four chambers that are curled into an S shape: the sinus venosus, the atrium, the ventricle, and a fourth chamber that is muscular and contractile in non-teleost fishes (the conus arteriosus) but is elastic in teleosts (the bulbus). In groups that use lungs for respiration (e.g. *Polypterus, Lepisosteus, Amia*), and in most groups that use a lung-like gas bladder, these chambers are not septated and contain largely or totally an admixture of oxygen-rich pulmonary and oxygen-poor systemic blood (11, 34). Because the pulmonary and systemic admixture is pumped by the heart to the gills, fish with this circulatory design can lose oxygen from the blood to the environment when in hypoxic water. In contrast, the circulatory system of the lungfish (*Lepidosiren, Protopterus*) circumvents this problem.

The three genera of lungfish show progressive cardiovascular specialization correlating with their dependence on aerial oxygen, and therefore they have been depicted as a sequence of transitional grades from water- to air-breathers (49). However, these features may not be adaptations to air-breathing per se but rather may be specializations for life in hypoxic water. The lungfish are aquatic animals; the African and South American genera can survive without water only by metabolic depression and aestivation. Although they do not use gills to acquire oxygen, they use gills for the elimination of carbon dioxide, pH regulation, and the excretion of nitrogenous wastes (reviewed in 34). Consequently, they retain gill filaments for these purposes yet live in habitats that are often hypoxic. To prevent loss of oxygen to the water, their gills have atrophied, and their cardio-pulmonary systems contain partial septa in the atrium and ventricle and a spiral valve in the conus. Oxygen-rich blood from the lung enters the left atrium, remains on the left side of the heart, and is sent through the gill arches that have lost their capillary bed so that oxygen from the blood is not lost to the water (Figure 2*d*). Oxygen-poor blood enters the right atrium, remains in the right side of the ventricle, and is ejected into gill arches that have a capillary bed so that carbon dioxide, nitrogenous wastes, and hydrogen ions can be unloaded to the environment (45, 74). In contrast, the Australian lungfish, *Neoceratodus*, does not show the same degree of specialization. It does not aestivate, nor does it live in oxygen-poor environments. It has considerable mixing of oxygen-rich and -poor blood within the heart, a poorly divided conus that retains pocket valves, well-developed gills with all the branchial arteries subdivided into capillaries, and numerous other primitive features (e.g. large scales and dermal bones; big, fleshy, lobed fins; large opercular bone) (28, 37, 46, 61, 83). Hence, differences in these lungfish genera may not represent transitional grades from water- to air-breathers as much as transitional grades for progressively hypoxic aquatic environments. Identifying the factors that influenced the specialization of the lungfish cardiorespiratory system is useful when trying to sort out whether similar cardiovascular features found in tetrapods have resulted from convergent evolution or inheritance from a common ancestor.

THE TRANSITION TO LAND

Tetrapods probably descended from Rhipidistian fishes and inherited a spongy ventricle from these ancestors (59). With the transition to land came numerous changes in the cardio-respiratory system. In general, gills were lost, the lungs became the primary or only site of gas exchange, and separation of pulmonary and systemic blood was accomplished to varying degrees by subdivision of the ventral aorta into a pulmonary artery and systemic aortas and by subdivision of the heart into right and left sides [anatomically, the lumen of the ventricle was more nearly subdivided into dorsal and ventral than right and left chambers (42), but the description of right and left is used here for simplicity]. Although separation of oxygen-rich and oxygen-poor blood is advantageous in terms of the efficiency of gas exchange, it also results in very little oxygen in the right side of the heart. This may have posed a problem that was solved in various ways. In amphibians, oxygen-rich blood from cutaneous respiration enters the right side of the heart; in chelonians and lepidosaurs, the intracardiac shunt can carry oxygen into the right side of the heart; and in birds and mammals, the function of oxygenating the myocardium is carried out by a coronary circulation (this may also be true of crocodilians).

Amphibians have a full septum in the atrium; the left atrium receives oxygen-rich pulmonary blood while the right atrium receives systemic blood. Although amphibians lack a septum in the ventricle, the alignment of myocytes provides fairly good functional separation of pulmonary and systemic blood (47). Consequently, the right atrium and the right side of the ventricle, which are composed entirely of spongy myocardium, are isolated from pulmonary oxygen. However, the right side of the heart may receive oxygen from blood returning to the heart from the cutaneous and buccal circulation, which are oxygen-rich. Whether or not this occurs has not been investigated.

The heart of early amniotes also probably had a ventricle composed primarily of spongy myocardium, which has been retained in chelonians (turtles) and lepidosaurs (*Sphenodon*, amphisbaenids, snakes, lizards) (59). In turtles and lepidosaurs, the atrium is completely subdivided into two chambers, but the ventricle is generally subdivided into three chambers by two incomplete septa—the vertical and horizontal septa (42). Because the septa are incomplete, there can be mixing of blood between the chambers. When blood entering the ventricle from the right atrium is shunted from the right to the left side of the ventricle (the right-to-left shunt), oxygen-poor blood is ejected into the systemic aortas rather than into the pulmonary artery. When oxygen-rich blood entering the ventricle from the left atrium is shunted from the left to the right side of the ventricle (the left-to-right shunt), oxygen-rich blood is ejected into the pulmonary artery rather than into the systemic aortas. These shunts can constitute most of the cardiac output. Numerous studies have examined the function and mechanisms of shunts, and many have focused on the importance of the right-to-left shunt during diving (reviewed in 40). However, much cardiac morphology associated with shunts probably evolved in amniotes (42) along with features indicative of a terrestrial lifestyle (e.g. the amniotic egg, terrestrial locomotor features), suggesting an origin for this morphology unrelated to diving. Because the left-to-right shunt washes oxygen-rich blood into a region of the heart that would otherwise be oxygen-poor (41), it could function to supply oxygen to spongy myocardium (24).

As in fishes, myocardial oxygen demand in tetrapods is greatest during exercise. Furthermore, exercise induces an acidosis. Acidosis combined with anoxia is more debilitating for cardiac function than is either stress alone (43, 92). Hence, if the left-to-right shunt functions to supply the right side of the ventricle with oxygen, it should occur during exercise. Indeed, observations in turtles indicate that a left-to-right shunt occurs during exercise (56, 75, 93). The left-to-right shunt is also known to increase the oxygen content of the systemic arterial blood to levels that are equivalent to pulmonary venous values, suggesting that the shunt functions in systemic oxygen transport (39). However, this function does not exclude the left-to-right shunt from also serving as a source of myocardial oxygen. Indeed, myocardial electrical abnormalities (e.g. increase in the p-r interval, inversion of the t wave) that occur in turtles when effectively prevented from enriching ventricular blood with the left-to-right shunt during exercise suggest the function of myocardial oxygenation (25).

Archosaurs (birds and crocodilians) and mammals cannot shunt blood within the ventricle because it is completely subdivided by a septum. Nor do these animals enrich with oxygen the blood that enters the right side of the heart with cutaneous respiration. Consequently, another mechanism probably supplies oxygen to the myocardium. In birds and mammals, a coronary circulation carries oxygen to the heart, but the situation in crocodilians is not fully known. Crocodilian ventricles contain more spongy tissue than do those of birds or mammals (53). However, overall their ventricles more closely resemble those of birds than those of snakes and lizards (89). The crocodilian ventricle contains a significant proportion of compact myocardium that is completely supplied with oxygen through a coronary circulation, and the spongy myocardium is also well-endowed with coronary vasculature (53, 71). Furthermore, injections of ink into the coronary circulation show anastomosis of coronary vessels with the sinusoidal channels of the spongy myocardium (53). Hence, spongy regions that are avascular could still obtain oxygen from coronary blood through these anastomoses. Finally, comparisons of the right and left atria (which probably have similar workloads) indicate that the right atrium contains more coronary vasculature than the left (CG Farmer, unpublished observation). All of these factors suggest that a coronary circulation is critical to the crocodilian heart.

In summary, the ventricles of many tetrapods (amphibians, turtles, snakes, and lizards) are composed primarily of spongy myocardium. The separation of pulmonary and systemic blood that occurs in these animals therefore could result in regional myocardial hypoxia. However, this hypoxia could be overcome with cutaneous respiration and/or a left-to-right intracardiac shunt. For lineages that neither rely on cutaneous respiration nor have the ability to shunt blood within the ventricle, the primary source of myocardial oxygen appears to be from a coronary circulation. There are two noteworthy observations regarding complete subdivision of the cardio-pulmonary system and the replacement of spongy myocardium with compact tissue that is supplied with oxygen through a coronary circulation: First, several lineages independently evolved such a system (Figure 3); second, the evolution of this system is correlated with the ability to sustain high levels of exercise.

Ventricular Morphology and Coronary Circulation

Cardiac morphology varies dramatically among vertebrates in terms of the shape of the heart; the alignment of the chambers, septa, and outflow tracts; the density and composition of the cardiac walls; and the mode of oxygenation, etc. It appears that foraging strategy is an important factor in shaping this morphology. A benefit of active foraging is the procurement of more food than is obtained by sit-and-wait predators (81, 82), but active foraging requires the aerobic production of adenosine triphosphate. This, in turn, mandates high rates of flow of oxygen from the environment to the mitochondria, i.e. the oxygen cascade. Consequently, the evolution of stamina entails numerous adaptations in the cardio-respiratory system that facilitate the flux of oxygen through the cascade. In many cases, similar structures are found that are almost certainly the result of convergent evolution rather than inheritance from a common ancestor.

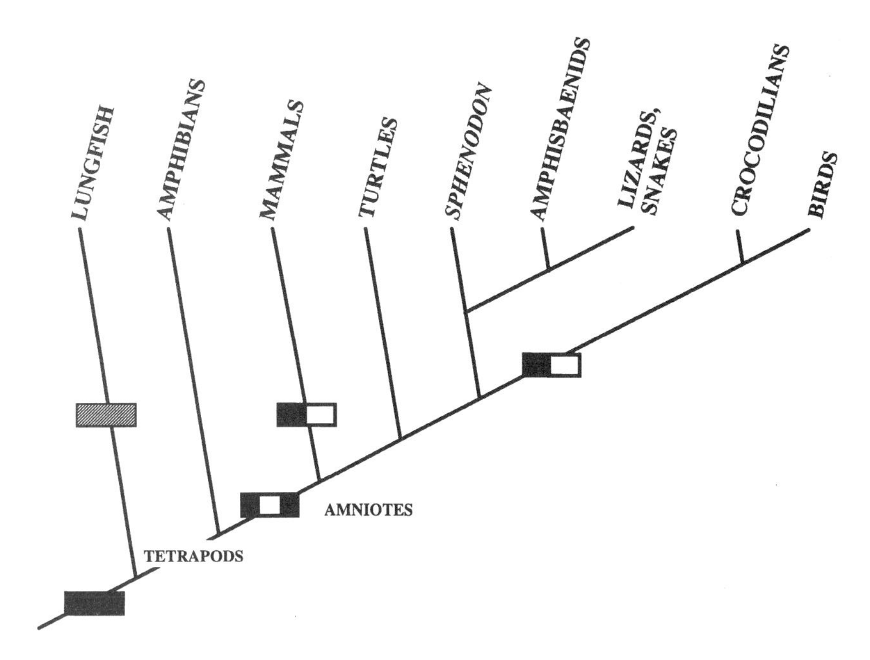

Figure 3 Hypothesis of the relationship of tetrapods, showing the number of chambers and the degree of subdivision of the ventricle. One ventricular chamber, no septum, ■; two ventricular chambers, incomplete septum, ▨; three ventricular chambers, incomplete septa, ■□■; two ventricular chambers, complete septum, ■□.

The ventricular septa of lungfish and amniotes have an independent origin and serve different functions. Independent evolution of these structures is suggested by the embryological association of the lungfish septum with the atrial septum, and of the main amniote septum (generally called the horizontal septum) with the conus arteriosus (42). The function of the septum in lungfish is probably to prevent loss of oxygen from the blood to hypoxic water (see above) and is not related to the creation of a dual-pressure circulatory system or expanded aerobic capacities. Indeed, the African and South American lungfish are noted for having exceptionally anaerobic rather than aerobic metabolisms (34). In contrast, the function of a well-developed septum in amniotes is associated with the ability to sustain exercise by enabling elevated systemic arterial pressures without elevated pulmonary pressures, preventing excessive stresses in the pulmonary capillaries (51, 65). Among amniotes there is great variation in the degree of development of the horizontal septum that is correlated with the lineages' ability to sustain locomotion. The septum is poorly developed in turtles, more fully developed in snakes and varanid lizards, and complete in archosaurs and mammals (Figure 3) (42). Evolution of a complete ventricular septum occurred independently in archosaurs and mammals. Likewise, a nearly complete septum evolved independently in varanid lizards (this septum totally divides the ventricle functionally but not anatomically) (65). Birds and mammals are well known for their endurance. Similarly, varanid lizards are noted among lepidosaurs for their ability to sustain exercise. Crocodilians, however, are better known for burst than sustained exercise.

The lifestyle of extant crocodilians might appear contradictory to the idea that a divided cardio-pulmonary system is an adaptation for sustained locomotion. Ancestrally, however, crocodilians were agile, terrestrial animals, and most of the specialized features found in the modern aquatic crocodilians were evolved in the late Triassic in highly terrestrial forms (15, 91). Hence, consideration of history is important in understanding these animals. Many extant crocodilian characters, including a fully septated ventricle, are probably vestigial. This idea is supported by similarities in the embryology of the avian and crocodilian ventricle that suggest the evolution of the septum took place early in the archosaurian lineage (42). Other characters of modern crocodilians were evolved later, probably as adaptations to an aquatic lifestyle, e.g. an ear lid that closes when the head passes through the air-water interface, preventing water from entering the ear (94). Cardiovascular features as unique to crocodilians as an ear lid may similarly have been acquired with the assumption of an aquatic lifestyle (e.g. an aorta originating in the right ventricle that enables a right-to-left shunt, the foramen of Panizza that enables blood flow between the right and lef aortas).

Animals with a well-developed ventricular septum also tend to have a well-developed coronary circulation. In turtles, the coronary arteries often originate from vessels far from the heart (e.g. from the subclavians), and coronary support is nonexistent to the atria and minimal to the ventricle (about 10% of the muscle mass). In snakes and lizards, the coronary artery is confined to posterior regions of the aortas. In snakes and the varanid lizard, there is compact tissue in the atria as well as the ventricle and more extensive coronary support than in turtles or other lizards (10, 59). In archosaurs and mammals, the coronary arteries originate from the base of the aorta (right aorta in crocodilians) and play a dominant role in nourishing the heart (see above). In general, these changes are accompanied by other adaptations for elevated aerobic metabolisms, e.g. high afterload, high hematocrit, and high heart rate. Some of these features are also present in gill-breathing fishes (e.g. scombrid fishes) noted for endurance (e.g. active foraging mode, compact ventricles, coronary support, high heart rate, high cardiac output, high afterload, and high hematocrit) (14, 50, 59, 72, 87).

It remains for future research to determine whether and how these adaptations for endurance interact to affect the form and function of the heart. Mechanisms that influence mammalian coronary angiogenesis and ventricular remodeling are complex and involve growth factors, extracellular matrix molecules, and inhibitory factors. Angiogenesis can be induced by thyroid hormones, hypoxia, dipyridamole or adenosine, and exercise. Exercise-associated angiogenesis is probably stimulated by mechanical stresses on the endothelial lining of the vasculature that trigger the release of growth factors and cause mitogenic, migratory, and tube formation of the endothelial cells (86). Exercise also induces ventricular remodeling that can vary with the type of exercise (44). An important bottom line to many of these changes is that sustained exercise confers great health benefits to humans, whereas a sedentary lifestyle is among the most significant risk factors for heart disease. The mechanisms by which an active lifestyle protects against disease are not fully understood (67). Although numerous potential mechanisms have been identified (e.g. improved lipoprotein profile, weight loss, lowered blood pressure), exercise confers health benefits that are independent of these mechanisms (8). Consequently, understanding how similar adaptations for endurance in groups as distantly related as birds, scombrid fishes, and mammals have resulted in similarities in cardiac form and function may prove important both for understanding the evolution of this system and for providing insight into the mammalian design.

SUMMARY

An adequate supply of oxygen to the heart is critical for proper cardiac function and probably has been a selection pressure during the evolution of the vertebrate cardio-respiratory system. The myocardium of essentially all vertebrates has primarily an aerobic metabolism that is depressed by hypoxia and acidosis; a combination of these factors inhibits the heart more significantly than either alone. Vertebrates have evolved two ways of oxygenating myocardium: (*a*) from channels that carry luminal blood to a spongy network of myocytes and (*b*) from a coronary circulation that carries oxygen-rich blood to compactly arranged myocytes. Ontogenetic studies and the phylogenetic distribution of these mechanisms indicate that spongy myocardium is primitive for vertebrates. The use of a coronary circulation and compact myocardium appears to have evolved convergently in several groups.

The cardiac performance of gill-breathing fishes may be limited by the fact that their spongy myocardium contains blood that is oxygen-poor. In air-breathing fishes that use a lung for respiration, there is mixing of oxygen-rich pulmonary and oxygen-poor systemic blood before it enters the heart. Hence, lungs may function to supply this myocardium with oxygen and could be an adaptation for an active lifestyle. Because both aerial predation and life in deep water preclude or diminish the usefulness of lungs, coronary support to the ventricle may have been requisite to an active lifestyle for fishes subject to these selection pressures.

With the transition from an aquatic to terrestrial life came numerous changes in the cardio-respiratory system. Subdivision of the cardiovascular system into a pulmonary and systemic circuit may have been a mixed blessing. Although improving the efficiency of gas exchange and enabling elevated systemic pressures, this subdivision isolates the spongy myocardium in the right side of the heart from oxygen-rich pulmonary blood. Cutaneous respiration in amphibians and the left-to-right shunt of chelonians and lepidosaurs could assuage this difficulty by enriching with oxygen the blood in the right side of the heart. Because a complete septum in the ventricle precludes this shunt, it may mandate coronary support to the heart in archosaurs and mammals. This idea is supported by the observation that progressive ventricular septation is accompanied by progressive coronary support to the heart and the replacement of spongy myocardium with compact tissue. Septation is important in the formation of a dual-pressure circulatory system and correlates well with lineages that have (or have had) an active foraging mode and therefore an aerobic exercise metabolism. Although numerous factors were probably involved in the evolution of compact myocardium and a coronary circulation, this selection pressure may have been among the most important. Along with this change in cardiac morphology are found other adaptations for sustained exercise (e.g. elevated hematocrit, heart rate, afterload).

It seems probable that many of these adaptations for sustained locomotion have interacted such that compact myocardium functions better for these organisms than spongy myocardium and therefore has been favored by natural selection. These interactions could involve changes in preload, afterload, blood viscosity, blood pH, heart rate, ejection fraction, etc, and are easy to imagine but have not been well studied. Consequently, comparative studies within an evolutionary context have potential to provide insight into basic mechanisms that may impact both the formation and the function of the coronary circulation. In humans, a sedentary lifestyle is among the most significant risk factors for heart disease, yet the mechanisms by which activity maintains the health of the coronary circulation are not fully understood. Research aimed at understanding the factors that have made a coronary circulation of importance in other groups of vertebrates that have experienced selection for an active lifestyle may not only be important for our understanding of vertebrate evolution but may also provide information important to understanding and maintaining the health of the mammalian coronary circulation.

ACKNOWLEDGMENTS

I thank DR Carrier, JW Hicks, DC Jackson, C Janis, C Kuhn III, and D Massaro for encouragement and insight regarding this work. This research has been supported by a National Science Foundation dissertation grant IBN-9423297 and a National Institutes of Health individual National Research Service award #1F32-HL09796-01.

Literature Cited

1. Barrell J. 1916. Influence of Silurian-Devonian climates on the rise of air-breathing vertebrates. *Bull. Geol. Soc. Am.* 27:387–436
2. Becker GC. 1983. *Fishes of Wisconsin.* Madison: Univ. Wisc. Press 1052 pp.
3. Bell CM, Padian K. 1995. Pterosaur fossils from the Cretaceous of Chile: evidence for a pterosaur colony on an inland desert plain. *Geol. Mag.* 132(1):31–38
4. Bevan DJ, Kramer DL. 1986. The effect of swimming depth on respiratory behavior of the honey gourami, *Colisa chuna* (Pisces Belontiidae). *Can. J. Zool.* 64:1893–96
5. Black EC. 1955. Blood levels of hemoglobin and lactic acid in some freshwater fishes following exercise. *J. Fish. Res. Board Can.* 12(6):917–29
6. Black EC. 1958. Hyperactivity as a lethal factor in fish. *J. Fish. Res. Board Can.* 15(4):573–86
7. Black EC, Connor AR, Lam K, Chiu W. 1962. Changes in glycogen, pyruvate and lactate in rainbow trout (*Salmo gairdneri*) during and following muscular activity. *J. Fish. Res. Board Can.* 19(3):409–36
8. Blair SN, Kampert JB, Kohl HW III, Barlow CE, Macera CA, et al. 1996. Influences of cardiorespiratory fitness and other precursors on cardiovascular disease and all-cause mortality in men and women. *J. Am. Med. Assoc.* 276(3):205–10
9. Boucot A, Janis C. 1983. Environment of the early Paleozoic vertebrates. *Palaeogeogr. Palaeoclimatol. Palaeoecol.* 41: 251–87
10. Brady AJ, Dubkin C. 1964. Coronary circulation in the turtle ventricle. *Biochem. Physiol.* 13:119–28
11. Brainerd EL. 1994. The evolution of lung-gill bimodal breathing and the homology of vertebrate respiratory pumps. *Am. Zool.* 34:289–99
12. Bray AA. 1985. The evolution of the terrestrial vertebrates: environmental and physiological considerations. *Philos. Trans. R. Soc. London Ser. B* 309:289–322
13. Breisch EA, White F, Jones HM, Laurs RM. 1983. Ultrastructural morphometry of the myocardium of *Thunnus alalunga*. *Cell Tiss. Res.* 233:427–38

13a. Burleson ML, Shipman BN, Smatresk NJ. 1998. Ventilation and acid-base recovery following exhaustive activity in an air-breathing fish. *J. Exp. Biol.* 201:1259–68

14. Cameron JN. 1975. Morphometric and flow indicator studies of the teleost heart. *Can. J. Zool.* 53:691–98
15. Carrier DR. 1987. The evolution of locomotor stamina in tetrapods: circumventing a mechanical constraint. *Paleobiology* 13:326–341
16. Carter GS. 1957. Air breathing. In *Physiology of Fishes 1*, ed. M Brown, pp. 65–79. New York: Academic
17. Davie PS, Farrell AP. 1991. The coronary and luminal circulations of the myocardium of fishes. *Can. J. Zool.* 69: 1993–2001
18. Denison RH. 1968. Early Devonian lungfishes from Wyoming, Utah and Idaho. *Fieldiana, Geol.* 17:353–413
19. Denison RH. 1951. Late Devonian freshwater fishes from the western United States. *Fieldiana, Geol.* 11:221–61
20. Denison RH. 1956. A review of the habitat of the earliest vertebrates. *Fieldiana, Geol.* 11:361–457
21. Diamond JM. 1984. Historic extinctions: a rosetta stone for understanding prehistoric extinctions. In *Quaternary Extinctions*, ed. PS Martin, RG Klein, pp. 824–62. Tucson: Univ. Ariz. Press
22. Driedzic WR, Gesser H. 1994. Energy metabolism and contractility in ectothermic vertebrate hearts: hypoxia, acidosis, and low temperature. *Physiol. Rev.* 74(1):221–58
23. Driedzic WR, Scott DL, Farrell AP. 1983. Aerobic and anaerobic contributions to energy metabolism in perfused isolated sea raven (*Hemitripterus americanus*) hearts. *Can. J. Zool.* 61:1880–83
24. Farmer C. 1997. Did lungs and the intracardiac shunt evolve to oxygenate the

heart in vertebrates? *Paleobiology* 23(3): 358–72
25. Farmer CG. 1998. *The influence of myocardial oxygenation on the evolution of the vertebrate cardio-pulmonary system*. PhD thesis. Brown University, Providence, RI. 103 pp.
26. Farmer CG, Jackson DC. 1998. Air-breathing during activity in the fishes *Amia calva* and *Lepisosteus oculatus*. *J. Exp. Biol.* 201:943–48
27. Farrell AP, Small S, Graham MS. 1989. Effect of heart rate and hypoxia on the performance of a perfused trout heart. *Can. J. Zool.* 67:274–80
28. Foxon GEH. 1955. Problems of the double circulation in vertebrates. *Biol. Rev.* 30:196–228
29. Fricke H, Hissmann K, Schauer J, Reinicke O, Kasang L, et al. 1991. Habitat and population size of the coelacanth *Latimeria chalumnae* at Grand Comoro. *Environ. Biol. F* 32:287–300
30. Gans C. 1989. Stages in the origin of vertebrates: analysis by means of scenarios. *Biol. Rev.* 64:221–68
31. Gesser H. 1985. Effects of hypoxia and acidosis on fish heart performance. In *Respiration and Metabolism*, ed. R Gilles, pp. 402–10. Berlin: Springer-Verlag
32. Gesser H, Andresen P, Brams P, Sund-Laursen J. 1982. Inotropic effects of adrenaline on the anoxic or hypercapnic myocardium of rainbow trout and eel. *J. Comp. Physiol.* 147:123–28
33. Gesser H, Poupa O. 1983. Acidosis and cardiac muscle contractility: comparative aspects. *Comp. Biochem. Physiol. A* 76:559–66
34. Graham JB. 1997. *Air-breathing Fishes: Evolution, Diversity, and Adaptation*. San Diego: Academic. 299 pp.
35. Graham JB. 1976. Respiratory adaptations of marine air-breathing fishes. In *Respiration of Amphibious Vertebrates*, ed. GM Hughes, pp. 165–87. London: Academic
36. Graham MS, Farrell AP. 1990. Myocardial oxygen consumption in trout acclimated to 5°C and 15°C. *Physiol. Zool.* 63(3):536–54
37. Grigg G. 1965. Studies on the Queensland lungfish, *Neoceratodus Forsteri* (Krefft) III. Aerial respiration in relation to habits. *Aust. J. Zool.* 13:413–21
38. Gunther A. 1871. The new Ganoid fish (*Ceratodus*) recently discovered in Queensland. *Nature* 1871:406–8
39. Hicks JW. 1994. Adrenergic and cholinergic regulation of intracardiac shunting. *Physiol. Zool.* 67:1325–46
40. Hicks JW. 1998. Cardiac shunting in reptiles: mechanisms, regulation and physiological function. In *Biology of the Reptilia G, The Visceral Organs*, ed. C Gans, AS Gaunt, 19:424–83. Ithaca, NY: Soc. Stud. Amphib. Reptiles
41. Hicks JW, Ishimatsu A, Malloi S, Erskin A, Heisler N. 1996. The mechanism of cardiac shunting in reptiles: a new synthesis. *J. Exp. Biol.* 199:1435–46
42. Holmes EB. 1975. A reconsideration of the phylogeny of the tetrapod heart. *J. Morphol.* 147:209–28
43. Jackson DC, Shi H, Singer JH, Hamm PH, Lawler RG. 1995. Effects of input pressure on in vitro turtle heart during anoxia and acidosis: a ^{31}P-NMR study. *Am. J. Physiol.* 268:R683–89
44. Janicki JS, Sheriff KK, Robotham JL, Wise RA. 1996. Cardiac output during exercise: contributions of the cardiac, circulatory and respiratory systems. In *Handbook of Physiology; Section 12: Exercise: Regulation and Integration of Multiple Systems*, ed. LB Rowell, JT Shepherd, pp. 649–704. New York: Am. Physiol. Soc.
45. Johansen K. 1970. Air breathing in fishes. In *Fish Physiology 4*, ed. WS Hoar, pp. 361–408. New York: Academic
46. Johansen K, Lenfant C, Grigg GC. 1967. Respiratory control in the lungfish, *Neoceratodus forsteri* (Krefft). *Comp. Biochem. Physiol.* 20:835–45
47. Johansen K, Hanson D. 1968. Functional anatomy of the hearts of lungfishes and amphibians. *Am. Zool.* 8:191–210
48. Johansen K, Hanson D, Lenfant C. 1970. Respiration in a primitive air breather, *Amia calva*. *Resp. Physiol.* 9:162–72
49. Johansen K, Lenfant C, Hanson D. 1968. Cardiovascular dynamics in the lungfishes. *Z. Vergl. Physiol.* 59:157–86
50. Jones DR, Randall DJ. 1978. The respiratory and circulatory systems during exercise. In *Fish Physiology*, ed. WS Hoar, DJ Randall, pp. 425–501. New York: Academic
51. Jones DR, Shelton G. 1993. The physiology of the alligator heart: left aortic flow patterns and right-to-left shunts. *J. Exp. Biol.* 176:247–69
52. Kiceniuk JW, Jones DR. 1977. The oxygen transport system in trout (*Salmo gairdneri*) during sustained exercise. *J. Exp. Biol.* 69:247–60
53. Kohmoto T, Argenziano M, Yamamoto N, Vliet KA, Gu A, et al. 1997. Assessment of transmyocardial perfusion in alligator hearts. *Circulation* 95:1585–91
54. Kramer DL, Lindsey CC, Moodie GEE,

Stevens ED. 1978. The fishes and the aquatic environment of the central Amazon basin, with particular reference to respiratory patterns. *Can. J. Zool.* 56:717–29
55. Kramer DL, McClure M. 1981. The transit cost of aerial respiration in the catfish *Corydoras aeneus* (Callichthyidae). *Physiol. Zool.* 54:189–94
56. Krosniunas EH, Hicks JW. 1994. Cardiovascular correlates of behavior in the turtle. *Physiologist* 37(5):A–95
57. Lauder GV, Liem KF. 1983. The evolution and interrelationships of the actinopterygian fishes. *Bull. Mus. Comp. Zool. Harv.* 150(3):95–197
58. Liem KF. 1988. Form and function of lungs: the evolution of air-breathing mechanisms. *Am. Zool.* 28:739–59
59. MacKinnon MR, Heatwole H. 1981. Comparative cardiac anatomy of the reptilia. IV. The coronary arterial circulation. *J. Morphol.* 170:1–27
60. Magid AMA. 1966. Breathing and function in the spiracles in *Polypterus senegalus*. *Anim. Behav.* 14:530–33
61. Maisey JG. 1996. *Discovering Fossil Fishes*. New York: Holt, Rinehart & Winston. 223 pp.
62. Mallatt J. 1985. Reconstructing the life cycle and the feeding of ancestral vertebrates. In *Evolutionary Biology of Primitive Fishes*, ed. RE Foreman, A Gorbman, JM Dodd, R Olsson, pp. 59–68. New York: Plenum
63. Martin D, Grably S, Royer F, Benchetrit G, Rossi A, et al. 1987. Metabolic alterations induced by hypoxia in the tortoise heart, comparison between spongy and compact myocardium. *Comp. Biochem. Physiol. A* 86(2):319–23
64. McKenzie DJ, Burleson ML, Randall DJ. 1991. The effects of branchial denervation and pseudobranch ablation on cardioventilatory control in an air-breathing fish. *J. Exp. Biol.* 161:347–65
65. Millard RW, Johansen K. 1973. Ventricular outflow dynamics in the lizard, *Varanus niloticus*: responses to hypoxia, hypercarbia and diving. *J. Exp. Biol.* 60: 871–80
66. Nelson JS. 1984. *Fishes of the World*. New York: Wiley & Sons. 523 pp.
67. NIH Consensus Development Panel on Physical Activity and Cardiovascular Health. 1996. Physical activity and cardiovascular health. *J. Am. Med. Assoc.* 276(3):241–46
68. Packard GC. 1974. The evolution of air breathing in Paleozoic gnathostome fishes. *Evolution* 28:320–25
69. Poupa O, Gesser H, Johansen K. 1978. Myocardial inotropy of CO_2 in water and air-breathing vertebrates. *Am. J. Physiol.* 234(3):R155–57
70. Rantin FT. 1993. Effects of environmental oxygen changes on cardio-respiratory function in fish. In *The Vertebrate Gas Cascade, Adaptations to Environment and Mode of Life*, ed. J Eduardo, PN Bicudo, pp. 233–41. Boca Raton, FL: CRC
71. Romenskii-Olu. 1978. Blood supply of the compact and spongy myocardium of fish, amphibia, and reptiles. *Arkh. Anat. Gistol. Embriol.* 75(7):91–95
72. Santer RM, Greer Walker M. 1980. Morphological studies on the ventricle of teleost and elasmobranch hearts. *J. Zool.* 190:259–72
73. Savidge JA. 1987. Extinction of an island forest avifauna by an introduced snake. *Ecology* 68(3):660–68
74. Shelton G. 1985. Functional and cardiovascular shunts in the amphibia. In *Cardiovascular Shunts: Phylogenetic, Ontogenetic and Clinical Aspects*, ed. K Johansen, W Burggren, pp. 100–16. Copenhagen: Munksgaard
75. Shelton G, Burggren WW. 1976. Cardiovascular dynamics of the chelonia during apnea and lung ventilation. *J. Exp. Biol.* 64:323–43
76. Shi H, Jackson DC. 1997. Effects of anoxia, acidosis and temperature on the contractile properties of turtle cardiac muscle strips. *J. Exp. Biol.* 200:1965–73
77. Shipman B. 1989. *Patterns of ventilation and acid-base recovery following exhausting activity in the air-breathing fish* Lepisosteus oculatus. MS thesis. Univ. Texas, Arlington. 92 pp.
78. Sidell BD, Driedzic WR, Stowe DB, Johnston IA. 1987. Biochemical correlations of power development and metabolic fuel preferenda in fish hearts. *Physiol. Zool.* 60:221–32
79. Smatresk NJ, Burleson ML, Azizi SQ. 1986. Chemoreflexive responses to hypoxia and NaCN in longnose gar: evidence for two chemoreceptor loci. *Am. J. Physiol.* 251(Regulatory Integrative Comp. Physiol. 20):R116–25
80. Smith RS, Kramer DL. 1986. The effect of apparent predation risk on the respiratory behavior of the Florida gar (*Lepisosteus platyrhincus*). *Can. J. Zool.* 64:2133–36
81. Taigen TL, Emerson SB, Pough FH. 1982. Ecological correlates of anuran exercise physiology. *Oecologia* 52:49–56
82. Taigen TL, Pough FH. 1983. Prey preference, foraging behavior, and metabolic

characteristics of frogs. *Am. Nat.* 122(4): 509–20
83. Thomson KS. 1969. The biology of the lobe-finned fishes. *Biol. Rev.* 44:91–154
84. Thomson KS. 1980. The ecology of Devonian lobe-finned fishes. In *The Terrestrial Environment and the Origin of Land Vertebrates*, ed. AL Panchen, pp. 187–222. New York: Academic
85. Thomson KS. 1969. The environment and distribution of Paleozoic sarcopterygian fishes. *Am. J. Sci.* 267:457–64
86. Tomanek RJ. 1994. Exercise-induced coronary angiogenesis: a review. *Med. Sci. Sports Exerc.* 26(10):1245–51
87. Tota B, Cimini V, Salvatore G, Zummo G. 1983. Comparative study of the ventricular myocardium of elasmobranch and teleost fishes. *Am. J. Anat.* 167:15–32
88. Turner JD, Driedzic WR. 1980. Mechanical and metabolic response of the perfused isolated fish heart to anoxia and acidosis. *Can. J. Zool.* 58:886–89
89. Van Mierop LHS, Kutsche LM. 1981. Comparative anatomy of the ventricular septum. In *The Ventricular Septum of the Heart*, ed. ACG Wenink, pp. 35–46. The Hague: Martinus Nijhoff
90. Vorobjeva E. 1975. Some peculiarities in evolution of the rhipidistian fishes. In *Problemes Actuels de Paleontologie Colloques Int. Cent. Natn. Rech. Scient. 218*, ed. JP Lehman, pp. 223–30
91. Walker AD. 1970. A revision of the Jurassic reptile *Hallopus victor* (Marsh), with remarks on the classification of crocodiles. *Phil. Trans. R. Soc. London Ser. B* 257:323–71
92. Wasser JS, Meinertz EA, Chang SY, Lawler RG, Jackson DC. 1992. Metabolic and cardiodynamic responses of isolated turtle hearts to ischemia and reperfusion. *Am. J. Physiol.* 262:R437–43
93. West NH, Butler PJ, Bevan RM. 1992. Pulmonary blood flow at rest and during swimming in the green turtle, *Chelonia mydas*. *Physiol. Zool.* 65(2):287–310
94. Wever EG. 1978. *The Reptile Ear*. Princeton, NJ: Princeton Univ. Press. 1024 pp.
95. Wood CM, Turner JD, Graham MS. 1983. Why do fish die after severe exercise? *J. Fish Biol.* 22:189–201

Annu. Rev. Physiol. 1999. 61:593–625

MOUSE MODELS OF AIRWAY RESPONSIVENESS: Physiological Basis of Observed Outcomes and Analysis of Selected Examples Using These Outcome Indicators

J. M. Drazen, P. W. Finn, and G. T. De Sanctis
Division of Pulmonary and Critical Care Medicine, Brigham and Women's Hospital, Boston, Massachusetts 02115; e-mail: jdrazen@rics.bwh.harvard.edu

KEY WORDS: barometric plethysmography, airway responsiveness, animal models of asthma, linkage analysis, T lymphocytes

ABSTRACT

The mouse is an ideal species for investigation at the interface of lung biology and lung function. As detailed in this review, there are well-developed methods for the quantitative study of lung function in mice. These methods can be applied to mice in both terminal and nonterminal experiments. Terminal experimental approaches provide more detailed physiological information, but nonterminal measurements provide adequate data for certain experiments. In this review, we provide two examples of how these models can be used to further understanding of the primary pathobiology of airway responsiveness in both the absence and the presence of induced airway inflammation. The first model is a dissection of chromosomal loci linked to the variance in airway responsiveness observed in the absence of any manipulation to induce airway inflammation. The second model explores the role of T-cell costimulatory signals in the induction of airway hyperresponsiveness. As the number of mice with targeted deletions of effector genes or insertion of informative transgenes grows, additional examples are likely to accrue.

0066-4278/99/0315-0593$08.00

INTRODUCTION

Experimental animal models are important tools for enhancing our understanding of the pathobiology of various diseases. In the past decade, many investigators have turned to murine models of disease for three related reasons. First, dense genetic and physical maps of the murine genome have been constructed. The availability, in the public domain, of such maps keyed to multiple microsatellite markers distributed with reasonable uniformity over the murine genome allows the identification of genetic loci linked to the physiological trait of interest (1, 2). Once a genetic locus has been isolated, candidate genes in the region of that locus that are mechanistically related to expression of the phenotype of interest can be identified by a survey of genetic maps, or the gene of interest can be identified by positional cloning methods. Because of similar synteny in murine and human genomes, knowledge of a defect in a murine gene leading to a disease phenotype may elucidate corresponding defects in human genes responsible for that phenotype. Second, substantive progress has been made in dissecting the various components of murine immunology. We now have a reasonably detailed understanding of the events associated with recurrent antigen presentation and the consequent development of an inflammatory response. Third, technology has been developed that allows in mice the programmed overexpression of targeted genes or the functional ablation of their protein products. The availability of such genetically engineered mice allows the experimentalist to address questions that heretofore have not been addressable. In this review we examine examples of how mouse models have been used to further understanding of human asthma.

For decades it has been appreciated that asthma in humans is characterized by airway obstruction and hyperresponsiveness, but in the past 10 years it has come to be recognized that asthma is also characterized by chronic airway inflammation. In the wake of these findings, asthma has emerged as an important disease target for which murine models are likely to be of value. However, to maximize the value of these models, it was necessary to develop methods for the quantitative assessment of airway function in mice. Such experimental techniques have been developed and used to probe various aspects of the asthmatic response.

In this review we focus on three topics with respect to the use of mice as models of the asthmatic response. First, we review the methods used to measure lung function in mice and to interpret the information derived from these measurements. Second, we review the factors that are known to modulate airway responsiveness in mice in the absence of an induced inflammatory response. Third, we address a specific facet of the immunology of asthma as reflected in murine models: the role of costimulatory molecules in modifying airway inflammation and responsiveness as a result of allergen challenge.

ASSESSMENT OF AIRWAY MECHANICS IN MICE

Human asthma is characterized by two distinct manifestations of altered airway mechanics: intermittent reversible airway obstruction, and hyperresponsiveness of the airways to a variety of bronchoconstrictor stimuli (3, 4). For an animal model of asthma to be credible, it must recapitulate both these aspects of the asthma phenotype (5). To document this phenotype requires techniques for quantitative assessment of airway patency. In this section, we evaluate such techniques that have been adopted over the past decade for use in murine systems.

Measurement of Airway Function in Humans

In human asthma, airway obstruction is most often measured with indices derived from tests of forced expiration. During such tests, patients are asked to inspire to total lung capacity and then to exhale as rapidly as possible into an instrument that records expired volume versus time. From this recording, the peak expiratory flow (PEF), the volume of air expired in the first second of exhalation [termed the forced expiratory volume in the first second (FEV_1)] and the mean flow over the middle one half of the vital capacity [termed the maximal midexpiratory flow (MMEF)] are calculated. Although the physiology of forced expiration is complex (6, 7), during a forced expiratory maneuver, it is the mechanical properties of the airways—namely, airway size and airway wall stiffness—that determine the rate at which air can be expelled from the lungs. The primary relationship governing the rate of expiratory airflow is the wave-speed equation for flow through collapsible tubes (6). This equation states that maximal expiratory airflow rate is proportional to airway size to the 3/2 power (decreasing airway size decreases maximal airflow) and to the square root of airway wall stiffness (increasing airway wall stiffness increases airflow). Thus, if a perturbation results in both airway narrowing and an increase in airway wall stiffness, the airway narrowing will predominate and expiratory airflow will be diminished. The advantage of measurements made during forced exhalation is that given a certain minimal level of expiratory effort, the values recorded are determined entirely by the mechanics of the lung, are independent of the level of effort, and require no invasive instrumentation of the test subject. Thus, human airway obstruction can be assessed easily and noninvasively. Although forced expiratory flow rates can be measured in mice (8), such measurements are technically demanding and the precise geometry at the junction

Table 1 Techniques available for the assessment of airway mechanics in the mouse

Techniques
Techniques requiring removal of the lungs from the host
Contraction of isolated airway segments
Trapped gas volume
Mechanical measurements on excised lungs
Techniques requiring anesthesia and instrumentation of the airway
Airway pressure measurements during mechanical ventilation
Occlusion mechanics
Measurement of pulmonary resistance and dynamic lung compliance
Measurement of lung tissue properties using alveolar capsules
Techniques that do not require instrumentation of the airway
Forced oscillatory mechanics
Airway resistance via dual chamber plethysmography
Barometric plethysmography

of the tracheal cannula and the trachea has a profound influence on flow rates. Thus, techniques have been developed to measure the mechanical properties of the lung and to infer from these measurements the state of the airways.

Measurement of Airway Function in Mice

Three techniques are used to measure lung mechanics in mice (Table 1). In the first, the physical properties of the lungs or airways are assessed after their removal from the host; in the second, animals are anesthetized and instrumented to allow the recording of airway mechanics; and in the third, neither anesthesia nor airway instrumentation is required. Each technique measures a different aspect of lung function, and each has its own strengths and weaknesses.

TECHNIQUES REQUIRING REMOVAL OF LUNGS FROM THE HOST *Contraction of isolated airway segments* In the lung-removal method, the trachea and lungs are removed and the airways are dissected and placed in organ baths for assessment of the contractile response (9, 10). Either isometric or isotonic responses can be measured after immersion of the tissue in an appropriate physiological buffer and connection of the tissues to appropriate force or motion transducers. Airway contraction is induced by bathing the tissue in physiological buffers containing appropriate contractile mediators (9, 11, 12) or by electrical-field stimulation of the airway smooth muscle in the preparation (10). Airway responses are quantitated by measuring the magnitude of response to a given stimulus or measuring the amount of a stimulus required to achieve a given contractile response. These techniques offer the precision of an isolated tissue assay in which the primary variables—i.e. initial length or tension and composition of the bathing medium—can be controlled; an additional advantage is the capacity to study a number of replicate tissues from the same animal. Finally, because contraction is measured directly rather than inferred from measures of airway mechanics, the complexities of the geometric and mechanical variables that complicate interpretation of data from intact systems are eliminated; all the contractile response observed is due to smooth muscle contraction.

The drawbacks of this approach are twofold. In vivo obstruction of the airway lumen occurs as a result of both smooth muscle contraction, which is measured in isolated tissue assays, and release of secretions into the airway lumen, which is not reflected in isolated tissue assays. Thus, only the component of airway obstruction due to muscular constriction can be assessed. Second, in situ, the airways are innervated by a variety of nerves and perfused by the bronchial circulation; these connections are interrupted in isolated tissue assays.

The contractile response of isolated tracheal tissues to neural stimulation has been shown to be modified by allergen sensitization and challenge. Specifically, tracheal tissues removed from animals exposed to antigen sensitization and challenge are more responsive to neural stimulation than are tissues removed from control animals (10, 13). These data indicate that enhanced responsiveness to contractile stimuli after allergen challenge is due, in part, to modifications of the contractile potential of airway smooth muscle.

Trapped gas volume In mice, because the chest wall has little outward recoil near functional residual capacity (FRC) (14), the lungs are the predominant determinant of respiratory system relaxation volume. In the normal murine lung, there appears to be enough airway tone that certain airways are closed even at FRC; in the presence of induced airway constriction, a greater proportion of airways are closed near FRC. When an airway closes, it traps a small volume of gas behind it. Investigators have taken advantage of this gas trapping by measuring the volume of gas in lungs excised from mice under varying experimental circumstances (15). The volume of gas trapped in a mouse lung can be precisely measured by monitoring the change in weight of an anchor suspended in a vessel filled with saline that occurs when the lung is attached to the anchor in such a way that the lung and anchor remain fully submerged in the saline (i.e. Archimedes' principle) (16). Because the density of lung tissue is close to that of saline, the apparent decrease in weight of the anchor is numerically equivalent to the gas volume of the lungs in milliliters. The lungs must be removed from the euthanized mouse to make this measurement.

This technique has a number of advantages. First, the measurements are technically easy to perform: All one needs to master is the technique of removing the lungs from the thoracic cavity without puncturing them. Because the volume of gas trapped does not change appreciably over the interval from euthanasia to measurement, the values obtained reflect the physiology of the lung at the moment the mouse is euthanized. This approach offers an advantage over isolated tissue strips in that all neural and anatomic relationships are intact at the time the lung volume is determined (i.e. the moment of euthanasia). Airway obstruction due to muscular airway narrowing, as well as that due to mucus occlusion of the airway, can result in an increase in trapped gas volume. Furthermore, because euthanasia can be quickly achieved, animals are free of the confounding effects of anesthetic use until the data of interest are obtained.

The disadvantages of this approach are that only one measurement can be made per mouse and that the precise relationship between airway obstruction and the amount of gas being trapped in the lung is not known. Our general knowledge of lung anatomy indicates that the airways whose closure is responsible for the gas trapping that contributes to the physiological signal measured are membranous bronchioles and smaller airways. Thus, it is possible that isolated large-airway constriction occurs without registering a change in this outcome indicator.

This method has been used to compare the bronchoconstrictor effects of aerosols generated from methacholine solutions in two inbred strains of mice, A/J and C3H/HeJ (15). In this experiment, the investigators showed that A/J mice were over 100 times more sensitive to these effects than were C3H/HeJ mice. Thus, the rank order of sensitivity of these two strains to the bronchoconstrictor actions of methacholine, as ascertained by the trapped gas volume technique, is similar to the rank order of methacholine sensitivity determined by means of other, more conventional outcome indicators (17, 18).

Mechanical measurements on excised lungs Isolated murine lungs can be prepared for the measurement of static compliance as well as dynamic mechanical properties during mechanical ventilation. To make such measurements, the lungs are excised from a euthanized host and placed in an apparatus that allows accurate and precise recording of delivered volume and transpulmonary pressure (19). From simultaneous measurements of pressure and flow, static and dynamic compliance as well as pulmonary resistance can be calculated. This method has been used to detect differences in the mechanical properties of the lung among mice of various ages, but it has not been used, to the best of our knowledge, to assess the effects of bronchoconstrictor mediators. Indeed, because of the possibility of nonuniform airway closure, it may well be difficult to obtain reproducible results with respect to the effects of bronchoconstrictor mediators in such a preparation.

This technique has the theoretical advantage of providing information about static pulmonary compliance. However, because asthma is believed to modify predominantly airway rather than parenchymal properties, there is likely to be little utility for measurements of static compliance.

TECHNIQUES REQUIRING ANESTHESIA AND INSTRUMENTATION OF THE AIRWAY

A number of techniques for assessing airway responses have been used in anesthetized and instrumented mice. These techniques share advantages and disadvantages. Among the advantages is the bypassing of the upper airway by a tracheal cannula, which eliminates noise due to narrowing of the upper airway in respiratory resistance measurements. Furthermore, because the mouse is an obligate, nose-breathing animal and the upper airway may comprise a large fraction of total respiratory resistance, bypassing the upper airway may increase the fraction of the total transrespiratory pressure signal that is attributable to changes in airway mechanics. Another advantage of these techniques is that ventilatory pattern is controlled by a mechanical ventilator. Thus, induction of airway inflammation does not cause changes in the respiratory rate or pattern that could influence measured pulmonary mechanics even in the absence of changes in the state of the airways. A further advantage is that all of these techniques retain the normal neural and anatomical relationships between the lung and its regulatory structures. In addition, within the timeframe of surgical anesthesia—i.e. up to 6 h—each of these techniques allows repeated measures of pulmonary mechanical indices in the same animal. Furthermore, because the animal remains alive, the full effects of cells recruited to the lung and of cytokines, chemokines, and mediators released by these cells can be appreciated.

A major disadvantage of these techniques is the need for general anesthesia before instrumentation of the airway and thorax. Anesthetic agents may alter neural traffic, modify lung blood flow, or exert agonist or antagonist effects on certain receptors.

Airway pressure measurements during mechanical ventilation Of the measurements made during mechanically assisted ventilation in an anesthetized animal, measuring airway pressure is the simplest (17, 20–22). Once the animal is anesthetized, a tracheal cannula with a side tap for measuring pressure is inserted into the trachea. For the data to be meaningful, the level of anesthesia must be deep enough to prevent ventilatory efforts by the mouse. During mechanical ventilation with a fixed tidal volume and frequency, a recording is made of transrespiratory pressure swings (Figure 1), and from this record, a baseline is established. Then the change that occurs in this pressure-time profile when a bronchoconstrictor stimulus is applied is measured, with the area under the peak pressure versus time envelope recorded as the airway pressure time index (APTI) resulting from the applied stimulus. This technique is simple because no measurements of respiratory flow or volume are made. Its disadvantage is that it measures only total respiratory impedance and does not allow a physiological dissection to determine whether the observed changes are in airway resistance or in lung elasticity.

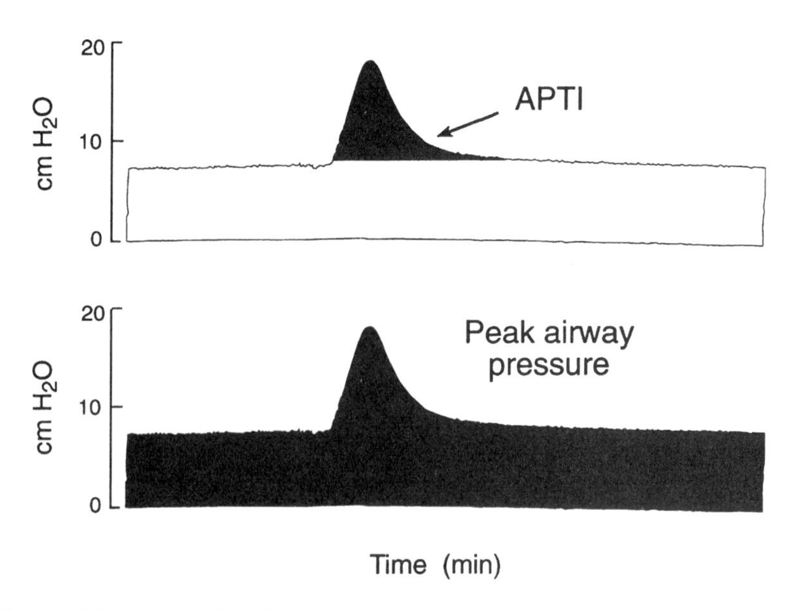

Figure 1 Measurement of the airway pressure time index (APTI), the area under the peak airway pressure curve over the baseline value, induced by administration of an agonist. [Modified from Levitt & Mitzner (17) with permission.]

Occlusion mechanics In the occlusion method, the animal is instrumented with a tracheal cannula connected to a flow transducer as well as to a tap for measuring tracheal pressure. Mechanical ventilation of the respiratory system is initiated and maintained throughout the experiment. Once again, a deep surgical plane of anesthesia must be maintained to prevent the mouse from initiating respiratory efforts. To measure respiratory resistance, simultaneous recordings are made of transrespiratory pressure and airflow (23). An electrical circuit through a solenoid valve is required to allow sudden occlusion of the airway at the instant of end inspiration. The airway occlusion is held until transrespiratory pressure reaches a plateau value (Figure 2). At that point, the occlusion is released, the change in transrespiratory pressure and exhaled volume (determined as the integral of expired flow) is recorded, and mechanical ventilation is reinstituted. Respiratory resistance (Rrs) is calculated by dividing the transrespiratory pressure difference in the presence and absence of airflow (Pr in Figure 2) by the magnitude of the inspiratory airflow. Respiratory compliance (Crs) is calculated by dividing the volume exhaled after the onset of occlusion to FRC by the transrespiratory pressure difference determined at the end of the occlusion and FRC (Pc in Figure 2). Values for Rrs and Crs computed by this technique have been used to assess airway responsiveness to methacholine; the data obtained agree closely with the data obtained by the APTI method (23).

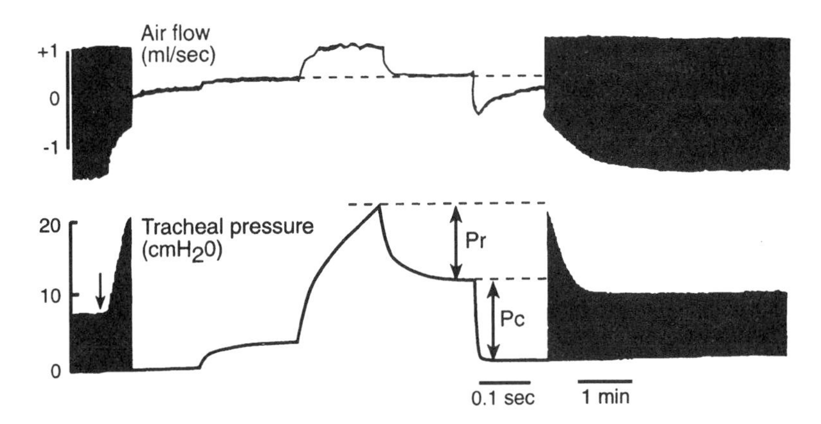

Figure 2 Measurement of respiratory mechanics by occlusion. Simultaneous measurements of airflow, tidal volume, and transrespiratory pressure are made. The airway is occluded suddenly during tidal mechanical ventilation at end-inspiration, and the occlusion held until transrespiratory pressure ceases to change. The occlusion is released, but tidal ventilation is not reinitiated until transrespiratory pressure reaches a new plateau value. P_r, Transrespiratory pressure due to resistive losses; P_c, transrespiratory pressure due to elastic losses. (Reproduced from Reference 23 with permission.)

The advantage of this technique over measurement of APTI is that it allows the investigator to ascertain respiratory resistance and compliance separately. Although a discussion of the physiological meaning of each of these parameters is beyond the scope of this review (24), two general points bear consideration. First, based on the airway size versus airway generation relationship that holds true for all mammalian lungs (25), isolated changes in respiratory (or pulmonary) resistance reflect the state of the large airways, whereas isolated changes in respiratory (or pulmonary) compliance reflect changes in small airways or the parenchyma. Thus, comparison of the effects of interventions on these various pulmonary mechanical outcomes allows insight into the anatomic locus of the observed changes; when isolated measures of APTI are reported, no such anatomic information is available.

There are two major disadvantages of the occlusion technique. First, only inspiratory resistance is determined. Second, because the respiratory pattern must be interrupted to acquire the data needed for the calculation of respiratory resistance and compliance, continuous recordings of these mechanical indices are not possible.

Measurement of pulmonary resistance and dynamic lung compliance Pulmonary resistance and pulmonary dynamic compliance represent fundamental physical properties of the lung. They are derived by fitting continuous data for tidal airflow, tidal volume, and transpulmonary pressure to the first-order differential equation describing the relationships among these variables:

$$P_{TP} = \dot{V} \cdot R_L + V_T/C_{dyn},$$

where P_{TP} is transpulmonary pressure, $\dot{V}$ is tidal airflow, R_L is pulmonary resistance, V_T is tidal volume, and C_{dyn} is the dynamic pulmonary compliance. A number of methods for deriving values for R_L and C_{dyn} from the primary measures of tidal airflow and transpulmonary pressure have been devised and tested (18, 26, 27).

Measurements of transpulmonary pressure and tidal airflow require more extensive instrumentation of the intact animal than any of the above methods (28). Transpulmonary pressure measurements necessitate calculation with a differential pressure transducer of the differential pressure between the tracheal cannula and the pleural surface. Pleural surface pressure measurements have typically been made in mice by bilateral thoracostomy, which equalizes pleural surface and body surface pressure. This approach requires a deep plane of surgical anesthesia and mechanical ventilation with a mechanism on the expiratory line to maintain an end-expiratory pressure above atmospheric. Tidal airflow has been measured by placing the mouse in a constant-mass body plethysmograph with the tracheal cannula leading out of the plethysmograph; in this configuration, changes in plethysmograph pressure—assuming that isothermal conditions are maintained—are proportional to changes in lung volume. If measurements are to be reliable, the transducer systems reporting tidal volume and transpulmonary pressure must be in phase and without dynamic distortion up to at least 10 Hz.

The advantage of this method is that breath-by-breath recordings of lung mechanics (both R_L and C_{dyn}) are available. Thus, the transient changes in lung mechanics resulting from an intervention such as the infusion of a bronchoactive mediator can be fully recorded. The measurement of R_L and C_{dyn} has been widely used in studies in which murine pulmonary physiology is the primary outcome indicator (28–35). Compared with the measurement of APTI, this approach is disadvantageous in that it is technically difficult to produce the high-fidelity recordings of transpulmonary pressure and airflow required for accurate solution of the equation of motion of the lung.

Measurement of lung tissue properties with alveolar capsules It is possible to obtain more information about the mechanical properties of the lung by adding a measurement—that of alveolar pressure derived from direct recording through an alveolar capsule (36)—to those needed to determine R_L. This approach yields additional information about the mechanical properties of the lung parenchyma (37). However, because asthma is thought to affect primarily the airways rather than the parenchyma, this approach is likely to be of little value to those interested in the use of pulmonary physiological outcome indicators as a measure of asthma-like changes in the lung.

TECHNIQUES THAT DO NOT REQUIRE INSTRUMENTATION OF THE AIRWAY A number of techniques have been developed for assessing lung mechanics in mice that have not been instrumented. Because these methods do not require the use of anesthetic agents or surgical preparation, the same mouse can be studied on a number of occasions. This is the major advantage of this group of techniques. However, convenience has its price: In the absence of instrumentation, no direct measures of the pressures driving ventilation are obtained, and the inferences that can be made with respect to lung mechanics are, therefore, less robust than those made with techniques utilizing direct-pressure measurements. In addition, because the airway is not instrumented, changes in glottal aperture or in the resistance of the nasal passages to airflow (the mouse being an obligate nose breather) are registered as changes in respiratory resistance. With respect to interventions intended to modify respiratory mechanics, bronchoactive agents also need to be administered by noninvasive techniques, such as subcutaneous injection or aerosol exposure.

Forced oscillatory mechanics The forced oscillatory method is derived from similar techniques used in humans (38) and larger animals (39, 40). An oscillating air pressure is applied at the body surface, and the subsequent flow generated at the airway opening is measured. Mice must be restrained in a tube the internal diameter of which is slightly larger than that of the animal. The tube is equipped with a movable, cone-shaped, spring-loaded facemask that provides an airtight seal around the nose (41). The mask allows fresh air to be directed into the lungs by high-impedance bias flow and permits inspiratory and expiratory airflow to be recorded. The rear chamber is sealed to a loudspeaker through which the investigator can systematically vary the pressure at the body surface. The relationship between the pressure applied at the body surface and the flow generated at the airway opening is used to calculate the pressure in phase with flow—i.e. total respiratory resistance. To prevent contamination of the signal applied at the body surface by the respiratory efforts of the mouse, filtering algorithms are used to examine the pressure-flow relationships at a frequency exceeding that of the mouse's spontaneous ventilation. This technique has been successfully used to assess the changes in airway responsiveness resulting from systemic allergen sensitization and aerosol challenge (41).

Among the techniques that do not require instrumentation of the respiratory system, this approach offers an advantage: The frequency of the pressure-flow relationships of the respiratory system is under the control of the investigator. This is also a disadvantage, as the respiratory resistance at a frequency above that used by the animal for spontaneous ventilation may not be physiologically relevant. A further disadvantage is that the face of the animal must be firmly wedged in a mask. It is possible, although not established, that facial stimulation modifies ventilatory mechanics through neural mechanisms.

Airway resistance via dual chamber plethysmography The technique for measuring specific airway conductance (S_{Gaw}) in humans has been adapted to the study of small animals (42); as of this writing (winter 1997–1998), no published reports have described the measurement of murine airway resistance by this technique. However, because there is theoretically no reason why this approach could not be adapted to the study of mice, the technique is briefly reviewed. S_{Gaw} is determined by separately measuring airflow at the airway opening and the chest wall and determining the relationship between these two signals. The technique is technically demanding in that a tight seal, usually achieved with a rubber dam, is required between the "body" and "head" chambers of the plethysmograph; any leak at the neck will result in spurious values. Furthermore, the entire system needs to be maintained in a precisely isothermal state if meaningful values of S_{Gaw} are to be obtained.

Successful application of this approach would allow repeated measurements of S_{Gaw} in the same animal. A potential disadvantage is that given that the value of S_{Gaw} is achieved by dividing airway conductance by lung volume, an intervention that decreased airway conductance (i.e. increased resistance) and increased lung volume could result in overestimation of the actual change in conductance. Furthermore, as noted above, this technique has not been adapted to mice, and other, as yet unappreciated problems could arise.

Barometric plethysmography In barometric plethysmopgraphy, unrestrained animals are placed in a chamber and the pressure fluctuations that occur during a ventilatory cycle are monitored (43–47). Although a complete theoretical analysis of this approach is beyond the scope of this review, the basic idea is that during inspiration, tidal air is warmed and heated up as it enters the thorax and the pressure change associated with this change is mirrored in the pressure within the chamber. With few assumptions, the timing of inspiration and expiration can be accurately assessed by this method. With the addition of a number of reasonable assumptions, it is possible to calculate tidal volume and minute ventilation from the changes in pressure over time. It is also possible to modify the chamber containing the mouse to provide fresh air for ventilation and to prevent thermal drift as the chamber temperature increases from the body heat of the enclosed animal (45).

Recently this approach was extended by empiric analysis of the respiratory pattern observed in unrestrained mice. Hamelmann and coworkers (47) divided the expiratory period into two phases: an early relaxation phase and a later phase

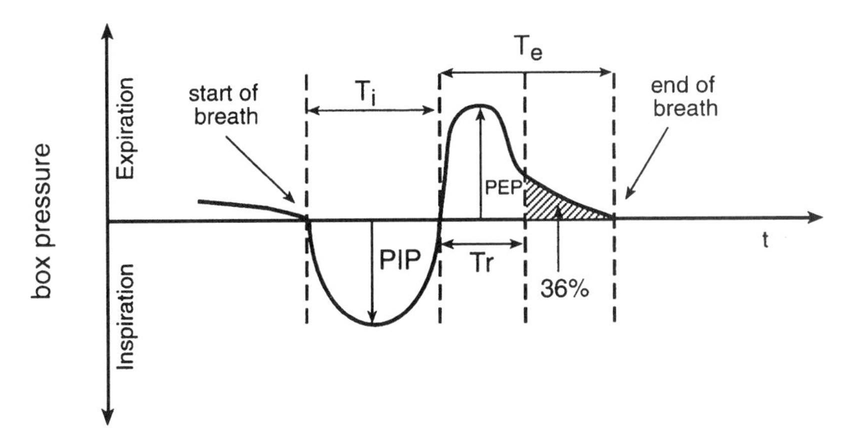

Figure 3 Computation of the parameters measured by barometric plethysmography. Schematic figure of a box pressure wave in inspiration (*down*) and expiration (*up*) explaining the computation of the parameters measured by whole body plethysmography. T_i, inspiratory time (in seconds), time from start of inspiration to end of inspiration; T_e, expiratory time (in seconds), time from end of inspiration to start of next inspiration; P_{IP}, peak inspiratory pressure, maximal negative box pressure occurring in one breath; P_{EP}, peak expiratory pressure, maximal positive box pressure occurring in one breath; f, frequency (breaths/min), respiratory rate; T_r, is the relaxation time (in seconds), time of the decay of the expiratory pressure-area plot to 36% of total box pressure during expiration. (Reproduced from Reference 47 with permission.)

(Figure 3). They computed respiratory pause with the equation

$$\text{Pause} = (T_e - T_r)/T_r,$$

where T_e is time of expiration and T_r is time required for the area under the chamber pressure-time curve during expiration to decrease to 36% of its total value. This relaxation time bears no relationship to the more commonly physiologically defined relaxation time observed when an animal is allowed to exhale without restraint (14). The researchers further noted that when breathing was unobstructed, the plethysmographic pressure signal during inspiration and expiration had equal deflections, whereas when breathing was obstructed, the expiratory pressure deflection was greater than was the inspiratory pressure deflection. Thus, they defined a parameter, termed enhanced pause (P_{enh}), as

$$P_{enh} = P_{EP}/P_{IP} \times (T_e - T_r)/T_r,$$

where P_{EP} is the peak expiratory pressure chamber deflection, P_{IP} is the peak inspiratory pressure chamber deflection, and the other terms are as defined above.

Hamelmann and coworkers demonstrated that the changes in P_{enh} closely reflected the changes observed in R_L and C_{dyn} during bronchoconstriction induced by aerosolized methacholine. They further showed that when test mice were sensitized and challenged with allergen, P_{enh} accurately reflected the enhanced response to methacholine observed with R_L and C_{dyn} as outcome indicators. They concluded that whole-body plethysmography was "a valid indicator of airway hyperresponsiveness after allergic sensitization in mice" (47).

The advantages of this technique are obvious. Mice are placed, relatively unrestrained, in the barometric plethysmograph, and airway responsiveness to inhaled bronchodilators is ascertained by their exposure to aerosols generated from solutions of a bronchoconstrictor agonist. Moreover, the same mouse can be studied on multiple occasions; through repeat study, experimental variance in the measurement of airway responsiveness can be minimized.

There are two major disadvantages of this technique. First, the parameter measured, P_{enh}, unlike all of the other outcome parameters reviewed in this chapter, is not derived from first physical principles but rather is an outcome indicator based entirely on empiric signal processing. As a consequence, the absolute value of P_{enh} has no physical meaning, and this parameter cannot be compared from mouse to mouse. Second, if an intervention is undertaken that results in a change in the respiratory pattern during induced bronchoconstriction, then P_{enh} can change without true airway obstruction—or dilation—occurring. Thus, investigators who use P_{enh} as an outcome indicator must at least inspect the barometric plethysmograph pressure tracings to assure themselves that the pressure variations noted correspond to those from which the P_{enh} parameter was derived; this validity check should be noted when the experimental results are reported. Ideally, until further experience with this novel technique is gained and the reliability of P_{enh} as a surrogate for bronchoconstriction is established, P_{enh} measures should be confirmed with a measurement of airway obstruction based on physical principles rather than signal processing.

GENETIC VARIATIONS IN AIRWAY RESPONSIVENESS

The above-noted measures of airway responses have been used to assess dose-response relationships in which an agonist capable of inducing airway narrowing in mice is administered in geometrically increasing doses while the effects of the agonist on indices of pulmonary obstruction are monitored. Although airway hyperresponsiveness has been shown to be inducible by environmental agents, including allergens (48, 49), low-molecular-weight chemical sensitizers (50), and ozone (51–53), in both humans and animals, the variability in airway responsiveness attributable to genetic influences has been scantly addressed in the past and has only recently been investigated in humans (54, 55) and animals

(17, 18, 22, 56). This section reviews the genetic basis of airway responsiveness in inbred mice.

Distribution of Airway Responsiveness Among Strains of Inbred Mice

All mice within an inbred strain carry the same allele at a given genetic locus and can be considered as a family of "identical twins" at all autosomes. Thus, in a group of inbred mice, variability of a given parameter reflects environmental influences. Outbred populations, on the other hand, demonstrate considerable heterogeneity at every genetic locus across the entire genome. Therefore, variability of a trait is due to both genetic and environmental components. When multiple genes are interacting with the environment to control a complex phenotypic trait in a population, the use of inbred rather than outbred populations is desirable because the putatively responsible genes will segregate randomly in a heterogeneous outbred population. For example, although the distribution of airway responsiveness can vary as much as 300-fold in outbred populations such as dogs (57), rats (58), and guinea pigs (59), that described in inbred strains of mice is considerably less—i.e. on the order of 10-fold (20, 60, 61).

Several investigators have screened numerous inbred strains of mice for differences in airway responsiveness (17, 20, 60, 61) and have reported significantly greater interstrain than intrastrain variability. This finding is consistent with the hypothesis that airway responsiveness is a heritable trait. Levitt & Mitzner first described interstrain differences in airway responsiveness among nine common inbred strains of mice (17). They measured the APTI after an intravenous bolus of either acetylcholine or serotonin (17, 20). Of the nine strains (Figure 4), the C57BL6/J, SJL/J, and C3H/HeJ strains exhibited the least responsiveness, whereas the A/J and AKR/J strains exhibited the greatest degree of airway narrowing (17). Indeed, there was a sixfold difference in airway responsiveness between the phenotypically divergent C3H/HeJ and A/J strains.

A subsequent study by Konno and coworkers (60) confirmed these findings. In this study, differences in airway responsiveness were assessed after intravenous challenge with methacholine, a congener of acetylcholine. Among the six strains of inbred mice investigated (A/J, DBA/2, WBB6F1-W/Wv, WBB6F1-+/+, C3H/HeN, and C57BL/6 mice), A/J and DBA/2 were designated high-responder strains and C57BL/6 and C3H/HeN were designated low-responder strains.

Several other studies have reported strain distribution patterns of airway responsiveness similar to those published by Levitt & Mitzner (17). Chiba and coworkers (62) ascertained the effects of strain and route of administration on airway responsiveness in C57BL/6 and DBA/2 mice. No differences in baseline respiratory resistance were noted between strains prior to challenge with

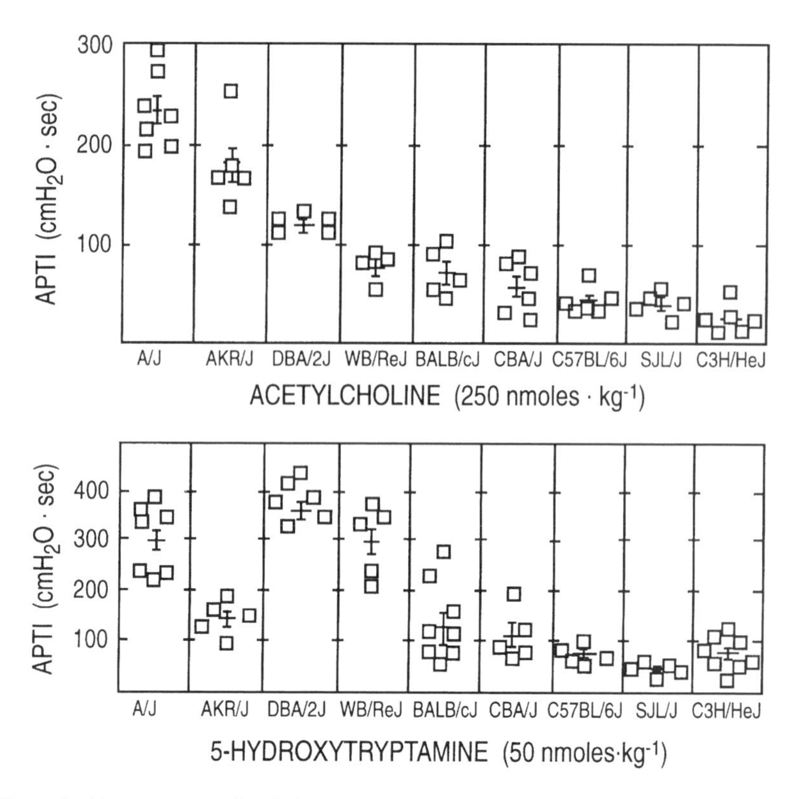

Figure 4 Airway pressure-time index (APTI) response to either acetylcholine (250 nmol/kg) or 5-hydroxytryptamine (50 nmol/kg intravenously) in different strains of inbred mice. Each symbol represents APTI response for an individual mouse. (Reprinted from Reference 20 with permission.)

acetylcholine; airway responsiveness was significantly greater in the DBA/2 strain than in the C57BL/6 strain only after intravenous challenge and not after inhalation. These results not only confirmed the genetic differences described by Levitt & Mitzner for these two strains, they also illustrated the problems that can arise when genetic differences in airway responsiveness are assessed with challenge by different routes. In two additional studies using the APTI method of phenotyping, Zhang et al (21) and Longphre & Kleeberger (61) showed a rank order among inbred strains of mice for airway responsiveness to acetylcholine in the absence of antigen or environmental exposure. They demonstrated the C3H/HeJ and C57BL/6J strains to be hyporesponsive and the A/J and AKR/J strains to be most responsive. An investigation into the mechanism(s) underlying the difference in airway responsiveness between the C3H/HeJ and A/J strains suggested that the hyperresponsiveness of the A/J strain may be a result of enhanced muscarinic receptor signal transduction, which in turn is due to increased agonist affinity for muscarinic receptors and up-regulation of G-protein levels (63).

Studies of serotonin-induced airway responses (assessed by APTI) have been carried out in a number of standardized laboratory inbred strains of mice (20). The rank order of airway responsiveness to serotonin is similar but not identical to that of airway responsiveness to acetylcholine (Figure 4). Specifically, although the C3H/HeJ, SJL/J, C57BL/6J, and CBA/J strains exhibited a diminished response and the A/J strain exhibited a significant response to the two agonists, the DBA/2J, AKR/J, WBA/2J, and WB/ReJ strains exhibited varying degrees of airway reactivity to the two agonists (Figure 4). For example, Levitt & Mitzner demonstrated that the AKR/J strain was the least reactive to serotonin, yet it was among the most reactive to acetylcholine (17). In view of the results, the authors hypothesized that the dissimilarity in responsiveness to acetylcholine and serotonin was attributable to different genes that are inherited independently. The differential responses observed by Levitt & Mitzner among certain strains to both agonists are inconsistent with the findings of Konno and coworkers, who examined bronchial reactivity to both serotonin and methacholine in C57BL/6, WBB6F1-W/Wv, WBB6F1-+/+, A/J, DBA/2, and C3H/HeN mice and found no difference in the rank order of responsiveness to both agonists (60). The discrepancy between the findings of these two studies may be explained by several factors, including the age of the mice at the time of study, methods of assessment of airway reactivity, and housing conditions.

Mendelian Models of Airway Responsiveness

Mendelian traits differ from complex traits in that they are the result of the contribution of a single mutant gene and not multiple genes. The gene can exert a large effect on the phenotype, and the transmission of the trait follows simple patterns of inheritance. Mendelian traits of autosomal origin are encoded by genes on chromosomes other than the sex chromosomes and are considered dominant if they are expressed in animals heterozygous at the locus of interest. Recessive traits, on the other hand, are not expressed in heterozygous animals and manifest only when two recessive mutant alleles are present in the organism at the locus of interest. If one assumes that there is only one normal allele and one mutant allele, three genotypes are possible: heterozygous, homozygous normal, and homozygous mutant. In order to determine the pattern of inheritance of a Mendelian trait, a segregation analysis is performed whereby the transmission of the trait is followed in the F_1 (first filial), in F_2 intercross progeny produced by crossing the F_1 progeny ($F_1 \times F_1$), and in the backcross (B_1) offspring produced by crossing the F_1 progeny back to either parental strain ($F_1 \times$ Parent). The F_2 and backcross offspring are regarded as segregating progeny because genetic loci will segregate independently at meiosis, resulting in a different array of progenitor alleles on each chromosome. If the ratio of affected to unaffected progeny in the segregating generations follows a Mendelian mode of inheritance, the genetic trait of interest is most likely controlled by a single gene. The variance of the phenotype in the nonsegregating F_1 progeny represents environmental effects, whereas the variance in the segregating F_2 intercross and backcross progeny reflects both genetic and environmental effects.

Levitt & Mitzner (17) were the first to adapt this genetic strategy to determine the pattern of inheritance for acetylcholine-induced airway hyperreactivity in various inbred strains of mice and progeny derived from simple crosses. Specifically, they carried out a genetic analysis of progeny derived from a cross between a hyporesponsive (C3H/HeJ) and a hyperresponsive (A/J) mouse strain, using the APTI as their outcome indicator. On the basis of their segregation analysis of airway responsiveness in a cross between A/J and C3H/HeJ progenitor strains (reviewed below), they concluded that airway responsiveness to acetylcholine was inherited as a simple (Mendelian) autosomal recessive trait in mice (17). APTI measurements followed a single fixed dose of acetylcholine, and animals were designated as hyporesponsive or hyperresponsive depending on whether they achieved a given preestablished threshold value for APTI. From an initial screen of many inbred strains, two strains were chosen for the segregation analysis: one hyporeactive [C3H/HeJ (C)] and the other hyperreactive [A/J (A)]. The A/J mice were sixfold more responsive than the C3H/HeJ mice. When the F_1 progeny (CAF_1 or ACF_1, with the female represented by the first letter) were phenotyped, they were uniformly hyporeactive; when C3H/HeJ were crossed with CAF_1 progeny, the backcross progeny were exclusively hyporeactive. When the authors examined the variance of the APTI in the F_2 intercross ($ACF_1 \times CAF_1$) progeny, two phenotypic groups were easily distinguishable, with an observed 3:1 ratio of hyporeactive to hyperreactive progeny (Figure 5). These results led the authors to postulate that mice homozygous for the mutant allele were hyperreactive whereas heterozygotes exhibited a hyporeactive phenotype. Because recessive Mendelian inheritance is characterized by a trait that is latent in the heterozygote and because the observed frequencies in the backcross and F_2 progeny were consistent with this mode of inheritance, the authors concluded that a single autosomal recessive locus regulated acetylcholine-mediated airway reactivity in the C3H/HeJ and A/J cross.

In a later study, Levitt & Mitzner carried out a similar segregation analysis using serotonin, rather than acetylcholine, as a bronchoconstrictor agonist (20). In this study, DBA/2J mice were hyperresponsive and C57BL/6J mice were hyporesponsive. The APTI response was four- to fivefold greater in DBA/2J than in C57BL/6J mice, with no overlap in responses. Given these differences,

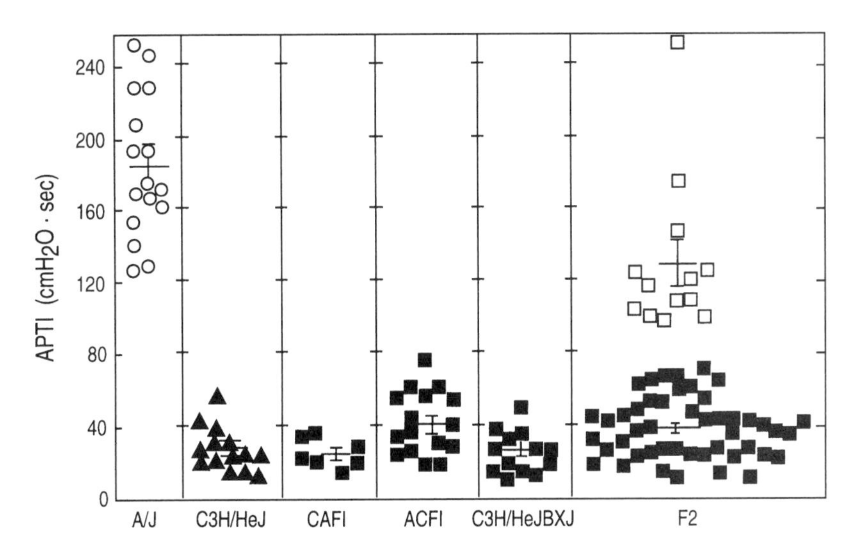

Figure 5 Airway responses to 25 μg Ach, intravenously, in C3H/HeJ and A/J and their progeny. Means $\pm$ standard error are presented. The relationship of APTI from individual animals of each cross is illustrated. CAF1, C3H/HeJ female $\times$ A/J male; ACF1, A/J female $\times$ C3H/HeJ male; C3H/HeJ BX, C3H/HeJ female $\times$ CAF1 male; F2, ACF1 $\times$ CAF1. (Reprinted from Reference 17 with permission.)

the authors phenotyped the progeny of crosses derived from the two parental strains. Once again, animals with a given APTI threshold were designated hyperreactive and those falling below that threshold were designated hyporeactive. Although the nonsegregating F_1 progeny exhibited a phenotype similar to that of the hyporesponsive C57BL/6J parent, analysis of the segregating progeny led the investigators to conclude that the inheritance of airway hyperreactivity to serotonin was attributable to a single autosomal recessive gene.

Thus, although a similar mode of inheritance was found for acetylcholine and serotonin, the distinct strain distribution patterns for airway hyperresponsiveness to both agonists in segregating F_2 mice led the authors to conclude that the putative responsiveness genes do not cosegregate, are not closely linked, and are inherited independently. They therefore postulated that nonspecific airway hyperresponsiveness to these two bronchoconstrictor agents is controlled by more than one gene and is agonist-specific in the mouse.

Complex (Polygenic) Models of Airway Responsiveness

Although Mendelian traits are believed to be caused by a single gene, complex or polygenic traits are caused by the action of multiple genes, with each gene contributing to the overall phenotype. In the case of native or intrinsic airway responsiveness, recent studies suggest that the pattern of inheritance is more complex than was suggested by Levitt & Mitzner (17, 20). Like earlier studies, these recent studies have used parental inbred strains differing substantially in airway responsiveness. However, they have extended previous studies by considering airway responsiveness as a quantitative trait, using the actual level of airway responsiveness rather than the observed airway responsiveness in the genetic analysis to determine whether a mouse is a high or a low responder. Such a genetic analysis allows the recognition of specific regions linked to the expression of the relevant trait. In particular, the identification of a comprehensive set of unique genetic markers that are distributed across the mouse genome and are polymorphic among various standardized laboratory inbred strains has made it possible to identify linkages to defined areas of the genome through the use of quantitative trait locus (QTL) linkage analysis (64). These linkage studies utilize progeny of mouse crosses to correlate quantitative data, such as airway responsiveness levels, with genotypic data in order to map loci contributing to the overall phenotype. This whole-genome search strategy employs interval mapping in which both phenotypic and genotypic data are used to estimate the probable genotype and the most likely QTL effect across the whole genome. In this manner, investigators have successfully identified region(s) of the genome linked to the expression of several quantitative traits, including hypertension (65) in rats and, more recently, airway hyperresponsiveness in mice (18, 22).

Two recent studies have successfully mapped QTLs linked to airway hyperresponsiveness in mice. These studies employed different methods of phenotyping airway responsiveness and investigated hybrid crosses derived from different parental strains; in both studies, however, the airway responsiveness phenotype of the two strains investigated varied substantially. In the first study (18), De Sanctis and coworkers used measurements of pulmonary resistance (R_L) before and after a series of increasing doses of intravenously delivered methacholine, a congener of acetylcholine that is not subject to degradation by acetylcholinesterase. From the relationship between the pulmonary resistance (R_L) measured and the dose of methacholine administered, the effective dose of methacholine required to cause a doubling of pulmonary resistance (ED_{200} R_L) was calculated by log-linear interpolation in the parental strains [A/J (hyperresponsive) and C57BL/6J (B) (hyporesponsive)] and progeny derived from hybrid crosses. Numerically low values of the log ED_{200} R_L index are consistent with a heightened bronchoconstrictor response to methacholine—a phenotype characteristically observed in asthmatics. Numerically high values indicate the opposite: a hyporesponsive phenotype consistent with a low level of sensitivity. To control for any confounding effects of age, gender, or airway infection on airway responsiveness, De Sanctis and coworkers studied only age- and gender-matched mice raised under barrier conditions. Of the inbred

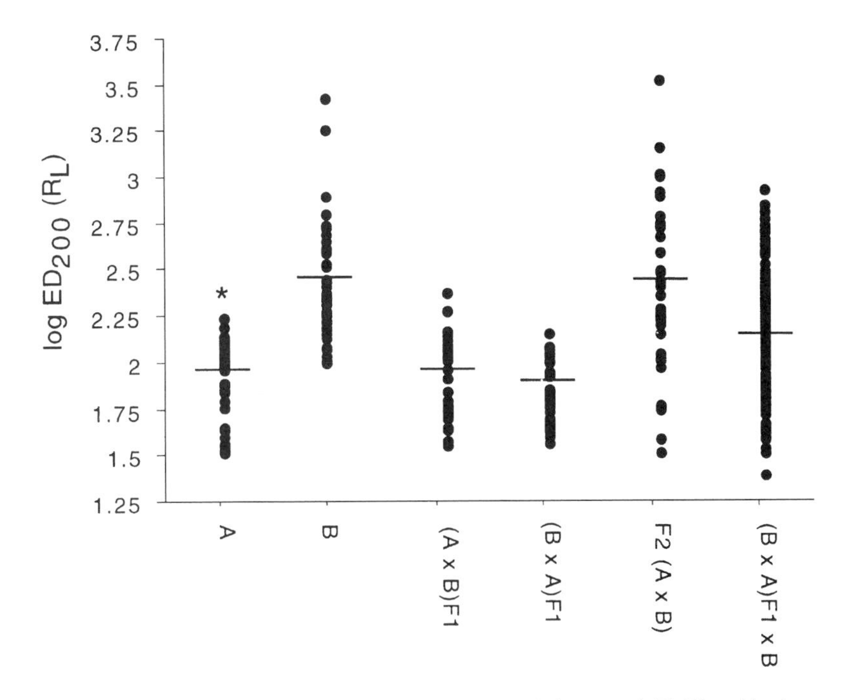

Figure 6 Scatterplot of log ED_{200} R_L from individual animals in parental, F1, F2, and backcross mice. (*Asterisk*) Significantly different from C57BL/6J mice ($P < 0.05$). (A, A/J; B, C57BL/6J). (Reprinted from Reference 18 with permission.)

strains, the A/J strain exhibited, on average, a threefold greater degree of airway responsiveness than did the C57BL6/J strain, a finding consistent with previously published data (18). F_1 progeny derived from reciprocal parental crosses (ABF_1 and BAF_1) were similar in phenotype to the A/J group (Figure 6). Thus, no parental influence was inferred. Normal quantile analysis of airway responsiveness in a segregating F_2 intercross derived from an A/J and C57BL/6J background segregated in a unimodal normal distribution. This result suggested that the airway responsiveness phenotype in this study was in fact a polygenic trait and not a simple Mendelian trait, with a distribution similar to that observed in human populations by Pattemore and coworkers (66).

Because the F_1 progeny exhibited a hyperresponsive phenotype similar to that in the A/J parental strain, De Sanctis and coworkers backcrossed the F_1 progeny (A/J $\times$ C57BL/6J) to the hyporesponsive C57BL/6J strain (ABF_1 $\times$ B) (18). Normal quantile analysis of 321 backcross progeny revealed that airway responsiveness was normally distributed, with 50% of the variance attributable to genetic factors and the remaining variance to environmental influences.

Because the pattern of inheritance did not segregate as would be expected with a single locus, De Sanctis and coworkers estimated the number of loci that were contributing to the manifestation of the airway responsiveness phenotype. They used the approach described by Wright (67), which assumes that all loci contribute equally and positively to the expression of the phenotype of interest; two loci were estimated to be involved in regulating airway responsiveness to methacholine in the mouse.

To localize QTLs affecting airway responsiveness, De Sanctis and coworkers initially selected the phenotypically extreme backcross progeny for genotyping because they are the most genetically informative animals. They carried out a genome-wide scan of these progeny with 157 simple sequence-length polymorphic genetic markers spaced approximately 9 cM apart to identify potential regions of interest. Genotype and phenotype data were analyzed with the QTL/MAPMAKER computer program (68), and several regions of interest were identified. After this initial analysis, all 321 backcross progeny were genotyped in these regions with 31 additional simple sequence-length polymorphic markers. Genetic markers that are informative will cosegregate with the airway hyperresponsiveness phenotype and are localized within a short distance of the QTLs; the closer a marker is to the trait locus, the fewer the recombinations occurring and the greater the value of the information obtained. Genetic markers that are not informative will not cosegregate with the phenotype and will show no linkage. With this approach, a correlation between genotypic and phenotypic data revealed three QTLs influencing airway responsiveness in the mouse. De Sanctis and coworkers designated the three loci *Bhr1*, *Bhr2*, and *Bhr3* (bronchial hyperresponsiveness loci one through three). Interestingly, each QTL mapped close to the mouse homologue of several candidate genes previously implicated in the biology of asthma (Figure 7).

Using an approach similar to the one employed by De Sanctis and colleagues, Ewart and coworkers examined the genetics of acetylcholine-induced airway responsiveness (with both the APTI and respiratory resistance as outcome indicators) in the A/J and C3H/HeJ genetic background (22). In contrast to the previous findings of Levitt & Mitzner (17), who observed a Mendelian pattern of inheritance in this background, the APTI findings of Ewart et al (22) indicated that the observed and expected ratios of hyperreactive and hyporeactive phenotypes in the segregating progeny were not consistent with single-gene control of acetylcholine-induced airway hyperresponsiveness. When Ewart and

→

Figure 7 Calculation of LOD scores from genotypes of murine simple sequence length polymorphic polymorphic markers on 321 backcross progeny [(C57BL/6J × A/J) × C57BL/6J] on chromosomes 2, 15, and 17. (Reprinted from Reference 18 with permission.)

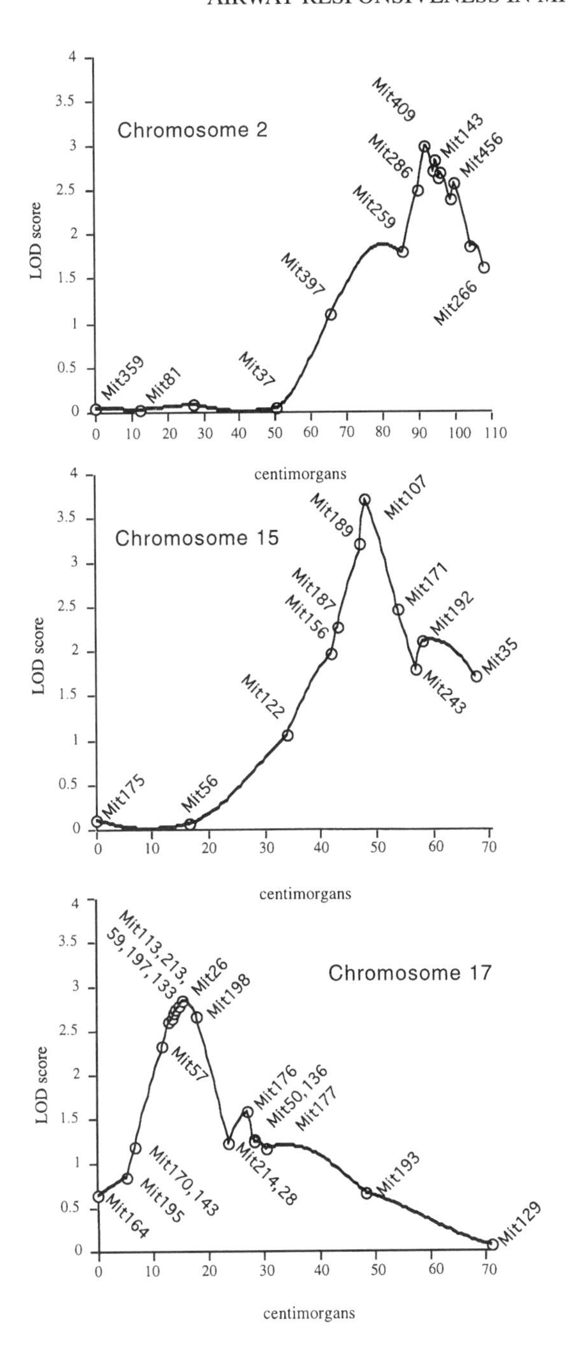
Chromosome 2
LOD score
centimorgans
Mit359
Mit81
Mit37
Mit397
Mit259
Mit286
Mit409
Mit143
Mit456
Mit266
Chromosome 15
LOD score
centimorgans
Mit175
Mit56
Mit122
Mit187
Mit156
Mit189
Mit107
Mit171
Mit192
Mit35
Mit243
Chromosome 17
LOD score
centimorgans
Mit113,213,
59,197,133
Mit26
Mit198
Mit57
Mit176
Mit50,136
Mit177
Mit214,28
Mit170,143
Mit195
Mit164
Mit193
Mit129

coworkers compared the APTI and respiratory resistance methods of phenotyping, the frequency distributions of the F_2 and backcross progeny were somewhat discordant; the investigators concluded that the two methods of phenotyping measured slightly different physiological parameters. When the genotype and phenotype data for 42 backcross mice were analyzed with the QTL/MAPMAKER program, a single QTL was identified. This QTL reached the nominal significance level, indicated by a LOD score of 3.0 (69), only with the APTI—and not the respiratory resistance—phenotype. When Ewart and colleagues tested multiple inheritance models by maximum likelihood techniques, they concluded that the segregation data were best described by a mixed general model in which the inheritance pattern was determined by one major locus along with a polygenic component. Several candidate genes of interest in the biology of asthma were identified within the confidence interval of the quantitative trait locus in their study.

These data indicate the utility of quantitative measures of airway responsiveness in mice and demonstrate how such measures can be used to achieve a mechanistic understanding unachievable by other means. Thus, the phenotype of airway responsiveness has value on its own. In addition, as is detailed below, it can be used as one component of a complex phenotype indicating the "asthmatic state" of the animal under study.

MURINE MODELS OF ALLERGEN-INDUCED PULMONARY INFLAMMATION AND AIRWAY HYPERRESPONSIVENESS

Features of Models That Mirror Human Asthma

T lymphocytes are recognized as critical to the pathogenesis of inflammation and airway hyperresponsiveness of human allergic asthma (70–72). Studies in mice have provided the strongest data indicating the critical role of T lymphocytes in mediating the airway hyperresponsiveness induced by systemic sensitization followed by allergen exposure. The relevant mouse models are reviewed in general, with a focus on the role of T-cell stimulation in the chain of events leading to airway eosinophilia and hyperresponsiveness.

Several investigators have developed murine models that reproduce certain features of asthma. Inbred strains of mice are first sensitized systemically and then challenged by aerosol. A variety of antigens, including ovalbumin (32, 48, 49, 73–76), picryl chloride (77), sheep erythrocytes (78), and *Shistosoma mansoni* (soluble egg antigen, SEA) (79) have been used in these systems with similar results. Each model has demonstrated some of the features characteristic of human asthma, including, but not limited to, increased bronchial reactivity (48, 49, 80), increased numbers of eosinophils in bronchoalveolar lavage fluid (74), increased immunoglobulin (Ig) E production (32), and airway infiltration with lymphocytes, monocytes, and eosinophils (73). One of the critical features of these models is that specific antigen sensitization and challenge protocols are used to induce changes in airway function that are thought to reflect downstream events resulting in airway inflammation. Thus, a primary thrust of the research conducted with these models has been to investigate the mechanisms leading to inflammation and the consequences of manipulating the inflammatory response on airway physiology. The greatest attention has been paid to T-cell activation pathways that couple allergen sensitization to allergic pulmonary inflammation; this aspect of these models and the consequences with respect to altered airway function form the basis of the material reviewed herein.

Role of Costimulatory Signals in T-Cell Activation

ANATOMY OF COSTIMULATION T-cell activation requires an antigen-presenting cell (APC) to process and present antigen to a T cell expressing an antigen-specific T-cell receptor (TCR). However, TCR recognition of antigen is not sufficient by itself to induce complete T-cell activation. A second set of costimulatory signals is required for the full complement of T cell–mediated events. Among the costimulatory pathways, the CD28/B7-1/B7-2 pathway is the best characterized (Figure 8). CD28, which is expressed on T cells, binds

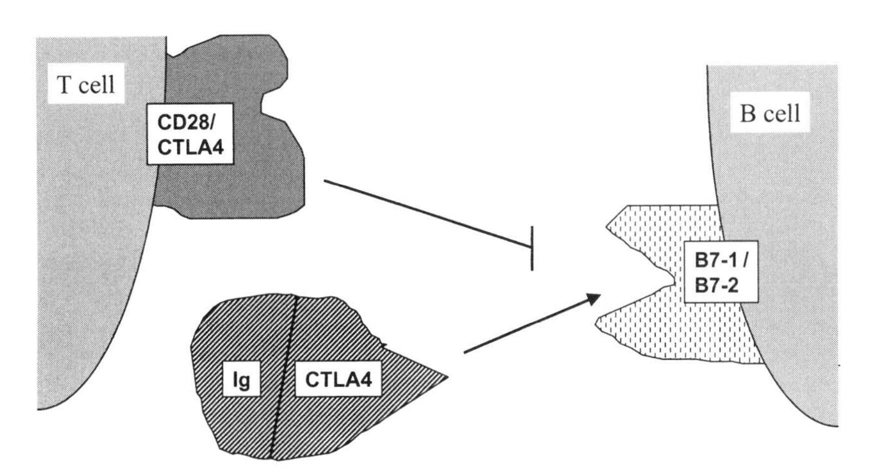

Figure 8 CTLA4-Ig inhibits the CD28 costimulatory pathway. The fusion protein CTLA4-Ig, composed of a soluble form of CTLA4 linked to the Fc portion of human IgG1, inhibits antigen-specific T-cell responses. CTLA4-Ig is thought to function by binding B7 molecules on the surface of antigen-presenting cells such as B cells and interrupting activation through the CD28/B7 costimulatory pathway.

the ligands B7-1 and B7-2 (CD80, CD86), which are expressed primarily on APCs (81, 82). This binding initiates a series of events that culminates in full T-cell activation. CTLA4, an alternative counterreceptor for B7-1 and B7-2, has been shown primarily to promote negative signals for T-cell activation (81, 82). Thus, full activation of T cells requires an antigen-specific TCR signal plus an antigen-nonspecific costimulatory signal transduced by CD28. After receiving the CD28 plus TCR signal, the T cell is activated and can perform regulatory and effector functions (83).

There are four costimulatory molecules in this pathway: the CD28 and CTLA4 receptors and the B7-1 and B7-2 ligands. All possible combinations of binding between CD28/CTLA4 and B7-1/B7-2 have been observed. CTLA4 has an approximately 15- to 20-fold higher affinity for B7 than does CD28, and B7-1 has a higher affinity for CTLA4 than does B7-2 (81, 82). An important observation is the cell type–specific expression of costimulatory molecules. To date, CD28 and CTLA4 expression have been reported primarily on T cells, although a previous report shows low levels of CTLA4 expression on human B cells (84). Naive T cells express CD28 constitutively, whereas CTLA4 is expressed only after T-cell activation (85, 86). The B7 ligands are expressed predominantly on APCs. B7-2 is typically expressed prior to B7-1 during activation of APCs. Interestingly, both B7-1 and B7-2 are expressed by activated T cells in addition to APCs, although the precise function of B7 on T cells remains undetermined. The costimulation process is regulated in part by differential kinetics and cell type–specific expression of costimulatory molecules and receptors; the implication is that these differential responses may influence the physiological consequences of inflammation.

The CD28 signal is not necessary to the initiation of T-cell activation but is important as a late signal (24–48 h after the T cell encounters the APC). The late CD28 signal is crucial to the promotion of T-cell proliferation and interleukin 2 production. In vivo studies show that CD28 engagement contributes to T-cell expansion and prolonged survival during an immune response (87). These results are consistent with previous analyses of mice with targeted deletions in CD28, which showed positive initial activation in response to antigen but decreased proliferation and survival of T cells (88–90). In CD28-deficient mice, other costimulatory receptors including 4-1BB and HSA, which are less well understood, may at least partially compensate for the lack of CD28. Together, these studies show that blockade of the CD28 costimulatory pathway inhibits the development of T-cell responses in a number of in vitro and in vivo experimental models.

INHIBITION OF CD28/B7 COSTIMULATION LEADS TO DIMINISHED PULMONARY INFLAMMATION Blocking the costimulatory pathway in vivo with an inhibitor of the CD28/B7 pathway selectively inhibits antigen-specific T-cell responses. For example, blockade of the pathway with CTLA4-Ig, a fusion protein composed of a soluble form of CTLA4 linked to the Fc portion of human IgG1 (91), prolongs xeno- and allograft survival and inhibits autoimmunity. CTLA4-Ig is thought to function by binding B7 molecules on the cell surface and, thus, inhibiting costimulation (Figure 8). In a model of xenogeneic pancreatic islet cell transplantation, CTLA4-Ig treatment for 10 days resulted in long-term graft survival (92). Similar results were obtained in a model of murine cardiac allograft treated with CTLA4-Ig plus blood transfusions (93). In this model, the cardiac allograft also survived indefinitely without further treatment—a result that suggests the induction of graft-specific tolerance.

In a model of allergen-induced airway inflammation, treatment with CTLA4-Ig during the ovalbumin aerosol challenge period of pulmonary sensitization protocols significantly lowered airway responsiveness to methacholine, diminished serum IgE levels, reduced bronchoalveolar lavage (BAL) inflammatory cells thereby decreasing the number of activated thoracic T-cell numbers, and increased amounts of interferon γ recovered from the BAL fluid but decreased the amount of interleukin 4 (94). Pathological changes usually seen in ovalbumin-treated mice, including perivascular and peribronchiolar infiltrates composed of lymphocytes, neutrophils, and eosinophils as well as bronchiolar goblet cell metaplasia, were greatly reduced after treatment with CTLA4-Ig. Functional assessment of the thoracic lymph nodes indicated that proliferation of lymphocytes after ovalbumin exposure was greatly reduced in the CTLA4-Ig group but not in the L6 control group. These findings were originally made by Krinzman et al (94) (Figure 9) and confirmed by others (95).

CONTRIBUTION OF BOTH B7-1 AND B7-2 TO THE DEVELOPMENT OF AIRWAY HYPERRESPONSIVENESS AND PULMONARY INFLAMMATION The individual roles of B7-1 and B7-2 in allergic pulmonary responses were analyzed in studies with in vivo antagonists to either ligand. Ovalbumin challenge has been shown to increase airway eosinophilia detected by histologic characterization of Cytospin® preparations from BAL (49). To examine the effect of individual B7 ligands on the development of BAL eosinophilia, ovalbumin-sensitized and -challenged mice treated with inhibitors specific for either B7-1 or B7-2 were analyzed. The inhibitors of costimulation used by Mark et al were monoclonal antibodies (mAb) or Fab to B7-1 and B7-2, alone or in combination (96). In addition, for selective B7-1 interruption, possible agonist activity of mAb to B7-1 was avoided by use of a mutated form of CTLA4-Ig (Y100F) that selectively binds B7-1. Y100F, a fusion protein linking a mutated form of the extracellular portion of CTLA4 (containing a tyrosine to phenylalanine substitution at position 100 that eliminates binding to B7-2) to the Fc portion of IgG1,

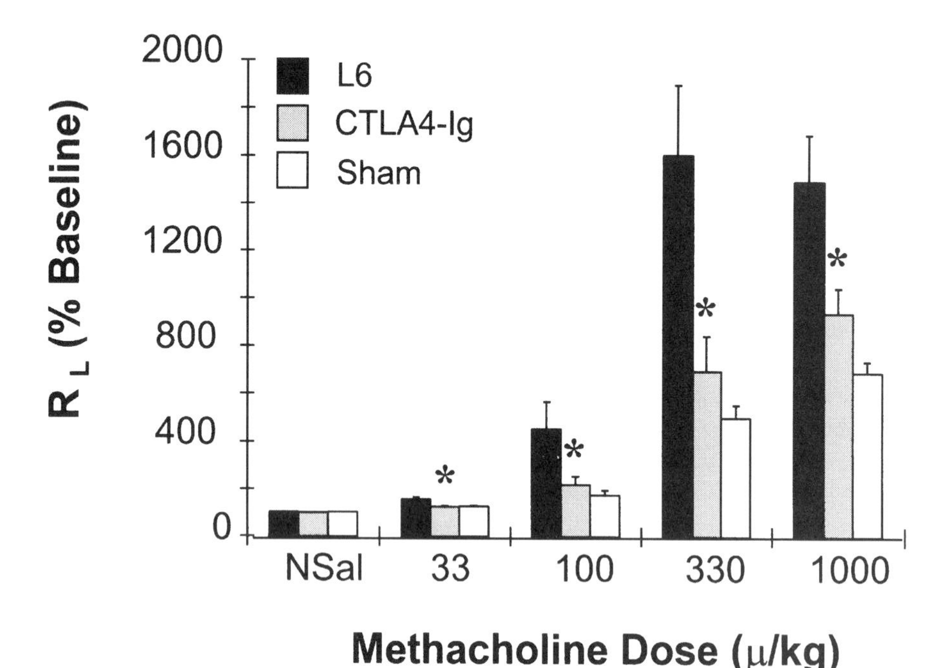

Figure 9 CTLA4-Ig significantly decreases airway responsiveness. BALB/c mice were sensitized and aerosol challenged with the allergen ovalbumin (OVA). Either CTLA4-Ig or control antibody (L6) (100 μg) was administered on days 14, 16, 18, and 20 during the OVA aerosol challenge. An additional control group received sensitization and aerosol challenge with phosphate-buffered saline (PBS) alone (Sham). $N = 13$ for CTLA4-Ig, $N = 11$ for L6 groups, and $N = 7$ for the Sham group. Mice were studied one day after the final aerosol. Each mouse was anesthetized intraperitoneally with pentobarbital sodium (70–80 μg/kg). An internal jugular vein cannulated with a saline-filled Silastic catheter was used to administer methacholine (acetyl-b-methylcholine chloride). Pulmonary resistance and dynamic compliance were determined. Dose-response curves for methacholine were obtained by administering sequentially increasing doses of methacholine (33–1000 μg/kg). Resistance (R_L) in response to methacholine was measured and calculated as percentage of baseline (y axis). $\pm$SEM. $P < 0.05$ for CTLA4-Ig versus L6 groups. There was no significant difference between CTLA4-Ig and Sham groups alone. (Reprinted from Reference 94 with permission.)

does not show evidence of agonist effects (96). Mark et al showed that administration of Y100F or a mAb to B7-2, or a combination of the mAb with either Y100F or Fab to B7-1, prevented increased BAL eosinophilia (97). Harris et al used only Y100F and found decreased BAL eosinophilia (96). Tsuyuki et al found that anti-B7-2 mAb decreased eosinophilia (95). Taken together, these results suggest that recruitment of eosinophils to the lung is mediated by both B7-1 and B7-2.

Consistent with previous reports (95), Mark et al found that treatment with a mAb to B7-2 during aerosol challenge significantly decreased airway responsiveness, which suggests bronchial reactivity is at least partially dependent on B7-2 interactions (97). Inhibition of bronchial responsiveness was also achieved with Y100F alone and in combination with anti-B7-2. Treatment with a combination of mAbs to B7-1 and B7-2 had no significant effect on airway responsiveness, nor did treatment with mAb to B7-1 alone. Given the potential agonist properties of the intact mAb to B7-1, signaling through the B7-1 pathway, rather than its blockade, may account for the lack of diminution in airway responsiveness when the intact antibodies to B7-1 were administered either alone or in combination.

Blocking either molecule alone decreases pulmonary eosinophilia and airway responsiveness, which suggests that both B7-1 and B7-2 interactions support the development of allergen-induced pulmonary inflammation. The concept that B7-1 and B7-2 can have overlapping functions is supported by analyses of B7-deficient mice: Animals lacking either B7-1 or B7-2 can still produce high-titer IgG responses when adjuvant is used in immunization (98).

Summary of Costimulation Data with Respect to Airway Responses

The costimulatory pathway has multiple ligands binding to multiple receptors, different functions of individual costimulatory molecules and receptors, different kinetics of expression following activation, and differential expression on specific cell types. Interaction between the B7-1 and B7-2 ligands and the CD28/CTLA4 receptors is complex, with both positive and negative regulation of T-cell activation. In models of allergen-induced airway responsiveness, inhibition of the CD28/B7 costimulatory pathway decreases airway responsiveness, eosinophilia, and inflammation, and both B7-1 and B7-2 are required for full expression of the airway hyperresponsiveness phenotype.

Literature Cited

1. Schork NJ, Nath SP, Lindpaintner K, Jacob HJ. 1996. Extensions to quantitative trait locus mapping in experimental organisms. *Hypertension* 28:1104–11
2. Fisler JS, Warden CH. 1997. Mapping of mouse obesity genes: a generic approach to a complex trait. *J. Nutr.* 127:S1909–16
3. Natl. Asthma Educ. Program. 1991. *Guidelines for the Diagnosis and Management of Asthma*. Bethesda, MD: US Dept. Health & Hum. Serv.
4. Natl. Heart Lung Blood Inst. 1995. *NHLBI/WHO Workshop Report: Global strategy for asthma management and prevention. Global Initiative for Asthma*. Publication #95–3659. Bethesda, MD: Natl. Heart Lung Blood Inst.
5. Richards IM. 1996. Mouse models of aller-

gic disease; how do they relate to asthma in man? *Clin. Exp. Allergy* 26:618–20
6. Dawson SV, Elliott EA. 1977. Wave-speed limitation on expiratory flow—a unifying concept. *J. Appl. Physiol.* 43:498–515
7. Lambert RK, Wilson TA, Hyatt RE, Rodarte JR. 1982. A computational model for expiratory flow. *J. Appl. Physiol.* 52:44–56
8. Hipfner DR, Almquist KC, Leslie EM, Gerlach JH, Grant CE, et al. 1997. Membrane topology of the multidrug resistance protein (MRP)—a study of glycosylation-site mutants reveals an extracytosolic NH2 terminus. *J. Biol. Chem.* 272:23623–30
9. Hooker CS, Calkins PJ, Fleisch JH. 1977. On the measurement of vascular and respiratory smooth muscle responses in vitro. *Blood Vessels* 14:1–11
10. Larsen GL, Renz H, Loader JE, Bradley KL, Gelfand EW. 1992. Airway response to electrical field stimulation in sensitized inbred mice. Passive transfer of increased responsiveness with peribronchial lymph nodes. *J. Clin. Invest.* 89:747–52
11. Manzini S. 1992. Bronchodilatation by tachykinins and capsaicin in the mouse main bronchus. *Br. J. Pharmacol.* 105:968–72
12. Henry PJ, Goldie RG. 1994. ET(b) but not ET(a) receptor-mediated contractions to endothelin-1 attenuated by respiratory tract viral infection in mouse airways. *Br. J. Pharmacol.* 112:1188–94
13. Larsen GL, Fame TM, Renz H, Loader JE, Graves J, et al. 1994. Increased acetylcholine release in tracheas from allergen-exposed IgE-immune mice. *Am. J. Physiol.* 266:L263–70
14. Vinegar A, Sinnett EE, Leith DE. 1979. Dynamic mechanisms determine functional residual capacity in mice, *Mus musculus*. *J. Appl. Physiol.* 46:867–71
15. Yiamouyiannis CA, Stengel PW, Cockerham SL, Silbaugh SA. 1995. Effect of bronchoconstrictive aerosols on pulmonary gas trapping in the A/J mouse. *Respir. Physiol.* 102:97–104
16. Silbaugh SA, Stengel PW, Dillard RD, Bemis KG. 1987. Pulmonary gas trapping in the guinea pig and its application in pharmacological testing. *J. Pharmacol. Methods* 18:295–303
17. Levitt RC, Mitzner W. 1988. Expression of airway hyperreactivity to acetylcholine as a simple autosomal recessive trait in mice. *FASEB J.* 2:2605–8
18. De Sanctis GT, Merchant M, Beier DR, Dredge RD, Grobholz JK, et al. 1995. Quantitative locus analysis of airway hyperresponsiveness in A/J and C57BL/6J mice. *Nat. Genet.* 11:150–54
19. Hirai T, Hosokawa M, Kawakami K, Takubo Y, Sakai N, et al. 1995. Age-related changes in the static and dynamic mechanical properties of mouse lungs. *Respir. Physiol.* 102:195–203
20. Levitt RC, Mitzner W. 1989. Autosomal recessive inheritance of airway hyperreactivity to 5-hydroxytryptamine. *J. Appl. Physiol.* 67:1125–32
21. Zhang LY, Levitt RC, Kleeberger SR. 1995. Differential susceptibility to ozone-induced airways hyperreactivity in inbred strains of mice. *Exp. Lung Res.* 21:503–18
22. Ewart SL, Mitzner W, Disilvestre DA, Meyers DA, Levitt RC. 1996. Airway hyperresponsiveness to acetylcholine: segregation analysis and evidence for linkage to murine chromosome 6. *Am. J. Respir. Cell. Mol. Biol.* 14:487–95
23. Ewart S, Levitt R, Mitzner W. 1995. Respiratory system mechanics in mice measured by end-inflation occlusion. *J. Appl. Physiol.* 79:560–66
24. Drazen JM. 1976. Physiologic basis and interpretation of common indices of respiratory mechanical function. *Environ. Health Perspect.* 16:11–16
25. Weibel ER. 1963. *Morphometry of the Human Lung*. Berlin: Springer-Verlag
26. Amdur MO, Mead J. 1958. Mechanics of respiration in unanesthetized guinea pigs. *Am. J. Physiol.* 192:364–68
27. Mead J, Whittenberger JL. 1953. Physical properties of human lungs measured during spontaneous respiration. *J. Appl. Physiol.* 5:779–96
28. Martin TR, Gerard NP, Galli SJ, Drazen JM. 1988. Pulmonary responses to bronchoconstrictor agonists in the mouse. *J. Appl. Physiol.* 64:2318–23
29. Martin TR, Galli SJ, Katona IM, Drazen JM. 1989. Role of mast cells in anaphylaxis. Evidence for the importance of mast cells in the cardiopulmonary alterations and death induced by anti-IgE in mice. *J. Clin. Invest.* 83:1375–83
30. Martin TR, Takeishi T, Katz HR, Austen KF, Drazen JM, et al. 1993. Mast cell activation enhances airway responsiveness to methacholine in the mouse. *J. Clin. Invest.* 91:1176–82
31. Martin TR, Cohen ML, Drazen JM. 1994. Serotonin-induced pulmonary responses are mediated by the 5-HT2 receptor in the mouse. *J. Pharmacol. Exp. Ther.* 268:104–9
32. Renz H, Bradley K, Saloga J, Loader J, Larsen GL, et al. 1993. T cells expressing specific V beta elements regulate immunoglobulin E production and airways responsiveness in vivo. *J. Exp. Med.* 177:1175–80

33. Hamelmann E, Oshiba A, Paluh J, Bradley K, Loader J, et al. 1996. Requirement for CD8(+)T cells in the development of airway hyperresponsiveness in a murine model of airway sensitization. *J. Exp. Med.* 183:1719–29
34. Corry DB, Folkesson HG, Warnock ML, Erle DJ, Matthay MA, et al. 1997. Interleukin 4, but not interleukin 5 or eosinophils, is required in a murine model of acute airway hyperreactivity. *J. Exp. Med.* 185:1715–19
35. Tang WL, Geba GP, Zheng T, Ray P, Homer RJ, et al. 1996. Targeted expression of IL-11 in the murine airway causes lymphocytic inflammation, bronchial remodeling, and airways obstruction. *J. Clin. Invest.* 98:2845–53
36. Hantos Z, Petak F, Adamicza A, Daroczy B, Fredberg JJ. 1995. Differential responses of global airway, terminal airway, and tissue impedances to histamine. *J. Appl. Physiol.* 79:1440–48
37. Nagase T, Matsui H, Aoki T, Ouchi Y, Fukuchi Y. 1996. Lung tissue behavior in the mouse during constriction induced by methacholine and endothelin-1. *J. Appl. Physiol.* 81:2373–78
38. Goldman M, Knudson RJ, Mead J, Peterson N, Schwaber JR, et al. 1970. A simplified measurement of respiratory resistance by forced oscillation. *J. Appl. Physiol.* 28:113–16
39. Jackson AC, Loring SH, Drazen JM. 1981. Serial distribution of bronchoconstriction induced by vagal stimulation or histamine. *J. Appl. Physiol.* 50:1286–92
40. Watson JW, Jackson AC, Drazen JM. 1986. Effect of lung volume on pulmonary mechanics in guinea pigs. *J. Appl. Physiol.* 61:304–11
41. Hessel EM, Vanoosterhout AJM, Hofstra CL, Debie JJ, Garssen J, et al. 1995. Bronchoconstriction and airway hyperresponsiveness after ovalbumin inhalation in sensitized mice. *Eur. J. Pharmacol. Environ. Toxicol.* 293:401–12
42. Johanson WG Jr, Pierce AK. 1971. A noninvasive technique for measurement of airway conductance in small animals. *J. Appl. Physiol.* 30:146–50
43. Drorbaugh JE, Fenn WO. 1955. A barometric method for measuring ventilation in newborn infants. *Pediatrics* 16:81–86
44. Bartlett DJ, Tenney SM. 1970. Control of breathing in experimental anemia. *Respir. Physiol.* 10:384–95
45. Jacky JP. 1978. A plethysmograph for long-term measurements of ventilation in unrestrained animals. *J. Appl. Physiol.* 45:644–47
46. Epstein MA, Epstein RA. 1978. A theoretical analysis of the barometric method for measurement of tidal volume. *Respir. Physiol.* 32:105–20
47. Hamelmann E, Schwarze J, Takeda K, Oshiba A, Larsen GL, et al. 1997. Noninvasive measurement of airway responsiveness in allergic mice using barometric plethysmography. *Am. J. Respir. Crit. Care Med.* 156:766–75
48. Renz H, Lack G, Saloga J, Schwinzer R, Bradley K, et al. 1994. Inhibition of IgE production and normalization of airways responsiveness by sensitized CD8 T cells in a mouse model of allergen-induced sensitization. *J. Immunol.* 152:351–60
49. Krinzman SJ, De Sanctis GT, Cernadas M, Kobzik L, Listman JA, et al. 1996. T cell activation in a murine model of asthma. *Am. J. Physiol.* 15: L476–83
50. Fabbri LM, Chiesura-Corona P, Dal Vecchio L, di Giacomo GR, Zocca E, et al. 1985. Prednisone inhibits late asthmatic reactions and the associated increase in airway responsiveness induced by toluenediisocyanate in sensitized subjects. *Am. Rev. Respir. Dis.* 132:1010–14
51. Kleeberger SR, Bassett DJ, Jakab GJ, Levitt RC. 1990. A genetic model for evaluation of susceptibility to ozone-induced inflammation. *Am. J. Physiol.* 258:L313–20
52. Prows DR, Shertzer HG, Daly MJ, Sidman CL, Leikauf GD. 1997. Genetic analysis of ozone-induced acute lung injury in sensitive and resistant strains of mice. *Nat. Genet.* 17:471–74
53. Kleeberger SR, Levitt RC, Zhang LY, Longphre M, Harkema L, et al. 1997. Linkage analysis of susceptibility to ozone-induced lung inflammation in inbred mice. *Nat. Genet.* 17:475–78
54. Postma DS, Bleecker ER, Amelung PJ, Holroyd KJ, Xu JF, et al. 1995. Genetic susceptibility to asthma—bronchial hyperresponsiveness coinherited with a major gene for atopy. *N. Engl. J. Med.* 333:894–900
55. Vanherwerden L, Harrap SB, Wong ZYH, Abramson MJ, Kutin JJ, et al. 1995. Linkage of high-affinity IgE receptor gene with bronchial hyperreactivity, even in absence of atopy. *Lancet* 346:1262–65
56. Snapper JR, Lefferts PL, Stecenko AA, Hinson JM Jr, Dyer EL. 1986. Bronchial responsiveness to nonantigenic bronchoconstrictors in awake sheep. *J. Appl. Physiol.* 61:752–59
57. Snapper JR, Drazen JM, Loring SH, Schneider W, Ingram RH Jr. 1978. Distribution of pulmonary responsiveness to

aerosol histamine in dogs. *J. Appl. Physiol.* 44:738–42
58. Pauwels R, Van der Straeten M, Weyne J, Bazin H. 1985. Genetic factors in nonspecific bronchial reactivity in rats. *Eur. J. Respir. Dis.* 66:98–104
59. Douglas JS, Ridgway P, Brink C. 1977. Airway responses of the guinea pig in vivo and in vitro. *J. Pharmacol. Exp. Ther.* 202:116–24
60. Konno S, Adachi M, Matsuura T, Sunochi K, Hoshino H, et al. 1993. Bronchial reactivity to methacholine and serotonin in six inred mouse strains. *Arerugi* 42:42–47
61. Longphre M, Kleeberger SR. 1995. Susceptibility to platelet-activating factor-induced airway hyperreactivity and hyperpermeability: interstrain variation and genetic control. *Am. J. Respir. Cell. Mol. Biol.* 13:586–94
62. Chiba Y, Yanagisawa R, Sagai M. 1995. Strain and route differences in airway responsiveness to acetylcholine in mice. *Res. Commun. Mol. Pathol. Pharmacol.* 90: 169–72
63. Gavett SH, Willskarp M. 1993. Elevated lung G-protein levels and muscarinic receptor affinity in a mouse model of airway hyperreactivity. *Am. J. Physiol.* 265:L493–L500
64. Dietrich WF, Miller JC, Steen RG, Merchant M, Damron D, et al. 1994. A genetic map of the mouse with 4,006 simple sequence length polymorphisms. *Nat. Genet.* 7:220–45
65. Jacob HJ, Lindpaintner K, Lincoln SE, Kusumi K, Bunker RK, et al. 1991. Genetic mapping of a gene causing hypertension in the stroke-prone spontaneously hypertensive rat. *Cell* 67:213–24
66. Pattemore PK, Asher MI, Harrison AC, Mitchell EA, Rea HH, et al. 1990. The interrelationship among bronchial hyperresponsiveness, the diagnosis of asthma, and asthma symptoms. *Am. Rev. Respir. Dis.* 142:549–54
67. Wright S. 1968. *Evolution and the Genetics of Populations: Genetic and Biometric Foundations.* Chicago: Univ. Chicago Press
68. Lander ES, Green P, Abrahamson J, Barlow A, Daly MJ, et al. 1987. MAPMAKER: an interactive computer package for constructing primary genetic linkage maps of experimental and natural populations. *Genomics* 1:174–81
69. Lander ES, Kruglyak L. 1995. Genetic dissection of complex traits: guidelines for interpreting and reporting linkage results. *Nat. Genet.* 11:241–47
70. Azzawi M, Bradley B, Jeffery PK, Frew AJ, Wardlaw AJ, et al. 1990. Identification of activated T lymphocytes and eosinophils in bronchial biopsies in stable atopic asthma. *Am. Rev. Respir. Dis.* 142:1407–13
71. Wardlaw AJ, Dunnette S, Gleich GJ, Collins JV, Kay AB. 1988. Eosinophils and mast cells in bronchoalveolar lavage in subjects with mild asthma. Relationship to bronchial hyperreactivity. *Am. Rev. Respir. Dis.* 137:62–69
72. Corrigan CJ, Kay AB. 1990. CD4 T-lymphocyte activation in acute severe asthma. Relationship to disease severity and atopic status. *Am. Rev. Respir. Dis.* 141:970–77
73. Brusselle GG, Kips JC, Tavernier JH, Vanderheyden JG, Cuvelier CA, et al. 1994. Attenuation of allergic airway inflammation in IL-4 deficient mice. *Clin. Exp. Allergy* 24:73–80
74. Kung TT, Stelts D, Zurcher JA, Jones H, Umland SP, et al. 1995. Mast cells modulate allergic pulmonary eosinophilia in mice. *Am. J. Respir. Cell. Mol. Biol.* 12: 404–9
75. Foster PS, Hogan SP, Ramsay AJ, Matthaei KI, Young IG. 1996. Interleukin 5 deficiency abolishes eosinophilia, airways hyperreactivity, and lung damage in a mouse asthma model. *J. Exp. Med.* 183:195–201
76. Corry DB, Folkesson HG, Warnock ML, Erle DJ, Matthay MA, et al. 1996. Interleukin 4, but not interleukin 5 or eosinophils, is required in a murine model of acute airway hyperreactivity. *J. Exp. Med.* 183:109–17
77. Garssen J, Nijkamp FP, Vanvugt E, Vandervliet H, Vanloveren H. 1994. T cell-derived antigen binding molecules play a role in the induction of airway hyperresponsiveness. *Am. J. Respir. Crit. Care Med.* 150:1528–38
78. Kaltreider HB, Curtis JL, Arraj SM. 1987. The mechanism of appearance of specific antibody-forming cells in lungs of inbred mice after immunization with sheep erythrocytes intratracheally. II. Dose-dependence and kinetics of appearance of antibody-forming cells in hilar lymph nodes and lungs of unprimed and primed mice. *Am. Rev. Respir. Dis.* 135:87–92
79. Lukacs NW, Strieter RM, Chensue SW, Kunkel SL. 1994. Interleukin-4-dependent pulmonary eosinophil infiltration in a murine model of asthma. *Am. J. Respir. Cell. Mol. Biol.* 10:526–32
80. Renz H, Bradley KL, Marrack P, Gelfand EW. 1992. T cells expressing variable elements of T-cell receptor beta 8 and beta 2 chain regulate murine IgE production. *Proc. Natl. Acad. Sci. USA* 89:6438–42

81. Allison JP. 1994. CD28-B7 interactions in T-cell activation. *Curr. Opin. Immunol.* 6:414–19
82. Bluestone JA. 1995. New perspectives of CD28-B7-mediated T cell costimulation. *Immunity* 2:555–59
83. Schwartz RH. 1990. A cell culture model for T lymphocyte clonal anergy. *Science* 248:1349–56
84. Kuiper HM, Brouwer M, Linsley PS, van Lier RA. 1995. Activated T cells can induce high levels of CTLA-4 expression on B cells. *J. Immunol.* 155:1776–83
85. Freeman GJ, Lombard DB, Gimmi CD, Brod SA, Lee K, et al. 1992. CTLA-4 and CD28 mRNA are coexpressed in most T cells after activation. Expression of CTLA-4 and CD28 mRNA does not correlate with the pattern of lymphokine production. *J. Immunol.* 149:3795–801
86. Perkins D, Wang Z, Donovan C, He H, Mark D, et al. 1996. Regulation of CTLA-4 expression during T cell activation. *J. Immunol.* 156:4154–59
87. Vella AT, Mitchell T, Groth B, Linsley PS, Green JM, et al. 1997. CD28 engagement and proinflammatory cytokines contribute to T cell expansion and long-term survival in vivo. *J. Immunol.* 158:4714–20
88. Shahinian A, Pfeffer K, Lee KP, Kundig TM, Kishihara K, et al. 1993. Differential T cell costimulatory requirements in CD28-deficient mice. *Science* 261:609–12
89. Boise LH, Minn AJ, Noel PJ, June CH, Accavitti MA, et al. 1995. CD28 costimulation can promote T cell survival by enhancing the expression of Bcl-XL. *Immunity* 3:87–98
90. Lucas PJ, Negishi I, Nakayama K, Fields LE, Loh DY. 1995. Naive CD28-deficient T cells can initiate but not sustain an in vitro antigen-specific immune response. *J. Immunol.* 154:5757–68
91. Liu Y, Linsley PS. 1992. Costimulation of T-cell growth. *Curr. Opin. Immunol.* 4: 265–70
92. Lenschow DJ, Zeng Y, Thistlethwaite JR, Montag A, Brady W, et al. 1992. Long-term survival of xenogeneic pancreatic islet grafts induced by CTLA4lg. *Science* 257:789–92
93. Bolling SF, Lin H, Wei RQ, Linsley P, Turka LA. 1994. The effect of combination cyclosporine and CTLA4-Ig therapy on cardiac allograft survival. *J. Surg. Res.* 57:60–64
94. Krinzman SJ, De Sanctis GT, Cernadas M, Mark D, Wang YS, et al. 1996. Inhibition of T cell costimulation abrogates airway hyperresponsiveness in a murine model. *J. Clin. Invest.* 98:2693–99
95. Tsuyuki S, Tsuyuki J, Einsle K, Kopf M, Coyle AJ. 1997. Costimulation through B7-2 (CD86) is required for the induction of a lung mucosal t helper cell 2 (TH2) immune response and altered airway responsiveness. *J. Exp. Med.* 185:1671–79
96. Harris N, Peach R, Naemura J, Linsley PS, Le Gros G, et al. 1997. CD80 costimulation is essential for the induction of airway eosinophilia. *J. Exp. Med.* 185:177–82
97. Mark DA, Donovan CE, Krinzman SJ, De Sanctis GT, Kobzik L, et al. 1998. Both CD80 and CD86 constimulatory molecules inhibit allergic pulmonary inflammation. *Int. Immunol.* 10:1647–55
98. Borriello F, Sethna MP, Boyd SD, Schweitzer AN, Tivol EA, et al. 1997. B7-1 and B7-2 have overlapping, critical roles in immunoglobulin class switching and germinal center formation. *Immunity* 6:303–13

Annu. Rev. Physiol. 1999. 61:627–61

SODIUM CHANNELS IN ALVEOLAR EPITHELIAL CELLS: Molecular Characterization, Biophysical Properties, and Physiological Significance

Sadis Matalon
Department of Anesthesiology, University of Alabama at Birmingham, Birmingham, Alabama 35233; e-mail: Sadis.Matalon@ccc.uab.edu

Hugh O'Brodovich
Department of Pediatrics, Hospital for Sick Children, University of Toronto, Toronto, Ontario, Canada M5G1X8; e-mail: hugh.obrodovich@mailhub.sickkids.on.ca

KEY WORDS: alveolar type II cells, patch clamp, fetal distal lung epithelial cells, cyclic AMP, nitric oxide

ABSTRACT

At birth, fetal distal lung epithelial (FDLE) cells switch from active chloride secretion to active sodium (Na^+) reabsorption. Sodium ions enter the FDLE and alveolar type II (ATII) cells mainly through apical nonselective cation and Na^+-selective channels, with conductances of 4–26 pS (picoSiemens) in FDLE and 20–25 pS in ATII cells. All these channels are inhibited by amiloride with a 50% inhibitory concentration of <1 μM, and some are also inhibited by [N-ethyl-N-isopropyl]-2′-4′-amiloride (50% inhibitory concentration of <1 μM). Both FDLE and ATII cells contain the α-, β-, and γ-rENaC (rat epithelial Na^+ channels) mRNAs; reconstitution of an ATII cell Na^+-channel protein into lipid bilayers revealed the presence of 25-pS Na^+ single channels, inhibited by amiloride and [N-ethyl-N-isopropyl]-2′-4′-amiloride. A variety of agents, including cAMP, oxygen, glucocorticoids, and in some cases Ca^{2+}, increased the activity and/or rENaC mRNA levels. The phenotypic properties of these channels differ from those observed in other Na^+-absorbing epithelia. Pharmacological blockade of alveolar Na^+ transport in vivo, as well as experiments with newborn α-rENaC knock-out mice, demonstrate the importance of active Na^+ transport in the

0066-4278/99/0315-0627$08.00

reabsorption of fluid from the fetal lung and in reabsorbing alveolar fluid in the injured adult lung. Indeed, in a number of inflammatory diseases, increased production of reactive oxygen-nitrogen intermediates, such as peroxynitrite ($ONOO^-$), may damage ATII and FDLE Na^+ channels, decrease Na^+ reabsorption in vivo, and thus contribute to the formation of alveolar edema.

INTRODUCTION

In order for gas exchange to occur optimally, the alveoli must remain open and free from fluid. In the fetus, gas exchange occurs across the placenta, and the future gas exchange areas of the lung are filled with fluid that is essential for normal lung development (for reviews see 23, 119). Studies of fetal lambs, guinea pigs, and rhesus monkeys have shown that chloride (Cl^-) concentration in the fetal fluid is much higher than in plasma (2) and that fluid secretion is secondary to active Cl^- secretion across the tracheal and distal lung epithelium (133). Thus, for mammals to survive in an air-breathing environment, at birth or shortly thereafter, their lungs must rapidly convert from a fluid-secreting to a fluid-absorbing organ.

Presently, convincing evidence indicates that active Na^+ transport across the alveolar epithelium in vivo helps both in the reabsorption of the fetal fluid (23, 132) and in keeping the adult alveolar spaces free of fluid, especially when alveolar permeability to plasma proteins has been increased (108, 130, 185, 186). Epithelial Na^+ channels represent the rate-limiting step in Na^+ absorption.

Various strategies have been undertaken to identify and characterize the structure and regulation of these channels. Initial efforts focused on biochemical purification of Na^+ channels from A6 cells and bovine kidney papilla (17), bovine trachea (35), and adult alveolar type II (ATII) cells (157). More recently, molecular techniques have been used and an amiloride-sensitive epithelial Na^+ channel (ENaC), consisting of at least three different subunits, has been cloned from rat colon (27, 92), human lung (179), and a variety of other organs (for reviews see 8, 54).

The purpose of this review is to summarize current knowledge of the properties of Na^+ channels in fetal distal lung epithelial (FDLE) and ATII cells. We also wish to indicate the similarities and, most important, the differences in the expression, characteristics, and regulation of Na^+ channels in FDLE and ATII cells relative to those in other Na^+ transporting epithelia. As the reader will appreciate, there is considerable controversy concerning the biophysical properties of these channels and whether they are coded by rENaC. Space does not permit a discussion of much of the epithelial Na^+ channel literature, and the interested reader is referred to reviews related to this topic (8, 54, 178).

THE CONVERSION OF THE PERINATAL LUNG FROM Cl^- SECRETION TO Na^+ ABSORPTION

As mentioned above, for a successful transition from prenatal to postnatal life, mammals' airspaces must become air filled. Thus, fluid secretion must stop, greatly decrease, or be overwhelmed by a much greater fluid absorptive process (reviewed in 23, 119). Fluid absorption is largely mediated by active Na^+ absorption by the lung epithelium (122, 132). It is known that β (25) and β_2 (33) agonists, membrane-permeant analogues of cAMP (181), and phosphodiesterase inhibitors (33) can, within minutes, reversibly convert the mature in utero fetal lung from a fluid-secreting to a fluid-absorbing organ. In an analogous manner, primary cultures of FDLE cells have been shown to increase Na^+ transport in response to β agonists (124, 125), which are known to circulate at high levels at birth (25). The fact that the immature lung is unable to convert from fluid secretion to fluid absorption in response to such stimuli (10, 25, 181) suggests that inadequate Na^+ transport may contribute to the development of neonatal respiratory distress syndromes (126).

The voluminous literature summarizing the presence of active Na^+ reabsorption across the adult alveolar epithelium in vivo in a number of species, including man, has recently been summarized (108). Several groups have demonstrated the reabsorption of intratracheally instilled isotonic fluid or plasma from the alveolar into the interstitial space both in anesthetized animals and in isolated perfused lungs (52, 83, 108, 109, 130). Sodium transport inhibitors [amiloride or *N*-ethyl-*N*-isopropyl amiloride (EIPA)] added to the alveolar space and Na^+-K^+-ATPase inhibitors (ouabain), injected into the vascular compartment, decreased the rate of fluid reabsorption by approximately 40–50% and 70–80%, respectively (14, 60, 107, 131, 185).

The adult mammalian alveolar epithelium consists of two cell types: (*a*) large squamous alveolar type I cells (ATI), and (*b*) cuboidal type II (ATII) cells. The latter make up most of the alveolar epithelial cells but constitute only 3% of the alveolar surface area in the adult lung (40). An important function of ATII and FDLE cells is the production and storage of pulmonary surfactant, a complex mixture of phospholipids and specific apoproteins (183). In addition, they serve as progenitors to the squamous ATI cells during normal lung development as well as in the reparative response of the alveolar epithelium to injury (47, 64). Immunocytochemical and Western blotting studies demonstrate the presence of proteins antigenically related to Na^+ channels and Na^+-K^+-ATPase in the apical and basolateral membranes of both ATII and FDLE cells, respectively (100, 104, 116, 156). Northern blotting studies showed that both ATII and late gestational FDLE cells contain the mRNAs for the Na^+-channel proteins (120, 171, 179, 186).

When grown to confluence on permeable supports, both ATII and FDLE cells form tight monolayers that generate apical-to-basolateral potential differences (PD) of 2–10 mV (apical membrane negative) (reviewed in 99, 101, 119). When mounted in Ussing chambers and clamped to zero potential difference, FDLE and ATII cell monolayers develop Na^+ short-circuit currents inhibited to a large extent (50–90%) by 1–10 μM amiloride added into the apical compartment or by 1 mM basolateral ouabain (24, 34, 59, 63, 121, 125). Taken as a whole, the results of the in vivo and in vitro studies indicate that Na^+ ions in the alveolar lining fluid passively diffuse into FDLE and ATII cells through cation- and Na^+-selective channels located in their apical membranes (96, 101, 104, 121, 132, 134, 151, 187). Under normal conditions, other Na^+ entry pathways—such as the Na^+/H^+ antiport (118), the Na^+-D-glucose symport (85), and amino acid–Na^+ cotransporters (26)—contribute only a small fraction of the total Na^+ influx (102, 121, 151). The favorable electrochemical driving force for Na^+ influx is maintained by the ouabain-sensitive basolateral Na^+-K^+-ATPase that also transports Na^+ ions into the interstitial space. K^+ ions, which enter the cells in exchange for Na^+, exit down its electrochemical gradient through basolateral K^+ channels (43, 123). Although airway cells also reabsorb Na^+, distal lung epithelial cells (FDLE and ATII) are most likely the primary site for Na^+ transport in the lung in view of their massive surface area (e.g. the alveolar surface area in newborns and adult humans is ~3 and 100 m^2, respectively).

Recently, ATI cells have been isolated from adult rat lungs and, like ATII and FDLE cells, have been shown to possess very high permeability to water, consistent with the presence of aquaporins (45, 51, 150). However, no information about vectorial Na^+ transport across ATI cells exists at this time. Patch-clamp and lipid bilayer reconstitution studies indicating the presence of various functional types of Na^+ channels in both FDLE and ATII cells are reviewed below.

BIOPHYSICAL PROPERTIES OF Na^+ CHANNELS IN LUNG ALVEOLAR EPITHELIAL CELLS

FDLE and ATII Cells

SINGLE CHANNELS Definitive information as to the presence of Na^+ channels, their ionic selectivity, and their regulation by various agents and second messengers was obtained by the detection of unitary currents in ATII and FDLE cell membranes patched in the "cell-attached" or the "excised" patch configuration (71). Because FDLE and ATII cells orient themselves with their basal membranes attached to the substratum and the apical membranes pointing up

(104, 187), channels in excised or cell-attached patches are likely to be located in the apical membranes of FDLE cells.

Several groups have provided evidence for the existence of different types of Na^+ and cation channels in apical membranes of FDLE cells (Table 1). Orser et al (134) isolated FDLE cells from the lungs of rats delivered by cesarean section at 20 days gestation (term 22 days) and cultured them on collagen-coated coverslips for 24–96 h. In the presence of symmetrical solutions (140 mM NaCl), inside-out patches revealed the presence of 23-pS single channels, equally permeable to Na^+ and K^+ ($P_{Na}/P_K = 0.9$), but essentially impermeable to Cl^-. Amiloride (1 μM) applied to the pipette solution (apical side of the membrane) decreased the open probability (*Po*) of these channels without affecting their unitary conductance. Cation channels with identical biophysical characteristics and conductance values of 25 pS and 26.9 pS were subsequently reported in rat FDLE cells by Marunaka et al (96, 98). This group also reported that the 50% inhibitory concentration (IC_{50}) of this cation channel is 100 nM for amiloride and 10 nM for benzamil.

The activity of these nonselective cation (NSC) channels is dependent upon the intracellular calcium ($[Ca^{2+}]_i$); an increase in intracellular $[Ca^{2+}]_i$ from 0.001 to 1 mM increased the *Po* from almost 0 to about 0.4, and decreased the P_{Na}/P_K of these channels (98, 134). Because $[Ca^{2+}]_i$ in both FDLE and adult ATII cells is below 50 nM (57, 98), these cation channels are probably closed under normal conditions, and it was questioned whether they could be activated in any situation. Subsequent work (173) showed that terbutaline, a β agonist, increased the *Po* of this NSC channel by a complex strategy: First, terbutaline increased $[Ca^{2+}]_i$ from 35 nM to 1.5 μM by inducing both Ca^{2+} influx from the extracellular space and Ca^{2+} release from intracellular stores; second, it increased the sensitivity of the NSC to $[Ca^{2+}]_i$; and third, it reduced $[Cl^-]_i$ from 45 to 25 mM, which further activated this NSC channel. The decrease in $[Cl^-]_i$ was attributed to the iso-osmotic loss of KCl due to the opening of K^+- and Cl^--activated Ca^{2+} channels in these cells. Under these conditions, the channel displayed a negative correlation between the value of its *Po* and $[Cl^-]_i$. Although the exact mechanisms of these actions have not been elucidated, the ability of $[Cl^-]_i$ to act as a signal transducing agent has been reported in other cells (62).

Tohda & Marunaka (96, 174) also identified a Na^+-selective, Ca^{2+}-activated channel in the apical membranes of the FDLE cells. This channel has a conductance of about 12 pS around normal resting potential, is selective for Na^+ over K^+ [$(P_{Na}/P_K) > 10$], is practically nonpermeable to anions [$(P_{Na}/P_{Cl}) \geq 40$], and is blocked by amiloride with an IC_{50} of 1–2 μM. Furthermore, in excised patches, the *Po* of this moderately selective Na^+ channel increased from 0.02 to 0.4 as the $[Ca^{2+}]_i$ increased from 50 to 100 nM, indicating that it is likely that it

Table 1 Single-channel characteristics of Na^+ channels recorded across fetal distal lung epithelial cells from late gestational fetuses[a]

Species (days in cult)	Type of patch	[Na^+ pip/Na^+ bath] (mM)	g (pS)	Rect	[P_{Na^+}/P_{K^+}]	IC_{50} (μM) Amil	EIPA	Regulation	Reference
Guinea pig	IO	145/145	11.1	Linear	NM	<4	NM	GTPγS	94
(0–0.5)	IO	145/5	5.6	Linear	1.8	NM	NM	GTPγS	94
Rat (1–4)	IO	140/140	23	Linear	0.9	<1	NM	Ca^{2+}	134
Rat (2)	CA	140/140	27	Linear	NM	1–2	NM	Ca^{2+}, insulin	96
	IO	140/10	27	Linear	1.1	1–2	NM	Ca^+	96
	CA	140/140	12	Inward	NM	1	NM	Ca^{2+}, insulin	96
	IO	140/10	12	Inward	>10	1	NM	Ca^{2+}	96
Rat (2–3)	CA	140/140	28	Linear	NM	NM	NM	Cl^-, terb.	173
	IA	140/5	28	Linear	~1	NM	NM	Ca^{+2}	
								NM	
Rat (1–8)	OO	140/10	4	Linear	>10	0.09	100		179

[a]Abbreviations: g, single-channel conductance; pS, picoSiemens; Rect, rectification of single-channel current-voltage relationship; P_{Na^+}/P_{K^+}, ratio of sodium to potassium permeability of ion channels; IC_{50}, concentration (micromolar) of Amil (amiloride) or EIPA (5-*N*-ethyl-*N*-isopropyl-2′-4′-amiloride) to achieve 50% inhibition of single channel current; IO, inside-out patch; NM, not measured; CA, cell-attached patch; OO, outside-out patch.

will be open under physiological conditions. However, this channel is difficult to detect in the open state because its apical membrane density is nine times lower than that of the NSC channel. Furthermore, it is activated by insulin but not terbutaline (174). Changes in the membrane potential had mild or no effect in the *Po* of either channel (96, 134).

The activation of these channels by an increase in $[Ca^{2+}]_i$ is a variance on what has been observed in other epithelial cells containing amiloride-sensitive channels. For example, in the frequently studied amphibian renal A6 epithelial cell line, an increase in Ca^{2+} concentration has been shown to down-regulate Na^+-channel activity (53, 158) via a protein kinase C–dependent mechanism (91).

Another type of a nonselective cation channel in FDLE cells from fetal guinea pigs was reported by MacGregor et al (94). Inside-out patches in about 20% of these cells using symmetrical Na^+ solutions (145 mM NaCl) showed single-channel activity with a linear current-voltage relationship and a unitary conductance of 11 pS. When patched using bionic solutions (145 mM NaCl in the pipette, 145 mM KCl in the bath), channels with conductance to 5.6 pS and a P_{Na}/P_K of 1.8 were observed. Addition of 10 μM amiloride in the pipette (apical side) completely abolished channel activity, whereas in the range of 0.4–4 μM, amiloride reduced channel density and caused the channels to flicker.

In these experiments, all single-channel recordings in inside-out patches were obtained in the presence of a 1.2 mM Ca^{2+} in the bath. Decreasing Ca^{2+} to 100 nM did not affect channel density. In this respect, the Ca^{2+} dependence of this channel (if any) is different from that reported by Orser et al (134) and Marunaka et al (98, 117, 173). It should also be stressed that single-channel recordings using physiological intracellular Ca^{2+} concentrations (i.e. $<$50 nM) were not performed.

A novel property of this channel was its regulation by G-proteins. Addition of 0.1 mM guanosine 5′-O-(3-thiotriphosphate) to the cytoplasmic site of inside-out patches in the absence of ATP caused activation of single-channel activity in previously quiescent patches and increased channel density in active patches, presumably by coupling the G protein to the ion-channel complex. A subunit of the Na^+-channel protein isolated from A6 cells has also been identified as the α subunit of $G_{\alpha i3}$ (4), and treatment of A6 monolayers with pertussis toxin inhibited transepithelial Na^+ transport (4). However, there is no evidence for the association of G protein with the immunopurified ATII Na^+-channel protein, and neither pertussis toxin nor GTPγS affected single ATII Na^+ channels in lipid bilayers (19).

The existence of a Ca^{2+}-independent, Na^+-selective channel in apical membranes of rat FDLE cells was reported by Voilley et al (179). These investigators isolated and cultured rat FDLE cells using the methods of Orser et al (134) for

24 h to 8 days and recorded single-channel currents from outside-out patches. In symmetrical Na^+ solutions (140 mM NaCl), channels with linear current-voltage relationships and unitary conductance of 4.4 pS were observed. Benzamil, phenamil, and amiloride inhibited the currents with $K_{0.5}$ values of 14 nM, 19 nM, and 90 nM, respectively. These currents were practically insensitive to EIPA ($K_{0.5} = 400$ nM). When patched with bionic solutions (140 mM K^+ in the pipette, 140 mM Na^+ in the bath), current-voltage relationships were consistent with a high selectivity of these channels for Na^+ over K^+ ($P_{Na}/P_K > 10$). The activity of this channel was also characterized by very slow kinetics, with opening and closing times lasting for seconds. These biophysical characteristics place these channels in Palmer's Na [5] category (137) and are identical to the biophysical properties of Na^+ channels obtained when cRNAs encoding for the α-, β-, and γ-rENaC were injected in *Xenopus laevis* oocytes (29).

It should be stressed that these FDLE cells were isolated and cultured under conditions identical to those of Orser et al (134), with the only exception being the type of patches obtained (outside-out vs inside-out). Yet channels with markedly different biophysical properties were reported. It is possible that the biophysical properties of channels may be affected by the method of patching. For example, Chinet et al (36) found that the ion selectivity of Na^+ channels in tracheal cells depended on whether measurements were made in the cell-attached mode ($P_{Na}/P_K > 6$) or inside-out mode ($P_{Na}/P_K = 1.33$). Thus, it would have been interesting to compare the results of inside-out recordings between these two studies. Unfortunately, these measurements were not performed. Furthermore, it is surprising that the same biophysical properties of these channels were obtained in both freshly isolated FDLE cells and after they were maintained in culture for 8 days because phenotypic and electrophysiologic properties of these cells may change after 4 days in culture. Presently, no other group has reported the existence of this 4-pS channel in either ATII or FDLE cells.

A diverse number of Na^+ and cation channels have been identified in ATII cells isolated from the lungs of adult animals (Table 2). Feng et al (49) obtained single-channel recordings across rat ATII cells maintained in primary culture for 24 to 72 h on collagen-coated coverslips for 24 and 72 h patched in the inside-out mode. Their data are consistent with the presence of nonselective ($P_{Na}/P_K = 1$), voltage-independent, Ca^{2+}-activated (>0.1 mM) cation channels with a conductance of 20.4 pS in symmetrical NaCl (150 mM) solutions. Addition of amiloride (1–10 μM) into the pipette solution decreased the *Po* but did not alter the single-channel conductance. Amiloride-sensitive cation channels were not found in alveolar macrophages, which are present, albeit in a small percentage, in almost all ATII cultures. The biophysical properties of these channels closely resemble those recorded in FDLE cells by Orser et al (134).

Table 2 Single-channel characteristics of Na^+ channels recorded across isolated adult alveolar type II (ATII) cells or reconstituted Na^+-channel proteins in lipid bilayer[a]

Species (days in cult)	Type of patch	[Na^+ pip/Na^+ bath] (mM)	g (pS)	Rect	[P_{Na^+}/P_{K^+}]	IC_{50} (μM) Amil	IC_{50} (μM) EIPA	Regulation	Reference
ATII cells									
Rat (1–4)	CA	140/140	20.6	Linear	0.97	<1	NM	cGMP/PKG	82
Rat (1–4)	IO	140/5	20.6	Linear	0.97	<1	NM	cGMP	82
Rat (1–4)	IO	150/150	20.4	Linear	1.15	<1	NM	Ca^{2+}	49
Rat (1–4)	CA	150/150	27	Inward	NM	NM	NM	Terbut.;	187
								hyperoxia	186
Rat (1–4)	IO	150/0	25	Linear	7	<1	<1	cAMP/PKA	187
Na^+-channel proteins from ATII cells (lipid bilayers)									
Rabbit	(Bilayers)	100/100	25	Linear	9	8	1	PKA	157
Rabbit	(Bilayers)	100/100	11	Linear	NM	NM	NM	$G\alpha i$-2, $GTP\gamma S$	20

[a]Abbreviations: g, single-channel conductance; Rect, rectification of single-channel current-voltage relationship; P_{Na^+}/P_{K^+}, ratio of sodium to potassium permeability of ion channels; IC_{50}, concentration (micromolar) of Amil (amiloride) or EIPA (5-*N*-ethyl-*N*-isopropyl-2′-4′-amiloride) to achieve 50% inhibition of single-channel current; CA, cell-attached patch; NM, not measured; PKG, protein kinase G; IO, inside-out patch; PKA, protein kinase A. Conductance measured in the presence of actin.

Yue et al (187) patched ATII cells, isolated from the lungs of adult rats and kept in primary culture for periods of 12–24 h, in either the cell-attached or inside-out modes. When patched in the cell-attached mode using symmetrical Na^+ solutions (150 mM Na^+), single-channel currents were observed for holding potentials between −80 and 30 mV. These channels had a single-channel conductance of 27 pS, a mean open time (τ_1) of 3.3 ms, and a *Po* of 0.36. Single-channel currents with a conductance of 25 pS were also recorded across ATII cells patched in the inside-out mode (cytosolic $Ca^{2+} < 10$ nM). Ion substitution studies showed a relative permeability of Na^+ to (K^+ P_{Na}/P_K) of 7:1. This channel was also activated by an increase in intracellular cAMP.

The activity of these moderately selective Na^+ channels in ATII cells was inhibited almost completely by inclusion of either 1 μM amiloride or 1 μM EIPA into the pipette solution. EIPA also blocked electrogenic $^{22}Na^+$ uptake into plasma membrane vesicles from ATII cells (102), $^{22}Na^+$ fluxes into freshly isolated ATII cells (104), Na^+ currents across ATII and FDLE cells patched in the whole-cell mode (104, 182), and single-channel activity of an ATII Na^+-channel protein reconstituted in lipid bilayers (20, 157). Finally, Yue & Matalon showed that intratracheal instillation of equimolar concentrations of amiloride or EIPA inhibited Na^+ reabsorption across the alveolar epithelium of anesthetized rats in vivo and increased the amount of lung edema when rats were exposed to hyperoxia (185). These so-called L-type Na^+ channels (159) have been found in a variety of tissues, including in LLC-PK_1 and MDCK cells (114), the brush border membranes of rat kidney cortex (7), rabbit blastocyst trophectodermal cells (147), the basolateral membranes of toad urinary bladder (55), and brain endothelial cells (177). However, EIPA did not inhibit Na^+ short-circuit current (I_{sc}) across resistive monolayers of ATII cells grown on permeable supports (63, 151).

Jain et al (82) reported the existence of a 20-pS Na^+ channel in cell-attached patches of ATII cells cultured for 24 to 96 h. The current reversed at the resting membrane potential of the ATII cells (about −30 mV) (31), indicating that this channel had equal permeability to Na^+ and K^+. Addition of amiloride (0.1–1 μM) in the pipette reduced the *Po* from 0.31 to 0.03 without affecting the conductance. Cation channels with similar permeability to Na^+ and K^+ were also observed when ATII cells were patched in the inside-out mode using 145 mM NaCl in the pipette and 145 mM KCl in the bath. They concluded that this channel was similar to the one described by Orser et al (134) in FDLE cells and by Feng et al (49) in adult ATII cells. However, the channels described by Orser et al and Feng et al became active only at very high intracellular Ca^{2+} concentrations ($[Ca^{2+}]_i > 1$ mM). In contrast, the channel recorded by Jain et al (82) was active at normal intracellular Ca^{2+} concentrations ($\approx$100 nM for cultured ATII cells) (57) but was activated by a cGMP-dependent protein kinase.

Light et al (90) also demonstrated the presence of a 28-pS cation channel in rat renal inner-medullary collecting duct cells, the activity of which was modulated both by cGMP per se and via cGMP kinase-induced phosphorylation. When this channel was cloned (84), mRNA could not be detected within cultured FDLE cells using reverse transcriptase–polymerase chain reaction (H O'Brodovich, unpublished observations). Furthermore, previous studies reported that large increases in intracellular cGMP levels failed to alter Na^+ reabsorption across adult and isolated perfused lungs (58), monolayers of ATII or FDLE cells (59, 63, 124), or ATII cells patched in the whole-cell mode (S Matalon, unpublished observations).

Taken together, the results of these studies indicate that the apical membranes of ATII and FDLE cells contain a Ca^{2+}-activated NSC and Na^+-selective channels. In addition, FDLE cells contain a Ca^{2+}-insensitive, 4-pS Na^+-selective channel, with biophysical properties similar to those of α-, β-, and γ-rENaC, reconstituted in *Xenopus* oocytes (27, 29). On the other hand, none of the channels identified in adult ATII cells resemble the 4-pS channel. Because all three rENaC subunits are present in both fetal and adult ATII cells (120, 171, 186), it is possible that the stochiometry of the Na^+ channel in ATII cells is different from that found in the colon. Indeed, Kizer et al (86) reported that expression of the α-rENaC from osteoblasts into a null cell line resulted in a 24-pS cation channel.

WHOLE-CELL CURRENTS Only about 10% of the cell-attached or inside-out patches in ATII cells demonstrate single-channel activity. Furthermore, the contribution of various types of channels with different conductances and densities to overall Na^+ transport is difficult to ascertain. Additional information can be obtained from measurements of current-voltage relationships across the entire ATII cell membranes.

Several laboratories have reported successful whole-cell recordings in ATII cells (71). When patched using symmetrical solutions with Na^+, with the sole cation present, both freshly isolated and cultured rabbit or rat ATII cells exhibit outwardly rectified Na^+ currents (72, 104, 184). Substitution of Na^+-glutamate with an equimolar concentration of $NMDG^+$ (N-Methyl-D-glucamine)-glutamate either in the bath or the pipette resulted in complete loss (except for leak current) of the inward or outward currents, respectively. Addition of 10 mM tetraethyl ammonium to the bath solution did not alter the values of these currents, indicating that the movement of Na^+ ions did not occur through tetraethyl ammonium–sensitive K^+ channels known to exist in cultured ATII cells (42, 43). At 0 h and 24 h in culture, more than 60% of the outward currents were inhibited by amiloride, benzamil, or EIPA with an $IC_{50} \leq 1\ \mu M$ for each inhibitor, in a reversible manner. However, after 48 h in culture, the magnitude of the amiloride-sensitive current decreased to the extent that none of the Na^+ current was amiloride sensitive at 72 h post-isolation.

When patched using bionic solutions (bath = 150 mM Na^+-glutamate; pipette = 150 mM K^+-glutamate), both amiloride and EIPA (1 μM) reversibly inhibited the inward (Na^+) but not the outward (K^+) current. In this experiment, addition of tetraethyl ammonium (10 mM) to the bath solution decreased the outward (K^+) current but had no effect on the inward (Na^+) currents. It is interesting to note that loss of amiloride-sensitive Na^+ currents coincided with movement of proteins antigenically related to Na^+ channels from the area of plasma membrane to the cytoplasm (detected by confocal microscopy utilizing an antibody raised against Na^+-channel protein purified from bovine kidney papilla) (184). The magnitude of the inhibition of the Na^+ current is similar to the extent of inhibition of Na^+ reabsorption across the alveolar epithelium in vivo following intratracheal instillation of amiloride both in human (152) and in sheep lungs (22) and of EIPA in rat lungs (185).

When whole-cell currents were measured in rat ATII cells using the aforementioned bionic conditions, the currents reversed around a zero membrane potential, indicating that the channels were equally permeable for Na^+ as for K^+. This is in contrast to the findings of Yue et al (187), who reported the presence of moderately selective Na^+ channels using single-channel measurements ($P_{Na}/P_K = 7$). These differences can be reconciled by the existence of additional channels in the cell membrane. In addition to Na^+ channels, whole-cell patch clamp measurements have identified two different populations of voltage-activated K^+ channels (low- and high-threshold types) in both freshly isolated and cultured rat ATII cells (43, 138).

The most serious drawback of the whole-cell technique is that dilution of the cytoplasmic contents by the pipette solution may cause the concentration of a critical factor to fall below a given threshold, which in turn may modify channel behavior. This limitation may be circumvented by the addition of pore-forming antibiotics, such as nystatin or amphotericin B, in the pipette solution. These agents create conduits allowing the free movement of small monovalent ions through the membrane patch while restricting the movement of larger solutes (perforated patch) (73). FDLE cells patched with this technique using bionic (bath, 135 mM NaCl; pipette, 135 mM KCl and 1 mM $CaCl_2$) exhibited linear currents reversing around -15 mV, indicating the presence of cation channels with similar permeability to Na^+ and K^+ (182). The magnitude of the inward Na^+ currents were diminished considerably by the additions of either amiloride or EIPA (20 μM) into the bath solution but were not affected by dimethylamiloride. Thus, ATII and FDLE Na^+ channels are sensitive to EIPA.

Reconstitution of ATII Na^+-Channel Proteins in Lipid Bilayers

Additional proof for the existence of Na^+ channels in ATII cells was obtained by purifying to homogeneity a Na^+-channel protein from freshly isolated rabbit ATII cells using ion exchange chromatography, followed by immunoaffinity purification over a column to which rabbit polyclonal antibodies raised against purified bovine renal Na^+-channel protein were bound (157). Under denatured and either reduced or nonreduced conditions, the ATII cell Na^+ channel protein consists of two peptides of ~130 and 70 kDa and is quite different from the Na^+-channel protein (~700 kDa under nonreduced conditions), which was purified from bovine papillary collecting ducts and A6 cells (18). Studies utilizing a photoreactive amiloride analog (2′-methoxy-5′-nitrobenzamil) and antiamiloride antibodies, as well as monoclonal antiidiotypic antibodies (RA 6.3) directed against antiamiloride antibodies, identified the 130-kDa polypeptide as an amiloride binding protein in both the lung and kidney proteins (128).

The amiloride binding site in adult ATII cells was further characterized by equilibrium binding assays using [^{3}H]Br-benzamil as a ligand (128). Scatchard analysis of specific [^{3}H]Br-benzamil binding to cell membranes from freshly isolated rabbit ATII cells showed a single binding site population with an apparent dissociation constant (K_d) of 370 nM. Similar studies in FDLE cells revealed the presence of two distinct populations. The first had an average K_d value of 19.2 nM, with a maximal number of binding sites (B_{max}) of 8.36 pmol/mg of protein; the second had a K_d of 1525 nM, with a B_{max} of 260 pmol/mg of protein (100). The large ratio of the low/high affinity binding studies (31:1) accounts for the fact that Na^+ transport into these cells is inhibited to the same extent by amiloride and EIPA (100, 182). These biochemical findings are in agreement with the results of physiological studies reviewed above, indicating the presence of multiple types of Na^+ channels in FDLE cells (174).

When this ATII cell Na^+-channel protein was reconstituted in lipid bilayers, single-channel currents with a linear conductance of 20–25 pS were seen (20, 157). In agreement with what was observed in ATII cells (187), addition of the catalytic subunit of protein kinase A (PKA) plus ATP to the presumed cytoplasmic side of the bilayer resulted in a significant increase in *Po* without altering single-channel conductance. The addition of amiloride or EIPA to the *trans* (extracellular) side reduced *Po* with no change in single-channel conductance. The IC_{50} values for amiloride and EIPA were 8 μM and 1 μM, respectively. In additional studies, Berdiev et al (20) showed that the apparent inhibition constants for amiloride and EIPA increased significantly following addition of PKA and ATP in the cytoplasmic side of the bilayer (from 8 to

15 μM for amiloride and from 1 to 2 μM for EIPA). In contrast, reconstitution of the Na^+-channel protein isolated from kidney papilla or A6 cells into the same type of lipid bilayers at 100 mN Na^+ resulted in channels with unitary conductances of 35–40 and 5.6 pS, fully blocked by 0.1 μM amiloride but insensitive to EIPA (127).

CLONING AND GENE EXPRESSION OF EPITHELIAL Na^+ CHANNELS

Cloning of the Amiloride-Sensitive Epithelial Na^+ Channel

A complementary DNA (cDNA) encoding an amiloride-sensitive Na^+ channel was cloned from the colon of salt-deprived rats using functional expression cloning techniques (27, 29, 93). This clone, termed α-rENaC (for the α subunit of the rat epithelial Na^+ channel), contains a 2094-nucleotide open reading frame corresponding to 698 amino acids with a predicted molecular mass of 79 kDa. Furthermore, it shares significant homology with *mec-4* and *deg-1*, members of a family of *Caenorhabditis elegans* genes involved in sensory touch expression. When expressed in *Xenopus* oocytes, α-rENaC displayed the characteristics of the Na[5] Na^+ channels of Palmer's classification (137), i.e. much higher affinity to amiloride ($K_i = 0.1$ μM) than to EIPA ($K_i = 10$ μM), no significant K^+ conductance, and high permeability to Li^+ ions ($P_{Li}/P_{Na} = 1.6$). Subsequently, Canessa et al (29) identified and cloned two additional subunits of this channel, named β-rENaC and γ-rENaC, with molecular masses of 72 kDa and 75 kDa, respectively. Coexpression of all three subunits in oocytes generated 100-fold higher amiloride-sensitive currents than did α-rENaC alone (29). Each subunit has two putative transmembrane domains, yielding a protein with a large (~50 kDa) hydrophilic loop and short hydrophilic NH_2 and COOH termini. The α-rENaC spans the membrane twice, with the short terminal ends on the cytoplasmic side and a large hydrophilic loop in the extracellular space (28). The α-rENaC message was identified only in organs known to contain epithelial Na^+ channels, such as kidney medulla and cortex and distal colon. Results from experiments utilizing point mutations suggest that all three subunits are involved in pore formation (155), although the exact stoichiometry is debated, with different groups reporting either four (50) or nine subunits (161) in the complex.

The three subunits are part of a novel cation-channel super family (reviewed in 8, 148) that is highly conserved from an evolutionary point of view. They share homology with relevant proteins in *C. elegans*, mammalian homologues δ-ENaC, $BNaC_1$, and $BNaC_2$, and ligand-gated channels such as FaNaC in *Helix aspersa* and the mammalian ASIC (acid-sensing ion channel) (8). All three human and some bovine and murine homologue subunits have now been cloned (8, 54).

There are some data regarding the structure and regulation of the α-rENaC subunit gene. Southern blot analyses indicate that a single gene accounts for α-rENaC and at least two alternatively spliced variants (89). The alternatively spliced transcripts have deletions that result in proteins shortened by 199 or 216 amino acids at the carboxyl terminus. Expression of one of these truncated transcripts (α-rENaCa) in *Xenopus* oocytes results in loss of amiloride-sensitive Na^+ currents. The α-rENaCa transcript is less abundant than the α-rENaC in kidney, lung, and taste tissues.

The actual genomic structure and regulation of the promoter has been determined for rat α-ENaC gene (135); 12 exons and 2 transcriptional start sites were detected, with a longer 5′ UTR being more prevalent in fetal than in adult rat lung or kidney. The α-ENaC promoter yielded low levels of reporter gene activity, which could be increased by dexamethasone treatment. Triiodothyronine (T_3) alone had no effect but potentiated dexamethasone stimulation of promoter activity. These functional studies agree with the known physiologic regulation of α-ENaC activity by these hormones (10, 32, 171) (see below). The relatively weak promoter activity raised the question of why high levels of α-rENaC mRNA are detected in mature lung (32, 120, 186). Although one cannot discard the possibility that promoter activity is much higher in vivo, a more likely reason relates to the observation that the half life ($t_{1/2}$) of α-rENaC mRNA is ~24 h in mature FDLE cells (135). These observations combined with the extremely low abundance of ENaC protein suggests that ENaC may be regulated on a posttranscriptional basis.

The intron/exon structure, along with approximately 450 bp of 5′ flanking DNA sequence of the gene encoding the γ subunit of human ENaC has also been identified (172). The 5′ flanking region contains no CCAAT- or TATA-like elements but does contain two GC boxes as well as several putative transcription factor binding sites, including AP-2, Sp1, CRE, PEA-3, and NF-IL6.

Cloning of ENaC from Lung Tissue

There has been one report of a Na^+ channel cloned directly from lung tissue. Voilley et al (179) used a fragment of the rat colon Na^+-channel cDNA to screen a human lung cDNA library. One of the hybridizing clones contained a 2007-bp open reading frame, encoding a 699–amino acid protein of 76 kDa. When injected into oocytes, the cloned channel also exhibited the biophysical characteristics of the channel identified in their FDLE cells (was sensitive to amiloride but insensitive to EIPA). The sequence shares 81% identity with α-rENaC, if methionine-27 of the rat colon sequence is aligned with the first methionine of the human sequence, and is identical with α-hENaC cloned from a human kidney cDNA library (111). Northern blot analysis with the mRNA of this channel identified the presence of a 3.8-kb transcript, similar in size to the α-rENaC transcript, in both human and rat lung tissue. Furthermore, expression of the mRNA increased significantly shortly before birth. However, it should be emphasized that because the Na^+-channel subunit was cloned from a whole lung cDNA library containing more than 40 different types of epithelial cells, its relationship to the native amiloride-sensitive Na^+ channel in FDLE and ATII cells has yet to be determined.

EXPRESSION AND HORMONAL REGULATION OF ENaC IN NORMAL LUNG ALVEOLAR EPITHELIAL CELLS

When total RNA is extracted from whole lungs, there are very low levels of α-ENaC mRNA during early stages of fetal rat (120), mouse (41), and human (179) development. Although α-rENaC mRNA does increase prior to birth (120), β- and γ-rENaC subunits are differentially regulated, with maximal expression shortly after birth (171). On a functional basis, bioelectric (144) and lung explant (13) studies similarly indicate that mature, relative to immature, rat FDLE cells have a significant capacity for Na^+ transport. Recently, it has also been shown that mature human FDLE cells possess similar bioelectric properties (9) and ENaC mRNA levels (176) to those described for rats.

Expression of α-rENaC mRNA in adult rat ATII cells was also demonstrated by Northern blot analysis (186), polymerase chain reaction (48), and in situ hybridization (186) (Table 3) (48, 106). Additional in situ studies indicate that although β and γ mRNAs are detected in large and small airways, they are less abundant in ATII cells as compared with α-rENaC (48). Antibodies, raised against the α, β, and γ subunits, labeled surface epithelial cells on rat trachea, bronchi, and bronchioles but not on normal alveoli (146, 146). In contrast, antibodies raised against a protein isolated from kidney papillae (162) immunostained in a specific fashion alveolar epithelial cells both in vivo and in vitro (104, 105, 186). Subsequently, Michaut et al (112) identified the presence of mRNAs for all three subunits in rat FDLE cells immortalized by transfection with the simian virus (SV40) large T antigen gene (37).

The in vivo relation between the absolute levels of α-, β-, and γ-hENaC mRNA and amiloride-sensitive PD in normal adult human male nasal respiratory epithelia was recently determined using a newly developed quantitative reverse transcriptase–polymerase chain reaction assay that was specific for each subunit (136). The assay used in vitro transcribed cRNAs identical to each target mRNA (but containing a small internal deletion) as competitive internal controls, and results were normalized to epithelial-specific cytokeratin

Table 3 Detection of Na^+-channel mRNAs and proteins in fetal distal lung epithelial (FDLE) and aveolar type II (ATII) cells[a]

Probe	Method	Cell type	Comments	References
$NaAb^+$	Immunofluorence	Lung sections & ATII cells	Immunostaining of ATII cell apical membrane; ↑ hyperoxia	104, 105, 186
$NaAb^+$ $An.Id\text{-}Am^{++}$	Western blot Photoaffinity lab.	FDLE, ATII	Immunostaining of 135–150 and 90 kDa; ↑ hyperoxia	72, 100, 104, 128
α-rENaC cDNA	Northern blots	FDLE RNA	3.7-kb transcripts; ↑ expression before birth; ↑ Po_2	120, 139, 171
α-rENaC cDNA	Northern blots	FDLE RNA	3.6-kb transcripts ↑ dexam	32, 171
α-rENaC cDNA	Western blot	ATII RNA	3.7-kb transcript ↑ hyperoxia	186
α-rENaC cRNA	In situ hybrid	Lung sections	Signal detected in ATII cells; ↑ hyperoxia	186
βγ-rENaC cDNA	Northern blots	FDLE RNA	Detected just prior to birth; ↑ after birth	48, 106, 171
β-rENaC cRNA	In situ hybrid	Lung sections	very low abundance in ATII cells	48, 106

[a]Abbreviations: NaAb, polyclonal antibody raised against Na^+-channel protein from bovine kidney papilla; An.Ib-Ab, monoclonal antiidiotypic antibodies directed against antiamiloride antibodies; ENaC, epithelial Na^+ channel.

18 mRNA. The respective values for α-, β-, and γ-hENaC mRNA levels were 39 ± 4, 7.5 ± 0.92, and 1.8 ± 0.25 attomol/fmol cytokeratin mRNA. Respiratory epithelial PD decreased with increasing γ-hENaC mRNA levels ($r^2 = 0.62, p < 0.05$). There was no correlation between either α- or β-hENaC mRNA levels and PD. This assay may provide a useful tool to evaluate Na^+ transport in patients with cystic fibrosis, neonatal respiratory distress syndrome, and pulmonary edema.

Cell-Derived Matrix Products

Several factors are now known to influence both ENaC mRNA levels and amiloride-sensitive Na^+ transport in the developing lung. Consistent with our understanding of the in vivo ontogeny of fetal lung epithelial ion transport, fetal mixed lung cell-derived matrix produced from canalicular staged (i.e. immature) lungs decreases the mRNA levels of α-, β-, and γ-rENaC in overlying FDLE cells (140, 150). This matrix concomitantly induces a more immature ion transporting phenotype secretion in the FDLE cells, which then exhibit a lower amiloride-sensitive I_{sc} and evidence of Cl^-secretion.

Glucocorticoids and Mineralocorticoids

Glucocorticosteroids increase α-ENaC mRNA and amiloride-sensitive I_{sc} in primary cultures of rat (32) and human (176) FDLE cells, whereas in euthyroid rat fetuses (171) or cultured fetal rat (32) and human FDLE cells (176), T_3 alone does not increase ENaC expression. These results are compatible with the recent evaluation of rENaC promoter activity (135). In vivo experiments in rats have demonstrated a differential regulation of ENaC subunits by glucocorticosteroids: α- but neither β- nor γ-rENaC mRNA levels increase within 8 h of treatment (171). However, in studies using primary cultures of human FDLE cells, glucocorticosteroids increased the levels of all three subunits. The difference in this study may relate to the higher concentrations of steroids used in these in vitro experiments (176).

Aldosterone plays a major role in the regulation of Na^+ transport in epithelial tissues known to contain Na^+ channels (53). Exposure of toad bladder to aldosterone leads, after a 30- to 90-min latent period, to a large increase in I_{sc}, lasting up to 6 h, that is due solely to an increase in the Na^+ permeability of the apical membranes. Tousson et al (175) showed that treatment of the amphibian A6 renal epithelial line with aldosterone significantly increased I_{sc} by causing the conversion of inactive apical Na^+ channels to active ones. The molecular mechanisms of this conversion are not known, but they may be related to transmethylation of the Na^+-channel protein (80, 153). Both adult and fetal lungs may be potential targets for aldosterone regulation because they contain mineralocorticoid receptors (88). However, specific cellular targets have not been identified. Overnight incubation of ATII cell monolayers with aldosterone concentrations ranging between 10^{-7} and 10^{-4} M did not increase I_{sc} (39). Addition of aldosterone (10^{-6} M) to FDLE cells did not alter their bioelectric properties (124). On the other hand, pretreatment of FDLE cells with aldosterone (10^{-6} M) for 8 h induced a large increase in α-rENaC mRNA and amiloride-sensitive Na^+ currents, as detected by patch-clamp measurements (32). The results were consistent with aldosterone stimulating Na^+-channel protein synthesis in FDLE cells by binding to type II glucocorticoid and not mineralocorticoid receptors (32). This contrasts with the effect of aldosterone in A6 cells (see above). Recent studies have shown that gender hormones modulate both the mRNA levels and amiloride-sensitive I_{sc} in adult rat lung and cultured ATII cells (170).

Oxygen

Although catecholamines and cAMP rapidly convert the mature fetal lung from Cl^- secretion to Na^+ absorption, the lung rapidly reverts to fluid secretion when the infusion is discontinued (25). The change from fetal (~3%) to postnatal (~21%) O_2 concentrations at birth may be one of the lung's "permanent switching mechanisms" to fluid absorption. Ambient PO_2 affects fetal lung cyst fluid formation in vitro (11), and studies have shown that the perinatal increase in PO_2 increases the mRNA levels of both α-, β-, and γ-rENaC and amiloride-sensitive I_{sc} in FDLE cells (139). The O_2-induced increase of ENaC expression in FDLE is associated with NF-κB but not AP-1 activation and is blocked by a superoxide scavenger (143). These studies are consistent with the identification of NF-κB transcription binding sites in the α-rENaC promoter region (135). In adult cells, changes in ambient PO_2 have induced a biphasic response. Exposure of cultured ATII cells to severe hypoxia (3% or 0% ambient O_2) results in time-dependent down-regulation of amiloride-sensitive $^{22}Na^+$ influx in ATII cells, decreased mRNA levels of the α-, β-, and γ-rENaC subunits and a significant decrease in α-rENaC protein synthesis (141). However, more moderate hypoxia levels (5% O_2) had no effect on these variables. Severe hypoxia (3% O_2) also down-regulated $^{22}Na^+$ uptake in A549 cells, a human carcinoma cell line that resembles some features of ATII cells (95). On the other hand, exposure of rats to sublethal hyperoxia (85% O_2) up-regulated whole-cell and single-channel currents in ATII cells and increased ATII cell α-rENaC and Na^+-channel protein levels significantly (72, 186; for review see 101).

POSTTRANSLATIONAL REGULATION OF Na^+ CHANNEL ACTIVITY IN LUNG ALVEOLAR EPITHELIAL CELLS AND ATII Na^+-CHANNEL PROTEINS

β-Agonists and cAMP

As mentioned above, infusion of terbutaline in mature lamb fetuses (>135 days) results in the reabsorption of the fetal lung fluid by increasing active Na^+ transport from lung lumen to plasma (25, 132). In the adult lung, intratracheal instillation of β-agonists increases Na^+ reabsorption across sheep and rat lungs in situ (22, 108). The fact that propranolol, a β_2-antagonist, prevented these changes shows that they were mediated via activation of β_2-receptors. The presence of both β_1 and β_2 receptors in ATII cells has been demonstrated in vivo by autoradiographic techniques (30). Activation of β_2 receptors generally stimulates adenylate cyclase that in turn increases intracellular cAMP levels. Sakuma et al (152) showed that intratracheal instillation of terbutaline increases Na^+ reabsorption across resected human lungs. β-agonists, or agents that increase intracellular cAMP levels, such as cholera toxin, 8-bromo-cAMP, and 3-isobutyl-1-methylxanthine, increase short-circuit current (I_{sc}) across ATII or FDLE monolayers (34, 124, 125). Based on the results of these in vivo and in vitro studies, it was proposed that an increase in intracellular cAMP results in increased Na^+ transport across ATII cells by up-regulating apical Na^+

conductive pathways. These agents also increase ATII cell Na^+-K^+-ATPase activity by a Na^+-independent mechanism (169).

Existing evidence also indicates that agents that increase cAMP alter intracellular Cl^-- movement across ATII cells. Measurements of ^{22}Na and $^{36}Cl^-$ fluxes across monolayers of ATII cells indicated that addition of terbutaline into the basolateral compartment increased transepithelial Na^+ and Cl^- reabsorption (85a). Jiang et al (83a) showed that treatment of rat ATII cells with terbutaline stimulated Cl^- and Na^+ influx into the cells, which increased net NaCl absorption without affecting the apical membrane Na^+ conductance. On the other hand, Nielsen et al (116a) showed that agents that elevated intracellular cAMP in rabbit ATII cells mounted in Ussing chambers, augmented I_{sc} by increasing Cl^- secretion Na^+ reabsorption. The CFTR channel blocker glybenclamide and the loop diuretic bumetanide partially decreased the forskolin-induced increase in I_{sc}, suggesting that Cl^- occurred through CFTR. Furthermore, Nielsen et al (116a) also demonstrated that intratracheal instillation of forskolin into rabbits, may result in some cases in Cl^- secretion and net fluid movement into the alveolar space, resulting in pulmonary edema.

More definitive evidence of up-regulation of the ATII Na^+ channels by agents that increase intracellular cAMP was provided by several patch-clamp studies. Addition of 10 μM terbutaline to the bath solution of ATII cells patched in the cell-attached mode using symmetrical Na^+ solutions increased the single-channel mean open time (τ_1) from 3.3 ms to 6.4 ms and the *Po* from 0.36 to 0.62 without affecting single-channel conductance (187). These effects were totally blocked by the addition of the β-antagonist propranolol into the bath solution.

The observed increase in *Po* by PKA may have been brought about by direct phosphorylation of channel proteins, phosphorylation of cytoskeletal protein interacting with Na^+-channel proteins (such as actin, ankyrin, spectrin, or fodrin) (149, 160), or by insertion of new channel protein from a cytoplasmic pool to the apical membrane. In subsequent studies of ATII cells patched in the inside-out mode, addition of 250 U of PKA per ml with 1 mM ATP and 5 mM $MgCl_2$ to the bath solution increased the single-channel τ_1 from 3.26 to 7.38 and *Po* from 0.41 to 0.72 without altering conductance. Addition of PKA plus ATP to the presumed cytoplasmic side of planar bilayers containing the putative immunopurified ATII Na^+-channel protein also resulted in a significant increase in the single-channel open probability (P_O) (from 0.40 to 0.8) without altering single-channel conductance (157). These data support the hypothesis that phosphorylation of the Na^+-channel complex is involved in cAMP activation and the demonstrated increase in *Po*.

Indeed, Berdiev et al (20) showed that PKA phosphorylated both the 135-kDa and the 70-kDa polypeptides of the immunopurified ATII Na^+-channel protein.

In A6 cells, PKA phosphorylated a 315-kDa protein, which is one of the subunits of the Na^+-channel protein isolated by Benos et al (17, 18), and increased Na^+ transport (154). PKA also phosphorylated the 315-kDa polypeptide of a highly purified Na^+-channel protein inserted into lipid bilayers and increased the *Po* of these channels without affecting their conductance (129). ENaC do not contain consensus phosphorylation sites in their cytoplasmic domain (145), and PKA did not activate amiloride-sensitive currents in *Xenopus* oocytes injected with ENaC cRNAs (5). On the other hand, MDCK cells transfected with α-, β-, and γ-rENaC developed significant levels of amiloride-sensitive currents that were activated by forskolin (166). Furthermore, reconstitution of ENaCs into planar lipid bilayers results in a channel that is activated by PKA and ATP in the presence, but not in the absence of short actin filaments (19). Thus, it should be stressed that it is possible that the increase in *Po*, observed in excised inside-out patches of ATII cells following addition of PKA, may have been the result of increased phosphorylation of the short actin filaments or other cytoskeletal proteins.

Marunaka et al (98, 173) also reported that addition of 10 μM terbutaline to the bath solution of FDLE cells, patched in the cell-attached mode, increased the *Po* of the Ca^{2+}-activated, nonselective cation channels without increasing single-channel conductance. Furthermore, in the presence of brefeldin A, terbutaline did not alter the *Po* of the Ca^{2+}-activated cation channel, indicating that in FDLE cells, terbutaline may promote the trafficking of this cation channel to the apical cell surface (81). The mechanisms responsible for the increase in *Po* are more difficult to elucidate because, in this system, terbutaline also increased the intracellular Ca^{2+} from 40 nM to more than 1 μM and decreased the intracellular Cl^- concentration from 45 to 25 nM, which will activate this nonselective cation channel. It is unclear if brefeldin also prevented the increase in intracellular Ca^{2+} noted by Tohda et al (173). The Na^+-channel protein, as a result of its SH3 binding domain interaction with spectrin, may be maintained at the apical membrane of FDLE cells (149) or undergo degradation, because the ubiquitin protein ligase NEDD4 binds to the proline rich sequence in the C terminus of ENaC (163, 164). Their results are in agreement with the findings of Kleyman et al (87), who reported that exposure of A6 cells to vasopressin doubled the amount of proteins antigenically related to Na^+ channels in their apical membrane and that this response was inhibited by brefeldin A. Furthermore, Marunaka & Eaton (97) reported that exposure of A6 cells to agents that increase cAMP levels resulted in an increase in the density of single channels but not in their *Po*, consistent with—but not proof of—the insertion of new channels in the apical cell membranes. Clearly, terbutaline increases Na^+ transport across ATII and FDLE cells via a number of different mechanisms.

Insulin

Insulin seems to increase Na^+ transport across ATII cells. Addition of 60 ng of insulin per ml to the basolateral side of Ussing chambers containing rat ATII cells increased I_{sc} from 2.1 to 3.2 $\mu A/cm^2$ and changed the PD from -1.1 to -1.6 mV (apical membrane negative), without altering transepithelial resistance (167). Insulin was much less effective in increasing Na^+ transport when added to the apical membrane side of the chambers. Hagiwara et al (69) reported that insulin increased both the amiloride-sensitive and the amiloride-insensitive components of I_{sc} across FDLE cells. Inhibition studies suggested that the latter effect was mediated via phosphorylation of tyrosine kinase. Tohda & Marunaka (174) showed that insulin increased the *Po* of both types of ion channels in FDLE without increasing their conductance. Thus, insulin may be one of several hormones involved in the regulation of Na^+ transport across the alveolar epithelium. However, it is unclear as to whether the concentrations needed to increase Na^+ transport in vitro will be encountered in lung interstitium in vivo.

MODIFICATION OF Na^+-CHANNEL ACTIVITY IN LUNG ALVEOLAR EPITHELIAL CELLS BY •NO AND $ONOO^-$

A number of studies have clearly demonstrated the importance of Na^+ reabsorption in fluid balance across the neonatal lung. Instillation of amiloride or benzamil into the fluid-filled airspaces of newborn guinea pigs prior to their first breath resulted in decreased clearance of the fetal fluid and the development of respiratory distress and arterial hypoxemia (121, 122). Neonatal mice, in which α-mENaC gene was inactivated by gene targeting, were unable to clear the fetal lung fluid and died within 40 h of birth (75). It was also shown that transgenic expression of α-rENaC driven by a cytomegalovirus promoter in α-mENaC (−/−) knockout mice rescued the perinatal lethal pulmonary phenotype and partially restored Na^+ transport in renal, colonic, and pulmonary epithelia (76). In addition, studies showing that newborn infants with either transient tachypnea (61) or neonatal respiratory distress syndrome (12) had more negative nasal transepithelial PD that were poorly inhibited by amiloride (12), which suggests that impairment of Na^+ absorption across the respiratory epithelia of very premature infants may be one of the factors contributing to the pathogenesis of respiratory distress syndrome. The importance of active transport in fluid clearance across the injured alveolar epithelium was demonstrated by the studies of Matthay & Wiener-Kronish (110), who found a positive correlation between the ability of the human alveolar epithelium to transport Na^+ actively and the rate of resolution of noncardiogenic pulmonary edema. Finally, instillation of phenamil, an irreversible blocker of epithelial Na^+ channels, into the lungs of rats exposed to hyperoxia resulted in higher levels of extravascular lung fluid volumes after 24 h compared with those receiving vehicle alone (185). Thus, lung Na^+ transport is highly relevant to human lung disease.

In Vitro Studies

Pathophysiological processes in a variety of pulmonary diseases, including neonatal and adult respiratory distress syndrome, cystic fibrosis, bronchopulmonary dysplasia, etc, may damage or alter the respiratory epithelium and alter the ability of FDLE and ATII cells to actively transport Na^+, thereby impairing the clearance of pulmonary edema. A common factor that may account for this injury is overproduction of reactive oxygen and nitrogen intermediates. For example, in response to proinflammatory cytokines, activated neutrophils and macrophages migrate to the lungs and release reactive oxygen species by the membrane-bound enzyme-complex NADPH oxidase (6) and nitric oxide (•NO) via the Ca^{2+}-insensitive (iNOS) form of •NO synthase (3, 79).

•NO binding to the heme group of soluble guanylate cyclase and the subsequent increase in cellular cGMP levels is probably the best-characterized interaction of •NO with a biological target. Many of the physiological effects of •NO, including smooth muscle vasodilation, are mediated by cGMP through various isoforms of cGMP-dependent protein kinase (PKG) and protein phosphorylation (77).

CGMP AND PKG PHOSPHORYLATION There is convincing evidence that redox states of •NO modulate cation-channel activity by increasing cGMP. Light et al (90) demonstrated the presence of a 28-pS cation channel in rat renal inner-medullary collecting duct cells, the activity of which was modulated both by cGMP per se and via PKG-induced phosphorylation. •NO released from endothelial cells specifically inhibited the apical membrane Na^+ conductance in permeabilized monolayers of cultured collecting duct cells (165), leading to an increased urinary Na^+ excretion (90, 165). Jain et al (82) reported that S-nitrosoglutathione and S-nitroso-N-acetylpenicillamine increased ATII cell cGMP content and significantly reduced the *Po* of a 20-pS NSC channel in cell-attached patches of ATII cells. Pretreatment with a PKG inhibitor prevented the inhibitory effects of S-nitrosoglutathione on this channel; incubation of ATII cells with a cell-permeable analogue of cGMP (8-BrcCMP) also decreased the *Po*. They concluded that •NO decreased the activity of this channel by activating a cGMP-dependent protein kinase.

Guo et al (63) also reported that •NO, generated by spermine NONOate and papa NONOate, decreased I_{sc} across rat ATII cells with an IC_{50} of 0.4 μM without affecting transepithelial resistance. •NO also inhibited ~60% of the amiloride-sensitive I_{sc} across ATII cell monolayers following permeabilization of the basolateral membrane with amphotericin B. However, in contrast to the findings of Jain et al (82), incubation of ATII monolayers with 8-bromo-GMP (400 μM) did not decrease I_{sc}. These results suggest that the effects of •NO on amiloride-sensitive currents occurred through cGMP-independent mechanisms and were caused by direct interaction of reactive oxygen-nitrogen intermediates with channel or cytoskeletal proteins.

PEROXYNITRITE •NO with $O_2^{\bullet -}$ react at a near-diffusion rate to form peroxynitrite ($ONOO^-$) (16), a potent oxidant and nitrating species that directly oxidizes a wide spectrum of biological molecules, such as DNA constituents (78), lipids (142), and proteins (56, 115). The cytotoxic effects of $ONOO^-$ on the components of the alveolar epithelium have been well documented (for review see 67). Exposure of surfactant protein A (SP-A), the most abundant apoprotein of pulmonary surfactant, to $ONOO^-$ led to nitration of a single tyrosine residue in its carbohydrate recognition domain and diminished the ability of SP-A to aggregate lipids and bind to mannose (65, 188). SP-A, isolated from the lungs of lambs breathing •NO and 95% O_2, also had decreased ability to aggregate lipids, indicating that reactive nitrogen-oxygen intermediates may damage surfactant proteins in vivo (103).

Hu et al (74) showed that addition of boluses of $ONOO^-$ (0.5 or 1 mM) into suspensions of freshly isolated rabbit ATII cells decreased amiloride-inhibitable $^{22}Na^+$ uptake to 68% and 56% of their control values, respectively, without affecting cell viability. Peroxynitrite, but not reactive oxygen species, also decreased $^{22}Na^+$ uptake into membrane vesicles of colonic cells of dexamethasone-treated rats known to contain Na^+-channels (15). At physiological pH values, $ONOO^-$ decomposes spontaneously with a half-time of about 1 s (16). Thus, a bolus instillation of 1 mM $ONOO^-$ resulted in a steady-state concentration of 2.6 μM during a 10-min period (15, 74). Significantly higher concentrations may be generated in the epithelial lining fluid by activated alveolar macrophages (79).

Reactive oxygen-nitrogen species may interfere with Na^+ transport across epithelial cells by damaging important structural proteins necessary for the proper function of these transporters. Compeau et al (38) assessed changes in Na^+ transport across monolayers of rat FDLE cells following incubation of these cells with macrophages stimulated with endotoxin for 16 h. They reported a 75% decline in transepithelial resistance (*Rt*) and a 60% reduction in amiloride-sensitive I_{sc}. Single-channel patch-clamp analysis demonstrated a 60% decrease in the density of a 25-pS nonselective cation (NSC) channel present in the apical membrane of these cells. However, single-channel conductance and open probability were not affected. A concurrent reduction in epithelial F-actin content suggested a role for actin depolymerization in mediating this effect. Incubation of cocultures of FDLE cells and alveolar macrophages with the methylated L-arginine (Arg) derivative NG-monomethyl-L-arginine prevented the reduction in epithelial I_{sc}, as did substitution of L-Arg with D-Arg or incubation in L-Arg-free medium. The products of activated macrophages exerted their effect by expression of inducible •NO synthase in the lung epithelium (44), and the down-regulation of amiloride-sensitive I_{sc} was associated with a decrease in rENaC mRNA levels (H O'Brodovich, unpublished observations). These data indicate that reactive oxygen-nitrogen species may affect amiloride-sensitive cation channels by reducing F-actin or other cytoskeletal structures.

In a recent report, DuVall et al (46) demonstrated that 3-morpholinosydnonimine, a generator of $ONOO^-$ profoundly inhibited the amiloride-sensitive whole-cell conductance in *Xenopus* oocytes expressing the three cloned subunits of the wild-type rat epithelial Na^+ channel α-, β-, γ-rENaC. Importantly, this effect was observed at very low $ONOO^-$ concentrations ($\sim$10 μM) suggesting that $ONOO^-$ may produce similar effects in vivo where concentrations have been estimated to occur at higher levels during inflammation (79). On the other hand, even supraphysiological concentrations of •NO, generated by a variety of •NO donors, had no effect on the amiloride-sensitive current. The inhibitory effects of 3-morpholinosydnonimine were mimicked by tetranitromethane at pH 6, a condition that results in the oxidation of sulfhydryl groups (68). In contrast, at pH 7.4, tetranitromethane both oxidizes sulfhydryl groups and nitrates tyrosine and tryptophan residues, but it does not affect the amiloride-sensitive whole-cell current. The external loop of α-rENaC contains 26 tyrosines, 6 tryptophans, and 14 cysteines (28), any or all of which may be subject to modification (nitration and/or oxidation) by reactive oxygen-nitrogen species. These data suggested that oxidation of critical sulfhydryl groups within rENaC by $ONOO^-$ directly inhibits amiloride-sensitive Na^+-channel activity (46).

In Vivo Studies

The toxicity of •NO per se, as well as the production of reactive oxygen nitrogen intermediates formed by the interaction of •NO with superoxide, has raised concerns that increased levels of •NO or $ONOO^-$ may damage ion transporters and thus interfere with Na^+ reabsorption across the alveolar epithelium in vivo. The detection of nitrotyrosine (the stable by-product of $ONOO^-$ reaction with tyrosine residues) in the lungs of patients with acute respiratory distress syndrome (66), as well as the detection of both nitrotyrosine and large amounts of nitrate in the epithelial lining fluid of patients with acute respiratory distress syndrome (S Matalon, unpublished observations), indicates that $ONOO^-$ is produced in the lungs of patients with inflammatory disease. In a recent study, Modelska et al

(113) showed that reabsorption of isotonic fluid, secondary to Na^+ reabsorption across the alveolar space, was inhibited followed prolonged hemorrhagic shock. Moreover, instillation of aminoguanidine, an inhibitor of the inducible form of •NO synthase, restored fluid reabsorption to normal levels. Thus, in agreement with the aforementioned in vitro studies across isolated type II cells, this study demonstrates that increased production of •NO by lung epithelial or inflammatory cells may damage Na^+ transporters, leading to decreased Na^+ reabsorption.

CONCLUSIONS

Currently, the following question is debated in a variety of forums: Is ENaC the major channel in fetal and adult alveolar epithelial cells? There is evidence in favor of this hypothesis. First, all the various rENaC subunits have been identified in FDLE and ATII cells (Table 3). Second, α-rENaC mRNA levels increase immediately before birth (120) and following sublethal injury to the alveolar epithelium (186), situations associated with up-regulation of Na^+ reabsorption across the alveolar epithelium. Third, genetically transformed mice lacking α-rENaC are unable to clear their fetal lung fluid and die from respiratory distress shortly after birth (75). Fourth, one group of investigators identified a 4-pS Na^+ channel in FDLE cells with biophysical properties identical to those observed when α-, β-, and γ-rENaC cRNAs are expressed in *Xenopus* oocytes (179). These facts have led a number of investigators to state that indeed ENaC is the major channel in lung epithelial cells (8, 54).

On the other hand, the following evidence argues against this hypothesis. First, with the exception of the study by Voilley et al (179), the biophysical properties of the identified Na^+ channels in FDLE and ATII cells are markedly different from those of ENaC (see Tables 1 and 2). Second, a Na^+-channel protein isolated from ATII cells and expressed in lipid bilayers exhibits a 25-pS Na^+ channel that is inhibited to the same extent by both amiloride and EIPA (20, 157). Although bilayer reconstitution studies have been criticized as being artificial, the fact remains that reconstitution of a protein isolated from bovine renal papilla expressed Na^+ channels that were insensitive to EIPA (127). Third, intratracheal instillation of EIPA inhibits Na^+ reabsorption across the normal and injured alveolar epithelium in vivo (185).

How can these diverse findings be reconciled? Clearly, the molecular cloning of the Na^+ channel from FDLE and ATII cells will help to answer this question. As mentioned in the text, a Na^+ channel has been cloned from human lung (179). However, the adult lung contains more than 40 different cells, only 14% of which are ATII cells (70). It is possible that the FDLE and ATII cell Na^+ channel is indeed coded by the same gene as ENaC but that it has a different stochiometry or even contains the δ subunit, which alters the biophysical properties of the α-, β-, and γ-rENaC ENaC channels (180). Alternatively, it may be identical to ENaC but a variety of factors, including cytoskeletal proteins and components present in the interstitial matrix may modify its biophysical properties posttranslationally.

Finally, there is considerable interest in identifying the fundamental mechanisms responsible for the modulation of Na^+-channel activity in vivo in a number of diseased states. The demonstration that reactive oxygen-nitrogen intermediates released by activated alveolar macrophages down-regulate the activity of FDLE and ATII Na^+ channels (38, 44, 63), as well as amiloride-sensitive currents in oocytes injected with ENaCs (46), has shed considerable insight into this question. Clearly, additional work is needed to understand the cellular and molecular mechanisms by which reactive species regulate Na^+ gene and protein expression.

ACKNOWLEDGMENTS

This project was supported by NIH Grants HL31197 and HL51173 and by a grant from the Office of Naval Research (N00014-97-1-0309) (Matalon) and by the MRC Group in Lung Development (O'Brodovich). The authors acknowledge the assistance of Ms. Mary Beth Campbell in editing this manuscript.

Literature Cited

1. Adamson IY, Young L, Bowden DH. 1988. Relationship of alveolar epithelial injury and repair to the induction of pulmonary fibrosis. *Am. J. Pathol.* 130:377–183
2. Adamson TM, Boyd RD, Platt HS, Strang LB. 1969. Composition of alveolar liquid in the foetal lamb. *J. Physiol. London* 204:159–68
3. Assreuy J, Cunha FQ, Epperlein M, Noronha-Dutra A, O'Donnell CA, et al. 1994. Production of nitric oxide and superoxide by activated macrophages and killing of Leishmania major. *Eur. J. Immunol.* 24:672–76
4. Ausiello DA, Stow JL, Cantiello HF, de Almeida JB, Benos DJ. 1992. Purified epithelial Na^+ channel complex contains the pertussis toxin-sensitive G alpha i-3 protein. *J. Biol. Chem.* 267: 4759–65
5. Awayda MS, Ismailov II, Berdiev BK, Fuller CM, Benos DJ. 1996. Protein kinase regulation of a cloned epithelial Na^+ channel. *J. Gen. Physiol.* 108:49–65
6. Babior BM. 1994. Activation of the respiratory burst oxidase. *Environ. Health Perspect.* 102(Suppl. 10):53–56
7. Barbry P, Chassande O, Vigne P, Frelin C, Ellory C, et al. 1987. Purification and subunit structure of the [^{3}H]phenamil receptor associated with the renal apical Na^+ channel. *Proc. Natl. Acad. Sci. USA* 84:4836–40
8. Barbry P, Hofman P. 1997. Molecular biology of Na^+ absorption. *Am. J. Physiol.* 273:G571–85
9. Barker PM, Boucher RC, Yankaskas JR. 1995. Bioelectric properties of cultured monolayers from epithelium of distal human fetal lung. *Am. J. Physiol.* 268:L270–77
10. Barker PM, Brown MJ, Ramsden CA,

Strang LB, Walters DV. 1988. The effect of thyroidectomy in the fetal sheep on lung liquid reabsorption induced by adrenaline or cyclic AMP. *J. Physiol. London* 407:373–83
11. Barker PM, Gatzy JT. 1993. Effect of gas composition on liquid secretion by explants of distal lung of fetal rat in submersion culture. *Am. J. Physiol.* 265:L512–17
12. Barker PM, Gowen CW, Lawson EE, Knowles MR. 1997. Decreased sodium ion absorption across nasal epithelium of very premature infants with respiratory distress syndrome. *J. Pediatr.* 130:373–77
13. Barker PM, Stiles AD, Boucher RC, Gatzy JT. 1992. Bioelectric properties of cultured epithelial monolayers from distal lung of 18-day fetal rat. *Am. J. Physiol.* 262:L628–36
14. Basset G, Crone C, Saumon G. 1987. Fluid absorption by rat lung in situ: pathways for sodium entry in the luminal membrane of alveolar epithelium. *J. Physiol. London* 384:325–45
15. Bauer ML, Beckman JS, Bridges RJ, Fuller CM, Matalon S. 1992. Peroxynitrite inhibits sodium uptake in rat colonic membrane vesicles. *Biochim. Biophys. Acta* 1104:87–94
16. Beckman JS, Beckman TW, Chen J, Marshall PA, Freeman BA. 1990. Apparent hydroxyl radical production by peroxynitrite: implications for endothelial injury from nitric oxide and superoxide. *Proc. Natl. Acad. Sci. USA* 87:1620–24
17. Benos DJ, Saccomani G, Brenner BM, Sariban-Sohraby S. 1986. Purification and characterization of the amiloride-sensitive sodium channel from A6 cultured cells and bovine renal papilla. *Proc. Natl. Acad. Sci. USA* 83:8525–29
18. Benos DJ, Saccomani G, Sariban-Sohraby S. 1987. The epithelial sodium channel. Subunit number and location of the amiloride binding site. *J. Biol. Chem.* 262:10613–18
19. Berdiev BK, Prat AG, Cantiello HF, Ausiello DA, Fuller CM, et al. 1996. Regulation of epithelial sodium channels by short actin filaments. *J. Biol. Chem.* 271:17704–10
20. Berdiev BK, Shlyonsky VG, Senyk O, Keeton D, Guo Y, et al. 1997. Protein kinase A phosphorylation and G protein regulation of type II pneumocyte Na^+ channels in lipid bilayers. *Am. J. Physiol.* 272:C1262–70
21. Berg MM, Kim KJ, Lubman RL, Crandall ED. 1989. Hydrophilic solute transport across rat alveolar epithelium. *J. Appl. Physiol.* 66:2320–27
22. Berthiaume Y, Staub NC, Matthay MA. 1987. Beta-adrenergic agonists increase lung liquid clearance in anesthetized sheep. *J. Clin. Invest.* 79:335–43
23. Bland RD, Nielson DW. 1992. Developmental changes in lung epithelial ion transport and liquid movement. *Annu. Rev. Physiol.* 54:373–94
24. Borok Z, Hami A, Danto SI, Zabski AM, Crandall ED. 1995. Rat serum inhibits progression of alveolar epithelial cells toward the type I cell phenotype in vitro. *Am. J. Respir. Cell Mol. Biol.* 12:50–55
25. Brown MJ, Olver RE, Ramsden CA, Strang LB, Walters DV. 1983. Effects of adrenaline and of spontaneous labour on the secretion and absorption of lung liquid in the fetal lamb. *J. Physiol. London* 344:137–52
26. Brown SE, Kim KJ, Goodman BE, Wells JR, Crandall ED. 1985. Sodium-amino acid cotransport by type II alveolar epithelial cells. *J. Appl. Physiol.* 59:1616–22
27. Canessa CM, Horisberger JD, Rossier BC. 1993. Epithelial sodium channel related to proteins involved in neurodegeneration. *Nature* 361:467–70
28. Canessa CM, Merillat AM, Rossier BC. 1994. Membrane topology of the epithelial sodium channel in intact cells. *Am. J. Physiol.* 267:C1682–90
29. Canessa CM, Schild L, Buell G, Thorens B, Gautschi I, et al. 1994. Amiloride-sensitive epithelial Na^+ channel is made of three homologous subunits. *Nature* 367:463–67
30. Carstairs R, Nimmo AJ, Barnes PJ. 1985. Autoradiographic visualization of beta-adrenoreceptor subtypes in human lung. *Am. Rev. Respir. Dis.* 132:541–47
31. Castranova V, Jones GS, Miles PR. 1983. Transmembrane potential of isolated rat alveolar type II cells. *J. Appl. Physiol.* 54:1511–17
32. Champigny G, Voilley N, Lingueglia E, Friend V, Barbry P, Lazdunski M. 1994. Regulation of expression of the lung amiloride-sensitive Na^+ channel by steroid hormones. *EMBO J.* 13:2177–81
33. Chapman DL, Carlton DP, Cummings JJ, Poulain FR, Bland RD. 1991. Intrapulmonary terbutaline and aminophylline decrease lung liquid in fetal lambs. *Pediatr. Res.* 29:357–61
34. Cheek JM, Kim KJ, Crandall ED. 1989. Tight monolayers of rat alveolar epithe-

lial cells: bioelectric properties and active sodium transport. *Am. J. Physiol.* 256:C688–93
35. Cherksey BD. 1988. Functional reconstitution of an isolated sodium channel from bovine trachea. *Comp. Biochem. Physiol. A* 90:771–73
36. Chinet TC, Fullton JM, Yankaskas JR, Boucher RC, Stutts MJ. 1993. Sodium-permeable channels in the apical membrane of human nasal epithelial cells. *Am. J. Physiol.* 265:C1050–60
37. Clement A, Steele MP, Brody JS, Riedel N. 1991. SV40T-immortalized lung alveolar epithelial cells display post-transcriptional regulation of proliferation-related genes. *Exp. Cell Res.* 196:198–205
38. Compeau CG, Rotstein OD, Tohda H, Marunaka Y, Rafii B, et al. 1994. Endotoxin-stimulated alveolar macrophages impair lung epithelial Na^+ transport by an L-Arg-dependent mechanism. *Am. J. Physiol.* 266:C1330–41
39. Cott GR. 1989. Modulation of bioelectric properties across alveolar type II cells by substratum. *Am. J. Physiol.* 257: C678–88
40. Crapo JD, Barry BE, Foscue HA, Shelburne J. 1980. Structural and biochemical changes in rat lungs occurring during exposures to lethal and adaptive doses of oxygen. *Am. Rev. Respir. Dis.* 122:123–43
41. Dagenais A, Kothary R, Berthiaume Y. 1997. The alpha subunit of the epithelial sodium channel in the mouse: developmental regulation of its expression. *Pediatr. Res.* 42:327–34
42. DeCoursey TE. 1990. State-dependent inactivation of K^+ currents in rat type II alveolar epithelial cells. *J. Gen. Physiol.* 95:617–46
43. DeCoursey TE, Jacobs ER, Silver MR. 1988. Potassium currents in rat type II alveolar epithelial cells. *J. Physiol. London* 395:487–505
44. Ding JW, Dickie J, O'Brodovich H, Shintani Y, Rafii B, et al. 1998. Inhibition of amiloride-sensitive sodium-channel activity in distal lung epithelial cells by nitric oxide. *Am. J. Physiol.* 274:L378–87
45. Dobbs LG, Gonzalez R, Matthay MA, Carter EP, Allen L, Verkman AS. 1998. Highly water-permeable type I alveolar epithelial cells confer high water permeability between the airspace and vasculature in rat lung. *Proc. Natl. Acad. Sci. USA* 95:2991–96
46. DuVall MD, Zhu A, Fuller CM, Matalon S. 1998. Peroxynitrite inhibits amiloride-sensitve Na^+ currents in *Xenopus* oocytes expressing α,β,γrENaC. *Am. J. Physiol.* 274:C1417–23
47. Evans MJ, Cabral LJ, Stephens RJ, Freeman G. 1975. Transformation of alveolar type 2 cells to type 1 cells following exposure to NO2. *Exp. Mol. Pathol.* 22:142–50
48. Farman N, Talbot CR, Boucher R, Fay M, Canessa C, et al. 1997. Noncoordinated expression of alpha-, beta-, gamma-subunit mRNAs of epithelial Na^+ channel along rat respiratory tract. *Am. J. Physiol.* 272:C131–41
49. Feng ZP, Clark RB, Berthiaume Y. 1993. Identification of nonselective cation channels in cultured adult rat alveolar type II cells. *Am. J. Respir. Cell Mol. Biol.* 9:248–54
50. Firsov D, Gautschi I, Merillat AM, Rossier BC, Schild L. 1998. The heterotetrameric architecture of the epithelial sodium channel (ENaC). *EMBO J.* 17:344–52
51. Folkesson HG, Matthay MA, Hasegawa H, Kheradmand F, Verkman AS. 1994. Transcellular water transport in lung alveolar epithelium through mercury-sensitive water channels. *Proc. Natl. Acad. Sci. USA* 91:4970–74
52. Garat C, Meignan M, Matthay MA, Luo DF, Jayr C. 1997. Alveolar epithelial fluid clearance mechanisms are intact after moderate hyperoxic lung injury in rats. *Chest* 111:1381–88
53. Garty H, Benos DJ. 1988. Characteristics and regulatory mechanisms of the amiloride-blockable Na^+ channel. *Physiol. Rev.* 68:309–73
54. Garty H, Palmer LG. 1997. Epithelial sodium channels: function, structure, regulation. *Physiol. Rev.* 77:359–96
55. Garty H, Warncke J, Lindemann B. 1987. An amiloride-sensitive Na^+ conductance in the basolateral membrane of toad urinary bladder. *J. Membr. Biol.* 95:91–103
56. Gatti RM, Radi R, Augusto O. 1994. Peroxynitrite-mediated oxidation of albumin to the protein-thiyl free radical. *FEBS Lett.* 348:287–90
57. Gerboth GD, Effros RM, Roman RJ, Jacobs ER. 1993. pH-induced calcium transients in type II alveolar epithelial cells. *Am. J. Physiol.* 264:L448–57
58. Goodman BE, Anderson JL, Clemens JW. 1989. Evidence for regulation of sodium transport from airspace to vascular space by cAMP. *Am. J. Physiol.* 257:L86–93

59. Goodman BE, Fleischer RS, Crandall ED. 1983. Evidence for active Na^+ transport by cultured monolayers of pulmonary alveolar epithelial cells. *Am. J. Physiol.* 245:C78–83
60. Goodman BE, Kim KJ, Crandall ED. 1987. Evidence for active sodium transport across alveolar epithelium of isolated rat lung. *J. Appl. Physiol.* 62:2460–66
61. Gowen CWJ, Lawson EE, Gingras J, Boucher RC, Gatzy JT, Knowles MR. 1988. Electrical potential difference and ion transport across nasal epithelium of term neonates: correlation with mode of delivery, transient tachypnea of the newborn, respiratory rate. *J. Pediatr.* 113:121–27
62. Grinstein S, Furuya W, Downey GP. 1992. Activation of permeabilized neutrophils: role of anions. *Am. J. Physiol.* 263:C78–85
63. Guo Y, Duvall MD, Crow JP, Matalon S. 1998. Nitric oxide inhibits Na^+ absorption across cultured alveolar type II monolayers. *Am. J. Physiol.* 274:L369–77
64. Hackney JD, Spier CE, Anzar UT, Clark KW, Evans MJ. 1981. Effect of high concentrations of oxygen on reparative regeneration of damaged alveolar epithelium in mice. *Exp. Mol. Pathol.* 34: 338–44
65. Haddad IY, Crow JP, Hu P, Ye Y, Beckman J, Matalon S. 1994. Concurrent generation of nitric oxide and superoxide damages surfactant protein A. *Am. J. Physiol.* 267:L242–49
66. Haddad IY, Pataki G, Hu P, Galliani C, Beckman JS, Matalon S. 1994. Quantitation of nitrotyrosine levels in lung sections of patients and animals with acute lung injury. *J. Clin. Invest.* 94:2407–13
67. Haddad IY, Pitt BR, Matalon S. 1996. Nitric oxide and lung injury. In *Pulmonary Diseases and Disorders*, ed. AP Fishman, pp. 337–46. New York: McGraw-Hill
68. Haddad IY, Zhu A, Ischiropoulos H, Matalon S. 1996. Nitration of surfactant protein A results in decreased ability to aggregate lipids. *Am. J. Physiol.* 270:L281–88
69. Hagiwara N, Tohda H, Doi Y, O'Brodovich H, Marunaka Y. 1992. Effects of insulin and tyrosine kinase inhibitor on ion transport in the alveolar cell of the fetal lung. *Biochem. Biophys. Res. Commun.* 187:802–8
70. Haies DM, Gil M, Weibel ER. 1981. Morphometric study of rat lung cells. *Am. Rev. Respir. Dis.* 123:533–41
71. Hamill OP, Marty A, Neher E, Sackman B, Sigworth FJ. 1981. Improved patch-clamp technique for high-resolution current recording from cells and cell-free patches. *Pflugers Arch.* 391:85–100
72. Haskell JF, Yue G, Benos DJ, Matalon S. 1994. Upregulation of sodium conductive pathways in alveolar type II cells in sublethal hyperoxia. *Am. J. Physiol.* 266:L30–37
73. Horn R, Marty A. 1988. Muscarinic activation of ionic currents measured by a new whole-cell recording method. *J. Gen. Physiol.* 92:145–59
74. Hu P, Ischiropoulos H, Beckman JS, Matalon S. 1994. Peroxynitrite inhibition of oxygen consumption and sodium transport in alveolar type II cells. *Am. J. Physiol.* 266:L628–34
75. Hummler E, Barker P, Gatzy J, Beermann F, Verdumo C, et al. 1996. Early death due to defective neonatal lung liquid clearance in *αENaC*-deficient mice. *Nat. Genet.* 12:325–28
76. Hummler E, Barker P, Talbot C, Wang W, Verdumo C, et al. 1997. A mouse model for the renal salt-wasting syndrome pseudohypoaldosteronism. *Proc. Natl. Acad. Sci. USA* 94:11710–15
77. Ignarro LJ. 1992. Haem-dependent activation of cytosolic guanylate cyclase by nitric oxide: a widespread signal transduction mechanism. *Biochem. Soc. Trans.* 20:465–69
78. Inoue S, Kawanishi S. 1995. Oxidative DNA damage induced by simultaneous generation of nitric oxide and superoxide. *FEBS Lett.* 371:86–88
79. Ischiropoulos H, Zhu L, Beckman JS. 1992. Peroxynitrite formation from macrophage-derived nitric oxide. *Arch. Biochem. Biophys.* 298:446–51
80. Ismailov II, McDuffie JH, Sariban-Sohraby S, Johnson JP, Benos DJ. 1994. Carboxyl methylation activates purified renal amiloride-sensitive Na^+ channels in planar lipid bilayers. *J. Biol. Chem.* 269:22193–97
81. Ito Y, Niisato N, O'Brodovich H, Marunaka Y. 1997. The effect of brefeldin A on terbutaline-induced sodium absorption in fetal rat distal lung epithelium. *Pflugers Arch.* 434:492–94
82. Jain L, Chen XJ, Brown LA, Eaton DC. 1998. Nitric oxide inhibits lung sodium transport through a cGMP-mediated inhibition of epithelial cation channels. *Am. J. Physiol.* 274:L475–84
83. Jayr C, Garat C, Meignan M, Pittet JF,

Zelter M, Matthay MA. 1994. Alveolar liquid and protein clearance in anesthetized ventilated rats. *J. Appl. Physiol.* 76:2636–42

83a. Jiang X, Ingbar DH, O'Grady SM. 1998. Adenergic activation of an apical Cl^- channel in cultured adult rat alveolar epithelial cells. *Am. J. Physiol. (Cell Physiol.)* In press

84. Karlson KH, Ciampolillo-Bates F, McCoy DE, Kizer NL, Stanton BA. 1995. Cloning of a cGMP-gated cation channel from mouse kidney inner medullary collecting duct. *Biochim. Biophys. Acta* 1236:197–200; Erratum. 1995. *Biochim. Biophys. Acta* 1238(2):197

85. Kerr JS, Reicherter J, Fisher AB. 1982. 2-Deoxy-D-glucose uptake by rat granular pneumocytes in primary culture. *Am. J. Physiol.* 243:C14–19

85a. Kim KJ, Cheek JM, Crandall ED. 1991. Contribution of active Na^+ and Cl^- fluxes to net ion transport by alveolar epithelium. *Respir. Physiol.* 85:245–56

86. Kizer N, Guo XL, Hruska K. 1997. Reconstitution of stretch-activated cation channels by expression of the alpha-subunit of the epithelial sodium channel cloned from osteoblasts. *Proc. Natl. Acad. Sci. USA* 94:1013–18; Erratum. 1997. *Proc. Natl. Acad. Sci. USA* 94(8):4233

87. Kleyman TR, Ernst SA, Coupaye-Gerard B. 1994. Arginine vasopressin and forskolin regulate apical cell surface expression of epithelial Na^+ channels in A6 cells. *Am. J. Physiol.* 266:F506–11

88. Krozowski Z, Funder JW. 1981. Mineralocorticoid receptors in the rat lung. *Endocrinology* 109:1811–13

89. Li XJ, Xu RH, Guggino WB, Snyder SH. 1995. Alternatively spliced forms of the alpha subunit of the epithelial sodium channel: distinct sites for amiloride binding and channel pore. *Mol. Pharmacol.* 47:1133–40

90. Light DB, Corbin JD, Stanton BA. 1990. Dual ion-channel regulation by cyclic GMP and cyclic GMP-dependent protein kinase. *Nature* 344:336–39

91. Ling BN, Eaton DC. 1989. Effects of luminal Na^+ on single Na^+ channels in A6 cells, a regulatory role for protein kinase C. *Am. J. Physiol.* 256:F1094–103

92. Lingueglia E, Renard S, Voilley N, Waldmann R, Chassande O, et al. 1993. Molecular cloning and functional expression of different molecular forms of rat amiloride-binding proteins. *Eur. J. Biochem.* 216:679–87

93. Lingueglia E, Voilley N, Waldmann R, Lazdunski M, Barbry P. 1993. Expression cloning of an epithelial amiloride-sensitive Na^+ channel. A new channel type with homologies to *Caenorhabditis elegans* degenerins. *FEBS Lett.* 318:95–99

94. MacGregor GG, Olver RE, Kemp PJ. 1994. Amiloride-sensitive Na^+ channels in fetal type II pneumocytes are regulated by G proteins. *Am. J. Physiol.* 267:L1–8

95. Mairbaurl H, Wodopia R, Eckes S, Schulz S, Bartsch P. 1997. Impairment of cation transport in A549 cells and rat alveolar epithelial cells by hypoxia. *Am. J. Physiol.* 273:L797–806

96. Marunaka Y. 1996. Amiloride-blockable Ca^{2+}-activated Na^+-permeant channels in the fetal distal lung epithelium. *Pflugers Arch.* 431:748–56

97. Marunaka Y, Eaton DC. 1991. Effects of vasopressin and cAMP on single amiloride-blockable Na channels. *Am. J. Physiol.* 260:C1071–84

98. Marunaka Y, Tohda H, Hagiwara N, O'Brodovich H. 1992. Cytosolic $Ca(^{2+})$-induced modulation of ion selectivity and amiloride sensitivity of a cation channel and beta agonist action in fetal lung epithelium. *Biochem. Biophys. Res. Commun.* 187:648–56

99. Matalon S. 1993. Mechanisms and regulation of ion transport in adult mammalian alveolar type II pneumocytes. *Am. J. Physiol.* 261:C727–38

100. Matalon S, Bauer ML, Benos DJ, Kleyman TR, Lin C, et al. 1993. Fetal lung epithelial cells contain two populations of amiloride-sensitive Na^+ channels. *Am. J. Physiol.* 264:L357–64

101. Matalon S, Benos DJ, Jackson RM. 1996. Biophysical and molecular properties of amiloride-inhibitable Na^+ channels in alveolar epithelial cells. *Am. J. Physiol.* 271:L1–22

102. Matalon S, Bridges RJ, Benos DJ. 1991. Amiloride-inhibitable Na^+ conductive pathways in alveolar type II pneumocytes. *Am. J. Physiol.* 260:L90–96

103. Matalon S, DeMarco V, Haddad IY, Myles C, Skimming JW, et al. 1996. Inhaled nitric oxide injures the pulmonary surfactant system of lambs in vivo. *Am. J. Physiol.* 270:L273–80

104. Matalon S, Kirk KL, Bubien JK, Oh Y, Hu P, et al. 1992. Immunocytochemical and functional characterization of Na^+ conductance in adult alveolar pneumocytes. *Am. J. Physiol.* 262:C1228–38

105. Matalon S, Yue G, Hu P, Oh Y, Benos DJ. 1994. Mechanisms of active Na^+

transport across freshly isolated and cultured adult alveolar type II pneumocytes. In *Fluid and Solute Transport in the Airspaces of the Lungs*, ed. RM Effros, HK Chang, pp. 179–217. New York: Dekker

106. Matsushita K, McCray PBJ, Sigmund RD, Welsh MJ, Stokes JB. 1996. Localization of epithelial sodium channel subunit mRNAs in adult rat lung by in situ hybridization. *Am. J. Physiol.* 271:L332–39
107. Matthay MA, Berthiaume Y, Staub NC. 1985. Long-term clearance of liquid and protein from the lungs of unanesthetized sheep. *J. Appl. Physiol.* 59:928–34
108. Matthay MA, Folkesson HG, Verkman AS. 1996. Salt and water transport across alveolar and distal airway epithelia in the adult lung. *Am. J. Physiol.* 270:L487–503
109. Matthay MA, Landolt CC, Staub NC. 1982. Differential liquid and protein clearance from the alveoli of anesthetized sheep. *J. Appl. Physiol.* 53:96–104
110. Matthay MA, Wiener-Kronish JP. 1990. Intact epithelial barrier function is critical for the resolution of alveolar edema in humans. *Am. Rev. Respir. Dis.* 142:1250–57
111. McDonald FJ, Snyder PM, McCray PB Jr, Welsh MJ. 1994. Cloning, expression, and tissue distribution of a human amiloride-sensitive Na^+ channel. *Am. J. Physiol.* 266:L728–34
112. Michaut P, Planes C, Escoubet B, Clement A, Amiel C, Clerici C. 1996. Rat lung alveolar type II cell line maintains sodium transport characteristics of primary culture. *J. Cell Physiol.* 169:78–86
113. Modelska K, Matthay MA, Pittet JF. 1998. Inhibition of inducible NO synthase activity (iNOS) after prolonged hemorrhagic shock attenuates oxidant-mediated decrease in alveolar epithelial fluid transport in rats. *FASEB J.* 12:A39 (Abstr.)
114. Moran A, Asher C, Cragoe EJ Jr, Garty H. 1988. Conductive sodium pathway with low affinity to amiloride in LLC-PK1 cells and other epithelia. *J. Biol. Chem.* 263:19586–91
115. Moreno JJ, Pryor WA. 1992. Inactivation of alpha 1-proteinase inhibitor by peroxynitrite. *Chem. Res. Toxicol.* 5:425–31
116. Nici L, Dowin R, Gilmore-Hebert M, Jamieson JD, Ingbar DH. 1991. Upregulation of rat lung Na-K-ATPase during hyperoxic injury. *Am. J. Physiol.* 261:L307–14

116a. Nielsen VG, DuVall MD, Baird MS, Matalon S. 1998. cAMP activation of chloride and fluid secretion across the rabbit alveolar epithelium. *Am. J. Physiol. (Lung Cell. Mol. Biol.)* In press

117. Niisato N, Nakahari T, Tanswell AK, Marunaka Y. 1997. Beta 2-agonist regulation of cell volume in fetal distal lung epithelium by cAMP-independent Ca^{2+} release from intracellular stores. *Can. J. Physiol. Pharmacol.* 75:1030–33
118. Nord EP, Brown SE, Crandall ED. 1987. Characterization of Na^+-H^+ antiport in type II alveolar epithelial cells. *Am. J. Physiol.* 252:C490–98
119. O'Brodovich H. 1993. Epithelial ion transport in the fetal and perinatal lung. *Am. J. Physiol.* 261:C555–64
120. O'Brodovich H, Canessa C, Ueda J, Rafii B, Rossier BC, Edelson J. 1993. Expression of the epithelial Na^+ channel in the developing rat lung. *Am. J. Physiol.* 265:C491–96
121. O'Brodovich H, Hannam V, Rafii B. 1991. Sodium channel but neither $Na^{(+)}$-H^+ nor Na-glucose symport inhibitors slow neonatal lung water clearance. *Am. J. Respir. Cell Mol. Biol.* 5:377–84
122. O'Brodovich H, Hannam V, Seear M, Mullen JB. 1990. Amiloride impairs lung water clearance in newborn guinea pigs. *J. Appl. Physiol.* 68:1758–62
123. O'Brodovich H, Rafii B. 1993. Effect of K channel blockers on basal and beta-agonist stimulated ion transport by fetal distal lung epithelium. *Can. J. Physiol. Pharmacol.* 71:54–57
124. O'Brodovich H, Rafii B, Perlon P. 1992. Arginine vasopressin and atrial natriuretic peptide do not alter ion transport by cultured fetal distal lung epithelium. *Pediatr. Res.* 31:318–22
125. O'Brodovich H, Rafii B, Post M. 1990. Bioelectric properties of fetal alveolar epithelial monolayers. *Am. J. Physiol.* 258:L201–6
126. O'Brodovich HM. 1996. Immature epithelial Na^+ channel expression is one of the pathogenetic mechanisms leading to human neonatal respiratory distress syndrome. *Proc. Assoc. Am. Physicians* 108:345–55
127. Oh Y, Benos DJ. 1993. Single-channel characteristics of a purified bovine renal amiloride-sensitive Na^+ channel in planar lipid bilayers. *Am. J. Physiol.* 264:C1489–99
128. Oh Y, Matalon S, Kleyman TR, Benos DJ. 1992. Biochemical evidence for the

presence of an amiloride binding protein in adult alveolar type II pneumocytes. *J. Biol. Chem.* 267:18498–504; Erratum. 1992. *J. Biol. Chem.* 267(36):26200
129. Oh Y, Smith PR, Bradford AL, Keeton D, Benos DJ. 1993. Regulation by phosphorylation of purified epithelial Na^+ channels in planar lipid bilayers. *Am. J. Physiol.* 265:C85–91
130. Olivera W, Ridge K, Wood LD, Sznajder JI. 1994. Active sodium transport and alveolar epithelial Na-K-ATPase increase during subacute hyperoxia in rats. *Am. J. Physiol.* 266:L577–84
131. Olivera WG, Ridge KM, Sznajder JI. 1995. Lung liquid clearance and Na,K-ATPase during acute hyperoxia and recovery in rats. *Am. J. Respir. Crit. Care Med.* 152:1229–34
132. Olver RE, Ramsden CA, Strang LB, Walters DV. 1986. The role of amiloride-blockable sodium transport in adrenaline-induced lung liquid reabsorption in the fetal lamb. *J. Physiol. London* 376:321–40
133. Olver RE, LB Strang. 1974. Ion fluxes across the pulmonary epithelium and the secretion of lung liquid in the foetal lamb. *J. Physiol. London* 241:327–57
134. Orser BA, Bertlik M, Fedorko L, O'Brodovich H. 1991. Cation selective channel in fetal alveolar type II epithelium. *Biochim. Biophys. Acta* 1094:19–26
135. Otulakowski G, Rafii B, Bremmer HR, O'Brodovich H. 1998. Structure and hormone responsiveness of the gene encoding the α-subunit of the amiloride-sensitive epithelial sodium channel. *Am. J. Respir. Cell Mol. Biol.* In press
136. Otulakowski G, Staub S, Ellis L, Ramlall K, Staub O, et al. 1998. Relation between α,β,γ-hENaC mRNA levels and respiratory epithelial potential difference in healthy men. *Am. J. Respir. Crit. Care Med.* 158(4):1213–20
137. Palmer LG. 1992. Epithelial Na channels: function and diversity. *Annu. Rev. Physiol.* 54:51–66
138. Peers C, Kemp PJ, Boyd CA, Nye PC. 1990. Whole-cell K^+ currents in type II pneumocytes freshly isolated from rat lung: pharmacological evidence for two subpopulations of cells. *Biochim. Biophys. Acta* 1052:113–18
139. Pitkanen O, Transwell AK, Downey G, O'Brodovich H. 1996. Increased Po2 alters the bioelectric properties of fetal distal lung epithelium. *Am. J. Physiol.* 270:L1060–66
140. Pitkanen OM, Tanswell AK, O'Brodovich HM. 1995. Fetal lung cell derived matrix alters distal lung epithelial ion transport. *Am. J. Physiol.* 268:L762–71
141. Planes C, Escoubet B, Blot-Chabaud M, Friedlander G, Farman N, Clerici C. 1997. Hypoxia downregulates expression and activity of epithelial sodium channels in rat alveolar epithelial cells. *Am. J. Respir. Cell Mol. Biol.* 17:508–18
142. Radi R, Beckman JS, Bush KM, Freeman BA. 1991. Peroxynitrite-induced membrane lipid peroxidation: the cytotoxic potential of superoxide and nitric oxide. *Arch. Biochem. Biophys.* 288:481–87
143. Rafii B, Tanswell AK, Otulakowski G, Pitkanen O, Belcastro-Taylor R, O'Brodovich H. 1998. O_2 induced Na channel expression is associated with Nf-kB activation and blocked by superoxide scavenger. *Am. J. Physiol.* 275: L764–70
144. Rao AK, Cott GR. 1991. Ontogeny of ion transport across fetal pulmonary epithelial cells in monolayer culture. *Am. J. Physiol.* 261:L178–87
145. Renard S, Lingueglia E, Voilley N, Lazdunski M, Barbry P. 1994. Biochemical analysis of the membrane topology of the amiloride-sensitive Na^+ channel. *J. Biol. Chem.* 269:12981–86
146. Renard S, Voilley N, Bassilana F, Lazdunski M, Barbry P. 1995. Localization and regulation by steroids of the alpha, beta, and gamma subunits of the amiloride-sensitive Na^+ channel in colon, lung and kidney. *Pflugers Arch.* 430:299–307
147. Robinson DH, Bubien JK, Smith PR, Benos DJ. 1991. Epithelial sodium conductance in rabbit preimplantation trophectodermal cells. *Dev. Biol.* 147:313–21
148. Rossier BC, Canessa CM, Schild L, Horisberger JD. 1994. Epithelial sodium channels. *Curr. Opin. Nephrol. Hypertens.* 3:487–96
149. Rotin D, Bar-Sagi D, O'Brodovich H, Merilainen J, Lehto VP, et al. 1994. An SH3 binding region in the epithelial Na^+ channel (alpha rENaC) mediates its localization at the apical membrane. *EMBO J.* 13:4440–50
150. Ruddy MK, Drazen JM, Pitkanen OM, Rafii B, O'Brodovich HM, Harris HW. 1998. Modulation of aquaporin 4 and the amiloride-inhibitable sodium channel in perinatal rat lung epithelial cells. *Am. J. Physiol.* 274:L1066–72
151. Russo RM, Lubman RL, Crandall ED. 1992. Evidence for amiloride-sensitive

sodium channels in alveolar epithelial cells. *Am. J. Physiol.* 262:L405–11

152. Sakuma T, Okaniwa G, Nakada T, Nishimura T, Fujimura S, Matthay MA. 1994. Alveolar fluid clearance in the resected human lung. *Am. J. Respir. Crit. Care Med.* 150:305–10
153. Sariban-Sohraby S, Burger M, Wiesmann WP, Chiang PK, Johnson JP. 1984. Methylation increases sodium transport into A6 apical membrane vesicles: possible mode of aldosterone action. *Science* 225:745–46
154. Sariban-Sohraby S, Sorscher EJ, Brenner BM, Benos DJ. 1988. Phosphorylation of a single subunit of the epithelial Na^+ channel protein following vasopressin treatment of A6 cells. *J. Biol. Chem.* 263:13875–79
155. Schild L, Schneeberger E, Gautschi I, Firsov D. 1997. Identification of amino acid residues in the alpha, beta, gamma subunits of the epithelial sodium channel (ENaC) involved in amiloride block and ion permeation. *J. Gen. Physiol.* 109:15–26
156. Schneeberger EE, McCarthy KM. 1986. Cytochemical localization of Na^+-K^+-ATPase in rat type II pneumocytes. *J. Appl. Physiol.* 60:1584–89
157. Senyk O, Ismailov I, Bradford AL, Baker RR, Matalon S, Benos DJ. 1995. Reconstitution of immunopurified alveolar type II cell Na^+ channel protein into planar lipid bilayers. *Am. J. Physiol.* 268:C1148–56
158. Silver RB, Frindt G, Windhager EE, Palmer LG. 1993. Feedback regulation of Na channels in rat CCT. I. Effects of inhibition of Na pump. *Am. J. Physiol.* 264:F557–64
159. Smith PR, Benos DJ. 1991. Epithelial Na^+ channels. *Annu. Rev. Physiol.* 53:509–30
160. Smith PR, Saccomani G, Joe EH, Angelides KJ, Benos DJ. 1991. Amiloride-sensitive sodium channel is linked to the cytoskeleton in renal epithelial cells. *Proc. Natl. Acad. Sci. USA* 88:6971–75
161. Snyder PM, Cheng C, Prince LS, Rogers JC, Welsh MJ. 1998. Electrophysiological and biochemical evidence that DEG/ENaC cation channels are composed of nine subunits. *J. Biol. Chem.* 273:681–84
162. Sorscher EJ, Accavitti MA, Keeton D, Steadman E, Frizzell RA, Benos DJ. 1988. Antibodies against purified epithelial sodium channel protein from bovine renal papilla. *Am. J. Physiol.* 255:C835–43
163. Staub O, Gautschi I, Ishikawa T, Breitschopf K, Ciechanover A, et al. 1997. Regulation of stability and function of the epithelial Na^+ channel (ENaC) by ubiquitination. *EMBO J.* 16:6325–36
164. Staub O, Yeger H, Plant PJ, Kim H, Ernst SA, Rotin D. 1997. Immunolocalization of the ubiquitin-protein ligase Nedd4 in tissues expressing the epithelial Na^+ channel (ENaC). *Am. J. Physiol.* 272:C1871–80
165. Stoos BA, Carretero OA, Garvin JL. 1994. Endothelial-derived nitric oxide inhibits sodium transport by affecting apical membrane channels in cultured collecting duct cells. *J. Am. Soc. Nephrol.* 4:1855–60
166. Stutts MJ, Canessa CM, Olsen JC, Hamrick M, Cohn JA, et al. 1995. CFTR as a cAMP-dependent regulator of sodium channels. *Science* 269:847–50
167. Sugahara K, Freidenberg GR, Mason RJ. 1984. Insulin binding and effects of glucose and transepithelial transport by alveolar type II cells. *Am. J. Physiol. Cell Physiol.* 247:C472–77
168. Suwabe A, Panos RJ, Voelker DR. 1991. Alveolar type II cells isolated after silica-induced lung injury in rats have increased surfactant protein A (SP-A) receptor activity. *Am. J. Respir. Cell Mol. Biol.* 4:264–72
169. Suzuki S, Zuege D, Berthiaume Y. 1995. Sodium-independent modulation of Na(+)-K(+)-ATPase activity by beta-adrenergic agonist in alveolar type II cells. *Am. J. Physiol.* 268:L983–90
170. Sweezey N, Tchepichev S, Gagnon S, Fertuck K, O'Brodovich H. 1998. Female gender hormones regulate mRNA levels and function of the rat lung epithelial Na channel. *Am. J. Physiol.* 274:C379–86
171. Tchepichev S, Ueda J, Canessa C, Rossier BC, O'Brodovich H. 1995. Lung epithelial Na channel subunits are differentially regulated during development and by steroids. *Am. J. Physiol.* 269:C805–12
172. Thomas CP, Doggett NA, Fisher R, Stokes JB. 1996. Genomic organization and the 5′ flanking region of the gamma subunit of the human amiloride-sensitive epithelial sodium channel. *J. Biol. Chem.* 271:26062–66
173. Tohda H, Foskett JK, O'Brodovich H, Marunaka Y. 1994. Cl-regulation of a $Ca^{(2+)}$-activated nonselective cation channel in beta-agonist-treated fetal distal lung epithelium. *Am. J. Physiol.* 266:C104–9

174. Tohda H, Marunaka Y. 1995. Insulin-activated amiloride-blockable nonselective cation and Na^+ channels in the fetal distal lung epithelium. *Gen. Pharmacol.* 26:755–63
175. Tousson A, Alley CD, Sorscher EJ, Brinkley BR, Benos DJ. 1989. Immunochemical localization of amiloride-sensitive sodium channels in sodium-transporting epithelia. *J. Cell Sci.* 93: 349–62
176. Venkatesh VC, Katzberg HD. 1997. Glucocorticoid regulation of epithelial sodium channel genes in human fetal lung. *Am. J. Physiol.* 273:L227–33
177. Vigne P, Champigny G, Marsault R, Barbry P, Frelin C, Lazdunski M. 1989. A new type of amiloride-sensitive cationic channel in endothelial cells of brain microvessels. *J. Biol. Chem.* 264:7663–68
178. Voilley N, Galibert A, Bassilana F, Renard S, Lingueglia E, et al. 1997. The amiloride-sensitive Na^+ channel: from primary structure to function. *Comp. Biochem. Physiol. A* 118:193–200
179. Voilley N, Lingueglia E, Champigny G, Mattei MG, Waldmann R, et al. 1994. The lung amiloride-sensitive Na^+ channel: biophysical properties, pharmacology, ontogenesis, molecular cloning. *Proc. Natl. Acad. Sci. USA* 91:247–51
180. Waldmann R, Champigny G, Bassilana F, Voilley N, Lazdunski M. 1995. Molecular cloning and functional expression of a novel amiloride-sensitive Na^+ channel. *J. Biol. Chem.* 270:27411–14
181. Walters DV, Ramsden CA, Olver RE. 1990. Dibutyryl cAMP induces a gestation-dependent absorption of fetal lung liquid. *J. Appl. Physiol.* 68:2054–59
182. Wang X, Kleyman TR, Tohda H, Marunaka Y, O'Brodovich H. 1993. 5-(N-ethyl-N-isopropyl)amiloride sensitive Na+ currents in intact fetal distal lung epithelial cells. *Can. J. Physiol. Pharmacol.* 71:58–62
183. Wright JR, Dobbs LG. 1991. Regulation of pulmonary surfactant secretion and clearance. *Annu. Rev. Physiol.* 53:395–414
184. Yue G, Hu P, Oh Y, Jilling T, Shoemaker RL, et al. 1993. Culture-induced alterations in alveolar type II cell Na+ conductance. *Am. J. Physiol.* 265:C630–40
185. Yue G, Matalon S. 1997. Mechanisms and sequelae of increased alveolar fluid clearance in hyperoxic rats. *Am. J. Physiol.* 272:L407–12
186. Yue G, Russell WJ, Benos DJ, Jackson RM, Olman MA, Matalon S. 1995. Increased expression and activity of sodium channels in alveolar type II cells of hyperoxic rats. *Proc. Natl. Acad. Sci. USA* 92:8418–22
187. Yue G, Shoemaker RL, Matalon S. 1994. Regulation of low-amiloride-affinity sodium channels in alveolar type II cells. *Am. J. Physiol.* 267:L94–100
188. Zhu S, Haddad IY, Matalon S. 1996. Nitration of surfactant protein A (SP-A) tyrosine residues results in decreased mannose binding ability. *Arch. Biochem. Biophys.* 333:282–90

Annu. Rev. Physiol. 1999. 61:663–82

SODIUM-COUPLED TRANSPORTERS FOR KREBS CYCLE INTERMEDIATES

Ana M. Pajor
Department of Physiology and Biophysics, University of Texas Medical Branch, Galveston, Texas; e-mail: ampajor@utmb.edu

KEY WORDS: succinate, citrate, α-ketoglutarate, sodium, citric acid cycle intermediates

ABSTRACT

Krebs cycle intermediates such as succinate, citrate, and α-ketoglutarate are transferred across plasma membranes of cells by secondary active transporters that couple the downhill movement of sodium to the concentrative uptake of substrate. Several transporters have been identified in isolated membrane vesicles and cells based on their functional properties, suggesting the existence of at least three or more Na^+/dicarboxylate cotransporter proteins in a given species. Recently, several cDNAs, called NaDC-1, coding for the low-affinity Na^+/dicarboxylate cotransporters have been isolated from rabbit, human, and rat kidney. The Na^+/dicarboxylate cotransporters are part of a distinct gene family that includes the renal and intestinal Na^+/sulfate cotransporters. Other members of this family include a Na^+- and Li^+-dependent dicarboxylate transporter from *Xenopus* intestine and a putative Na^+/dicarboxylate cotransporter from rat intestine. The current model of secondary structure in NaDC-1 contains 11 transmembrane domains and an extracellular N-glycosylated carboxy terminus.

INTRODUCTION

The metabolic intermediates of the Krebs or citric acid cycle constitute a group of organic anions that include dicarboxylates such as succinate and α-ketoglutarate and tricarboxylates such as citrate. The Krebs cycle intermediates are transported across plasma membranes of cells by secondary active transporters that couple the downhill movement of sodium to the concentrative

0066-4278/99/0315-0663$08.00

uptake of substrate. Tricarboxylates are often carried in protonated form, and therefore, the transporters are referred to as Na^+/dicarboxylate cotransporters. These transporters have broad substrate specificities and carry a wide range of di- and tricarboxylic acids. The primary distribution of Na^+/dicarboxylate cotransporters is in the epithelial cells of the renal proximal tubule and small intestine. However, these transporters are also found in organs such as colon, liver, placenta, and brain.

The sodium-coupled transport of Krebs cycle intermediates in the kidney has been reviewed previously by Wright (71), Hamm (21), and Murer et al (38). This review discusses the different classes of Na^+/dicarboxylate cotransporters that have been characterized in kidney as well as other organs. This review also provides an update on the molecular advances in the field. Several of the low-affinity Na^+/dicarboxylate cotransporter cDNAs have now been isolated. The Na^+/dicarboxylate cotransporters, called NaDC, are related in sequence and probably also in structure to the Na^+/sulfate cotransporter, NaSi-1. The Na^+/dicarboxylate and Na^+/sulfate cotransporters belong to a distinct gene family that is not related to any of the other known families of transport proteins.

FUNCTIONAL CHARACTERIZATION OF SODIUM-COUPLED DICARBOXYLATE TRANSPORTERS

Functional studies in isolated cells and membrane vesicles have identified several categories of sodium-coupled transporters for Krebs cycle intermediates (Table 1). The transporters differ in substrate affinity and selectivity, in sensitivity to inhibition by lithium, and in tissue distribution and species distribution. In addition to providing information on the physiological role of these transporters, the identification of functional differences between transport pathways may be a useful predictor of the number of different transport proteins that are likely to exist.

Low-Affinity Transporters for Krebs Cycle Intermediates

The best characterized of the Na^+/dicarboxylate cotransporters is the low-affinity transporter found on the apical membranes of proximal tubule cells in rabbit kidney (Table 1). This transporter has been studied in isolated, perfused tubules and in brush border membrane vesicles. The primary function of this pathway is to reabsorb Krebs cycle intermediates from the tubular filtrate.

SUBSTRATE SPECIFICITY The substrate specificity of the low-affinity transport pathway is very broad (63, 74). The transporter accepts a wide variety of di- and tricarboxylates, including succinate, citrate, and α-ketoglutarate. The

Table 1 Functional properties of Na^+/dicarboxylate cotransporters

K_m (succinate or αKG)	Lithium inhibition	Electrogenic	Species	Organ/cell type	Reference
0.5–1 mM	Yes	Yes	Rabbit	Renal cortex bbm[1]	29, 76
			Rat	Small intestine bbm	67
0.4 mM	No	Yes	Rat	Colon bbm	67
0.5 (citrate)	n.d.	n.d.	Opossum	OK cell line	30
100–175 μM	Yes	Yes	Rat	Renal cortex bbm	14, 58
			Pig	Intestinal bbm	69
5–30 μM	Yes	Yes	Rat, rabbit	Renal cortex blm	10, 14, 76
			Human	Placenta bbm	18, 40
			Rat	Liver blm	37, 77
2 μM	n.d.	n.d.	Rat, mouse	Brain synaptosomes	56, 57
25 μM	n.d.	No	Chick	Intestinal cells	28

[1]Abbreviations: bbm, brush border membranes; blm, basolateral membranes; n.d., not determined.

preferred structure consists of a four-carbon, terminal carboxylic acid with the carboxylate groups in *trans* configuration (74). The transporter has a high affinity for succinate, with a K_m of approximately 0.5–1 mM, and for this reason, succinate is often used as a test substrate. The kinetic properties of Na^+/succinate cotransport are asymmetrical: The succinate K_m measured from influx experiments was approximately the same as that measured in efflux experiments, but the V_{max} for influx was threefold faster than for efflux (22).

The low-affinity Na^+/dicarboxylate cotransporter is characterized by an insensitivity of dicarboxylate transport to changes in pH (19, 75). In contrast, the transport of tricarboxylates such as citrate is strongly stimulated by acidic pH, in parallel with the concentrations of protonated citrate in the medium (7, 19, 75). Therefore the preferred substrates of the transporter appear to be divalent anions, which suggests that the affinity for protonated citrate is very high. As an example, in rabbit renal brush border membrane vesicles the apparent K_m for total citrate was calculated as 0.4 mM, but when the concentrations of protonated citrate were taken into account, the K_m was approximately 15 μM (3). High concentrations of trivalent citrate appear to inhibit transport of protonated citrate (3).

CATIONS The transport of Krebs cycle intermediates is coupled to the movement of sodium. In rabbit renal brush border membrane vesicles, the replacement of sodium by other cations, with the exception of lithium (see below), abolished transport (72). Sodium acts as an essential activator of dicarboxylate transport. It is thought that three sodium ions bind first to the transporter and trigger a conformational change that results in an increased substrate affinity (23, 73). Transport kinetics measured at different sodium concentrations showed that the K_m for succinate became larger as the sodium concentration decreased (73). Direct measurements of sodium and succinate transport in brush border membrane vesicles showed that three sodium ions are coupled to the transport of succinate (23). The coupling coefficient was independent of succinate and sodium concentrations.

LITHIUM Treatment of human patients with therapeutic doses of lithium salts led to a rapid increase in the renal excretion of α-ketoglutarate and glutarate (6). This response was also seen in rats (5). In rabbit renal brush border membrane vesicles, the effects of lithium were shown to be a result of competition with sodium in the Na^+/dicarboxylate cotransporter (72). The inhibition by millimolar concentrations of lithium (K_i 1.2 mM) occurs in the presence of 100 mM sodium, suggesting that at least one of the cation binding sites has a high affinity for lithium (72). Lithium can replace sodium in the transport of succinate, but succinate transport occurs at a greatly reduced rate and the K_m for succinate in Li^+ is very high, about 30 mM (72). This result indicates that the binding of lithium to the Na^+/dicarboxylate cotransporter does not produce the optimal conformation for succinate binding.

ELECTROGENICITY Sodium-coupled transport of dicarboxylates in rabbit renal brush border membranes is an electrogenic process. The coupled transport of succinate and sodium was sensitive to changes in membrane potential (73), and the transport of succinate also depolarized the membrane potential in vesicles (54). The predominant effect of voltage on transport in vesicles was on the K_m for succinate; the K_m became smaller when measured at more negative membrane potentials (73). Interestingly, there is one report of electrogenic Na^+/succinate cotransport in outer cortical membrane vesicles that predicts a coupling stoichiometry of only 2:1 based on static-head experiments (17).

DISTRIBUTION AND FUNCTION The primary function of the Na^+/dicarboxylate cotransporter on the apical membrane of renal proximal tubule cells is to recover Krebs cycle intermediates from the tubular filtrate. These transported substrates are transferred to the mitochondria and metabolized. Estimates of citrate contribution to proximal tubule oxygen consumption are as high as 10% (21). Recently, it was shown that the cytosolic enzyme, ATP citrate lyase, is abundant in kidney and plays an important role in citrate metabolism, suggesting that transported citrate could be used in cholesterol and lipid biosynthesis (35).

The renal Na^+/dicarboxylate cotransporter is involved in regulating urinary citrate concentrations. Citrate prevents urinary stone formation by chelating calcium. Approximately 50% of patients with kidney stones exhibit hypocitraturia (49), but there is no direct evidence that a defect in the transporter is involved in the hypocitraturia that results in stone formation. Hypocitraturia is often accompanied by acidosis, and approximately half of the hypocitraturia seen in acidosis can be attributed to increased activity of ATP citrate lyase (35).

Low-affinity Na^+/dicarboxylate cotransport with properties similar to that of the renal transporter has been characterized in isolated brush border membranes from the rat small intestine (67) (Table 1). Sodium-coupled transport of succinate, citrate, and α-ketoglutarate has also been reported in everted sacs of hamster small intestine (8) and in brush border membrane vesicles of calves (68). The small intestine Na^+/dicarboxylate cotransporter functions to absorb dicarboxylates from the diet, as well as to recover citrate that is secreted in pancreatic and gastric juice (32, 52). There is evidence for net transepithelial transfer of citrate in hamster intestine (8). The efflux of di- and tricarboxylates across the intestinal basolateral membrane appears to be mediated by an anion exchanger (70). Evidence exists for intestinal absorption of citrate in humans: Oral administration of citrate results in increased serum citrate concentrations within 30 min (53a).

Functional differences observed between low-affinity sodium-dicarboxylate cotransporters suggest that different transport proteins may exist (Table 1). The brush border membrane of rat colon contains a low-affinity transporter that is not sensitive to inhibition by lithium (Table 1), whereas the same study showed that the transporter in small intestine is sensitive to lithium (67). Therefore, different proteins are likely to mediate uptake of dicarboxylates in the colon and small intestine (67). Another sodium-dependent transporter for Krebs cycle intermediates has been reported in OK cells (opossum kidney) (30) (Table 1). The OK cell transporter has a relatively low-affinity for citrate, which may be carried in trivalent form, and an unusual substrate specificity: It does not appear to handle succinate. It is not known whether the OK cell transporter is found in native opossum kidney membranes or whether transporters with these properties are found in other organs or species. The differences in transport properties suggest that there are at least three different sodium-coupled transport proteins that carry di- and tricarboxylates with low-affinity.

Intermediate-Affinity Transporters for Krebs Cycle Intermediates

The Na^+/dicarboxylate cotransporters found on renal and intestinal brush border membranes exhibit functional differences between species (Table 1). Apical membrane transporters have been reported with intermediate substrate affinities, with K_ms for succinate or α-ketoglutarate around 100 μM. For example, rat kidney contains a sodium-dependent transport pathway with substrate specificity similar to the one found in rabbit kidney (58). The rat transporter has an apparent K_m for methylsuccinate of 130 μM (58) and a K_m for α-ketoglutarate of 158 μM (14). Aside from the difference in substrate affinity, the apical membrane transporters in rat and rabbit are very similar in their sodium dependence and sensitivity to inhibition by millimolar concentrations of lithium, K_i 1.8 mM (58). In addition, the insensitivity of dicarboxylate transport to pH and the stimulation of tricarboxylate transport at acidic pH is similar in both rats and rabbits.

Intestinal brush border membrane vesicles from pig also express an intermediate affinity Na^+/dicarboxylate cotransporter with a K_m for succinate of 175 μM (69). The transport of both fumarate and citrate was sensitive to changes in membrane potential, and there was a strong stimulation of citrate uptake at pH 5.5. This study is consistent with electrogenic transport of divalent citrate in pig intestine and supports a coupling stoichiometry of 3 Na^+:1 divalent anion substrate (69). Interestingly, another study of succinate transport in pig intestine reported very low rates of sodium-coupled transport and what appears to be a very large diffusive component (36). It is possible that the differences between studies are a result of dietary regulation of Na^+/dicarboxylate cotransport in the pig intestine. To my knowledge no studies have examined the dietary regulation of intestinal dicarboxylate transport, but it is well established that many nutrients regulate the activity of their transporters in the intestine (16). The dietary induction of transporters could also explain why Na^+/succinate transport in brush border membrane vesicles from rabbit small intestine was measured in some studies (44) but not in others (61).

Note that the conditions used for uptake experiments can contribute to differences in apparent substrate affinities. If initial rates of transport are not used at all substrate concentrations in kinetic studies, the transport rates measured at higher substrate concentrations can be underestimates of the true rates (73). The calculated V_{max} from those data would be lower than the true V_{max}, and the K_m (or the concentration that produces 1/2 V_{max}) would appear to be smaller than the true K_m. For example, the K_m for succinate transport in rabbit renal brush border membrane vesicles was found to be 110 μM when 15-s uptakes were used (74), whereas the K_m for succinate measured with 1-s uptakes was 0.7 mM (73). Although the succinate K_m reported for rat kidney is consistently lower than that reported for rabbit, more studies are necessary to rule out the possibility that the intermediate affinity transporters are in fact a subset of the low-affinity transporters.

High-Affinity Transporters for Krebs Cycle Intermediates

The functional properties of the high-affinity transporters appear to exhibit a number of differences compared with the low- and intermediate-affinity transporters (Table 1). Of high-affinity transporters, the best characterized are those found on the basolateral membranes of kidney proximal tubule cells. However, high-affinity transporters have also been reported on other cells and organs, including liver, placenta, and brain.

SUBSTRATES The high-affinity Na^+/dicarboxylate cotransporters that have been functionally characterized have K_ms for succinate or α-ketoglutarate between 5 and 33 μM. Comparison of transport in brush border and basolateral membranes from the same organs has shown that the high-affinity transporter has a much lower transport capacity than the transporter on the apical membrane (14, 76). Although the high-affinity and low-affinity transport pathways have many substrates in common, some differences appear in substrate specificity. Citrate appears to be carried by the low-affinity transporter but is not a good substrate of the high-affinity pathway. The apparent K_m for citrate in rabbit renal basolateral membrane vesicles is around 2.5 mM (25). The transport of citrate is also relatively insensitive to pH changes, suggesting that trivalent citrate is the transported species (76). The pH dependence of succinate transport in the high-affinity pathway has a pH optimum at 7.5 (10, 76). The high-affinity Na^+/dicarboxylate transporter interacts with substrates such as dimethylsuccinate, meso-2,3-dimercaptosuccinate, and *cis*-aconitate (63), which do not inhibit the low-affinity transporter.

CATIONS The high-affinity Na^+/dicarboxylate cotransporters also couple multiple sodium ions to the transport of dicarboxylates, and transport is thought to be electrogenic. The transport of dicarboxylates but not of citrate appears to be sensitive to changes in membrane potential (10, 14, 76), which also supports the idea that citrate is carried in trivalent form.

There may be differences between the high-affinity transporters in their sensitivity to inhibition by lithium. The Na^+/dicarboxylate cotransporters in rat kidney basolateral membranes (10, 14) and rat liver basolateral membranes (37, 77) are sensitive to inhibition by millimolar concentrations of lithium. However, Na^+/dicarboxylate cotransport in human placenta is much less sensitive, with an apparent IC_{50} for Li^+ of around 10 mM (18), which could indicate some species or tissue differences in the transporter proteins.

TISSUE DISTRIBUTION AND FUNCTION High-affinity Na^+/dicarboxylate cotransport has been characterized in the basolateral membranes of renal proximal tubules of rat and rabbit (10, 14, 76), rat liver sinusoidal basolateral membranes (37, 77), human placental brush border membranes (18, 40), mouse and rat brain synaptosomes (56, 57), and isolated chick intestinal cells (28) (Table 1).

One of the primary functions of the high-affinity transporter on the renal basolateral membrane appears to be in organic anion secretion (53). Organic anions, such as *p*-aminohippurate (PAH), enter the cells of the proximal tubule on an organic anion/dicarboxylate exchanger located on the basolateral membrane (53). The dicarboxylates preferred by this exchanger include glutarate and α-ketoglutarate; succinate and citrate are not substrates of the exchanger. Glutarate and α-ketoglutarate are accumulated in proximal tubule cells by the Na^+/dicarboxylate cotransporters on the apical (13) and basolateral membranes. The organic anion/dicarboxylate exchanger couples the efflux of dicarboxylates down their electrochemical gradients to the concentrative uptake of organic anions into the cells. The functional coupling between Na^+/dicarboxylate cotransporters and organic anion secretory pathways may also operate in other organs such as liver (77).

The Na^+/dicarboxylate cotransporter in liver may play a role in regulating the synthesis of glutamine (62). The high-affinity Na^+/dicarboxylate cotransporter in rat liver is found on the basolateral membranes of a subset ($\sim$7%) of hepatocytes located in perivenous regions (62). The perivenous hepatocytes express glutamine synthetase, and the α-ketoglutarate transported into these hepatocytes is quickly converted to glutamine (62). In brain, the transport of α-ketoglutarate into synaptic terminals is thought to be the first step in replenishing pools of neurotransmitters such as glutamate (56). Synaptosome membranes contain at least one high-affinity Na^+-dependent α-ketoglutarate transport pathway (56, 57). This transport pathway is inhibited by glutamate and aspartate, which do not inhibit other high-affinity transporters, suggesting that the isoform found in brain is a different protein than the renal isoform. Chick intestinal cells also contain a high-affinity Na^+/dicarboxylate cotransporter, with a K_m for succinate of 25 μM (28). The chick intestinal transporter does not appear to be sensitive to membrane potential and may couple only 2 Na^+ to the transport of each succinate. Because the experiments were done with dissociated enterocytes, it is not known whether this transporter is on the apical or basolateral membrane.

REGULATION OF SODIUM-DICARBOXYLATE COTRANSPORTERS

Relatively little information is available about the regulation of Na^+/dicarboxylate cotransporters. All studies to date have dealt with the effects of chronic conditions on transport in the kidney. For example, studies with perfused proximal tubules and isolated brush border membranes from fasted rats have shown increased transport of α-ketoglutarate (58) and citrate (66). After three-day starvation, the K_m for α-ketoglutarate remained unchanged but the V_{max} doubled (58). Interestingly, no corresponding change appeared in basolateral Na^+/dicarboxylate cotransport with starvation (64). Transport of citrate is also increased under conditions of metabolic acidosis (24) and chronic K^+ depletion, which is also mediated by an increased V_{max} with no change in K_m (31). There are no reports of regulation of Na^+/dicarboxylate transport in other organs or short-term changes induced by hormones, although parathyroid hormone may affect citrate transport in human kidney (12).

MOLECULAR STUDIES OF SODIUM-DICARBOXYLATE COTRANSPORTERS

Cloning and Characterization of NaDC-1 Family Members

The cDNA coding for the rabbit renal low-affinity Na^+/dicarboxylate cotransporter, NaDC-1, was isolated by expression cloning in *Xenopus* oocytes (41). The primary amino acid sequence of NaDC-1 contains 593 amino acids and has a predicted mass of 66 kDa. The amino acid sequence of NaDC-1 is 43% identical to that of the renal and intestinal Na^+/sulfate cotransporter NaSi-1 (34, 39). The transporters in this gene family are not related to any of the other transporter superfamilies.

Functionally, NaDC-1 corresponds to the low-affinity Na^+/dicarboxylate cotransporter of the brush border membrane of the renal proximal tubule (71). NaDC-1 expressed in *Xenopus* oocytes has an apparent K_m for succinate of 0.5 mM and a K_m for citrate of about 0.9 mM (45). NaDC-1 has also been expressed in COS-7 cells and exhibits similar functional properties, including a K_m for succinate of 0.5 mM (48). The substrate specificity of NaDC-1 resembles that of the rabbit low-affinity Na^+/dicarboxylate cotransporter (71); succinate transport in NaDC-1 was inhibited by a range of di- and tricarboxylates but not by monocarboxylates such as lactate. Transport by NaDC-1 was also insensitive to inhibition by dimethylsuccinate, a test substrate of the high-affinity transporter (63). As seen previously in brush border membrane vesicles (75), the transport of succinate by NaDC-1 was insensitive to changes in pH, whereas the transport of citrate was stimulated at acidic pH values (45). The primary effect of pH on citrate transport in NaDC-1 is on K_m with no change in V_{max}, consistent with the idea that NaDC-1 prefers protonated citrate as a substrate (45). NaDC-1 is inhibited by furosemide, IC_{50} 1.5 mM, and flufenamate, IC_{50} 250 μM, but it is not affected by anion transport inhibitors such as bumetanide, probenecid, or 4,4′-diisothiocyanostilbene-2,2′-disulfonic acid (DIDS) (45).

The cation specificity of NaDC-1 is also similar to that of rabbit renal brush border membrane vesicles. Sodium activation curves with NaDC-1 are sigmoidal, with apparent Hill coefficients of 1.6–2.9 (41, 48), indicating that multiple sodium ions are involved in the transport of succinate. The half-saturation constant for sodium in NaDC-1 is approximately 50 mM (41). The transport of succinate is dependent on the presence of sodium, and replacement of sodium by cations such as choline results in the reduction of activity to background levels (41). Replacement of sodium by lithium, however, results in a low rate of transport, approximately 5% of that seen in sodium (46). NaDC-1 is also sensitive to inhibition by lithium. In the presence of saturating concentrations of sodium, millimolar concentrations of lithium inhibit transport by NaDC-1, with an apparent K_i of 1.8 mM (45), similar to the K_i reported in renal membranes (72).

The mRNA coding for NaDC-1 is found in kidney cortex and small intestine (41), a distribution similar to that of low-affinity Na^+/dicarboxylate cotransport activity. However, after long exposure of Northern blots probed at high stringency with NaDC-1 cDNA, hybridization signals also appear in liver, lung, and adrenal, suggesting either low abundance of NaDC-1 or related messages in those organs (41). More recently, antibodies have been prepared against a fusion protein consisting of 60 amino acids from NaDC-1 and glutathione-*S*-transferase (44). The antibodies were originally raised in chickens (44) but were also raised in rabbits (46) because of background problems with the chicken antibodies. NaDC-1 protein is found in kidney and intestine brush border membrane vesicles (44). The antibodies recognized a glycosylated protein of approximately 63 kDa in rabbit renal brush border membranes and two proteins of 57 and 115 kDa in rabbit intestinal brush border membranes (44). Recent studies have verified that chronic metabolic acidosis in rats leads to an increase in NaDC-1 protein, up to 5.6-fold higher than controls (1). Chronic metabolic acidosis also resulted in an increased amount of NaDC-1 message in the kidney, up to 3.5-fold, which was correlated with the decrease in serum HCO_3^- (1).

The cDNA coding for the human ortholog of NaDC-1, called hNaDC-1, was isolated by hybridization with the rabbit NaDC-1 cDNA (42). The amino acid sequence of hNaDC-1 is 78% identical to NaDC-1 and 47% identical to NaSi-1 (42). Functionally, hNaDC-1 also appears to correspond to a low-affinity transporter, with a K_m for succinate of about 0.4 mM (42). In general, the functional properties of NaDC-1 and hNaDC-1 are similar: Both transporters have a relatively low affinity for succinate and glutarate, both are sodium dependent, and both exhibit similar responses to pH (45). However, the two transporters have some interesting differences. The K_m for citrate is about eightfold higher in hNaDC-1 (7 mM) than in NaDC-1 (0.9 mM) (45). Humans appear to have a higher fractional excretion of citrate in the urine—between 10 and 35% of the filtered load—compared with species, such as dog or rat, that excrete about 2–7% of the filtered load (59). It is possible that the differences in citrate K_m could contribute to the species differences in citrate handling.

The human Na^+/dicarboxylate cotransporter, hNaDC-1, appears to have a low cation affinity, with an apparent K_{Na} of around 80 mM compared with 50 mM for NaDC-1 (45). The Hill coefficient is around 2.1, again consistent with multiple sodium ions being coupled to the movement of substrate. Human patients receiving therapeutic doses of lithium exhibit increased excretion of glutarate and α-ketoglutarate, indicating that the Na^+/dicarboxylate cotransporter in human kidney is sensitive to inhibition by lithium, similar to the rabbit transporter (6). In contrast, hNaDC-1 expressed in oocytes is insensitive to inhibition by lithium, with an apparent K_i of 10 mM (45). The reason for the apparent difference is not known. It is possible that either multiple isoforms of hNaDC-1 exist in the apical membrane of kidney proximal tubule, or the conditions used in the oocyte experiments, such as membrane potential or cation concentrations, affect lithium sensitivity.

The mRNA coding for hNaDC-1 was found in kidney and small intestine, suggesting that the same protein is expressed in both organs (42). In addition, the gene coding for hNaDC-1 was found on chromosome 17 using mouse-hamster somatic hybrid cell lines, but it has not been localized further (42).

The cDNA coding for the rat renal Na^+/dicarboxylate cotransporter, rNaDC-1, was recently isolated by hybridization screening (55). The amino acid sequence of rNaDC-1 is 73% identical to that to NaDC-1 (Table 2). The rat transporter is sodium dependent and sensitive to inhibition by lithium, and it carries a variety of di- and tricarboxylic acids in divalent anion form (12a, 54a). The rNaDC-1 protein is found on the apical membranes of proximal tubules, predominantly from S2 and S3 segments (54a). The cDNA coding for rNaDC-1 was independently cloned by a second group and given the name SDCT1 (12a). In situ hybridization experiments identified rNaDC-1 (SDCT1) mRNA in the kidney, small intestine, lung, liver, and epididymis (12a).

A cDNA related to NaDC-1, called RI-19, was isolated from a rat intestinal cDNA library (27). The carboxy terminus of NaDC-1 contains approximately 60 amino acids with about 80% sequence identity with rat intestinal mucin (41). Khatri and colleagues used homology screening with mucin cDNA to isolate the RI-19 cDNA from rat intestine (27). RI-19 has not been functionally

Table 2 Properties of cloned Na^+/dicarboxylate and Na^+/sulfate cotransporters

Name	Source	% identity with NaDC-1	K_m succinate	Lithium inhibition	Electrogenic	Genbank number	Reference
NaDC-1	Rabbit kidney	100	0.5 mM	Yes	Yes	U12186	41, 45
hNaDC-1	Human kidney	78	0.8 mM	No	Yes[1]	U26029	42, 45
rNaDC-1	Rat kidney	73	n.d.	n.d.	n.d.	AB001321	55
RI-19	Rat intestine	60	n.d.	n.d.	n.d.	U51153	27
NaDC-2	*Xenopus* intestine	62	0.3 mM	No	Yes[1]	U87318	2
NaSi-1	Rat kidney, intestine	43	—	No	Yes	L19102	11, 34, 39

[1]AM Pajor, unpublished observations.

characterized. The predicted amino acid sequence of RI-19 is 60% identical in sequence to NaDC-1 (27). However, there appear to be several frame shifts in the sequence, and by adding or deleting a total of five nucleotides, the sequence identity with NaDC-1 rises to 73% (AM Pajor, unpublished observations). This suggests either that RI-19 represents a nonfunctional pseudogene or that the published sequence contains errors. At the nucleotide level, RI-19 is 98.5% identical to rNaDC-1.

A cDNA called NaDC-2, coding for the intestinal Na^+/dicarboxylate cotransporter from the African clawed frog, *Xenopus laevis*, was isolated by functional expression in *Xenopus* oocytes (2). The amino acid sequence of NaDC-2 is approximately 63% identical to the sequence of NaDC-1. NaDC-2 message was found only in intestine and not in any other organ such as kidney and liver (2). When expressed in *Xenopus* oocytes, NaDC-2 transports succinate, citrate, and glutarate, and transport was not inhibited by dimethylsuccinate or sulfate (2). NaDC-2 exhibits an unusual cation selectivity compared with NaDC-1. Replacement of sodium by lithium results in little or no decrease in transport rate in NaDC-2 (2). The K_m for succinate measured in sodium is approximately 0.3 mM and the K_m for succinate measured in lithium is 0.7 mM. The apparent sodium and lithium affinities are the same (K_{Na} or K_{Li} ~45 mM), and the apparent Hill coefficients are around 1.3 in either sodium or lithium.

Relatively little information exists about the high-affinity Na^+/dicarboxylate cotransporters. A high-affinity Na^+/dicarboxylate cotransporter was expressed in *Xenopus* oocytes microinjected with a 2–3 kb size fraction of mRNA from rat kidney (60). The high-affinity Na^+/dicarboxylate cotransporter NaDC-3 has recently been isolated from rat placenta (V Ganapathy, personal communication). NaDC-3 is 42% identical in amino acid sequence to NaDC-1, and it exhibits properties of a high-affinity transporter, including a K_m for succinate of 2 μM and interaction with dimethylsuccinate. The tissue distribution of NaDC-3 mRNA in placenta, kidney, liver, and brain also resembles the distribution of high-affinity Na^+/dicarboxylate transport.

Genbank and other databases have a number of sequences related to the NaDC-1 gene family. The function of these proteins from organisms such as *Caenorhabditis elegans* and yeast have not been determined. However, a distinct family of transporters in bacteria, called the 2-hydroxy-carboxylate carriers, includes sodium- and proton-coupled dicarboxylate transporters (65). The members of this family are unrelated in either primary sequence or predicted secondary structure to NaDC-1 or NaSi-1. Despite the lack of sequence similarity, the Na^+/citrate cotransporter of *Klebsiella pneumoniae*, called CitS, exhibits interesting functional parallels with NaDC-1. CitS also appears to carry citrate as a divalent anion, and lithium can substitute for sodium but with much reduced affinity (33). The coupling stoichiometry is thought to be 2 Na^+:1H^+: 1 citrate^{2-}, and therefore transport by CitS should be electrogenic (33).

Structure of NaDC-1-Related Family Members

Relatively little information is available regarding the structure of transporters related to NaDC-1, but members of the same gene family will likely have strong similarities in their structures. Initial hydrophobicity analysis of NaDC-1 using the Kyte-Doolittle hydropathy scale resulted in a predicted secondary structure containing 8 transmembrane domains (34, 41). This model has since been revised (Figure 1) after reanalysis using the Rao-Argos buried helix parameter scale, which predicts that NaDC-1 contains 11–12 hydrophobic regions long enough to span the membrane as α-helices (44).

The sequence of NaDC-1 contains two consensus sites for N-glycosylation, at Asn-160, in a large polar region, and Asn-578 near the carboxy terminus (44). However, mutagenesis experiments showed that Asn-578 is the site that is glycosylated, which places the carboxy terminus of NaDC-1 on the outside of the cell (44) (Figure 1). Interestingly, all members of the family related to NaDC-1 contain one or two consensus sequences for N-glycosylation located close to the carboxy terminus. Some of the family members, including NaSi-1

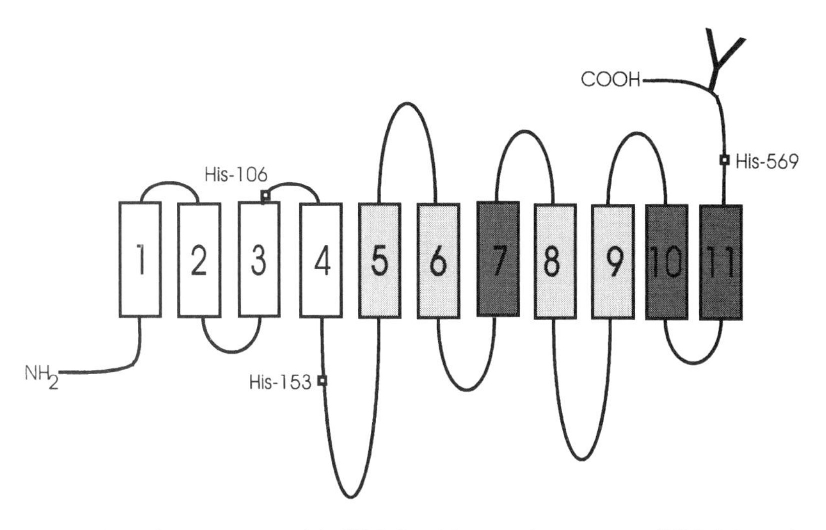

Figure 1 Secondary structure model of NaDC-1. The secondary structure of NaDC-1 contains 11 putative transmembrane domains, shown by the *numbered rectangles*. The amino terminus is on the cytoplasmic side of the membrane, and the carboxy terminus is on the outside of the cell. **Y** designates the N-glycosylation site at Asn-576. The *shaded* transmembrane domains represent regions of the protein important in substrate binding. Transmembrane domains 5–11 contain the substrate recognition domain (46). The *darker shaded* transmembrane domains, 7, 10, and 11 contain residues that determine affinity for citrate (26). Transmembrane domains 8 and 9 contain acidic residues that may interact with sodium (20). The histidines at positions 153 and 569 bind diethylpyrocarbonate, which inhibits transport; histidine-106 is involved in protein stability or trafficking (47).

and rNaDC-1, contain additional N-glycosylation sequences around amino acids 140–250. The human hNaDC-1 has both of its N-glycosylation sites at the carboxy terminus, and the size increase after in vitro translation experiments suggests that both sites are glycosylated (42). Aside from the extracellular carboxy terminus, the rest of the secondary structure model in NaDC-1 and the rest of the family remain to be tested in detail.

The role of N-glycosylation in NaDC-1 appears to be in protein trafficking or stability, which also seems to be the case in other transport proteins (44). A mutant of NaDC-1 lacking N-glycosylation sites, called GM2, exhibited a decrease in transport activity of about 50% (44), which was paralleled by a 65% reduction in the abundance of GM2 protein at the plasma membrane (46).

Structure-Function Studies of Na^+/Dicarboxylate Cotransporters

Structure-function studies of membrane transport proteins are somewhat limited by the lack of good structural information about integral membrane proteins. Two general approaches have been taken in studies of structure-function relationships in transporters: site-directed mutagenesis and chimera formation. In the absence of structural information that might lead to hypotheses about locations of binding sites, we have used site-directed mutagenesis based on previous studies with amino acid selective reagents and suggestions of amino acids that might be involved in coordinating cation binding. In addition, the differences in function between the members of the NaDC-1 family have been exploited by formation of chimeric transporters.

Previous studies using the histidine-selective reagent diethylpyrocarbonate (DEPC) suggested that a histidine might be found at or near the substrate binding site in the rabbit renal low-affinity Na^+/dicarboxylate cotransporter (4). In order to test this hypothesis, each of the 11 histidines in NaDC-1 was mutated to alanine, and the mutant transporters were expressed in *Xenopus* oocytes (47). Replacement of 10 of the 11 histidines by alanine had no effect on the function of NaDC-1. However, replacement of His-106 by alanine resulted in a 98% decrease in transport activity. The H106A mutant had no change in the K_m for succinate but a large decrease in V_{max}. The abundance of H106A protein at the plasma membrane was correspondingly reduced, although there was very little decrease in the total amount of H106A protein in the oocyte. Therefore histidine does not appear to be required for transport in NaDC-1, although His-106 is likely to be involved in trafficking or stability. The DEPC binding sites in NaDC-1 were identified as histidines 153 and 569, and the inhibition of transport by DEPC binding at these sites probably occurs by steric hindrance (47).

A second experimental approach, the formation of chimeric transporters, was used to identify the substrate recognition domains in the Na^+/dicarboxylate and Na^+/sulfate cotransporters (46). The amino acid sequence of NaDC-1 is 43%

identical to that of the Na^+/sulfate cotransporter, NaSi-1 (34). The two transporters have very distinct substrate specificities. NaDC-1 does not transport sulfate, and succinate transport is not inhibited by sulfate. Similarly, NaSi-1 does not interact with succinate. The technique of homologous recombination (9) was used to prepare chimeras between NaDC-1 and NaSi-1. Only one functional chimera resulted, probably because of the difference in sequence between the two transporters. Chimera SiDC-4 contained the first four transmembrane domains from NaSi-1 and the last seven transmembrane domains from NaDC-1. The substrate specificity of SiDC-4 was identical to that of the parent NaDC-1, suggesting that the substrate recognition domain is found in the carboxy terminal twothirds of the protein (Figure 1). Residues affecting substrate affinity and inhibition by furosemide and flufenamate were found in the amino terminal portion of the protein. Finally, it appears that residues involved in cation binding may be found in both the amino- and carboxy-terminal portions of the transporters (34).

A similar chimera formation strategy has been taken to identify the domains that determine the differences in substrate affinity between the human and rabbit NaDC-1. The rabbit NaDC-1 has a K_m for citrate of 0.9 mM, whereas the human hNaDC-1 has a K_m of about 7 mM (42). Chimeras formed between NaDC-1 and hNaDC-1 confirmed that the carboxy-terminal half of the protein, transmembrane domains 7–11, contains residues that determine the differences in citrate affinity (26) (Figure 1). The differences in citrate affinity appear to be the result of interactions between residues in three transmembrane domains, 7, 10, and 11. A chimera with substitutions of all three transmembrane domains (7, 10, and 11) had the same K_m for citrate as the donor of the three transmembrane domains, whereas substitution of one or two of these transmembrane domains resulted in only a partial change in affinity (26).

In an effort to identify individual residues involved in substrate or cation binding, conserved anionic amino acids in NaDC-1 were mutated to alanines (20). Of the amino acids mutated, only Asp-373 and Glu-475 appear to be required for transport function. Asp-373 is in transmembrane domain 8, and Glu-475 is in transmembrane domain 9 (Figure 1). Replacement of these amino acids resulted in changes in cation selectivity and affinity, as well as substrate affinity. The results suggest that these acidic residues contribute to the structure of the cation binding sites or participate in the coordination of cations (20).

Electrophysiological Analysis of NaDC-1 Function

Electrophysiological methods have been used to study a number of cloned electrogenic transporters expressed in *Xenopus* oocytes or cultured cells. The approach was first used to study currents generated by the Na^+/glucose cotransporter, SGLT1 (50, 51). The use of electrophysiological measurements provides some advantages over measurements of radiolabeled uptakes. It is possible to make rapid measurements of transport activity, and the ability to control membrane potential provides more precise information about the kinetics of transport, which is particularly important when interpreting the effects of mutations on function.

NaDC-1 is an electrogenic transporter, with a transport cycle that moves one net positive charge across the membrane. In voltage-clamped oocytes expressing NaDC-1, superfusion with substrates such as succinate, citrate or methylsuccinate resulted in inward currents as large as 3 μA (43). The production of currents in the presence of tricarboxylate substrates supports the idea that divalent anions are the preferred substrates of NaDC-1. At -50 mV, the $K_{0.5}^{\text{succinate}}$ was 180 μM and the $K_{0.5}^{Na^+}$ was 19 mM. The Hill coefficient for sodium was 2.3, which is consistent with the predicted transport stoichiometry of $3Na^+$:1 divalent anion substrate. Although Na^+ is the preferred cation, Li^+ was also able to support transport, although much less effectively (the $K_{0.5}^{\text{succinate}}$ in Li^+ was 3 mM). However, in the presence of sodium, lithium binds with high affinity to one of the cation binding sites, resulting in transport inhibition (43).

Electrophysiological characterization of the rat ortholog, rNaDC-1 (SDCT1), has revealed some interesting differences with NaDC-1. Both NaDC-1 and rNaDC-1 (SDCT1) exhibit voltage-dependent steps in translocation but voltage independence of substrate binding (43, 12a). Unlike NaDC-1, however, rNaDC-1 (SDCT1) does not exhibit inward currents in the presence of lithium, although lithium is a potent inhibitor of transport (12a). Under voltage-clamp conditions, the $K_{0.5}$ for succinate in rNaDC-1 (SDCT1) is around 25 μM (12a, 54a) compared with 180 μM for NaDC-1, which verifies previous suggestions that the rat transporter has an intermediate substrate affinity. The stoichiometry of transport in rNaDC-1 (SDCT1) is three sodium ions for each succinate or citrate molecule transported, determined from the simultaneous measurement of currents and radiotracer uptakes under voltage-clamp conditions (12a, 54a).

The renal Na^+/sulfate transporter, NaSi-1, is also electrogenic. Earlier radiotracer transport studies with NaSi-1 suggested that transport was electroneutral, based on an apparent Hill coefficient for sodium of about 1.8 (34). However, the presence of substrates such as sulfate, thiosulfate, and selenate induced inward currents in oocytes expressing NaSi-1 (11). Under voltage-clamp conditions, the Hill coefficient for sodium is 2.8, which indicates a coupling stoichiometry in NaSi-1 similar to that of NaDC-1:3 Na^+:1 sulfate^{2-}, resulting in the net movement of one positive charge across the membrane (11). In preliminary studies, we have also observed substrate-induced currents in oocytes expressing hNaDC-1 and NaDC-2 (AM Pajor, unpublished observations), which have Hill coefficients for sodium of 2.1 (hNaDC-1) and 1.3 (NaDC-2). The results suggest that the coupling stoichiometry in hNaDC-1 and NaDC-2 is also likely to be 3 Na^+:1 succinate^{2-}. The differences in Hill coefficients could be due to the effects of membrane potential on transport in nonvoltage-clamped oocytes, or there may be differences in the extent of cooperativity between cation binding sites in these transporters.

CONCLUSIONS AND FUTURE DIRECTIONS

The characterization of sodium-coupled dicarboxylate transporters in isolated cells and membrane vesicles has identified transport pathways with functional differences such as substrate affinity, substrate specificity, and sensitivity to inhibition by lithium. The functional studies suggest that a number of different isoforms of Na^+/dicarboxylate cotransporters are likely to be found in a given organism, and there may be species differences in transporters as well. The recent cloning of cDNAs coding for Na^+/dicarboxylate cotransporters shows that a family of related proteins exists, with differences in kinetics and other functional properties. Cloning of additional members of the family will allow the identification and functional characterization of the different transporter isoforms and the determination of their tissue distribution, and will also provide a more complete picture of the handling of Krebs cycle intermediates. Although there is some information on regions of the proteins that may be involved in specific functions, a well-tested model of protein structure of the NaDC-1-related family is needed. The use of mutants and chimeric transporters, in the context of a good model of protein structure, should help to identify substrate and cation binding sites and will provide information on the mechanism of transport. There is also relatively little information on the regulation of the transporters; increased availability of such information would be greatly facilitated by the development of a cell culture model. The combination of molecular and functional approaches will provide powerful tools in future studies of the NaDC-1-related family of transporters.

ACKNOWLEDGMENTS

Thanks to Drs. Stephen Wright and Bruce Hirayama for discussions. The author's work in this area is supported by National Institutes of Health grants DK46269 and DK02429.

Literature Cited

1. Aruga S, Preisig PA, Moe OW, Pajor AM, Alpern RJ. 1997. Chronic metabolic acidosis (CMA) increases renal cortical NaDC-1 mRNA and protein abundance in rats. *J. Am. Soc. Nephrol.* 8:A0006
2. Bai L, Pajor AM. 1997. Expression cloning of NaDC-2, an intestinal Na^+- or Li^+-dependent dicarboxylate transporter.

Am. J. Physiol. 273:G267–74
3. Barac-Nieto M. 1984. Effects of pH, calcium, and succinate on sodium citrate cotransport in renal microvilli. *Am. J. Physiol.* 247:F282–90
4. Bindslev N, Wright EM. 1984. Histidyl residues at the active site of the Na^+/succinate cotransporter in rabbit renal brush borders. *J. Biol.* 81:159–70
5. Bond PA, Jenner FA. 1974. The effect of lithium and related metal ions on the urinary excretion of 2-oxoglutarate and citrate in the rat. *Br. J. Pharmacol.* 50:283–39
6. Bond PA, Jenner FA, Lee CR, Lenton E, Pollitt RJ, Sampson GA. 1972. The effect of lithium salts on the urinary excretion of 2-oxoglutarate in man. *Br. J. Pharmacol.* 46:116–23
7. Brennan S, Hering-Smith K, Hamm LL. 1988. Effect of pH on citrate reabsorption in the proximal convoluted tubule. *Am. J. Physiol.* 255:F301–6
8. Browne JL, Sanford PA, Smyth DH. 1978. Transfer and metabolism of citrate, succinate, α-ketoglutarate and pyruvate by hamster small intestine. *Proc. R. Soc. London Ser. B* 200:117–35
9. Buck KJ, Amara SG. 1994. Chimeric dopamine-norepinephrine transporters delineate structural domains influencing selectivity for catecholamines and 1-methyl-4-phenylpyridinium. *Proc. Natl. Acad. Sci. USA* 91:12584–88
10. Burckhardt G. 1984. Sodium-dependent dicarboxylate transport in rat renal basolateral membrane vesicles. *Pflügers Arch.* 401:254–61
11. Busch AE, Waldegger S, Herzer T, Biber J, Markovich D, et al. 1994. Electrogenic cotransport of Na^+ and sulfate in *Xenopus* oocytes expressing the cloned Na^+/SO_4^{2-} transport protein NaSi-1. *J. Biol. Chem.* 269:12407–9
12. Canary JJ, Meloni CR, Clive D, Grossman E. 1964. The renal clearance of citrate in man. *Metabolism* 13:21–30

12a. Chen X-Z, Shayakul C, Berger UV, Tian W, Hediger MA. 1998. Characterization of a rat Na^+-dicarboxylate cotransporter. *J. Biol. Chem.* 273:20972–81

13. Dantzler WH, Evans KK. 1996. Effect of αKG in lumen on PAH transport by isolated-perfused rabbit renal proximal tubules. *Am. J. Physiol.* 271:F521–26
14. Edwards RM, Stack E, Trizna W. 1997. α-ketoglutarate transport in rat renal brush-border and basolateral membrane-vesicles. *J. Pharmacol. Exp. Ther.* 281: 1059–64
15. Deleted in proof
16. Ferraris RP. 1994. Regulation of intestinal nutrient transport. In *Physiology of the Gastrointestinal Tract*, ed. LR Johnson, pp. 1821–44. New York: Raven
17. Fukuhara Y, Turner RJ. 1983. Sodium-dependent succinate transport in renal outer cortical brush border membrane vesicles. *Am. J. Physiol.* 245:F374–81
18. Ganapathy V, Ganapathy ME, Tiruppathi C, Miyamoto Y, Mahesh VB, Leibach FH. 1988. Sodium-gradient-driven, high-affinity, uphill transport of succinate in human placental brush-border membrane vesicles. *Biochem. J.* 249:179–84
19. Grassl SM, Heinz E, Kinne R. 1983. Effect of K^+ and H^+ on sodium/citrate cotransport in renal brush-border vesicles. *Biochim. Biophys. Acta* 736:178–88
20. Griffith DA, Pajor AM. 1998. Acidic residues of the sodium-dicarboxylate cotransporter NaDC-1 involved in cation binding and selectivity. *FASEB J.* 12: A1018 (Abstr.)
21. Hamm LL. 1990. Renal handling of citrate. *Kidney Int.* 38:728–35
22. Hirayama B, Wright EM. 1984. Asymmetry of the Na^+-succinate cotransporter in rabbit renal brush-border membranes. *Biochim. Biophys. Acta* 775:17–21
23. Hirayama B, Wright EM. 1986. Coupling between sodium and succinate transport across renal brush border membrane vesicles. *Pflügers Arch.* 407:S174–79 (Suppl.)
24. Jenkins AD, Dousa TP, Smith LH. 1985. Transport of citrate across renal brush border membrane: effects of dietary acid and alkali loading. *Am. J. Physiol.* 249:F590–95
25. Jorgensen KE, Kragh-Hansen U, Roigaard-Petersen H, Iqbal Sheik M. 1983. Citrate uptake by basolateral and luminal membrane vesicles from rabbit kidney cortex. *Am. J. Physiol.* 244: F686–95
26. Kahn ES, Pajor AM. 1998. Identification of citrate binding domains of sodium-dicarboxylate transporters using human/rabbit chimeric transporters. *FASEB J.* 12:A424 (Abstr.)
27. Khatri IA, Kovacs SVB, Forstner JF. 1996. Cloning of the cDNA for a rat intestinal Na^+/dicarboxylate cotransporter reveals partial sequence homology with a rat intestinal mucin. *Biochim. Biophys. Acta* 1309:58–62
28. Kimmich GA, Randles J, Bennett E. 1991. Sodium-dependent succinate transport by isolated chick intestinal cells. *Am. J. Physiol.* 260:C1151–57
29. Kippen I, Hirayama B, Klinenberg JR, Wright EM. 1979. Transport of tricar-

boxylic acid cycle intermediates by membrane vesicles from renal brush border. *Proc. Natl. Acad. Sci. USA* 76:3397–400
30. Law D, Hering-Smith KS, Hamm LL. 1992. Citrate transport in proximal cell line. *Am. J. Physiol.* 263:C220–25
31. Levi M, McDonald LA, Preisig PA, Alpern RJ. 1991. Chronic K depletion stimulates rat renal brush-border membrane Na-citrate cotransporter. *Am. J. Physiol.* 261:F767–73
32. Lohse J, Verine HJ, Charbit JJ, Sarles H. 1981. Studies on pancreatic stones. II. Citrate secretion in the canine pancreatic juice. *Digestion* 21:198–204
33. Lolkema JS, Enequist H, van der Rest ME. 1994. Transport of citrate catalyzed by the sodium-dependent citrate carrier of *Klebsiella pneumoniae* is obligatorily coupled to the transport of two sodium ions. *Eur. J. Biochem.* 220:469–75
34. Markovich D, Forgo J, Stange G, Biber J, Murer H. 1993. Expression cloning of rat renal Na^+/SO_4^{2-} cotransport. *Proc. Natl. Acad. Sci. USA* 90:8073–77
35. Melnick JZ, Srere PA, Elshourbagy NA, Moe OW, Preisig PA, Alpern RJ. 1996. Adenosine triphosphate citrate lyase mediates hypocitraturia in rats. *J. Clin. Invest.* 98:2381–87
36. Moe AJ, Mallet RT, Jackson MJ, Hollywood JA, Kelleher JK. 1988. Effect of Na^+ on intestinal succinate transport and metabolism in vitro. *Am. J. Physiol.* 255:C95–101
37. Moseley RH, Jarose S, Permoad P. 1992. Hepatic Na^+-dicarboxylate cotransport: identification, characterization, and acinar location. *Am. J. Physiol.* 263:G871–79
38. Murer H, Manganel M, Roch-Ramel F. 1992. Tubular transport of monocarboxylates, Krebs cycle intermediates, and inorganic sulfate. In *Handbook of Physiology-Renal Physiology*, ed. EE Windhager, pp. 2165–88 New York: Am. Physiol. Soc.
39. Norbis F, Perego C, Markovich D, Stange G, Verri T, Murer H. 1994. cDNA cloning of a rat small intestinal Na^+/SO_4^{2-} cotransporter. *Pflügers Arch.* 428:217–23
40. Ogin C, Grassl SM. 1989. Dicarboxylate transport in human placental brush-border membrane vesicles. *Biochim. Biophys. Acta* 980:248–54
41. Pajor AM. 1995. Sequence and functional characterization of a renal sodium/dicarboxylate cotransporter. *J. Biol. Chem.* 270:5779–85
42. Pajor AM. 1996. Molecular cloning and functional expression of a sodium-dicarboxylate cotransporter from human kidney. *Am. J. Physiol.* 270:F642–48
43. Pajor AM, Hirayama BA, Loo DDF. 1998. Sodium and lithium interactions with the Na^+/dicarboxylate cotransporter. *J. Biol. Chem.* 273:18923–29
44. Pajor AM, Sun N. 1996. Characterization of the rabbit renal Na^+/dicarboxylate cotransporter using anti-fusion protein antibodies. *Am. J. Physiol.* 271:C1808–16
45. Pajor AM, Sun N. 1996. Functional differences between rabbit and human Na^+-dicarboxylate cotransporters, NaDC-1 and hNaDC-1. *Am. J. Physiol.* 271:F1093–99
46. Pajor AM, Sun N, Bai L, Markovich D, Sule P. 1998. The substrate recognition domain in the Na^+/dicarboxylate and Na^+/sulfate cotransporters is located in the carboxy-terminal portion of the protein. *Biochim. Biophys. Acta* 1370:98–106
47. Pajor AM, Sun N, Valmonte HG. 1998. Mutational analysis of histidines in the Na^+/dicarboxylate cotransporter, NaDC-1. *Biochem. J.* 331:257–64
48. Pajor AM, Valmonte HG. 1996. Expression of the renal Na^+/dicarboxylate cotransporter, NaDC-1, in COS-7 cells. *Pflügers Arch.* 431:645–51
49. Pak CYC. 1991. Etiology and treatment of urolithiasis. *Am. J. Kidney Dis.* 18:624–37
50. Parent L, Supplisson S, Loo DDF, Wright EM. 1992. Electrogenic properties of the cloned Na^+/glucose cotransporter: I. Voltage-clamp studies. *J. Biol.* 125:49–6
51. Parent L, Supplisson S, Loo DDF, Wright EM. 1992. Electrogenic properties of the cloned Na^+/glucose cotransporter: II. A transport model under nonrapid equilibrium conditions. *J. Membr. Biol.* 125:63–79
52. Piper DW, Fenton BH, Goodman LR. 1967. Lactic, pyruvic, citric and uric acid and urea content of human gastric juice. *Gastroenterology* 53:42–48
53. Pritchard JB, Miller DS. 1993. Mechanisms mediating renal secretion of organic anions and cations. *Physiol. Rev.* 73:765–96
53a. Sakhaee K, Alpern RJ, Pointdexter J, Pak CYC. 1998. Citraturic response to oral citric acid load. *J. Urol.* 147:975–76
54. Schell RE, Wright EM. 1985. Electrophysiology of succinate transport across rabbit renal brush border membranes. *J. Physiol.* 360:95–104
54a. Sekine T, Cha SH, Hosoyamada M, Kanai Y, Watanabe N, et al. 1998. Cloning, functional characterization, and localization of a rat renal Na^+-dicarboxylate transporter. *Am. J. Physiol.* 275:F298–305

55. Sekine T, Watanabe N, Hosoyamada M, Kanai Y, Endou H. 1997. Expression cloning and characterization of a novel multispecific organic anion transporter. *J. Biol. Chem.* 272:18526–29
56. Shank RP, Bennett DJ. 1993. 2-Oxoglutarate transport: a potential mechanism for regulating glutamate and tricarboxylic-acid cycle intermediates in neurons. *Neurochem. Res.* 18:401–10
57. Shank RP, Campbell GL. 1981. Avid Na^+-dependent, high affinity uptake of alpha-ketoglutarate by nerve terminal enriched material from mouse cerebellum. *Life Sci.* 28:843–50
58. Sheridan E, Rumrich G, Ullrich KJ. 1983. Reabsorption of dicarboxylic acids from the proximal convolution of rat kidney. *Pflügers Arch.* 399:18–28
59. Simpson DP. 1983. Citrate excretion: a window on renal metabolism. *Am. J. Physiol.* 244:F223–34
60. Steffgen J, Kienle S, Scheyerl F, Franz HE. 1994. Expression of a rat renal sodium-dependent dicarboxylate transporter in *Xenopus* oocytes. *Biochem. J.* 297:35–39
61. Stevens BR, Wright SH, Hirayama B, Gunther RD, Ross HJ, et al. 1982. Organic and inorganic solute transport in renal and intestinal membrane vesicles preserved in liquid nitrogen. *Membr. Biochem.* 4:271–82
62. Stoll B, McNelly S, Buscher HP, Haussinger D. 1991. Functional hepatocyte heterogeneity in glutamate, aspartate and α-ketoglutarate uptake: a histoautoradiographical study. *Hepatology* 13:247–53
63. Ullrich KJ. 1997. Renal transporters for organic anions and organic cations. Structural requirements for substrates. *J. Membr. Biol.* 158:95–107
64. Ullrich KJ, Fasold H, Rumrich G, Kloss S. 1984. Secretion and contraluminal uptake of dicarboxylic acids in the proximal convolution of rat kidney. *Pflügers Arch.* 400:241–49
65. van der Rest ME, Siewe RM, Abee T, Schwarz E, Oesterhelt D, Konings WN. 1992. Nucleotide sequence and functional properties of a sodium-dependent citrate transport system from *Klebsiella pneumoniae*. *J. Biol. Chem.* 267:8971–76
66. Windus DW, Cohn DE, Heifets M. 1986. Effects of fasting on citrate transport by the brush-border membrane of the rat kidney. *Am. J. Physiol.* 251:F678–82
67. Wolffram S, Badertscher M, Scharrer E. 1994. Carrier-mediated transport is involved in mucosal succinate uptake by rat large intestine. *Exp. Physiol* 79:215–26
68. Wolffram S, Bisang B, Grenacher B, Scharrer E. 1990. Transport of tri- and dicarboxylic acids across the intestinal brush-border membrane of calves. *J. Nutr.* 120:767–74
69. Wolffram S, Hagemann C, Grenacher B, Scharrer E. 1992. Characterization of the transport of tri- and dicarboxylates by pig intestinal brush-border membrane vesicles. *Comp. Biochem. Physiol. A* 101:759–67
70. Wolffram S, Unternahrer R, Grenacher B, Scharrer E. 1994. Transport of citrate across the brush border and basolateral membrane of rat small intestine. *Comp. Biochem. Physiol. A* 109:39–52
71. Wright EM. 1985. Transport of carboxylic acids by renal membrane vesicles. *Annu. Rev. Physiol.* 47:127–41
72. Wright EM, Wright SH, Hirayama BA, Kippen I. 1982. Interactions between lithium and renal transport of Krebs cycle intermediates. *Proc. Natl. Acad. Sci. USA* 79:7514–17
73. Wright SH, Hirayama B, Kaunitz JD, Kippen I, Wright EM. 1983. Kinetics of sodium succinate cotransport across renal brush-border membranes. *J. Biol. Chem.* 258:5456–62
74. Wright SH, Kippen I, Klinenberg JR, Wright EM. 1980. Specificity of the transport system for tricarboxylic acid cycle intermediates in renal brush borders. *J. Membr. Biol.* 57:73–82
75. Wright SH, Kippen I, Wright EM. 1982. Effect of pH on the transport of Krebs cycle intermediates in renal brush border membranes. *Biochim. Biophys. Acta* 684:287–90
76. Wright SH, Wunz TM. 1987. Succinate and citrate transport in renal basolateral and brush-border membranes. *Am. J. Physiol.* 253:F432–39
77. Zimmerli B, O'Neill B, Meier PJ. 1992. Identification of sodium-dependent and sodium-independent dicarboxylate transport systems in rat liver basolateral membrane vesicles. *Pflügers Arch.* 421:329–35

Annu. Rev. Physiol. 1999. 61:683–97

MODULATION OF VASOPRESSIN-ELICITED WATER TRANSPORT BY TRAFFICKING OF AQUAPORIN2-CONTAINING VESICLES[1]

Donald T. Ward[2], *Timothy G. Hammond*[3], *and H. William Harris*[2]
[2]Division of Nephrology, Children's Hospital, Harvard Medical School, Boston, Massachusetts 02115; e-mail: harris@a1.tch.harvard.edu
[3]Renal Electrolyte Division and Veterans Administration Medical Center, Tulane University Medical Center, New Orleans, Louisiana 70118

KEY WORDS: water channels, endosomes, membrane transporters, kidney, collecting duct

ABSTRACT

Vasopressin or AVP regulates water reabsorption by the kidney inner medullary collecting duct (IMCD) through the insertion and removal of aquaporin (AQP) 2 water channels into the IMCD apical membrane. AVP-elicited trafficking of AQP2 with the apical membrane occurs via a specialized population of vesicles that resemble synaptic vesicles in neurons. AQP2 vesicles and the IMCD apical membrane contain homologs of vesicle-targeting and signal transduction proteins found in neurons. Expression studies of AQP2, including human AQP2 mutants, suggest that the carboxyl-terminal domain of AQP2 is important in AQP2 trafficking, particularly as a site for cAMP-dependent protein kinase phosphorylation. These present data reveal that IMCD cells possess a complex integrated-signaling and vesicle-trafficking machinery that provides integration of AVP-elicited water transport with many other parameters within the IMCD cell as well as kidney.

INTRODUCTION

The importance of the peptide hormone vasopressin (AVP)[2] in the regulation of water reabsorption in the kidney has long been appreciated by both physiologists (reviewed in 1, 2) and clinicians (reviewed in 3). Recent efforts by multiple investigators have yielded much information that provides fundamental new insights into the molecular regulation of the urinary concentrating mechanism and total body water balance. In this regard, data obtained from both animals and humans now serve to link earlier physiological observations with specific alterations in renal epithelial cell function. Moreover, studies on AVP-responsive epithelial cells have begun to serve as an experimental paradigm to address several fundamental issues in epithelial cell biology.

The purpose of this review is to summarize these recent developments in studies of AVP-elicited water transport that link renal physiology and medicine to other areas of cell and molecular biology, particularly neurobiology, and to trafficking of membrane transporter proteins by epithelial cells. Although AVP has important actions on a variety of kidney cells, this review focuses exclusively on AVP actions in the mammalian collecting duct (CD), particularly the inner medullary collecting duct (IMCD). In this regard, recent research has focused on two interrelated questions concerning AVP's actions in IMCD. First, how does the IMCD cell target similar AQP water channel proteins (AQP2, AQP3, and AQP4) to either the apical or basolateral membrane within the same cell? Second, what mechanisms permit the AVP-stimulated IMCD cell to efficiently activate or target entirely different transporters–AQP2, the vasopressin-regulated urea transporter (VRUT), and the epithelial sodium channel (ENaC)–in its apical membrane?

Overview of the AVP-Elicited Urinary Concentrating Mechanism

In the absence of AVP stimulation, CD epithelia exhibit very low permeabilities to sodium, urea, and water (4–6). These specialized permeability properties permit the excretion of large volumes of hypotonic urine formed during intervals of water diuresis. In contrast, AVP stimulation of CD cells causes selective increases in their apical membrane water (P_f), urea (P_{urea}), and sodium (P_{Na}) permeabilities (4–7). These AVP-elicited membrane permeability changes allow for the renal reclamation of water and a portion of the filtered solutes and provide the basis for water conservation during intervals of antidiuresis.

[2]Arginine vasopressin, or AVP, is the principal peptide hormone in mammals. These antidiuretic hormones (ADH) are highly conserved throughout evolution and are given various other designations in other animal classes.

In CD segments located in the renal cortex (CCD), passive water reabsorption occurs from hypotonic luminal fluid (100 mOsm/kg H_2O) to isotonic renal cortex (300 mOsm/kg H_2O), where approximately two thirds of total AVP water reabsorption takes place (2, 3). Because facilitated urea absorption is much less in the CCD compared with that in the IMCD, there is greater entrapment of urea in the renal medulla as solute for the creation of hypertonic urine (8, 9). In kidney medulla, there is a progressive increase in interstitial osmolality reaching 1200–2000 mOsm/kg H_2O in the inner medulla. This increased tissue osmolality is achieved by trapping of urea and NaCl by countercurrent multiplication (2, 3). Thus increases in luminal osmolality via loss of water increases luminal urea concentrations, thereby allowing for passive urea reabsorption and recycling in IMCD.

AVP-responsive CD epithelia are not only the major intrarenal target for AVP action. These cells also possess a highly complex cellular machinery that integrates other extracellular signals, including peptide and steroid hormones, prostaglandins, and ions such as calcium, with AVP that together preserve body homeostasis (1). For example, dietary alterations in protein intake will alter the rates of urea generation, thus obligating changes in renal solute handling by the IMCD (10). Therefore, IMCD cells must possess complex systems to integrate these signal transduction pathways to maintain a nearly constant total body water, urea, and sodium content.

AVP Modulates P_f of IMCD Apical Membrane by Alterations in the Location and Content of AQP2

As shown in Figure 1, specialized vesicles containing AQP2 are clustered in the immediate vicinity of the IMCD apical membrane in the absence of ADH stimulation (11). The binding of AVP to its basolateral V2 receptor activates adenyl cyclase via a G_s protein and increases intracellular cAMP (1). Increases in cAMP cause insertion of AQP2 water channels into the apical membrane and an increase in apical membrane P_f (9, 11, 12). Removal of AVP stimulation as well as other stimuli results in the retrieval of water channel–containing membrane via vesicle endocytosis into a specialized endocytic compartment and the return of apical membrane P_f to low baseline levels (9, 11–13). Retrieved water channel membrane is then processed by an apical endocytic compartment within the IMCD cell (14, 15). Studies in renal epithelia have demonstrated that both the insertion and retrieval of water channel vesicles is a dynamic process occurring throughout AVP stimulation (7, 11, 16). Therefore, the resulting membrane P_f represents the difference of vesicle insertion and retrieval at any given moment (16). These data have confirmed previous work summarized as the shuttle hypothesis (17) and have established vesicle-mediated AQP2 trafficking as the major regulator of ADH elicited P_f. Water entering the cell is

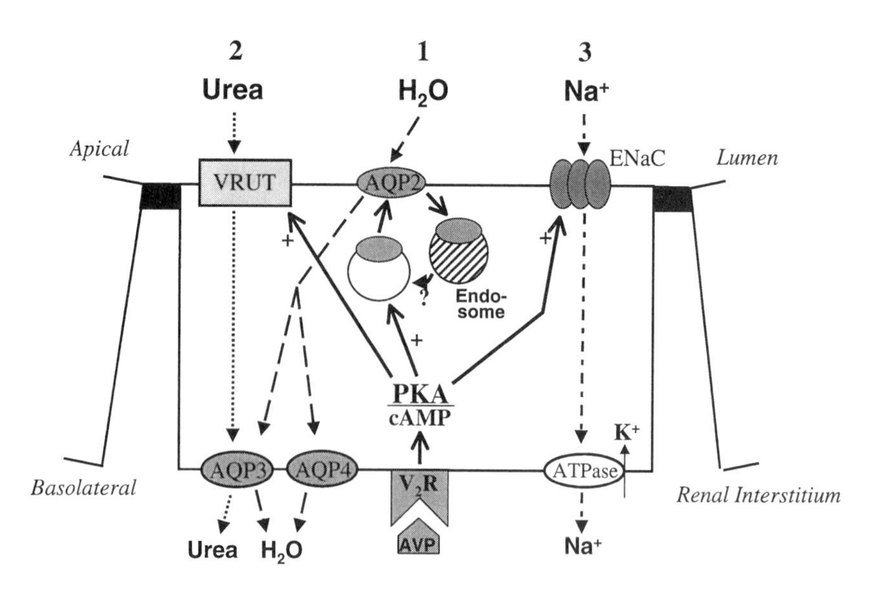

Figure 1 Schematic diagram showing AVP-elicited urea, H_2O, and Na^+ reabsorption in inner medullary collecting duct (IMCD) cells. In response to AVP-induced PKA activation, there is an increase in apical membrane permeability of (1) H_2O, which enters the IMCD cell via AQP2 water channel and is postulated to exit through both AQP3 and AQP4; (2) urea, which crosses that apical membrane by way of VRUT and then exits via AQP3; and (3) Na^+, which after traversing the apical membrane via ENaC, is transported out of the cell via the basolateral membrane Na^+K^+ATPase. AQP2 protein is present in subapical membrane endosomes that are shuttled into the apical membrane in response to AVP and retrieved endocytically. At present, it is not clear whether these AQP2-containing endosomes are recycled back into the exocytic pathway or degraded. Abbreviations: AQP, aquaporin; AVP, vasopressin; ENaC, amiloride-sensitive epithelial sodium channel; PKA, cAMP-dependent protein kinase A; VRUT, vasopressin-regulated urea transporter.

postulated to exit via either AQP3 (18, 19) or AQP4 (20–22) water channels that are localized to the basolateral membrane of the IMCD cell. AQP3 possesses significant permeabilities to both water and urea and thus provides a conduit for transepithelial transport of water and urea that cross the IMCD apical membrane via AQP2 and VRUT, respectively (18, 19).

A second important AQP2 regulatory mechanism occurs at the transcriptional level and alters the steady-state levels of AQP2 mRNA and protein within IMCD cells. Both AQP2 protein and mRNA are increased in IMCD upon exposure of rats to stimuli that activate renal water conservation mechanisms (23–27). The augmentation of IMCD P_f that results from an increase in IMCD AQP2 content has been termed conditioning (28). In contrast, maneuvers that cause pathological defects in urinary concentration (29–32) reduce IMCD AQP2 content. Recent studies suggest that these alterations in AQP2 mRNA occur through activation or repression of both cAMP and the hypertonicity-responsive elements in the promoter region of the AQP2 gene (33).

Structural Aspects of Aquaporin 2, 3, and 4 Water Channel Proteins

AQP2 is a member of the family of aquaporin water channel proteins (34–36). Molecular cloning and expression studies of various AQPs show that these proteins contain six membrane-spanning domains and possess a common structural motif (termed an hourglass) forming a single water-selective aqueous channel that spans the plasma membrane (37). Both rat (38) and human (39) AQP2 homologs have been cloned, and each consists of a cytoplasmic amino (N)-terminal domain, six membrane-spanning domains, and a cytoplasmic carboxyl (C)-terminal portion believed to be important in AQP2 trafficking (Figure 2; see below). AQP2 contains a consensus sequence for N-linked glycosylation and migrates in SDS-PAGE as a 29-kDa nonglycosylated or as a

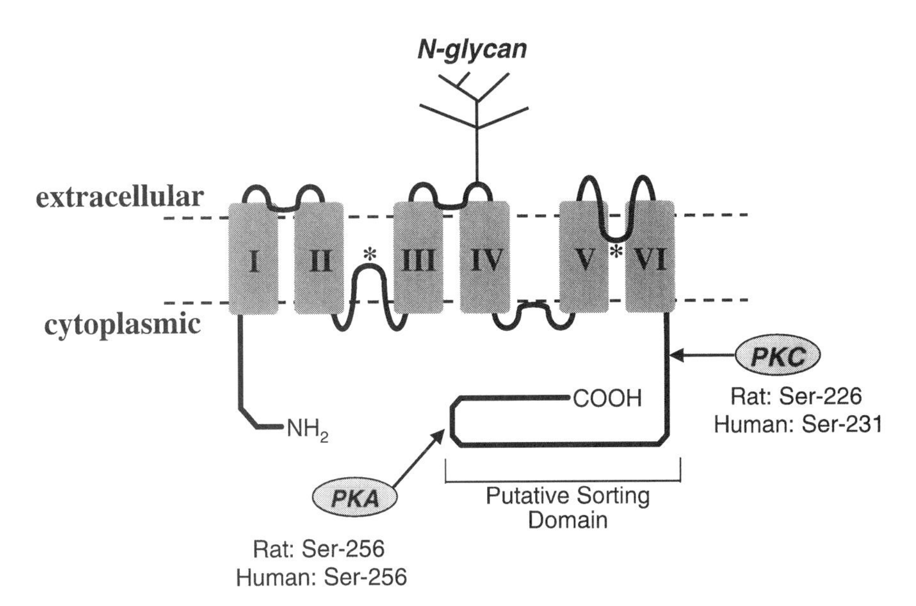

Figure 2 Schematic representation of the membrane topology of AQP2. The AVP-elicited AQP2 water channel is composed of six-transmembrane domains with five connecting loops containing a single glycosylation site. Loops two and five (*asterisks*) are proposed to associate to produce an hourglass structure that forms the water pore (85) in a manner similar to that originally proposed for AQP1 (86). The C termini of both human and rat AQP2s possess single consensus sequences for PKA and PKC phosphorylation and represent the putative sorting or targeting domain for the routing of AQP2 to the apical membrane of IMCD cells.

35-50-kDa glycosylated polypeptide. However, present evidence suggests that glycosylation of AQP2 does not play a major role in either the trafficking or water permeability of the channel because in Madin-Darby canine kidney (MDCK) cells transfected with AQP2, tunicamycin (an inhibitor of protein glycosylation) fail to alter transcellular water transport under basal and AVP-simulated conditions (40).

Two other AQPs, AQP3 and AQP4, are also expressed by IMCD cells (18–21). Although AQPs 3 and 4 both contain similar membrane-spanning water channel pores, their respective cytoplasmic portions each contain distinct amino acid sequences compared with those of AQP2. As described below, since AQPs 3 and 4 are localized to the basolateral membranes of IMCD cells, and because AQP2 is primarily localized to the apical membrane and associated vesicles, it is possible that IMCD cells maintain this highly polarized distribution of AQPs 2, 3, and 4 via cellular sorting machinery that permits the efficient trafficking of each different AQP protein through recognition of their divergent cytoplasmic domains. Although immunocytochemistry studies in other nonrenal epithelia (34, 41) show that AQPs 3 and 4 exhibit basolateral distributions similar to that observed for IMCD, it is presently unclear whether this represents the presence of similar sorting mechanisms in these cells.

Molecular cloning of both the amiloride-inhibitable epithelial apical sodium channel (ENaC) subunits (42, 43), as well as the AVP-regulated urea transporter (VRUT) (44), permits comparisons of the structural features of AQP2, ENaC, and VRUT to search for common targeting or regulatory domains within these proteins that are expressed by IMCD cells. AQP2 does not possess either of the specific peptide motifs postulated to permit ENaC to specifically interact with other proteins. The C-terminal intracellular domain of αENaC contains a proline-rich sequence that binds proteins containing SH_3 domains, such as ankyrin and α-spectrin (45). The ENaC α, β, and γ subunits possess a proline-rich PY motif (XPPXY) that binds proteins containing WW domains (46). VRUT contains 7 potential phosphorylation sites for cAMP-dependent protein kinase A (PKA), 6 potential sites for protein kinase C (PKC), and 11 potential sites for CaM Kinase II (44). Although there is evidence for VRUT phosphorylation in intact IMCD cells (47), its significance either to VRUT function or to VRUT trafficking is unknown. In summary, inspection of cytoplasmic domains of AQP2, ENaC, and VRUT provides no evidence of a common structural motif(s) that might permit coordinated regulation of CD water, urea, and sodium transport after AVP stimulation.

Mutations of AQP2 That Impair Its Trafficking

Humans with autosomal recessive nephrogenic diabetes insipidus (NDI) fail to concentrate the urine normally and possess mutations of the AQP2 gene that interfere with AQP2 protein functions including trafficking (48). Expression of these mutant human AQP2s in *Xenopus* oocytes shows that some AQP2 mutations (Gly64Arg, Asn68Ser, Arg187Cys, and Ser216Pro) result in completely nonfunctional proteins in oocytes (49), whereas other mutations (Thr126Met and Ala147Thr) produce only a smaller increase in oocyte P_f compared with that of wild-type AQP2 (50). In contrast to wild-type AQP2 protein, only a small portion of these various mutant AQP2 proteins are localized to the oocyte plasma membrane. Instead, AQP2 mutants are retarded in the oocyte endoplasmic reticulum as a 32-kDa AQP2 translation product (49) or in the Golgi complex (51). These data are similar to studies of mutants of the CFTR Cl^- channel (52) and suggest that misfolded mutant AQP2 proteins (some of which are actual functional water channels) are targeted abnormally and thus fail to reach the plasma membrane. Recent studies in both CFTR (53) and AQP2 (50) suggest that synthesis or misrouting of some mutant proteins may be corrected by exposure to chemical chaperones that presumably facilitate the synthesis and/or correct folding of mutant polypeptides.

Data from one recently discovered AQP2 mutant, Glu258Lys, suggests that the C-terminal domain of AQP2 is important in vesicle trafficking of AQP2 (51). This AQP2 mutant is retained in the Golgi (and not in the ER, unlike the other mutants described above), despite the fact that the adjacent Ser256 residue is phosphorylated normally (51).

Significance of AQP2 C Terminus and Ser256 to Trafficking

Present evidence suggests that the C-terminal domain of AQP2 contains a peptide sequence important for normal membrane trafficking of AQP2. Replacement of the C-terminal domain of an aquaporin, AQP-1, not normally sequestered in intracellular vesicles with 41 amino acids from the C terminus of AQP2 increased the transepithelial water flux of LLC-PK1 cells expressing the AQP-1/AQP2 chimera after combined forskolin/AVP stimulation. In contrast, cells expressing wild-type AQP-1 exhibited no increased P_f in response to identical stimulation (54). Similarly, transfection with either N- or C-terminal AQP2/green fluorescent protein (GFP) chimeras produced different subcellular localization patterns within LLC-PK1 cells. While the response of N-terminal AQP2/GFP chimeras to forskolin/AVP stimulation was similar to that of wild type AQP2, targeting of C-terminal AQP2/GFP chimeras was abnormal, suggesting that the presence of C-terminal GFP interfered with the C-terminal AQP2 domain (55, 56).

Interpretation of these data cited above is complicated by the fact that LLC-PK1 cells expressing either AQP1/AQP2 or AQP2/GFP chimeras insert both of the resulting constructs into their basolateral rather than apical membranes as expected after stimulation with forskolin/AVP (56, 57). These observations suggest that LLC-PK1 cells may lack some necessary components present in IMCD cells to permit all aspects of AVP-elicited membrane trafficking events. However, recent work shows that wild-type AQP2 is targeted correctly to the apical membrane of a cultured CD cell line, RC.SV3, following AVP treatment (58).

Ser256 located within the C terminus of AQP2 is a potential phosphorylation site for cAMP-dependent protein kinase A (PKA) (38). Studies using both purified AQP2-containing vesicles (59) and oocytes (60) suggest that PKA-mediated phosphorylation of AQP2 does not alter its intrinsic P_f, but rather may be a key event permitting AQP2 access to the plasma membranes of IMCD cells or *Xenopus* oocytes.

The rat homolog of AQP2 also contains a consensus sequence for phosphorylation by PKC at Ser-226 within its C-terminal region (38). It was initially believed that human AQP2 contained no potential PKC phosphorylation sites because a proline residue replaces Ser-226 in the human sequence (39). However, a recent reexamination of the human AQP2 protein reveals that a putative PKC site exists at Ser-231, which in the rat sequence is a glutamine residue (S Sasaki, personal communication). These new data raise the possibility that phosphorylation of AQP2 by PKC may represent a general mechanism of regulation, perhaps involving AQP2 trafficking. Further studies are needed to determine the relevance of these PKC sites to AQP2 function.

Characterization of IMCD AQP2 Apical Membrane Vesicles

A large body of data demonstrates that AQP2 is inserted and removed from the IMCD apical membrane after stimulation with AVP (Figure 3). Modulation of apical membrane P_f by shuttling of AQP2 vesicles is similar to other hormonally mediated membrane transport processes, including insulin-stimulated vesicle shuttling of GLUT4 in adipocytes (61). Present studies of AQP2 trafficking have been hampered by an inability to isolate AQP2 vesicles from the exocytic portion of the AQP2 shuttling pathway (Figure 1, *open circle*). However, data obtained from study of apical membrane endocytic endosomes (Figure 1, *hatched circle*) highly enriched for AQP2 have yielded insights into the basic mechanisms of AQP2 trafficking. This evidence suggests that IMCD cells and their constituent AQP2 vesicles possess many similarities to neurons and their resident synaptic vesicles. These data provide support for the hypothesis by Kelly (62) that epithelial basolateral and apical membranes are analogous to neuronal cell bodies and synaptic termini, respectively. Since movement of ions and water by epithelial cells likely preceeded development of a complex nervous system on an evolutionary basis, features present in renal epithelial cells may have provided the basis for development of synaptic vesicle transmission by neurons.

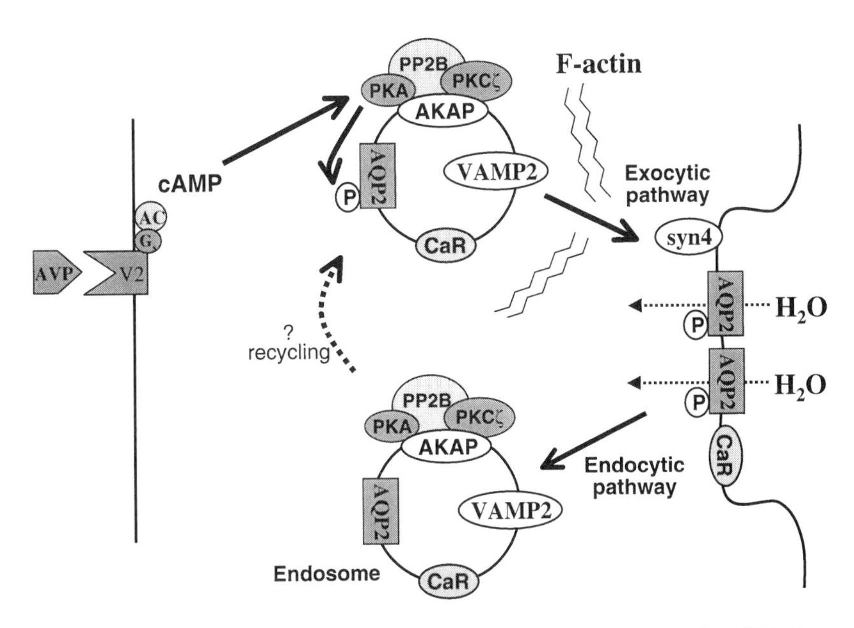

Figure 3 Diagramatic representation of proposed AQP2 trafficking in IMCD cells. AVP induces generation of cAMP after binding to the IMCD basolateral membrane and activates PKA. This action results in a series of events including AQP2 phosphorylation via bound PKA, localized reorganization of the subapical cytoskeleton, and insertion of AQP2-vesicles into the IMCD apical membrane. The targeting of AQP2-containing vesicles to the apical membrane may involve the association of VAMP2 with a membrane-bound syntaxin-4 (syn-4). Studies using purified AQP2 endosomes have identified multiple constituent proteins that have been demonstrated to be signaling complexes in other cell types. One complex consists of an A kinase-anchoring protein (AKAP) that binds PKA, PKC ζ and the protein phosphatase calcineurin (PP2B). This complex may participate in local cycles of phosphorylation and dephosphorylation of AQP2. AQP2 endosomes also possess a calcium/polyvalent cation receptor protein or CaR that is capable of sensing both luminal and intravesicular concentrations of Ca^{2+}. Pathways for the potential recycling of AQP2 endosomes have not yet been identified. AQP2 vesicles also contain the microtubule-associated motor protein dynein (87) (not shown), which could transport the vesicles to the apical membrane.

Data from intact (14) and purified AQP2 vesicle preparations (15) suggest that AQP2 is retrieved from the apical membrane into a specialized endocytic compartment that lacks a full complement of vacuolar proton ATPase components and thus cannot acidify its luminal contents. In addition to the AQP2 present in the membranes of these endosomes, multiple functional signaling proteins are present that may interact with various cellular components to modulate AQP2 trafficking in IMCD cells.

Purified IMCD AQP2 endosomes contain endogenous PKA and phosphatase activities capable of phosphorylation and dephosphorylation of resident AQP2 (59). Recent studies (63) reveal that binding of PKA to AQP2 vesicles occurs via a multiprotein complex consisting of an A kinase anchoring protein (AKAP), type II PKA regulatory subunit (RII), protein kinase C ζ (PKC ζ), and protein phosphatase 2B or calcineurin (PP2B). A similar complex has been characterized from hippocampal neurons, where it is postulated to provide molecular specificity for cycles of PKA-mediated phosphorylation and dephosphorylation of membrane protein components including ion channels (64, 65). Further experiments will be necessary to determine if the AKAP complex in AQP2 vesicles of IMCD cells contributes to the insertion and retrieval of AQP2 from the apical membrane by similar repeated cycles of PKA-mediated phosphorylation and dephosphorylation of AQP2 Ser-256. At present, the role of bound PKC ζ is unclear, but it may participate in inhibition of the AVP-elicited increase in P_f, (see 1) perhaps via phosphorylation of AQP2 within its C-terminal domain as described above.

Studies in both AVP-responsive toad bladder epithelia (66) as well as rat IMCD (67) suggest the presence of a subapical filamentous actin (F-actin) network immediately adjacent to the apical membrane. It has been postulated that this F-actin network acts as a barrier to the movement of AQP2 vesicles and prevents their constitutive fusion with the apical membrane (67). Accordingly, AVP induces F-actin depolymerization, suggesting that dissociation of this subapical cytoskeleton is required to permit vesicle trafficking to the membrane. Present data suggest that movement of AQP2 vesicles to the apical membrane also involves microtubules, particularly during the initial phases of AVP stimulation (61). Vesicles isolated with anti-AQP2 antisera contain myosin-1, which has been demonstrated to associate with microtubules (68). The specific roles of each of these proteins await further study.

Purified AQP2 endosomes also contain a calcium/polyvalent cation-sensing protein (CaR) (69) similar to that identified in both parathyroid gland and kidney renal thick ascending limb (TAL) (70). CaRs have been shown to sense the extracellular concentration of divalent cations, including Ca^{2+} or Mg^{2+}, and activate various signal transduction pathways in multiple cell types (70). Although little significant transepithelial transport of Ca^{2+} or Mg^{2+} occurs in IMCD (3), the luminal concentrations of these divalent cations undergo significant alterations as a result of AVP-elicited water reabsorption such that elevated IMCD luminal Ca^{2+} concentrations occurring during intervals of either antidiuresis or chronic hypercalcemia likely contribute to the formation of Ca^{2+}-containing renal stones. Studies in isolated perfused rat IMCD show that apical membrane exposure to CaR agonists rapidly reduces AVP-elicited P_f without alteration in P_{urea} (69). Thus this apical membrane CaR may provide a mechanism for the modulation of AVP-elicited water transport in IMCD, perhaps by altering AQP2 vesicle apical membrane retrieval. The presence of this apical CaR permits the IMCD cell to continuously integrate AVP water transport with alterations in luminal Ca^{2+}.

The fusion of synaptic vesicles with the presynaptic membrane in neurons is promoted and specifically regulated by a series of vesicle-targeting proteins collectively known as SNAREs [soluble NSF-attachment protein (SNAP) receptors], that include VAMPs (vesicle-associated membrane proteins or synaptobrevins) and syntaxins (71, 72). It has been postulated that isoform-specific interactions between a vesicle-associated VAMP and a membrane-associated syntaxin confer the specificity necessary to permit synaptic vesicles to fuse selectively with presynaptic membrane (73). The association of VAMP, syntaxin, and a third protein called SNAP-25 (synaptosome-associated protein of 25 kDa) is termed a SNARE complex, which is highly conserved in evolution. SNARE components including VAMP1 (synaptobrevin a) are reported to be present in mammalian neurons (74) and in various tissues of *Drosophila* (75) and the marine ray *Torpedo* (76). Similarly, other SNARE proteins have also been found in nonneuronal tissues such as pancreatic endocrine cells (77). Two other proteins are known to interact with the SNARE complex: NSF (for N-ethylmaleimide-sensitive factor), which possesses intrinsic ATPase activity, and a-SNAP (for a-soluble NSF-attachment protein). Vesicle fusion is dependent on both the formation of an a-SNAP:NSF:SNARE complex and NSF-mediated hydrolysis of ATP (78). The exact chronology of the events that precede bilayer fusion remains under active investigation (71).

AQP2-containing endosomes have been demonstrated to contain a synaptobrevin isoform called VAMP-2 and to possess the ability to fuse with each other in vitro after exposure to cytosolic soluble fusion proteins, as described above (79, 80). Localization of syntaxin-4 in the apical membrane of IMCD (81), together with the observation that VAMP-2 binds syntaxin-4 (and syntaxin-1) with high affinity (82), suggests that these vesicle-targeting proteins are components of a specific vesicle targeting system that permits selective trafficking of AQP2 vesicles to IMCD apical membrane (Figure 3). Interestingly, various syntaxin isoforms have been localized to distinct membrane compartments within MDCK cells (83). However, present lack of the ability to purify AQP2 vesicles prior to their fusion with the apical membrane has limited these investigations because AQP2 endosomes retrieved from the apical membrane may contain both vesicle and apical membrane SNARE components. A kidney equivalent to neuronal SNAP25, termed SNAP23, has also recently been reported in rat IMCD cells (84). The function of renal SNAP23 is currently unclear, although it is known that neuronal SNAP25 increases the affinity of VAMP-2 for syntaxins 1 and 4 (82).

FUTURE STUDIES

The data summarized above show that recent research focused on AVP-elicited water transport in CD has provided many new insights into the molecular regulation of AQP2 water channel trafficking and expression. The combination of molecular cloning and expression studies, together with experiments utilizing both intact IMCD as well as subcellular fractions derived from its constituent epithelial cells, have begun to address how the IMCD cell specifically targets various AQP water channel proteins and other transporters involved in the AVP water permeability response. Future studies focused on the molecular cloning and expression of new IMCD proteins identified from biochemical studies, improvements in the cell culture of AVP-responsive CD cells, and isolation of newly processed AQP2 vesicles that have not fused previously with the IMCD apical membrane promise to provide more information regarding mechanisms of AQP2 trafficking in IMCD.

Literature Cited

1. Breyer M, Ando Y. 1989. Hormonal signaling and regulation of salt and water transport in the collecting duct. *Annu. Rev. Physiol.* 56:711–39
2. Verkman A. 1989. Mechanisms and regulation of water permeability in renal epithelia. *Am. J. Physiol.* 257:C837–50
3. Harris HW Jr, Zeidel ML. 1996. Cell biology of vasopressin. In *The Kidney*, ed. BM Brenner, 12:516–31. Philadelphia: Saunders. 5th ed.
4. Flamion B, Spring KS. 1990. Water permeability of apical and basolateral membrane of rat inner medullary collecting duct. *Am. J. Physiol.* 259:F986–99
5. Duchatelle P, Ohara A, Ling B, Kemendy A, Kokko K, et al. 1992. Regulation of renal epithelial sodium channels. *Mol. Cell. Biochem.* 114:27–34
6. Star R. 1990. Apical membrane limits urea permeation across the rat inner medullary collecting duct. *J. Clin. Invest.* 86:1172–78
7. Wall SM, Han JK, Chou C-L, Knepper MA. 1992. Kinetics of urea and water permeability activation by vasopressin in rat terminal IMCD. *Am. J. Physiol.* 262:F989–98
8. Morgan T, Berliner RW. 1968. Permeability of the loop of Henle, vasa recta and collecting duct to water, urea and sodium. *Am. J. Physiol.* 215:108–15
9. Sands J, Nonoguchi H, Knepper M. 1987. Vasopressin effects on urea and water transport in inner medullary collecting duct subsegments. *Am. J. Physiol.* 253:F823–32
10. Ashkar Z, Martial S, Isozaki T, Price SR, Sands JM. 1995. Urea transport in initial IMCD of rats fed a low-protein diet: functional properties and mRNA abundance. *Am. J. Physiol.* 268:F1218–23
11. Nielsen S, Muller J, Knepper MA. 1993. Vasopressin and cAMP induced changes in ultrastructure of isolated perfused inner medullary collecting ducts. *Am. J. Physiol.* 265:F225–38
12. Nielsen S, DiGiovanni SR, Christensen EI, Knepper MA, Harris HW. 1993. Cellular and subcellular immunolocalization of vasopressin-regulated water channel in rat kidney. *Proc. Natl. Acad. Sci. USA* 90: 11663–67
13. Marples D, Knepper MA, Christensen E, Nielsen S. 1995. Redistribution of aquaporin 2 water channels induced by vasopressin in rat kidney inner medullary collecting duct. *Am. J. Physiol.* 269:C655–64
14. Lencer WI, Verkman AS, Arnout MA, Ausiello DA, Brown D. 1990. Endocytic vesicles from renal papilla which retrieve the vasopressin-sensitive water channel do not contain a functional H^+ ATPase. *J. Cell Biol.* 111:379–89
15. Harris HW, Zeidel ML, Jo I, Hammond TG. 1994. Characterization of purified endosomes containing the antidiuretic hormone sensitive water channel from rat renal papilla. *J. Biol. Chem.* 269:11993–12000
16. Harris H, Wade JB, Handler JS. 1986. Transepithelial water flow regulates apical membrane retrieval in antidiuretic hormone-stimulated toad urinary bladder. *J. Clin. Invest.* 78:703–12
17. Wade JB, Stetson DL, Lewis SA. 1981.

ADH action: evidence for a membrane shuttle mechanism. *Ann. NY Acad. Sci.* 372:106–17
18. Ishibashi K, Sasaki S, Fushimi K, Uchida S, Kuwahara M, Saito H, et al. 1994. Molecular cloning and expression of a member of the aquaporin family with permeability to glycerol and urea in addition to water expressed at the basolateral membrane of kidney collecting duct cells. *Proc. Natl. Acad. Sci. USA* 91:6269–73
19. Echevarria M, Windhager E, Tate S, Frindt G. 1994. Cloning and expression of AQP-3, a water channel from the medullary collecting duct of rat kidney. *Proc. Natl. Acad. Sci. USA* 91:10997–1001
20. Hasegawa H, Ma T, Scatch W, Matthay MA, Verkman AS. 1994. Molecular cloning of a mercurial-insensitive water channel expressed in selected water-transporting tissues. *J. Biol. Chem.* 269:5497–500
21. Frigeri A, Gropper MA, Turck CW, Verkman AS. 1995. Immunolocalization of the mercurial-insensitive water channel and glycerol intrinsic protein in epithelial cell plasma membranes. *Proc. Natl. Acad. Sci. USA* 92:4328–31
22. Ma T, Yang B, Gillespie A, Carlson EJ, Epstein CJ, Verkman AS. 1997. Generation and phenotype of a transgenic knockout mouse lacking the mercurial-insensitive water channel aquaporin-4. *J. Clin. Invest.* 100:957–62
23. Hayashi, M, Sasaki S, Tsuganezawa H, Monkawa T, Kitajima W, Konishi I, et al. 1994. Expression and distribution of aquaporin of collecting duct are regulated by vasopressin V2 receptor in rat kidney. *J. Clin. Invest.* 94:1778–83
24. DiGiovanni S, Nielsen S, Christensen E, Knepper MA. 1994. Regulation of collecting duct water channel expression by vasopressin in Brattleboro rat. *Proc. Natl. Acad. Sci. USA* 91:8984–88
25. Eklof A, Yasui M, Belusa R, Nielsen S, Marples D, Aperia A. 1996. Development of urinary concentrating capacity: role of aquaporin 2. *Am. J. Physiol.* 271:F234–39
26. Nielsen S, Terris J, Andersen D, Ecelbarger C, Frokiaer J, et al. 1997. Congestive heart failure in rats is associated with increased expression and targeting of aquaporin-2 water channel in collecting duct. *Proc. Natl. Acad. Sci. USA* 94:5450–55
27. Xu DL, Martin PY, Ohara M, St. John J, Pattison T, et al. 1997. Upregulation of aquaporin-2 water channel expression in chronic heart failure rat. *J. Clin. Invest.* 99:1500–5
28. Lankford SP, Chou C, Terada Y, Wall SM, Wade JB, Knepper MA. 1993. Regulation of collecting duct water permeability independent of cAMP-mediated AVP response. *Am. J. Physiol.* 261:F554–66
29. Sands JM, Naruse M, Jacobs JD, Wilcox JN, Klein JD. 1996. Changes in aquaporin 2 protein contribute to the urine concentrating defect in rats fed a low-protein diet. *J. Clin. Invest.* 97:2807–14
30. Marples D, Christensen S, Christensen E, Ottosen P, Nielsen S. 1995. Lithium induced downregulation of aquaporin 2 water channel expression in rat kidney medulla. *J. Clin. Invest.* 95:1838–45
31. Marples D, Frokiaer J, Dorup J, Knepper M, Nielsen S. 1996. Hypokalemia-induced downregulation of aquaporin 2 water channel expression in rat kidney medulla and cortex. *J. Clin. Invest.* 97:1960–68
32. Frokiaer J, Marples D, Knepper MA, Nielsen S. 1996. Bilateral ureteral obstruction downregulates expression of the vasopressin-sensitive aquaporin-2 water channel in rat kidney. *Am. J. Physiol.* 270: F657–68
33. Uchida S, Sasaki S, Fushimi K, Marumo F. 1994. Isolation of human aquaporin-CD gene. *J. Biol. Chem.* 269:23451–55
34. Knepper MA. 1994. The aquaporin family of molecular water channels. *Proc. Natl. Acad. Sci. USA* 91:6255–58
35. Chrispeels MJ, Agre P. 1994. Aquaporins: water channel proteins of plant and animal cells. *Trends Biochem. Sci.* 19:421–25
36. Agre P, Bonhivers M, Borgnia MJ. 1998. The aquaporins, blueprints for cellular plumbing systems. *J. Biol. Chem.* 273: 14659–62
37. Bai L, Fushimi K, Sasaki S, Marumo F. 1996. Structure of aquaporin-2 vasopressin water channel. *J. Biol. Chem.* 271:5171–76
38. Fushimi K, Uchida S, Hara Y, Hirata Y, Marumo F, Sasaki S. 1993. Cloning and expression of apical membrane water channel of rat kidney collecting tubule. *Nature* 361:549–52
39. Sasaki S, Fushimi K, Saito H, Saito F, Uchida S, et al. 1994. Cloning, characterization and chromosomal mapping of human aquaporin of collecting duct. *J. Clin. Invest.* 93:1250–56
40. Baumgarten R, Wetzels JFM, Van Os CH, Deen PMT. 1997. Glycosylation of aquaporin-2 is not essential for routing and functioning in mammalian cells. *J. Am. Soc. Nephrol.* 8:A71 (Abstr.)
41. Ruddy MK, Drazen JM, Pitakanen OM, Raffi M, O'Brodovich HM, Harris HW. 1998. Epithelial cells in perinatal rat lung coordinately express the AQP-4 water

channel and components of the amiloride-sensitive Na^+ channel. *Am. J. Physiol.* 274: L1066–72
42. Canessa CM, Schild L, Buell G, Thorens B, Gautschi B. 1994. Amiloride-sensitive epithelial Na^+ channel is made of three homologous subunits. *Nature* 367:463–67
43. Xiao-Jiang L, Ruo-Hui X, Guggino WB, Snyder SH. 1995. Alternatively spliced forms of the α subunit of the epithelial sodium channel: distinct sites for amiloride binding and channel pore. *Am. J. Pharm. Exp. Therap.* 47:1133–40
44. Sands JM, Timmer RT, Gunn RB. 1997. Urea transporters in kidney and erythrocytes. *Am. J. Physiol.* 273:F321–39
45. Rotin D, Bar-Sagi D, O'Brodovich H, Merilainen J, Lehto VP, et al. 1994. An SH3 binding region in the epithelial Na^+ channel (αrENaC) mediates its localization at the apical membrane. *EMBO J.* 13:4440–50
46. Staub O, Dho S, Henry PC, Correa J, Ishikawa T, et al. 1996. WW domains of Nedd4 bind to the proline-rich PY motifs in the epithelial Na^+ channel deleted in Liddle's syndrome. *EMBO J.* 15:2371–80
47. Klein JD, Rouillard P, Kato A, Sands JM. 1997. The vasopressin-regulated urea transporter is phosphorylated in rat inner medulla. *J. Am. Soc. Nephrol.* 8:A94 (Abstr.)
48. Deen PMT, Verdijk MAJ, Knoers NVAM, Wieringa B, Monnens LAH, et al. 1994. Requirement of human renal water channel aquaporin-2 for vasopressin-dependent concentration of urine. *Science* 264:92–95
49. Deen PMT, Croes H, van Aubel RAMH, Ginsel LA, van Os CH. 1995. Water channels encoded by mutant aquaporin-2 genes in nephrogenic diabetes insipidus are impaired in their cellular routing. *J. Clin. Invest.* 95:2291–96
50. Tamarappoo BK, Verkman AS. 1998. Defective aquaporin-2 trafficking in nephrogenic diabetes insipidus and correction by chemical chaperones. *J. Clin. Invest.* 101: 2257–67
51. Mulders SM, Bichet DG, Rijss JPL, Kamsteeg E-J, Arthus M-F, et al. 1998. An aquaporin-2 water channel mutant which causes autosomal dominant nephrogenic diabetes insipidus is retained in the Golgi complex. *J. Clin. Invest.* 102:57–66
52. Morris AP, Cunningham SA, Tousson A, Benos DJ, Frizzell RA. 1994. Polarization-dependent apical membrane CFTR targeting underlies cAMP-stimulated Cl^- secretion in epithelial cells. *Am. J. Physiol.* 263:C254–68
53. Howard MB, Frizzell RA, Bedwell D. 1996. Aminoglycoside antibiotics restore CFTR function by suppressing CFTR stop mutations. *Nature Med.* 2:467–69
54. Toriano R, Ford P, Rivarola V, Tamarappoo BK, Verkman AS, Parisi M. 1998. Reconstitution of a regulated transepithelial water pathway in cells transfected with AQP2 and an AQP1/AQP2 hybrid containing the AQP2-C terminus. *J. Membr. Biol.* 161:141–49
55. Katsura T, Gustafson CE, Ausiello DA, Brown D. 1997. Protein kinase A phosphorylation is involved in regulated exocytosis of aquaporin-2 in transfected LLC-PK1 cells. *Am. J. Physiol.* 272:F817–22
56. Gustafson CE, Levine S, Deize AM, Brown D. 1997. Trafficking of aquaporin 2/green fluorescent protein chimeras in $LLC\text{-}PK_1$ cells. *J. Am. Soc. Nephrol.* 8:A83 (Abstr.)
57. Katsura T, Verbavatz J-M, Farinas J, Ma T, Ausiello DA, et al. 1995. Constitutive and regulated membrane expression of aquaporin 1 and aquaporin 2 water channels in stably transfected LLC-PK1 epithelial cells. *Proc. Natl. Acad. Sci.* 92:7212–16
58. Valenti G, Frigeri A, Ronco PM, Dí Ettorre C, Svelto M. 1996. Expression and functional analysis of water channels in a stably AQP2-transfected human collecting duct cell line. *J. Biol. Chem.* 271:24365–70. Eratum: 1997. *J. Biol. Chem.* 272:25694
59. Lande MB, Jo I, Zeidel ML, Somers M, Harris HW. 1996. Phosphorylation of aquaporin-2 does not alter the membrane permeability of rat papillary water channel-containing vesicles. *J. Biol. Chem.* 271: 5552–57
60. Kurahara M, Fushimi K, Terada Y, Bai L, Marumo F, Sasaki S. 1995. cAMP-dependent phosphorylation stimulates water permeability of aquaporin-collecting duct water channel protein expressed in *Xenopus* oocytes. *J. Biol. Chem.* 270: 10384–87
61. Bradbury N, Bridges R. 1994. Role of membrane trafficking in plasma membrane solute transport. *Am. J. Physiol.* 267:C1–24
62. Kelly RB. 1993. A question of endosomes. *Science* 364:487–88
63. Jo I, Baum M, Scott JD, Coghlan VM, Harris HW. 1997. Aquaporin 2 containing apical membrane endosomes possess a multiprotein signalling complex similar to that present in brain neurons. *J. Am. Soc. Nephrol.* 8:A87 (Abstr.)
64. Rosenmund C, Carr D, Bergeson S, Nilaver G, Scott J, Westbrook G. 1994. Anchoring of protein kinase A is required for modu-

lation of AMPA/kainate receptors on hippocampal neurons. *Nature* 368:853–56
65. Dell'Acqua ML, Scott JD. 1997. Protein kinase A anchoring proteins. *J. Biol. Chem.* 272:12881–84
66. Ding G, Franki N, Condeelis J, Hays RM. 1991. Vasopressin depolymerizes F-actin in toad bladder epithelial cells. *Am. J. Physiol.* 260:C9–16
67. Simon H, Gao Y, Franki N, Hays RM. 1993. Vasopressin (AVP) depolymerizes apical actin in rat inner medullary collecting duct (IMCD). *Am. J. Physiol.* 265:C757–62
68. Marples D, Smith J, Nielsen S. 1997. Myosin-1 is associated with AQP2 water channel bearing vesicles in rat kidney and may be involved in the antidiuretic response to vasopressin. *J. Am. Soc. Nephrol.* 8:A300 (Abstr.)
69. Sands JM, Naruse M, Baum M, Jo I, Hebert SC, et al. 1997. An extracellular calcium/polyvalent cation-sensing receptor (CaR) localized to endosomes containing aquaporin 2 water channels modulates vasopressin-elicited water permeability in rat kidney inner medullary collecting duct. *J. Clin. Invest.* 99:1399–1405
70. Brown E, Pollack M, Seidman C, Seidman J, Chou Y-H, et al. 1995. Calcium ion sensing cell surface receptors. *New Engl. J. Med.* 333:234–40
71. Hay JC, Scheller RH. 1997. SNAREs and NSF in targeted membrane fusion. *Curr. Opin. Cell Biol.* 9:505–12
72. Linial M. 1997. SNARE proteins: Why so many, why so few? *J. Neurochem.* 69: 1781–92
73. Sollner T, Whiteheart SW, Brunner M, Erdjument-Bromage H, Geromanos S, et al. 1993. SNAP receptors implicated in vesicle targeting and fusion. *Nature* 362: 318–24
74. Elferink LA, Trimble WS, Scheller RH. 1989. Two vesicle-associated membrane protein genes are differentially expressed in the rat central nervous system. *J. Biol. Chem.* 264:11061–64
75. Südhof TC, Baumert M, Perin MT, Jahn R. 1989. A synaptic vesicle membrane protein is conserved from mammals to *Drosophila*. *Neuron.* 2:1475–81
76. Trimble WS, Cowan DM, Scheller RH. 1988. VAMP-1: a synaptic vesicle-associated integral membrane protein. *Proc. Natl. Acad. Sci. USA* 85:4538–42
77. Jacobsson G, Bean AJ, Scheller RH, Juntti-Berggren L, Deeney JT, et al. 1994. Identification of synaptic proteins and their isoform mRNAs in compartments of pancreatic endocrine cells. *Proc. Natl. Acad. Sci. USA* 91:12487–91
78. Whiteheart SW, Rossnagel K, Buhrow SA, Brunner M, Jaenicke R, Rothman JE. 1994. N-ethylmaleimide-sensitive fusion protein: a trimeric ATPase whose hydrolysis of ATP is required for membrane fusion. *J. Cell Biol.* 126:945–54
79. Franki N, Macaluso F, Schubert W, Gunther L, Hays R. 1995. Water channel-carrying vesicles in rat IMCD contain cellubrevin. *Am. J. Physiol.* 269:C797–801
80. Harris HW, Jo I, Amendt-Raduege AM, Majewski RR, Hammond TG. 1995. Rat kidney papilla contains abundant synaptobrevin protein that participates in the fusion of antidiuretic hormone-regulated water channel-containing endosomes in vitro. *Proc. Natl. Acad. Sci. USA.* 92:1876–80
81. Mandon B, Chou C-C, Nielsen S, Knepper MA. 1996. Syntaxin-4 is localized to the apical plasma membrane of rat renal collecting duct cells: possible role in aquaporin-2 trafficking. *J. Clin. Invest.* 98: 906–13
82. Pevsner J, Hsu S-C, Braun JEA, Calakos N, Ting AE, et al. 1994. Specificity and regulation of a synaptic vesicle docking complex. *Neuron* 13:353–61
83. Low S-H, Chaplin SJ, Weimbs T, Komuves LG, Bennett MK, Mostov KE. 1996. Differential localization of syntaxin isoforms in polarized Madin-Darby canine kidney cells. *Mol. Biol. Cell* 7:2007–18
84. Inoue T, Mandon B, Nielsen S, Knepper MA. 1997. Expression of SNAP23, the "missing snare," in rat collecting duct principal cells. *J. Am. Soc. Nephrol.* 8: A296 (Abstr.)
85. Bai L, Fushimi K, Sasaki S, Marumo F. 1996. Structure of aquaporin-2 vasopressin water channel. *J. Biol. Chem.* 271:5171–76
86. Jung JS, Preston GM, Smith BL, Guggino WB, Agre P. 1994. Molecular structure of the water channel through aquaporin CHIP. The hourglass model. *J. Biol. Chem.* 269:14648–54
87. Marples D, Schroer TA, Ahrens N, Taylor A, Knepper MA, Nielsen S. 1998. Dynein and actin colocalize with AQP2 water channels in intracellular vesicles from kidney collecting duct. *Am. J. Physiol.* 274: F384–94

Annu. Rev. Physiol. 1999. 61:699–723

ELECTROGENIC Na^+/HCO_3^- COTRANSPORTERS: Cloning and Physiology

Michael F. Romero
Department of Physiology and Biophysics and Pharmacology, Case Western Reserve University School of Medicine, Cleveland, Ohio 44106-4790; e-mail: mfr2@po.cwru.edu

Walter F. Boron
Department of Cellular and Molecular Physiology, Yale University School of Medicine, New Haven, Connecticut 06520; e-mail: walter.boron@yale.edu

KEY WORDS: homology cloning, *Xenopus* oocyte expression, intracellular pH, Na^+ transport, HCO_3^- transport, rat

ABSTRACT

Bicarbonate and CO_2 comprise the major pH buffer of biological fluids. In the renal proximal tubule most of the filtered HCO_3^- is reabsorbed by an electrogenic Na/HCO_3 cotransporter located at the basolateral membrane. This Na^+ bicarbonate cotransporter (NBC) was recently cloned. This review highlights the recent developments leading to and since the cloning of NBC: NBC expression cloning, protein features, clone physiology, isoforms and genes, mRNA distribution, and protein distribution. With the NBC amino acid sequence 30–35% identical to the anion exchangers (AE1-3), a superfamily of HCO_3^- transporters is emerging. Physiologically, NBC is electrogenic, Na^+ dependent, HCO_3^- dependent, Cl^- independent, and inhibited by stilbenes (DIDS and SITS). NBC clones and proteins have been isolated from several tissues (other than kidney) thought to have physiologically distinct HCO_3^- transporters. For example, NBC occurs in pancreas, prostate, brain, heart, small and large intestine, stomach, and epididymis. Finally, there are at least two genes that encode NBC proteins. Possible future directions of research are discussed.

0066-4278/99/0315-0699$08.00

INTRODUCTION

Bicarbonate, along with CO_2, is the major pH buffer of biological fluids. And HCO_3^- is a special ion in that it coexists with CO_2 gas in solution. The reaction

$$CO_2 + H_2O \leftrightarrow H_2CO_3 \leftrightarrow H^+ + HCO_3^-$$

is well known to every chemistry and biology student. This reaction is readily reversible. In biological systems, the interconversion of CO_2 to HCO_3^- is greatly potentiated by the family of carbonic anhydrase enzymes (1, 2).

Certain organ systems have evolved to be particularly good at HCO_3^- transport. The pancreatic ducts move CO_2 and HCO_3^- from the blood into pancreatic secretions. Humans can secrete a pancreatic fluid that is virtually isotonic $NaHCO_3$ (i.e. roughly 130 mM) and has a pH of about 8.1. Similar, although not as extreme, HCO_3^- secretions seem to occur in several other exocrine organs, such as salivary glands and the prostate. The kidneys reabsorb massive amounts of HCO_3^- daily. In humans, the glomeruli filter ~180 liters of blood plasma each day containing more than 4 mol of $NaHCO_3$—or roughly the amount contained in a pound of baking soda. To prevent the development of a massive metabolic acidosis, the epithelial cells in the remainder of the nephron subsequently reabsorb virtually all of this $NaHCO_3$. The proximal tubule (PT) isotonically reabsorbs the bulk of the filtered HCO_3^-, about 80%–90%, as well as most of the filtered Na^+, Cl^-, and H_2O.

How does the PT reabsorb the $NaHCO_3$? Luminal Na^+ enters the PT cell via an array of Na^+-coupled transport systems (e.g. Na-H exchanger, Na/glucose cotransporter) and perhaps Na^+ channels as well. The PT cell then extrudes Na^+ across the basolateral membrane via basolateral Na-K pumps, maintaining a low intracellular $[Na^+]$. H^+ secreted into the lumen by Na-H exchangers and H^+ pumps titrates the filtered HCO_3^- in the lumen, forming CO_2 in a reaction-facilitated carbonic anhydrase IV tethered to the luminal membrane via a GPI linkage. CO_2 and H_2O then rapidly enter the PT cell, where soluble carbonic anhydrase II—in effect—regenerates H^+ and HCO_3^-. For early segments of the PT, the vast majority of the intracellular HCO_3^- moves across the basolateral membrane into the blood via the electrogenic Na/HCO_3 cotransporter (3).

CLONING OF THE ELECTROGENIC NA^+/HCO_3^- COTRANSPORTER: NBC

The Physiological Family of HCO_3^- Transporters

Bicarbonate transporters are often the major pH regulators in animal cells and play vital roles in acid-based movement in a number of epithelia, including those in the stomach, pancreas, intestine, kidney, reproductive system, and central nervous system. The functional family of HCO_3^- transporters includes Cl-HCO_3 exchangers, Na/HCO_3 cotransporters with as many as three different stoichiometries (3–5), a K/HCO_3 cotransporter (6, 7), and a Na^+-driven Cl-HCO_3 exchanger (8, 9). Yet until 1997, there had been no molecular information on any HCO_3^- transporter except for the Cl-HCO_3 exchangers [anion exchangers (AEs)], whose cDNAs were cloned several years ago (10–13).

Several groups, including one of our laboratories, unsuccessfully used a number of approaches in attempts to purify the proteins or clone the cDNAs of Na^+-coupled HCO_3^- transporters. These approaches included binding of inhibitors, protein purification, and screening of cDNA libraries based on homology to the AEs.

The Expression Cloning Strategy

Encouraged by the success of others, who have expression cloned several membrane proteins using the oocytes of *Xenopus laevis* (for review see 14), we attempted to clone one of these HCO_3^- transporters, the renal electrogenic Na/HCO_3 cotransporter. This approach, although time consuming, allows functional evaluation of properties attributed to a single or functional group of proteins. Expression cloning has had a major impact on the cloning of integral membrane proteins because the technique relies on a functional property rather than requiring an antibody, cDNA probe, or some other insight to the putative protein's structure.

In cloning a HCO_3^- transporter, the ability to monitor multiple features of the transporter to make the correct molecular diagnosis is important. All HCO_3^- transporters produce a change in intracellular pH (pH_i) that can be followed easily by using microelectrodes. Moreover, with the exception of the K/HCO_3 cotransporter, members of the functional family outlined above are almost always blocked by stilbene derivatives such as DIDS (4,4′-diisothiocyano-2,2′-stilbene disulfonate). However, the Na/HCO_3 cotransporter activity is unique among HCO_3^- transporters in that, for most tissues described, the cotransport is electrogenic, moving net negative charge in the direction of Na^+ and HCO_3^- cotransport (see below for assay). It is easy to use microelectrodes to monitor the changes in membrane potential (V_m) or membrane current produced by such an electrogenic transporter. Because the activity of the electrogenic Na/HCO_3 cotransporter was first described in the kidney, and its electrophysiology there had been described in detail (3), we attempted cloning this cotransporter from renal tissue. Our general approach was to simultaneously monitor changes in pH_i and V_m and to devise an assay that would identify the cotransporter unambiguously, easily, and with great sensitivity.

The Diagnostic Assay for Electrogenic Na^+/HCO_3^- Cotransport

To test more precisely for electrogenic Na/HCO_3 cotransporter activity, we set several criteria that when simultaneously observed should be characteristic of the cotransporter. The expressed protein should be (*a*) electrogenic, (*b*) Na^+ dependent, (*c*) HCO_3^- dependent, and (*d*) blocked by stilbenes such as DIDS. Our basic assay was to monitor pH_i and V_m in *Xenopus* oocytes injected with renal poly(A)$^+$ RNA. Adding CO_2/HCO_3^- to the extracellular solution bathing an oocyte rapidly acidifies the cell because of the entry of CO_2 and the subsequent formation of HCO_3^- and H^+ inside the cell. In control oocytes, i.e. those injected either with nothing (native oocytes) or with H_2O instead of RNA, pH_i does not recover from the CO_2-induced acidification (15). Removing permeant ions such as Cl^- and Na^+ does not unmask any native HCO_3^- or other acid-base transporters (e.g. Na-H exchangers or H^+ pumps) (15, 16). It is interesting to note that the control *Xenopus* oocyte does have both a native Na-H exchanger and a native H^+ pump. However, both of these are silent unless the cell is osmotically shrunken (17–19). Although the pH_i of control oocytes does not recover from the initial CO_2-induced acidification, oocytes expressing NBC do exhibit a slow pH_i recovery (i.e. alkalinization).

Once the CO_2/HCO_3^- exposure has acidified the oocyte and pH_i has either stabilized or begun to recover, bath Na^+ is removed. The expectation is that in a CO_2/HCO_3^--buffered solution, Na^+ removal should cause the cotransporter to operate as it normally does in the proximal tubule. That is, Na^+ and HCO_3^- should exit the cell and thereby elicit a simultaneous depolarization (due to the exit of Na^+ and more than one HCO_3^-) and fall of pH_i (due to the exit of the HCO_3^-). This two-pronged signal should be reversible and blocked by stilbenes such as DIDS.

Initially, we injected *Xenopus* oocytes with poly(A)$^+$ RNA isolated from rabbit renal cortex, but the expected signal did not occur. Reasoning that an amphibian cell might express amphibian mRNA better than mammalian mRNA, we isolated and injected poly(A)$^+$ RNA from the kidney of a salamander *Ambystoma tigrinum*, the preparation from which the cotransporter was first described (3). The oocytes injected with salamander RNA expressed an activity that was robust and fit all our criteria. However, the activity became apparent no sooner than 6 days after injection of the mRNA (15).

Characteristics of the NBC cDNA and Protein

BASIC PHYSIOLOGICAL CHARACTERISTICS OF aNBC After developing the diagnostic assay, we size fractionated poly(A)$^+$ RNA from *Ambystoma* and constructed a directional cDNA library from the 3.5- to 5.0-kb fraction, which yielded a positive assay. Four rounds of functional screening of this library yielded a single clone, 9h5g, named the renal electrogenic **Na** **b**icarbonate **c**otransporter (NBC). Because several species forms of NBC have now been cloned, we refer to the *Ambystoma* clone as aNBC (GenBank #AF001958). When this aNBC protein is expressed in *Xenopus* oocytes, it has all the hallmarks of the electrogenic Na/HCO_3 cotransporter: It is electrogenic, produces the expected pH_i changes, is Na^+ dependent, is HCO_3^- dependent, and is blocked by DIDS (15). The electrogenicity can be observed either as a shift in V_m or a current (in voltage-clamped oocytes) that can be blocked by DIDS. The V_m or current change can be evoked either by changing $[HCO_3^-]_o$ or $[Na^+]_o$. As far as the Na^+ dependence is concerned, the removal of extracellular Na^+ halts the pH_i recovery in oocytes exposed to CO_2/HCO_3^- and instead produces a slow pH_i decrease. In addition, Na^+ removal elicits either a depolarization (i.e. Na moves as if it were an anion) or an inward current. Demonstrating the HCO_3^- dependence requires more effort. We applied a butyric acid/butyrate solution and acidified oocytes to the same extent as when applying a CO_2/HCO_3^- solution. In oocytes acidified with butyric acid, no activity was observed in either control or NBC-expressing oocytes. Only NBC-expressing oocytes acidified with CO_2/HCO_3^- showed NBC activity.

ANALYSIS OF THE DEDUCED AMINO-ACID SEQUENCE OF aNBC The aNBC cDNA encodes a protein of 1035 amino acids. Hydropathy analysis indicates that NBC should have at least ten membrane-spanning segments. Interestingly, NBC is 30%–35% identical at the protein level to the AE gene family; the homology is strongest to AE3 and AE2. Figure 1 shows a multiple sequence alignment of the cloned NBCs and the AEs. Deduced amino-acid sequences indicate that aNBC and the AEs share many areas of identity, both in the putative membrane-spanning segments and in the putative cytoplasmic regions, especially in the NH_2 terminus. The hydropathy plots of these proteins are virtually superimposable, which suggests that the folding of the NBC and the AE proteins are likely to be similar. Figure 2*A* illustrates that several basic features of the AEs are preserved in aNBC: (*a*) both the NH_2 and COOH termini are presumably intracellular; (*b*) there is a large, glycosylated, extracellular loop between the fifth and sixth transmembrane (TM) segments; and (*c*) lysine residues are conserved at predicted DIDS-reactive sites. Thus, NBC and the AEs appear to be the first two major families of HCO_3^- transporters (Figure 2*B*), likely forming a HCO_3^- transporter superfamily.

OTHER NBC-RELATED cDNAS Shortly after cloning aNBC, we also isolated and characterized NBC from rat kidney (rkNBC) (GenBank #AF004017). The rat clone is 86% identical to aNBC at the amino acid level (16, 20). Within

```
rkNBC MSTE-NVEGKPNNL-----------------GERGRARSST----FLRVFQPM-----------------FNH------------------------------------------   34
 aNBC MSSE-K--ECLENML------------NGYAESGRVLSRTSL----VIN---------------------------------------------------------------   30
hkNBC MSTE-NVEGKPSNL-----------------GERGRARSST----FLRVVQPM-----------------FNH------------------------------------------   34
hhNBC MEDE-AVLDRGASFL------------KHVCDEEEVEGHHTI----YIGVHVPKS-----------------YRRR---------------RRHKRKTGHKEKKEKERISENY   64
AE1   M----------------------------EELQ-----DDYEDMMEEN-------------LEQEEY-------------------------------------------   21
AE2   MSSAPRLPAKGADSFCTPEPESLGPGTPGFPEQEEDELHRTLGVERFEEILQEAGSRGGEEPGRSYGMEDFEYRRQSSHHIHHPLSTHLPPGARRRKTPQGPGRKPRRRPGASPT  115
AE3   MTSP-------------------------------------LDKVMEPNGALGPK------------------------------------PGDTEDRGPGRNPA   32

rkNBC ----------------------SIFTSAVSPAAERIRFILGEEDD--------SPAPP---------------------------------------------------------   62
 aNBC ---------Q---------AVNRSIFTSTVSPAAERIRFILGEEDD--------SPAPP---------------------------------------------------------   63
hkNBC ----------------------SIFTSAVSPAAERIRFILGEEDD--------SPAPP---------------------------------------------------------   62
hhNBC SDKSDIENAD---------ESSSSILKPLISPAAERIRFILGEEDD--------SPAPP---------------------------------------------------------  106
AE1   -EDPDIPESQMEEPAAHDTEATAT--------------------------------------------------------------------------------------------   44
AE2   GETPTIVEGEEDEDEASEAEGARALTQPSPVSTPSSVQFFLREDDSADRKAERTSPSSPAPLPHQEATPRASKGAQAGTQVEEAEAEAVAVASGTAGGDDGGASGRPLPKAQPGH  230
AE3   PGTGDLVASEDLE--------------------------MFVLDFED-----------------------------------------------------------------   53
                                             f l   d

rkNBC ---------------------------------------------------------------------------------------------QLFTELDELLAVD-GQEME   80
 aNBC ---------------------------------------------------------------------------------------------QLFTELDELLAVD-GQEME   81
hkNBC ---------------------------------------------------------------------------------------------QLFTELDELLAVD-GQEME   80
hhNBC ---------------------------------------------------------------------------------------------QLFTELDELLAVD-GQEME  124
AE1   -DY-------------------------------------------------HTTSHPG----------------THEVYVELQELVMDEKNQELR   74
AE2   RSYNLQERRRIGSMTGARQALLPRVPTDEIEAQTLATADLDLMKSHRFEDVPGVRRHLVRKNAKGSTQSGREGREPGPTP-----RARPRAPHKPHEVFVELNELLLD-KNQEPQ  339
AE3   --YGLWEPMR------GHPSPLAGVAA-----------------CHRLEDNPGVRRHLVKKPSR--IQGGR-GSPSGLAPILRRKKKKKLDRRPHEVFVELNELMLD-RSQEPH  139
                                                                                              265 EL EL6    QE

rkNBC WKETARWIKFEEKVEQGGERWSKPHVATLSLHSLFELRTCMEKGSIMLDREASSLPQLVEMIADHQIETGLLKPDLKDKVTYTLLRKHRHQTKKSNLR------SLADIGKTVSS  189
 aNBC WKETARWIKFEEKVEQGGERWSKPHVATLSLHSLFELRTCIEKGTILLDLEATSLPQIVEIVINNQIELGLLKADMKENVTRTLLRKHRHQTKKSNLR------SLADIGKTVSS  190
hkNBC WKETARWIKFEEKVEQGGERWSKPHVATLSLHSLFELRTCMEKGSIMLDREASSLPQLVEMIVDHQIETGLLKPELKDKVTYTLLRKHRHQTKKSNLR------SLADIGKTVSS  189
hhNBC WKETARWIKFEEKVEQGGERWSKPHVATLSLHSLFELRTCMEKGSIMLDREASSLPQLVEMIVDHQIETGLLKPELKDKVTYTLLRKHRHQTKKSNLR------SLADIGKTVSS  233
AE1   WMEAARWVQLEENLGENGA-WGRPHLSHLTFWSLLELRRVFTKGTVLLDLQETSLAGVANQLLDRFIFEDQIRPQDREELLRALLLKHSHAGE---------------LEALGGV  173
AE2   WRETARWIKFEEDVEEETERWGKPHVASLSFRSLLELRRTLAHGAVLLDLDQQTLPGVAHQVVEQMVISDQIKAEDRANVLRALLLKHSHPSDEKDFSF-PRNISAGSLGSLLGH  453
AE3   WRETARWIKFEEDVEEETERWGKPHVASLSFRSLLELRRTIAQGAALLDLEQTTLPGIAHLVVETMIVSDQIRPEDRASVLRTLLLKHSHPNDDKDSGFFPRNPSSSSVNSVLGN  254
      W EtARW6kfEE 6e2  erW 4PH6a L3  SL ELR    G  6LD    3Lp 6   6    6   64   4  6   LL KH H                 s  6

rkNBC ASRMFSNPDNGSPAMTHRNLT-------------SSSLNDISDKPEKDQLKN--KFMKKLPRDAEASNVLVGEVDFLDTPFIAFVRLQQAVMLGALTEVPVPTRFLFILLGPKGK  289
 aNBC ASRLFSTPDNGSPTMTHRNLT-------------STSLNDVSDKPDKEQLKN--KFMKKLPRDAEASNVLVGEVDFLESPFIAFVRLQQAVMLGSLTEVPVPTRFLFILLGPKGK  290
hkNBC ASRMFTNPDNGSPAMTHRNLT-------------SSSLNDISDKPEKDQLKN--KFMKKLPRDAEASNVLVGEVDFLDTPFIAFVRLQQAVMLGALTEVPVPTRFLFILLGPKGK  289
hhNBC ASRMFTNPDNGSPAMTHRNLT-------------SFSLNDISDKPEKDQLKN--KFMKKLPRDAEASNVLVGEVDFLDTPFIAFVRLQQAVMLGALTEVPVPTRFLFILLGPKGK  333
AE1   KPAVLTRSGDPSQPLLPQHSSLETQLFCEQGDG-GTEGHSPSG-----------ILEKIPPDSEATLVLVGRADFLEQPVLGFVRLQEAAELEAV-ELPVPIRFLFVLLGPEAP  274
AE2   HH---GQGAESDPHVTEPLMGGVPETRLEVERERDVPPPAPPAGITRSKSKHELKLLEKIPENAEATVVLVGCVEFLSRPTMAFVRLREAVELDAVLEVPVPVRFLFLLLGPSSA  565
AE3   HHPTPSHGPDGAVPTMADDLGEPAPLWPHDPDAKEKPLHMPGGDGHRGKS---LKLLEKIPEDAEATVVLVGSVPFLEQPAAAFVRLSEAVLLESVLEVPVPVRFLFVMLGPSHT  366
                                                          k 6 K6P 1aEA3 VLVG v FL  P  aFVRL 2Av L  6 E6PVP RFLF66LGP

rkNBC AKSYHEIGRAIATLMSDEVFHDIAYKAKDRHDLIAGIDEFLDEVIVLPPGEWDPAIRIEPPKSLPSSDKRKNMYSGGENVQMNGDTPHDGG------HGGGGHGDCEE--LQRTG  396
 aNBC AKSYHEIGRSIATLMSDEVFHDIAYKAKNREDLIAGIDEFLDEVIVLLGEWDPTIRIEPPKSLPSSDKRKNMYSGGDNLQMNGDAPHDDG--------GGGHGDSEE--LQRTG  395
hkNBC AKSYHEIGRAIATLMSDEVFHDIAYKAKDRHDLIAGIDEFLDEVIVLPPGEWDPAIRIEPPKSLPSSDKRKNMYSGGENVQMNGDTPHDGG------HGGGGHGDCEE--LQRTG  396
hhNBC AKSYHEIGRAIATLMSDEVFHDIAYKAKDRHDLIAGIDEFLDEVIVLPPGEWDPAIRIEPPKSLPSSDKRKNMYSGGENVQMNGDTPHDGG------HGGGGHGDCEE--LQRTG  440
AE1   HIDYTQLGRAAATLMSERVFRIDAYMAQSRGELLHSLEGFLDCSLVLPPTDAPSEQALLSLVPVQRELLRRRYQSSPAKPDSSFY-------KGLDLNGGPDD------PLQQTG  376
AE2   NMDYHEIGRSISTLMSDKQFHEAAYLADEREDLLTAINAFLDCSVVLPPSEVQGEELLRSVAHFQRQMLKKREEQGRLLPTGAGLEPKSAQDKAL-LQMVERQGQLKMIPSA-DG  678
AE3   STDYHELGRSIATLMSDKLFHEAAYQADDRQDLLGAISEFLDGSIVIPPSEVEGRDLLRSVAAFQRELLRKRREREQTKVEMTTRGGYVAPGKELSLEMGGSEATSEDDPLQRTG  481
         Yh26GR iaTLMSd  Fh  AY A  R dL6  6  FLD  6V6Pp e       6        44                     g                 lq tG
                                 ----------------1----------------          --------2--------  -------3-------
rkNBC RFCGGLIKDIKRKAPFFASDFYDALNIQALSAILFIYLATVTNAITFGGLLGDATDNMQGVLESFLGTAVSGAIFCLFAGQPLTILSSTGPVLVFERLLFNFSKDHSFDYLEFRL  511
 aNBC RFCGGLIKDIQRKAPFFASDFYDALSIQSLSAILFIYLGTVTNAITFGGLLGDATENMQGVLESFLGTAVSGAVFCLFGGQPLTILSSTGPVLVFERLLFNFSKDNDFDYLEFRL  510
hkNBC RFCGGLIKDIKRKAPFFASDFYDALNIQALSAILFIYLATVTNAITFGGLLGDATDNMQGVLESFLGTAVSGAIFCLFAGQPLTILSSTGPVLVFERLLFNFSKDNNFDYLEFRL  511
hhNBC RFCGGLIKDIKRKAPFFASDFYDALNIQALSAILFIYLATVTNAITFGGLLGDATDNMQGVLESFLGTAVSGAIFCLFAGQPLTILSSTGPVLVFERLLFNFSKDNNFDYLEFRL  555
AE1   QLFGGLVRDIRRRYPYYLSDITDAFSPQVLAAVIFIYFAALSPAITFGGLLGEKTRNQMGVSELLISTAVQGILFALLGAQPLLVVGFSGPLLVFEEAFFSFCETNGLEYIVGRV  491
AE2   AAFGGLIRDVRRRYPHYLSDFRDALDPQCLAAVIFIYFAALSPAITFGGLLGEKTQDLIGVSELLISTALQGVVFCLLGAQPLLVIGFSGPLLVFEEAFFSFCSSNHLEYLVGRV  793
AE3   SVFGGLVRDVKRRYPHYPSDLRDALHSQCVAAVLFIYFAALSPAITFGGLLGEKTEGLMGVSELIVSTAVLGVLFSLLGAQPLLVVGFSGPLLVFEEAFFKFCRAQDLEYLTGRV  596
         GGL64D6 R4 P 5 SD  DA1  Q 6 A66FIY a 63 AITFGGLLG  T    GV E  6 TA6 G 6F L  QPL 66  3GP6LVFE  F F        Y6 R6
      ------------4------------    -----------5-----------
rkNBC WIGLWSAFMCLILVATDASFLVQYFTRFTEEGFSSLISFIFIYDAFKKMIKLADYYPINSDFRVGYNTHFSCACLPPDPVNLS-VSNDTTLAPEDLPTVSSTDMYHNATFDWAYL  625
 aNBC WIGLWSAFQCLILVATDASFLVKYFTRFTEEGFSSLISFIFIYDAFKKMIKLADYYPINSHFKVDYITQYSCACFPPEPANSSWFNMTTAATTTQFLTNASTDMAYNGTIDWSLL  625
hkNBC WIGLWSAFLCLILVATDASFLVQYFTRFTEEGFSSLISFIFIYDAFKKMIKLADYYPINSNFKVGYNTLFSCTCVPPDPANIS-ISNDTTLAPEYLPTMSSTDMYHNTTFDWAFL  625
hhNBC WIGLWSAFLCLILVATDASFLVQYFTRFTEEGFSSLISFIFIYDAFKKMIKLADYYPINSNFKVGYNTLFSCTCVPPDPANIS-ISNDTTLAPEYLPTMSSTDMYHNTTFDWAFL  669
AE1   WIGFWLILLVVLVVAFEGSFLVRFISRYTQEIFSFLISLIFIYETFSKLIKIFQDHPLQKTYNYNVLMV-----------------------------------------------  560
AE2   WIGFWLVFLALLMVALEGSFLVRFVSRFTREIFAFLISLIFIYETFYKLVKIFQEHPLHGCSASNSSEV-------DGGENMTWAGARPTLGPG----------------NRSLA  885
AE3   WVGLWLVVFVLALVAAEGSFLVRYISPFTQEIFAFLISLIFIYETFHKLYKVFTEHPLLPFYPPEE-----------------------ALEPGLELN----------------SSALP  676
      W6G W     6 6VA    SFLV 5 3r5T E F  LIS IFIY   F K6 K6     P6
                                                                -------------6-------------                         ------
rkNBC SKKECVKFGGKLVGNNCDFVPDITLMSFILFLGTYTSSMAMKKFKTSRYFPTTARKLISDFAIILSILIFCVIDALVGVD-TPKLIVPSEFKPTSPH-RGWFVPPFGGN---PWW  735
 aNBC SKKECLKYGGLLVGSNCKYVPDITLMSFILFLGTYTCSMALKKFKTSRYFPTTARKLISDFAIILSILIFCGLDALLGVD-TPKLIVPSEFKPTSPN-RGWFVPPFGGN---PWW  735
hkNBC SKKECSKYGGNLVGNNCNFVPDITLMSFILFLGTYTSSMALKKFKTSPYFPTTARKLISDFAIILSILIFCVIDALVGVD-TPKLIVPSEFKPTSPN-RGWFVPPFGEN---PWW  735
hhNBC SKKECSKYGGNLVGNNCNFVPDITLMSFILFLGTYTSSMALKKFKTSPYFPTTARKLISDFAIILSILIFCVIDALVGVD-TPKLIVPSEFKPTSPN-RGWFVPPFGEN---PWW  779
AE1   -----PKPQGPL---------PNTALLSLVLMAGTFFFAMMLRKFKNSSYFPGKLRRVIGDFGVPISILIMVLVDFFIQDTYTQKLSVPDGFKVSNSSARGWVIHPLGLRSEFPIW  662
AE2   GQSGQGKPRGQ----------PNTAPLSLVLMAGTFFIAFFLRKFKNSRFFPGRIRRVIGDFGVPIAILIMVLVDYSIEDTYTQKLSVPSGFSVTAPEKRGWVINPLGEKSPFPVW  991
AE3   PTEGPPGPRNQ----------PNTALLSLILMLGTFLIAFFLRKFRNSRFLGGKARRVIGDFGIPISILVMVLVDYSITDTYTQKLTVPTGLSVTSPHKRTWFIPPLGSARPFPPW  782
          k  g             P1  16S 6L  GT5     64KF4 S 5fp  R46I DF 6  6sIL6  6D  6    T KL VP  f  3 p  RgW 6 P G     P W
      ---------7---------             -------------8-------------                            ------------9------------
rkNBC VCLAAAIPALLVTILIFMDQQITAVIVNRKEHKLKKGAGYHLDLFWVAILMVVCSFMALPWYVAATVISIAHIDSLKMETETSAPGEQPKFLGVREQRVTGTLVFILTGLSVFMA  850
 aNBC VYLAAAIPALLVTILIFMDQQITGVIVNRKEHKLKKGAGYHLDLFWVAILMVVCSFMALPWYVAATVISIAHIDSLKMETETSAPGEQPKFLGVREQRVTGTVVFLLTGLSVFMA  850
hkNBC VCLAAAIPALLVTILIFMDQQITAVIVNRKEHKLKKGAGYHLDLFWVAILMVICSLMALPWYVAATVISIAHIDSLKMETETSAPGEQPKFLGVREQRVTGTLVFILTGLSVFMA  850
hhNBC VCLAAAIPALLVTILIFMDQQITAVIVNRKEHKLKKGAGYHLDLFWVAILMVICSLMALPWYVAATVISIAHIDSLKMETETSAPGEQPKFLGVREQRVTGTLVFILTGLSVFMA  894
AE1   MMFASALPALLVFILIFLESQITTLIVSKPERKMVKGSGFHLDLLLVVGMGGVAALFGMPWLSATTVRSVTHANALTVMGKASTPGAAAQIQEVKEQRISGLLVAVLVGLSILME  777
AE2   MMVASLLPAILVFILIFMETQITTLIISKKERMLQKGSGFHLDLLLIVAMGGICALFGLPWLAAATVRSVTHANALTVMSKAVAPGDKPKIQEVKEQRVTGLLVALLVGLSIVIG 1106
AE3   MMVAAAVPALLVLILIFMETQITALIVSQKARRLLKGSGFHLDLLLIGSLGGLCGLFGLPWLTAATVRSVTHVNALTVMRTAIAPGDKPQIQEVREQRVTGVLIASLVGLSIVMG  897
      6  A a6PA6LV ILIF6  QIT 6I6  ke  6 KG G5HLDL   6  6  6c   6PW  AaTV S6 H 1 L 6     aPG  p   V4EQR63G 66  L GLS6 6
      -----------9-----------                   --------------10--------------
rkNBC PILKFIPMPVLYGVFLYMGVASLNGVQFMDRLKLLLMPLKHQPDFIYLRHVPLRRVHLFTSLQVLCLALLWILKSTVAAIIFPVMILALVAVRKGM-DYLFSQHDLSFLDDVIPE  964
 aNBC PILKFIPMPVLYGVFLYMGVASLNGVQFMDRLKLLLMPPRYQPDFIYLRHVPLRRVHLFTFLQVVCLAMLWILKSTVAAIIFPVMILALVAVRKAM-DYFFSQHDLSFLDDVIPE  964
hkNBC PILKFIPMPVLYGVFLYMGVASLNGVQFMDRLKLLLMPLKHQPDFIYLRHVPLRRVHLFTFLQVLCLALLWILKSTVAAIIFPVMILALVAVRKGM-DYLFSQHDLSFLDDVIPE  964
hhNBC PILKFIPMPVLYGVFLYMGVASLNGVQFMDRLKLLLMPLKHQPDFIYLRHVPLRRVHLFTFLQVLCLALLWILKSTVAAIIFPVMILALVAVRKGM-DYLFSQHDLSFLDDVIPE 1008
AE1   PILSRIPLAVLFGIFLYMGVTSLSGIQLFDRILLLFKPPKYHPDVPYVKRVKTWRMHLFTGIQIICLAVLWVVKSTPASLALPFVLILTVPLRRVLLPLIFRNVELQCLD-----  887
AE2   DLLRQIPLAVLFGIFLYMGVTSLNGIQFYERLHLLLMPPKHHPDVTYVKKVRTLRMHLFTALQLLCLALLWAVMSTAASLAFPFILILTVPLRMVVLTRIFTDREMKCLD----- 1216
AE3   AVLRRIPLAVLFGIFLYMGVTSLSGIQLSQRLLLIFMPAKHHPEQPYVTKVKTWRMHLFTFIQLGCIALLWVVKSTVASLAFPFLLLLTVPLRRCLLPRLFQDRELQALD----- 1007
       6L  IP6 VL5G6FLYMGV SL G6Q    R6 L6 mP K  Pd  Y6  V   R6HLFT 6Q6 C6A6LW 6kST A 6 fP 666  V 6R  6   F    6 LD

rkNBC KDKKKKEDEKKKKKKKGSLDSDNDDSDCPYSEKVPSIKIPMDITEQQPFLSDNKPLDRERSSTFLERHTSC 1035
 aNBC KDKKKKEDEKKKKKKKGSIDSDVEDSDCPYPEKVPSIKIPMDIMEKEPFLIDSKPSDRENSPTFLERHTSC 1035
hkNBC KDKKKKEDEKKKKKKKGSLDSDNDDSDCPYSEKVPSIKIPMDIMEQQPFLSDSKPSDRERSPTFLERHTSC 1035
hhNBC KDKKKKEDEKKKKKKKGSLDSDNDDSDCPYSEKVPSIKIPMDIMEQQPFLSDSKPSDRERSPTFLERHTSC 1079
AE1   ---------------------ADDAKATFDE--------------------------EEGRDEYDEVAMPV  911
AE2   ---------------------ANEAEPVFDE--------------------------REGVDEYNEMPMPV 1240
AE3   ---------------------SEDAEPNFDE---------------------------DGQDEYNELHMPV 1030
                            d   5 E                           e   5 E
```

the last year, Burnham and coworkers (21) isolated a NBC-cDNA from human kidney (hNBC1 or hkNBC) (GenBank #AF007216) that is 86% identical to aNBC and 97% identical to rkNBC. All these renal clones have 1035 amino acids and have many conserved putative phosphorylation sites (Figure 2*A*; see also Table 2).

CHARACTERISTICS OF THE HCO_3^--TRANSPORTER SUPERFAMILY With rkNBC added to the superfamily, two general sequence features become more apparent: (*a*) signature sequences of the superfamily (Table 1) and (*b*) an additional potential DIDS-reaction-site motif. As illustrated in Figure 1 and highlighted in Table 1, several areas of amino acids identity or high similarity seem characteristic of HCO_3^- transporter superfamily members. In particular, ETARWIKFEE, AITFGGLLG, VREQRVTG, and FLYMGV are blocks of six or more amino acids that are almost absolutely conserved among members. Both LISxIFIY and PALLVxILIF are also long blocks of conserved amino acids encompassing only one variant amino acid. (T/S)GP(V/L)LVFE in the NH_2 terminus of the superfamily is noteworthy because in the AEs the sequence is SGPLLVFE whereas in the NBCs the invariant sequence is TGPVLVFE. Table 1 lists other examples of this sequence conservation within AE and conservation within NBC contained in a larger identity group. These sequences are particularly interesting because they appear invariant among amphibians and mammals.

The DIDS motif KL(X)K (X = I,V,Y) was originally identified after the cloning of AE3 (12), aided by a biochemical analysis of AE1 with which DIDS had covalently reacted (22, 23). The cognate sequence in both *Ambystoma* and rat NBC is KMIK (558–561). In addition, at a more C-terminal site, both NBC clones have the original AE consensus motif sequence KLKK (768–771).

Figure 1 Multiple amino acid sequence alignment of electrogenic Na bicarbonate cotransporters (NBCs) and anion exchangers (AEs). The cDNAs for *Ambystoma* kidney NBC (aNBC), rat kidney NBC (rkNBC), and human kidney NBC (hkNBC) encode proteins of 1035 amino acids (GenBank #AF001958, AF004017, AF007216, respectively), whereas human heart NBC (hhNBC) (#AF069510 or #AF011390 from pancreas) encodes a 1079–amino acid protein. Clones identical to hhNBC have been isolated from human kidney (76), pancreas (25, 76), and prostate (MF Romero, unpublished results). The multiple sequence alignment was generated using DNAstar (Lasergene, Madison, WI) and the alignment shaded and annotated using GeneDoc© (available free at http://www.cris.com/~ketchup/genedoc.shtml). The consensus of the seven amino acid sequences appears below the alignment. (*Capital letter*) Indicates identity in all seven; (*number*) indicates all seven have a member of the functional group; (*small letter*) indicates identity in six of seven. (*Highlighting* and *reverse type*) In the multiple sequence alignment, AE sequences (GenBank Accession numbers S03074, S21086, A42497) identical or similar in functional group across all seven sequences. Similar amino acids are defined in six groups: 1 (DN), 2 (EQ), 3 (ST), 4 (KR), 5 (FYW), and 6 (LIVM). (*Shaded* and *normal type*) Identity or similarity across at least four members. (*Line over sequence*) NBC-predicted TMs.

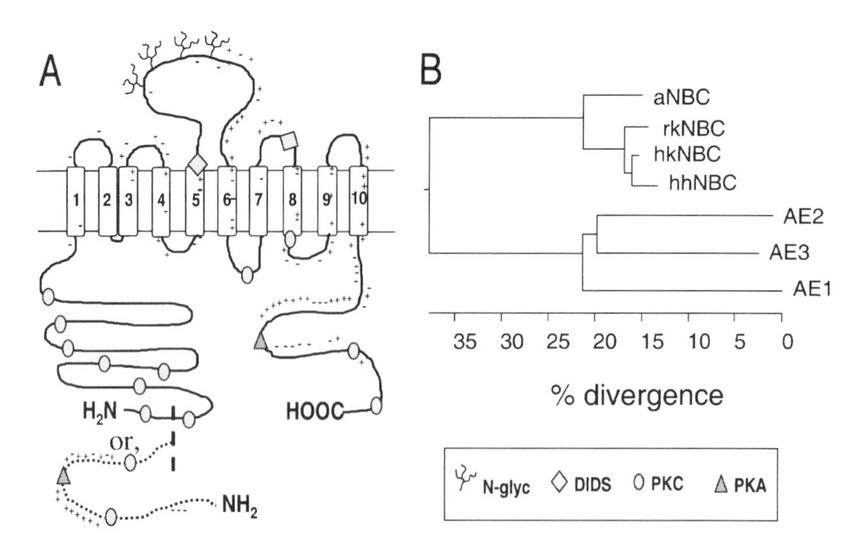

Figure 2 HCO_3^- transporter superfamily relationships. (*A*) Membrane model of electrogenic Na bicarbonate cotransporter (NBC) protein. (*Numbered rectangles*) Putative transmembranes. (*Diamonds*) DIDS-binding motifs. Of eight consensus N-linked glycosylation sites, only three are predicted to be extracellular (four amino acids in aNBC). Ser 982, predicted to be intracellular, is the only consensus protein kinase A [PKA (*triangle*)] site; the hhNBC-like clones that have 1079 amino acids (*dotted line*: additional amino acids MEDE start; MSTE start and 1035 amino acids) have an additional PKA site (T49) at the NH_2 terminus. Of the many consensus sites for protein kinase C [PKC (*circles*)], not all are predicted to be intracellular (see Table 2 for details). (+, −) Charged residues closely associated with transmembranes, or those at a high density. (*B*) This dendrogram shows the percentage of divergence of the amino acid sequences of members from the HCO_3^- transporter superfamily [the NBCs and the most homologous anion exchangers (AEs), as in Figure 1]. The divergence is indicated by the total length of the *horizontal line* segments from one label [e.g. aNBC (see Figure 1 legend for abbreviations) to another. aNBC is 35%, 33%, and 34% similar to AE3, AE2, and AE3, respectively. (Modified from Reference 15.)

Thus, the NBC sequence data suggest a more generalized DIDS-binding motif: K-(Y)(X)-K, where Y = M,L and X = I,V,Y.

The single-consensus PKA phosphorylation site (S982) is conserved in salamander, rat, and human kidney clones. Recently, a longer human NBC clone was found to have an additional PKA site at T49 (24, 25). Several groups have shown that PKA pathways can modulate the activity of Na/HCO_3 cotransporters. In tissue preparations, angiotensin II (26, 27) stimulates the cotransporter via inhibition of PKA signaling pathways. Measuring ^{22}Na uptake after direct stimulation of basolateral membrane vesicles (BLMV) with angiotensin II (28) or endothelin-1 (29) also stimulated Na/HCO_3 cotransport, whereas directly activating PKA in BLMVs is reported to inhibit Na/HCO_3 cotransport

Table 1 Signature sequences of the HCO_3^--transporter superfamily[a]

NBC topology location	Conserved amino acid sequence	rkNBC amino acid location
NH_2-terminal cytoplasmic tail	ETARWIKFEE	83...92
NH_2-terminal cytoplasmic tail	E(V/L)PVPxRFLFxxxLGP	272...286
TM-1	AITFGGLLG	440...448
TM-3	(T/S)GP(V/L)LVFE	485...492
TM-5 prior to KMIK	LISxIFIY	547...555
TM-7	PALLVxILIF	743...754
Beginning of TM-8	KGxG(Y/F)HLDL	771...779
Beginning of TM-9	V(R/K)EQRVTG	829...836
Central TM-9	IPmpVL(F/Y)G(V/I)FLYMGV	856...870
TM-10	R(V/M)HLFTx(L/I)Q(V/I)xC(L/I)AxLW	905...921

[a]Identity sequences between the anion exchangers and the electrogenic Na bicarbonate cotransporters (NBCs). NBC topology corresponds to that illustrated in Figure 2*A*. TM, Transmembrane; KMIK, NBC's sequence that comprises the first DIDS-binding motif K(Y)(X)K.

(30). Interestingly, in the pancreas, both secretin and forskolin stimulate pancreatic HCO_3^- secretion and appear to increase Na/HCO_3 cotransporter activity in guinea pig pancreas (31). Perhaps T49 provides the crucial PKA phosphorylation site for NBC in the pancreas.

All NBC clones have multiple consensus PKC- and casein kinase II–phosphorylation sites. There are also either one or two predicted tyrosine phosphorylation sites (Y897 in rkNBC). Though the pathway is currently unknown, norepinephrine decreases electrogenic Na/HCO_3 cotransporter activity in both *Ambystoma* (32) and rat proximal tubules (33). This attenuated activity presumably occurs via second messenger signaling.

Other predicted modification sites include several consensus myristylation and N-linked glycosylation sites (Table 2). Additionally, based on the identity with the AEs, palmitoylation (AE1-C843(34)) of NBC-C916 (C960 in hhNBC) is possible.

PHYSIOLOGY OF NBC

Modes of Na/HCO_3 Cotransport

The aNBC clone encodes the renal electrogenic Na/HCO_3 cotransporter that normally mediates Na^+ and HCO_3^- efflux across the basolateral membrane of the proximal tubule. This cotransporter presumably has a Na^+:HCO_3^- stoichiometry of 1:3 (35, 36), at least as it functions in the proximal tubule. A functionally related cotransporter, which mediates both HCO_3^- influx and efflux and has a

Table 2 Putative modification sites of NBC[a]

Predicted type	Consensus site	Sites (hhNBC)	Sites (hk-, rk-, and aNBC)
N-linked glycosylation	N-{P}-[ST]-{P}	541, 636, 641, 661	(590), 592, 597, 617
PKA	[RK](2)-x-[ST].	T49, S1026	S982
PKC	[ST]-x-[RK]	S38, S65, T128, T216, T249, S262, S400, T439, T750, S854, S1039, S1044, S1064	T84, T172, T205, S218, S356, T395, T706, S810, S995, and S1000, S1020 (not rkNBC)
Casein kinase II	[ST]-x(2)-[DE].	S68, T110, S157, T163, S223, S239, S257, S336, S408, T419, S995, S1000, S1029, S1064, T1071	T66, S113, T119, S179, S195, S213, S292, S364, T375, S951, S956, S985, and T1027
Tyrosine phosphorylation	[RK]-x(2,3)-[DE]-x(2,3)-Y	Y941	Y897
Myristylation	G-{EDRKHPFYW}-x(2)-[STA GCN]-{P}	G423, G427, G488, G500, G507, G512, G520, G558, G679, G683, G702, G1025	G379, G383, G444, G456, G463, G468, G476, G514, (G635, G639), G658, (G759, G981)

[a][], Indicates that one of the listed amino acids is present; {}, indicates an optional amino acid may be present; (), indicates sites found in aNBC or hkNBC but not rkNBC (see Figure 1 legend for abbreviations).

stoichiometry of 1:3, also has been identified in retinal Müller cells (37, 38) and corneal endothelial cells (39, 40).

Other electrogenic or electroneutral Na/HCO_3 cotransporters mediate net HCO_3^- influx (i.e. acid extrusion mode) in their native cells. Generally, net HCO_3^- influx requires a $Na^+:HCO_3^-$ stoichiometry of less than 1:3 (i.e. 1:2 or 1:1). Cotransporters with $Na^+:HCO_3^-$ stoichiometries of 1:2 are found in invertebrate glia (4), mammalian astrocytes (41, 42), liver (43–45), pancreas (46) and colon (47), and parotid (48). However, electrogenicity of the cotransporter has not been explicitly demonstrated in colon, pancreas, and parotid. Vaughan-Jones and associates (5, 5a) have evidence for a cotransporter with a 1:1 stoichiometry in mammalian heart. Such a cotransporter would be electroneutral. On the other hand, Camilion de Hurtado et al (49) have provided evidence for an electrogenic Na^+-dependent HCO_3^--uptake mechanism in cardiac cells. It is attractive to speculate that NBC-related clones may underlie these physiologically identified Na/HCO_3 cotransport activities. In fact, the possibility has not been ruled out that the same clone is capable of mediating Na/HCO_3 cotransport with two or more different stoichiometries. Indeed, two groups have suggested that the electrogenic Na/HCO_3 cotransporter is capable of functioning in either the 1:3 or 1:2 modes (33, 50).

Stoichiometry of the Renal Electrogenic Na/HCO_3 Cotransporter

In their original work on the electrogenic Na/HCO_3 cotransporter of the salamander proximal tubule, Boron & Boulpaep (3) demonstrated that the cotransporter moves more HCO_3^- than Na^+. Based on measurements of pH_i, V_m, and intracellular Na^+ activity, they made a thermodynamic argument that the $Na^+:HCO_3^-$ stoichiometry had to be at least 1:2. However, they could not rule out the possibility that it was higher (e.g. 1:3). Subsequent work by Lopes et al (51) on Necturus proximal tubules suggested, again on thermodynamic grounds, that the $Na^+:HCO_3^-$ stoichiometry had to be at least 1:3.

Using rabbit renal BLMV, Soleimani et al (36) reasoned that the net transport direction depends on both the $Na^+:HCO_3^-$ coupling ratio and the electrochemical gradients for Na^+ and HCO_3^-. By altering these gradients and measuring the direction of net transport in rabbit BLMV, these workers concluded that the renal electrogenic Na/HCO_3 cotransporter must have a stoichiometry of 1:3. Any of three models could account for this apparent 1:3 stoichiometry of the cotransporter: (*a*) Na^+ plus 3 HCO_3^-, (*b*) Na^+ plus HCO_3^- plus $CO_3^=$, or (*c*) the $NaCO_3^-$ ion pair and HCO_3^-.

Two groups working with isolated proximal tubules have suggested that, under special conditions, the renal electrogenic Na/HCO_3 cotransporter can alter its stoichiometry from 1:3 to 1:2 and thereby change the net direction of net HCO_3^- transport (50, 52).

Even though the data obtained under physiological conditions, on native renal cells or native cell-derived materials point to a stoichiometry of 1:3, it should be pointed out that the Na^+:HCO_3^- coupling ratio has never been measured directly.

Characterization of NBC Clones

Both aNBC and rkNBC have been functionally characterized by monitoring intracellular pH (pH_i) and voltage (V_m) or current when cRNA is injected and expressed in *Xenopus* oocytes (15, 16). A human renal homolog (hkNBC) has been studied using pH-sensitive dyes in HEK-293 cells transiently transfected (21). Both akNBC and rkNBC are electrogenic, and recently hhNBC and hkNBC were shown to be electrogenic (24).

Figure 3 illustrates several of the fundamental properties of aNBC and rkNBC as expressed in *Xenopus* oocytes. The NBC proteins expressed in *Xenopus*

Figure 3 Expression of electrogenic Na bicarbonate cotransporters (NBCs) in *Xenopus* oocytes. Expression of aNBC and rkNBC (see Figure 1 legend for abbreviations) (10 ng/50 nl of cRNA solution) was first obvious on day 3 after injection of cRNA and continued until at least day 13. (*A–D*) aNBC expressed in *Xenopus* oocytes; (*E, F*) rkNBC expressed in *Xenopus* oocytes. (*A*) DIDS sensitivity. The bathing solution was switched from ND96 solution (CO_2/HCO_3^- free) to 1.5% CO_2/10 mM HCO_3^- (pH 7.5). Na^+ was then removed four times in CO_2/HCO_3^-. The last two Na^+ removals were in the presence of 200 μM DIDS. With DIDS, the response to Na^+ removal was similar to that observed in water-injected oocytes in the absence of DIDS (not shown). (*B*) HCO_3^- dependence. From a resting value of 7.2-7.4 in ND96, pH_i decreased to ~7.0 within 10 min of adding either 1.5% CO_2/10 mM HCO_3^- or 10 mM butyrate (not shown). Na^+ was removed five times, twice in CO_2/HCO_3^- and three times in butyrate. The hyperpolarizing response to Na^+ removal in butyrate is similar to that observed in water-injected oocytes in the presence of CO_2/HCO_3^- (not shown). (*C*) Changing $[HCO_3^-]_o$ at a fixed $[CO_2]$ by altering extracellular pH (pH_o). Maintaining a PCO_2 of 1.5%, we changed $[HCO_3^-]_o$ from 10 to 2 mM (pH_o: 7.5 to 6.8). After two 0-Na^+ pulses, we changed $[HCO_3^-]_o$ from 10 to 32 mM (pH_o: 7.5 to 8.0). (*D*) NBC currents. The oocyte was voltage clamped at −60 mV as we switched from ND96 to 1.5% CO_2/10 mM HCO_3^-. The ~50 nA outward current elicited by CO_2/HCO_3^- corresponds to a ~50 mV hyperpolarization observed in unclamped cells; the ~50 nA inward current elicited by Na^+ removal corresponds to a ~50 mV depolarization observed in unclamped cells. Hence, aNBC expression does not significantly change the native oocyte resistance of ~1 MΩ. (*E*) The bath solution was switched from ND96 solution to 5% CO_2/33 mM HCO_3^- (pH 7.5). Na^+ was removed two times in CO_2/HCO_3^- and once in Cl^-. In comparison with aNBC, the rkNBC clone expresses poorly in oocytes even when bathed with threefold increased HCO_3^-. (*F*) rNBC-pTLN2 expression in oocytes. The rkNBC-cDNA was subcloned into a *Xenopus* expression vector, pTLN2 (93), a derivative of pSP6 (94, 95). The 5′- and 3′-untranslated regions of the *Xenopus* β-globin mRNA flank the rkNBC cDNA. An experiment is shown in which the bath solution was switched from ND96 solution (CO_2/HCO_3^- free) to only 1.5% CO_2/10 mM HCO_3^- (pH 7.5). Na^+ was removed three times in CO_2/HCO_3^-. Expression of rkNBC is increased by ~50-fold. Thus, placing the mammalian rkNBC cDNA within this *Xenopus* context is apparently beneficial for expression in *Xenopus* oocytes. (Modified from References 15, 16.)

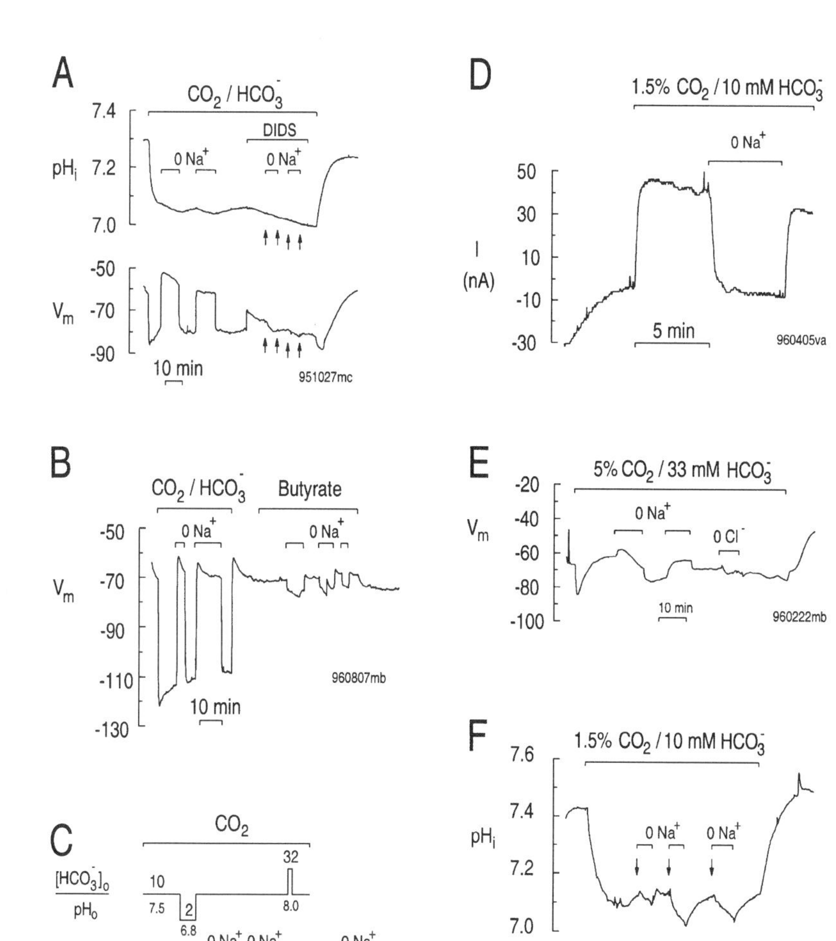
A
CO_2 / HCO_3^-
DIDS
0 Na+
0 Na+
pHi
7.4
7.2
7.0
-50
Vm
-70
-90
10 min
951027mc
B
CO_2 / HCO_3^-
Butyrate
0 Na+
0 Na+
Vm
-50
-70
-90
-110
-130
10 min
960807mb
C
CO_2
[HCO_3^-]o
pHo
10
7.5
2
6.8
32
8.0
0 Na+
0 Na+
0 Na+
-50
-70
-90
Vm
-110
-130
-150
10 min
960402mc
D
1.5% CO_2 / 10 mM HCO_3^-
0 Na+
50
30
I
(nA)
10
-10
-30
5 min
960405va
E
5% CO_2 / 33 mM HCO_3^-
-20
-40
Vm
-60
-80
-100
0 Na+
0 Cl-
10 min
960222mb
F
1.5% CO_2 / 10 mM HCO_3^-
7.6
7.4
pHi
7.2
7.0
0 Na+
0 Na+
-30
-50
Vm
-70
-90
-110
10 min
960730mb

oocytes are electrogenic, Na^+ dependent, and HCO_3^- dependent and are blocked by extracellular DIDS. As shown in Figure 3*A*, bath addition of CO_2/HCO_3^- to NBC-expressing oocytes elicits an immediate hyperpolarization that slowly relaxes; this relaxation of the hyperpolarization presumably reflects the slow increase in $[HCO_3^-]_i$ produced as NBC transports HCO_3^- into the cell. Figure 3*B* shows that although acidifying an oocyte with CO_2/HCO_3^- can produce a sizeable hyperpolarization, applying butyrate (which acidifies the cell to the same extent; not shown) has no effect on V_m. In the presence of CO_2/HCO_3^-, removing bath Na^+ (Figure 3*A,E,F*) or lowering bath HCO_3^- (Figure 3*C*) depolarizes NBC-expressing oocytes. Readdition of bath Na^+ or HCO_3^- reverses these effects. Expression of rkNBC may be substantially increased by placing the rkNBC-cDNA into a *Xenopus* expression plasmid (compare Figure 3*E* and *F*) (16). Finally, most if not all of these NBC-mediated transport processes are blocked by extracellular DIDS (Figure 3*A*).

Na^+ Dependence

In experiments using ^{22}Na uptake on BLMVs of rabbit kidney cortex, Li^+, K^+, and choline each appeared to partially support Na/HCO_3 cotransporter activity (53). Studying ^{22}Na uptake, Jentsch and coworkers (54) determined electrogenic, DIDS-inhibitable Na/HCO_3 cotransporter activity in BSC-1 cells. They found an apparent K_m for Na^+ of 20–40 mM at 28 mM HCO_3^-. These investigators also found that Na/HCO_3 cotransporter activity was specific for Na^+; neither Li^+ nor K^+ could substitute. Amlal and colleagues (55) recently reported that after transfecting hkNBC into HEK-293 cells, a low affinity for Li^+ and a lesser affinity for K^+ (they conclude no K^+ substitution; however, their data show measureable transport) is measured when monitoring pH_i using 2′7′-bis(carboxethyl)-5(and 6)-carboxy fluorescein (BCECF). When expressed in *Xenopus* oocytes and studied electrophysiologically, neither aNBC nor rkNBC seems to be able to transport Li^+ (56, 57). Moreover, voltage-clamp experiments using rkNBC show that neither Li^+ nor K^+ could substitute for Na^+ (58). Both influx (outward current, as for aNBC in Figure 3*D*) and efflux (inward current, as for aNBC in Figure 3*D*) of $NaHCO_3$ depend on extracellular Na^+ and voltage (58). Regardless of extracellular $[Na^+]$, influx (outward I increasing with depolarization) is always measured for V_m more positive than −40 mV; and efflux (inward I increasing with hyperpolarization) is always measured for V_m more negative than −100 mV. The apparent affinity for extracellular Na^+ is ~30 mM between −160 and −100 mV ($NaHCO_3$ efflux) and also between −20 and +60 mV ($NaHCO_3$ influx). For more typically physiologic V_ms (−40 to −100 mV) both influx and efflux transport modes may be measured, depending on both extracellular $[Na^+]$ and V_m. In general, reducing $[Na^+]_o$ in this physiologic V_m range enables NBC to predominantly efflux $NaHCO_3$ from the cell.

HCO_3^- *Dependence*

The NBC protein in the renal proximal tubule is probably the major, perhaps exclusive, mode of HCO_3^- exit from the cell into the blood; it may mediate the reabsorption of as much as 90% of renal HCO_3^- absorption (59). However, the chemical form of HCO_3^- (i.e. HCO_3^-, $CO_3^=$, or the $NaCO_3^-$ ion pair) transported by the NBC protein has not yet been elucidated.

Soleimani & Aronson (60), working on BLMV from rabbit renal cortex, found that raising $[CO_3^=]_o$ at constant $[HCO_3^-]_o$ stimulates the influx of ^{22}Na, consistent with the hypothesis that $CO_3^=$ is a substrate of NBC. On the other hand, raising $[CO_3^=]_o$ at constant $[HCO_3^-]_o$ under equilibrium conditions necessarily involves raising pH_o. Therefore this result does not unambiguously prove that NBC transports $CO_3^=$. In other experiments, Soleimani & Aronson (60) found that in the presence of low $[HCO_3^-]$, adding $SO_3^=$ stimulates ^{22}Na uptake, consistent with the idea that $SO_3^=$ substitutes for $CO_3^=$ at a $CO_3^=$ binding site on NBC. On the other hand, $SO_3^=$ solutions at physiological pH also contain HSO_3^-. Thus, one could also hypothesize that HSO_3^- substitutes for HCO_3^- at a HCO_3^- binding site. More recent work on rkNBC expressed in *Xenopus* oocytes shows that—at least as expressed in oocytes—rkNBC transports neither $SO_3^=$ nor HSO_3^- (61). Thus, there is currently no convincing evidence that NBC transports $CO_3^=$.

Recent experiments with the NBC clones have provided data on the specificity and affinity for HCO_3^- transport. In contrast to the anion promiscuity of the AEs (62–65), neither aNBC nor rkNBC expressed in oocytes seems to accept other organic anions (15, 56) or inorganic anions (II Grichtchenko, MF Romero, WF Boron, unpublished observations). For example, when an oocyte is acidified by exposing it to butyrate/butyric acid rather than to CO_2/HCO_3^-, there is no negative shift in V_m, and removing extracellular Na^+ fails to elicit a depolarization (Figure 3*B*) (15, 56). A recent report indicates that hkNBC expressed in HEK-293 cells may also have a Na^+:OH^- cotransport mode (55).

Grichtchenko and colleagues have preliminary data on the extracellular $[HCO_3^-]$ dependence of aNBC and rkNBC expressed in *Xenopus* oocytes. They exposed oocytes briefly to pH 7.5 solutions containing a range of HCO_3^- concentrations [they also varied (CO_2) to keep pH_o constant] and assessed transport either from the hyperpolarization or outward current mediated by NBC. They found that the apparent K_m for external HCO_3^-, with the cotransporter running in the inward direction, is ~12 mM for both NBCs (61, 67).

pH_i *Dependence*

Several acid-base transporters are pH dependent (62, 68, 69). In studies on BBMV studies using ^{22}Na uptake to access Na/HCO_3 cotransporter activity,

Soleimani and coworkers (70) found that ^{22}Na uptake increased as the pH gradient increased (pH_i constant while varying pH_o). This same study indicated that maintaining $pH_i = pH_o$ or maintaining a constant ratio of ($[Na^+]_i/[Na^+]_o$) had a bell-shaped uptake profile (low uptake at $pH_o = 6.8$, maximal uptake at 7.4, and low uptake at 8.0) (70). Transfecting hkNBC into HEK-293 cells, this same group has observed increases of pH_i elicited by raising pH_o from 7.4 to 7.8 (55).

Voltage Dependence

A priori, one would expect that transport via a membrane transport protein should be sensitive to the voltage difference across a membrane, i.e. membrane potential (V_m). Newman & Astion (37) used whole cell recordings of retinal glial cells and found a voltage-dependent electrogenic Na/HCO_3 cotransporter (outward I for $V_m > -37$ mV, and inward for $V_m < -37$ mV) with a stoichiometry of 1 Na^+:3 HCO_3^-. Recently, by permeablizing the apical membrane of monolayers of proximal tubule cell-lines, Gross & Hopfer (71) found a linear voltage dependence on the DNDS-inhibitable short-circuit current across the epithelial basolateral membrane. Cotransporter currents of aNBC expressed in oocytes, although measurable, are small (Figure 3*D*). Interestingly, both giant patch (72) and 2-electrode voltage-clamp experiments (58) of rkNBC show not only a voltage dependence of both inward and outward NBC transport (i.e. larger outward I with depolarization, or larger inward I with hyperpolarization), but also a Na^+:HCO_3^- stoichiometry of less than 1:3.

NBC CLONES

Because electrogenic Na/HCO_3 cotransporters apparently have a variety of stoichiometries, we have tried to clone and characterize NBC from several tissues and organisms (*Ambystoma*, rats, and humans).

Mammalian, Non-Human, NBC cDNAs and Genes

Presently, only the renal NBC clone (rkNBC) is a full-length open reading frame (ORF) from the rat (16). Screening rat brain libraries, Bevensee and coworkers (73) identified at least two varieties of NBC in the brain. One clone is identical to rkNBC. The second clone contains a 3′ deletion that shifts the reading frame to result in a slightly larger encoded protein. Recently, using gene-specific primers and polymerase chain reaction, Shepard & Rae (74) provided evidence that NBC-mRNA is present in rabbit corneal epithelium, rabbit corneal endothelium, and human lens epithelium. At the same time, Rimmer and colleagues (75) obtained partial NBC clones from rabbit corneal endothelium. These partial clones have not yet been functionally characterized.

Human NBC cDNAs and Genes

KIDNEY Knowing that NBC is related to the AEs, Burnham and associates (21) identified and obtained expressed sequence tags encoding a human analog of NBC. After screening a kidney library, they assembled a full-length clone 97% identical to rkNBC. This hkNBC clone has been characterized by transient transfections of HEK-293 cells and monitoring BCECF fluorescence to measure pH_i. Recent work of Choi et al (76, 77) has shown that this transporter is indeed electrogenic. These investigators also isolated a second NBC form from human kidney with an alternative NH_2 terminus (MEDE-start and 5′ region) (76) and have shown it to be electrogenic (44, 77).

PANCREAS Because the pancreas secretes HCO_3^-, one might expect that NBC in the pancreas should have different sequence than that of the kidney. Abuladze et al (25) recently reported cloning a variant of NBC from human pancreas (pNBC is identical to hhNBC). When these investigators expressed this human clone in *Xenopus* oocytes, they measured both HCO_3^--stimulated ^{22}Na-uptake and decreases of pH_i upon extracellular Na^+ removal (monitored by BCECF-fluorescence) (25). Working at the same time, Choi et al (24) cloned an identical cDNA from human heart but found it to be identical to the dominant NBC in pancreas (see below).

HEART As noted earlier, physiological studies of mammalian heart indicate that the cells express an electroneutral Na/HCO_3 cotransporter (5, 5a). On the other hand, work on cat papillary muscle suggests that there is an electrogenic Na/HCO_3 cotransporter in the heart, presumably with a $Na^+:HCO_3^-$ stoichiometry of 1:2 (49). Choi et al recently cloned an NBC-related cDNA from human heart (hhNBC). It is identical to the cDNA cloned from human kidney except that the 41 NH_2-terminal amino acids of hkNBC are replaced by 85 in hhNBC. Thus, hhNBC has an open reading frame of 1079 amino acids. The 5′ end includes the unique 5′ MEDE start. hhNBC is identical to the pancreatic NBC. Electrophysiological studies on oocytes indicate that hhNBC is an electrogenic Na/HCO_3 cotransporter (44, 77). Thus, the NH_2 terminus of NBC does not appear responsible for conferring electrogenicity.

An electroneutral Na/HCO_3 cotransporter has yet to be cloned and expressed from any mammalian tissue.

PROSTATE Using high-stringency Northern analysis, we identified the NBC mRNA in tissues for which there is little or no HCO_3^- transporter physiology known. The prostate is one such tissue. This NBC cotransporter also contains the MEDE start and is virtually identical to the clone from other tissues (MF Romero, unpublished results; GenBank#AF053753).

HUMAN NBC GENES Two groups have obtained Pl artificial chromosome clones and used fluorescent in situ hybridization (FISH) to localize the NBC gene(s) to human chromosome 4q (25, 78). Our analysis of several NBC P1-derived artificial chromosome clones indicates that there are two human NBC genes on chromosome 4q2 and two human NBC-related genes (78). Studies are under way to determine gene structure and more precise chromosomal localization. Currently, it is difficult to distinguish the encoded cDNAs. Perhaps the genes contain tissue-specific response elements to direct these virtually identical clones to tissues of varying apparent Na/HCO_3 cotransporter activity.

LOCALIZATION OF NBC mRNA

Localization of NBC mRNAs by Northern Analysis

By Northern analysis, two groups have observed an rkNBC mRNA at ~7.5 kb (16, 79). The rkNBC mRNA is abundant in kidney but present in substantial amounts in liver and brain, and at lower levels in heart, lung, and spleen. The rkNBC-ORF encodes a protein of 1035 amino acids, indicating that the message has additional untranslated regions of more than 4 kb. In *Ambystoma*, the message was smaller (4.4 kb); there was no reactivity in the liver, lung, and spleen; and an even smaller message (~2 kb) was in the heart (15). Similarly, several groups have observed with human Northern blots that NBC-like transcripts (7.5 to ~9 kb) are abundant in pancreas, kidney, brain, and prostate but detectable in liver, lung, small intestine, large intestine, and heart (21, 24, 25, 76). Recently, similar results were reported with the refinement of using transcript-specific probes to distinguish forms (25). These data indicate that the 1035–amino acid form of human NBC (or hkNBC) is predominant in the kidney whereas the 1079–amino acid form of human NBC is prominent in the pancreas and prostate.

Localization of NBC mRNAs by In Situ Hybridization

Examining NBC-mRNA distribution by in situ hybridization appears to give conflicting results. Rat kidney NBC-mRNA predominates in the straight portion of the S2 renal nephron with no mRNA in S1 or S3 (16). The in situ localization of NBC is more restricted spatially than the well-documented cotransporter activity in isolated perfused tubules. This activity has been detected in S1 and convoluted segments of S2 (27, 35, 80–85), as well as in S3 (86, 87). In rabbit kidney, the expected distribution of NBC mRNA was observed (88). The basis for the difference in the rat and rabbit localizations is unclear. One possibility is that the rat has other NBC isoforms not yet detected with existing probes. Alternatively, NBC mRNA and NBC protein may be controlled differently along the proximal tubule (see below).

Physiological experiments indicate the presence of a Na^+-coupled HCO_3^- transporter in acini (89) and on the basolateral membrane of pancreatic duct cells (46). In the mouse pancreas, NBC-mRNA has been recently reported to be in both ductal epithelial cells and in acini (25).

In adult rat brain, NBC mRNA expression has been shown by both Northern blotting and in situ hybridization (89a). NBC is expressed throughout the neuraxis, but prominently in olfactory bulb, hippocampus, and cerebellum. Interestingly, NBC was present not only in glial cells (e.g. hippocampal astrocytes and Bergmann glia) but was also found at similar levels in neurons (e.g. in cortex and hippocampus).

Antibody Localization of NBC Protein

Schmitt and coworkers (90) generated polyclonal antibodies directed against both the middle (amino acids 338–391) and carboxy terminus (amino acids 928–1035) of rat kidney NBC. These epitopes are conserved from salamander to human. Additionally, the NBC-epitopes are distinct from AE sequences (see Figure 1). Thus, it was expected that the antibodies would recognize NBC in a variety of species and yet not show cross-reactivity to the AEs. These expectations have proven true.

In immunoblot experiments, the NBC antibodies react with a rat- and rabbit-kidney protein with a molecular weight of ~130,000. Smaller bands are seen at molecular weights of ~100,000 and ~85,000. rkNBC expressed in *Xenopus* oocyte also has an apparent molecular weight of ~130,000. In the *Ambystoma* kidney, the antibodies recognize a band at a substantially higher molecular weight, ~160,000. Because the predicted molecular weight for these NBCs is ~116,000, it is likely that the NBC protein is partially glycosylated both in vivo and in vitro (91, 92).

In immunocytochemistry studies, NBC immunoreactivity is observed exclusively in basolateral membranes of rat, rabbit, and *Ambystoma* kidneys (90, 91). In rabbit kidney, the immunoreactivity is limited to the S1 and S2 segments of the proximal tubule; no reactivity was detected in the more distal S3 segment. Differences between the immunocytochemistry data and the in situ hybridization data could reflect differences in the sensitivities of the methods, differences in the relative abundances of NBC mRNA vs protein, or differences in isoforms expressed in different segments of the proximal tubule. In the salamander, immunoreactivity was intense in a portion of the distal nephron with high rates of H^+ secretion and was present but less intense in the proximal tubule.

Preliminary work with these NBC antibodies has identified NBC-related proteins in the basolateral membranes of parietal cells, colonic crypts (not mucus-secreting cells), ductuli efferentes, and caput and cauda epididymis of rats (92, 92a). These NBC antibodies do not recognize species or isoform differences.

By immunoblotting and immunohistochemistry, Schmitt et al (89a) have demonstrated that NBC protein is widely expressed in the central nervous system, especially in olfactory bulb, hippocampus, and cerebellum. As with mRNA, NBC protein was present in both glial cells and in neurons. Immunoblotting on primary cultured cells confirmed that the characteristic ~130-kDa protein is present at similar levels in hippocampal astrocytes and cortical neurons from rat. A study by Douglas et al (92b) showed that NBC is expressed at early developmental stages and reaches adult levels soon after birth, with regional differences. Furthermore, exposing rats to chronic hypoxia in utero appeared to upregulate the NBC protein levels.

By screening a rat brain cDNA library using a portion of rat kidney NBC, Bevensee and coworkers isolated a partial-length NBC-like clone that is identical to rkNBC except for a 97 base pair deletion near the 3′ end (MO Bevensee, BM Schmitt, M Romero & WF Boron, unpublished observations). This novel clone encodes a protein that has 61 unique C-terminal amino acids instead of the 46 C-terminal amino acids of rkNBC. These investigators have developed a pair of polyclonal antibodies that distinguishes rkNBC from a variant brain cDNA that has a unique NH_2 terminus. The rat brain NBC variant also has an apparent molecular weight of 130 when detected using an isoform-specific NBC antibody (73).

SUMMARY AND CONCLUSIONS

With the cloning of NBC from several species and tissues, interest in acid-base transporters and particularly HCO_3^- transporters appears renewed. Although some of the elemental transport processes of NBC are beginnig to be characterized, there are still many avenues of transporter function and regulation to be elucidated. Future studies, we hope, will determine (*a*) what ions are transported, (*b*) whether voltage dependence and/or stoichiometry is changeable, and (*c*) whether there are complementary proteins interacting with NBC to alter measured properties. It is clear that there are NBC isoforms. Yet it is unclear whether these NBC-variants arise from the same or different NBC genes. What signals and/or binding proteins regulate the NBC genes, mRNAs, and protein? Are there pathophysiologic stimuli such as acidosis, alkalosis, hypertension, hypotension, or cancers that influence NBC activity, mRNA expression, protein production, or protein regulation?

Finally, there are now two branches of what seems to be a HCO_3^- transporter superfamily. Several physiologically important HCO_3^- transporters have yet to be identified at the molecular level. We hope interest in HCO_3^- transport will flourish. Perhaps with the aid of several genome sequencing projects, the ever-growing expressed sequence tags databases, cloning projects, and the fervent interest in functional genomics (physiology), many, if not all, putative superfamily members will be identified.

ACKNOWLEDGMENTS

We thank our colleagues and collaborators, in particular Emile L Boulpaep, Matthias A Hediger, Mark O Bevensee, Urs V Berger, Inyoung Choi, Bruce A Davis, Peying Fong, Irina I Grichtchenko, Nazih L Nakhoul, Chris M Sciortino, Caroline R Sussman, Bernhard M Schmitt, Patricia Bray-Ward, David Ward, and Duncan Wong who have been involved in many ways and in several phases of this work. This work was supported by National Institutes of Health grants DK30344, DK17433, and DK43171 to WFB. MFR was supported by grants from the National Kidney Foundation, National Institutes of Health grant NRSA DK09342, the American Heart Association, American Cancer Society Award IRg-91-022-05-IRg and a HHMI-institutional grant to Case Western Reserve University.

Literature Cited

1. Sly WS, Hu PY. 1995. Human carbonic anhydrases and carbonic anhydrase deficiencies. *Annu. Rev. Biochem.* 64:375–401
2. Nakhoul NL, Romero MF, Waheed A, Davis BA, Mullins R, et al. 1996. Processing and functional expression of carbonic anhydrase isoforms in *Xenopus laevis* oocytes. *FASEB J.* 10:A88 (Abstr.)
3. Boron WF, Boulpaep EL. 1983. Intracellular pH regulation in the renal proximal tubule of the salamander. Basolateral HCO_3^- transport. *J. Gen. Physiol.* 81:53–94
4. Deitmer JW, Schlue WR. 1987. The regulation of intracellular pH by identified glial cells and neurones in the central nervous system of the leech. *J. Physiol.* 388:261–83
5. Dart C, Vaughan-Jones RD. 1992. Na^+-HCO_3^- symport in the sheep cardiac Purkinje fibre. *J. Physiol.* 451:365–85

5a. Lagadic-Gossmann D, Buckler KJ, Vaughn-Jones RD. 1992. Role of bicarbonate in pH recovery from intracellular acidosis in the guinea pig ventricle myocyte. *J. Physiol.* 458:361–84

6. Hogan EM, Cohen MA, Boron WF. 1995. K^+- and HCO_3^--dependent acid-base transport in squid giant axons. I. Base efflux. *J. Gen. Physiol.* 106:821–44
7. Hogan EM, Cohen MA, Boron WF. 1995. K^+- and HCO_3^--dependent acid-base transport in squid giant axons. II. Base influx. *J. Gen. Physiol.* 106:845–62
8. Russell JM, Boron WF. 1976. Role of chloride transport in regulation of intracellular pH. *Nature* 264:73–74
9. Thomas RC. 1977. The role of bicarbonate, chloride and sodium ions in the regulation of intracellular pH in snail neurones. *J. Physiol.* 273:317–38
10. Kopito RR, Lodish HF. 1985. Primary structure and transmembrane orientation of the murine anion exchange protein. *Nature* 316:234–38
11. Alper SL, Kopito RR, Libresco SM, Lodish HF. 1988. Cloning and characterization of a murine band 3-related cDNA from kidney and from a lymphoid cell line. *J. Biol. Chem.* 263:17092–99
12. Kopito RR, Lee BS, Simmons DM, Lindsey AE, Morgans CW, Schneider K. 1989. Regulation of intracellular pH by a neuronal homolog of the erythrocyte anion exchanger. *Cell* 59:927–37
13. Linn SC, Kudrycki KE, Shull GE. 1992. The predicted translation product of a

cardiac AE3 mRNA contains an N terminus distinct from that of the brain AE3 Cl^-/HCO_3^- exchanger. Cloning of a cardiac AE3 cDNA, organization of the AE3 gene, identification of an alternative transcription initiation site. *J. Biol. Chem.* 267:7927–35
14. Romero MF, Kanai Y, Gunshin H, Hediger MA. 1998. Expression cloning using *Xenopus laevis* oocytes. *Methods Enzymol.* 296:17–52
15. Romero MF, Hediger MA, Boulpaep EL, Boron WF. 1997. Expression cloning and characterization of a renal electrogenic Na^+/HCO_3^- cotransporter. *Nature* 387:409–13
16. Romero MF, Fong P, Berger UV, Hediger MA, Boron WF. 1998. Cloning and functional expression of rNBC, an electrogenic Na^+/HCO_3^- cotransporter from rat kidney. *Am. J. Physiol.* 274:F425–32
17. Hogan EM, Romero MF, Davis BA, Boron WF. 1993. Shrinkage-induced activation of Na-H exchange in *Xenopus* oocytes. *FASEB J.* 7:A442 (Abstr.)
18. Humphreys BD, Jiang L, Chernova MN, Alper SL. 1995. Hypertonic activation of AE2 anion exchanger in *Xenopus* oocytes via NHE-mediated intracellular alkalinization. *Am. J. Physiol.* 268:C201–9
19. Hogan EM, Davis BA, Apkon M, Boron WF. 1997. Effect of shrinkage on pH_i and V_m in *Xenopus* oocytes expressing AQP1. *J. Am. Soc. Nephrol.* 8:A26 (Abstr.)
20. Romero MF, Hediger MA, Boron WF. 1996. Cloning and functional expression of the rat renal electrogenic Na/HCO_3 cotransporter (rNBC). *J. Am. Soc. Nephrol.* 7:1259 (Abstr.)
21. Burnham CE, Amlal H, Wang Z, Shull GE, Soleimani M. 1997. Cloning and functional expression of a human kidney $Na^+:HCO_3^-$ cotransporter. *J. Biol. Chem.* 272:19111–14
22. Bartel D, Hans H, Passow H. 1989. Identification by site-directed mutagenesis of Lys-558 as the covalent attachment site of H2DIDS in the mouse erythroid band 3 protein. *Biochim. Biophys. Acta* 985:355–58
23. Okubo K, Kang D, Hamasaki N, Jennings ML. 1994. Red blood cell band 3. Lysine 539 and lysine 851 react with the same H_2DIDS (4,4′-diisothiocyanodihydrostilbene-2,2′-disulfoniic acid) molecule. *J. Biol. Chem.* 269:1918–26
24. Choi I, Romero MF, Khandoudi N, Bril A, Boron WF. 1999. Cloning and characterization of an electrogenic Na/HCO_3 cotransporter from human heart. *Am. J. Physiol.* In press
25. Abuladze N, Lee I, Newman D, Hwang J, Boorer K, et al. 1998. Molecular cloning, chromosomal localization, tissue distribution, functional expression of the human pancreatic sodium bicarbonate cotransporter. *J. Biol. Chem.* 273:17689–95
26. Romero MF. 1992. *Angiotensin II mediated ion transport in the rabbit proximal tubule*. PhD thesis. Case Western Reserve Univ., OH. 220 pp.
27. Geibel J, Giebisch G, Boron WF. 1990. Angiotensin II stimulates both Na^+-H^+ exchange and Na^+/HCO_3^- cotransport in the rabbit proximal tubule. *Proc. Natl. Acad. Sci. USA* 87:7917–20
28. Eiam-Ong S, Hilden SA, Johns CA, Madias NE. 1993. Stimulation of basolateral Na^+-HCO_3^- cotransporter by angiotensin II in rabbit renal cortex. *Am. J. Physiol.* 265:F195–203
29. Eiam-Ong S, Hilden SA, King AJ, Johns CA, Madias NE. 1992. Endothelin-1 stimulates the Na^+/H^+ and Na^+/HCO_3^- transporters in rabbit renal cortex. *Kidney Int.* 42:18–24
30. Ruiz OS, Arruda JA. 1992. Regulation of the renal Na-HCO_3 cotransporter by cAMP and Ca-dependent protein kinases. *Am. J. Physiol.* 262:F560–65
31. Ishiguro H, Steward MC, Wilson RW, Case RM. 1996. Bicarbonate secretion in interlobular ducts from guinea-pig pancreas. *J. Physiol.* 495:179–91
32. Abdulnour-Nakhoul S, Khuri RN, Nakhoul NL. 1998. Effect of norepinephrine on intracellular pH in kidney proximal tubule: role of Na^+-$(HCO_3^-)_n$ cotransport. *Am. J. Physiol.* 275:F33–45
33. Müller-Berger S, Nesterov VV, Frömter E. 1997. Partial recovery of in vivo function by improved incubation conditions of isolated renal proximal tubule. II. Change of Na-HCO_3 cotransport stoichiometry and of response to acetazolamide. *Pflügers Arch.* 434:383–91
34. Okubo K, Hamasaki N, Hara K, Kageura M. 1991. Palmitoylation of cysteine 69 from the COOH-terminal of band 3 protein in the human erythrocyte membrane. Acylation occurs in the middle of the consensus sequence of F–I-IICLAVL found in band 3 protein and G2 protein of Rift Valley fever virus. *J. Biol. Chem.* 266:16420–24
35. Yoshitomi K, Burckhardt BC, Frömter E. 1985. Rheogenic sodium-bicarbonate cotransport in the peritubular cell membrane of rat renal proximal tubule. *Pflügers Arch.* 405:360–66
36. Soleimani M, Grassi SM, Aronson PS. 1987. Stoichiometry of Na^+/HCO_3^- co-

transport in basolateral membrane vesicles isolated from rabbit renal cortex. *J. Clin. Invest.* 79:1276–80
37. Newman EA, Astion ML. 1991. Localization and stoichiometry of electrogenic sodium bicarbonate cotransport in retinal glial cells. *Glia* 4:424–28
38. Newman EA. 1996. Acid efflux from retinal glial cells generated by sodium bicarbonate cotransport. *J. Neurosci.* 16:159–68
39. Jentsch TJ, Keller SK, Koch M, Wiederholt M. 1984. Evidence for coupled transport of bicarbonate and sodium in cultured bovine corneal endothelial cells. *J. Membr. Biol.* 81:189–204
40. Jentsch TJ, Stahlknecht TR, Hollwede H, Fischer DG, Keller SK, Wiederholt M. 1985. A bicarbonate-dependent process inhibitable by disulfonic stilbenes and a Na^+/H^+ exchange mediate $^{22}Na^+$ uptake into cultured bovine corneal endothelium. *J. Biol. Chem.* 260:795–801
41. Bevensee MO, Apkon M, Boron WF. 1997. Intracellular pH regulation in cultured astrocytes from rat hippocampus. II. Electrogenic Na/HCO_3 cotransport. *J. Gen. Physiol.* 110:467–83
42. Bevensee MO, Weed RA, Boron WF. 1997. Intracellular pH regulation in cultured astrocytes from rat hippocampus. I. Role of HCO_3^-. *J. Gen. Physiol.* 110:453–65
43. Fitz JG, Persico M, Scharschmidt BF. 1989. Electrophysiological evidence for Na^+-coupled bicarbonate transport in cultured rat hepatocytes. *Am. J. Physiol.* 256:G491–500
44. Gleeson D, Smith ND, Boyer JL. 1989. Bicarbonate-dependent and -independent intracellular pH regulatory mechanisms in rat hepatocytes. Evidence for Na^+-HCO_3^- cotransport. *J. Clin. Invest.* 84:312–21
45. Townsley MC, Machen TE. 1989. Na-HCO_3 cotransport in rabbit parietal cells. *Am. J. Physiol.* 257:G350–56
46. Ishiguro H, Steward MC, Lindsay AR, Case RM. 1996. Accumulation of intracellular HCO_3^- by Na^+-HCO_3^- cotransport in interlobular ducts from guinea-pig pancreas. *J. Physiol.* 495:169–78
47. Rajendran VM, Oesterlin M, Binder HJ. 1991. Sodium uptake across basolateral membrane of rat distal colon. Evidence for Na-H exchange and Na-anion cotransport. *J. Clin. Invest.* 88:1379–85
48. Poronnik P, Schumann SY, Cook DI. 1995. HCO_3^--dependent ACh-activated Na^+ influx in sheep parotid secretory endpieces. *Pflügers Arch.* 429:852–58
49. Camilion de Hurtado MC, Perez NG, Cingolani HE. 1995. An electrogenic sodium-bicarbonate cotransport in the regulation of myocardial intracellular pH. *J. Mol. Cell. Cardiol.* 27:231–42
50. Planelles G, Thomas SR, Anagnostopoulos T. 1993. Change of apparent stoichiometry of proximal-tubule Na^+-HCO_3^- cotransport upon experimental reversal of its orientation. *Proc. Natl. Acad. Sci. USA* 90:7406–10
51. Lopes AG, Siebens AW, Giebisch G, Boron WF. 1987. Electrogenic Na/HCO_3 cotransport across basolateral membrane of isolated perfused Necturus proximal tubule. *Am. J. Physiol.* 253:F340–50
52. Seki G, Coppola S, Fromter E. 1993. The Na^+-HCO_3^- cotransporter operates with a coupling ratio of 2 HCO_3^- to 1 Na^+ in isolated rabbit renal proximal tubule. *Pflugers Arch.* 425:409–16
53. Soleimani M, Lesoine GA, Bergman JA, Aronson PS. 1991. Cation specificity and modes of the Na^+:CO_3^{-2}:HCO_3^- cotransporter in renal basolateral membrane vesicles. *J. Biol. Chem.* 266:8706–10
54. Jentsch TJ, Schill BS, Schwartz P, Matthes H, Keller SK, Wiederholt M. 1985. Kidney epithelial cells of monkey origin (BSC-1) express a sodium bicarbonate cotransport. Characterization by $^{22}Na^+$ flux measurements. *J. Biol. Chem.* 260:15554–60
55. Amlal H, Wang Z, Burnham C, Soleimani M. 1998. Functional characterization of a cloned human kidney Na^+:HCO_3^- cotransporter. *J. Biol. Chem.* 273:16810–15
56. Romero MF, Hediger MA, Fong P, Boron WF. 1997. Expression of the rat renal electrogenic Na/HCO_3 cotransporter (rNBC). *FASEB J.* 11:A25 (Abstr.)
57. Romero MF, Hediger MA, Boulpaep EL, Boron WF. 1996. Physiology of the cloned *Ambystoma tigrinum* renal electrogenic Na/HCO_3 cotransporter (aNBC): II. Localization and Na^+ dependence. *J. Am. Soc. Nephrol.* 7:1260 (Abstr.)
58. Sciortino CM, Romero MF. 1998. Na^+ and voltage dependence of the rat kidney electrogenic Na/HCO_3 cotransporter (rkNBC) expressed in *Xenopus* oocytes. *J. Am. Soc. Nephrol.* 9:12A (Abstr.)
59. Boron WF, Fong P, Hediger MA, Boulpaep EL, Romero MF. 1997. The electrogenic Na/HCO_3 cotransporter. *Wien Klin. Wochenschr.* 109:445–56
60. Soleimani M, Aronson PS. 1989. Ionic mechanism of Na^+-HCO_3^- cotransport in rabbit renal basolateral membrane vesicles. *J. Biol. Chem.* 264:18302–8

61. Grichtchenko II, Romero MF, Boron WF. 1998. Electrogenic Na/HCO_3 cotransporters (NBC) from rat and salamander kidney have similar external HCO_3^- dependencies. *FASEB J.* 12:A638 (Abstr.)
62. Alper SL. 1991. The band 3-related anion exchanger (AE) gene family. *Annu. Rev. Physiol.* 53:549–64
63. Jennings ML. 1992. Anion transport proteins. See Ref. 96, pp. 503–35
64. Jennings ML. 1995. Rapid electrogenic sulfate-chloride exchange mediated by chemically modified band 3 in human erythrocytes. *J. Gen. Physiol.* 105:21–47
65. Jennings ML, Adame MF. 1996. Characterization of oxalate transport by the human erythrocyte band 3 protein. *J. Gen. Physiol.* 107:145–59
66. Chernova MN, Jiang L, Crest M, Hand M, Vandorpe DH, et al. 1997. Electrogenic sulfate/chloride exchange in *Xenopus* oocytes mediated by murine AE1 E699Q. *J. Gen. Physiol.* 109:345–60
67. Grichtchenko II, Romero MF, Boron WF. 1996. Extracellular bicarbonate dependence of aNBC, the electrogenic Na/HCO_3 cotransporter cloned from tiger salamander (*Ambystoma tigrinum*). *J. Am. Soc. Nephrol.* 7:1255 (Abstr.)
68. Boron WF. 1986. Intracellular pH regulation in epithelial cells. *Annu. Rev. Physiol.* 48:377–88
69. Boron WF. 1992. Control of intracellular pH. See Ref. 96, pp. 219–63
70. Soleimani M, Hattabaugh YJ, Bizal GL. 1992. pH sensitivity of the Na^+:HCO_3^- cotransporter in basolateral membrane vesicles isolated from rabbit kidney cortex. *J. Biol. Chem.* 267:18349–55
71. Gross E, Hopfer U. 1996. Activity and stoichiometry of Na^+:HCO_3^- cotransport in immortalized renal proximal tubule cells. *J. Membr. Biol.* 152:245–52
72. Müller-Berger S, Heyer M, Romero MF, Boron WF, Frömter E. 1998. Stoichiometry of rat Na^+-HCO_3^- cotransporter (rkNBC) overexpressed in *Xenopus laevis* oocytes measured using giant patches. *J. Am. Soc. Nephrol.* 9:9A (Abstr.)
73. Bevensee MO, Schmitt BM, Romero MF, Boron WF. 1998. Cloning of a putative Na/HCO_3 cotransporter (NBC) from rat brain. *FASEB J.* 12:A1031 (Abstr.)
74. Shepard AR, Rae JL. 1998. Ion transporters and receptors in cDNA libraries from lens and cornea epithelia. *Curr. Eye Res.* 17:708–19
75. Rimmer SJ, Romero MF, Guggenheim JG, Wigham CG, Hodson SA. 1998. Demonstration of a sodium-bicarbonate cotransporter (NBC) mRNA in rabbit corneal endothelium. *Exp. Eye Res.* 67:58 (Abstr.)
76. Romero MF, Sussman CR, Choi I, Hediger MA, Boron WF. 1998. Cloning of an electrogenic Na/HCO_3 cotransporter (NBC) isoform from human kidney and pancreas. *J. Am. Soc. Nephrol.* 9:11A
77. Choi I, Aalkjaer C, Bril A, Boron WF. 1998. Cloning of putative sodium bicarbonate cotransporters expressed in human heart ant rat pulmonary arteries. *FASEB J.* 12:A1031
78. Romero MF, Davis BA, Sussman CR, Bray-Ward P, Ward D, Boron WF. 1998. Identification of multiple genes for human electrogenic Na/HCO_3 cotransporters (NBC) on 4q. *J. Am. Soc. Nephrol.* 9:11A (Abstr.)
79. Burnham CE, Flagella M, Wang Z, Amlal H, Shull GE, Soleimani M. 1998. Cloning, renal distribution, regulation of the rat Na^+-HCO_3^- cotransporter. *Am. J. Physiol.* 274:F1119–26
80. Yoshitomi K, Frömter E. 1985. How big is the electrochemical potential difference of Na^+ across rat renal proximal tubular cell membranes in vivo? *Pflügers Arch.* 405:S121–26
81. Alpern RJ. 1985. Mechanism of basolateral membrane H^+/OH^-/HCO_3^- transport in the rat proximal convoluted tubule. A sodium-coupled electrogenic process. *J. Gen. Physiol.* 86:613–36
82. Biagi BA, Sohtell M. 1986. Electrophysiology of basolateral bicarbonate transport in the rabbit proximal tubule. *Am. J. Physiol.* 250:F267–72
83. Krapf R, Alpern RJ, Rector FC Jr, Berry CA. 1987. Basolateral membrane Na/base cotransport is dependent on CO_2/HCO_3^- in the proximal convoluted tubule. *J. Gen. Physiol.* 90:833–53
84. Preisig PA, Alpern RJ. 1988. Chronic metabolic acidosis causes an adaptation in the apical membrane Na/H antiporter and basolateral membrane $Na(HCO_3)_3$ symporter in the rat proximal convoluted tubule. *J. Clin. Invest.* 82:1445–53
85. Geibel J, Giebisch G, Boron WF. 1989. Basolateral sodium-coupled acid-base transport mechanisms of the rabbit proximal tubule. *Am. J. Physiol.* 257:F790–97
86. Kurtz I. 1989. Basolateral membrane Na^+/H^+ antiport, Na^+/base cotransport, Na^+-independent Cl^-/base exchange in the rabbit S3 proximal tubule. *J. Clin. Invest.* 83:616–22
87. Nakhoul NL, Chen LK, Boron WF. 1990. Intracellular pH regulation in rabbit S3 proximal tubule: basolateral Cl-HCO_3

exchange and Na-HCO_3 cotransport. *Am. J. Physiol.* 258:F371–81

88. Abuladze N, Lee I, Newman D, Hwang J, Pushkin A, Kurtz I. 1998. Axial heterogeneity of sodium-bicarbonate cotransporter expression in the rabbit proximal tubule. *Am. J. Physiol.* 274:F628–33
89. Muallem S, Loessberg PA. 1990. Intracellular pH-regulatory mechanisms in pancreatic acinar cells. I. Characterization of H^+ and HCO_3^- transporters. *J. Biol. Chem.* 265:12806-12

89a. Schmitt BM, Bevensee MO, Douglas R, Berger UV, Hediger MA, et al. 1998. Expression and localization of Na/HCO_3 cotransporter (NBC) mRNA and protein in adult rat brain. *Soc. Neurosci. Abstr.* 24: 1066

90. Schmitt BM, Biemesderfer D, Boulpaep EL, Romero MF, Boron WF. 1999. Immunolocalization of the electrogenic Na^+/HCO_3^- cotransporter in mammalian and amphibian kidney. *Am. J. Physiol.* 276: In press
91. Schmitt BM, Biemesderfer D, Boulpaep EL, Romero MF, Boron WF. 1997. Immunolocalization of the electrogenic Na^+/HCO_3^- cotransporter (NBC) in mammalian and amphibian kidney. *J. Am. Soc. Nephrol.* 8:10a (Abstr.)
92. Schmitt BM, Biemesderfer D, Breton S, Brown D, Caroppo R, et al. 1998. Immunolocalization of the electrogenic Na^+/HCO_3^- cotransporter (NBC) in mammalian epithelia. *Pflügers Arch.* 435: R59 (Abstr.)

92a. Jensen LJ, Schmitt BM, Berger UV, Nsumu NN, Boron WF, et al. 1998. Localization of sodium bicarbonate cotransporter (NBC) protein and mRNA in rat epididymis. *Biol. Reprod.* In press

92b. Douglas R, Xia Y, Schmitt BM, Bevensee MO, Biemesderfer M, et al. 1998. Developmental and stress-induced profile of two CNS pH regulatory proteins: the Na/H exchanger and the Na/HCO_3 contransporter. *Soc. Neurosci. Abstr.* 24: 1605

93. Lorenz C, Pusch M, Jentsch TJ. 1996. Heteromultimeric CLC chloride channels with novel properties. *Proc. Natl. Acad. Sci. USA* 93:13362–66
94. Melton DA, Krieg PA, Rebagliati MR, Maniatis T, Zinn K, Green MR. 1984. Efficient in vitro synthesis of biologically active RNA and RNA hybridization probes from plasmids containing a bacteriophage SP6 promoter. *Nucleic Acids Res.* 12:7035–56
95. Krieg PA, Melton DA. 1984. Functional messenger RNAs are produced by SP6 in vitro transcription of cloned cDNAs. *Nucleic Acids Res.* 12:7057–70
96. Seldin DW, Giebisch G, eds. 1992. *The Kidney: Physiology and Pathophysiology*. New York: Raven. 2nd ed.

Annu. Rev. Physiol. 1999. 61:725–52

ELECTROPHYSIOLOGY OF SYNAPTIC VESICLE CYCLING

Henrique von Gersdorff[1,*] *and Gary Matthews*[2]
[1]Max Planck Institute for Biophysical Chemistry, Department of Membrane Biophysics, Am Fassberg, D-37077, Göttingen, Germany; *present address: Vollum Institute, Oregon Health Sciences University, Portland, Oregon 97201; e-mail: vongersh@ohsu.edu; and [2]Department of Neurobiology and Behavior, State University of New York at Stony Brook, Stony Brook, New York 11794–5230; e-mail: gary.g.matthews@sunysb.edu

KEY WORDS: exocytosis, endocytosis, glutamate secretion, patch-clamp capacitance

ABSTRACT

Patch-clamp capacitance measurements can monitor in real time the kinetics of exocytosis and endocytosis in living cells. We review the application of this technique to the giant presynaptic terminals of goldfish bipolar cells. These terminals secrete glutamate via the fusion of small, clear-core vesicles at specialized, active zones of release called synaptic ribbons. We compare the functional characteristics of transmitter release at ribbon-type and conventional synapses, both of which have a unique capacity for fast and focal vesicle fusion. Subsequent rapid retrieval and recycling of fused synaptic vesicle membrane allow presynaptic terminals to function independently of the cell soma and, thus, as autonomous computational units. Together with the mobilization of reserve vesicle pools, local cycling of synaptic vesicles may delay the onset of vesicle pool depletion and sustain neuronal output during high stimulation frequencies.

What was life? No one knew...it was not matter and it was not spirit, but something between the two, a phenomenon conveyed by matter, like the rainbow on the waterfall, and like the flame...it was a stolen and voluptuous impurity of sucking and secreting; an exhalation...of mysterious origin and composition.

The Magic Mountain, Thomas Mann

0066-4278/99/0315-0725$08.00

INTRODUCTION

Temporal fidelity for rapidly changing signals in synaptic transmission is attained by means of a transmitter release process that closely ties depolarization-elicited Ca^{2+} influx to vesicle fusion on a submillisecond timescale. To avoid cross talk among closely spaced synaptic inputs, neurotransmitter release from a particular presynaptic terminal is precisely targeted to its own complement of postsynaptic receptors. This requirement for fast, spatially precise secretion sets neurotransmitter release apart from other types of secretion. The specialized architecture of the active zone, where vesicle docking and fusion machinery is brought into molecular proximity with Ca^{2+} channels (101, 107, 134), is thought to be a prime factor in achieving the high speed and precise targeting of exocytosis in neurons.

This review focuses on studies of stimulus-triggered exocytosis and the ensuing endocytosis at presynaptic terminals. Time-resolved membrane capacitance measurements (80) are emphasized as an assay for secretion, with an emphasis on the giant synaptic terminals of goldfish retinal bipolar cells. Capacitance measurements can achieve submillisecond time resolution and, thus, are well suited for monitoring the kinetics of fast exocytosis. Furthermore, capacitance measurements also track membrane retrieval (endocytosis) (13, 21) in real time. Recent findings with this technique have revealed both differences and similarities between the secretory processes of neurons and other secretory cells. The similarities suggest common exocytotic mechanisms among distinct cells, whereas the differences reflect specific functional requirements imposed by the physiological roles of the different cell types. Whenever possible, the findings from capacitance measurements are compared with results from other techniques used to study presynaptic exocytosis and endocytosis.

MEMBRANE CAPACITANCE: AN INDEX OF EXOCYTOSIS AND ENDOCYTOSIS

Because time-resolved membrane capacitance measurements are a major focus of this review, we briefly discuss the basis of the technique. A full discussion is given by Gillis (34). During exocytosis, the surface area of the secreting cell increases as secretory vesicles fuse with the plasma membrane. Conversely, the surface area decreases when membrane is retrieved during endocytosis. These changes in surface area can be monitored in single cells by measuring the electrical capacitance of the cell. The scaling factor between area and capacitance is the specific capacitance of biological membranes, which is typically in the range of 0.8–1.1 $\mu F/cm^2$ (12, 29). The first reports of cellular membrane capacitance changes following stimulation (fertilization) came from studies of sea urchin egg (16, 50), whereas it was in squid giant synapse (33) that the first nerve terminal capacitance measurements were performed.

To measure the time-resolved membrane capacitance of single cells in whole-cell patch-clamp recordings, the cell and cell-attached pipette are modeled as a linear three-element circuit with an access resistance, R_a, in series with the parallel membrane resistance, R_m, and membrane capacitance, C_m. In the frequency-domain method of measuring capacitance, a sinusoidal voltage command is superimposed on the holding potential, and the resulting current is analyzed. This method has been used to study exocytosis and endocytosis in a variety of isolated secretory cells. The increase in capacitance, ΔC, due to the incorporation of a single vesicle of capacitance C_{ves} is given by

$$\Delta C = C_{ves}/[1 + (\omega C_{ves} R_p)^2],$$

where ω is the frequency of the sine wave and R_p is the resistance of the fusion pore between vesicle and plasma membrane (3, 4). The extremely small capacitance of synaptic vesicles (30 to 50 nm in diameter) causes virtually its entire capacitance to be measured immediately upon opening of the fusion pore, even if the fusion pore has the conductance of a single ion channel ($\sim$100 pS; see 65).

It is important to keep in mind that capacitance changes do not always correspond to secretion (82). For example, capacitance may also change because of gating charge movement in transmembrane proteins (48). Several other sources of artifact must also be considered, including nonexocytotic change in passive membrane electrical parameters, calcium-dependent conductance changes, access resistance changes, and improperly compensated pipette capacitance. Because the techniques used to calculate capacitance assume linear circuit behavior, care must also be taken to avoid activation of nonlinear voltage-dependent conductances. Furthermore, the three-element passive circuit model used to calculate capacitance applies only to spherical cells in which there is equal electrical access to all parts of the cell surface. Cells with more complex morphology require more complicated electrical models and alternative methods of estimating capacitance (73). Another consideration is that capacitance detects net change in surface area, and thus, simultaneous membrane retrieval can lead to an underestimate of the amount of ongoing exocytosis. Given these numerous caveats, it is desirable that capacitance measurements be coupled whenever possible with techniques of equivalent time-resolution that detect the actual secreted substance. This has been done for mast cells (4) and chromaffin cells (15, 78), where comparisons of the integral of the amperometric current (a measure of catecholamine release) and simultaneously recorded capacitance increases are in good agreement (122). As described below, a comparison between glutamate secretion and capacitance responses has also now been accomplished for bipolar-cell terminals.

CAPACITANCE MEASUREMENTS IN BIPOLAR CELL TERMINALS

Active Zone Architecture: Synaptic Ribbons as Output Sites

Bipolar cells are interneurons that connect photoreceptors to ganglion and amacrine cells in the vertebrate retina (25). Certain classes of bipolar cells in goldfish retina have a single, large, bulbous terminal, 8–12 μm in diameter (103). The largest terminals belong to type Mb1 bipolar cells, which are a class of rod-dominant, depolarizing (ON-type) bipolar cell. The response to light of dark-adapted Mb1 bipolar cells is a depolarization (98) that has a fast phasic component (>20 mV for about 200 ms, as measured by conventional intracellular recordings) and a long plateau component, depending on light intensity. Synaptic terminals of Mb1 bipolar cells are densely packed with small, clear-core vesicles and contain no dense-core vesicles (120). The neurotransmitter released by the bipolar cell is glutamate (109, 110). The active zone where the bipolar cell makes synaptic contact with postsynaptic amacrine cells is marked by a specialized synaptic ribbon, which is a short, electron-dense sheet oriented perpendicular to the plasma membrane (see Figure 1*A*,*B*). Each ribbon is surrounded by a halo of tethered synaptic vesicles, which form five rows of about 11 vesicles on each face of the ribbon, for a total of approximately 110 tethered vesicles [see figure 9 in Zucker & Yazulla (133) for another *en face* view of a bipolar-cell ribbon]. Three-dimensional reconstruction of a Mb1 bipolar terminal from serial electron microscopy (EM) sections revealed that a terminal ~10 μm in diameter has 65 synaptic ribbons (Figure 1*C*).

The synaptic ribbon may help to anchor and deliver vesicles to their precise sites of fusion. The synaptic terminals of retinal photoreceptors also possess ribbons, and presynaptic dense bodies resembling ribbons are also found in hair cells (91), fish electroreceptors (84), pinealocytes (116), and several invertebrate neuromuscular junction nerve terminals, including from *Drosophila* (58), crayfish (18), and lobster (53). In high-resolution EM studies of frog photoreceptors, three to five thin filaments about 25 nm long are seen attaching vesicles to the surface of the ribbon (114). The ribbon is much smaller in bipolar cells than in rods and cones, implying that the latter may need a larger pool of release-ready vesicles for their tonic mode of operation. Indeed, spontaneous excitatory postsynaptic currents in bipolar cells indicate that photoreceptor synapses may release vesicles in clusters (67). Ribbon synapses

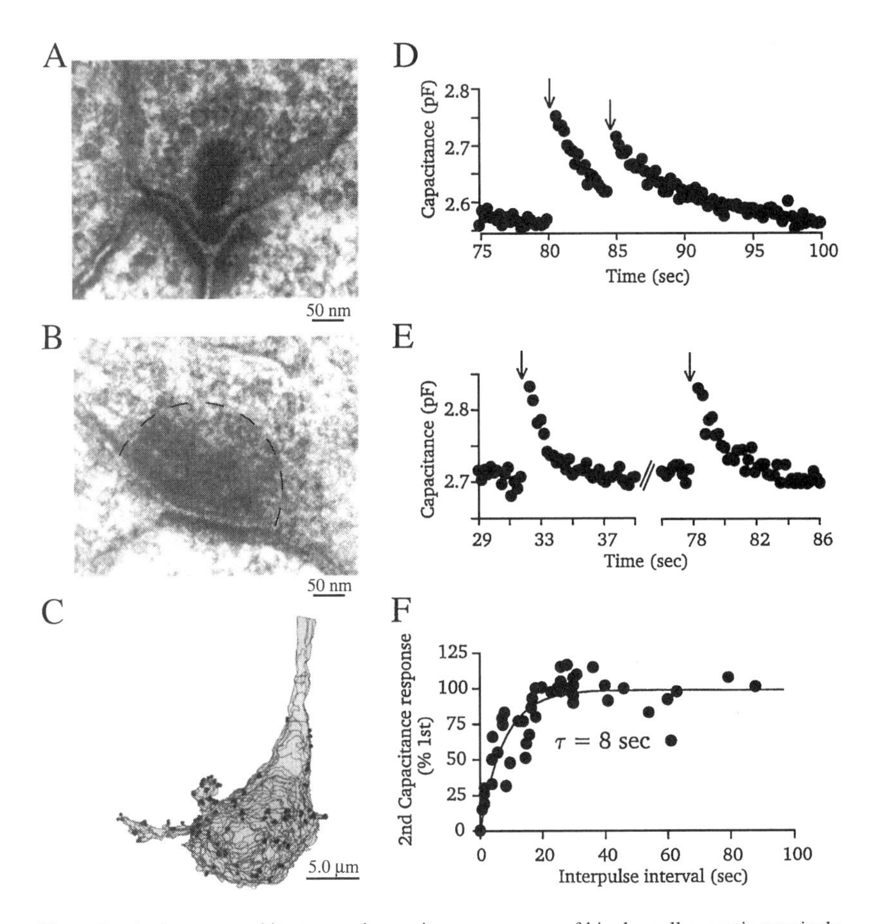

Figure 1 Active zone architecture and capacitance responses of bipolar-cell synaptic terminals. (*A*) Electron micrographs of a synaptic ribbon cut perpendicular to the face of the ribbon. Vesicles are tethered to both faces of the ribbon. Two postsynaptic processes with membrane thickenings oppose the ribbon structure. (*B*) *En face* view of ribbon with overlaid synaptic vesicles. Notice the postsynaptic membrane thickening. The *dashed line* delineates the ribbon boundary. Each face of the ribbon can accommodate about 55 vesicles. (*C*) Three-dimensional reconstruction of a bipolar terminal from serial EM sections. (*Circles*) The location of synaptic ribbons: total of 65 (reproduced from 120). (*D*) Time-resolved membrane capacitance measurements showing responses to two depolarizations ~4 s apart, given at the *arrows* (pulse of 250 ms from −60 mV to −10 mV). The indicated time is relative to break-in. (*E*) Two capacitance jumps were elicited ~46 s apart. (*F*) Summary of experiments like those depicted in *D* and *E*. To compare results across terminals, the second capacitance response is expressed as a percentage of the first. (*Solid line*) A best-fit single exponential with a time constant $\tau = 7.6$ s (reproduced from 121).

do not express synapsin (66), a protein involved in vesicle attachment to the cytoskeleton at conventional synapses (39), but they do express other synaptic proteins involved in exocytosis, albeit in specific isoforms (77).

Interestingly, the bipolar-cell synaptic terminals of goldfish undergo pronounced morphological rearrangement during light and dark adaptation, developing prominent spinules on their plasma membrane during dark adaptation that disappear with light adaptation (124, 131). Thus, synaptic morphology may change on a timescale of hours. So the dynamic amoebae-like behavior of growth cones may still be present in mature synaptic terminals to some degree. Such remodeling of the synaptic terminal suggests that the terminal is not a static structure and may possess mechanisms of membrane addition and membrane retrieval in addition to those involved in neurotransmitter release at active zones.

Depression of Capacitance Jumps

Single synaptic terminals of the retinal bipolar neurons of goldfish are particularly well suited for capacitance measurements. They are approximately spherical, once cut off from their axon, and have a resting capacitance ranging from 1 to 4 pF. Isolated terminals have a high input-resistance of >10 GΩ. The large number of output sites (ribbons) and vesicles per output site make the total membrane area added during secretion large enough to be detected in capacitance measurements from single terminals, even though the terminals secrete via small clear-core vesicles of about 30 nm in mean diameter (120). The capacitance jump evoked by activation of Ca^{2+} current is shown in Figure 1*D*. On average, capacitance increases by 150 fF for a 250-ms depolarization from −60 to 0 mV, which elicits the peak calcium current (117). The time constant for recovery of capacitance back to baseline after a single 250-ms pulse is 1–2 s, which presumably reflects vesicle membrane endocytosis. Furthermore, the total surface area of the terminal is tightly conserved, as evidenced by the return of membrane capacitance back to prestimulus baseline after the exocytotic bout (Figure 1*D,E*).

Figure 1*D* also shows that a second pulse given 4 s after the first elicits a second capacitance jump that is much smaller than the first. When the second pulse is given >20 s after the first pulse, the second capacitance jump has about the same amplitude as the first (Figure 1*E*). Such double-pulse experiments with variable interpulse intervals reveal that the recovery from paired-pulse depression has an exponential time constant of about 8 s in bipolar-cell terminals (Figure 1*F*). Inactivation of the calcium current could not account for the depression of the capacitance responses, and thus, depletion of the readily releasable pool (i.e. the vesicles tethered to ribbons) is the most likely explanation. Experiments on the lobster neuromuscular junction (53), squid giant synapse (60, 108), and hippocampal neurons (74, 106) give time constants of recovery from depression in the range of 4–12 s. Thus, the refilling rate of depleted vesicle pools in retinal bipolar-cell synaptic terminals is similar to that in other synaptic terminals, assuming depression is due to pool depletion.

Following repetitive stimulation with a train of pulses for several seconds, recovery of the capacitance responses was significantly slower, taking >20 s to recover fully (121), whereas calcium current recovered fully from inactivation within 20 s. This slower recovery time may indicate the depletion of a reserve pool of vesicles in the vicinity of the synaptic ribbons. At conventional synapses, similar behavior has been reported in experiments using FM1-43 fluorescence to monitor vesicle dynamics in single hippocampal boutons. Stevens & Tsujimoto (106) report a recovery time of 10 s for brief stimuli (~20 vesicles released), whereas Liu & Tsien (63) find that recovery requires 40 s after more prolonged stimulation (~90 vesicles released). Stronger stimulation, thus, seems to lead to slower recovery from depression in both conventional and ribbon-type synapses (129).

Depletion of Vesicle Pools

Capacitance responses from bipolar-cell synaptic terminals saturate at about 150 fF for depolarizing pulses that range from 200 ms to 1 s in duration (Figure 2*A*) (see 122), which suggests that a readily releasable pool has been exhausted. To convert this capacitance plateau into number of vesicles, one needs to know the capacitance of a single vesicle. In bipolar-cell terminals of goldfish, the mean vesicle diameter (average of inner and outer diameters of vesicle membrane) is about 29 nm (120). Thus, a single synaptic vesicle has a capacitance of approximately 26 pF, assuming vesicle membrane has a specific capacitance of 1 $\mu F/cm^2$. A capacitance jump of 150 fF corresponds then to the fusion of about 5700 vesicles. This estimate agrees well with the total number of vesicles tethered to synaptic ribbons (about 6000) and suggests that the vesicles on ribbons can be rapidly released (120).

Thus, we interpret the saturation of the capacitance jumps as being due to the full stripping of the vesicles attached to synaptic ribbons by strong depolarizations. This implies that ribbons denuded of their halo of vesicles should be present at bipolar terminals immediately after a strong depolarizing pulse. Indeed, bipolar ribbons fixed in normal external Ca^{2+} (1.4–1.8 mM) often display synaptic ribbons partially or fully stripped of their vesicles [see figure 4 of Witkovsky & Dowling (128) and figure 5 of Townes-Anderson & Vogt (113)], whereas bipolar ribbons fixed in low external Ca^{2+} display a complete halo of vesicles (120, 133). In fish electroreceptors, which also have ribbon-type synapses, depression of postsynaptic responses is associated with depletion of vesicles from the ribbons (31). If this is also true for bipolar-cell ribbons, then

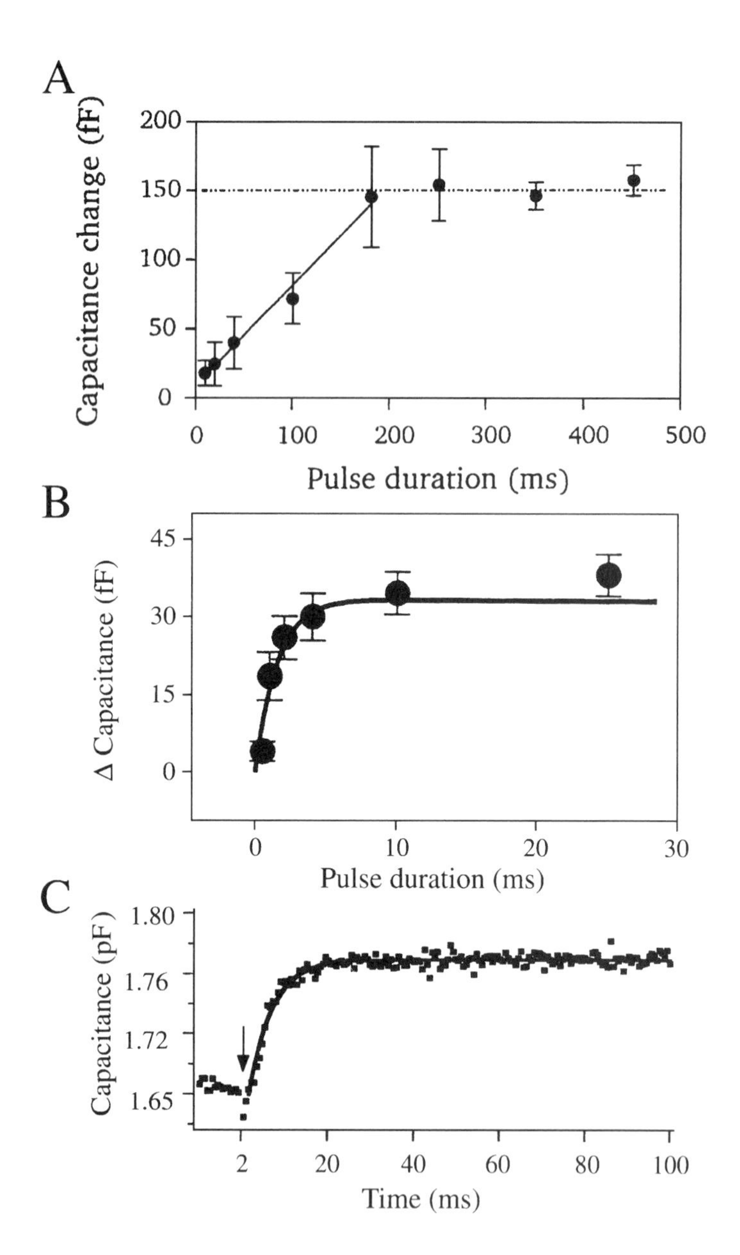
A
Capacitance change (fF)
200
150
100
50
0
0
100
200
300
400
500
Pulse duration (ms)
B
Δ Capacitance (fF)
45
30
15
0
0
10
20
30
Pulse duration (ms)
C
Capacitance (pF)
1.80
1.76
1.72
1.65
2
20
40
60
80
100
Time (ms)

the time course of recovery from depression may represent the rate of repopulation of denuded ribbons by synaptic vesicles. Fast endocytosis was not required for recovery from depression (121), and thus, the replenishment of the release-ready pool occurs from preformed reserve vesicles, which are highly abundant in bipolar-cell terminals.

Depletion of vesicle pools following prolonged stimulation has been documented in several synaptic preparations with conventional active zones at the EM level (40, 46, 57, 76, 87, 127). However, electrophysiological studies have been plagued by the fact that a decrease in synaptic transmission may be due to factors other than decreased release, including postsynaptic receptor desensitization, presynaptic Ca-current inactivation, presynaptic autoreceptor activation, and/or decreases in external Ca^{2+} concentration during stimulation (115). Synaptic depression, therefore, may result from multiple factors. Thus, capacitance measurements may, in some instances, provide a more reliable assay of changes in transmitter release than the sensitive, but noisy and saturable, postsynaptic receptor (27).

Rate of Release: Conventional Versus Ribbon-Type Synapses

The size of capacitance change elicited by Ca^{2+} currents of different durations is shown in Figure 2*A*. For pulse durations of 10–450 ms, Ca^{2+} influx correlates well with pulse duration because Ca^{2+} current inactivation is slow (55, 119). A straight line fit to the initial rise in capacitance with increasing pulse duration gives a slope of 730 fF/s, corresponding to an initial rate of fusion of 28,000 vesicles/s. Because an average bipolar terminal contains about 55 synaptic

←

Figure 2 Kinetics of exocytosis. (*A*) Capacitance versus depolarizing pulse duration. Voltage was stepped from −60 to 0 mV for a variable duration, and the corresponding capacitance jump was measured. Capacitance jumps saturated after approximately 200 ms at a value of approximately 150 fF, even though calcium influx continued to increase with pulse duration because I_{Ca} inactivated slowly. Data points show averages (± standard error of the mean) from 5 to 27 terminals. For pulse durations <100 ms, responses from 5 to 25 pulses were averaged for each terminal to reduce capacitance noise levels. The patch-pipette solution contained 0.4 mM BAPTA and 0.1 mM fura-2 as calcium buffers (reproduced from 117). (*B*) A fast component of exocytosis triggered by Ca current. Capacitance measurements using pulse durations from 0.5 to 25 ms reveal an extremely fast component of capacitance rise. (*Solid line*) A single exponential fit with a time constant of 1.5 ms and an amplitude of 33 fF. Note the deviation of the last data point from the fit, which suggests that a slower component of release is beginning to become evident with longer pulses. The patch-pipette solution contained 0.5 mM EGTA (reproduced from 72). (*C*) Flash photolysis of caged Ca triggers rapid capacitance increase. (*Arrow*) A flash of light triggered the photolysis of Ca-loaded DM-nitrophen (10 mM) dialyzed into the bipolar terminal and an increase in $[Ca^{2+}]_i$ of ~40 μM, as measured by furaptra, a low-affinity Ca-indicator dye. The exponential fit had a time constant of 5.2 ms, and the capacitance increased by approximately 100 fF (reproduced from 42).

ribbons, the release rate per active zone would be ~500 vesicles/s. Similar estimates were also found from capacitance measurements in hair cells, which are presynaptic cells whose synaptic output sites are marked by synaptic dense bodies (86). The spherical dense bodies are thought to be functionally similar to synaptic ribbons. However, in hair cells, capacitance responses continue to increase linearly with pulse duration up to the maximum tested duration (2 s). During a 2-s depolarization, the number of vesicles released in hair cells was more than twice the estimated total number of vesicles attached to the dense bodies. Hair cells, therefore, differ from bipolar cells with respect to saturation of their response and may have active zones specialized for rapid replenishment of vesicles.

Notice that the straight line fit of Figure 2*A* does not intercept the vertical capacitance axis at zero, indicating that release rates may be even higher during the first few milliseconds of depolarization, as observed for amacrine cell synapses (36). This is indeed the case, as shown in Figure 2*B*. For pulse durations from 0.5 to 5 ms, capacitance increases with a single exponential time constant of approximately 1.5 ms to a plateau value of ~30 fF (72). This ultrafast pool corresponds to approximately 1200 29-nm synaptic vesicles, which is approximately the number of vesicles tethered closest to the plasma membrane, in the bottom row of vesicles on the synaptic ribbon. This ultrafast component of capacitance increase, thus, may correspond to the fusion of docked vesicles at the base of the synaptic ribbon, whereas the slower component of capacitance increase of Figure 2*A* may represent more distal vesicles on the ribbon.

Variable pulse-duration experiments at frog neuromuscular junctions (52), amacrine-cell synapses (36), lamprey synapses (69), *Aplysia* synapses (102), and squid giant synapses (64) also show an approximate linear rise, with increasing presynaptic pulse duration followed by a saturation of the postsynaptic response. Saturation is reached within 2 ms at the neuromuscular junction, within 5 ms for squid giant synapse, and within 35 ms for *Aplysia* neurons, whereas capacitance responses saturate only at 200 ms for bipolar terminals. Differences in the readily releasable vesicle pool size, calcium buffering, and release rates among different synaptic terminals may account for these results.

At conventional synapses between cultured amacrine cells (35), sustained release rates of 20 vesicles/s at a single docking site are estimated during stimulation. However, quantal analysis reveals a faster component of 150 vesicles/s per release site, which is thought to be due to those vesicles initially docked at the plasma membrane (10). These results have been interpreted in the context of a fire and reload scheme, where a release site will be refractory to vesicle fusion for 45 ms before a vesicle is able to fuse again at that same site (10). Similar numbers are also obtained independently (106) in cultured rat hippocampal neurons (20 quanta per s per synapse for sustained release and ~20 ms for reloading). Thus, conventional synapses appear to have much slower rates of sustained release than do ribbon synapses. However, assuming each of the ~22 docking sites at the base of the ribbon are individual release sites, then each fusion site produces 23 fusions/s, to achieve the total rate per ribbon of 500 vesicles/s (120). This similarity in the rate per fusion site suggests that the basic mechanism underlying fusion and redocking may be the same for conventional and ribbon-type synapses. However, at conventional synapses, the number of morphologically docked vesicles per active zone is ~10, whereas the releasable pool size averages 8 quanta (23, 100). Ribbon synapses, thus, may serve to increase the number of release sites and the pool of readily releasable vesicles, and their compactness may aid in the transmission of high signal rates (22).

Calcium-Dependence of Exocytosis in Bipolar-Cell Terminals: Dialysis, Flash Photolysis, and Ca^{2+} Buffers

Dialysis of highly buffered levels of Ca^{2+} via the patch-pipette (117) causes a significant capacitance increase in bipolar-cell terminals, provided $[Ca^{2+}]_i$ exceeds ~20 μM. Levels of 1–2 μM $[Ca^{2+}]_i$ have no effect on capacitance or calcium current, whereas levels of ~50 μM did cause a slow sigmoidal increase in capacitance after a diffusion-related delay. On average, an increase of 340 fF was observed with ~50 μM $[Ca^{2+}]_i$. Similar experiments in chromaffin cells indicate that 0.5–1 μM $[Ca^{2+}]_i$ is sufficient to elicit secretion (8). Chromaffin cells and bipolar-cell synaptic terminals, thus, differ 20-fold or more in terms of the calcium-threshold for secretion. Rapid superfusion of high concentrations of ionomycin (10 μg/ml) also can elicit capacitance increases in bipolar-cell terminals, but at rates 20-fold lower than those elicited by Ca^{2+} current (117). The faster rate elicited by depolarization reflects, in part, the more synchronous activation of secretion throughout the terminal from voltage-clamp pulses and also the strategic colocalization of synaptic vesicles and Ca^{2+} channels (93).

Heidelberger et al (42) studied the calcium-dependence of the rate of exocytosis in bipolar-cell synaptic terminals using flash photolysis of DM-nitrophen to rapidly elevate Ca^{2+} to high concentrations. High-time-resolution capacitance measurements were used to track fast changes in capacitance, whereas the Ca^{2+} level achieved by the flash was monitored with the low-affinity Ca^{2+} indicator furaptra (88). Figure 2*C* shows the capacitance response to a flash that caused an increase in $[Ca^{2+}]_i$ to about 40 μM. The rise in capacitance was well described by a single exponential. The threshold level of $[Ca^{2+}]_i$ that elicited detectable capacitance responses was 10–20 μM, confirming the results obtained with Ca^{2+}-dialysis. The time constant of the single exponential fit was steeply dependent on $[Ca^{2+}]_i$, and the results could be fit by a model assuming sequential and cooperative binding of calcium to four sites. Half-saturation was at 194 μM, implicating a low-affinity calcium sensor protein in synaptic vesicle fusion. The high rates of release observed indicate that bipolar-cell synapses are capable of extremely rapid signaling if $[Ca^{2+}]_i$ is elevated to levels above

50 μM, as can occur transiently in the vicinity of Ca^{2+} channels. A fourth power relationship between Ca^{2+} and postsynaptic response was also reported in studies of squid giant synapses (7) and frog neuromuscular junctions (24). This Ca-dependence of exocytosis was found to be independent of ATP-Mg; however, the ability of terminals to respond to multiple stimuli was greatly reduced in the absence of ATP-Mg (41), as also occurs in neuroendocrine cells (85).

Similar to its effect at the giant synapse of squid (1), internally perfused BAPTA (5 mM), a fast Ca^{2+} chelator, completely eliminated capacitance jumps elicited by a 250-ms depolarizing pulse (117). However, 0.5 mM BAPTA had little effect. Prolonged trains of depolarizing pulses were necessary to overcome the effect of 5 mM BAPTA and, finally, evoke capacitance increases. EGTA, a slow Ca^{2+} buffer, was less effective than BAPTA in attenuating the capacitance responses elicited by pulse trains (121). Similar effects were also observed at the neuromuscular junction of frogs (94), but at the calyx of Held synapse (11), EGTA is more potent at attenuating evoked transmitter release, albeit not as effectively as BAPTA. The relative density and distance of Ca^{2+} channels from release sites, thus, may vary between synapses and perhaps during development.

In summary, the release characteristics of bipolar-cell terminals differ from neuroendocrine cells in several respects. Salient features of neuroendocrine secretion are the relatively low level of $[Ca^{2+}]_i$ triggering (8, 15) granule fusion (0.5–4 μM), the triggering of exocytosis by GTP-γ-S (83), and the considerable delay in secretion after stimulus reception (15). Bursts of action potentials are required to produce significant release in neuroendocrine cells (30, 132). Stimulus-secretion coupling, thus, is less tight than in neurons, where release occurs within <1 ms following a single action potential. A weaker spatial coupling between Ca^{2+} channels and secretory granules (15) may account in part for this difference.

Phasic and Tonic Synapses

Synapses in the retina (25) and in several neuromuscular junction preparations, such as crayfish (6) and lizard (125), can be either phasic or tonic. Phasic spinal motor neurons are associated with rapid twitch muscles and tonic motor neurons with slow, nonfatiguing muscles involved in endurance-requiring responses. Phasic neurons characteristically release most of their transmitter initially when stimulated by a series of impulses and depress subsequently, whereas tonic synapses are resistant to depression and display facilitation for sustained stimulation (18). The lobster neuromuscular junction, for example, has ribbon-type synapses that facilitate or depress depending on the muscle type innervated (53). Hair cells, which have synaptic dense bodies, also release in tonic and phasic modes (130). Likewise, squid giant synapse, a premier example of a fast, phasic synapse, can release in a slow, asynchronous manner at a low level for long depolarizations of small amplitude, indicating that transmitter release does not have an abrupt threshold (14). Thus, both ribbon-type and conventional synapses may operate in tonic and/or phasic modes.

In bipolar-cell terminals, the rapid change in capacitance, the saturation of the capacitance response with pulses longer than 200 ms, and the depression of subsequent responses point toward a more phasic behavior. By contrast, photoreceptors release transmitter tonically in darkness, and increases of 1–2 μM $[Ca^{2+}]_i$ cause capacitance changes (90), indicating that photoreceptor synapses may operate differently from bipolar-cell synapses, in spite of the fact that both have ribbon-type active zones. Differentially expressed isoforms of the presumed calcium sensor, synaptotagmin, with different Ca^{2+}-affinities may explain these findings. At lizard neuromuscular junctions, both phasic and tonic presynaptic terminals contain conventional active zones with similar vesicle concentrations, but an action potential releases at least 10 times more quanta at phasic terminals. Because the number of active zone particles (putative Ca^{2+} channels) flanking vesicles in active zones of phasic terminals is larger than at tonic terminals, Walrond & Reese (125) hypothesize that the resulting greater calcium influx in the phasic terminals is responsible for their greater probability of release. In recent agreement with this hypothesis, Cooper et al (18), using calcium indicator dyes, found in the neuromuscular junction of crayfish greater calcium influx in proximal nerve terminals (phasic) than in central nerve terminals (tonic). Thus mechanisms that regulate calcium channel density and anchoring at active zones may determine synaptic output characteristics.

At conventional synapses, evoked neurotransmitter release has a rapid component (synchronous release) followed by a period, lasting up to 0.5 s, of asynchronous release, during which small, spontaneous release events occur with enhanced probability (19, 37). Hippocampal neurons lacking synaptotagmin I express only the asynchronous form of release, implicating synaptotagmin I as a major Ca^{2+} sensor for phasic release (32). At cultured amacrine cell synapses, the asynchronous component of release can last for seconds, depending on calcium current amplitude and duration (36). Thus, different isoforms of the Ca^{2+} sensor for release, with different Ca^{2+} affinities, may also be differentially expressed across conventional synapses and during development.

GLUTAMATE SECRETION FROM BIPOLAR CELL TERMINALS

Two Components of Glutamate Release

Bipolar cells have prominent glutamate immunohistochemical signatures (68), and electrophysiological recordings reveal excitatory synapses between

ON-type bipolar cells and ON-OFF transient amacrine cells (20, 59). Direct evidence for glutamate secretion from goldfish bipolar-cell terminals was first obtained by Tachibana & Okada (109) in a series of double patch-clamp experiments in which retinal horizontal cells were used to detect glutamate release from closely apposed bipolar cells. The postsynaptic current evoked in the horizontal cell (held at +30 mV) by depolarization of the bipolar cell was similar to the response evoked in horizontal cells by iontophoretically applied glutamate and was blocked reversibly by the application of 50 μM D-AP5, a NMDA receptor antagonist (99). The postsynaptic responses in horizontal cells were found to correlate well with the Ca^{2+} current I–V relation of the bipolar cell, and superfusion of Cd^{2+} or dihydropyridines, which block the bipolar-cell L-type Ca^{2+} current (43, 110), eliminated the postsynaptic response (110). Thus, L-type channels control secretion from bipolar-cell terminals, as they do in the lizard neuromuscular junction (62). Taken together, these results indicate that Mb1 bipolar terminals of goldfish release glutamate.

As described previously (see Figure 2), capacitance measurements reveal two components of exocytosis in bipolar-cell synaptic terminals (72, 99). Experiments using horizontal cells to detect glutamate release from bipolar cells also reveal two temporally distinct components of release. Figure 3 shows that when a long depolarization (3 s) is given to a terminal loaded with 5 mM EGTA, the postsynaptic response of the horizontal cell has a double-peaked shape (99). A rapid component of release was evoked after the onset of depolarization, and then a slow, delayed component was elicited during the sustained depolarization. The delay of this second component of release depended on the amplitude of the depolarizing pulse (Figure 3). These results demonstrate that bipolar terminals have at least two distinct pools of synaptic vesicles: a small readily releasable pool (first component), and a larger reserve pool that is released more slowly (second component) during Ca^{2+} current activation. These components may correspond to the vesicles in the bottom-most row tethered at the base of the ribbon (first component) and to those tethered to the upper rows (second component), which are subsequently mobilized to release sites. This mobilization process apparently is modulated by Ca because it can be accelerated by increasing Ca influx (122). Interestingly, biphasic transmitter release kinetics has also been observed during a long depolarizing pulse at the inhibitory neuromuscular synapse of crayfish (123).

Recently, AMPA receptor-mediated responses were observed in horizontal cells induced by glutamate release from bipolar-cell terminals at the same time capacitance measurements were used to track presynaptic exocytosis (122a). These experiments provide direct comparison between glutamate release and capacitance changes in the presynaptic terminal. Figure 4 shows an example of the results of one such simultaneous pre-/postsynaptic recording. Here,

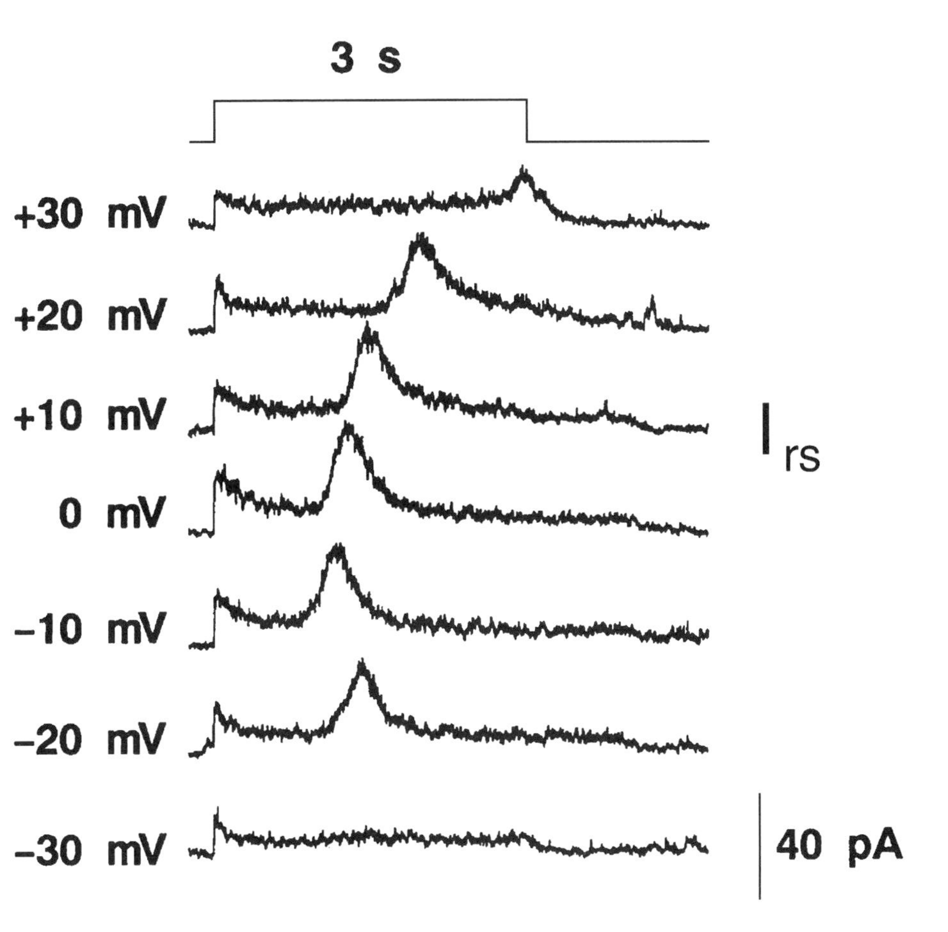

Figure 3 Bipolar-cell glutamate release: two components. Goldfish bipolar-cell terminals were depolarized for 3 s (*top trace*) from −60 mV to the values shown on the *left*, which evoked calcium currents of different amplitudes. Glutamate was released from the bipolar-cell terminal onto an apposed catfish horizontal cell held at −30 mV, evoking a current I_{rs}, which was double-peaked. The glutamate receptors of the catfish horizontal cell are of the NMDA type (slowly inactivating even with a 10-s application of glutamate). A likely explanation for the eventual decay of I_{rs} during Ca-current activation is the complete depletion of the readily releasable pool of vesicles attached to synaptic ribbons. The whole-cell pipette solution of the bipolar terminal contained 5 mM EGTA. (Reproduced from Reference 99).

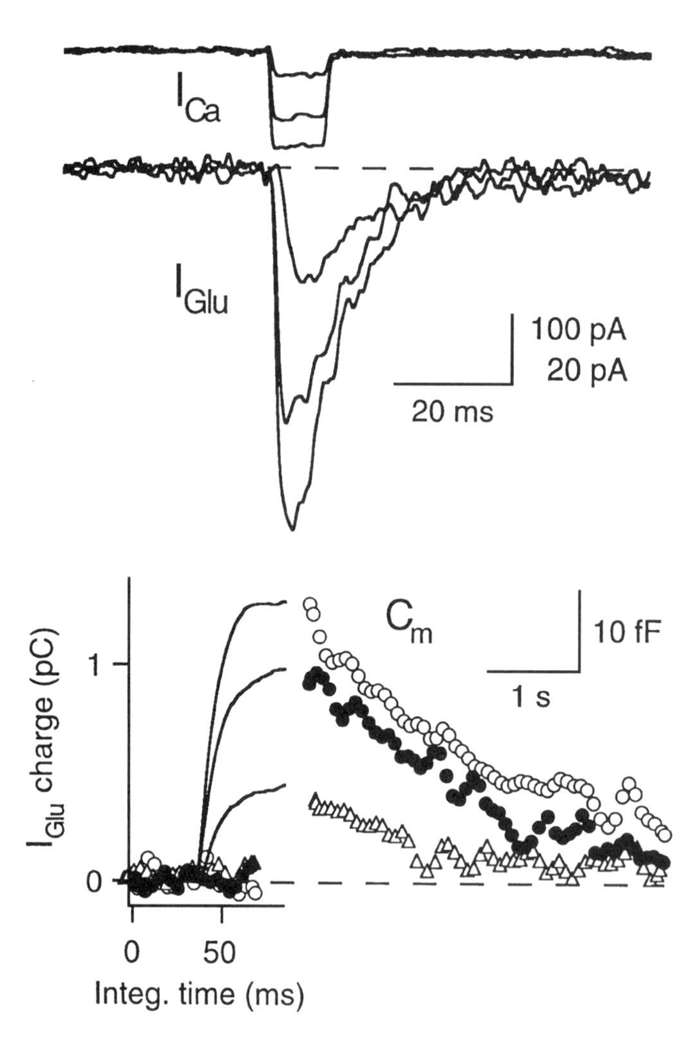

Figure 4 Simultaneous glutamate release and capacitance measurements. (*Top trace*) The Ca current evoked by 10-ms depolarizing pulses to −30, −20, and −10 mV from a holding potential of −60 mV. The horizontal cell was held at −70 mV. The external solution contained 100 μM cyclothiazide to block AMPA receptor desensitization and 50 μM D-AP5 to block NMDA receptors. The resting capacitance of the terminal was 2.1 pF. (*Open circle*) −10 mV; (*black circle*) −20 mV; and (*triangle*) −30 mV (122a).

10-ms pulses of −30, −20, and −10 mV were given, eliciting, respectively, greater Ca currents and correspondingly larger excitatory currents (I_{glu}) in the horizontal cell. These currents were completely blocked by 10 μM 6-cyano-7-nitroquinoxaline-2,3-dione (CNQX), an AMPA receptor antagonist, and 100 μM cyclothiazide enhanced the response by reducing desensitization. The integral of I_{glu} is shown, as are the respective capacitance responses (notice the difference in timescales between the panels). The amount of glutamate release, as measured by the integral of the glutamate current, correlated well with the respective jumps in capacitance. The recovery of the capacitance back to baseline is well fit by single exponentials with time constants of 1–2 s, indicating that for these short pulses, the rate of endocytosis does not depend on the amount of previous exocytosis (97). Capacitance jumps, thus, are a faithful indicator of the amount of glutamate secretion from bipolar-cell terminals, since the rate of endocytosis is at least 100-fold slower than the rate of exocytosis.

ENDOCYTOSIS IN NERVE TERMINALS

Anatomical and Molecular Studies

Efficient local recycling of synaptic vesicles is a crucial requirement for normal nervous system operation (21). This is clearly evident by considering the temperature-sensitive *Drosophila* mutant *shibire* (58). This mutant displays normal behavior at the permissive temperature (19°C) but is paralyzed at higher temperatures (29°C). The effect is rapid (within 30 s, flies are completely paralyzed) and reversible (full recovery takes 20 min). EM micrographs show that synaptic transmission fails in *shibire* flies at 29°C because of synaptic vesicle depletion at nerve terminals, owing to a block of vesicle recycling at the endocytosis step (57). The mutation has been traced to a single gene whose product is dynamin, a GTPase that is regulated by Ca (92) following nerve terminal depolarization. *Shibire* flies form clathrin-coated vesicles that invaginate normally but cannot pinch off to complete the endocytotic fission. Incubation of synaptosomes with GTP-γ-S induces long, tube-like invaginations capped by coated or uncoated vesicles on the plasma membrane. The tube-like invagination is covered by an electron-dense spiral of dynamin, thus resembling the *shibire* phenotype at nonpermissive temperature. It is thought that *shibire* dynamin cannot constrict the neck of the budding vesicle because of a defect in its GTPase activity (111).

Antibodies to lumenal epitopes of synaptotagmin have been used to show that synaptic vesicle protein does not remain on the plasma membrane even after extensive depolarization (70). Conversely, antibodies to the plasma membrane protein neural cell adhesion molecule (NCAM) do not appear to be rapidly internalized (81), which suggests that the two membranes do not mix considerably and that synaptic vesicle membrane proteins may be selectively tagged for rapid retrieval. Fused synaptic vesicle membrane proteins may remain somewhat linked for some time and tagged for endocytosis as a unit by the retrieval machinery of the cell (13). A complex sequence of molecular events, thus, leads to vesicle membrane internalization.

Endocytosis depends steeply on temperature (76) and on the metabolic state of the cell (126). In conditions that inhibit oxidative phosphorylation, stimulated nerve terminals are severely depleted of vesicles at active zones (6). Clathrin-coated vesicles (71) are clearly involved in some forms of presynaptic endocytosis, as evidenced by the accumulation of coated pits that do not undergo full fission in *Drosophila shibire* mutants (58) and by the large increase in coated vesicle density at strongly stimulated active zones (13, 38). However, budding vesicles without identifiable coats are also observed, which suggests that in nerve terminals, some forms of endocytosis may be independent of clathrin (5, 111, 117).

Two Types of Endocytosis Are Observed: Fast and Slow

Through a combination of electron microscopy and horseradish peroxidase uptake techniques, several groups have reported at least two types of membrane retrieval mechanisms. In photoreceptor terminals, two kinds of membrane retrieval mechanisms have been described (17). First, some synaptic vesicles seem to recycle rapidly without going through a coated vesicle stage. Second, a diventricular membrane infolding was observed and thought to result from the fusion and coalescence of synaptic vesicle membrane with the presynaptic plasma membrane. Retrieval and recycling via this second process did involve coat formation. Miller & Heuser (75), using quick-frozen 4-AP–treated frog neuromuscular junction, also report two types for membrane retrieval mechanisms. One occurred within the first few seconds after exocytosis, as large vacuoles ($\sim$0.1 μm) pinched off from the plasma membrane at the active zone and away from it. This process was not mediated via coated pits. The second process was a slower, clathrin-coat–dependent endocytosis and appeared to be selective because large intramembrane particles were internalized. This slower process occurred everywhere on the synaptic terminal, except at the active zone.

Using capacitance measurements, we have reported similar results for bipolar-cell synaptic terminals (117). Rapid recovery of capacitance occurs after brief stimuli (τ = 1–2 s), and a slower recovery was observed after sustained stimulation with a train of pulses (average τ = 20 s). Rapid endocytosis was also observed at neurohypophysial nerve terminals (54), where fast (τ = 0.4 s) and slow endocytosis were observed for short and long pulses, respectively (49). Because these nerve terminals contain both small, clear-core vesicles and large, dense-core vesicles, the faster rates may be due to endocytosis of membrane associated with the former, whereas the slower rates may be due to retrieval of membrane associated with the latter. Clonal PC12 cells, which also have both types of vesicles, may behave similarly (51). A slowing of endocytosis with repetitive flashes of caged Ca^{2+} is also observed in pituitary cells (112). Endocytosis may, however, occur simultaneously with slow, asynchronous exocytosis in some neuroendocrine cells because of their low $[Ca^{2+}]_i$ threshold for exocytosis (8).

Clathrin-dependent endocytosis may be too slow to mediate rapid endocytosis (5). Coated-pit–mediated endocytosis, independent of ligand-receptor binding, is reported to occur within 25 s, whereas even slower rates are reported for receptor-mediated endocytosis (44). In nerve terminals, rapid clathrin-independent endocytosis may serve to quickly clear fused vesicular membrane from release sites and, hence, reestablish conditions for vesicle docking at the same fusion site. Following prolonged stimulation, slower endocytosis may result from the accumulation of synaptic vesicle membrane away from active zones and the need for selective retrieval of large amounts of synaptic vesicle membrane proteins through coated-pit formation. The location of endocytosis in synapses may depend on the levels of release (56, 75), and recent evidence indicates retrieved vesicles do not fuse with endosomes during recycling (79).

Ca-Dependent and Ca-Independent Forms of Endocytosis

The onset of endocytosis at bipolar-cell terminals is delayed after depolarizing pulses exceeding 500 ms in duration (118). With such long-duration pulses, $[Ca^{2+}]_i$ typically rises to >1 μM in the terminal. As $[Ca^{2+}]_i$ fell below $\sim$700 nM, capacitance began to recover, albeit slowly, with $\tau \sim 8$ s. The delay and the slow recovery of capacitance contrasts sharply with the behavior of capacitance for briefer depolarizations ($\leq$250 ms), after which recovery is rapid, with $\tau = 1$–2 s. The slower endocytosis with longer depolarizations can be attributed to the higher level of $[Ca^{2+}]_i$ achieved by longer pulses (118). Elevation of $[Ca^{2+}]_i$ by application of the Ca^{2+} ionophore ionomycin also slowed the rate of capacitance recovery, as did dialysis with pipette solutions containing buffered $[Ca^{2+}]_i$ in the range of 0.3–2 μM. Calcium current was not inactivated by these levels of $[Ca^{2+}]_i$, and the ability of the terminal to exocytose repeatedly was not compromised (see Figure 5). Global levels of Ca^{2+} near 1 μM or above were sufficient to completely inhibit fast endocytosis, whereas resting levels of $[Ca^{2+}]_i$ in the range of 50–300 nM gave approximately equal rates of fast endocytosis.

After a train of depolarizations, endocytosis proceeds slowly, with $\tau = 20$ s in bipolar terminals. The $[Ca^{2+}]_i$ transient induced by a train of pulses decays with $\tau = 2$–4 s, which means this slow form of endocytosis is not correlated

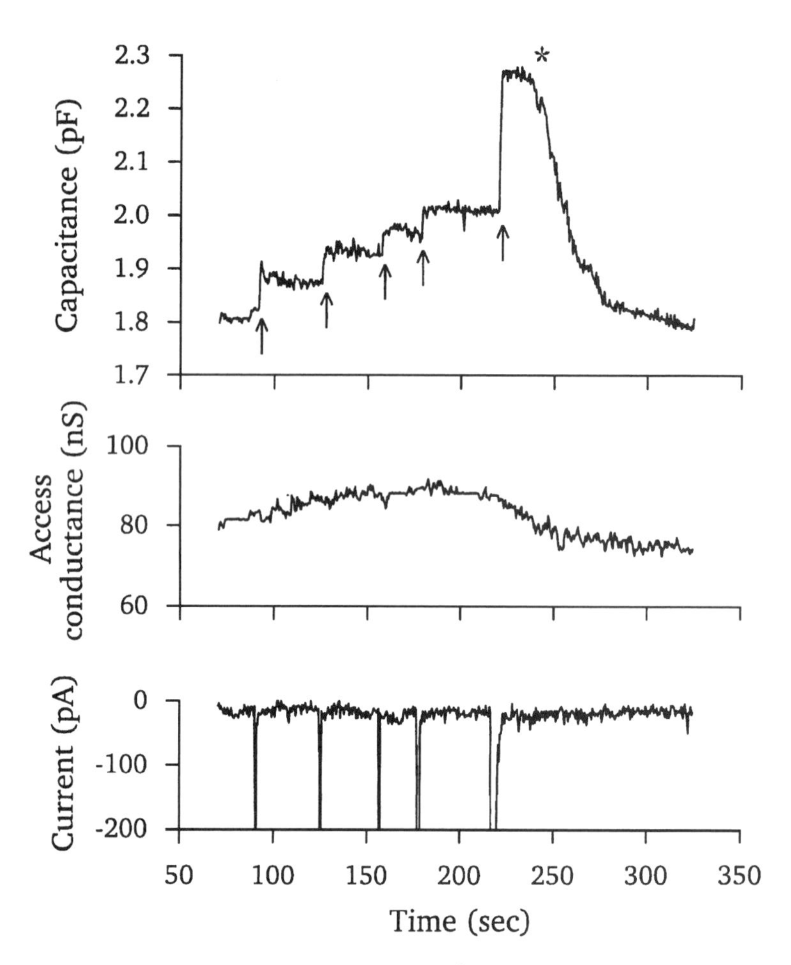

Figure 5 Fast endocytosis is blocked by elevated $[Ca^{2+}]_i$. Fast endocytosis was inhibited by buffering $[Ca^{2+}]_i$ to approximately 2 μM by including 7 mM diazo-2 and 4 mM $CaCl_2$ in the patch-pipette solution. In addition, the pipette solution contained, in mM: Cs-glutamate, 103; TEA-Cl, 5; Cs-HEPES, 34; fura-2, 0.5; Mg-ATP, 2; and GTP, 0.5 (pH = 7.2). Break-in occurred at 70 s. (*Arrows*) Timing of depolarizations from −60 mV to 0 mV, with durations of 250 ms (first 3 pulses), 1 s (pulse 4), or 3 s (pulse 5). The amplitude of the Ca current was 270 pA. (*Top trace*) Capacitance; (*middle trace*) access conductance; (*bottom trace*) membrane current. The capacitance responses to the first four pulses may have been reduced in size because of the added calcium buffer in the pipette solution. Notice that repetitive responses, totaling a capacitance increase of about 450 fF, occurred in the absence of fast endocytosis. Access conductance and membrane current (at the holding potential of −60 mV) showed no consistent changes during the recording and no changes correlated with stimulation. (*Asterisk, top trace*) The onset of a delayed form of endocytosis, which appeared in this cell after the large capacitance response evoked by the 3-s depolarization. This delayed form of slow endocytosis was observed only after a large cumulative increase in capacitance. The large capacitance jump evoked by the 3-s pulse (pulse 5) may be due to a Ca-dependent increase in the rate of mobilization of reserve vesicles during stimulation (122).

with the instantaneous level of $[Ca^{2+}]_i$ (117). A similar conclusion was reached at the neuromuscular junction for endocytosis following repetitive stimulation (129). Although the recovery of capacitance to baseline is not correlated with the recovery of calcium concentration, slow endocytosis after a train of depolarizations is usually blocked when bipolar terminals are dialyzed with $[Ca^{2+}]_i = 1\text{–}2\ \mu M$. Thus, tonically elevated $[Ca^{2+}]_i$ can inhibit slow endocytosis as well as fast endocytosis. Alternatively, because capacitance measures only net surface area changes, it is possible that at these levels of $[Ca^{2+}]_i$, a continuous form of exo-endocytosis is elicited (61) that produces no net capacitance changes (90). In some rare cases, we have observed endocytosis with $\tau \sim 20$ s occurring even at $[Ca^{2+}]_i = 1\text{–}2\ \mu M$. An example is shown in Figure 5. An avalanche-like, Ca^{2+}-independent form of slow endocytosis is, therefore, present in bipolar cells following a large cumulative increase in capacitance and may be a fail-safe mechanism that is invoked after large bouts of exocytosis to avoid catastrophic increases in cellular surface area (104). Because this Ca^{2+}-independent form of endocytosis was observed only rarely, we have not been able to study its regulation.

Perforated patch recordings in pancreatic β cells (26) show that short depolarizing pulses elicited no endocytosis or very slow endocytosis, whereas long depolarizations had faster endocytosis. This behavior is in striking contrast to that observed in bipolar-cell terminals (118) and neurohypophysial nerve terminals (49), where short (10–200 ms) pulses display fast endocytosis. These differences in the calcium dependence of endocytosis may indicate that cells have several modes of membrane retrieval (105, 112).

Optical Monitoring of Endocytosis

Studies with the activity-dependent dye FM1-43 (9) have shown that the duration of stimulation determines the rate of endocytosis at the neuromuscular junction of frogs (129). The fastest rate of endocytosis had $\tau \sim 20$ s (10-s stimulation at 30 Hz). Increasing the duration of stimulation slowed endocytosis ($\tau \sim 57$ s for 60-s stimulation at 30 Hz). Interestingly, endocytosis occurred during stimulation and was not determined by the instantaneous level of $[Ca^{2+}]_i$. Somewhat different conclusions were reported in the pioneering work of Holtzman et al (47), where horseradish peroxidase (HRP) uptake into vesicles within nerve endings was first demonstrated. Both a complete lack of stimulation and continuous stimulation up to the point of fixation produced little uptake of HRP. However, stimulation interspersed with rest periods produced nerve terminals with 20–50% of their vesicles stained with HRP, consistent with the hypothesis that sustained stimulation slows endocytosis and that endocytosis is not significant during stimulation. Exocytosis induced by treatment with ouabain, a Na^+/K^+-ATPase inhibitor that induces a steady increase in $[Ca^{2+}]_i$, depletes vesicle pools and is also not accompanied by HRP uptake in frog neuromuscular junction nerve terminals (40). A caveat to these findings is that HRP is a relatively large molecule and, thus, may not serve as an appropriate fluid phase marker for fast forms of endocytosis mediated by small, 50-nm endocytic vesicles.

Ryan & Smith (96) also report half-times for endocytosis of about 20 s in cultured hippocampal neurons after 10-Hz electrical stimulation. At least 15 s were needed to reprime an endocytosed vesicle so it could re-exocytose. However, with prolonged potassium depolarization (60-s application of high potassium), half-times for endocytosis of 60 s (24°C) were measured (95), and ~30 s were needed for repriming of vesicles. Thus, very prolonged stimulation seems to slow the rate of endocytosis in hippocampal boutons. However, inhibition of the Na^+/Ca^{2+} exchanger, which is expected to elevate $[Ca^{2+}]_i$, did not affect the rate of endocytosis (89). Thus, in contrast to bipolar terminals, internal Ca^{2+} does not seem to affect the rate of endocytosis in hippocampal boutons. Furthermore, the intensity of brief stimulation also does not seem to affect the rate of endocytosis (97). When either 5% or 25% of the releasable vesicle pool was exocytosed by evoking 20 or 100 action potentials, respectively, the half-time of endocytosis was still ~20 s. Likewise in bipolar terminals, depolarizing pulse durations from 10 ms (~15% of the releasable vesicle pool) to 250 ms (~100% of the releasable pool) also give similar time constants of endocytosis (τ = 1–2 s) (118). Therefore, for both hippocampal boutons and bipolar terminals the rate of endocytosis is independent of stimulus duration until very strong and prolonged stimulation is used (e.g. > 250-ms pulse for bipolar terminals and 60 s in high potassium for hippocampal boutons).

Flicker-Fusion Endocytosis

Capacitance measurements in mast cells (3) and chromaffin cells (2) occasionally show flickering fusion events, during which secretion can occur (2, 4). The opening of the fusion pore, thus, is reversible so that dense core granules can be rapidly reinternalized. This mechanism could operate with finite capacity in briefly stimulated neurons, whereas in strongly stimulated cells full collapse of vesicle membrane would ensue (28). Is the fast endocytosis seen in bipolar-cell synaptic terminals evidence for flicker-fusion? We do not think so because very short stimuli (e.g. 10-ms pulses) (Figure 4) have the same rate of endocytosis as do much longer stimuli (200 ms), namely a τ = 1–2 s. This mode of endocytosis is, however, attractive as a mechanism of vesicle recycling because vesicle membrane would quickly be retrieved, obviating the need for future sorting of synaptic vesicle protein. A transient vesicle pore of 300 nm lasting only 260 μs can be sufficient for the full voiding of transmitter from a 50-nm vesicle (3). Full collapse of vesicular membrane onto the plasma membrane, thus, would not be a necessary requirement for synaptic transmission. Interestingly, staurosporin-treated frog neuromuscular junctions can release neurotransmitter without FM1-43 destaining (45). Synaptic transmission in this "kiss-and-run" mode, thus, is not ruled out, but there is still no direct evidence for its occurrence at synapses.

CONCLUSION

Secretion at bipolar-cell ribbon synapses and at conventional synapses are similar in several aspects, and it appears the ribbon structure allows for an active zone with a compact and large pool of readily releasable vesicles. Presynaptic exocytosis and endocytosis have rates that vary with stimulus strength, with both being initially high for strong and brief stimuli and both slowing down under sustained stimulation. The two phenomena are, however, temporally well separated because rates of endocytosis are at least ten to hundreds of times slower than those of exocytosis. The dependence of endocytosis on Ca^{2+} may turn out to be complicated, and several parallel processes of membrane retrieval are likely to be present in cells, especially when they are strongly stimulated. Thus, Ca^{2+} emerges as a versatile master switch that regulates the synaptic vesicle cycle at different levels and locations. The recruitment of vesicles from reserve to readily releasable pools during stimulation may also be regulated by internal Ca^{2+} levels. This interplay of multiple effects of Ca^{2+} allows many possible varieties of responses to repetitive stimulation at individual synapses and may account for some forms of short-term plasticity.

Literature Cited

1. Adler EM, Augustine GJ, Duffy SN, Charlton MP. 1991. Alien intracellular calcium chelators attenuate neurotransmitter release at the squid synapse. *J. Neurosci.* 11:1496–507
2. Albillos A, Dernick G, Horstmann H, Almers W, Alvarez de Toledo G, Lindau M. 1997. The exocytotic event in chromaffin cells revealed by patch amperometry. *Nature* 389:509–12
3. Almers W, Breckenridge LJ, Iwata A, Lee AK, Spruce AE, Tse FW. 1991. Millisecond studies of single membrane fusion events. *Ann. NY Acad. Sci.* 635:318–27
4. Alvarez de Toledo G, Fernández-Chacón R, Fernández JM. 1993. Release of secretory products during transient vesicle fusion. *Nature* 363:554–57
5. Artalejo CR, Henley JR, McNiven MA, Palfrey HC. 1995. Rapid endocytosis coupled to exocytosis in adrenal chromaffin cells involves Ca^{2+}, GTP, and dynamin but not clathrin. *Proc. Natl. Acad. Sci. USA* 92:8328–32
6. Atwood HL, Lang F, Morin WA. 1972. Synaptic vesicles: selective depletion in crayfish excitatory and inhibitory axons. *Science* 176:1353–55
7. Augustine GJ, Charlton MP, Smith SJ. 1985. Calcium entry and transmitter release at voltage-clamped nerve terminals of squid. *J. Physiol.* 367:143–62
8. Augustine GJ, Neher E. 1992. Calcium

requirements for secretion in bovine chromaffin cells. *J. Physiol.* 450:247–71
9. Betz WJ, Bewick GS. 1993. Optical monitoring of transmitter release and synaptic vesicle recycling at the frog neuromuscular junction. *J. Physiol.* 460: 287–309
10. Borges S, Gleason E, Turelli M, Wilson M. 1995. The kinetics of quantal transmitter release from retinal amacrine cells. *Proc. Natl. Acad. Sci. USA* 92: 6896–900
11. Borst JGG, Sakmann B. 1996. Calcium influx and transmitter release in a fast CNS synapse. *Nature* 383:431–34
12. Breckenridge LJ, Almers W. 1987. Final steps in exocytosis observed in a cell with giant secretory granules. *Proc. Natl. Acad. Sci. USA* 84:1945–49
13. Brodin L, Löw P, Gad H, Gustafsson J, Pieribone VA, Shupliakov O. 1997. Sustained neurotransmitter release: new molecular clues. *Eur. J. Neurosci.* 9: 2503–11
14. Charlton MP, Atwood HL. 1977. Slow release of transmitter at the squid giant synapse. *Neurosci. Lett.* 5:165–69
15. Chow RH, Klingauf J, Neher E. 1994. Time course of Ca^{2+} concentration triggering exocytosis in neuroendocrine cells. *Proc. Natl. Acad. Sci. USA* 91: 12765–69
16. Cole KS. 1968. *Membranes, Ions, and Impulses*, pp. 1–36. Berkeley, CA: Univ. Calif. Press
17. Cooper NG, McLaughlin B. 1983. Tracer uptake by photoreceptor synaptic terminals. I. Dark-mediated effects. *J. Ultrastruct. Res.* 84:252–67
18. Cooper RL, Marin L, Atwood HL. 1995. Synaptic differentiation of a single motor neuron: conjoint definition of transmitter release, presynaptic calcium signals, and ultrastructure. *J. Neurosci.* 15: 4209–22
19. Cummings DD, Wilcox KS, Dichter MA. 1996. Calcium-dependent paired-pulse facilitation of miniature EPSC frequency accompanies depression of EPSCs at hippocampal synapses in culture. *J. Neurosci.* 16:5312–23
20. Dacheux RF, Raviola E. 1986. The rod pathway in the rabbit retina: a depolarizing bipolar and amacrine cell. *J. Neurosci.* 6:331–45
21. De Camilli P, Takei K. 1996. Molecular mechanisms in synaptic vesicle endocytosis and recycling. *Neuron* 16:481–86
22. de Ruyter van Steveninck RR, Laughlin SB. 1996. The rate of information transfer at graded-potential synapses. *Nature* 379:642–45
23. Dobrunz LE, Stevens CF. 1997. Heterogeneity of release probability, facilitation, and depletion at central synapses. *Neuron* 18:995–1008
24. Dodge FA, Rahamimoff R. 1967. Co-operative action of calcium ions in transmitter release at the neuromuscular junction. *J. Physiol.* 193:419–32
25. Dowling JE. 1987. *The Retina: An approachable part of the brain.* Cambridge, MA: Harvard Univ. Press
26. Eliasson L, Proks P, Ämmälä C, Ashcroft FM, Bokvist K, et al. 1996. Endocytosis of secretory granules in mouse pancreatic b-cells evoked by transient elevation of cytosolic calcium. *J. Physiol.* 493:755–67
27. Faber DS, Young WS, Legendre P, Korn H. 1992. Intrinsic quantal variability due to stochastic properties of receptor-transmitter interactions. *Science* 258:1494–98
28. Fesce R, Grohovaz F, Valtorta F, Meldolesi J. 1994. Neurotransmitter release: fusion or 'kiss-and-run'? *Trends Cell Biol.* 4:1–4
29. Fettiplace R, Andrews DM, Haydon DA. 1971. The thickness, composition and structure of some lipid bilayers and natural membranes. *J. Membr. Biol.* 5:277–96
30. Fidler Lim N, Nowycky MC, Bookman RJ. 1990. Direct measurement of exocytosis and calcium currents in single vertebrate nerve terminals. *Nature* 344:449–51
31. Fields RD, Ellisman MH. 1985. Synaptic morphology and differences in sensitivity. *Science* 228:197–99
32. Geppert M, Goda Y, Hammer RE, Li C, Rosahl TW, et al. 1994. Synaptotagmin I: a major Ca^{2+} sensor for neurotransmitter release at a central synapse. *Cell* 79:717–27
33. Gillespie JI. 1979. The effect of repetitive stimulation on the passive electrical properties of the presynaptic terminal of the squid giant synapse. *Proc. R. Soc. London Ser. B* 206:293–306
34. Gillis KD. 1995. Techniques for membrane capacitance measurements. In *Single-Channel Recording*, ed. B Sakmann, E Neher, pp. 155–98. New York: Plenum. 2nd ed.
35. Gleason E, Borges S, Wilson M. 1993. Synaptic transmission between pairs of retinal amacrine cells in culture. *J. Neurosci.* 13:2359–70
36. Gleason E, Borges S, Wilson M. 1994.

Control of transmitter release from retinal amacrine cells by Ca^{2+} influx and efflux. *Neuron* 13:1109–17
37. Goda Y, Stevens CF. 1994. Two components of transmitter release at a central synapse. *Proc. Natl. Acad. Sci. USA* 91: 12942–46
38. Gray EG, Pease HL. 1971. On understanding the organization of retinal receptor synapses. *Brain Res.* 35:1–15
39. Greengard P, Valtorta F, Czernik AJ, Benfenati F. 1993. Synaptic vesicle phosphoproteins and regulation of synaptic function. *Science* 259:780–85
40. Haimann C, Torri-Tarelli F, Fesce R, Ceccarelli B. 1985. Measurement of quantal secretion induced by ouabain and its correlation with depletion of synaptic vesicles. *J. Cell Biol.* 101: 1953–65
41. Heidelberger R. 1998. Adenosine triphosphate and the late steps in calcium-dependent exocytosis at a ribbon synapse. *J. Gen. Physiol.* 111:225–41
42. Heidelberger R, Heinemann C, Neher E, Matthews G. 1994. Calcium dependence of the rate of exocytosis in a synaptic terminal. *Nature* 371:513–15
43. Heidelberger R, Matthews G. 1992. Calcium influx and calcium current in single synaptic terminals of goldfish retinal bipolar neurons. *J. Physiol.* 447: 235–56
44. Henkel AW, Almers W. 1996. Fast steps in exocytosis and endocytosis studied by capacitance measurements in endocrine cells. *Curr. Opin. Neurobiol.* 6: 350–57
45. Henkel AW, Betz WJ. 1995. Staurosporine blocks evoked release of FM1-43 but not acetylcholine from frog motor nerve terminals. *J. Neurosci.* 15:8246–58
46. Heuser JE, Reese TS. 1981. Structural changes after transmitter release at the frog neuromuscular junction. *J. Cell Biol.* 88:564–80
47. Holtzman E, Freeman AR, Kashner LA. 1971. Stimulation-dependent alterations in peroxidase uptake at lobster neuromuscular junctions. *Science* 173:733–36
48. Horrigan FT, Bookman RJ. 1994. Releasable pools and the kinetics of exocytosis in adrenal chromaffin cells. *Neuron* 13:1119–29
49. Hsu S-F, Jackson MB. 1996. Rapid exocytosis and endocytosis in nerve terminals of the rat posterior pituitary. *J. Physiol.* 494:539–53
50. Jaffe LA, Hagiwara S, Kado RT. 1978. The time course of cortical vesicle fusion in sea urchin eggs observed as membrane capacitance changes. *Dev. Biol.* 67:243–48
51. Kasai H, Takagi H, Ninomiya Y, Kishimoto T, Ito K, et al. 1996. Two components of exocytosis and endocytosis in phaeochromocytoma cells studied using caged Ca^{2+} compounds. *J. Physiol.* 494:53–65
52. Katz B, Miledi R. 1967. The release of acetylcholine from nerve endings by graded electric pulses. *Proc. R. Soc. London Ser. B* 167:23–38
53. Katz PS, Kirk MD, Govind CK. 1993. Facilitation and depression at different branches of the same motor axon: evidence for presynaptic differences in release. *J. Neurosci.* 13:3075–89
54. Knoll G, Plattner H, Nordmann JJ. 1992. Exo-endocytosis in isolated peptidergic nerve terminals occurs in sub-second range. *Biosci. Rep.* 12:495–501
55. Kobayashi K, Tachibana M. 1995. Ca regulation in the presynaptic terminals of goldfish retinal bipolar cells. *J. Physiol.* 483(1):79–94
56. Koenig JH, Ikeda K. 1996. Synaptic vesicles have two distinct recycling pathways. *J. Cell Biol.* 135:797–808
57. Koenig JH, Kosaka T, Ikeda K. 1989. The relationship between the number of synaptic vesicles and the amount of transmitter released. *J. Neurosci.* 9: 1937–42
58. Kosaka T, Ikeda K. 1983. Possible temperature-dependent blockage of single synaptic vesicle recycling induced by a single gene mutation in Drosophila. *J. Neurobiol.* 14:207–25
59. Kujiraoka T, Saito T, Toyoda J-I. 1988. Analysis of synaptic inputs to ON-OFF amacrine cells of the carp retina. *J. Gen. Physiol.* 92:475–87
60. Kusano K, Landau EM. 1975. Depression and recovery of transmission at the squid giant synapse. *J. Physiol.* 245:13–32
61. Lagnado L, Gomis A, Job C. 1996. Continuous vesicle cycling in the synaptic terminal of retinal bipolar cells. *Neuron* 17:957–67
62. Lindgren CA, Moore JW. 1989. Identification of ionic currents at presynaptic nerve endings of the lizard. *J. Physiol.* 414:201–22
63. Liu G, Tsien RW. 1995. Properties of synaptic transmission at single hippocampal synaptic boutons. *Nature* 375: 404–8
64. Llinás R, Steinberg IZ, Walton K. 1981. Relationship between presynaptic and

postsynaptic potential in squid giant synapse. *Biophys. J.* 33:323–52
65. Lollike K, Borregaard N, Lindau M. 1995. The exocytotic fusion pore of small granules has a conductance similar to an ion channel. *J. Cell Biol.* 129:99–104
66. Mandell JW, Townes-Anderson E, Czernik AJ, Cameron R, Greengard P, De Camilli P. 1990. Synapsins in vertebrate retina: absence from ribbon synapses and heterogeneous distribution among conventional synapses. *Neuron* 5:19–33
67. Maple BR, Werblin FS, Wu SM. 1994. Miniature excitatory postsynaptic currents in bipolar cells of the tiger salamander retina. *Vision Res.* 34:2357–62
68. Marc RE, Liu WL, Kalloniatis M, Raiguel SF, Van Haesendonck E. 1990. Patterns of glutamate immunoreactivity in the goldfish retina. *J. Neurosci.* 10:4006–43
69. Martin AR, Ringham GL. 1975. Synaptic transfer at a vertebrate central nervous system synapse. *J. Physiol.* 251:409–26
70. Matteoli M, Takei K, Perin MS, Südhof TC, De Camilli P. 1992. Exo-endocytosis recycling of synaptic vesicles in developing processes of cultured hippocampal neurons. *J. Cell Biol.* 117:849–61
71. Maycox PR, Link E, Reetz A, Morris SA, Jahn R. 1992. Clathrin-coated vesicles in nervous tissue are involved primarily in synaptic vesicle recycling. *J. Cell Biol.* 118:1379–88
72. Mennerick S, Matthews G. 1996. Ultrafast exocytosis elicited by calcium current in synaptic terminals of retinal bipolar neurons. *Neuron* 17:1241–49
73. Mennerick S, Zenisek D, Matthews G. 1997. Static and dynamic membrane properties of large terminal bipolar cells from goldfish retina: experimental test of a compartment model. *J. Neurophysiol.* 78:51–62
74. Mennerick S, Zorumski CF. 1996. Paired-pulse modulation of fast excitatory synaptic currents in microcultures of rat hippocampal neurons. *J. Physiol.* 488:85–101
75. Miller TM, Heuser JE. 1984. Endocytosis of synaptic vesicle membrane at the frog neuromuscular junction. *J. Cell Biol.* 98:685–98
76. Model PG, Highstein SM, Bennett MVL. 1975. Depletion of vesicles and fatigue of transmission at a vertebrate control synapse. *Brain Res.* 98:209–28
77. Morgans CW, Brandstätter JH, Kellerman J, Betz H, Wässle HA. 1996. SNARE complex containing syntaxin 3 is present in ribbon synapses of the retina. *J. Neurosci.* 16:6713–21
78. Moser T, Neher E. 1997. Estimation of the mean exocytotic vesicle capacitance in mouse adrenal chromaffin cells. *Proc. Natl. Acad. Sci. USA* 94:6735–40
79. Murthy VN, Stevens CF. 1998. Synaptic vesicles retain their identity through the endocytic cycle. *Nature* 392:497–501
80. Neher E, Marty A. 1982. Discrete changes of cell membrane capacitance observed under conditions of enhanced secretion in bovine adrenal chromaffin cells. *Proc. Natl. Acad. Sci. USA* 79:6712–16
81. Nordmann JJ, Artault J-C. 1992. Membrane retrieval following exocytosis in isolated neurosecretory nerve endings. *Neuroscience* 49:201–7
82. Oberhauser AF, Robinson IM, Fernandez JM. 1996. Simultaneous capacitance and amperometric measurements of exocytosis: a comparison. *Biophys. J.* 71:1131–39
83. Okano K, Monck JR, Fernandez JM. 1993. GTP-γ-S stimulates exocytosis in patch-clamped rat melanotrophs. *Neuron* 11:165–72
84. Pappas GD, Waxman SG. 1972. Synaptic fine structure—morphological correlates of chemical and electrotonic transmission. In *Structure and Function of Synapses*, ed. GD Pappas, DP Purpura, pp. 1–43. New York: Raven
85. Parsons TD, Coorssen JR, Horstmann H, Almers W. 1995. Docked granules, the exocytotic burst and the need for ATP hydrolysis in endocrine cells. *Neuron* 15:1085–96
86. Parsons TD, Lenzi D, Almers W, Roberts WM. 1994. Calcium-triggered exocytosis and endocytosis in an isolated presynaptic cell: capacitance measurements in saccular hair cells. *Neuron* 13:875–83
87. Pieribone VA, Shupliakov O, Brodin L, Hilfiker-Rothenfluh S, Czernik AJ, Greengard P. 1995. Distinct pools of synaptic vesicles in neurotransmitter release. *Nature* 375:493–97
88. Regehr WG, Atluri PP. 1995. Calcium transients in cerebellar granule cell presynaptic terminals. *Biophys. J.* 68:2156–70
89. Reuter H, Porzig H. 1995. Localization and functional significance of the Na^+/Ca^{2+} exchanger in presynaptic boutons of hippocampal cells in culture. *Neuron* 15:1077–84

90. Rieke F, Schwartz EA. 1996. Asynchronous transmitter release: control of exocytosis and endocytosis at the salamander rod synapse. *J. Physiol.* 493:1–8
91. Roberts WM, Jacobs RA, Hudspeth AJ. 1990. Colocalization of ion channels involved in frequency selectivity and synaptic transmission at presynaptic active zones of hair cells. *J. Neurosci.* 10:3664–84
92. Robinson PJ, Sontag J-M, Liu J-P, Fykse EM, Slaughter C, et al. 1993. Dynamin GTPase regulated by protein kinase C phosphorylation in nerve terminals. *Nature* 365:163–66
93. Robitaille R, Adler EM, Charlton MP. 1990. Strategic location of calcium channels at transmitter release sites of frog neuromuscular synapses. *Neuron* 5:773–79
94. Robitaille R, Garcia ML, Kaczorowski GJ, Charlton MP. 1993. Functional colocalization of Ca and Ca-gated potassium channels in control of transmitter release. *Neuron* 11:645–55
95. Ryan TA, Reuter H, Wendland B, Schweizer FE, Tsien RW, Smith SJ. 1993. The kinetics of synaptic vesicle recycling measured at single presynaptic boutons. *Neuron* 11:713–24
96. Ryan TA, Smith SJ. 1995. Vesicle pool mobilization during action potential firing at hippocampal synapses. *Neuron* 14: 983–89
97. Ryan TA, Smith SJ, Reuter H. 1996. The timing of synaptic vesicle endocytosis. *Proc. Natl. Acad. Sci. USA* 93:5567–71
98. Saito T, Kondo H, Toyoda J-I. 1979. Ionic mechanisms of two types of on-center bipolar cells in the carp retina. I. The responses to central illumination. *J. Gen. Physiol.* 73:73–90
99. Sakaba T, Tachibana M, Matsui K, Minami N. 1997. Two components of transmitter release in retinal bipolar cells: exocytosis and mobilization of synaptic vesicles. *Neurosci. Res.* 27:357–70
100. Schikorski T, Stevens CF. 1997. Quantitative ultrastructural analysis of hippocampal excitatory synapses. *J. Neurosci.* 17:5858–67
101. Schweizer FE, Betz H, Augustine GJ. 1995. From vesicle docking to endocytosis: intermediate reactions of exocytosis. *Neuron* 14:689–96
102. Shapiro E, Castellucci VF, Kandel ER. 1980. Presynaptic membrane potential affects transmitter release in an identified neuron in *Aplysia* by modulating the Ca^{2+} and K^{+} currents. *Proc. Natl. Acad. Sci. USA* 77:629–33
103. Sherry DM, Yazulla S. 1993. Goldfish bipolar cells and axon terminal patterns: a Golgi study. *J. Comp. Neurol.* 329:188–200
104. Smith CB, Betz WJ. 1996. Simultaneous independent measurement of endocytosis and exocytosis. *Nature* 380:531–34
105. Smith CB, Neher E. 1997. Multiple forms of endocytosis in bovine adrenal chromaffin cells. *J. Cell Biol.* 139:885–94
106. Stevens CF, Tsujimoto T. 1995. Estimates for the pool size of releasable quanta at a single central synapse and for the time required to refill the pool. *Proc. Natl. Acad. Sci. USA* 92:846–49
107. Südhof TC. 1995. The synaptic vesicle cycle: a cascade of protein-protein interactions. *Nature* 375:645–53
108. Swandulla D, Hans M, Zipser K, Augustine GJ. 1991. Role of residual calcium in synaptic depression and posttetanic potentiation: fast and slow calcium signaling in nerve terminals. *Neuron* 7:915–26
109. Tachibana M, Okada T. 1991. Release of endogenous excitatory amino acids from ON-type bipolar cells isolated from the goldfish retina. *J. Neurosci.* 11:2199–208
110. Tachibana M, Okada T, Arimura T, Kobayashi K, Piccolino M. 1993. Dihydropyridine-sensitive calcium current mediates neurotransmitter release from bipolar cells of the goldfish retina. *J. Neurosci.* 13:2898–909
111. Takei K, McPherson PS, Schmid SL, De Camilli P. 1995. Tubular membrane invaginations coated by dynamin rings are induced by GTP-γ-S in nerve terminals. *Nature* 374:186–92
112. Thomas P, Lee AK, Wong JG, Almers WA. 1994. Triggered mechanism retrieves membrane in seconds after Ca^{2+}-stimulated exocytosis in single pituitary cells. *J. Cell Biol.* 124:667–75
113. Townes-Anderson E, Vogt BA. 1989. Distribution of muscarinic acetylcholine receptors on processes of isolated retinal cells. *J. Comp. Neurol.* 290:369–83
114. Usukura J, Yamada E. 1987. Ultrastructure of the synaptic ribbons in photoreceptor cells of Rana Catesbeiana revealed by freeze-etching and freeze-substitution. *Cell Tissue Res.* 247:483–88
115. Vassilev PM, Mitchel J, Vassilev M, Kanazirska M, Brown EM. 1997. Assessment of frequency-dependent alterations in the level of extracellular Ca^{2+} in

the synaptic cleft. *Biophys. J.* 72:2103–16

116. Vollrath L, Huss H. 1973. The synaptic ribbons in the guinea-pig pineal gland under normal and experimental conditions. *Z. Zellforsch.* 139:417–29
117. von Gersdorff H, Matthews G. 1994. Dynamics of synaptic vesicle fusion and membrane retrieval in synaptic terminals. *Nature* 367:735–39
118. von Gersdorff H, Matthews G. 1994. Inhibition of endocytosis by elevated internal calcium in a synaptic terminal. *Nature* 370:652–55
119. von Gersdorff H, Matthews G. 1996. Calcium-dependent inactivation of calcium current in synaptic terminals of retinal bipolar neurons. *J. Neurosci.* 16:115–22
120. von Gersdorff H, Vardi E, Matthews G, Sterling P. 1996. Evidence that vesicles on the synaptic ribbon of retinal bipolar neurons can be rapidly released. *Neuron* 16:1221–27
121. von Gersdorff H, Matthews G. 1997. Depletion and replenishment of vesicle pools at a ribbon-type synaptic terminal. *J. Neurosci.* 17:1919–27
122. von Rüden L, Neher EA. 1993. Ca-dependent early step in the release of catecholamines from adrenal chromaffin cells. *Science* 262:1061–65

122a. von Gersdorff H, Sakaba T, Berglund K, Tachibana M. 1998. Submillisecond kinetics of glutamate release from a sensory synapse. *Neuron* 21:1177–88

123. Vyshedskiy A, Lin J-W. 1997. Change of transmitter release kinetics during facilitation revealed by prolonged test pulses at the inhibitor of the crayfish opener muscle. *J. Neurophysiol.* 78:1791–99
124. Wagner H-J, Djamgoz MBA. 1993. Spinules: a case for retinal synaptic plasticity. *Trends Neurosci.* 16:201–6
125. Walrond JP, Reese TS. 1985. Structure of axon terminals and active zones at synapses on the lizard twitch and tonic muscle fibers. *J. Neurosci.* 5:1118–31
126. Webster HdeF, Ames A. 1965. Reversible and irreversible changes in the fine structure of nervous tissue during oxygen and glucose deprivation. *J. Cell Biol.* 26:885–909
127. Wiley RG, Spencer C, Pysh JJ. 1987. Time course and frequency dependence of synaptic vesicle depletion and recovery in electrically stimulated sympathetic ganglia. *J. Neurocytol.* 16:359–72
128. Witkovsky P, Dowling JE. 1969. Synaptic relationships in the plexiform layers of carp retina. *Z. Zellforsch. Mikrosk. Anat.* 100:60–82
129. Wu L-G, Betz WJ. 1996. Nerve activity but not intracellular calcium determines the time course of endocytosis at the frog neuromuscular junction. *Neuron* 17:769–79
130. Yamashita M, Ohmori H. 1990. Synaptic responses to mechanical stimulation in calyceal and bouton type vestibular afferents studied in an isolated preparation of semicircular canal ampullae of chicken. *Exp. Brain Res.* 80:475–88
131. Yazulla S, Studholme KM. 1992. Light-dependent plasticity of the synaptic terminals of Mb bipolar cells in goldfish retina. *J. Comp. Neurol.* 320:521–30
132. Zhou Z, Misler S. 1995. Action potential-induced quantal secretion of catecholamines from rat adrenal chromaffin cells. *J. Biol. Chem.* 270:3498–505
133. Zucker C, Yazulla S. 1982. Localization of synaptic and nonsynaptic nicotinic-acetylcholine receptors in the goldfish retina. *J. Comp. Neurol.* 204:188–95
134. Zucker RS. 1996. Exocytosis: a molecular and physiological perspective. *Neuron* 17:1049–55

Annu. Rev. Physiol. 1999. 61:753–76

GENETICS OF SYNAPTIC VESICLE FUNCTION: Toward the Complete Functional Anatomy of an Organelle

Rafael Fernández-Chacón and Thomas C. Südhof
Center for Basic Neuroscience, Howard Hughes Medical Institute and Department of Molecular Genetics, The University of Texas Southwestern Medical School, Dallas, Texas 75235-9050; e-mail: RFerna@mednet.swmed.edu; TSudho@mednet.swmed.edu

KEY WORDS: synapse, neurotransmitter release, exocytosis, rab proteins, synaptotagmin

ABSTRACT
Synaptic transmission starts with the release of neurotransmitters by exocytosis of synaptic vesicles. As a relatively simple organelle with a limited number of components, synaptic vesicles are in principle accessible to complete structural and functional genetic analysis. At present, the majority of synaptic vesicle proteins has been characterized, and many have been genetically analyzed in mice, *Drosophila*, and *Caenorhabditis elegans*. These studies have shown that synaptic vesicles contain proteins with diverse structures and functions. Although the genetic studies are as yet unfinished, they promise to lead to a full description of synaptic vesicles as macromolecular machines involved in all aspects of presynaptic neurotransmitter release.

INTRODUCTION

Synaptic Vesicles in Neurotransmitter Release

Synaptic vesicles (SVs) are abundant secretory organelles of presynaptic nerve terminals. SVs accumulate high concentrations of neurotransmitters and secrete them by fusion with the presynaptic plasma membrane (1). SV fusion occurs at only a specialized area of the presynaptic plasma membrane, the active zone. The active zone is precisely aligned with the synaptic cleft and the postsynaptic density to form the synaptic signaling complex (2). At any given time,

0066-4278/99/0315-0753$08.00

5–20 docked SVs are bound to the active zone of a synapse. Hundreds of SVs lie in a tight cluster immediately adjacent to the active zone. Synaptic transmission is initiated by exocytosis of docked SVs at the active zone, which results in secretion of transmitters into the synaptic cleft with subsequent activation of postsynaptic receptors. After exocytosis, empty SVs rapidly endocytose and recycle (3). The trafficking pathway of SVs in the nerve terminal is schematically shown in Figure 1. A fundamental cycle of SV exocytosis, endocytosis, and recycling constitutes the basis of the SV pathway. SVs may fully exocytose (4) or form a transient fusion pore that is closed rapidly after transmitters have diffused out ("kiss-and-run" exocytosis) (5–7). After exo- and endocytosis, most SVs probably recycle and re-exocytose without passing through an endosomal intermediate (8). Some SVs undergo a more complex recycling pathway that involves an endosomal intermediate (Figure 1). Evidence for this is derived from two observations: SVs contain rab5, a rab protein typical for endosomes (9, 10), and stimulation of nerve terminals in the presence of extracellular tracers leads to the sequestration of these tracers in endosomes (11). It is unclear

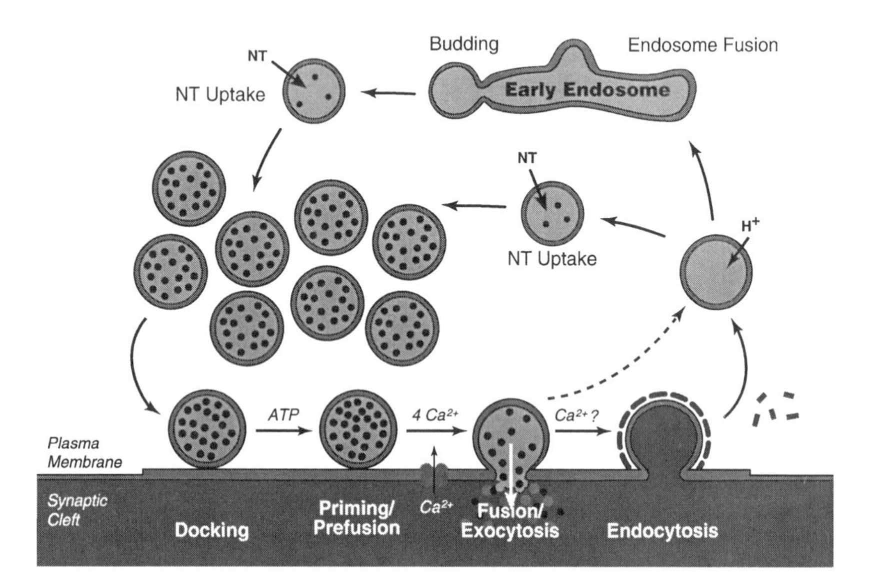

Figure 1 Trafficking of SVs in the nerve terminal. SVs are clustered close to the active zone by an unknown mechanism prior to recruitment for docking and fusion. Neurotransmitter release by fusion is triggered by Ca^{2+} influx via voltage-gated Ca^{2+} channels strategically localized close to the active zone. After exocytosis, SVs are rapidly endocytosed by a mechanism that probably involves clathrin, followed by recycling either directly or via an endosomal intermediate.

if SV recycling via endosomes is a frequent event or is only used as a sorting station to eliminate aged and abnormal SVs.

SVs are clustered in the vicinity of the active zone and interconnected by unidentified proteins that are neither actin filaments nor microtubules (12). When synapses are continuously stimulated, SVs are recruited to the active zone. For recruitment, SVs may simply diffuse away from the clusters, or they may be actively moved by a motor protein. In nerve terminals, SVs are part of functionally distinct pools with different probabilities of exocytosis. When nerve terminals are stimulated in the presence of labeled neurotransmitters, recycling SVs that have recently undergone a cycle of exo- and endocytosis are preferentially filled with labeled neurotransmitters. SVs that did not undergo exocytosis contain a much lower concentration of labeled transmitter. When nerve terminals are stimulated again, the recently filled SVs with the highest concentrations of labeled transmitter are the first to undergo exocytosis (13). The SVs containing primarily unlabeled transmitters undergo exocytosis only after intense stimulation. This result suggests a pool of active SVs that participate in continuous cycles of exo- and endocytosis, and a pool of reserve SVs that are recruited only under conditions of massive stimulation. These pools may correspond morphologically to SVs close to the active zone and to SVs located at a more distant location.

In this review, we discuss nerve terminal function from the perspective of SVs. We outline an inherently descriptive approach that derives its focus from the central role of SVs in neurotransmitter release. This approach aims to achieve a complete molecular and functional description of SVs in two phases: (*a*) a molecular characterization of all protein components of SVs and (*b*) a genetic determination of the functions of these components. The overall goal is a systematic analysis of an eukaryotic organelle to completion. For space reasons, we do not deal with many other important aspects of nerve terminal function such as synaptic plasticity or the mechanisms of endocytosis, which are described in several excellent recent reviews (14–16).

Molecular Anatomy of Synaptic Vesicles

SVs are relatively small organelles (≈50 nm diameter) of uniform size. Their membrane can accommodate only a limited number of proteins and phospholipids (17). The structures of most SV proteins are known (a current list is presented in Table 1). A 50-nm vesicle composed entirely of phospholipids would contain approximately 20,000 phospholipid molecules (based on a cross-sectional area of 0.65 nm^2 per phospholipid) (18). Because SVs contain phospholipids and cholesterol in a ratio of ≈2:1 (19), each SV contains approximately 12,000 phospholipid molecules. The mass ratio of phospholipids

Table 1 Structural and genetic analysis of synaptic vesicles

SV proteins	Characteristics	Organism	Knock-out phenotype	Function
Transport proteins				
Monoamine transporter	Transports catecholamines, dopamine, serotonin, and possibly histamine. Two isoforms with 12 TMRs (20, 23)[a]	M	Lethal for brain isoform. Heterozygotes are hypersensitive to cocaine and amphetamine (47, 48)	Transports monoamines into SVs
Acetylcholine transporter	Protein with 12 TMRs. Homologous to monoamine transporters (25)	C	Unc17 in *C. elegans*: paralyzed (24)	SV transport of acetilcholine
GABA transporter	Protein with 12 TMRs. Homologous to other vesicular transporters (26)	C	Unc47 in *C. elegans*: paralyzed (49)	SV transport of GABA
ATP transporter	Unknown	—	Unknown	SV transport of ATP
Glutamate transporter	Unknown	—	Unknown	SV transport of acetylcholine
Chloride channel	Unknown	—	Unknown	Countertransport of Cl^- into SVs
Proton pump	Protein complex of at least 13 subunits (21)	—	Unknown	Establishment of electrochemical transmembrane gradient
Zn^{2+} transporter (ZnT-3)	Protein with 6 TMRs. Homologous to endosomal Zn^{2+} transporter (52)	M	Increased sensitivity to seizures	SV transport of Zn^{2+}
Brain-specific Na^+-dependent inorganic phosphate transporter	(See 52b)		Unknown	Unknown

Trafficking proteins				
Cysteine string protein (CSP)	Palmitoylated peripheral membrane protein with DNA-J homology domain (35)	D	Paralysis and early death (90). Ca^{2+}/exocytosis coupling impaired (91)	Coupling Ca^{2+} channels to exocytosis
Rab3A, B, and C	Low-molecular-weight binding proteins	M, C	Rab3A KO mice lack mossy fiber LTP (81); exhibit increase in glutamate release (80)	Regulation of SV fusion
Rabphilin-3A	N-terminal domain binds GTP-rab3 but not GDP-rab3; C terminus contains two C2-domains; central region is substrate for PKA and CAM kinase II (36, 43, 87, 88)	M	No major phenotype in mice	Putative minor rab3 effector
SCAMPs 1 and 4[b]	Integral membrane proteins with 4 TMRs. Ubiquitous and SV-specific isoforms (38)	M	Unknown	Unknown
SV2A, 2B, and 2C	Glycosylated protein with 12 TMRs; homologous to bacterial transporters (27–29)	M	In mice, SV2A KOs are lethal; SV2B KOs are not[c]	Unknown
SVOP	Non-glycosylated protein with 12 TMRs; homologous to bacterial transporters (29)		Unknown	Unknown
Synaptobrevins (VAMPS)	Type II membrane proteins; most abundant SV proteins; cleaved by tetanus and botulinum toxins (30, 54–57)	M, D, C	Lethal in mice; residual synaptic transmission in *C. elegans* and *Drosophila* (63, 64)	Direct or indirect function in membrane fusion

(*Continued*)

Table 1 (*Continued*)

SV proteins	Characteristics	Organism	Knock-out phenotype	Function
Synaptotagmins	Type I membrane proteins with two C_2 domains; bind Ca^{2+} and phospholipids, neurexins, AP2, SNAP-25, and syntaxins (68)	M, D, C	In mice, fast component of Ca^{2+}-dependent release is impaired in sytI KO (70)	Essential for Ca^{2+}-triggered fusion but not general fusion
Synaptogyrins	Membrane proteins with 4 TMRs and tyrosine-phosphorylated C terminus distantly related to synaptophysins (41)	M	In mice, essential for posttetanic potentiation. With synaptophysins redundant function in synaptic plasticity (104)	Effector for synaptic plasticity
Synaptophysins	Membrane proteins with 4 TMRs and tyrosine-phosphorylated C terminus distantly related to synaptogyrin (32, 33)	M	In mice, single KO of synaptophysin I has no phenotype (103). Double KO with synaptogyrin has multiple defects in synaptic plasticity (104)	Effector for synaptic plasticity

Table describes state as of June 1998. Under organism, (M), *C. elegans* (C), or *Drosophila* (D) indicate if a mutant was made. The mouse SCAMP1, CSP, rab3B, C, D, rabphilin, and SV2 mutants have not been analyzed. TMR (transmembrane region).

[a]Reference numbers, noted in parentheses.

[b]R Fernández-Chacón & TC Südhof, unpublished results.

[c]R Janz & TC Südhof, unpublished results.

($M_r \approx 800$) versus proteins is $\approx$1 (19). Assuming an average M_r per protein of 50, this would translate into $\approx$200 molecules of protein per SV. It seems likely that most proteins are present in multiple copies in a given SV, indicating that there may be 20–40 distinct SV proteins in total.

At present, we divide SV proteins into two functional classes: (*a*) transport proteins that execute the uptake of neurotransmitters and other components into SVs and (*b*) trafficking proteins that mediate the exo- and endocytosis of SVs and their recycling. SV proteins have no common structural theme. SV proteins include peripheral membrane proteins, proteins bound to SVs via hydrophobic posttranslational modifications, and proteins containing one or several transmembrane regions (see Figure 2). There is no common sorting sequence, and the mechanism by which proteins are targeted to SVs is unclear.

All neurotransmitter uptake into SVs is driven by an electrochemical transmembrane gradient (20). This gradient is generated by a vacuolar proton pump in SVs composed of at least 13 subunits (21). Each SV probably contains only one or two copies of the proton pump (22). With a size of $\approx 0.6–0.7 \times 10^6$ Daltons, a single proton pump accounts for $\approx$10% of the total SV protein. Each SV contains a transporter that mediates the energy-dependent uptake of a specific neurotransmitter. There are at least five distinct classes of vesicular transporters for neurotransmitters (20). Transporters that take up either glutamate, acetylcholine, or ATP have been biochemically characterized. In addition, polyfunctional transporters that translocate both GABA and glycine or all monoamines (dopamine, serotonin, catecholamines) have been identified. The monoamine, GABA, and acetylcholine transporters have been cloned (23–26), and the structures of the other transporters are likely to become available soon. It is unclear if the GABA transporter also functions in glycine uptake, and the number of the various transporters isoforms is unkown. In addition to proton pumps and neurotransmitter transporters, SVs contain ancillary transporters for zinc, chloride, and possibly other molecules.

Trafficking of SVs is mechanistically less well understood than neurotransmitter uptake into SVs. The current analysis of SVs focuses on proteins that are obligatory components of all SVs because all SVs, independent of transmitter type, are subject to similar trafficking processes. Ten classes of putative SV trafficking proteins were characterized (schematically pictured in Figure 2). These classes were identified as trafficking proteins by default because no obvious transport function could be associated with them. Two classes of the putative trafficking proteins (SV2s, SVOP), in fact, exhibit homology to transporters (27–29). It is possible that future studies will reveal a transport function for SV2s and SVOP. However, their distributions do not correlate with a known transport activity of SVs, making it difficult to envision what these proteins may transport.

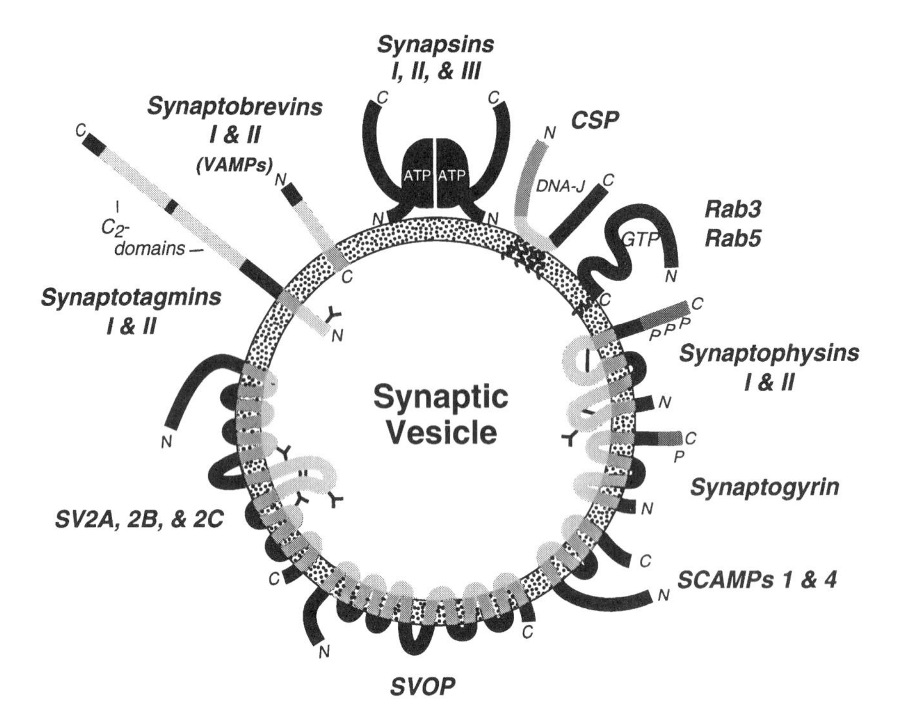

Figure 2 Trafficking proteins of synaptic vesicles. The structures of the major trafficking proteins of SVs are shown schematically. Trafficking proteins are defined as those proteins with a probable function in the SV cycle and no known involvement in neurotransmitter uptake. Only proteins tightly associated with SVs are shown; although the type of membrane attachment is well established for most proteins, it is unclear which synapsins will bind to SVs via their C-terminal regions instead of the N-terminal region shown here. Only a single isoform of CSP is known. In contrast, synapsins, synaptobrevins, synaptophysins, synaptogyrins, and rab3s are encoded by at least two genes whose products are located on SVs; SV2 proteins by 3, SCAMPs by an unknown number of genes, and synaptotagmins by at least 11 genes. Only one isoform of the multigene families is shown in each case.

Most transport and trafficking proteins of SVs are members of gene families with multiple isoforms. These isoforms can be either synaptic or ubiquitous. For example, synaptobrevins I and II (VAMP 1 and VAMP 2) are closely related proteins highly enriched on SVs (30). Synaptobrevins are homologous to a third protein called cellubrevin that, in contrast to synaptobrevins, is absent from SVs (31). However, cellubrevin is present on constitutive trafficking vesicles in all cells. Similarly, synaptophysin I and synaptophysin II/synaptoporin are related proteins on SVs (32, 33) that have a close relative, pantophysin, in constitutive trafficking vesicles (34). However, there is no general rule that governs the presence and distribution of SV proteins and their isoforms. Not all SV proteins are members of gene families because only single genes have been discovered for CSP (35), SVOP (29), and rabphilin (36). Most SV proteins appear to be relatively specific for SVs, but some SV proteins, such as CSP (37) and SCAMP1 (38), are also present on other cellular organelles. Conversely, at least two SV proteins (SV2s and synapsins) seem to be present only on SVs and related organelles without general isoforms (39, 40). For most SV proteins, multiple synaptic and/or general isoforms are expressed [e.g. synapto- and cellugyrin (41, 42; R Janz & TC Südhof, unpublished results), rab3 proteins (43, 44), SCAMPs (45; R Fernández-Chacón & TC Südhof, unpublished results), synaptotagmins (46)]. SV proteins with multiple isoforms are differentially expressed in brain in a pattern that does not correlate with neurotransmitter type or with functional brain regions (e.g. 39, 40). To complicate matters, no two families of SV proteins exhibit the same differential distribution. Therefore, the biological rationale, if any, for multiple isoforms of SV proteins with distinct expression patterns is unclear. In addition to the proteins described in Figure 2 and Table 1, other proteins, for example CaM Kinase II, $pp60^{c\text{-}src}$, and thy1, have been reported as potential components of SVs. It is unlikely that these proteins are obligatory components of SVs because they are not major constituents of purified SVs and are generally not enriched in nerve terminals.

The functions of most SV proteins are unknown. The trafficking pathway of SVs must be mediated mechanistically by protein-protein interactions involving SV proteins. Although SVs are functionally relatively simple compared with other organelles, their trafficking nevertheless involves multiple steps. The limited number of proteins in SVs suggests that some SV proteins may have multiple functions. The molecular description of SV proteins appears to be nearly complete, but their genetic analysis is only beginning. It is likely that SVs will be a rewarding subject for genetics because it should be possible to perform a genetic saturation analysis of SVs as an organelle in mice and in invertebrates. Such an approach targets an effector organelle that is centrally involved in the only mechanism by which neurotransmitters are released. Therefore, this approach excludes common problems of genetic analysis such as redundancy and compensation from other pathways. Results will likely have major implications for our understanding of intracellular trafficking and synaptic function, with a potential problem arising from multiple functions performed by each individual protein class. In the following, we discuss, for individual protein classes, where this analysis stands and what the future challenges are.

FUNCTIONAL GENETICS OF SYNAPTIC VESICLE PROTEINS

Transporters: Loading SVs with Neurotransmitters

The vesicular transporters for neurotransmitters that are already cloned (acetylcholine, GABA, and monoamine transporters; Table 1) form two families of proteins: the monoamine and acetylcholine transporters, which are homologous to each other, and the GABA transporter, which has an unrelated structure but is probably similar to the as yet uncloned glutamate transporter (23–26). Both groups of neurotransmitter transporters utilize an electrochemical gradient established by the proton pump to drive uptake. The functions of these transporters are essential for viability (47–49). The *Caenorhabditis elegans* mutants were not only invaluable for identifying the transporters for GABA and acetylcholine but also provided indisputable evidence that neurotransmitter uptake into SVs is essential for synaptic transmission as the final proof of the vesicle hypothesis (3, 5).

Can the neurotransmitter content of SVs be regulated either by modulation of the proton pump activity or by regulation of the transporters themselves? In other words, is the quantal size at a synapse controlled by the amount of transmitters taken up into SVs? Although some of the electrophysiological evidence argues against this possibility (e.g. the relatively uniform size of spontaneous miniature postsynaptic currents), it cannot be excluded. Three lines of evidence suggest that the activity of neurotransmitter transporters may be rate-limiting. First, when electromotor nerve terminals in *Torpedo* are extensively stimulated, SVs recover much faster as organelles than they re-fill with transmitter (50). Second, in heterozygous mutant mice lacking one of the two copies of the brain monoamine transporter VMAT2, catecholamine release appears to be decreased, which is indicative of a decrease in the filling of the SVs (48). Third, overexpression of the vesicular acetylcholine transporter in frog neuromuscular junctions led to a large increase in the amplitude and frequency of miniature endplate currents (51). Although these results suggest that transporter activity may be limiting, direct evidence that it is regulated has not been presented.

In addition to neurotransmitters and chloride, a subset of SVs contains high concentrations of Zn^{2+}. As a modulator of NMDA-receptors, Zn^{2+} may serve as a co-transmitter with glutamate. Curiously, the highest Zn^{2+} content in brain is found in mossy fiber nerve terminals in the CA3 region of the hippocampus, a synapse that is best known for an NMDA receptor–independent form of LTP. Zn^{2+} is transported into SVs by ZnT-3, a transporter protein homologous to other Zn^{2+} transporters (52). Knockouts of ZnT-3 revealed that Zn^{2+} is not essential for synaptic transmission or survival (as opposed to neurotransmitter transporters). However, in the absence of ZnT-3, mice are more sensitive to seizure-inducing agents, thus indicating that Zn^{2+} functions as a protective neuromodulator (RD Palmiter, personal communication). A new additional Zn^{2+} transporter, ZnT-4, has recently been identified (52a). The gene encoding ZnT-4 is responsible for the inherited Zn^{2+} deficiency in the *lethal milk* mutation in mice. ZnT-4 is strongly expressed in brain, and *lethal milk* has a neurological phenotype, possibly because of defective Zn^{2+} transport in SVs. It will be interesting to investigate if both ZnT-3 and ZnT-4 are synaptic vesicle transporters and have similar functions.

Synaptobrevin and the Core Complex of Membrane Fusion

During exocytosis, the SV protein synaptobrevin (also referred to as VAMP or as SV v-SNARE) and the plasma membrane proteins SNAP-25 and syntaxin 1 (also called synaptic t-SNAREs) assemble into a complex called the core complex. Synaptobrevin, syntaxin, and SNAP-25 form a tight SDS-resistant complex only in ternary interactions (53). Complex formation is energetically favorable so that the complex assembles spontaneously whenever tissues are homogenized. Experiments with tetanus and botulinum toxins, which irreversibly inhibit SV exocytosis, revealed that the core complex is essential for exocytosis. Tetanus toxin and the various botulinum toxins enter the cytosol and act as site-specific proteases. Most toxins primarily attack synaptobrevin (tetanus toxin and botulinum toxins B, D, F, and G) (54–57), although some botulinum toxins also cleave SNAP-25 alone (botulinum toxins A and E) or both SNAP-25 and syntaxin (botulinum toxin C1) (58–60). When synaptobrevin, syntaxin, or SNAP-25 are proteolysed by one of these toxins, they become unable to form stable, membrane-anchored core complexes and to participate in exocytosis (53).

Although it is well established that the core complex is essential for exocytosis, it is not known when it forms and what it does. The core complex is assembled after docking because synaptobrevin is not essential for docking. Does the core complex form prior to fusion, with fusion performed by other proteins, or does the assembly of the core complex drive fusion? The energy released on core complex formation may be utilized in membrane fusion (44, 61). This is supported by the architecture of the core complex in which all three components are arranged in a parallel orientation (61). However, in recent reconstitution experiments, fusion driven by core complex formation was very slow and uncontrolled, making it unlikely that this by itself is sufficient for fusion (62). An alternative hypothesis is that the core complex assembles before fusion to position the membranes, with the actual fusion reaction performed by a separate activity.

Mutants of synaptobrevin have been obtained in *Drosophila*, *C. elegans*, and mice (63, 64; S Schoch, TC Südhof & A Koenigstorffer, unpublished observation). In all organisms, synaptobrevin null mutants are lethal, as would be expected. However, not all exocytosis appears to be abolished in *C. elegans* and *Drosophila* mutants, which suggests that some membrane fusion persists even in the absence of synaptobrevin. This result indicates that synaptobrevin is not absolutely essential for fusion but it increases the catalytic rate. If this is correct, the core complex formation might provide the energy for fusion but not actually initiate the merging of the two membranes. It may be possible to test this hypothesis more decisively in the future using electrophysiology and biochemistry in mouse mutants.

Ca^{2+} Triggering of Fusion: Role of Synaptotagmins

The speed with which Ca^{2+} stimulates SV exocytosis is arguably the most fascinating property of the SV pathway. Ca^{2+} triggers release in less than 1 ms, maybe less than 100 μs (65, 66). In central synapses, two components of Ca^{2+}-induced glutamate release were observed: a major fast component of synchronous release, and a minor slow component of asynchronous release (67). Both components exhibit a similar Ca^{2+} cooperativity but distinct apparent Ca^{2+} affinities, indicating that the underlying Ca^{2+}-dependent regulatory processes involve Ca^{2+}-binding proteins. Because of the speed with which Ca^{2+} acts, it is likely that Ca^{2+} enters the nerve terminal at the site of exocytosis (the active zone) to activate a pre-assembled fusion complex. This model predicts that the fusion reaction is largely executed prior to Ca^{2+} entry. The relation of Ca^{2+} action to the assembly of the core complex is unknown. It is possible either that the core complex has already been assembled before Ca^{2+} acts but is not sufficient for fusion or that Ca^{2+} unleashes a rapid assembly reaction that drives fusion.

Synaptotagmins are SV proteins present in multiple isoforms (46). All SVs appear to contain synaptotagmin I and/or II, the most abundant synaptotagmins. Synaptotagmin is composed of a small intravesicular sequence, a single transmembrane region, and a large cytoplasmic sequence with two C_2-domains (68). Each of the two C_2-domains probably binds at least three Ca^{2+} ions (69). Synaptotagmins form Ca^{2+}-independent multimers on the SV surface, resulting in protein complexes in which each subunit binds at least six Ca^{2+} ions, creating an enormous apparent Ca^{2+} cooperativity. Studies of knockout mice (KO mice) with mutations in the synaptotagmin I gene showed that synaptotagmin I is essential for Ca^{2+}-triggered exocytosis (70). Mutant mice die immediately after birth. No structural or biochemical abnormalities in brain were noted, and no developmental changes were detected. Electrophysiological recordings, however, revealed that the fast component of Ca^{2+}-dependent neurotransmitter release was severely depressed in the mutant mice. By contrast, Ca^{2+}-independent release processes were entirely normal (70). These data showed that in mice, synaptotagmin I is selectively required for fast Ca^{2+}-dependent exocytosis but not directly involved in the fusion reaction itself or in development of synapses.

These findings are compatible with observations in *Drosophila* and *C. elegans* in which synaptotagmin mutations also severely impair synaptic activity but leave some Ca^{2+}-dependent neurotransmitter release intact (71–73).

It is uncertain if Ca^{2+} binding to synaptotagmin I triggers exocytosis or if synaptotagmin happens to be a Ca^{2+}-binding protein that is also essential for Ca^{2+}-triggered fusion. The localization of synaptotagmin I on SVs, its Ca^{2+}-binding properties, and its essential nature for only fast Ca^{2+}-triggered release support the hypothesis that Ca^{2+} is the sensor but do not prove it. The question arises if Ca^{2+} binding to one or both of the C_2-domains of synaptotagmin does in fact trigger release, and if so, how Ca^{2+} binding triggers fusion. Because the interactions involved are probably low-affinity, high-speed interactions, verification will require in vivo approaches dealing with a combination of genetics and physiology.

Regulation of Fusion by rab3

At rest, most active zones contain several docked SVs (2). Stimulation by Ca^{2+} leads to exocytosis only infrequently and usually releases only a single vesicle (74). At most active zones, SV fusion occurs only once for every 5 to 10 Ca^{2+} signals (75, 76). In nerve terminals, SV exocytosis can be stimulated by hypertonic solutions, such as hypertonic sucrose, by a Ca^{2+}-independent pathway. The mechanism by which sucrose acts is unknown, but it also depends on the core complex similar to Ca^{2+}-triggered exocytosis (77). Different from Ca^{2+}-triggered exocytosis, hypertonic sucrose stimulates exocytosis of all docked SVs, thereby defining a pool of readily releasable SVs (78). All docked SVs at an active zone appear to be ready for fusion, but Ca^{2+} selectively picks out only one SV and leaves other SVs unscathed. These observations indicate that the Ca^{2+}-regulated step in the fusion reaction is strongly inhibited and can be activated only occasionally.

Rab3 is a synaptic vesicle protein that belongs to the rab family of low-molecular-weight GTP-binding proteins. Four closely related rab3 isoforms are expressed in mammals, rab3A, B, C, and D. Rab3A is by far the most abundant rab3 isoform in brain. Rab3A and 3C are present on SVs (and, to a lesser extent, on other secretory organelles); the localization of rab3B and rab3D in brain has not been explored (43). In nerve terminals, rab3A and 3C dissociate from SVs after exocytosis, indicating an activity-dependent cycling between soluble and vesicular forms. This cycling most likely involves GTP hydrolysis, leading to the presence of GDP-rab3 in the cytosol or GTP-rab3 on SVs.

KO mice lacking rab3A are viable and fertile but exhibit major changes in synaptic transmission (79, 80). The amount of evoked glutamate release per stimulus is enhanced (Figure 3). This enhancement is not from an increase in release probability per synapse but may be caused by an augmentation of the number of SVs released per active zone if exocytosis is activated (80).

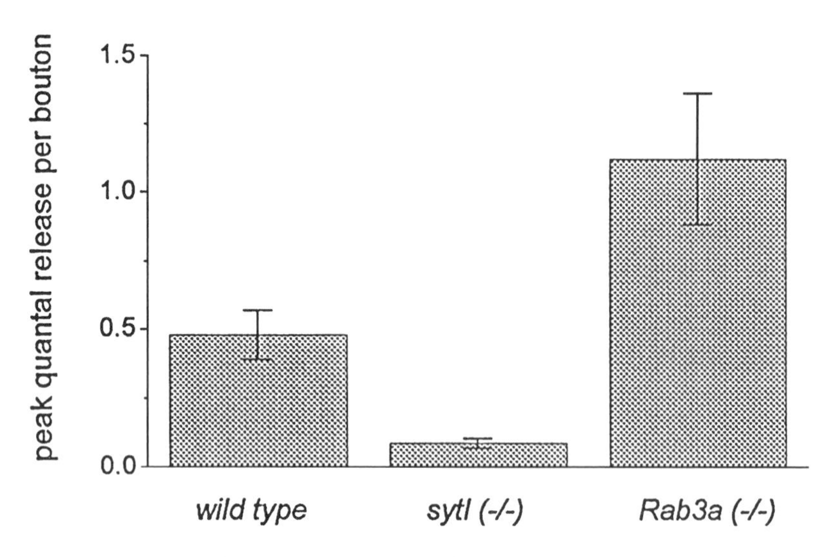

Figure 3 The amount of transmitter released per stimulus is increased in synapses of rab3a KO mice. In these experiments, a wild-type synapse releases on average 0.5 quanta per stimulus (peak quantal release per bouton ≈0.5). A synapse of synaptotagmin I KO mice, which lacks fast Ca^{2+}-dependent synaptic transmission, shows a severe reduction in peak quantal release. In contrast, synapses from rab3a KO mice shows a peak quantal release per bouton higher than 1, indicating a twofold increase in the number of quanta released per stimulus versus a wild-type synapse [modified with permission from *Nature* (80); copyright 1997, Macmillan Mag. Ltd.].

Based on these results, rab3A appears to be a constitutive negative regulator of fusion that acts at a late step in fusion, coincidental with synaptotagmin (44). However, rab3A is by far not the only negative regulator, since the disinhibition of fusion affects only a few SVs; most of the docked SVs that can be stimulated with hypertonic sucrose are still refractory to Ca^{2+} in the rab3A KO mice (80). The regulatory role of rab3A in fusion is physiologically relevant because it is essential for long-term potentiation (LTP) in mossy fiber nerve terminals of the CA3 region of the hippocampus (81). In rab3A KO mice, this type of LTP cannot be normally produced, presumably because the synapses are already in an activated state. Because rab3A is a member of a protein family with at least four isoforms, it is possible that it has additional redundant functions that were not detected in the rab3A KO mice. In *C. elegans*, only a single isoform of rab3 is present. Mutations in this gene produce no major aberration in synaptic transmission (82), suggesting that rab3 has no more fundamental functions than those revealed in mice.

As a regulator of fusion, two questions about rab3 arise: What part of the docking and fusion reaction does it regulate, and how does it regulate fusion?

The first question is similar to the question of how synaptotagmin acts and relates to the general problem of when the core complex assembles. The fact that rab3A and synaptotagmin I deficiencies become apparent in the last step of fusion does not prove they act here; they could act earlier in a manner that would phenotypically manifest itself later. The most attractive hypothesis, independent of whether the core complex assembles before fusion or during fusion, is that rab3 regulates this assembly. Rab proteins in other systems have been postulated to functionally interact with the assembly of the fusion complex (83), but no creditable molecular link has been discovered.

How does rab3 regulate fusion? Because rab3 is a GTP-binding protein with a GTP-dependent cycle of SV association and dissociation, it presumably activates effector molecules in a GTP-dependent manner. Three potential targets have been identified: rabphilin, RIM, and NOC2 (36, 84, 85). All three proteins interact with rab3 in a GTP-dependent fashion via an N-terminal Zn^{2+} finger domain. Rabphilin is reversibly recruited to SVs by rab3, resulting in a cycle of association and dissociation in which rab3 is first bound to SVs and then recruits rabphilin, and both dissociate from SVs in the reverse order after GTP hydrolysis (86). Rabphilin is phosphorylated by cAMP-dependent protein kinase A (PKA) (87) in a region-specific manner in the mossy fibers of the hippocampus (88). The second putative effector, RIM, is an active zone protein that binds only to rab3 when SVs dock with GTP-bound rab3 attached (84). The third putative effector, NOC2, exhibits no detectable expression in brain and is primarily synthesized in endocrine cells (85).

Immunocytochemistry shows that both putative effectors in neurons, rabphilin and RIM, are co-localized in the same synapses (84). Why would a rab protein have two effectors? Both rabphilin and RIM contain C_2-domains in addition to a similar Zn^{2+} finger for rab3 binding, but their C_2-domains are very different. Rabphilin binds PIP and PIP_2 as a function of Ca^{2+}, suggesting a potential role in Ca^{2+}-dependent regulation of exocytosis (89). Another potential function for rabphilin could be that of a competitor with RIM, which might explain the negative regulatory action of rab3. Surprisingly, preliminary analysis of rabphilin KO mice failed to substantiate these ideas. In these KO mice, the phenotype of the rab3A KO mice is not reproduced (O Schlüter & TC Südhof, unpublished observation). Thus, at this point, the role of rabphilin, if any, must be considered to be subtle because it clearly does not serve as an essential regulator of fusion. Future studies on the other effectors of rab3 may shed more light on this question.

Cysteine-String Protein

Cysteine-string protein (CSP) is a peripheral SV membrane protein with multiple covalently bound fatty acids that attach CSP to SVs (35). CSP is unusual among SV proteins because it contains a DNA-J domain, which functions as a chaperone by interaction with DNA-K domains in a separate protein. CSP has been characterized genetically only in *Drosophila* (90a). Interestingly, the *Drosophila* CSP mutation is a null mutant with a temperature-sensitive phenotype. Although null mutants generally do not result in temperature-sensitive phenotypes, CSP mutants present a temperature-sensitive block of SV exocytosis (90a). This agrees well with the presence of the DNA-J domain in CSP and with the fact that most heat shock proteins are DNA-K domain proteins, which interact with DNA-J domains.

Interesting data have been presented about the phenotype of the *Drosophila* CSP mutant. All reports agree that normal SV exocytosis is impaired in the absence of CSP, one paper reported that lack of CSP results in the absence of SVs and signs of degeneration (90). In contrast, another study showed that in CSP mutants, SV exocytosis is not impaired if induced by Ca^{2+} ionophores but is defective when initiated by membrane depolarization (91). This observation implies that SVs are in fact present in CSP mutants and that CSP may be required for coupling Ca^{2+} influx to SV exocytosis (91, 91a). A role for CSP in the assembly of Ca^{2+} channels at the active zone has not been directly demonstrated, but such a role is supported by the finding that CSP is essential for the assembly of N-type Ca^{2+} channels in *Xenopus* oocytes when co-injected with total brain mRNA (92). The mechanism by which Ca^{2+} channels are assembled presynaptically remains a mystery. It is unclear how a molecular chaperone (DNA-J and DNA-K domains) could function here. However, the CSP data raise the possibility that this SV protein serves as an organizer of Ca^{2+} channel assembly at the active zone, an attractive idea to explain the speed of neurotransmitter release triggered by Ca^{2+}.

Synapsins as Synaptic Regulators

Synapsins are abundant dimeric proteins on the surface of SVs, where they constitute approximately 10% of the total SV protein. There are at least five synapsins—synapsins Ia, Ib, IIa, IIb, and IIIa—that are produced from three genes (93–95). Structurally, synapsins are composed of a large, highly conserved central domain (the C-domain) that is flanked by smaller and less conserved N- and C-terminal regions. In the N-terminal region, synapsins contain two short domains that are present in all vertebrate synapsins and carry a conserved phosphorylation site for CaM Kinase I and PKA. In the C-terminal region, combinations or variable domains with different sizes are observed in synapsins. Interestingly, synapsins Ia, IIa, and IIIa share a common C-terminal sequence of unknown function called the E-domain. The abundance, regulated phosphorylation, and specific localization of synapsins to SVs have been fascinating, and have resulted in hundreds of papers over the last 10 years about their in vitro properties, thus making synapsins the most published SV proteins.

For many years the function of synapsins was a mystery. The recent crystal structure of the C-domain of synapsin I provided a major surprise: It showed that synapsins structurally resemble a family of prokaryotic enzymes that utilize ATP to synthesize a variety of small molecules (96). Direct binding measurements confirmed that all synapsins constitute high-affinity ATP-binding proteins (97). Unexpectedly, ATP binding is regulated by Ca^{2+} in a subtype-specific manner. ATP-binding to the C-domain of synapsins Ia and Ib requires Ca^{2+}; the C-domain of synapsins IIa and IIb is Ca^{2+} independent, and ATP-binding to the C-domain of synapsin IIIa is inhibited by Ca^{2+} (94, 97). Thus, in spite of their great similarity, the synapsins exhibit differential types of direct Ca^{2+} regulation in addition to their phosphorylation by Ca^{2+}-dependent kinases. The structural homology and ATP-binding characteristics of synapsins indicate that they function as Ca^{2+}-regulated enzymes on the SV surface, although their substrates are currently unknown.

A second surprise regarding the functions of synapsins came from the analysis of the KO mice (98–100). Deletion of synapsins I and II, accounting for 10% of SV proteins and more than 98% of all synapsins (synapsin IIIa levels are very low), had major effects on synaptic transmission but still allowed the animals to live and procreate. Thus synapsins are not required for the fundamental mechanics of SV exocytosis, endocytosis, and recycling. In the absence of synapsins, SVs were destabilized and the number of SVs were decreased, but all other structural parameters of synapses were normal: the number of synapses, the clustering of SVs at the active zone, and the exocytosis of SVs appeared to be unimpaired. As determined electrophysiologically, the major phenotype in the KO mice consisted of changes in short-term synaptic plasticity (98, 99). Long-term synaptic plasticity, however, was unaffected (101). These data indicate that the primary function of synapsins is to maintain a stable pool of SVs that can be rapidly recruited during processes of synaptic plasticity. Since the synapsins probably function as enzymes, it is possible that their enzyme activity relates to an increased average stability of SVs required for normal short-term regulation of SV exocytosis.

Synaptophysins and Synaptogyrin

SVs contain two closely related proteins called synaptophysin I and synaptoporin/synaptophysin II, and a third more distantly related protein called synaptogyrin (Figure 2). These three proteins are composed of four transmembrane regions and relatively short, variable C- and N-terminal sequences (32, 41). Synaptophysins and synaptogyrin are abundant proteins, with synaptophysin

I alone accounting for ≈7% of the total SV protein (102). All SVs contain both synaptogyrin and either synaptophysin I and/or synaptophysin II. Furthermore, ubiquitous isoforms of synaptogyrin and synaptophysins, called cellugyrin and pantophysin, are apparently co-expressed in all cells (34, 42). Thus synaptogyrin and synaptophysins represent invariant components of trafficking organelles with synaptic and ubiquitous forms. Synaptophysin I and synaptogyrin contain tyrosine-phosphorylated cytoplasmic C termini that are substrates for kinases of the src family. Such kinases are associated with SVs, and synaptophysin I and synaptogyrin appear to be phosphorylated in vivo (42). Surprisingly, synaptophysin II, which is otherwise homologous to synaptophysin I, probably is not tyrosine phosphorylated (R Janz & TC Südhof, unpublished observation).

The functions of synaptophysins and synaptogyrin are unknown. In view of their abundance, synthesis of ubiquitous and synaptic isoforms, and presence in all SVs, one would assume that synaptogyrin and synaptophysins perform fundamental, essential functions. Unexpectedly, single-mutant KO mice, lacking synaptophysin I or synaptogyrin, and double-mutant KO mice, lacking both, experience no apparent morbidity or enhanced mortality (103, 104). Detailed biochemical, morphological, and electrophysiological studies failed to reveal developmental abnormalities, structural changes, or biochemical compensatory mechanisms. The KO mice do, however, exhibit a phenotype. This phenotype was unexpected in view of the characteristics of synaptogyrin and synaptophysin: In synaptogyrin-deficient hippocampal synapses, a selective decrease in post-tetanic potentiation was present, whereas no abnormality was detected in synaptophysin I-deficient mice (104). In double KO mice, synapses lacking both synaptophysin I and synaptogyrin suffered from major impairments in all forms of synaptic plasticity and exhibited decreases in paired pulse facilitation, post-tetanic potentiation, and LTP. Thus these proteins are not required for the fundamental operations of SVs but appear to be necessary for adaptive changes during synaptic plasticity (104). Although the mechanism of this action is unclear, it is tempting to speculate that the observed requirement for tyrosine phosphorylation in synaptic plasticity (105, 106) may, at least in part, be based on the phosphorylation of these proteins.

What do these results teach us? First, the phenotype of the double synaptophysin/synaptogyrin KO mice is more severe than that of the single KO mice, indicating that synaptogyrin and synaptophysin I are functionally redundant. Thus, although these proteins are only weakly homologous (<25% sequence identity) and are represented in all cells by their ubiquitous isoforms, they do not perform partly related functions. Second, it is possible to remove a large part of the intrinsic membrane proteins of SVs without major consequences. Thus these proteins either perform only subtle functions, or their functions are redundant. Redundancy appears to be a more plausible explanation in view of the characteristics of these proteins.

SUMMARY AND OUTLOOK

SVs are composed of at least ten classes of putative trafficking proteins in addition to proteins that transport neurotransmitters, protons, chloride, and Zn^{2+}. The working hypothesis of the SV project is that SVs are composed of a limited number of proteins that perform distinct, identifiable functions. For example, one protein may mediate the recognition of SVs by the active zone in SV docking, another may link SVs into clusters as they are waiting to be recruited to the active zone, and a third may regulate endosomal traffic of SVs. According to this paradigm, knockouts of specific proteins should create selective defects in these processes. As in all biological systems, several proteins may perform redundant or overlapping functions, requiring multiple knockouts to uncover the full biological role of a protein.

Members of eight of the ten classes of putative trafficking proteins have been mutated in animals: synaptogyrin, synaptophysin I, rab3A, synapsins, synaptotagmin, SV2A/B, synaptobrevin II, and CSP (Table 1). In addition, rabphilin, which is recruited to SVs by rab3, has also been genetically analyzed. All these mutants were obtained in mice except for CSP, which was obtained only in *Drosophila*; some of the other mutants were also generated in flies and *C. elegans* (synaptobrevin, synaptotagmin, rab3). In addition to the mutants in trafficking proteins, mutants in the vertebrate monoamine SV transporter and the invertebrate GABA and acetylcholine transporters were characterized.

Of the trafficking protein mutants, only synaptobrevin was found to be essential for the fundamental process of release. Synaptotagmin, SV2, and CSP were observed to be essential for viability but able to perform via a regulatory function. Mutants of the other proteins exhibited more subtle phenotypes suggestive of functions in the modulation instead of the execution of SV exocytosis. Thus at this point, the paradigm of the SV project, to characterize all SV components and to assign identifiable and discrete functions to the individual components, has been fulfilled for some of the major proteins (synaptobrevin, synaptotagmin, rab3A, transporters), whereas for others (SV2, rabphilin, synaptogyrin, synaptophysin, CSP), the current analysis does not permit definitive functional conclusions.

Eventually, it will be possible to delete all SV proteins and to obtain a complete description of the SV pathway in terms of SV proteins. At the present level of analysis, many essential functions of SVs remain unexplained. For example, we have no idea how SV docking works, we do not know how SVs are linked into clusters, and it is unclear how their biogenesis as a separate organelle is organized. These questions are not answered for any eukaryotic organelle. There is a good chance that mutations in the remaining genes will address these questions. Redundant functions that could cover them have not been investigated for synaptophysins (the synaptophysin II KO mouse is not yet analyzed), SV2s, SVOP, SCAMPs, and rab3 (B, C, and D are as yet not analyzed). Thus it is too early to rethink the guiding hypothesis that single identified proteins are involved in specific functions.

ACKNOWLEDGMENTS

We are grateful to MS Brown and JL Goldstein for support and advice. RFC has been supported by a postdoctoral fellowship from the Spanish Ministry of Education and Culture and the Fulbright Commission.

Literature Cited

1. Katz B. 1969. *The Release of Neural Transmitter Substances*. Liverpool, UK: Liverpool Univ. Press. 60 pp.
2. Peters A, Palay SL, Webster Hde F. 1991. *The Fine Structure of the Nervous System*. New York/Oxford: Oxford Univ. Press
3. Südhof TC. 1995. The synaptic vesicle cycle: a cascade of protein-protein-interactions. *Nature* 375:645–53
4. Heuser JE, Reese TS, Dennis MJ, Jan Y, Jan L. 1979. Synaptic vesicle exocytosis captured by quick freezing and correlated with quantal transmitter release. *J. Cell Biol.* 81:725–30
5. Ceccarelli B, Hurlbut WP. 1980. Vesicle hypothesis of the release of quanta of acetylcholine. *Physiol. Rev.* 60:396–441
6. Alvarez de Toledo G, Fernández-Chacón R, Fernández JM. 1993. Release of secretory products during transient vesicle fusion. *Nature* 363:554–57
7. Henkel AW, Betz WJ. 1995. Staurosporine blocks evoked release of FM1-43 but not acetylcholine from frog motor nerve terminals. *J. Neurosci.* 15:8246–58
8. Murthy VM, Stevens CF. 1998 Synaptic vesicles retain their identity through the endocytic cycle. *Nature* 392:497–501
9. Fischer von Mollard G, Stahl B, Walch-Solimena C, Takei K, Daniels L, et al. 1994. Localization of rab5 to synaptic vesicles identifies endosomal intermediate in synaptic vesicle recycling pathway. *Eur. J. Cell Biol.* 65:319–26
10. de Hoop MJ, Huber LA, Stenmark H, Williamson E, Zerial M, et al. 1994. The involvement of the small GTP-binding protein rab5a in neuronal endocytosis. *Neuron* 13:11–22
11. Sulzer D, Holtzman E. 1989. Acidification and endosome-like compartments in the presynaptic terminals of frog retinal photoreceptors. *J. Neurocytol.* 18:529–40
12. Landis DMD, Hall AK, Weinstgei LA, Reese TS. 1988. The organization of cytoplasm at the presynaptic active zone of a central nervous system synapse. *Neuron* 1:201–9
13. von Schwarzenfeld I. 1979. Origin of transmitter released by electrical stimulation from a small, metabolically very active vesicular pool of cholinergic synapses in guinea-pig cerebral cortex. *Neuroscience* 4:477–93
14. Stevens CF, Sullivan J. 1998. Synaptic plasticity. *Curr. Biol.* 8:R151–53
15. Scheller RH. 1995. Membrane trafficking in the presynaptic nerve terminal. *Neuron* 14:893–97
16. Cremona O, De Camilli P. 1997. Synaptic vesicle endocytosis. *Curr. Opin. Neurobiol.* 7:323–30
17. Jahn R, Südhof TC. 1993. Synaptic vesicle traffic: rush hour in the nerve terminal. *J. Neurochem.* 61:12–21
18. Huang C, Mason JT. 1978. Geometric packing constraints in egg phosphatidyl-

choline vesicles. *Proc. Natl. Acad. Sci. USA* 75:308–10

19. Nagy A, Baker RR, Morris SJ, Whittaker VP. 1976. The preparation and characterization of synaptic vesicles of high purity. *Brain Res.* 109:285–309
20. Liu Y, Edwards RH. 1997. The role of vesicular transport proteins in synaptic transmission and neural degeneration. *Annu. Rev. Neurosci.* 20:125–56
21. Stevens TH, Forgac M. 1997. Structure, function and regulation of the vacuolar (H^+)-ATPase. *Annu. Rev. Cell Dev. Biol.* 13:779–808
22. Stadler HS, Tsukita S. 1984. Synaptic vesicles contain an ATP-dependent proton pump and show "knob-like" protrusions on their surface. *EMBO J.* 3:3333–37
23. Erickson JD, Eiden LE, Hoffman BJ. 1992. Expression cloning of a reserpine-sensitive vesicular monoamine transporter. *Proc. Natl. Acad. Sci. USA* 89: 10993–97
24. Alfonso A, Grundahl K. Duerr JS, Han H-P, Rand JB. 1993. The *Caenorhabditis elegans unc-17* gene: a putative vesicular acetylcholine transporter. *Science* 261:617–19
25. Roghani A, Feldman J, Kohan SA, Shirzadi A, Gundersen CB, et al. 1994. Molecular cloning of a putative vesicular transporter for acetylcholine. *Proc. Natl. Acad. USA* 91:10620–24
26. McIntire SL, Reimer RJ, Schuske K, Edwards RH, Jorgensen EM. 1997. Identification and characterization of the vesicular GABA transporter. *Nature* 389:870–76
27. Bajjalieh SM, Peterson K, Linial, M, Scheller RH. 1993. Brain contains two forms of synaptic vesicle protein 2. *Proc. Natl. Acad. Sci. USA* 90:2150–54
28. Feany MB, Lee S, Edwards RH, Buckley KM. 1992. The synaptic vesicle protein SV2 is a novel type of transmembrane transporter. *Cell* 70:861–67
29. Janz R, Hofmann K, Südhof TC. 1998. SVOP, an evolutionarily conserved synaptic vesicle protein, suggests novel transport functions of synaptic vesicles. *J. Neurosci.* In press
30. Elferink LA, Trimble WS, Scheller RH. 1989. Two vesicle-associated membrane protein genes are differentially expressed in the rat central nervous system. *J. Biol. Chem.* 264:11061–64
31. McMahon HT, Ushkaryov YA, Edelman L, Link E, Binz T, et al. 1993. Cellubrevin is a ubiquitous tetanus-toxin substrate homologous to a putative synaptic vesicle fusion protein. *Nature* 364:346–49
32. Südhof TC, Lottspeich F, Greengard P, Mehl E, Jahn R. 1987. Synaptophysin: a synaptic vesicle protein with four transmembrane regions and a novel cytoplasmic domain. *Science* 238:1142–44
33. Fykse EM, Takei K, Walch-Solimena C, Geppert M, Jahn R, et al. 1993. Relative properties and localizations of synaptic vesicle protein isoforms: the case of the synaptophysins. *J. Neurosci.* 13:4997–5007
34. Haass NK, Kartenbeck MA, Leube RE. 1996. Pantophysin is a ubiquitously expressed synaptophysin homologue and defines constitutive transport vesicles. *J. Cell Biol.* 134:731–46
35. Mastrogiacomo A, Parsons SM, Zampighi GA, Jenden DJ, Umbach JA, et al. 1994. Cysteine string proteins: a potential link between synaptic vesicles and presynaptic Ca^{2+} channels. *Science* 263:981–82
36. Shirataki H, Kaibuchi K, Sakoda T, Kishida S, Yamaguchi T, et al. 1993. Rabphilin-3A, a putative target protein for smg p25/rab3A small GTP-binding protein related to synaptotagmin. *Mol. Cell Biol.* 13:2061–68
37. Braun JE, Scheller RH. 1995. Cysteine string protein, a DnaJ family member, is present on diverse secretory vesicles. *Neuropharmacology* 34:1361–69
38. Brand SH, Castle JD. 1993. SCAMP37, a new marker within the general cell surface recycling system. *EMBO J.* 12:3753–61
39. Bajjalieh SM, Frantz GD, Weimann JM, McConnell SK, Scheller RH. 1994. Differential expression of synaptic vesicle protein 2 (SV2) isoforms. *J. Neurosci.* 14:5223–35
40. Südhof TC, Czernik AJ, Kao H, Takei K, Johnston PA, et al. 1989. Synapsins: mosaics of shared and individual domains in a family of synaptic vesicle phosphoproteins. *Science* 245:1474–80
41. Stenius K, Janz R, Südhof TC, Jahn R. 1995. Structure of synaptogyrin (p29) defines a novel family of synaptic vesicle proteins. *J. Cell Biol.* 131:1801–9
42. Janz R, Südhof TC. 1998. Cellugyrin, a novel ubiquitous form of synaptogyrin that is phosphorylated by $pp60^{c\text{-}src}$. *J. Biol. Chem.* 273:2851–57
43. Li C, Takei K, Geppert M, Daniell L, Stenius K, et al. 1994. Synaptic targeting of rabphilin-3A, a synaptic vesicle Ca^{2+}phospholipid-binding protein, depends on rab3A/3C. *Neuron* 13:885–98

44. Geppert M, Südhof TC. 1998. Rab3 and synaptotagmin: the yin and yang of synaptic membrane fusion. *Annu. Rev. Neurosci.* 21:75–95
45. Singleton DR, Wu TT, Castle JD. 1997. Three mammalian SCAMPs (secretory carrier membrane proteins) are highly related products of distinct genes having similar subcellular distribution *J. Cell. Sci.* 110:2099–107
46. Li C, Ullrich B, Zhang JZ, Anderson RGW, Brose N, Südhof TC. 1995. Ca^{2+}-dependent and independent activities of neural and non neural synaptotagmins. *Nature* 375:594–99
47. Wang, YM, Gainetdinov RR, Fumagalli F, Xu F, Jones SR, et al. 1997. Knockout of the vesicular monoamine transporter 2 gene results in neonatal death and supersensitivity to cocaine and amphetamine. *Neuron* 19:1285–96
48. Takahashi N, Miner LL, Sora I, Ukike H, Revay RS, et al. 1997. VMAT2 knockout mice: Heterozygotes display reduced amphetamine-conditioned reward, enhanced amphetamine locomotion, and enhanced MPTP toxicity. *Proc. Natl. Acad. Sci. USA* 94:9938–43
49. McIntire SL, Jorgensen E, Horvitz HR. 1992. Genes required for GABA function in *Caenorhabditis elegans*. *Nature* 364:334–37
50. Zimmermann H, Whittaker VP. 1974. Different recovery rates of the electrophysiological, biochemical, and morphological parameters in the cholinergic synapses of the *Torpedo* electric organ after stimulation. *J. Neurochem.* 22:1109–14
51. Song H-J, Ming G-L, Fon E, Bellocchio E, Edwards RH, Poo M-M. 1997. Expression of a putative vesicular acetylcholine transporter facilitates quantal transmitter packaging. *Neuron* 18:815–26
52. Palmiter RD, Cole TB, Quaife CJ, Findley SD. 1996. ZnT-3, a putative transporter of zinc into synaptic vesicles. *Proc. Natl. Acad. Sci. USA* 93:14934–39
52a. Huang L, Gitschier J. 1997. A novel gene involved in zinc transport is deficient in the *lethal milk* mouse. *Nat. Genet.* 17:292–97
52b. Bellocchio EE, Hu H, Pohorille A, Chan J, Pickel VM, et al. 1998. The localization of the brain-specific inorganic phosphate transporter suggests a specific presynaptic role in glutamatergic transmission. *J. Neurosci.* 18:8648–59
53. Hayashi T, McMahon H, Yamasaki S, Binz T, Hata Y, et al. 1994. Synaptic vesicle membrane fusion complex: action of clostridial neurotoxins on assembly. *EMBO J.* 13:5051–61
54. Link E, Edelmann L, Chow JH, Binz T, Yamasaki S, et al. 1992. Tetanus toxin action: inhibition of neurotransmitter release linked to synaptobrevin proteolysis. *Biochem. Biophys. Res. Comm.* 189:1017–23
55. Link E, Edelman L, Chou JH, Binz T, Yamasaki S, et al. 1992. Tetanus toxin action: inhibition of neurotransmitter release linked to synaptobrevin proteolysis. *Biochem. Biophys. Res. Commun.* 189: 1017–23
56. Schiavo G, Benfenati F, Poulain B, Rossetto O, Polverino de Laureto P. 1992. Tetanus and botulinum-B neurotoxins block neurotransmitter release by proteolytic cleavage of synaptobrevin. *Nature* 359:832–35
57. Yamasaki KS, Baumeister A, Binz T, Link E, Cornille F, et al. 1994. Cleavage of members of the synaptobrevin/VAMP family by types D and F botulinal neurotoxins and tetanus toxin. *J. Biol. Chem.* 269:12764–72
58. Blasi J, Chapman ER, Link E, Binz T, Yamasaki S, et al. 1993. Botulinum neurotoxin A selectively cleaves the synaptic protein SNAP-25. *Nature* 365:160–63
59. Blasi J, Chapman ER, Yamasaki S, Binz T, Niemann H, Jahn R. 1993. Botulinum neurotoxin C1 blocks neurotransmitter release by means of cleaving HPC-1/syntaxin. *EMBO J.* 12:4821–28
60. Foran P, Lawrence GW, Shone CC, Foster KA, Dolly JO. 1996. Botulinum neurotoxin C1 cleaves both syntaxin and SNAP-25 in intact and permeabilized chromaffin cells: correlation with its blockade of catecholamine release. *Biochemistry* 35:2630–36
61. Hanson PI, Roth R, Morisaki H, Jahn R, Heuser JE. 1997. Structure and conformational changes in NSF and its membrane receptor complexes visualized by quick-freeze\deep-etch electron microscopy. *Cell* 90:523–35
62. Weber T, Zemelman BV, McNew JA, Westermann B, Gmalch M, et al. 1998. SNAREpins: minimal machinery for membrane fusion. *Cell* 92:759–72
63. Nonet ML, Saifee O, Zhao H, Rand JB, Wei L. 1998 Synaptic transmission deficits in *Caenorhabditis elegans* synaptobrevin mutants. *J. Neurosci.* 18:70–80
64. Deitcher DL, Ueda A, Stewart BA, Burgess RW, Kidokoro Y, Schwarz TL. 1998. Distinct requirements for evoked and spontaneous release of neurotransmitter are revealed by mutations in the

Drosophila gene neuronal-synaptobrevin. *J. Neurosci.* 18:2028–39
65. Bruns D, Jahn R. 1995. Real-time measurement of transmitter release from single synaptic vesicles. *Nature* 377:62–65
66. Sabatini BL, Regehr WG. 1996. Timing of neurotransmission at fast synapses in the mammalian brain. *Nature* 384:170–72
67. Goda Y, Stevens CF. 1994. Two components of transmitter release at a central synapse. *Proc. Natl. Acad. Sci. USA* 91:12942–46
68. Südhof TC, Rizo J. 1996. Synaptotagmins: C_2-domain proteins that regulate membrane traffic. *Neuron* 17:379–88
69. Ubach J, Zhang X, Shao X, Südhof TC, Rizo J. 1998. Ca^{2+} binding to synaptotagmin: how many Ca^{2+} ions bind to the tip of a C_2-domain. *EMBO J.* 17:3921–30
70. Geppert M, Goda Y, Hammer RE, Li C, Rosahl TW, et al. 1994. Synaptotagmin I: a major Ca^{2+}-sensor for transmitter release at a central synapse. *Cell* 79:717–27
71. DiAntonio A, Parfitt KD, Schwarz TL. 1993. Synaptic transmission persists in synaptotagmin mutants of *Drosophila*. *Cell* 3:1281–90
72. Littleton JT, Stern M, Schulze K, Perin M, Bellen HJ. 1993. Mutational analysis of *Drosophila* synaptotagmin demonstrates its essential role in Ca^{2+}-activated neurotransmitter release. *Cell* 74:1125–34
73. Nonet ML, Grundahl K, Meyer BJ, Rand JB. 1993. Synaptic function is impaired but not eliminated in *C. elegans* mutants lacking synaptotagmin. *Cell* 73:1291–305
74. Raastad M, Storm JF, Andersen P. 1992. Putative single quantum and single fibre excitatory postsynaptic currents show similar amplitude range and variability in rat hippocampal slices. *Eur. J. Neurosci.* 4:113–17
75. Hessler NA, Shirke AM, Malinow R. 1993. The probability of transmitter release at a mammalian central synapse. *Nature* 366:569–72
76. Rosenmund C, Clements JD, Westbrook GL. 1993. Nonuniform probability of glutamate release at a hippocampal synapse. *Science* 262:754–57
77. Capogna M, McKinney RA, O'Connor V, Gähwiler BH, Thompson SM. 1997. Ca^{2+} or Sr^{2+} partially rescues synaptic transmission in hippocampal cultures treated with botulinum toxin A and C, but not tetanus toxin. *J. Neurosci.* 17:7190–202
78. Rosenmund C, Stevens CF. 1996. Definition of the readily releasable pool of vesicles at hippocampal synapses. *Neuron* 16:1197–207
79. Geppert M, Bolshakov V, Siegelbaum SA, Takei K, De Camilli P, et al. 1994. The role of Rab3A in neurotransmitter release. *Nature* 369:493–97
80. Geppert M, Goda Y, Stevens CF, Südhof TC. 1997. Rab3A regulates a late step in synaptic vesicle fusion. *Nature* 387:810–14
81. Castillo PE, Janz R, Tzounopoulos T, Südhof TC, Malenka RC, Nicoll RA. 1997. The synaptic vesicle protein rab3A is essential for mossy fiber long-term potentiation in the hippocampus. *Nature* 388:590–93
82. Nonet ML, Staunton JE, Kilgard MP, Fergestad T, Hartwieg E, et al. 1997. *Caenorhabditis elegans* rab3 mutant synapses exhibit impaired function and are partially depleted of vesicles. *J. Neurosci.* 17:8061–73
83. Brennwald P, Kearns B, Champion K, Keranen S, Bankiatis V. 1994. Sec9 is a SNAP-25-like component of a yeast SNARE complex that may be the effector of Sec4 function in exocytosis. *Cell* 79:245–58
84. Wang Y, Okamoto M, Schmitz F, Hofmann K, Südhof TC. 1997. RIM: A putative rab3 effector in regulating synaptic vesicle fusion. *Nature* 388:593–98
85. Kotake K, Ozaki N, Mizuta M, Sekiya S, Inagaki N, Seino S. 1997. Noc2, a putative zinc finger protein involved in exocytosis in endocrine cells. *J. Biol. Chem.* 272:29407–10
86. Stahl B, Chou JH, Li C, Südhof TC, Jahn R. 1996. Rab3 reversibly recruits rabphilin to synaptic vesicles by a mechanism analogous to raf recruitment by ras. *EMBO J.* 15:1799–809
87. Fykse EM, Li C, Südhof TC. 1995. Phosphorylation of rabphilin-3a by Ca^{2+}/Calmodulin- and cAMP-dependent protein kinases in vitro. *J. Neurosci.* 15:2385–95
88. Lönart G, Südhof TC. 1998. Region-specific phosphorylation of rabphilin in mossy fiber nerve terminals of the hippocampus. *J. Neurosci.* 18:634–40
89. Chung SH, Song WJ, Kim K, Bednarski JJ, Chen J, et al. 1998. The C2 domains of rabphilin-3A specifically bind phosphatidylinositol 4,5-bisphosphate containing vesicles in a Ca^{2+}-dependent manner. In vitro characteristics and possible significance. *J. Biol. Chem.* 273: 10240–48
90. Zinsmaier KE, Eberle KK, Buchner E, Walter N, Benzer S. 1994. Paralysis and early death in cysteine string protein mutants of *Drosophila*. *Science* 263:977–80

90a. Umbach JA. Zinsmaier KE, Eberle KK, Buchner E, Benzer S, Gundersen CB. 1994. Presynaptic dysfunction in *Drosophila csp* mutants. *Neuron* 13:899–907
91. Ranjan R, Brink P, Zinsmaier KE. 1998. Cysteine string protein is required for calcium secretion coupling of evoked neurotransmitter in *Drosophila* but not for vesicle recycling. *J. Neurosci.* 18:956–64
91a. Umbach JA, Saitoe M, Kidokoro Y, Gundersen CB. 1998. Attenuated influx of calcium ions at nerve endings of *csp* and *shibire* mutant *Drosophila. J. Neurosci.* 18:3233–40
92. Gundersen CB, Umbach JA. 1992. Suppression cloning of the cDNA for a candidate subunit of a presynaptic calcium channel. *Neuron* 9:527–37
93. Südhof TC. 1990. The structure of the human synapsin I gene and protein. *J. Biol. Chem.* 165:7849–52
94. Hosaka M, Südhof TC. 1998. Synapsin III, a novel synapsin with an unusual regulation by Ca^{2+}. *J. Biol. Chem.* 273:13371–74
95. Kao HT, Porton B, Czernik AJ, Feng J, Yiu G, et al. 1998. A third member of the synapsin gene family. *Proc. Natl. Acad. Sci. USA* 95:4667–72
96. Esser L, Wang C-R, Hosaka M, Smagula CS, Südhof TC, Deisenhofer J. 1998. Synapsin I is structurally homologous to ATP-utilizing enzymes. *EMBO J.* 17: 977–84
97. Hosaka M, Südhof TC. 1998. Synapsins I and II are ATP-binding proteins with differential Ca^{2+} regulation. *J. Biol. Chem.* 273:1425–29
98. Rosahl TW, Geppert M, Spillane D, Herz J, Hammer RE, et al. 1993. Short-term synaptic plasticity is altered in mice lacking synapsin I. *Cell* 75:661–70
99. Rosahl TW, Spillane D, Missler M, Herz J, Wolff J, et al. 1995. Essential functions of synapsins I and II in synaptic vesicle regulation. *Nature* 375:488–93
100. Ryan TA, Li L, Chin LS, Greengard P, Smith SJ. Synaptic vesicle recycling in synapsin I knock-out mice. *J. Cell Biol.* 134:1219–27
101. Spillane D, Rosahl T, Südhof TC, Malenka RC. 1995. Long-term potentiation in mice lacking synapsins. *Neuropharmacology* 34:1573–79
102. Jahn R, Schiebler W, Ouimet C, Greengard P. 1985. A 38,000-dalton membrane protein (p38) present in synaptic vesicles. *Proc. Natl. Acad. Sci. USA* 82:4137–41
103. McMahon H, Bolshakov VY, Janz R, Hammer RE, Siegelbaum SA, Südhof TC. 1996. Synaptophysin, a major synaptic vesicle protein, is not essential for neurotransmitter release. *Proc. Natl. Acad. Sci. USA* 75:308–10
104. Janz R, Bolshakov VY, Hammer RH, Siegelbaum S, Südhof TC. 1998. Synaptogyrin and synaptophysin, abundant tyrosine-phosphorylated proteins of synaptic vesicles, are essential for synaptic plasticity. *Neuron.* Submitted
105. O'Dell TJ, Kandel ER, Grant SG. 1991. Long-term potentiation in the hippocampus is blocked by tyrosine kinase inhibitors. *Nature* 353:558–60
106. Grant SG, O'Dell TJ, Karl KA, Stein PL, Soriano P, Kandel ER. 1992. Impaired long-term potentiation, spatial learning, and hippocampal development in *fyn* mutant mice. *Science* 258:1903–10

Annu. Rev. Physiol. 1999. 61:777–807

RECONSTITUTION OF REGULATED EXOCYTOSIS IN CELL-FREE SYSTEMS: A Critical Appraisal

Julia Avery and Reinhard Jahn
Department of Neurobiology, Max-Planck-Institute for Biophysical Chemistry, Am Fassberg, D-37077 Göttingen, Germany; e-mail: rjahn@gwdg.de

J. Michael Edwardson
Department of Pharmacology, University of Cambridge, Tennis Court Road, Cambridge CB2 1QJ, United Kingdom; e-mail:

KEY WORDS: permeabilized cells, in vitro membrane fusion

ABSTRACT

Regulated exocytosis involves the tightly controlled fusion of a transport vesicle with the plasma membrane. It includes processes as diverse as the release of neurotransmitters from presynaptic nerve endings and the sperm-triggered deposition of a barrier preventing polyspermy in oocytes. Cell-free model systems have been developed for studying the biochemical events underlying exocytosis. They range from semi-intact permeabilized cells to the reconstitution of membrane fusion from isolated secretory vesicles and their target plasma membranes. Interest in such cell-free systems has recently been reinvigorated by new evidence suggesting that membrane fusion is mediated by a basic mechanism common to all intracellular fusion events. In this chapter, we review some of the literature in the light of these new developments and attempt to provide a critical discussion of the strengths and limitations of the various cell-free systems.

INTRODUCTION

The fusion of a trafficking vesicle with its target membrane is a basic feature of every eukaryotic cell. Recent evidence suggests that membrane fusion is governed by conserved sets of proteins that have evolved into small protein families. These proteins include three membrane proteins, commonly referred

0066-4278/99/0315-0777$08.00

to as SNAREs, which undergo cyclic assembly and disassembly reactions with the assistance of chaperone-like molecules known as NSF and SNAPs (1–3). Although it is still debated as to how these reactions bring about membrane fusion (4, 5), SNAREs appear to be responsible for virtually every membrane fusion step, in cell types as diverse as yeast and mammalian neurons (6–8). This is regardless of whether intracellular organelles fuse together or whether fusion occurs between trafficking vesicles and the plasma membrane. Several other protein families required for membrane fusion appear to be similarly ubiquitous and conserved, such as the GTPases of the rab family (9–12) and the Sec1p/munc-18 protein family (13, 14). Thus, regulated exocytosis, which has long been considered a unique feature of highly specialized cells, represents a pathway in which a common membrane fusion apparatus is regulated by cell-specific control mechanisms.

Despite recent developments, the complex molecular events underlying regulated exocytosis are still unclear. The docking and controlled fusion of a secretory vesicle with the plasma membrane require multiple steps that need to be coordinated both spatially and temporally and that involve many different molecules. Membrane fusion can be monitored with high precision and kinetic resolution using electrophysiological techniques (15, 16), but the preceding steps are more difficult to analyze. In addition, the mechanisms regulating exocytosis appear to differ between cell types. For example, Ca^{2+} ions trigger exocytosis in many regulated secretory cells, but the rate-limiting steps controlled by Ca^{2+} may not be identical in all cases. Furthermore, in at least some cell types, Ca^{2+} is required for multiple steps, each with different kinetic properties, along the pathway leading to fusion (17–20). In other cell types, exocytosis can be triggered independently of changes in intracellular Ca^{2+} by means of molecules such as GTP analogs, e.g. mast cells (21) and platelets (22), or cyclic AMP, e.g. parotid gland (23).

Although more and more trafficking proteins are being identified, refined assays are urgently needed to clarify the precise role of these proteins in the sequence of events leading to exocytosis. A large gap exists between approaches involving intact organisms or cells and those involving the biochemistry of isolated proteins. For example, the functional relevance of a protein can be investigated by means of genetic alteration, transfection, or microinjection of probes affecting its behavior. However, it remains a challenge to identify the precise step at which a particular protein is operating. On the other hand, the protein-protein interactions these gene products undergo in the test tube may yield detailed pieces of the puzzle but cast little light on how these pieces fit together to form the complete picture.

One way in which to bridge this gap would be to study the fusion of vesicles with plasma membranes under cell-free conditions. In principle, such in vitro systems should allow direct biochemical access to the exocytotic apparatus and the factors controlling it. Several attempts have been made to establish such systems. The first in vitro exocytotic system was developed from the sea urchin egg (24): Flat carrier-supported membranes, complete with their array of secretory granules, were obtained by shearing eggs attached to polylysine-coated surfaces. Exocytosis was elicited simply by the addition of micromolar Ca^{2+}. Surprisingly, it has been difficult to develop comparable cell-free systems using mammalian cells, which can largely be attributed to methodological problems (discussed further below).

In contrast, fusion between intracellular trafficking vesicles can be readily studied in vitro (25–29). When intracellular vesicles fuse with each other, the inner lumen remains completely separated from the external surroundings. Taking advantage of this feature, ingenious and powerful assays have been developed that use vesicle populations containing different and interacting components (25–29). Signals are generated only when the vesicular contents and/or the inner leaflets of the vesicle membranes mix. The assays are highly sensitive in that they will detect fusion of even a small proportion of the vesicles. Furthermore, they are highly specific because fusion can easily be distinguished from vesicle lysis by adding membrane-impermeant inhibitors of the reporter reaction to the outside medium. These methods have led to the discovery of essential proteins and have been instrumental in shaping current understanding of intracellular membrane fusion.

During exocytosis, a secretory vesicle fuses with a flat membrane and releases its content into the medium. Thus, the convenient and sensitive content-mixing assays cannot be employed. To circumvent this problem, many investigators have used permeabilized cells, which permit access to the intracellular cytoplasm through holes in the plasma membrane. As in intact cells, exocytosis is measured through the release of secretory product into the medium. Although permeabilized cells still retain most of the complex cytoarchitecture involved in secretion, experiments performed on such systems have yielded important insights into the individual steps leading to exocytosis. In contrast, "true" in vitro assays for exocytosis, in which isolated vesicles fuse with plasma membranes, are tricky and fraught with technical problems. In this case, fusion is monitored by measuring the release of granule content and/or the mixing of the bilayers using exogenously added fluorescent probes. Because these assays lack the ease and sensitivity of intracellular fusion assays, they have so far been applied to only a few specialized systems.

In this article, we present an overview of the most commonly used approaches to study exocytosis in vitro and, without trying to be comprehensive, summarize some of the major findings these approaches have provided.

PERMEABILIZED CELLS

Baker & Knight (30, 31) were the first to demonstrate that secretion can be studied in cells with leaky plasma membranes. They used high-voltage discharges to cause the dielectric breakdown of the plasma membrane of suspended adrenal chromaffin cells and platelets, which rendered them permeable to exogenously applied compounds. Since these pioneering studies, several different techniques for cell permeabilization have been developed, including the application of detergents (e.g. digitonin and saponin), poreforming bacterial toxins (α-toxin and streptolysin *O*), ATP^{4-}, and exposure of cells to mechanical shearing forces (32, 33). Cells can also be dialyzed using a patch pipette in the whole cell configuration (for a detailed discussion of this approach, see 15, 34). In permeabilized cells, the intracellular space is directly accessible, allowing the use of biochemical methods to study secretion. Permeabilized cells are particularly suitable for examining the role of small effector molecules and of soluble proteins. For instance, there is often a progressive loss of the exocytotic response to Ca^{2+} due to the slow wash-out of cytosolic constituents necessary to maintain secretion (35–38). Exocytosis can be restored, at least for some time, by adding back cytosolic fractions, thereby allowing the identification of cytosolic proteins that are involved in exocytosis.

Stages of Exocytosis Defined by Their Dependence on Ca^{2+} and ATP

Permeabilized cells were instrumental in establishing that a rise of intracellular Ca^{2+} ions can trigger exocytosis. Exocytosis was stimulated in electropermeabilized adrenal chromaffin cells by the introduction of micromolar levels of Ca^{2+} directly into the cytosol (31, 39, 40). It was also established, early on, that MgATP was necessary for optimal secretion from a number of cell types, including adrenal chromaffin cells (31, 39, 41), platelets (42), pituitary tumor cells (43), and insulin-secreting tumor cells (44). The MgATP requirement of Ca^{2+}-stimulated secretion almost certainly indicates a need for ATP hydrolysis because nonhydrolyzable ATP analogues do not support secretion (39, 45).

Holz and colleagues (45; see also 18, 46) were the first to establish that ATP is required before Ca^{2+}-stimulated fusion can occur. Two components of exocytosis were identified in permeabilized adrenal chromaffin cells: an initial fast wave of exocytosis that is already past its MgATP-requirement when the cells are permeabilized and, thus, does not require exogenous MgATP for exocytosis; and a second, slower phase that requires exogenous MgATP for fusion to occur. It was suggested that in intact cells, the secretory apparatus is activated by intracellular ATP (a process commonly referred to as priming) so that, immediately upon permeabilization, there is a component of secretion that is independent of exogenous ATP. This MgATP-independent component of secretion is labile and rapidly lost with time after permeabilization (45).

Since these original observations, the differentiation of steps leading to exocytosis has been further refined. ATP-dependent priming was shown to be composed of a series of sequential reactions (18, 19). In digitonin-permeabilized adrenal chromaffin cells, priming was shown to include an ATP-dependent and Ca^{2+}-enhanced step, as well as a temperature-sensitive step, before the final primed state was reached (18). The two consecutive Ca^{2+}-requiring steps were shown to have different affinities for Ca^{2+} and, thus, most likely to involve distinct Ca^{2+}-binding proteins. In another study, on melanotrophs and chromaffin cells, priming was shown to consist of at least five sequential steps (19). The final primed state in both studies was one that could respond to Ca^{2+}, in the absence of MgATP, by initiating membrane fusion.

The discussion here focuses largely on results obtained from chromaffin cells or the closely related PC12 cell line, and it should be borne in mind that different results were reported from other cell types. For instance, in streptolysin *O*-permeabilized rat mast cells, exocytosis could be stimulated by a combination of GTPγS and Ca^{2+} even in the prolonged absence of ATP, which suggests that ATP is not required for exocytosis (47). For mast cells it may be sensible to maintain a postpriming state of all granules, as these cells literally explode upon stimulation (48).

Priming for Exocytosis

PROTEINS INVOLVED IN POLYPHOSPHOINOSITIDE METABOLISM Experiments with permeabilized PC12 cells established that distinct cytosolic factors were responsible for mediating ATP-dependent priming of Ca^{2+}-activated exocytosis (46). Two of these priming factors were shown to be phosphatidylinositol (PtdIns) transfer protein (49) and phosphatidylinositol-4-phosphate 5-kinase (50). PtdIns transfer protein transfers PtdIns and, to a lesser extent, phosphatidylcholine between membrane bilayers (51). Because phospholipid transfer does not require ATP, its role in ATP-dependent priming may be to provide precursors for the generation of polyphosphoinositides (50). Indeed, a strict correlation between the levels of the polyphosphoinositides (PIPs) and Ca^{2+}-stimulated exocytosis was demonstrated in permeabilized adrenal chromaffin cells (52). This function was independent of their being substrates for the generation of the signaling molecules inositol 1,4,5-trisphosphate and 1,2-diacylglycerol (52).

The dependence of exocytosis on PIPs is not currently understood. An increase in the level of PIPs in membranes would increase their negative surface charge, which would hinder fusion by means of electrostatic repulsion. Therefore, it is unlikely that PIPs promote exocytosis primarily by changing the biophysical properties of the participating membranes. Alternatively, it has been proposed that the transient generation of PIPs serves as a local signal for the recruitment and/or activation of proteins that function in the exocytotic process (for reviews see 53, 54). It is interesting that PIPs are also required for other membrane trafficking steps, where they have been associated with vesicle budding (55, 56). In yeast, both a PtdIns transfer protein and a PI-kinase (Sec14p and Vps34p, respectively) are involved in vesicle traffic from the Golgi to the vacuole (57, 58, 59, 60). Again, PIPs may serve as local signals for the recruitment of proteins such as coat proteins.

N-ETHYLMALEIMIDE–SENSITIVE FACTOR Permeabilized cells were also used to investigate the role in exocytosis of the cytoplasmic ATPase *N*-ethylmaleimide–sensitive factor (NSF). NSF, together with soluble NSF-attachment proteins (SNAPs), catalyzes ATP-dependent disassembly of the ternary SNARE complex (3, 61). NSF was originally proposed to act late in the sequence of events leading to exocytosis (61). However, this idea was inconsistent with previous observations that Ca^{2+}-stimulated exocytosis can occur in the absence of MgATP (18, 45, 46). Indeed, use of stage-specific assays in digitonin-permeabilized adrenal chromaffin cells demonstrated that exogenous α-SNAP stimulated the ATP-dependent and Ca^{2+}-enhanced priming of regulated exocytosis (20). Surprisingly, this effect occurred without the need for the addition of exogenous NSF. An explanation for this anomaly was provided by studies using permeabilized PC12 cells. Here a requirement for NSF was demonstrated only after incubation during repeated cycles of priming and depriming (62). These differences can probably be attributed to the fact that α-SNAP washes out more easily than NSF, thus becoming rate-limiting under these conditions. Conclusive evidence supporting a role of NSF in an early priming step was also provided by studying the fusion of yeast vacuoles in vitro (63, 64).

OTHER PROTEINS In addition to the proteins discussed above, other proteins have been proposed to operate in the priming reaction, but their role is less clear. In permeabilized adrenal chromaffin cells, the ATP-dependent, Ca^{2+}-enhanced priming was stimulated by the addition of 14-3-3 proteins (20). These proteins were originally identified as neuronal proteins that were essential for the normal development and functioning of the nervous system, although their precise function has remained enigmatic (65). An involvement of these proteins in Ca^{2+}-regulated exocytosis was first demonstrated through their ability to retard or reverse exocytotic rundown in digitonin-permeabilized adrenal chromaffin cells (66–69). The stimulatory effects of α-SNAP and 14-3-3 proteins on Ca^{2+}-regulated exocytosis were due to distinct mechanisms of action, and their effects were additive (20). This result supports the hypothesis that priming is a combination of many different biochemical reactions.

The role of cytoskeletal rearrangements during priming has also been investigated. In streptolysin *O*-permeabilized pancreatic acini, disassembly of the actin cytoskeleton beneath the apical plasma membrane was achieved by the introduction of specific actin monomer-binding proteins, such as the β-thymosins or a gelsolin fragment (70). It is interesting that this disassembly alone was sufficient to trigger exocytosis, even when the Ca^{2+} concentration was clamped at very low levels by EGTA. This result suggests that the primary role of Ca^{2+} in triggering exocytosis, at least in this cell type, may be to remove a physical barrier that prevents access of the secretory vesicles to their target membrane. Furthermore, it would appear that the fusion machinery on the two membranes is already primed in the resting cell and that during cell stimulation no further priming is necessary to elicit membrane fusion. Evidence for the notion that one of the priming steps may involve actin disassembly was also obtained from permeabilized chromaffin cells. It was proposed that Exo1, a member of the 14-3-3 protein family, brings about ATP-dependent priming by reorganizing the cortical actin cytoskeleton, thereby increasing the number of primed secretory vesicles at the plasma membrane (71).

Triggering of Exocytosis

SNARES As discussed above, it is well established that fusion is mediated by a conserved set of SNARE proteins. In neurons and neuroendocrine cells, these proteins include the vesicle membrane proteins synaptobrevin 1 and 2 (also referred to as VAMP1 and VAMP2, for vesicle–associated membrane protein) and the plasma membrane proteins SNAP-25 and syntaxin 1. The most compelling evidence for a direct involvement of these proteins in Ca^{2+}-regulated exocytosis was provided by studies using clostridial neurotoxins (for review see 72). In vitro, both tetanus toxin (TeNT) and the botulinum neurotoxins (BoNTs) selectively attack motorneurons and block neurotransmitter release. The toxins are all zinc proteases, and they each proteolyse one of the neuronal SNAREs. When introduced into permeabilized cells, the active light chains of these toxins were shown to inhibit Ca^{2+}-regulated secretion in a variety of cell types (73).

Since the original discovery of the neuronal isoforms of synaptobrevin, SNAP-25 and syntaxin, many mammalian homologues have been identified (5, 74–76). Many of these homologues are likely to be resistant to proteolytic attack by the clostridial neurotoxins because, as far as is known, the consensus sequences for cleavage are not preserved (75–77). In some cells, both toxin-sensitive and toxin-insensitive fusion events can be identified (77–79). For example, in permeabilized MDCK cells, a constitutively exocytosing epithelial cell line, transport from the *trans*-Golgi network to the basolateral plasma membrane, was sensitive to TeNT and BoNTs, whereas transport to the apical cell surface was not affected by either of these treatments (78). Thus, these toxins are useful tools in determining whether toxin-sensitive SNARE proteins are involved in a particular fusion event.

Ca^{2+}-BINDING PROTEINS Although there is agreement that assembly of the SNARE complex is essential for driving the fusion reaction, the molecular mechanisms by which Ca^{2+} exerts its trigger function are still being debated. As discussed above, Ca^{2+} may act at more than one step in the sequence of events leading to exocytosis. It is therefore not surprising that several Ca^{2+}-binding proteins have been implicated in the control of exocytosis.

In neurons, there is compelling evidence that synaptotagmin, a type-I integral membrane protein of synaptic vesicles (80, 81), plays a decisive role in linking the Ca^{2+} signal to exocytosis (82, 83). Synaptotagmin contains Ca^{2+}-binding C2 domains that are also found in a variety of other Ca^{2+}-dependent proteins, such as protein kinase C and phospholipase A_2 (PLA_2) (81). Disruption of the synaptotagmin gene in mice led to an almost complete loss of Ca^{2+}-dependent exocytosis in hippocampal neurons, whereas transmitter release was still evoked by other stimuli such as high osmolarity and α-latrotoxin (84). Synaptotagmin binds up to 4 mol of Ca^{2+} per mol when acidic phospholipids are present (85). The lack of a requirement for MgATP for Ca^{2+}-triggered fusion (see above) and the demonstration that synaptotagmin binding to syntaxin is enhanced by Ca^{2+} (86) suggest that synaptotagmin might be an activator of fusion that operates in conjunction with the SNAREs. Various synaptotagmin isoforms are expressed in other tissues, including neuroendocrine cells (87, 88), complicating an analysis of its function in such cells.

As with attempts to study the role of synaptotagmin using microinjection and transfection, it has been difficult to address its involvement in exocytosis using permeabilized cells. As an integral membrane protein, it does not wash out, a problem that highlights one of the shortcomings of permeabilized cell systems. Because no specific inhibitors of synaptotagmin are available, approaches have involved suppression of synaptotagmin expression by antisense oligonucleotides (89), overexpression of synaptotagmin fragments (89, 90), or injection of peptides corresponding to synaptotagmin domains (91, 92). Although popular, such approaches are limited in that they usually result in a loss of function and require high concentrations of the inhibitory agent. This is not surprising, because the protein fragment, in order to exert its effect, needs to compete with the endogenous native protein, which has the advantage of correct conformation and correct positioning at its site of action. For these reasons, data from such experiments should be interpreted with caution.

Attempts to identify soluble Ca^{2+}-dependent proteins involved in secretion using permeabilized cells have met with more success. In mechanically permeabilized PC12 cells, a novel protein, originally termed p145, was shown to function at a late, postdocking step in Ca^{2+}-stimulated exocytosis (46, 93). p145 was purified from rat brain cytosol, based on its ability to reconstitute norepinephrine secretion from permeabilized PC12 cells (94). More recently, this protein has been renamed CAPS, for Ca^{2+}-dependent activator protein for secretion (95). CAPS is the vertebrate homologue of the *Caenorhabditis elegans* unc-31 protein (95). Mutation of *unc-31* causes severe defects in neurotransmitter release (96), providing direct evidence that the protein is essential for exocytosis. However, its function in exocytosis is unknown.

Exogenous calmodulin was also shown to have a stimulatory effect at the Ca^{2+}-dependent triggering stage of exocytosis in digitonin-permeabilized adrenal chromaffin cells (20, 97). It should be noted, however, that exogenous calmodulin had no effect on secretion in saponin-permeabilized cells (98), emphasizing that whether a protein is rate limiting may depend on exactly how an experiment is performed. Calmodulin is a promiscuous protein and may have many sites of action. One possible calmodulin target is synaptotagmin, which is known to bind calmodulin in vitro (84).

Regulation of Exocytosis by GTPases

GTPases feature prominently among the potential regulators of intracellular membrane fusion events. Small, ras-like GTPases of the rab/ypt class are specifically localized on different organelles, and there is convincing genetic and biochemical evidence that these proteins are essential for many membrane docking and fusion reactions, both in yeast and in mammalian cells (for reviews see 10–12, 99, 100). Heterotrimeric GTPases, too, appear to be involved in controlling vesicular transport, but as yet, their role is less well defined.

GTP ANALOGS Gomperts and colleagues were the first to establish a role for GTP-binding proteins in regulated exocytosis (101). He investigated their function by introducing nonhydrolyzable GTP analogs, such as GTPγS, into permeabilized mast cells. Similar experiments were later performed by many investigators with different systems. However, the effects obtained with these compounds were often complicated and sometimes resulted in seemingly contradictory results, depending on the experimental conditions (see, for example, 102–108). Because nonhydrolyzable GTP analogs will affect all GTPases in the preparation, not only those involved in exocytosis, an interpretation of the data is often difficult. In several permeabilized cell systems, GTPγS is capable of potently stimulating exocytosis, either in conjunction with, or independent of, Ca^{2+}. For example, in permeabilized mast cells (and related cell lines), both Ca^{2+} and guanine nucleotides appear to be essential effectors of the exocytotic response (47). Guanine nucleotides influence a late step in exocytosis (109–111), which suggests a direct interaction of a GTPase with the exocytotic apparatus. Along similar lines, it was recently reported that cleavage of synaptobrevin 2 in permeabilized β-cells, by either TeNT or BoNT/B, abolished Ca^{2+}-stimulated exocytosis but did not affect GTPγS-stimulated exocytosis (112). This important observation needs verification, as it suggests the existence of parallel pathways leading to the exocytosis of insulin-containing granules, only one of which involves toxin-sensitive SNARE proteins. In permeabilized adrenal chromaffin cells, BoNT/D, C1, and E inhibited both Ca^{2+}- and GppNHp-induced catecholamine release to a similar extent (113).

RAB PROTEINS The genetic analysis of protein secretion in yeast led to the discovery that ypt/rab proteins function at various steps of the secretory pathway. For example, the ypt protein Sec4p is essential for the constitutive exocytosis of Golgi-derived vesicles (114). Similarly, in mammalian cells, rab proteins have been shown to be required for many intracellular membrane trafficking steps (10, 115–117). However, it has been difficult to prove unambiguously that a rab protein is required for regulated exocytosis. To date, the best candidate for an exocytotic rab protein is rab3 (for review see 118). Rab3 represents a small subfamily of rab proteins that are highly concentrated on secretory vesicles. For example, rab3A and rab3C are found on synaptic vesicles (119) and rab3D on pancreatic zymogen granules (120). Furthermore, rab3A (and rab3C) dissociates from synaptic vesicles (121, 122) and undergoes GTP hydrolysis (123) during the stimulation of exocytosis.

Numerous attempts have been made to elucidate the function of rab3 proteins in regulated exocytosis. Peptides corresponding to the rab effector domain were introduced into permeabilized cells to disrupt rab3 interactions. Such peptides stimulated exocytosis in permeabilized pancreatic acini (124) and chromaffin cells (125), which suggests an involvement of rab3A in the control of exocytosis in these cell types. However, it was subsequently concluded that most of the effects of these peptides on secretion were probably nonspecific side effects (99, 126). More recently, approaches for the elucidation of rab3 function have included gene disruption in *C. elegans* and mice (see 126a) and overexpression of GTP- and GDP-preferring mutants (127–130). Rab3A-deficient animals were viable and exhibited mild phenotypes (131, 132). Clearly, exocytosis was able to proceed in the absence of rab3A, and it was proposed that the active protein limits the number of vesicles fusing per action potential, thus playing an inhibitory rather than a permissive role (127, 132, 133). This conclusion is surprising in view of the essential role of rab proteins in membrane trafficking in yeast. There are several possible explanations for this discrepancy. First, the other isoforms of rab3 may be redundant to rab3A and thus functionally compensate for its loss. Second, it is also possible that, despite the abundance and specific localization of rab3A, another, hitherto unknown, rab protein functions in exocytosis in a manner equivalent to Sec4p. Third, regulated exocytosis may not have an absolute requirement for a rab protein. If, as has been suggested (128, 134), the function of rab proteins is to recruit SNARE proteins to the site of docking/fusion, they would be less important if the particular SNAREs are highly abundant, as is the case for the neuronal SNAREs (135).

Despite many efforts it is still unclear how rab proteins function in membrane trafficking. Both genetic interaction in yeast (134, 136–139) and immunoprecipitation studies (140) have suggested a link between rab proteins and SNAREs. However, it remains to be established whether the interaction is direct or mediated via additional proteins. Furthermore, for rab3, several putative downstream effectors have been characterized, such as the vesicle-associated protein rabphilin (141) and the plasma membrane–bound protein RIM (142). These proteins respond to the GTP-GDP status of rab3 and may provide the connection to the exocytotic fusion machinery.

HETEROTRIMERIC GTPASES Heterotrimeric GTPases are well-established transducers that link extracellular signals to intracellular effectors through coupling with plasma membrane receptors (for reviews see 143–145). In their inactive state, heterotrimeric GTPases exist in a complex of α, β, and γ subunits, each represented by multiple isoforms in which the guanine nucleotide binding site of the α subunit is occupied by GDP. The exchange of GTP for GDP, which is stimulated by a guanine nucleotide release factor, causes the dissociation of the GTPase into free α and a complex of β and γ subunits. The free GTP-bound α subunit is capable of activating a broad range of downstream effector molecules such as adenylyl cyclases, phospholipases, and ion channels. Spontaneous GTP hydrolysis returns the α subunit to its inactive form, and as a consequence, it reassociates with the $\beta\gamma$ subunit, thus returning the system to the beginning of the cycle (for reviews see 143–145).

In addition to their function in signal transduction at the plasma membrane, heterotrimeric GTPases have been implicated in the regulation of exocytosis and other membrane trafficking steps (110, 146). There is some evidence that these GTPases are activated by the "classical" pathway and couple to an unknown target at the exocytotic site. However, other findings are difficult to reconcile with this view and indicate a novel mode of action, with respect to both upstream regulators and downstream effectors. In addition, increasing evidence suggests that heterotrimeric GTPases operate at multiple steps along the secretory pathway and in regulated exocytosis.

It is well established that specific isoforms of Gα subunits are highly concentrated on various kinds of secretory vesicles. For example, both small synaptic and large, dense-core vesicles from neurons and neuroendocrine cells contain complete sets of heterotrimeric G proteins, including Gα_{o1}, Gα_{o2}, Gα_{i1}, Gα_{i2}, Gα_{o1}, and several β and γ subunits (147–149). In contrast, pancreatic zymogen granules selectively contain G$\alpha_{q/11}$ whereas no Gα_o subunits were detectable (150). Thus, the different vesicle types appear to contain different sets of GTPases. These localizations are specific and thus intriguing, but they do not preclude unrelated functions such as the "parking" of spare proteins for "rush-hour"-like needs at the plasma membrane. If, however, these GTPases are regulating exocytosis, they must be functioning in a novel manner because the only way they can be activated is by means of intracellular signals.

Further evidence for the involvement of heterotrimeric GTPases in regulated secretion came from pharmacological studies on permeabilized cells, in which the effects of various agents, such as specific effectors (e.g. activating or inhibitory peptides, pertussis toxin, AlF_3), antibodies, and purified proteins, were measured. Both peptide activators and inhibitory antibodies supported a role of Gα_o proteins in the priming step of regulated exocytosis in permeabilized adrenal chromaffin cells (149, 151). Furthermore, it was suggested that a plasma membrane-bound pool of Gα_{i3} controls a late step in exocytosis, which supports the previous conclusions obtained from permeabilized mast cells (152).

Some proposals have been made for both the activators and effectors of these GTPases. As activators, only classical plasma membrane receptors have been implicated, and there is no knowledge about activators of GTPases on intracellular membranes. In studies on β-cells, activation of α_2-adrenergic receptors caused a pertussis toxin–sensitive inhibition of Ca^{2+}-stimulated exocytosis that appears to operate at a late step (153). Furthermore, a novel seven–transmembrane domain receptor, termed CIRL or latrophilin, was recently identified as a main binding site for α-latrotoxin, the active constituent of black widow spider venom (154). α-Latrotoxin is known to stimulate exocytosis in various neurosecretory cells. However, it is possible that latrophilin's function might be limited to a recruitment of the toxin to the membrane, and the toxin might exert its effects by means of other proteins rather than activating a G protein–mediated signaling cascade.

As effectors, a variety of mechanisms have been proposed that, at least to some extent, are consistent with mechanisms previously implicated in steps leading to exocytosis. These include effects on the cortical cytoskeleton (151), activation of phospholipase A2 (149), activation of phospholipase D via ADP-ribosylation factor (155, 156), activation of PtdIns 4-kinase (151), and recruitment of cytosolic proteins required for vesicle docking or fusion (149).

To summarize, there are many indications that heterotrimeric GTPases are important regulators of exocytosis. However, despite many efforts, it has not been proven unambiguously that a granule- or plasma membrane–associated heterotrimeric G protein regulates a particular step in the exocytotic pathway. Many of the problems are of a methodological nature, highlighting some of the limitations of the permeabilized cell approach. For example, the specific peptide effectors may not be as specific as assumed, particularly if amphiphilic, like mastoparan, which is known to interact with phospholipid bilayers in a nonspecific way (157). Furthermore, it appears that control by heterotrimeric GTPases is complex: Different GTPases may control consecutive steps of the pathway, and their effects can be either stimulatory or inhibitory. Furthermore, the nature of G-protein control may be different in different cell types. Perhaps these GTPases convey cell-type–specific control of the conserved exocytotic apparatus, providing one explanation for the variety of such control mechanisms known to exist.

Summary: Advantages and Limitations of Permeabilized Cells

Cell permeabilization techniques have provided a wealth of information about the mechanisms controlling exocytotic membrane fusion. They have been instrumental in defining the stages of exocytosis and in identifying novel regulatory proteins involved in the pathway. Other potential regulatory factors have also been investigated in permeabilized cells, for instance specific protein kinases and phosphatases and the annexins (158, 159). However, the role, if any, of these proteins is not fully understood, and a comprehensive coverage is beyond the scope of this review. Undoubtedly, the use of permeabilized cells has its disadvantages. For example, the efficiency with which cytosolic constituents are washed out might vary between different experimental situations, and between individual proteins. This is illustrated by the difficulties in depleting cells of NSF and α-SNAP to the extent that they become rate limiting. A second limitation is that the only assay that can be applied is the release of granule content, because there is no direct experimental access to the participating membranes. Thus, it is difficult to assess important parameters, such as the status of the cytoskeleton or the extent to which vesicles are attached (docked) to the plasma membrane. As discussed above, investigations of the membrane proteins involved are limited: The only events that can be studied are those for which specific effectors or inhibitors are available, such as the SNARE-cleaving clostridial neurotoxins. Furthermore, the resolution of individual steps leading to exocytosis is still crude, so that many findings are open to multiple interpretations. In particular, upstream regulatory events may obscure the effects of exogenously applied compounds on the final membrane fusion event.

EXOCYTOTIC MEMBRANE FUSION IN VITRO

Methodological Considerations

A pure in vitro system, in which isolated secretory vesicles fuse with plasma membrane fragments, should allow a direct study of the properties of the final membrane fusion event, largely overcoming the limitations of the permeabilized cell systems. Such an in vitro system should permit the separate manipulation of the two interacting membranes and their resident proteins. Furthermore, it should permit a differentiation between vesicle attachment and fusion itself, a feature no other assay can contribute. The major obstacle to the development of such assays is the problem of validation, i.e. of establishing suitable detection systems, and of ensuring that what is being measured is a physiologically relevant membrane fusion event. This problem has proven difficult to overcome. Two basic types of in vitro assays for exocytotic fusion have been reported: content-release assays and lipid-mixing assays. In the former, fusion is measured through the release of the contents of secretory vesicles during incubation with plasma membranes. In the latter, the lipids of one membrane are labeled with a probe, and fusion is measured through the dilution of the probe into the unlabeled membrane. Neither type of assay offers the sensitivity and conclusiveness of the content mixing assays used for vesicle-vesicle fusion, and thus, both require rigorous control experiments.

Content-release assays are simple and rapid. Usually, content release is measured at the end of the fusion reaction by centrifuging the membranes and measuring the product in the supernatant. All such assays face the major inherent problem of differentiating true fusion from vesicle lysis. Isolated secretory vesicles, particularly when they are large, such as pancreatic zymogen granules, are often sensitive to environmental stress and to biochemical challenges that affect transmembrane ion and osmotic balances or the integrity of the phospholipid bilayer. It is of paramount importance, therefore, that every novel experimental condition is carefully controlled for nonspecific membrane damage. This inherent ambiguity has limited the application of content-release assays in the study of membrane fusion.

Lipid-mixing assays were first introduced by Hoekstra and colleagues (160). They rely on the self-quenching properties of amphiphilic fluorescent dyes such as octadecylrhodamine B-chloride (R18). R18 readily partitions into biological membranes, where its fluorescence becomes quenched because of radiationless energy dissipation between neighboring molecules. On fusion of the labeled membrane with an unlabeled target membrane, the surface density of the probe decreases, resulting in an increase in fluorescence that can be measured with high kinetic resolution. R18 dequenching was first used to measure the fusion of enveloped viruses, such as Sendai virus and influenza virus, with erythrocyte ghosts and liposomes (160).

As with content release, there are pitfalls with dequenching assays. Any substance that binds R18, however slightly, and thus increases its partitioning in the aqueous phase, will catalyze enhanced equilibration between labeled and unlabeled membranes. Furthermore, such compounds may increase fluorescence because of dilution, even in the absence of unlabeled acceptor membranes. Problems have also been reported with the use of R18 dequenching to measure fusion between cellular organelles in vitro. In some cases, dequenching was seen under circumstances where other assays did not detect fusion (161). Some of these artifacts can be overcome if fluorescently labeled phospholipids (usually derivatives of phosphatidylethanolamine) are used. However, these compounds are not soluble in water and can only be inserted efficiently into membranes by reconstitution, requiring prior solubilization of the membrane. Finally, the ability of some cytosolic phospholipid transfer proteins to transfer these probes efficiently from labeled to unlabeled membranes in the absence of fusion is a particularly troublesome artifact affecting all experiments involving addition of cytosol (162).

A Mammalian System: Fusion of Pancreatic Zymogen Granules with Isolated Plasma Membranes

Acinar cells of the exocrine pancreas secrete digestive enzymes, and it is a relatively simple matter to obtain large amounts of relatively pure secretory (zymogen) granules from this tissue (163). Furthermore, there are well-documented protocols for the purification of plasma membranes from these cells (164). For these reasons the exocrine pancreas is an attractive tissue on which to base an in vitro assay for regulated exocytosis. A further advantage is that several groups have studied the properties of exocytosis from streptolysin *O*-permeabilized acini (165–167); thus it is possible to compare the behavior of the in vitro assays with the properties of exocytosis in the permeabilized cells.

More than 20 years ago it was reported that radiolabeled cat pancreatic plasma membranes bound to zymogen granules in a Ca^{2+}-dependent manner, which suggests that these two membranes can interact in vitro in a physiologically meaningful way (168). More recently, it was shown that pancreatic plasma membranes trigger the release of amylase from zymogen granules in a time-dependent, concentration-dependent, saturable manner (163), which suggests membrane fusion. Similar results were obtained when fusion was measured directly using a dequenching assay (169). In both assays, the source of the target membranes was critically important. For instance, plasma membranes from another exocrine gland, the parotid, fused with zymogen granules whereas membranes from other sources did not (170). The triggering of amylase release was sensitive to protease pretreatment of the plasma membranes. Furthermore, both dequenching and amylase release were enhanced by GTPγS with a 50% effective concentration (EC_{50}) of 10–20 μM, as was exocytosis in permeabilized acini (165, 167), which suggests that exocytotic membrane fusion in this cell type is under the control of a stimulatory GTP-binding protein (163).

Exocytosis of zymogen granules in permeabilized acini is tightly controlled by Ca^{2+} with an EC_{50} of about 1 μM (165, 167), a concentration two orders of magnitude lower than the corresponding value in neurons and some neuroendocrine cells. However, it was surprisingly difficult to demonstrate Ca^{2+} dependence in the in vitro fusion assays. In fact, basal fusion occurred in the presence of ethylene glycol-bis(β-aminoethyl ether)-*N,N,N′,N′*-tetraacetic acid (EGTA), and stimulation by Ca^{2+} was rather modest, although its EC_{50} was similar to that measured in permeabilized cells (171). Thus, it is possible that unlike in other systems, such as the exocytosis of sea urchin egg cortical vesicles (discussed further below), the Ca^{2+}-control step operates more upstream of the fusion machine and is lost to some extent upon membrane isolation, resulting in a partially constitutive fusion. Furthermore, no priming with ATP is necessary, which suggests that unlike in PC12 and other neuroendocrine cells, a fusion-competent state of the membranes can be stably maintained in the absence of metabolic energy.

Currently, the SNARE proteins mediating the fusion of zymogen granules with the plasma membrane are not known, but some candidates have recently been identified. Synaptobrevin 2 is present on the granule membrane (172). However, tetanus toxin caused only a partial (30%) inhibition of exocytosis in streptolysin *O*-permeabilized pancreatic acini, although synaptobrevin was completely cleaved (172). Similarly, toxin treatment of the granules caused a minor (16%) inhibition of fusion using the in vitro dequenching assay, with synaptobrevin again being completely proteolyzed (173). These findings suggest that other TeNT-insensitive relatives of synaptobrevin operate alongside synaptobrevin 2 (see, for example, 174). The discovery of numerous novel synaptobrevin homologues (VAMPs) (76) raises the hope that the isoforms primarily responsible for pancreatic exocytosis will soon be identified. Similarly, neither the SNAP-25 nor the syntaxin isoforms involved in this fusion reaction are known. At least three syntaxin isoforms (syntaxins 2, 3, and 4) are expressed in the pancreatic acinar cell (175). Syntaxin 2 is concentrated in the apical domain of the plasma membrane with which the zymogen granules fuse. However, the syntaxin family has many members (5), and the possibility that further syntaxin isoforms are present in this cell type must be borne in mind.

As discussed above, the features of Ca^{2+}-control of exocytosis in the exocrine pancreas differ markedly from that of neurons, which suggests that the

Ca^{2+}-sensor(s) is different from synaptotagmin. Recently, a novel membrane protein of the zymogen granule membrane, termed syncollin, was characterized. Syncollin binds to syntaxins 1 and 2 at low Ca^{2+} concentrations and dissociates at concentrations known to trigger fusion, which suggests that this protein might play a role in the control of exocytosis in the acinar cell (171). When recombinant syncollin was added to an in vitro fusion reaction, R18 dequenching was inhibited in a concentration-dependent manner. Furthermore, its potency fell as Ca^{2+} concentration rose, which suggests that it might act as Ca^{2+}-sensitive clamp of syntaxin on the plasma membrane.

Other Mammalian Systems

There are few other reports describing the fusion of vesicles with isolated membranes, using either content release or fluorescence dequenching as an assay. It was recently shown that a fraction can be obtained from homogenates of PC12 cells that consists essentially of large, dense-core vesicles with attached plasma membrane fragments (176). This system retained the ability to respond to a Ca^{2+} stimulus, in the presence of MgATP and cytosol, by releasing norepinephrine. Secretion was blocked by pretreatment with either BoNT/B, BoNT/C, or BoNT/E, demonstrating that release involves SNAREs and is thus mediated by exocytosis (176). In contrast to the behavior of pancreatic zymogen granules and plasma membranes, however, attempts to entice free, large, dense-core vesicles to fuse with isolated plasma membranes were not successful.

R18 dequenching was also used in attempts to measure fusion between isolated chromaffin granules and chromaffin cell plasma membranes (177), and between isolated rat brain synaptic vesicles and plasma membranes (178). When R18-labeled chromaffin granules were incubated with chromaffin cell plasma membranes, dequenching was observed only after treatment of the plasma membranes with PLA_2 in the presence of Ca^{2+} (177). It was suggested that activation of PLA_2, and the subsequent liberation of arachidonic acid, represented the Ca^{2+}-dependent step in the triggering of exocytosis in this cell type. It should be noted, however, that the specificity of fusion in this system was not absolute: Chromaffin granules could not fuse with erythrocyte membranes but could fuse with liver cell plasma membranes. Furthermore, it is well known that lysophospholipids, which are generated by PLA_2, are capable of nonspecifically fusing phospholipid vesicles.

When R18-labeled synaptic vesicles were incubated with brain plasma membranes, dequenching required cytosolic proteins (178). Unfortunately, no dequenching traces were shown, and neither the time course nor the target membrane specificity of dequenching was reported. Furthermore, the membrane fractions were poorly defined. However, dequenching was almost completely blocked by pretreatment of the synaptic vesicles with BoNT/B, which should cleave synaptobrevin.

An Invertebrate System: The Sea Urchin Egg

BASIC FEATURES From the early days of physiology, experimental model systems derived from invertebrates have enjoyed widespread popularity. A major advantage lies in the fact that many invertebrates achieve an increase in efficiency of a cellular function by increasing size and/or redundancy. For example, many of the foundations of modern neurophysiology are based on studies of the giant axon and synapse of the squid. It is less well known that similarly convenient model systems derived from invertebrates are available for the study of exocytosis, some of which have astounding properties. In fact, Ca^{2+}-dependent exocytosis of cortical vesicles of sea urchin eggs was the first intracellular membrane trafficking step ever reconstituted in vitro (179, 180). Fusion of individual vesicles can be monitored with a resolution that is currently not achievable in other systems. For many years, however, progress was hampered by seemingly insurmountable problems concerning the characterization of proteins involved in exocytosis. Furthermore, the system cannot be manipulated by genetics or by the introduction of nucleic acids because the mature egg is arrested in interphase in a metabolically repressed state: DNA and protein synthesis are activated only upon fertilization (for a review see 181). Given these limitations, exocytosis of cortical vesicles was often dismissed as exotic, which in a sense it is, and thus not of relevance for the understanding of basic principles. This perception, however, is currently undergoing change as evidence is accumulating that fusion follows the same general pathway as in mainstream model systems, such as yeast and neurons.

When a sperm fertilizes a sea urchin egg, the intracellular Ca^{2+} concentration transiently increases from a resting level of around 100 nM to several micromolar (182–184). One of the events triggered by Ca^{2+} is the exocytosis of a layer of cortical secretory vesicles, which are docked at the cytoplasmic face of the plasma membrane in the unfertilized egg (185). The discharge of cortical vesicles results in the formation of a fertilization envelope around the egg, which acts as a physical barrier to further sperm and thereby prevents polyspermy (186).

Vacquier (24) prepared "cortical lawns" by shearing eggs attached to polylysine-coated surfaces, using a buffer similar to the internal milieu of the cell. When the cytoplasmic contents of the cells were washed away, the egg cortices, complete with their array of cortical secretory vesicles, were left attached to the surface via the vitelline layer. Exocytosis in vitro was achieved simply by the addition of buffers containing micromolar levels of Ca^{2+} (24; see also 183, 187). Furthermore, cortical secretory vesicles, purified from suspensions of egg cortices, attached to the cytoplasmic face of denuded plasma membrane lawns and fused in a Ca^{2+}-dependent manner (179).

Because of the sheer size of the vesicles (1 μm), individual fusion events can be monitored directly with the light microscope (24, 179, 185–188). Alternatively, exocytosis can be monitored in suspensions of isolated cortices via changes in turbidity (192, 193). The decrease in turbidity seen on addition of Ca^{2+} correlates with the release of a cortical granule enzyme (ovoperoxidase), and both parameters exhibit a similar Ca^{2+} dependence (192). Numerous control experiments have established that the observed disappearance of granules is due to true fusion rather than vesicle lysis (180, 192).

ATP AND Ca^{2+} Although in vitro fusion per se does not require ATP, cortical lawns incubated in the absence of ATP gradually lost their ability to respond to Ca^{2+} (183, 187, 193). Readmission of ATP restored the high Ca^{2+} affinity of the exocytotic reaction but failed to restore Ca^{2+} sensitivity to vesicles that had become entirely refractory (183). This result suggests that, as for other secretory systems, exocytosis in the sea urchin egg involves ATP-dependent priming followed by Ca^{2+}-dependent triggering of fusion. The nature of the ATP-dependent priming step is not known, although hydrolysis of ATP during priming does seem to be required. Microinjection of ATPγS into eggs completely blocked cortical vesicle exocytosis in response to fertilizing sperm, although the sperm-triggered Ca^{2+} wave remained unchanged (194). Furthermore, cortical lawns prepared from ATPγS-treated eggs failed to undergo exocytosis in response to Ca^{2+}. As expected for a priming event upstream of the Ca^{2+} signal, ATPγS did not affect exocytosis when applied directly to isolated cortical lawns. Protein phosphorylation was proposed to explain the effects of ATP, but so far there is no direct evidence in support of this view. Alternatively, ATP might be required for the maintenance of polyphosphoinositides in the egg cortex. In unfertilized eggs, both PtdIns 4-phosphate 5-kinase and PtdIns 4-kinase activities are associated with cortical membranes (195). A role for these proteins in the ATP-dependent priming of Ca^{2+}-regulated fusion has been shown for other secretory cell types (49, 50) (see above), but evidence for a similar requirement in the sea urchin egg is lacking.

The half-maximal [Ca^{2+}] for exocytosis is around 5 μM, and it becomes only slightly higher when vesicles are first purified and than readded to stripped membranes (179). Apparently, every vesicle has a predefined minimal [Ca^{2+}] for fusion: Depending on the [Ca^{2+}], a given vesicle will either fuse rapidly or never fuse, even when [Ca^{2+}] is returned to basal levels and then raised again to the threshold level. This remarkable property has been explained using a rather simple model that involves a randomly distributed number of Ca^{2+}-linked fusion complexes on the vesicle population (for a more detailed discussion see 196).

The model further proposes that Ca^{2+}-dependent activation of the complexes, once it occurs, is irreversible. These findings may have significance for other Ca^{2+}-dependent secretory systems.

Several attempts have been made to identify the Ca^{2+} receptor(s) responsible for triggering exocytosis. Sasaki (197) demonstrated that a KCl-extractable protein of approximately 100 kDa was required for conferring Ca^{2+} sensitivity on the exocytotic reaction. The 100-kDa protein has still not been identified, even though a protein factor functionally substituting for the 100-kDa protein was found in extracts of murine brain (198). Calmodulin has also been invoked in the control of exocytosis. For example, the calmodulin antagonist trifluoperazine inhibited cortical vesicle exocytosis in vitro when applied to isolated cortical lawns (199, 200). More persuasive was a complete block of exocytosis in cortical lawns that was achieved after incubation with an anti-calmodulin antibody, even in the presence of Ca^{2+} concentrations as high as 1 mM (201). Calmodulin was localized by immunofluorescence to the plasma membrane, beneath the layer of cortical vesicles, at the site of plasma membrane-cortical vesicle attachment (201).

Other Ca^{2+}-binding proteins have been identified in cortical lawns, but there is no direct evidence linking any of them to exocytosis. A protein reacting with antibodies to the neuronal Ca^{2+}-sensor synaptotagmin was shown, using immunoblotting of egg subcellular fractions, to be localized to the egg cortex (202). Furthermore, members of the annexin family of Ca^{2+}-dependent phospholipid-binding proteins (203) and a calcineurin-like protein (204) were identified in sea urchin eggs.

THE FUSION REACTION Evidently, a model system in which vesicle attachment and vesicle fusion can be distinguished so cleanly is ideally suited to the study of the details of the fusion reaction. However, the system lags behind in the characterization of proteins involved in fusion. Proteins cross-reacting with antibodies raised against mammalian synaptobrevin, syntaxin, SNAP-25, synaptotagmin, and rab3 were shown to be associated with the egg cortex (202, 205). When sea urchin egg cortical lawns were incubated with TeNT light chain, the synaptobrevin-immunoreactive protein was completely cleaved. At the same time, Ca^{2+}-dependent exocytosis was inhibited, but only partially (by about 63%) (202). So far, this finding is the best evidence that fusion is, at least in part, mediated by a mechanism involving SNARE proteins.

An involvement of toxin-sensitive SNARE proteins in cortical vesicle exocytosis is also supported by a different line of investigation. It is well established that plasma membranes reseal rapidly after injury, largely preventing leakage of intracellular contents (206–208). In sea urchin eggs and embryos, Steinhardt and colleagues (209, 210) observed that wounding of the cell membrane was followed by a rapid burst of localized Ca^{2+}-regulated exocytosis, which resulted in membrane resealing. In embryos, the resealing process was inhibited by the prior microinjection of either botulinum neurotoxins (BoNT) A, B, or C1 (209, 210). The source of the vesicles mediating resealing in embryos is unknown. However, it cannot be the layer of cortical secretory vesicles because they are no longer present after fertilization. In contrast, resealing was not affected by the toxins in unfertilized eggs. An inhibition was observed, however, when the cortical vesicles were reversibly undocked by stachyose treatment in the presence of either TeNT or BoNT/C1, whereas BoNT/A was ineffective (210). It was hypothesized that membrane resealing in the unfertilized egg was mediated by the cortical vesicles docked at the plasma membrane and that the responsible SNARE proteins were only accessible to the neurotoxins when the vesicles were undocked. Whether sperm-induced exocytosis is also blocked by such treatment needs to be investigated. The possibility that other vesicles, similarly affected by stachyose treatment, are responsible for resealing in the unfertilized egg currently cannot be excluded.

The attachment of cortical granules to inverted membranes appears to be specific for the type of membrane and requires proteins on both the granule and the plasma membrane (191). However, once contact is established, vesicle fusion can be elicited even when the target membrane is an artificial bilayer devoid of any proteins (211). This finding is difficult to reconcile with the current view of SNARE function, which requires complementary sets of SNAREs on the two membranes destined to fuse. It has been proposed that the main function of the SNAREs is to tie the participating membranes tightly together, thus overcoming the main energy barrier to fusion (4, 212). However, the possibility that the actual fusion reaction is mediated by other mechanisms that require only proteins on the vesicle cannot currently be excluded. This would explain why vesicles only fuse with artificial bilayers when they are first forced onto the membranes by centrifugation (211).

How membrane fusion then proceeds is still unclear. Chernomordik et al (213, 214) have proposed a model that unifies findings from studies on the fusion of enveloped viruses (which employ structurally unrelated fusion proteins) with those on exocytosis of cortical vesicles. According to this model, a lipidic stalk is formed at the onset of fusion that connects the outer (cytoplasmic) leaflets of the fusing membranes. At this stage, the inner leaflets are still separated, creating domains of high curvature for the cytoplasmic leaflets and triangular spaces with acyl chain–packing deficiencies in the hydrophobic interior. The luminal and extracellular leaflets then invaginate until they meet. At this point, the invaginating leaflets may either break apart (fusion) or form a bilayer, resulting in a single membrane separating the granule lumen from the extracellular space (hemifusion). Support for this model is provided by the effects of reagents that are thought to stabilize either negative curvature (oleic acid) or positive curvature (lysophosphatides) (213). For example, lysophosphatides and related molecules inhibit exocytosis of cortical granules, in agreement with their proposed destabilization of the negatively curved leaflet connecting the membranes via the stalk bridge. Thus, it appears that the final stages of fusion are primarily lipidic events that follow the laws of bilayer physics. Clearly, more work needs to be done until the fusion reaction is fully understood, but work on cortical vesicle exocytosis has provided a framework that, we hope, will initiate similar studies on other secretory systems.

CONCLUDING REMARKS

It is evident that in vitro assays for measuring exocytosis have not yet been developed to their full potential. In particular, the assays for measuring exocytosis in mammalian systems, most of which involve vesicles of sizes below the resolution of the light microscope, need to be refined. Both content-release and -dequenching assays are too crude when applied at the macroscopic scale. Using appropriate technology, it is conceivable for assays to have a much higher resolution with respect to space and time and to allow for a qualitative and quantitative differentiation between vesicle binding (docking) and fusion itself. Recent developments in fluorescent microscopy, for example the application of evanescent wave microscopy to exocytosis, raise the hope that such assays will soon be available. We have recently used high-resolution video microscopy to monitor the fusion of fluorescently labeled individual granules with flat, carrier-supported plasma membranes derived from a neuroendocrine cell line (J Avery & R Jahn, manuscript in preparation). Furthermore, attempts have recently been made to reconstitute fusion in liposomes loaded with SNARE proteins (215). Although these experiments are still fraught with numerous technical problems, it is hoped that the use of simple and defined membrane systems will aid in unraveling the molecular events underlying exocytotic membrane fusion.

Literature Cited

1. Söllner T, Bennett MK, Whiteheart SW, Scheller RH, Rothman JE. 1993. A protein assembly-disassembly pathway in vitro that may correspond to sequential steps of synaptic vesicle docking, activation, and fusion. *Cell* 75:409–18
2. Söllner T, Whiteheart SW, Brunner M, Erdjument-Bromage H, Geromanos S, et al. 1993. SNAP receptors implicated

in vesicle targeting and fusion. *Nature* 362:318–24
3. Hayashi T, Yamasaki S, Nauenburg S, Binz T, Niemann H. 1995. Disassembly of the reconstituted synaptic vesicle membrane fusion complex in vitro. *EMBO J.* 14:2317–25
4. Hanson PI, Heuser JE, Jahn R. 1997. Neurotransmitter release—four years of SNARE complexes. *Curr. Opin. Neurobiol.* 7:310–15
5. Bock JB, Scheller RH. 1997. Protein transport. A fusion of ideas. *Nature* 387:133–35
6. Bennett MK, Scheller RH. 1993. The molecular machinery for secretion is conserved from yeast to neurons. *Proc. Natl. Acad. Sci. USA* 90:2559–63
7. Ferro-Novick S, Jahn R. 1994. Vesicle fusion from yeast to man. *Nature* 370:191–93
8. Rothman JE, Warren G. 1994. Implications of the SNARE hypothesis for intracellular membrane topography and dynamics. *Curr. Biol.* 4:220–33
9. Simons K, Zerial M. 1993. Rab proteins and the road maps for intracellular transport. *Neuron* 11:789–99
10. Novick P, Zerial M. 1997. The diversity of Rab proteins in vesicle transport. *Curr. Opin. Cell Biol.* 9:496–504
11. Lazar T, Gotte M, Gallwitz D. 1997. Vesicular transport: How many Ypt/Rab-GTPases make a eukaryotic cell? *Trends Biochem. Sci.* 22:468–72
12. Olkkonen VM, Stenmark H. 1997. Role of Rab GTPases in membrane traffic. *Int. Rev. Cytol.* 176:1–85
13. Südhof TC. 1995. The synaptic vesicle cycle: a cascade of protein-protein interactions. *Nature* 375:645–53
14. Pevsner J. 1996. The role of Sec1p-related proteins in vesicle trafficking in the nerve terminal. *J. Neurosci. Res.* 45:89–95
15. Neher E. 1998. Vesicle pools and Ca^{2+} microdomains: new tools for understanding their roles in neurotransmitter release. *Neuron* 20:389–99
16. von Gersdorff H, Matthews G. 1994. Dynamics of synaptic vesicle fusion and membrane retrieval in synaptic terminals. *Nature* 367:735–39
17. Neher E, Zucker RS. 1993. Multiple calcium-dependent processes related to secretion in bovine chromaffin cells. *Neuron* 10:21–30
18. Bittner MA, Holz RW. 1992. Kinetic analysis of secretion from permeabilized adrenal chromaffin cells reveals distinct components. *J. Biol. Chem.* 267:16219–25
19. Parsons TD, Coorssen JR, Horstmann H, Almers W. 1995. Docked granules, the exocytic burst, and the need for ATP hydrolysis in endocrine cells. *Neuron* 15:1085–96
20. Chamberlain LH, Roth D, Morgan A, Burgoyne RD. 1995. Distinct effects of alpha-SNAP, 14-3-3 proteins, and calmodulin on priming and triggering of regulated exocytosis. *J. Cell Biol.* 130:1063–70
21. Fernandez JM, Neher E, Gomperts BD. 1984. Capacitance measurements reveal stepwise fusion events in degranulating mast cells. *Nature* 312:453–55
22. Coorssen JR, Haslam RJ. 1993. GTPγS and phorbol ester act synergistically to stimulate both Ca(2+)-independent secretion and phospholipase D activity in permeabilized human platelets. Inhibition by BAPTA and analogues. *FEBS Lett.* 316:170–74
23. Takuma T, Ichida T. 1988. Amylase secretion from saponin-permeabilized parotid cells evoked by cyclic AMP. *J. Biochem. Tokyo* 103:95–98
24. Vacquier V. 1975. The isolation of intact cortical granules from sea urchin eggs: calcium ions trigger granule discharge. *Dev. Biol.* 43:62–74
25. Balch WE, Glick BS, Rothman JE. 1984. Sequential intermediates in the pathway of intercompartmental transport in a cell-free system. *Cell* 39:525–36
26. Davey J, Hurtley SM, Warren G. 1985. Reconstitution of an endocytic fusion event in a cell-free system. *Cell* 43:643–52
27. Gruenberg JE, Howell KE. 1986. Reconstitution of vesicle fusion occurring in endocytosis with a cell-free system. *EMBO J.* 5:3091–101
28. Diaz R, Mayorga L, Stahl P. 1988. In vitro fusion of endosomes following receptor-mediated endocytosis. *J. Biol. Chem.* 263:6093–100
29. Haas A, Conradt B, Wickner W. 1994. G-protein ligands inhibit in vitro reactions of vacuole inheritance. *J. Cell Biol.* 126:87–97
30. Baker PF, Knight DE. 1978. A high-voltage technique for gaining rapid access to the interior of secretory cells. *J. Physiol.* 284:30–31P
31. Baker PF, Knight DE. 1981. Calcium control of exocytosis and endocytosis in bovine adrenal medullary cells. *Philos. Trans. R. Soc. London Ser. B* 296:83–103

32. Gomperts BD, Tatham PE. 1992. Regulated exocytotic secretion from permeabilized cells. *Methods Enyzmol.* 219:178–89
33. Hersey SJ, Perez A. 1990. Permeable cell models in stimulus-secretion coupling. *Annu. Rev. Physiol.* 52:345–61
34. von Gersdorff H, Matthews G. 1999. Electrophysiology of synaptic vesicle cycling. *Annu. Rev. Physiol.* 61:725–52
35. Peppers SC, Holz RW. 1986. Catecholamine secretion from digitonin-treated PC12 cells. Effects of Ca^{2+}, ATP, and protein kinase C activators. *J. Biol. Chem.* 261:14665–69
36. Sarafian T, Aunis D, Bader MF. 1987. Loss of proteins from digitonin-permeabilized adrenal chromaffin cells essential for exocytosis. *J. Biol. Chem.* 262:16671–76
37. Koffer A, Gomperts BD. 1989. Soluble proteins as modulators of the exocytotic reaction of permeabilised rat mast cells. *J. Cell Sci.* 94:585–91
38. Martin TF, Walent JH. 1989. A new method for cell permeabilization reveals a cytosolic protein requirement for Ca^{2+}-activated secretion in GH3 pituitary cells. *J. Biol. Chem.* 264:10299–308
39. Knight DE, Baker PF. 1982. Calcium-dependence of catecholamine release from bovine adrenal medullary cells after exposure to intense electric fields. *J. Membr. Biol.* 68:107–40
40. Knight DE, Scrutton MC. 1986. Gaining access to the cytosol: the technique and some applications of electropermeabilization. *Biochem. J.* 234:497–506
41. Dunn LA, Holz RW. 1983. Catecholamine secretion from digitonin-treated adrenal medullary chromaffin cells. *J. Biol. Chem.* 258:4989–93
42. Knight DE, Scrutton MC. 1980. Direct evidence for a role for Ca^{2+} in amine storage granule secretion by human platelets. *Thromb. Res.* 20:437–46
43. Ronning SA, Martin TF. 1986. Characterization of Ca^{2+}-stimulated secretion in permeable GH_3 pituitary cells. *J. Biol. Chem.* 264:7834–39
44. Vallar L, Biden TJ, Wollheim CB. 1987. Guanine nucleotides induce Ca^{2+}-independent insulin secretion from permeabilized RINm5F cells. *J. Biol. Chem.* 262:5049–56
45. Holz RW, Bittner MA, Peppers SC, Senter RA, Eberhard DA. 1989. MgATP-independent and MgATP-dependent exocytosis. *J. Biol. Chem.* 264:5412–19
46. Hay JC, Martin TF. 1992. Resolution of regulated secretion into sequential MgATP-dependent and calcium-dependent stages mediated by distinct cytosolic proteins. *J. Cell Biol.* 119:139–51
47. Howell TW, Cockcroft S, Gomperts BD. 1987. Essential synergy between Ca^{2+} and guanine nucleotides in exocytotic secretion from permeabilized rat mast cells. *J. Cell Biol.* 105:191–97
48. Gomperts BD, Hide I, Bennett JP, Pizzey A, Tatham PE. 1994. The exocytotic reaction of permeabilized rat mast cells. An all-or-none response. *Ann. NY Acad. Sci.* 710:217–31
49. Hay JC, Martin TF. 1993. Phosphatidylinositol transfer protein required for ATP-dependent priming of Ca^{2+}-activated secretion. *Nature* 366:572–75
50. Hay JC, Fisette PL, Jenkins GH, Fukami K, Takenawa T, et al. 1995. ATP-dependent inositide phosphorylation required for Ca^{2+}-activated secretion. *Nature* 374:173–77
51. Cleves A, McGee T, Bankaitis V. 1991. Phospholipid transfer proteins: a biological debut. *Trends Cell Biol.* 1:30–34
52. Eberhard DA, Cooper CL, Low MG, Holz RW. 1990. Evidence that the inositol phospholipids are necessary for exocytosis. *Biochem. J.* 268:15–25
53. De Camilli P, Emr SD, McPherson PS, Novick P. 1996. Phosphoinositides as regulators in membrane traffic. *Science* 271:1533–39
54. Martin TFJ. 1997. Phosphoinositides as spatial regulators of membrane traffic. *Curr. Opin. Neurobiol.* 7:331–38
55. Ohashi M, Jan de Vries K, Frank R, Snoek G, Bankaitis V, et al. 1995. A role for phosphatidylinositol transfer protein in secretory vesicle formation. *Nature* 377:544–47
56. Jones SM, Howell KE. 1998. Phosphatidylinositol 3-kinase is required for the formation of constitutive transport vesicles from the TGN. *J. Cell Biol.* 139:339–49
57. Bankaitis V, Malehorn DE, Emr SD, Greene R. 1989. The *Saccharomyces cerevisiae SEC14* gene encodes a cytosolic factor that is required for transport of secretory proteins from the yeast Golgi complex. *J. Cell Biol.* 108:1271–81
58. Bankaitis V, Aitken JR, Cleves AE, Dowhan W. 1990. An essential role for a phospholipid transfer protein in yeast Golgi function. *Nature* 347:561–62
59. Schu PV, Takegawa K, Fry MJ, Stack JH, Waterfield MD, Emr SD. 1993.

Phosphatidylinositol 3-kinase encoded by yeast *VPS34* gene essential for protein sorting. *Science* 260:88–91
60. Stack JH, Emr SD. 1994. Vsp34p required for yeast vacuolar protein sorting is a multiple specificity kinase that exhibits both protein kinase and phosphatidylinositol-specific PI 3-kinase activities. *J. Biol. Chem.* 269:31552–62
61. Söllner T, Bennett MK, Whiteheart SW, Scheller RH, Rothman JE. 1993. A protein assembly-disassembly pathway in vitro that may correspond to sequential steps of synaptic vesicle docking, activation, and fusion. *Cell* 75:409–18
62. Banerjee A, Barry VA, DasGupta BR, Martin TF. 1996. *N*-ethylmaleimide-sensitive factor acts at a prefusion ATP-dependent step in Ca^{2+}-activated exocytosis. *J. Biol. Chem.* 271:20223–26
63. Mayer A, Wickner W, Haas A. 1996. Sec18p (NSF)-driven release of Sec17p (alpha-SNAP) can precede docking and fusion of yeast vacuoles. *Cell* 85:83–94
64. Mayer A, Wickner W. 1997. Docking of yeast vacuoles is catalyzed by the Ras-like GTPase Ypt7p after symmetric priming by Sec18p (NSF). *J. Cell Biol.* 136:307–17
65. Aitken A, Collinge DB, van Heusden BP, Isobe T, Roseboom PH, et al. 1992. 14-3-3 proteins: a highly conserved, widespread family of eukaryotic proteins. *Trends Biochem. Sci.* 17:498–501
66. Ali SM, Geisow MJ, Burgoyne RD. 1989. A role for calpactin in calcium-dependent exocytosis in adrenal chromaffin cells. *Nature* 340:313–15
67. Burgoyne RD, Morgan A. 1990. Evidence for a role of calpactin in calcium-dependent exocytosis. *Biochem. Soc. Trans.* 18:1101–4
68. Sarafian T, Pradel L-A, Henry J-P, Aunis D, Bader MF. 1991. The participation of annexin II (calpactin I) in calcium-evoked exocytosis requires protein kinase C. *J. Cell Biol.* 114:1135–47
69. Morgan A, Burgoyne RD. 1992. Exo1 and Exo2 proteins stimulate calcium-dependent exocytosis in permeabilized adrenal chromaffin cells. *Nature* 355:833–36
70. Muallem S, Kwiatkowska K, Xu X, Zin HL. 1995. Actin filament disassembly is a sufficient final trigger for exocytosis in nonexcitable cells. *J. Cell Biol.* 128:589–98
71. Roth D, Burgoyne RD. 1995. Stimulation of catecholamine secretion from adrenal chromaffin cells by 14-3-3 proteins is due to reorganisation of the cortical actin network. *FEBS Lett.* 374:77–81
72. Niemann H, Blasi J, Jahn R. 1994. Clostridial neurotoxins: new tools for dissecting exocytosis. *Trends Cell. Biol.* 4:179–85
73. Ahnert-Hilger G, Bigalke H. 1995. Molecular aspects of tetanus and botulinum neurotoxin poisoning. *Prog. Neurobiol.* 46:83–96
74. Pelham HR. 1997. EJCB-lecture: SNAREs and the organization of the secretory pathway. *Eur. J. Cell Biol.* 74:311–14
75. Rossetto O, Gorza L, Schiavo G, Schiavo N, Scheller RH, Montecucco C. 1996. VAMP/synaptobrevin isoforms 1 and 2 are widely and differentially expressed in nonneuronal tissues. *J. Cell Biol.* 132:167–79
76. Advani RJ, Bae HR, Bock JB, Chao DS, Doung YC, et al. 1998. Seven novel mammalian SNARE proteins localize to distinct membrane compartments. *J. Biol. Chem.* 273:10317–24
77. Sadoul K, Berger A, Niemann H, Weller U, Roche PA, et al. 1997. SNAP-23 is not cleaved by botulinum neurotoxin E and can replace SNAP-25 in the process of insulin secretion. *J. Biol. Chem.* 272:33023–27
78. Ikonen E, Tagaya M, Ullrich O, Montecucco C, Simons K. 1995. Different requirements for NSF, SNAP, and rab proteins in apical and basolateral transport in MDCK cells. *Cell* 81:571–80
79. Land J, Zhang H, Vaidyanathan VV, Sadoul K, Niemann H, Wollheim CB. 1997. Transient expression of botulinum neurotoxin C1 light chain differentially inhibits calcium and glucose induced insulin secretion in clonal beta-cells. *FEBS Lett.* 8:13–17
80. Matthew WD, Tsavaler L, Reichardt LF. 1981. Identification of a synaptic vesicle-specific membrane protein with a wide distribution in neuronal and neurosecretory tissue. *J. Cell Biol.* 91:257–69
81. Perin M, Fried VA, Mignery GA, Jahn R, Südhof TC. 1990. Phospholipid binding by a synaptic vesicle protein homologous to the regulatory region of protein kinase C. *Nature* 345:260–63
82. Davletov BA, Südhof TC. 1993. A single C2 domain from synaptotagmin I is sufficient for high-affinity Ca^{2+} /phospholipid binding. *J. Biol. Chem.* 268: 26386–90
83. Davletov BA, Südhof TC. 1994. Ca(2+)-dependent conformational

change in synaptotagmin I. *J. Biol. Chem.* 269:28547–50
84. Geppert M, Goda Y, Hammer RE, Li C, Rosahl TW, et al. 1994. Synaptotagmin I: a major Ca^{2+} sensor for transmitter release at a central synapse. *Cell* 79:717–27
85. Brose N, Petrenko AG, Südhof TC, Jahn R. 1992. Synaptotagmin: a calcium sensor on the synaptic vesicle surface. *Science* 256:1021–25
86. Chapman ER, Hanson PI, An S, Jahn R. 1995. Ca^{2+} regulates the interaction between synaptotagmin and syntaxin 1. *J. Biol. Chem.* 270:23667–71
87. Mizuta M, Inagaki N, Nemoto Y, Matsukura S, Takahashi M, Seino S. 1994. Synaptotagmin III is a novel isoform of rat synaptotagmin expressed in endocrine and neuronal cells. *J. Biol. Chem.* 269:11675–78
88. Li C, Ulrich B, Zhang JZ, Anderson RG, Brose N, Südhof TC. 1995. Ca(2+)-dependent and -independent activities of neural and non-neural synaptotagmins. *Nature* 375:594–99
89. Martin KC, Armitage BA, Siegelbaum SA, Kandel ER, Kaang BK. 1995. Evidence for synaptotagmin as an inhibitory clamp on synaptic vesicle release in *Aplysia* neurons. *Proc. Natl. Acad. Sci. USA* 92:11307–11
90. Morimoto T, Wang XH, Poo MM. 1998. Overexpression of synaptotagmin modulates short-term synaptic plasticity at developing neuromuscular junctions. *Neuroscience* 82:969–78
91. Bommert K, Charlton MP, DeBello WM, Chin GJ, Betz H, Augustine GJ. 1993. Inhibition of neurotransmitter release by C2-domain peptides implicates synaptotagmin in exocytosis. *Nature* 363:163–65
92. Elferink LA, Peterson MR, Scheller RH. 1993. A role for synaptotagmin (p65) in regulated exocytosis. *Cell* 72:153–59
93. Banerjee A, Kowalchyk JA, DasGupta BR, Martin TF. 1996. SNAP-25 is required for a late postdocking step in Ca^{2+}-dependent exocytosis. *J. Biol. Chem.* 271:20227–30
94. Walent JH, Porter BW, Martin TF. 1992. A novel 145 kd brain cytosolic protein reconstitutes Ca^{2+}-regulated secretion in permeable neuroendocrine cells. *Cell* 70:765–75
95. Ann K, Kowalchyk JA, Martin TF. 1997. Novel Ca^{2+}-binding protein (CAPS) related to UNC-31 required for Ca^{2+}-activated exocytosis. *J. Biol. Chem.* 272:19637–40
96. Miller KG, Alfonso A, Nguyen M, Crowell JA, Johnson CD, Rand JB. 1996. A genetic selection for *Caenorhabditis elegans* synaptic transmission mutants. *Proc. Natl. Acad. Sci. USA* 93:12593–98
97. Okabe T, Sugimoto N, Matsuda M. 1992. Calmodulin is involved in catecholamine secretion from digitonin-permeabilized bovine adrenal medullary chromaffin cells. *Biochem. Biophys. Res. Commun.* 186:1006–11
98. Brooks JC, Treml S. 1983. Effect of trifluoperazine on catecholamine secretion by isolated bovine adrenal medullary chromaffin cells. *Biochem. Pharmacol.* 32:371–73
99. Fischer von Mollard G, Stahl B, Li C, Südhof TC, Jahn R. 1994. Rab proteins in regulated exocytosis. *Trends Biol. Sci* 19:164–68
100. Ferro-Novick S, Novick P. 1993. The role of GTP-binding proteins in transport along the exocytic pathway. *Annu. Rev. Cell Biol.* 9:575–99
101. Gomperts BD. 1983. Involvement of guanine nucleotide-binding protein in the gating of Ca^{2+} by receptors. *Nature* 306:64–66
102. Bittner MA, Holz RW, Neubig RR. 1986. Guanine nucleotide effects on catecholamine secretion from digitonin-permeabilized adrenal chromaffin cells. *J. Biol. Chem.* 261:10182–88
103. Knight DE, Baker PF. 1985. Guanine nucleotides and Ca^{2+}-dependent exocytosis. *FEBS Lett.* 189:345–49
104. Morgan A, Burgoyne RD. 1990. Stimulation of Ca^{2+}-independent catecholamine secretion from digitonin-permeabilized bovine adrenal chromaffin cells by guanine nucleotide analogues. *Biochem. J.* 269:521–26
105. Bader MF, Sontag JM, Thiersé D, Aunis D. 1989. A reassessment of guanine nucleotide effects on catecholamine secretion from permeabilized adrenal chromaffin cells. *J. Biol. Chem.* 264:16426–34
106. Burgoyne RD, Morgan A, O'Sullivan AJ. 1989. The control of cytoskeletal actin and exocytosis in intact and permeabilized adrenal chromaffin cells: role of calcium and protein kinase C. *Cell. Signal.* 1:323–34
107. Ahnert-Hilger G, Wegenhorst U, Stecher B, Spicher K, Rosenthal W, Gratzl M. 1992. Exocytosis from permeabilized bovine adrenal chromaffin cells is differently modulated by guanosine 5′-[γ-thio]triphosphate and guanosine

5′-[βγ-imido]triphosphate. *Biochem. J.* 284:321–26

108. Burgoyne RD, Handel SE, Morgan A. 1994. Control of exocytosis in adrenal chromaffin cells by GTP-binding proteins studied using permeabilized cells and patch-clamp capacitance measurements. *Biochem. Soc. Trans.* 22:468–71
109. Padfield PJ, Panesar N. 1998. The two phases of regulated exocytosis in permeabilized pancreatic acini are modulated differently by heterotrimeric G-proteins. *Biochem. Biophys. Res. Commun.* 245:332–36
110. Lillie TH, Gomperts BD. 1992. Nucleotides and divalent cations as effectors and modulators of exocytosis in permeabilized rat mast cells. *Philos. Trans. R. Soc. London Ser. B* 336:25–34
111. Barrowman MM, Cockcroft S, Gomperts BD. 1986. Two roles for guanine nucleotides in the stimulus-secretion sequence of neutrophils. *Nature* 319:504–7
112. Regazzi R, Wollheim CB, Lang J, Theler JM, Rossetto O, et al. 1995. VAMP-2 and cellubrevin are expressed in pancreatic beta-cells and are essential for Ca(2+)- but not for GTPγS-induced insulin secretion. *EMBO J.* 14:2723–30
113. Glenn DE, Burgoyne RD. 1996. Botulinum neurotoxin light chains inhibit both Ca(2+)-induced and GTP analogue-induced catecholamine release from permeabilised adrenal chromaffin cells. *FEBS Lett.* 386:137–40
114. Salminen A, Novick P. 1987. A ras-like protein is required for a post-Golgi event in yeast secretion. *Cell* 49:527–38
115. Gruenberg JE, Clague MJ. 1992. Regulation of intracellular membrane transport. *Curr. Opin. Cell Biol.* 4:593–99
116. Pfeffer SR. 1994. Rab GTPases: master regulators of membrane trafficking. *Curr. Opin. Cell Biol.* 6:522–26
117. Nuoffer C, Balch WE. 1994. GTPases: multifunctional molecular switches regulating vesicular traffic. *Annu. Rev. Biochem.* 63:949–90
118. Lledo PM, Johannes L, Vernier P, Zorec R, Darchen F, et al. 1994. Rab3 proteins: key players in the control of exocytosis. *Trends Neurosci.* 17:426–32
119. Fischer von Mollard G, Mignery GA, Baumert M, Perin MS, Hanson TJ, et al. 1990. rab3 is a small GTP-binding protein exclusively localized to synaptic vesicles. *Proc. Natl. Acad. Sci. USA* 87:1988–92
120. Valentijn JA, Sengupta D, Gumkowski FD, Tang LH, Konieczko EM, Jamieson JD. 1996. Rab3D localizes to secretory granules in rat pancreatic acinar cells. *Eur. J. Cell Biol.* 70:33–41
121. Fischer von Mollard G, Südhof TC, Jahn R. 1991. A small GTP-binding protein dissociates from synaptic vesicles during exocytosis. *Nature* 349:79–81
122. Fischer von Mollard G, Stahl B, Khokhlatchev A, Südhof TC, Jahn R. 1994. Rab3C is a synaptic vesicle protein that dissociates from synaptic vesicles after stimulation of exocytosis. *J. Biol. Chem.* 269:10971–74
123. Stahl B, Fischer von Mollard G, Walch-Solimena C, Jahn R. 1994. GTP cleavage by the small GTP-binding protein Rab3A is associated with exocytosis of synaptic vesicles induced by alpha-latrotoxin. *J. Biol. Chem.* 269:24770–76
124. Padfield PJ, Balch WE, Jamieson JD. 1992. A synthetic peptide of the rab3a effector domain stimulates amylase release from permeabilized pancreatic acini. *Proc. Natl. Acad. Sci. USA* 89: 1656–60
125. Senyshyn J, Balch WE, Holz RW. 1992. Synthetic peptides of the effector-binding domain of rab enhance secretion from digitonin-permeabilized chromaffin cells. *FEBS Lett.* 309:41–46
126. MacLean CM, Law GJ, Edwardson JM. 1993. Stimulation of exocytotic membrane fusion by modified peptides of the rab3 effector domain: re-evaluation of the role of rab3 in regulated exocytosis. *Biochem. J.* 294:325–28

126a. Fernández-Chacón R, Südhof T. 1999. Genetics of synaptic vesicle function: toward the complete functional anatomy of an organelle. *Annu. Rev. Physiol.* 61:753–76

127. Johannes L, Lledo PM, Roa M, Vincent JD, Henry JP, Darchen F. 1994. The GTPase Rab3a negatively controls calcium-dependent exocytosis in neuroendocrine cells. *EMBO J.* 13:2029–37
128. Johannes L, Doussau F, Clabecq A, Henry J-P, Darchen F, Poulain B. 1996. Evidence for a functional link between Rab3 and the SNARE complex. *J. Cell Sci.* 109:2875–84
129. Bean AJ, Scheller RH. 1997. Better late than never: a role for rabs late in exocytosis. *Neuron* 19:751–54
130. Geppert M, Südhof TC. 1998. Rab3 and synaptotagmin: the yin and yang of synaptic membrane fusion. *Annu. Rev Neurosci.* 21:75–95
131. Geppert M, Bolshakov SA, Siegelbaum K, Takel P, De Camilli P, et al. 1994.

The role of Rab3A in neurotransmitter release. *Nature* 369:493–97

132. Geppert M, Goda Y, Stevens CF, Südhof TC. 1997. The small GTP-binding protein Rab3A regulates a late step in synaptic vesicle fusion. *Nature* 387:810–14
133. Nonet ML, Staunton JE, Kilgard MP, Fergestad T, Hartwieg E, et al. 1997. *Caenorhabditis elegans* rab-3 mutant synapses exhibit impaired function and are partially depleted of vesicles. *J. Neurosci.* 17:8061–73
134. Søgaard M, Tani K, Ye RR, Geromanos S, Tempst S, et al. 1994. rab protein is required for the assembly of SNARE complexes in the docking of transport vesicles. *Cell* 78:937–48
135. Walch-Solimena C, Blasi J, Edelmann L, Chapman ER, Fischer von Mollard G, Jahn R. 1995. The t-SNAREs syntaxin 1 and SNAP-25 are present on organelles that participate in synaptic vesicle recycling. *J. Cell Biol.* 128:637–45
136. Newman AP, Shim J, Ferro-Novick S. 1990. BET1, BOS1, and SEC22 are members of a group of interacting yeast genes required for transport from the endoplasmic reticulum to the Golgi complex. *Mol. Cell Biol.* 10:3405–14
137. Newman AP, Groesch ME, Ferro-Novick S. 1992. Bos1p, a membrane protein required for ER to Golgi transport in yeast, co-purifies with the carrier vesicles and with Bet1p and the ER membrane. *EMBO J.* 11:3609–17
138. Dascher C, Ossig R, Gallwitz D, Schmitt HD. 1991. Identification and structure of four yeast genes (SLY) that are able to suppress the functional loss of YPT1, a member of the RAS superfamily. *Mol. Cell. Biol.* 11:872–85
139. Brennwald P, Kearns B, Champion K, Keranen S, Bankaitis V, Novick P. 1994. Sec9 is a SNAP-25-like component of a yeast SNARE complex that may be the effector of Sec4 function in exocytosis. *Cell* 79:245–58
140. Horikawa HPM, Saisu H, Ishizuka T, Sekine Y, Tsugita A, et al. 1993. A complex of rab3A, SNAP-25, VAMP/synaptobrevin-2 and syntaxins in brain presynaptic terminals. *FEBS Lett.* 330:236–40
141. Stahl B, Chou JH, Südhof TC, Jahn R. 1996. Rab3 reversibly recruits rabphilin to synaptic vesicles by a mechanism analogous to raf recruitment by ras. *EMBO J.* 15:1799–809
142. Wang Y, Okamoto M, Schmitz F, Hofmann K, Südhof TC. 1997. Rim is a putative Rab3 effector in regulating synaptic-vesicle fusion. *Nature* 388:593–98
143. Dessauer CW, Posner BA, Gilman AG. 1996. Visualizing signal transduction: receptors, G-proteins, and adenylate cyclases. *Clin. Sci. Colch* 91:527–37
144. Hepler JR, Gilman AG. 1992. G proteins. *Trends Biochem. Sci.* 17:383–87
145. Bomsel M, Mostov K. 1992. Role of heterotrimeric G proteins in membrane traffic. *Mol. Biol. Cell* 3:1317–28
146. Sontag JM, Thiersé D, Rouot B, Aunis D, Bader MF. 1991. A pertussis-toxin-sensitive protein controls exocytosis in chromaffin cells at a step distal to the generation of second messengers. *Biochem. J.* 274:339–47
147. Ahnert-Hilger G, Wiedenmann B. 1994. Requirements for exocytosis in permeabilized neuroendocrine cells. Possible involvement of heterotrimeric G proteins associated with secretory vesicles. *Ann. NY Acad. Sci.* 733:298–305
148. Konrad RJ, Young RA, Record RD, Smith RM, Butkerait P, et al. 1995. The heterotrimeric G-protein G_i is localized to the insulin secretory granules of beta-cells and is involved in insulin exocytosis. *J. Biol. Chem.* 270:12869–76
149. Vitale N, Gensse M, Chasserot-Golaz S, Aunis D, Bader MF. 1996. Trimeric G proteins control regulated exocytosis in bovine chromaffin cells: sequential involvement of G_o associated with secretory granules and G_{i3} bound to the plasma membrane. *Eur. J. Cell Biol.* 8:1275–85
150. Ohnishi H, Ernst SA, Yule DI, Baker CW, Williams JA. 1997. Heterotrimeric G-protein Gq/11 localized on pancreatic zymogen granules is involved in calcium-regulated amylase secretion. *J. Biol. Chem.* 272:16056–61
151. Gasman S, Chasserot-Golaz S, Hubert P, Aunis D, Bader MF. 1998. Identification of a potential effector pathway for the trimeric G_o protein associated with secretory granules. *J. Biol. Chem.* 273:16913–20
152. Aridor M, Rajmilevich G, Beaven MA, Sagai-Eisenberg R. 1993. Activation of exocytosis by the heterotrimeric G protein G_{i3}. *Science* 262:1569–72
153. Lang J, Nishimoto I, Okamoto T, Regazzi R, Kiraly C, et al. 1995. Direct control of exocytosis by receptor-mediated activation of the heterotrimeric GTPases G_i and G(o) or by the expression of their active G alpha subunits. *EMBO J.* 14:3635–44
154. Lang J, Ushkaryov Y, Grasso A, Woll-

heim CB. 1998. Ca^{2+}-independent insulin exocytosis induced by alpha-latrotoxin requires latrophilin, a G protein-coupled receptor. *EMBO J.* 17:648–57
155. Galas MC, Helms JB, Vitale N, Thiersé D, Aunis D, Bader MF. 1997. Regulated exocytosis in chromaffin cells. A potential role for a secretory granule-associated ARF6 protein. *J. Biol. Chem.* 272:2788–93
156. Caumont AS, Galas MC, Vitale N, Aunis D, Bader MF. 1998. Regulated exocytosis in chromaffin cells. Translocation of ARF6 stimulates a plasma membrane-associated phospholipase D. *J. Biol. Chem.* 273:1373–79
157. Weidman PJ, Winter WM. 1994. The G protein-activating peptide, mastoparan, and the synthetic NH2-terminal ARF peptide, ARFp13, inhibit in vitro Golgi transport by irreversibly damaging membranes. *J. Cell Biol.* 127:1815–27
158. Burgoyne RD. 1991. Control of exocytosis in adrenal chromaffin cells. *Biochem. Biophys. Acta* 1071:174–202
159. Burgoyne RD, Morgan A. 1993. Regulated exocytosis. *Biochem. J.* 293:305–16
160. Hoekstra D, de Boer T, Klappe K, Wilschut J. 1984. Fluorescence method for measuring the kinetics of fusion between biological membranes. *Biochemistry* 23:5675–81
161. Stegmann T, Schoen P, Bron R, Wey J, Bartoldus I, et al. 1993. Evaluation of viral membrane fusion assays. Comparison of the octadecylrhodamine dequenching assay with the pyrene excimer assay. *Biochemistry* 32:11330–37
162. Mullock BM, Perez JH, Kuwana T, Gray SR, Luzio JP. 1994. Lysosomes can fuse with a late endosomal compartment in a cell-free system from rat liver. *J. Cell Biol.* 126:1173–82
163. Nadin CY, Rogers J, Tomlinson S, Edwardson JM. 1989. A specific interaction in vitro between pancreatic zymogen granules and plasma membranes: stimulation by G-protein activators but not by Ca^{2+}. *J. Cell Biol.* 109:2801–8
164. Meldolesi J, Jamieson JD, Palade GE. 1971. Composition of cellular membranes in the pancreas of the guinea pig. II. Lipids. *J. Cell Biol.* 49:130–49
165. Edwardson JM, Vickery C, Christy LJ. 1990. Rat pancreatic acini permeabilized with streptolysin *O* secrete amylase at Ca^{2+} concentrations in the micromolar range, when provided with ATP and GTP gamma S. *Biochem. Biophys. Acta* 1053:32–36
166. Kitagawa M, Williams JA, De Lisle RC. 1990. Amylase release from streptolysin *O*-permeabilized pancreatic acini. *Am. J. Physiol.* 259:G157–64
167. Padfield PJ, Jamieson JD. 1991. Low molecular weight GTP-binding proteins associated with zymogen granule membranes from rat pancreas. *Biochem. Biophys. Res. Commun.* 174:600–5
168. Milutinovic S, Argent BE, Schulz I, Sachs G. 1977. Studies on isolated subcellular components of cat pancreas. II. A Ca^{2+}-dependent interaction between membranes and zymogen granules of cat pancreas. *J. Membr. Biol.* 36:281–95
169. MacLean CM, Edwardson JM. 1992. Fusion between rat pancreatic zymogen granules and plasma membranes. Modulation by a GTP-binding protein. *Biochem. J.* 286:747–53
170. Lee EG, Marciniak SJ, MacLean CM, Edwardson JM. 1994. Pancreatic plasma membranes: promiscuous partners in membrane fusion. *Biochem. J.* 298:599–604
171. Edwardson JM, An S, Jahn R. 1997. The secretory granule protein syncollin binds to syntaxin in a Ca(2+)-sensitive manner. *Cell* 90:325–33
172. Gaisano HY, Sheu L, Foskett JK, Trimble WS. 1994. Tetanus toxin light chain cleaves a vesicle-associated membrane protein (VAMP) isoform 2 in rat pancreatic zymogen granules and inhibits enzyme secretion. *J. Biol. Chem.* 269:17062–66
173. Edwardson JM. 1998. A cell-free system for Ca^{2+}-regulated exocytosis. *Methods Enzymol.* 16:In press
174. Braun JE, Fritz BA, Wong SM, Lowe AW. 1994. Identification of a vesicle-associated membrane protein (VAMP)-like membrane protein in zymogen granules of the rat exocrine pancreas. *J. Biol. Chem.* 269:5328–35
175. Gaisano HY, Ghai M, Malkus PN, Sheu L, Bouquillon A, et al. 1996. Distinct cellular locations of the syntaxin family of proteins in rat pancreatic acinar cells. *Mol. Biol. Cell* 7:2019–27
176. Martin TF, Kowalchyk JA. 1997. Docked secretory vesicles undergo Ca^{2+}-activated exocytosis in a cell-free system. *J. Biol. Chem.* 272:14447–53
177. Karli UO, Schäfer T, Burger MM. 1990. Fusion of neurotransmitter vesicles with target membrane is calcium independent in a cell-free system. *Proc. Natl. Acad. Sci. USA* 87:5912–15

178. Almeida MT, Ramalho-Santos J, Oliveira CR, Pedroso de Lima MC. 1997. Evidence that synaptobrevin is involved in fusion between synaptic vesicles and synaptic plasma membrane vesicles. *Biochem. Biophys. Res. Commun.* 236:184–88
179. Crabb JH, Jackson RC. 1985. In vitro reconstitution of exocytosis from plasma membrane and isolated secretory vesicles. *J. Cell Biol.* 101:2263–73
180. Crabb JH, Modern PA, Jackson RC. 1987. In vitro reconstitution of exocytosis from sea urchin egg plasma membrane and isolated cortical vesicles. *Biosci. Rep.* 7:399–409
181. Whitaker MJ, Steinhardt RA. 1982. Ionic regulation of egg activation. *Q. Rev. Biophys.* 15:593–666
182. Steinhardt RA, Zucker R, Schatten G. 1977. Intracellular calcium release at fertilization in the sea urchin egg. *Dev. Biol.* 58:185–96
183. Baker PF, Whitaker MJ. 1978. Influence of ATP and calcium on the cortical reaction in sea urchin eggs. *Nature* 276:513–15
184. Baker PF, Knight DE, Whitaker MJ. 1980. The relation between ionized calcium and cortical granule exocytosis in eggs of the sea urchin *Echinus esculentus*. *Proc. R. Soc. London Ser. B* 207:149–61
185. Schuel H. 1978. Secretory functions of egg cortical granules in fertilization and development: a critical review. *Gamete Res.* 1:299–382
186. Kay ES, Shapiro BM. 1985. The formation of the fertilization membrane of the sea urchin egg. In *Biology of Fertilization*. New York: Academic
187. Moy GW, Kopf GS, Gache C, Vacquier V. 1983. Calcium-mediated release of glucanase activity from cortical granules of sea urchin eggs. *Dev. Biol.* 100:267–74
188. Detering NK, Decker GL, Schmell ED, Lennarz WJ. 1977. Isolation and characterization of plasma membrane-associated cortical granules from sea urchin eggs. *J. Cell Biol.* 75:899–914
189. Zimmerberg J, Sardet C, Epel D. 1985. Exocytosis of sea urchin egg cortical vesicles in vitro is retarded by hyperosmotic sucrose: kinetics of fusion monitored by quantitative light-scattering microscopy. *J. Cell Biol.* 101:2398–410
190. Whalley T, Whitaker MJ. 1988. Exocytosis reconstituted from the sea urchin egg is unaffected by calcium pretreatment of granules and plasma membrane. *Biosci. Rep.* 8:335–43
191. Jackson RC, Modern PA. 1990. Reassociation of cortical secretory vesicles with sea urchin egg plasma membrane: assessment of binding specificity. *J. Membr. Biol.* 115:83–93
192. Haggerty JG, Jackson RC. 1983. Release of granule contents from sea urchin egg cortices. *J. Biol. Chem.* 258:1819–25
193. Sasaki H, Epel D. 1983. Cortical vesicle exocytosis in isolated cortices of sea urchin eggs: description of a turbidometric assay and its utilization in studying effects of different media on discharge. *Dev. Biol.* 98:327–37
194. Whalley T, Crossley I, Whitaker MJ. 1991. Phosphoprotein inhibition of calcium-stimulated exocytosis in sea urchin eggs. *J. Cell Biol.* 113:769–78
195. Oberdorf J, Vilar-Rojas C, Epel D. 1989. The localization of PI and PIP kinase activities in the sea urchin egg and their modulation following fertilization. *Dev. Biol.* 131:236–42
196. Vogel SS, Blank PS, Zimmerberg J. 1996. Poisson-distributed active fusion complexes underlie the control of the rate and extent of exocytosis by calcium. *J. Cell Biol.* 134:329–38
197. Sasaki H. 1984. Modulation of calcium sensitivity by a specific cortical protein during sea urchin egg cortical vesicle exocytosis. *Dev. Biol.* 101:125–35
198. Sasaki H. 1992. A protein factor extracted from murine brains confers physiological Ca^{2+} sensitivity to exocytosis in sea urchin eggs. *FEBS Lett.* 304:207–10
199. Baker PF, Whitaker MJ. 1979. Trifluoperazine inhibits exocytosis in sea urchin eggs. *J. Physiol.* 298:55P
200. Whitaker MJ, Baker PF. 1983. Calcium-dependent exocytosis in an in vitro secretory granule plasma membrane preparation from sea urchin eggs and the effects of some inhibitors of cytoskeletal function. *Proc. R. Soc. London Ser. B* 218:397–413
201. Steinhardt RA, Alderton JM. 1982. Calmodulin confers calcium sensitivity on secretory exocytosis. *Nature* 295: 154–55
202. Avery JC, Hodel A, Whitaker MJ. 1997. In vitro exocytosis in sea urchin eggs requires a synaptobrevin-related protein. *J. Cell Sci.* 110:1555–61
203. Shen W-J, Avery J, Totty NF, Hsuan JJ, Whitaker MJ, Moss SE. 1994. Identification and partial sequence analysis

of novel annexins in *Lytechinus pictus* oocytes. *Biochem. J.* 304:911–16

204. Iwasa F, Ishiguro K. 1986. Calmodulin-binding protein (55K+17K) of sea urchin eggs has a Ca^{2+}- and calmodulin-dependent phosphoprotein phosphatase activity. *J. Biochem.* 99:1353–58
205. Conner S, Leaf D, Wessel G. 1997. Members of the SNARE hypothesis are associated with cortical granule exocytosis in the sea urchin egg. *Mol. Reprod. Dev.* 48:106–18
206. Tatham PE, Gomperts BD. 1991. Rat mast cells degranulate in response to microinjection of guanine nucleotide. *J. Cell Sci.* 98:217–24
207. Baitinger C, Alderton JM, Poenie M, Schulman H, Steinhardt RA. 1990. Multifunctional Ca^{2+}/calmodulin-dependent protein kinase is necessary for nuclear envelope breakdown. *J. Cell Biol.* 111:1763–73
208. Swezey RR, Epel D. 1989. Stable, resealable pores formed in sea urchin eggs by electric discharge (electroporation) permit substrate loading for assay of enzymes in vivo. *Cell Reg.* 1:65–74
209. Steinhardt RA, Bi G, Alderton JM. 1994. Cell membrane resealing by a vesicular mechanism similar to neurotransmitter release. *Science* 263:390–93
210. Bi G-Q, Morris RL, Liao G, Alderton JM, Scholey JM, Steinhardt RA. 1997. Kinesin- and myosin-driven steps of vesicle recruitment for Ca^{2+}-regulated exocytosis. *J. Cell Biol.* 138:999–1008
211. Vogel SS, Chernomordik LV, Zimmerberg J. 1992. Calcium-triggered fusion of exocytotic granules requires proteins in only one membrane. *J. Biol. Chem.* 267:25640–43
212. Jahn R, Hanson PI. 1998. SNAREs line up in new environment. *Nature* 393:14–15
213. Chernomordik LV, Vogel SS, Sokoloff A, Onaran HO, Leikina EA, Zimmerberg J. 1993. Lysolipids reversibly inhibit Ca^{2+}-, GTP- and pH-dependent fusion of biological membranes. *FEBS Lett.* 318:71–76
214. Chernomordik LV, Frolov VA, Leikina EA, Bronk P, Zimmerberg J. 1998. The pathway of membrane fusion catalyzed by influenza hemagglutinin: restriction of lipids, hemifusion, and lipidic fusion pore formation. *J. Cell Biol.* 140:1369–82
215. Weber T, Zemelman BV, McNew JA, Westerman B, Gmachl M, et al. 1998. SNAREpins: minimal machinery for membrane fusion. *Cell* 92:759–72

Annu. Rev. Physiol. 1999. 61:809–34

MECHANISMS OF HAIR CELL TUNING

R. Fettiplace
Department of Physiology, University of Wisconsin, Madison, Wisconsin 53706; e-mail: fettiplace@physiology.wisc.edu

P. A. Fuchs
Center for Hearing Sciences, Department of Otolaryngology-Head and Neck Surgery, Johns Hopkins University, Baltimore Maryland, 21205; e-mail: pfuchs@bme.jhu.edu

KEY WORDS: alternative splicing, calcium, calcium-activated potassium channel, electrical tuning, mechanotransduction

ABSTRACT

Mechanosensory hair cells of the vertebrate inner ear contribute to acoustic tuning through feedback processes involving voltage-gated channels in the basolateral membrane and mechanotransduction channels in the apical hair bundle. The specific number and kinetics of calcium-activated (BK) potassium channels determine the resonant frequency of electrically tuned hair cells. Kinetic variation among BK channels may arise through alternative splicing of *slo* gene mRNA and combination with modulatory β subunits. The number of transduction channels and their rate of adaptation rise with hair cell response frequency along the cochlea's tonotopic axis. Calcium-dependent feedback onto transduction channels may underlie active hair bundle mechanics. The relative contributions of electrical and mechanical feedback to active tuning of hair cells may vary as a function of sound frequency.

INTRODUCTION

The auditory receptor, the cochlea in higher vertebrates, is responsible both for transforming the acoustic stimulus into an electrical signal and for resolving that stimulus into its component frequencies. The relative amplitudes of the different components are then signaled to the brain by activity in VIIIth nerve fibers, each tuned to a narrow frequency band. Acoustic frequency analysis

0066-4278/99/0315-0809$08.00

is an important aspect of sensory perception and helps to shape an animal's behavior. Thus competition and reproduction within most species depend on the spectral analysis of vocal or other acoustic signals. The frequency content of a sound also provides cues for localizing the source. Binaural disparities in sound intensity that are used for localization vary with the size of the animal's head and consequently depend on frequency. Moreover, the external ear reflects and filters sound differentially according to its direction, and thus confers spectral signatures onto defined regions of space (1, 2). Acoustic frequency analysis is therefore fundamental to sound localization, communication, and the detection of predators and prey.

Extrinsic Versus Intrinsic Tuning

The importance of frequency analysis in inner ear function is emphasized by the assortment of mechanisms that have evolved to implement this task in species ranging from insects to humans (3). Among this variety, two general design principles are found: an extrinsic mechanism in which the stimulus is filtered prior to hair cell transduction, and one where the filtering is intrinsic to the hair cell. The mammalian cochlea exemplifies an acoustic detector in which filtering is performed at least partly by the accessory structures in which the neural elements are embedded. Owing to the graded mechanical properties of the basilar membrane, different frequencies displace it maximally in different places, which results in a tonotopic map of vibration frequency (4). Thus a small range of frequencies is imparted to each inner hair cell, which transduces the narrow-band stimulus, thereby generating tuned receptor potentials. This filter is extrinsic to the hair cell, in analogy to that of the Pacinian corpuscle, where rapid adaptation arises largely from the mechanical properties of the accessory bulb that encapsulates the sensory ending.

In contrast, in the auditory papilla of the turtle, the filter is wholly intrinsic to the hair cell. Here the mechanics of the basilar membrane impart meager tuning, and transduction current is driven into the hair cell nearly equally by a broad range of stimulus frequencies. The amplitude of the receptor potential is then modulated by voltage-dependent ionic conductances that confer a property of electrical tuning onto the hair cells. An analogy may be drawn with color perception in the visual system, where different wavelengths in the light are detected by red, green, and blue cone photoreceptors, each maximally sensitive over a different spectral range. The resonant frequencies of turtle hair cells vary systematically along the length of the basilar papilla, resulting in a tonotopic organization similar to that arising from mechanical tuning in the mammal. The extrinsic and intrinsic acoustic tuning processes may not be totally independent because interactions between the two can occur by mechanical feedback from the hair cells, as is discussed below. Such feedback is thought to be involved in augmenting the tuning of the basilar membrane in the mammalian cochlea (5).

This review focuses on those features intrinsic to the hair cell that participate in their tuning and mechanosensitivity. The ion channels that comprise the mechanism of electrical tuning are discussed in the section ELECTRICAL TUNING. In the section MECHANICAL TUNING other hair cell properties that also vary along the tonotopic axis are described, with special emphasis on mechanical tuning by the transduction apparatus.

ELECTRICAL TUNING

Hair Cell Tuning in the Turtle Basilar Papilla

The low-frequency hearing (30–600 Hz) of the red-eared turtle *Trachemys scripta elegans* is served by a receptive epithelium, the basilar papilla, which contains roughly 1000 hair cells in a strip approximately 1 mm in length (6, 7). Direct measurements of basilar membrane motion using laser interferometry revealed no position-dependent mechanical tuning (8). Nonetheless, recordings from hair cells and afferent fibers in a semi-intact preparation showed sharp tuning and sensitivity, with an orderly sequence of best frequencies mapped along the basilar papilla (9, 10). The combined tuning curves of all afferent fibers possessed a minimum threshold and total frequency range matching the turtle's behavioral audiogram (11).

Intracellular recording from turtle hair cells showed that they were not passive reporters of mechanical input. Current pulses injected into hair cells caused a damped oscillation of the membrane potential (Figure 1) with frequency and decay rate similar to those elicited by an acoustic transient (click) to that same cell (12). This behavior, termed electrical resonance, was attributed to the voltage-dependent activation of a membrane K^+ conductance. The optimal frequencies and bandwidths of tuning for both the electrical and acoustic stimuli were essentially identical in each of a population of hair cells spanning much of the turtle's audible range. Therefore in the turtle there is little or no filtering of the acoustic stimulus prior to mechanoelectrical transduction (13).

BK Calcium-Activated Potassium Channels Tune Hair Cells

Electrical tuning has also been observed in hair cells of fish, frogs, alligators, and chicks (14–19). Voltage-clamp recording from frog saccular hair cells suggest that the interaction between a voltage-gated Ca^{2+} current and a K^+ current flowing through large conductance Ca^{2+}-activated K^+ (BK) channels produces the oscillatory voltage responses (17, 20, 21). The basis of the electrical resonance can be explained by considering the sequence of events following a current step: (*a*) depolarization opens voltage-gated Ca^{2+} channels, promoting

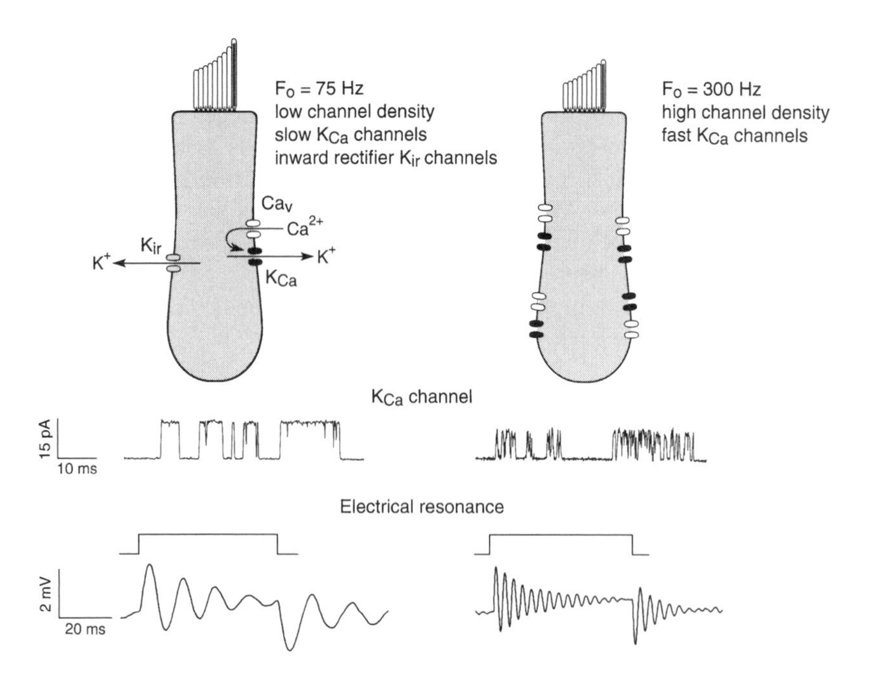

Figure 1 Schematic drawing of two hair cells from the turtle basilar papilla, with resonant frequencies (F_o) of 75 and 300 Hz. The low-frequency cell has a longer hair bundle, and a low density of Ca^{2+} and Ca^{2+}-activated K^+ (K_{Ca}) channel complexes. The number of channel complexes increases with (F_o). Beneath each cell are shown representative K_{Ca} (BK) single-channel records and ringing voltage responses to extrinsic current steps for cells tuned approximately to these two frequencies. The timing of the extrinsic current is shown above the voltage records. The single-channel records and the voltage ringing were from different sets of experiments (22, 23).

a rise in internal Ca^{2+} that activates BK channels; (*b*) the large outward K^+ current hyperpolarizes the membrane, closing the Ca^{2+} channels, which leads to the first cycle of the oscillation; (*c*) as the cell hyperpolarizes and intracellular Ca^{2+} transients dissipate, the BK channels partially close, but due to the continued extrinsic current, the membrane swings positive to initiate another cycle of Ca^{2+} influx. Since the BK channels are already partly activated, a smaller fraction of K^+ current is recruited on the second cycle, which will have a smaller amplitude than the first. Because the K^+ equilibrium potential (−80 mV) is negative to the resting potential (−50 mV), the BK channels behave as part of a negative feedback loop, but the time course of their activation delays the feedback and hence generates damped oscillatory responses.

Such negative feedback also produces sharp tuning for sinusoidal stimuli, and the frequency at which the cell is maximally sensitive, the resonant frequency, should be influenced by the size and speed of the feedback. The factors determining the resonant frequency were studied experimentally in turtle hair cells tuned to a range of frequencies (22). As in the frog, the electrical resonance was generated in most cells by the interaction of voltage-gated Ca^{2+} channels and large-conductance, Ca^{2+}-activated K^+ (BK) channels. A cell's resonant frequency was correlated with the characteristics of its BK channels, a higher frequency arising from an increase in the number of channels and, more importantly, from faster channel kinetics.

Analysis of single BK channels in membrane patches excised from turtle hair cells (23) demonstrated that the kinetic differences were intrinsic to the BK channel (Figure 1). The mean open time and relaxation time constant of ensemble-averaged currents at a fixed intracellular Ca^{2+} varied approximately 30-fold (0.4–13 ms) among BK channels from hair cells tuned to different frequencies. The Ca^{2+} sensitivity and unitary conductance in contrast were indistinguishable in all channels. A kinetic scheme of BK gating based on measurements from single channels, when combined with voltage-gated Ca^{2+} influx and accumulation, quantitatively accounts for electrical tuning over a frequency range from 40 to 600 Hz (24). For a subset of hair cells with resonant frequencies less than 40 Hz, tuning is achieved by replacing the BK channels with other voltage-gated K^+ channels.

Voltage-Gated Ca^{2+} Channels

Voltage-gated Ca^{2+} channels have been characterized in hair cells of several different species (20, 22, 25–29). In all cases, these channels activate with a time constant of less than 0.5 ms at −50 mV, do not inactivate, and deactivate very rapidly upon repolarization. The Ca^{2+} current is reduced by dihydropyridine antagonists, suggesting an L-type channel, but the hair cell Ca^{2+} channels differ from L-type channels in other cell types by more rapid gating kinetics, a more negative activation range, and lower sensitivity to dihydropyridine antagonists (29). The full-length sequence of an α_{1D} calcium channel has been cloned from the basilar papilla of the chick and is the most likely candidate for the hair cell's channel (30).

BK channels require a relatively high Ca^{2+} concentration to open ($K_{1/2}$ $\sim$12 μM at −50 mV) and so must be located in close proximity to the voltage-gated Ca^{2+} channels (24, 27). The co-localization of Ca^{2+} and BK channels, and high concentration of mobile Ca^{2+} buffer, ensure that excursions in Ca^{2+} concentration at the internal face of the BK channel follow with little delay the gating of the Ca^{2+} channels. Thus the kinetics of BK gating become the rate-limiting step in determining the frequency of electrical tuning. In the turtle, a hair cell's complement of voltage-gated Ca^{2+} channels increases with its resonant frequency, but the numbers of Ca^{2+} and BK channels maintain a fixed ratio of about 2:1 in all cells (31). This suggests that the two channel types are coregulated, which could be achieved by insertion into the membrane of channel complexes composed of two Ca^{2+} channels linked to each BK channel.

BK Channels–Alternatively Spliced slo Gene Products

To understand the regulation of the electrical tuning it is important to know the origin of the kinetic variation of the BK channels. There is currently no evidence that the channel kinetics are controlled by an intracellular modulator, and the simplest alternative hypothesis is that the variation arises from differential expression of distinct kinetic isoforms of the channel. What is the minimum number of channel variants that can account for the frequency range? Modeling of electrical tuning in the turtle indicated that five species of BK channel with different kinetics and overlapping distribution were sufficient to cover the animal's auditory range (40–600 Hz) (32). Extension of this model to the chick basilar papilla, which has a greater frequency range (150–4000 Hz) and operates at higher temperature, required a minimum of nine species of BK channel.

The BK channels that support electrical tuning in hair cells are most likely a product of a single *slo* gene originally described in *Drosophila* (33, 34) and subsequently found in mammals (35–37). A full-length homologue was cloned from a chick cochlear cDNA library and shown to encode the α-subunit of the BK channel when expressed in HEK 293 cells (38). The coding region of cSlo1 predicts an 1137 amino acid protein that is 94% identical to a human brain *slo* (hbr1) (36) and may correspond to a minimal length transcript (the fewest exons). The cSlo1 channels had a conductance of 224 pS in symmetrical K^+ solutions, were blocked by external charbydotoxin or iberiotoxin and by low concentrations of tetraethylammonium ions, and were sensitive to intracellular Ca^{2+}, with half-activation at 0 mV by approximately 20 μM Ca^{2+}. RT-PCR from the basilar papilla or from single isolated hair cells confirmed the expression of this cDNA in hair cells. A homologous minimal length cDNA has also been identified in turtle basilar papilla (39) and described in other studies on chick (40, 41).

The *slo* gene encodes a channel protein predicted to contain seven transmembrane segments, an extracellular N terminus (42), a pore region with homology to Shaker-type K^+ channels, and a long intracellular C-terminal segment that includes part of the Ca^{2+}-binding site (43). Multiple alternative exons are found at several splice sites within the *Drosophila* and mammalian transcripts. Some splice variants have altered gating kinetics (44, 45), suggesting that alternative splicing of *slo* mRNA could provide the functional heterogeneity found in hair cell BK channels. Indeed, hair cell *slo* transcripts are alternatively spliced (Figure 2). Eight potential splice sites have been identified and 15 alternative exons have been described to date (38–41).

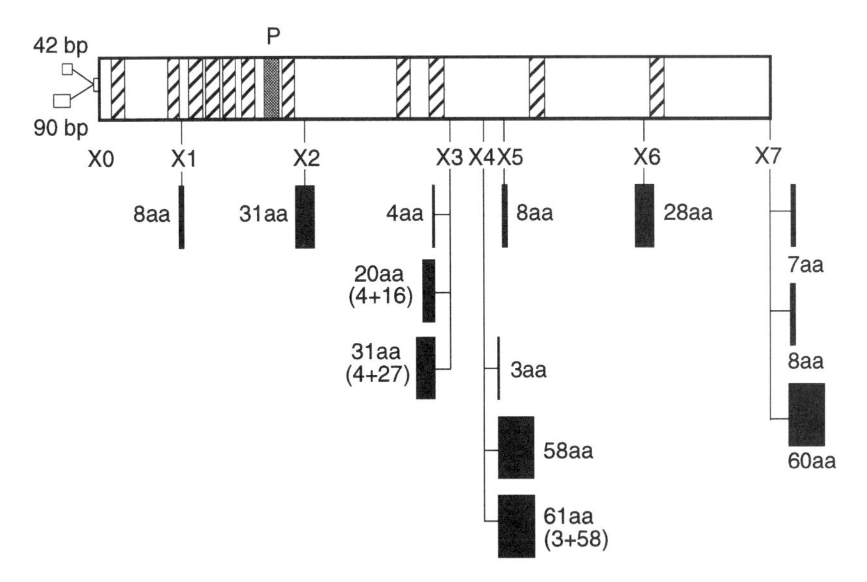

Figure 2 Schematic diagram of the cochlear Slo channel α-subunit open reading frame ($\sim$1150 amino acids in length), carboxy terminus to the right. *Hatched boxes* are putative amphipathic or transmembrane domains (S0–S10) based on data of Meera et al (42), and the *shaded area* is the pore (P). Eight splice sites, X0–X7, have been identified. Two 5′ sequences have been identified (38, 41). Both contain additional in-frame ATGs, but these are not necessary for producing a functional channel (36, 148) and may therefore be located in the untranslated region. At X7, three exons give rise to different carboxy termini of 7, 8, and 60 amino-acids (aa) (38–41; note a single residue difference in the 8 aa exon among these reports). X1–X6 may have no insert or contain a single exon or concatenated exons, the amino-acid sizes of which are noted below each site. X1, which is novel among all vertebrate and invertebrate BK transcripts, may contain an 8 aa insert (41); X2 may contain a 31 aa insert (40). X3 may contain a 4 aa (39–41), a 20 aa (41), or a 31 aa (39) insert. X4 may contain a 3 aa (39, 40), a 58 aa (41), or a 61 aa (39) insert. The 58 aa insert is reported as 59 but includes a modified 5′ flanking amino acid. X5 may contain an 8 aa insert (41) and X6 a 28 aa insert (40, 41; note the reported sequences differ by a single residue).

Distribution and Function of Alternatively-Spliced slo Variants in the Cochlea

Hair cells in both the avian and turtle basilar papillae are mapped tonotopically, with the cell's resonant frequency increasing monotonically along the length of the sensory epithelium. If alternative splicing underlies variations in hair cell tuning, then expression of BK splice variants should be spatially localized within the epithelium. In situ PCR showed that expression of the exon X3 = 4 was restricted to the middle third of the basilar papilla of the embryonic chick and was absent from the basal (high-frequency) tip of the post-hatch cochlea (41). Quantitative PCR from microdissected quadrants of the basilar papilla indicated that exon X2 = 31 was excluded from the low-frequency quarter of the cochlea (40). In this latter study, X3 = 4 appeared equally in all quadrants, in contrast to the result with in situ PCR (41). X4 = 0 was preferentially expressed in quadrants 2 and 3 from the apex. The distributions of two carboxy termini were found to differ, with X7 = 8 occurring at higher levels in quadrants 3 and 4.

In the turtle's basilar papilla, only a restricted subset of sites (X3 and X4 in Figure 2) appear to be alternatively spliced, and only the long (X7 = 60) form of the carboxy terminus is present. It was thus possible to determine some of the exon combinations occurring naturally (39). The combinations, specified by the amino acid insert sizes in X3 and X4, respectively, include 0-0, 4-0, 4-3, 4-61 and 31-3. The spatial distribution of the most prevalent isoforms was studied by RT-PCR on groups of hair cells isolated from different regions. The combinations 4-3 and 31-3 were absent from the highest frequency quadrant. It is worth noting that in both turtle and chick, the distributions observed are quite broad, involving 50% of the papilla or more. However, the amplification techniques do not as yet allow a conclusion about a gradient in the level of a particular mRNA transcript in these broad regions. Moreover, the occurrence of the message does not necessarily reflect the extent of channel incorporation into the membrane. It will be important to verify (by techniques such as antibody labeling) that the protein isoforms encoded by the different transcripts are indeed expressed in the hair cell plasma membrane.

The functional effects of alternative splicing are beginning to be explored. Two carboxy-terminal splice variants, X7 = 8 and X7 = 60 (homologous to the termini originally described in human and mouse Slo, respectively), produced functionally identical channels when expressed in HEK cells or *Xenopus* oocytes (46). Splice site X4 in turtle includes a 61amino acid exon that is related to the 59 or 61 amino acid exon described in adrenal chromaffin cells (45, 47). In studies of chick Slo variants, addition of X4 = 61 to the cSlo backbone caused a two- to threefold slowing of deactivation kinetics, as well as a 25 mV negative shift in the half-activation voltage (48). While studies of individual added exons can be instructive, ultimately it will be necessary to characterize and test those combinations of exons that predominate in hair cells if the native channels are to be reconstituted. In the chick, the occurrence of alternative splicing at seven sites within the coding region implies that a potentially large number of combinations may exist, which makes the task of assigning functional consequences to different variants daunting.

However, the restriction of splicing in the turtle channel to just two sites, X3 and X4, suggests that one or both of these sites is crucial for determining the channel properties, including its Ca^{2+} sensitivity and kinetics. Expression of the different turtle α-subunit variants in *Xenopus* oocytes has confirmed this notion (49). In order to match the performance of native channels, reconstitution will most likely require accessory β-subunits that are known to influence the channel's behavior (50). Preliminary results indicate that coexpression of hair cell α-subunit with a β-subunit both increased the channel's Ca^{2+} sensitivity and markedly slowed its kinetics (49, 51). Thus in theory a range of channel kinetics might be achieved by differential expression of different splice variants of the α-subunit in conjunction with an expression gradient of a β-subunit.

Hair Cell Tuning with Other K^+ Channels

As in turtles and frogs, electrical tuning in alligator and chick hair cells arises from the interaction of voltage-gated Ca^{2+} and Ca^{2+}-activated K^+ currents (18, 19). However the use of BK channels is confined to frequencies above 100 Hz, and at lower frequencies the outward current of hair cells in these species is dominated instead by a slowly activating calcium-independent, delayed-rectifier K^+ current (52). In addition, these cells have an inward rectifier K^+ current that makes a contribution to membrane conductance at potentials negative to −40 mV. Such cells have more negative resting membrane potentials and generate low frequency (<30 Hz) oscillations or slowly repetitive calcium action potentials. In alligator hair cells, a TTX-sensitive sodium current can assist with spiking (53).

Voltage-gated K^+ channels have also been shown to be involved in tuning of turtle auditory hair cells (54, 55). Slowly activating voltage-dependent K^+ currents and inward rectifier currents are responsible for tuning to the lowest frequencies (10–40 Hz) in apical hair cells. Use of a delayed rectifier may reflect the need to slow the activation kinetics of the K^+ current below that obtainable with a pure BK current. Inward rectifier K^+ currents also serve to augment the sharpness of tuning in cells containing BK channels tuned to frequencies less than 200 Hz (24, 55). The utilization of delayed rectifier and inward rectifier K^+ channels by low-frequency hair cells implies that expression of these types of K^+ channel may be confined to the apical region of the cochlea. RT-PCR was used to demonstrate that the inward rectifier cIRK1 (56) and a chick homologue of the Shaw K_v family, $cK_v3.1$ [a putative delayed rectifier (40)], were preferentially expressed in segments microdissected from the apical half of the chick's basilar papilla.

Determinants of Ion Channel Expression in Hair Cells

The expression of ion channels may be related to the synaptic organization of hair cells. It has been suggested that voltage-gated Ca^{2+} channels and BK channels cluster preferentially at transmitter release sites in frog saccular hair cells (27, 57), as observed at the neuromuscular junction (58). The relationship between Ca^{2+} channel expression and release site formation was examined in chick hair cells, among which afferent innervation density varies systematically by cochlear position (59). Release site size is greater in more basally located hair cells, but release site number falls across the cochlear width (see color insert C1, Figure 3, at back of volume). Ca^{2+} channel number was found to correlate with each hair cell's total release area—a product of release site number and size. A tonotopic gradient of Ca^{2+} channels in turtle hair cells also may be related to variations in presynaptic structure, with the highest frequency hair cells having the largest calcium currents (22, 31) and the greatest number of release sites (60).

Gradients of innervation and ion channel expression are observed across, as well as along, the sensory epithelium. The differential innervation by afferent and efferent neurons across the width of the chick's basilar papilla (61) corresponds to cell-specific expression of various voltage-gated potassium channels (62). Hair cells with predominately efferent innervation have rapidly inactivating A-type K^+ currents , whereas hair cells innervated by afferent neurons possess the delayed rectifier and inward rectifier currents described above. These pre- and postsynaptic K^+ currents are reminiscent of the synaptic distributions of K_v subtypes described in mammalian brain (63). It will be of interest to examine the distribution of ion channels in hair cells that have developed with altered innervation in vitro (64) or following denervation (65).

Studies of hair cell development may offer additional insights into potential regulatory mechanisms. BK-type whole-cell currents are first elicited from chick cochlear hair cells at about embryonic day 18 (66), coincident with a late stage of functional maturation of the cochlea (67, 68). In contrast, Ca^{2+} channels and delayed rectifier K^+ channels appear as many as 7 days earlier, and together support calcium spiking in the embryonic hair cell. Even at embryonic day 10, chick hair cells express different classes of voltage-gated K^+ channels depending on their cochlear position (69). Thus developmental schedules, and presumably the underlying regulatory mechanisms, are channel specific during hair cell differentiation. One might imagine that spontaneous (or driven) activity and associated Ca^{2+} flux in embryonic hair cells provides some instruction for the later expression of BK channels, as occurs during the developmental acquisition of K^+ channels by embryonic *Xenopus* neurons (70).

MECHANICAL TUNING

Passive Resonance of the Hair Bundle

The auditory signal can be filtered during the process of mechanotransduction in the hair bundle, as well as by the subsequent activity of voltage-dependent channels in the basolateral membrane. Acoustic stimuli give rise to vibrations of the basilar membrane, which are translated into a to-and-fro motion of the hair bundle, an array of 50 or more stereocilia that forms the hair cell's mechanosensory organelle. The bundle is wedge-shaped and the heights of sequential ranks of stereocilia increase from one side of the bundle to the other, thus defining an axis of symmetry along which the bundle normally rotates. Relative motion of adjacent stereocilia is detected by mechanotransducer channels located at the stereociliary tips (71–73). The channels are thought to be gated by force delivered through extracellular tip-links connecting the top of one stereocilium to the side wall of its taller neighbor (74, 75).

In most vertebrates, the structure of the hair bundle varies along the cochlea's tonotopic axis, with a decrease in the height of the stereocilia toward the high-frequency end (76–78). Reduction in bundle height is often accompanied by an increase in the number of stereocilia per bundle (7, 79, 80). The chick basilar papilla is a well-documented example, where bundle height decreases from 6 to 1.5 μm, and the number of stereocilia increases from 50 to 300 from the low- to high-frequency end (79). Direct manipulation of the bundle has shown that the stereocilia are rigid and move as a concerted array, pivoting about their base with no flexure along their length (81–83). At first glance, therefore, the hair bundles should behave as mechanical resonators like the arm of a tuning fork, with the resonant frequency being a function of the bundle's stiffness and mass. The number of stereocilia per hair cell, the links interconnecting them, and the maximum height of the bundle all contribute to the hair bundle stiffness (84). In a simple analysis, if the bundle contains stereocilia of mean length L, each with a rotational stiffness K_B, the free bundle's undamped resonant frequency F_B is given by

$$F_B = k\,K_B^{0.5} L^{-1.5}, \qquad 1.$$

where k is a constant. The resonant frequency is inversely proportional to the stereociliary length to the three halves power predicting that shorter bundles should resonate at a higher frequency (85). In this treatment, the bundle stiffness is assumed to be constant, but this is likely to be an oversimplification owing to the active bundle movements discussed below.

In the majority of species, passive resonance of the hair bundle probably contributes little to cochlear frequency selectivity. The resonant frequencies estimated from Equation 1 are inappropriately high (82, 86), and the predicted resonance is likely to be over-damped. A further limitation is that the bundles do not vibrate independently but are usually coupled laterally and longitudinally via attachments to an acellular tectorial membrane that carpets the entire papillar surface. Exceptions to this rule are found in several lizard species (87), where the basilar papilla is subdivided into regions with distinct morphologies. In one region, the hair bundles are connected to a continuous tectorial membrane in an arrangement common to most other vertebrates. In a second region, either the tectorial membrane is absent or there are a series of specialized tectorial structures, the sallets, each attached to only a small cohort of hair bundles. In the alligator lizard *Gerrhonotus multicarinatus*, cells in the high-frequency region of the papilla possess very long, free-standing bundles with no connection to a tectorial membrane (76). Both theoretical analysis (85, 88) and direct experimental observations (89, 90) indicate that the bundle resonance provides some frequency tuning. The bundle heights decrease from 30 to 12 μm in conjunction with an increase in characteristic frequency from 1 to 4 kHz, a correlation that is in good agreement with Equation 1 (85).

A sharply tuned passive resonance can also be achieved by employing shorter stereocilia but increasing the mass loading of the bundles with tectorial sallets coupled to a row of about ten hair bundles. This organization has been described and modeled in both the bobtail lizard *Tiliqua rugosa* (91) and the Tokay gecko *Gekko gecko* (92). For example, in the gecko, a gradient in hair bundle height from 16 to 5 μm (80) combined with the mass of tectorial sallets produces a passive resonance predicted to tune the hair cells to frequencies from 1 to 5 kHz. Both the free-standing bundles and sallet-loaded bundles are specializations that may have evolved to expand the high-frequency range of the hearing organ up to about 5 kHz. For these lizard species, there is an additional portion of the basilar papilla possessing a conventional tectorial canopy and receptor cells tuned to lower frequencies; in the gecko, hair cells in this portion probably employ an electrical tuning mechanism to encode frequencies from 0.15 to 0.8 kHz. (93).

There is at most a 5-fold variation in bundle height in a given cochlea, which (from Equation 1) yields only a 11-fold change in the passive resonant frequency. Without assuming variations in other factors, such as stereociliary rotational stiffness or tectorial mass loading, changes in bundle height are inadequate to explain the wide frequency range of most cochleae. What role then does the ubiquitous tonotopic variation in bundle structure play? One simple consequence of reducing bundle height and increasing stereociliary number at high frequencies will be to enhance the sensitivity of transduction. A given motion of the tectorial membrane will cause shorter bundles to undergo a larger angular rotation. When this factor is combined with the larger transducer current (from increases in numbers of both stereocilia and transducer channels per stereocilium; 94), it can, in theory, generate in the turtle a 10-fold increase in the sensitivity of transduction at high frequencies.

Transducer Currents and Adaptation

To examine other tuning processes intrinsic to the hair bundle, it is first necessary to document the properties of the transduction mechanism. Performance of the transducer channels has been assessed either by measuring extracellular microphonic currents (95, 96) or by recording transducer currents in isolated voltage-clamped hair cells (97–100) during manipulation of the hair bundle. Both methods have demonstrated that the channels respond maximally for bundle rotations of $\pm 5^\circ$ (equivalent to ± 0.5 μm deflection at the tip of a 6 μm bundle). The channels activate with time constants on the order of 0.1 ms at room temperature (95, 99), but in response to a maintained stimulus, they close again because of an adaptation process that resets the bundle's operating range. Depending on the measurement conditions and preparation, the adaptation time constant can range from 0.3 ms to more than 30 ms (94–96, 99, 101). Transduction in solitary hair cells is often compromised by mechanical damage incurred during the isolation procedure. Such damage can be minimized by patch-clamping hair cells in an intact cochlear epithelium (102), where larger currents and faster adaptation are observed. When this approach was applied to the turtle cochlea, the properties of the transducer current were found to vary with hair cell position along the tonotopic axis (94). In progressing from the low-frequency to the high-frequency end of the cochlea, the maximum transducer current increased more than fivefold and the time constant of adaptation decreased nearly tenfold. The turtle basilar papilla exhibits trends in hair bundle morphology similar to those described elsewhere (7), with a halving in bundle height (10 to 5 μm) and an approximate doubling in stereociliary number (50 to 90) in high-frequency hair cells compared with low-frequency hair cells. Variation in the number of stereocilia is insufficient alone to explain the gradient in the transducer current, and a change in the number of transducer channels per stereocilium must also be assumed (94). An increase in number of transducer channels per stereocilium will result in a larger Ca^{2+} influx that may partly account for the acceleration of adaptation in high frequency hair cells (see below).

The systematic variation in adaptation time constant along the cochlea (Figure 4) from 4 ms to less than 0.5 ms suggests that adaptation contributes to hair cell frequency selectivity. Dissection of the hair cell's acoustic tuning curve in the turtle cochlea (12) revealed that, apart from the major component endowed by the electrical resonance, there was a residual low-pass filter attributed to the middle ear mechanics and a single-pole high-pass filter of unknown origin. The high-pass filter varied from 29 to 350 Hz and was roughly scaled with the hair cell's characteristic frequency. A similar high-pass filter range was inferred from tuning curves during efferent stimulation that nullifies the electrical resonance (103). A variation in the time constant of transducer adaptation could account for this filter (94). The smooth curve in Figure 4 was calculated on the assumption that transducer adaptation contributes a high-pass filter with a 3 dB corner frequency of 0.7 of the cell's characteristic frequency. It should be emphasized that the absolute values of the time constant will vary

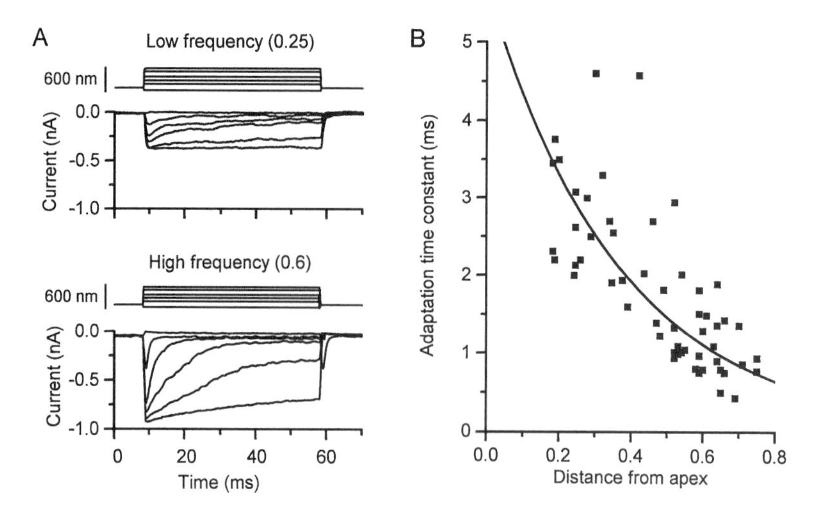

Figure 4 (*a*) Families of transducer currents from two hair cells near the low-frequency end (*top*) and high-frequency end of the turtle basilar papilla (*bottom*). Numbers in parentheses denote hair cell position as the fractional distance, d (0 to 1), from the low-frequency apical end. Note the currents in the high-frequency cell are larger and, for small stimuli, adapt more rapidly. Traces above current records represent deflections of the hair bundle. Holding potential −90 mV, intracellular Ca^{2+} buffer, 1 mM BAPTA. (*b*) Adaptation time constants, τ_a, of 53 cells against fractional distance of a cell from the low-frequency (apical) end of cochlea. *Smooth curve* was calculated on the assumption that adaptation contributes a high-pass filter with a 3 dB corner frequency of 0.7 of the cell's resonant frequency (F_o). The time constant of adaptation, τ_a, in milliseconds, is related to F_o and, assuming an exponential frequency map (32), to d, the fractional distance along the cochlea from the low-frequency end by $\tau_a = 1000/1.4\,\pi F_o = 5.68\,\exp(d/0.37)$.

to some extent depending on the external Ca^{2+} concentration and the intracellular Ca^{2+} buffer (94, 104), but nevertheless, the relative range is approximately correct.

The mechanism of transducer adaptation is still incompletely understood, but it is generally agreed to be regulated by changes in stereociliary Ca^{2+} concentration following influx of the divalent ion through open transducer channels (94, 98, 99, 105). The change in Ca^{2+} then resets the range of displacements detected by the channel. One mechanism by which this resetting might be accomplished entails a myosin motor connected to both the transducer channel and the actin cytoskeleton of the stereocilium (106). Ca^{2+} influx is postulated to inhibit the actomyosin interaction, causing the channel to slip down the side-wall of the stereocilium and thereby reduce the extension in the tip-link. Circumstantial evidence in support of this motor hypothesis includes the demonstration that myosin 1β is present near the tips of the stereocilia in frog saccular hair cells (107). In addition, adaptation is blocked by ADPβS (108) and by various phosphate analogs (109) that interfere with myosin ATPases. However, it should be stressed that all such agents also inhibit the Ca ATPases responsible for Ca^{2+} extrusion from hair cells (110, 111) and thus affect the stereociliary Ca^{2+}. Whether such an actomyosin interaction is rapid enough to account for the fastest adaptation time constants observed in turtle hair cells (<0.5 ms) is also presently unclear, and a more direct action of Ca^{2+} on the transducer channel may be required. Nevertheless, the scheme whereby the transducer channels are under negative feedback control is widely accepted.

Feedback Control and Tuning of the Transducer Current

Feedback control of the transducer channels arises because the transducer current is a function of the difference between the external stimulus and an internal set position for the channel determined by the level of intracellular free Ca^{2+}. As the transducer channels open during bundle deflection, Ca^{2+} enters the stereocilia and triggers adaptation, which acts to close the channels. As with other negative feedback systems, the transducer current may be tuned under certain conditions. Such tuning has been observed in turtle hair cells and is manifested as an under-damped oscillation of the voltage-clamped transducer current for small positive displacements. Resonant frequencies of 58 to 230 Hz have been measured (104). Whether adaptation displays an over-damped exponential decay or an under-damped oscillation depends on a variety of experimental factors including the magnitude of the transducer current, the intracellular Ca^{2+} buffering, and the external Ca^{2+} concentration. The resonance will occur at a frequency related to the rate of opening of the transducer channels and the speed of the adaptive feedback. It should be noted that this resonance in the transducer current does not require an active motor to produce the feedback. However, if the change in the channel's set point is achieved by a motor (101), then a mechanical output may be generated.

A useful analogy can be drawn between active transducer feedback and the electrical resonance. The passive electrical properties of the hair cell membrane, resulting from a leak resistance and a membrane capacitance, provide only a low-pass filter, but the addition of negative feedback by voltage-dependent activation of K^+ channels can generate a sharply tuned resonance. In a similar manner, a displacement-sensitive feedback on the transducer channels could generate a sharply tuned transducer current.

Active Hair Bundle Movements

Active movements of the hair bundles have been described in a number of lower vertebrate preparations. Such movements were manifested as spontaneous fluctuations in bundle position (82, 112–114), nonlinear responses to force steps (82, 112, 115), and motion evoked by intracellular current injection (82, 98, 101, 113, 116). The motion is regarded as active because its amplitude, ranging from 5 to 100 nm, exceeds that expected for the Brownian motion of a passive resonator (82). Whether the assorted observations reflect a single underlying mechanism is unclear.

In addressing the mechanism of the bundle motor, the experimental phenomenon may be categorized according to the speed of the active process. Some movements, epitomized by the responses to current injection reported by Assad & Corey (101), take place over 100 ms or more. This time course is correlated with that of transducer adaptation in bullfrog saccular hair cells and appears sufficiently slow to be mediated by the myosin motor detailed above. In contrast, some active movements occur on a millisecond time scale (82, 112) and have been referred to as rapid twitches (115) to distinguish them from the slower manifestations of adaptation. The faster motion may underlie the fast adaptation rates recently described in turtle hair cells (94).

A unifying hypothesis is that there are two Ca^{2+}-dependent processes to channel regulation, both of which could potentially involve myosin. In the slower component, myosin ratchets up and down the core of the stereocilium, detaching from and reattaching to the actin cytoskeleton and ferrying the channel with it in order to adjust the tension on the tip-links (106). In the faster component, there is a modulation of the transducer channel (99, 100) mediated either directly by an interaction of Ca^{2+} with the channel protein, or indirectly via myosin, which merely rocks back and forth without detachment from the actin cytoskeleton (106). Evidence that the hair cells are capable of creating a significant active force-output, even in lower vertebrates, is provided by the observations of spontaneous otoacoustic emissions. An especially compelling example was recently reported in the lizard *Anolis sagrei* (117), where the otoacoustic emissions were related to the number of hair cell generators in the high-frequency portion of the basilar papilla. In some other lizards and in some birds, the spontaneous otoacoustic emissions also appear to be confined to a frequency range corresponding to the high-frequency region of the papilla (118).

The role of active mechanical feedback in the tuning of individual hair cells is still poorly defined and remains an area for future exploration. How and where might it be employed? The obvious site for such a mechanism would be at high frequencies, where electrical tuning may have been abandoned because of the inordinately high densities and fast kinetics of K^+ channels required to achieve tuning at such frequencies (24). In lower vertebrates, electrical tuning seems adequate to explain auditory frequency selectivity at frequencies below 1 kHz. Avian cochleae utilize electrical resonance (19) and contain two types of hair cell (119), each arranged in multiple rows: a columnar inner hair cell (the tall cells) along the edge of the basilar membrane that receives the majority of the afferent innervation, and a flattened outer hair cell (the short hair cell) situated toward the center of the basilar membrane and innervated predominantly by efferent neurons (see color insert C1, Figure 3, at back of volume). This arrangement is striking in that it resembles the mammalian organization.

Although the role of the avian short outer hair cells is not established, it is tempting to suppose that, by analogy with their mammalian counterparts, they perform a motor function supplying tuned energy into the vibration of the cochlear partition, which itself displays some mechanical tuning (120). Because the cell bodies of the short hair cells are anchored to supporting cells in the basilar papilla, they can deliver force only via hair bundle motion. This movement in the short hair cells would be transmitted to the tall hair cells on the neural limbus via the overlying tectorial membrane. The proportion of short outer hair cells increases toward the basal end of the cochlea, consistent with their being used to extend the high-frequency range. The potential motor role of the short hair cells is an important area for future investigation.

Electromechanical Behavior in Mammalian Outer Hair Cells

The auditory frequency range in submammalian vertebrates rarely exceeds about 5 kHz, but in the evolution of the mammalian hearing organ, this range has been extended by an order of magnitude with the acquisition of new tuning mechanisms. The main morphological innovations are a modification of the middle ear structure, an increase in the length of the basilar membrane, and the specialization of cell types, both supporting and sensory, within the organ of Corti. This specialization includes a separation of the hair cells into two subtypes: a single row of inner hair cells through which most of the auditory information is funneled to the auditory nerve fibers, and three or four rows of long cylindrical outer hair cells with a conspicuous efferent but sparse afferent innervation. Each hair cell type has distinctive response properties (121–123) and makes a differential contribution to the cochlea's sensitivity and frequency selectivity (124). The elongated basilar membrane supports a traveling wave, with a maximum amplitude that moves systematically from apex to base with an increase in stimulation frequency (4). The basilar membrane thus possesses sharp mechanical tuning (125, 126), but as with other frequency-selective mechanisms, the tuning has both passive and active components. The passive component stems mainly from a gradient in the mechanical compliance of the cochlear partition (4). The amplitude of vibration and frequency selectivity are then augmented by active mechanical feedback from the outer hair cells, which generate forces predicted to cancel the viscous damping of the cochlear partition (127, 128).

The current notion of force generation by the outer hair cells involves their contracting longitudinally like miniature muscle fibers (129, 130). The contractions are fast and voltage-controlled – depolarization inducing cell shortening and hyperpolarization causing elongation. The molecular basis of the mechanism is thought to be a voltage-sensitive motor protein embedded at high densities in the lateral wall of the hair cell (131). Reorientation of the protein in the membrane field, which is envisioned to alter the area per molecule, has been followed by monitoring the associated charge movements (132, 133). Conformational changes in the motor protein are thought to change the surface area of the membrane thus altering the cell length at constant volume. Most of the characterization of outer hair cells has been performed on isolated cells, but in the organ of Corti these cells are constrained by apical attachments to the reticular lamina and by basal connections to Deiters cells. Evidence that outer hair cells can generate sufficient force to deform the organ of Corti is provided by the observation that current passed across the cochlear partition results in basilar membrane movements of tens of nanometers (134).

As with the active hair bundle movements discussed above, the mechanical output frequency is a function of the kinetics of the transducer channels and the speed of the motor. The motor appears to operate up to at least 25 kHz (135) and therefore may not be rate-limiting. However, because the process is voltage-controlled, it is also limited by the membrane time constant, which attentuates the receptor potential at high frequencies. The time constant is the product of the cell capacitance, C, and the input resistance, R, which is dominated by voltage-dependent K^+ conductances. At least two major types of K^+ channel contribute: (*a*) a high-threshold channel activated at membrane potentials positive to −35 mV and blocked by 0.1 mM 4-aminopyridine; and (*b*) a low-threshold channel activated between −90 and −50 mV, the identity of which is obscure (136–138). Some evidence also suggests the presence of a Ca^{2+}-activated K^+ channel similar to that found in lower vertebrate hair cells (136, 139).

It is clear that there are cochlear gradients both in the outer hair cell's membrane capacitance (from systematic changes in cell length), and in its complement of K^+ channels. Even the K^+ channel types are differentially expressed, with the high-threshold channel confined to the apical turn of the cochlea and the low-threshold channel predominating in the basal turns (138). Up to a fivefold reduction in cell capacitance from the low- to high-frequency end of the cochlea is accompanied by a severalfold decrease in input resistance (136, 138, 140). Consequently, the cell time constant of high-frequency outer hair cells is an order of magnitude faster than that of low-frequency cells. This is an appropriate trend for minimizing the high-frequency attenuation of the receptor potentials that are required to drive the motor on a cycle by cycle basis. However, absolute values of the time constant have so far yielded equivalent corner frequencies ($F_c = 1/2\pi RC$) of no more than ~1 kHz (138, 140, 141). These time constants present a significant rate-limiting step in the electromechanical feedback loop. The roll-off in sensitivity caused by the membrane time constant may be partially compensated if the magnitude of the transducer current increases in outer hair cells tuned to higher frequencies in mammals as it does in turtle (94).

The contractile behavior of the outer hair cells is a striking mammalian adaptation with properties appropriate for its presumed role as the cochlear amplifier. Owing to its robustness and relative insensitivity to cell metabolism or temperature (142), it has been fairly easy to study. In contrast, elucidating the mechanism and role of active hair bundle movements, which for their manifestation rely on proper functioning of the transduction mechanism, has proved difficult. Nevertheless, it remains a possibility that such bundle movements contribute to mechanical feedback especially at high frequencies. The calcium-dependent feedback described above is likely to be driven by transducer current and therefore is not constrained by the cell membrane time constant. Moreover, the apparent fragility of the hair bundle motor resembles that of the basilar membrane tuning, which is sensitive to the slightest mechanical or metabolic insult to the cochlea and rapidly deteriorates even in the best experimental preparations (e.g. 125). Such vulnerability is most likely located in the mechanoelectrical transduction mechanism. The importance of a fully functional transducer in cochlear mechanics is indicated by the effects of treatment with the diuretic furosemide. The main short-term action of furosemide is to reduce the endolymphatic potential, but this results in removal of the sharp tips of both neural and mechanical tuning curves (143, 144). Loss of the endolymphatic potential will reduce the electrical driving force across the stereociliary membrane from 150 to 70 mV, thus roughly halving the transducer current. This argues that the mechanical feedback is strongly sensitive to the gain of the mechanoelectrical transduction mechanism. Future experiments should seek to distinguish between the contribution of the transducer and of outer hair cell contractility in generating the active component of basilar membrane tuning.

CONCLUSIONS

The evolution of the auditory receptor is worth summarizing because it may illuminate the limitations of the various mechanisms for frequency selectivity and provide insight into the cellular processes employed in higher vertebrates. The turtle, which has been extensively studied, relies almost exclusively on electrical tuning of the hair cells, perhaps supplemented with active bundle movements driven by a tuned transducer current. The turtle is close to the primitive vertebrate condition, and in more evolutionarily recent amphibians and reptiles there has been an attempt to extend the upper frequency limit by introduction of various additional mechanisms. An increase in the high-frequency range may stem from selective pressure to improve sound localization in animals with small heads. Frogs possess both a low-frequency amphibian papilla, composed of hair cells endowed with an electrical tuning mechanism, and an organ unique to amphibians that is tuned to the major frequency components of the mating call (1–3 kHz) (145). In lizards, the low-frequency range may also be served by electrical tuning, but in some species the upper frequency limit has been extended to 5 kHz (at room temperature) by use of a secondary papillar region with distinct morphology that utilizes passive mechanical tuning of the hair bundle. These developments would argue that electrical tuning, as described in the turtle, can not be used above about 1 kHz. This may reflect limitations on both the achievable densities and kinetics of the BK channels.

Birds also employ electrical tuning, mediated by either Ca^{2+}-dependent or voltage-activated K^+ channels. The frequency range is partly expanded by elevated temperature, which raises the electrical resonant frequency with a Q_{10} of 2 (146). However, birds also possess other innovations that include a division of labor by inner and outer hair cells and a basilar membrane with some mechanical tuning. The simplest hypothesis is that this mechanical tuning is supplemented by electromechanical feedback from the short (outer) hair cells. Owing to the anchoring of the short hair cells in the basilar papilla, this feedback must be mediated via active hair bundle motion–perhaps transmitted through the tectorial membrane. The upper frequency limit attained is approximately 5 to 10 kHz. The developments found in birds are exaggerated in mammals that utilize a novel electromechanical feedback, by somatic contractions of the outer hair cells, to sharpen the passive mechanical tuning of the basilar membrane. There is no evidence that mammals employ electrical tuning over any frequency range (123, 147), and it may be that the active electromechanical output of the hair bundle also has intrinsic frequency limitations. This question may be settled only by more detailed studies of mammalian cochlear hair cells to investigate their ionic conductances and mechanoelectrical transduction mechanism.

ACKNOWLEDGMENTS

Authors' laboratories are supported by NIDCD DC 01362 (RF) and DC 00276, DC 01508 (PF). We thank D Geisler, P Gillespie, M Gray-Keller, G Jones, A Ricci, E Young, and M Zidanic for suggestions on the manuscript, and G Jones and C Dizack for help with the figures.

Literature Cited

1. Musicant AD, Chan JCK, Hind JE. 1990. Direction-dependent spectral properties of cat external ear: new data and cross-species comparisons. *J. Acoust Soc. Am.* 87:757–81
2. Rice JJ, May BJ, Spirou GA, Young ED. 1992. Pinna-based spectral cues for sound localization in the cat. *Hear. Res.* 58:132–52
3. Webster DB, Fay RR, Popper AN, eds. 1992. *The Evolutionary Biology of Hearing*. New York: Springer-Verlag
4. von Békésy G. 1960. *Experiments in Hearing*, New York: McGraw-Hill
5. Patuzzi R. 1996. Cochlear micromechanics and macromechanics. In *Springer Handbook of Auditory Research. The Cochlea*, ed. P Dallos, AN Popper, RR Fay, 8:186-257. New York: Springer-Verlag
6. Sneary MG. 1988. Auditory receptor of the red-eared turtle: general ultrastructure. *J. Comp. Neurol.* 276:573–87
7. Hackney CM, Fettiplace R, Furness DN. 1993. The functional morphology of stereociliary bundles on turtle cochlear hair cells. *Hear. Res.* 69:163–75
8. O'Neill MP, Bearden A. 1995. Laser feedback measurements of turtle basilar membrane motion using direct reflection. *Hear. Res.* 84:125–38
9. Fettiplace R, Crawford AC. 1978. The coding of sound pressure and frequency in cochlear hair cells of the terrapin. *Proc. R. Soc. London Ser. B* 203:209–18
10. Crawford AC, Fettiplace R. 1980. The frequency selectivity of auditory nerve fibers and hair cells in the cochlea of the turtle. *J. Physiol.* 306:79–125
11. Patterson WC. 1966. Hearing in the turtle. *J. Aud. Res.* 6:453–64
12. Crawford AC, Fettiplace R. 1981. An electrical tuning mechanism in turtle cochlear hair cells. *J. Physiol.* 312:377–412
13. Crawford AC, Fettiplace R. 1983. Auditory nerve responses to imposed displacements of the basilar membrane. *Hear. Res.* 12:199–208
14. Sugihara I, Furukawa T. 1989. Morphological and functional aspects of two different types of hair cells in the goldfish sacculus. *J. Neurophysiol.* 62:1330–43
15. Steinacker A, Romero A. 1992. Voltage-gated potassium current and resonance in toadfish saccular hair cells. *Brain Res.* 574:229–36
16. Ashmore JF. 1983. Frequency tuning in a frog vestibular organ. *Nature* 304:536–38
17. Lewis RS, Hudspeth AJ. 1983. Voltage- and ion-dependent conductances in solitary vertebrate hair cells. *Nature* 304:538–41
18. Fuchs PA, Evans MG. 1988. Voltage oscillations and ionic conductances in hair cells isolated from the alligator cochlea. *J. Comp. Physiol.* 164:151–63
19. Fuchs PA, Nagai T. Evans MG. 1988. Electrical tuning in hair cells isolated from the chick cochlea. *J. Neurosci.* 8: 2460–67
20. Hudspeth AJ, Lewis RS. 1988. Kinetic analysis of voltage- and ion-dependent conductances in saccular hair cells of the bullfrog, *Rana catesbeiana*. *J. Physiol.* 400:237–74
21. Hudspeth AJ, Lewis RS. 1988. A model for electrical resonance and frequency tuning in saccular hair cells of the bullfrog, *Rana catesbeiana*. *J. Physiol.* 400: 275–97
22. Art JJ, Fettiplace R. 1987. Variation of membrane properties in hair cells isolated from the turtle cochlea. *J. Physiol.* 385:207–42
23. Art JJ, Wu YC, Fettiplace R. 1995. The calcium-activated potassium channels of turtle hair cells. *J. Gen. Physiol.* 105:49–72
24. Wu YC, Art JJ, Goodman MB, Fettiplace R. 1995. A kinetic description of the calcium-activated potassium channel and its application to electrical tuning of hair cells. *Prog. Biophys. Mol. Biol.* 63:131–58
25. Ohmori H. 1984. Studies of ionic currents in the isolated vestibular hair cell of the chick. *J. Physiol.* 350:561–81
26. Fuchs PA, Evans MG, Murrow BW. 1990. Calcium current in hair cells isolated from the cochlea of the chick. *J. Physiol.* 429:553–68
27. Roberts WM, Jacobs RA, Hudspeth AJ. 1990. Co-localization of ion channels involved in frequency selectivity and synaptic transmission at presynaptic active zones of hair cells. *J. Neurosci.* 10:3664–84
28. Prigioni I, Masetto S, Russo G, Taglietti V. 1992. Calcium currents in solitary hair cells isolated from frog crista ampullaris. *J. Vestibular Res.* 2:31–9
29. Zidanic M, Fuchs PA. 1995. Kinetic analysis of barium currents in chick cochlear hair cells. *Biophys. J.* 68:1323–36
30. Kollmar R, Montgomery LG, Fak J,

Henry LJ, Hudspeth AJ. 1998. Predominance of the α_{1D} subunit in L-type voltage-gated Ca^{2+} channels of hair cells in the chicken's cochlea. *Proc. Natl. Acad. Sci. USA* 94:14883–88

31. Art JJ, Fettiplace R, Wu Y-C. 1993. The effects of low calcium on the voltage-dependent conductances involved in the tuning of turtle hair cells. *J. Physiol.* 470:109–26
32. Wu Y-C, Fettiplace R. 1996. A developmental model for generating frequency maps in the reptilian and avian cochleas. *Biophys. J.* 70:2557–70
33. Atkinson NS, Robertson GA, Ganetzky B. 1991. A component of calcium-activated potassium channels encoded by the *Drosophila slo* locus. *Science* 253:551–55
34. Adelman JP, Shen K-Z, Kavanaugh MP, Warren RA, Wu Y-N, et al. 1992. Calcium-activated potassium channels expressed from cloned complementary DNAs. *Neuron* 9:209–16
35. Butler A, Tsunoda S, McCobb DP, Wei A, Salkoff L. 1993. *mslo*, a complex mouse gene encoding "maxi" calcium-activated potassium channels. *Science* 261:221–24
36. Tseng-Crank J, Foster CD, Krause JD, Mertz R, Godinot N, et al. 1994. Cloning, expression and distribution of functionally distinct Ca^{2+}-activated K^+ channel isoforms from human brain. *Neuron* 13:1315–30
37. McCobb DP, Fowler NL, Featherstone T, Lingle CJ, Saito M, et al. 1995. A human calcium-activated potassium channel gene expressed in vascular smooth muscle. *Am. J. Physiol.* 269:H767–77
38. Jiang G-J, Zidanic M, Michaels R, Michael T, Griguer C, Fuchs PA. 1997. *cslo* encodes Ca^{2+}-activated potassium channels in the chick's cochlea. *Proc. R. Soc. London Ser. B* 264:731–37
39. Jones EMC, Laus C, Fettiplace R. 1998. Identification of Ca^{2+}-activated K^+ channel splice variants and their distribution in the turtle cochlea. *Proc. R. Soc. London Ser. B* 265:685–92
40. Navaratnam DS, Bell TJ, Tu TD, Cohen EL, Oberholtzer JC. 1997. Differential distribution of Ca^{2+}-activated K^+ channel splice variants among hair cells along the tonotopic axis of the chick cochlea. *Neuron* 19:1077–85
41. Rosenblatt KP, Sun Z-P, Heller S, Hudspeth AJ. 1997. Distribution of Ca^{2+}-activated K^+ channel isoforms along the tonotopic gradient of the chicken's cochlea. *Neuron* 19:1061–75
42. Meera P, Wallner M, Song M, Toro L. 1997. Large conductance voltage- and Ca^{2+}-activated K^+ channel, a distinct member of voltage-dependent ion channels with seven N-terminal transmembrane segments (S0–S6), an extracellular N-terminus and an intracellular (S9–S10) C-terminus. *Proc. Natl. Acad. Sci. USA* 94:14066–71
43. Wei A, Solaro C, Lingle C, Salkoff L. 1994. Calcium sensitivity of BK-type K_{Ca} channels determined by a separable domain. *Neuron* 13:671–81
44. Lagrutta A, Shen K-Z, North RA, Adelman JP. 1994. Functional differences among alternatively spliced variants of Slowpoke, a *Drosophila* calcium-activated potassium channel. *J. Biol. Chem.* 269:20347–51
45. Saito M, Nelson C, Salkoff L, Lingle CJ. 1997. A cysteine-rich domain defined by a novel exon in a *slo* variant in rat adrenal chromaffin cells and PC12 cells. *J. Biol. Chem.* 272:11710–17
46. Michael T, Ramanathan K, Jones EMC, Art JJ, Fettiplace R, Fuchs PA. 1997. Functional expression of cochlear Slo potassium channels in HEK293 cells and *Xenopus* oocytes. *Biophys. J.* 72:A352 (Abstr.)
47. Xie J, McCobb DP. 1998. Control of alternative splicing of potassium channels by stress hormones. *Science* 280:443–46
48. Michael T, Jiang G-J, Ramanathan K, Fuchs PA. 1998. BK channels encoded by cSlo splice variants from the chick's cochlea. *Assoc. Res. Otolarnygol.* 21:82 (Abstr.)
49. Jones EMC, Gray-Keller M, Art JJ, Fettiplace R. 1998. The functional role of alternative splicing of Ca^{2+}-activated K^+ channels in auditory hair cells. In *Molecular and Functional Diversity of Ion Channels and Receptors*, ed. B Rudy, P Seeburg. New York: Ann. NY Acad. Sci. In press
50. McManus OB, Helms LM, Pallanck L, Ganetzky B, Swanson R, Leonard RJ. 1995. Functional role of β-subunit of high-conductance calcium-activated potassium channels. *Neuron* 14:645–50
51. Ramanathan K, Michael T, Jiang G-J, Hiel H, Fuchs PA. 1998. A molecular mechanism for electrical tuning of cochlear hair cells. *Science.* In press
52. Fuchs PA, Evans MG. 1990. Potassium currents in hair cells isolated from the cochlea of the chick. *J. Physiol.* 429:529–51
53. Evans MG, Fuchs PA. 1987. Tetrodotoxin-sensitive voltage-dependent sodi-

um currents in hair cells from the alligator cochlea. *Biophys. J.* 52:649–52
54. Goodman M, Art JJ. 1996. Variations in the ensemble of potassium currents underlying resonance in turtle hair cells. *J. Physiol.* 497:395–412
55. Goodman M, Art JJ. 1996. Positive feedback by a potassium selective inward rectifier enhances tuning in vertebrate hair cells. *Biophys. J.* 71:430–42
56. Navaratnam DS, Escobar L, Covarrubias M, Oberholtzer JC. 1995. Permeation properties and differential expression across the auditory receptor epithelium of an inward rectifier K^+ channel cloned from the chick inner ear. *J. Biol. Chem.* 270:19238–45
57. Issa N, Hudspeth AJ. 1994. Clustering of Ca^{2+} channels and Ca^{2+}-activated K^+ channels at fluorescently labeled presynaptic active zones of hair cells. *Proc. Natl. Acad. Sci. USA* 91:7578–82
58. Robitaille R, Charlton MP. 1992. Presynaptic calcium signals and transmitter release are modulated by calcium-activated potassium channels. *J. Neurosci.* 12:297–305
59. Martinez-Dunst C, Michaels RL, Fuchs PA. 1997. Release sites and calcium channels in hair cells of the chick's cochlea. *J. Neurosci.* 17:9133–44
60. Sneary MG. 1988. Auditory receptor of the red-eared turtle. II. Afferent and efferent synapses and innervation patterns. *J. Comp. Neurol.* 276:588–606
61. Fischer F. 1992. Quantitative analysis of the innervation pattern of the chicken basilar papilla. *Hear. Res.* 61:167–78
62. Murrow BW. 1994. Position-dependent expression of potassium currents by hair cells of the chick's cochlea. *J. Physiol.* 480:247–59
63. Sheng M, Tsaur M-L, Jan YN, Jan LY. 1992. Subcellular segregation of two A-type K^+ channel proteins in rat central neurons. *Neuron* 9:271–84
64. Sokolowski BHA, Stahl L, Fuchs PA. 1993. Morphological and physiological development of vestibular hair cells in the organ-cultured otocyst of the chick. *Dev. Biol.* 155:134–46
65. Hirokawa N. 1977. Disappearance of afferent and efferent nerve terminals in the inner ear of the chick embryo after chronic treatment with beta-bungarotoxin. *J. Cell. Biol.* 73:27–46
66. Fuchs PA, Sokolowski BHA. 1990. The acquisition during development of Ca-activated potassium currents by cochlear hair cells of the chick. *Proc. R. Soc. London Ser. B* 241:122–26
67. Saunders JC, Coles RB, Gates GR. 1973. The development of auditory evoked responses in the cochlea and cochlear nuclei of the chick. *Brain Res.* 63:59–74
68. Jones SM, Jones TA. 1995. The tonotopic map in the embryonic chicken cochlea. *Hear. Res.* 82:149–57
69. Griguer C, Fuchs PA. 1996. Voltage-dependent potassium currents in cochlear hair cells of the embryonic chick. *J. Neurophysiol.* 75:508–13
70. Gu X, Spitzer NC. 1995. Distinct aspects of neuronal differentiation encoded by frequency of spontaneous Ca^{2+} transients. *Nature* 375:784–87
71. Hudspeth AJ. 1982. Extracellular current flow and the site of transduction by vertebrate hair cells. *J. Neurosci.* 2:1–10
72. Jaramillo F, Hudspeth AJ. 1992. Localization of the hair cell's transduction channels at the hair bundle's top by iontophoretic application of a channel blocker. *Neuron* 7:409–20
73. Denk W, Holt JR, Shepherd GMG, Corey DP. 1995. Calcium imaging of single stereocilia in hair cells: localization of transduction channels at both ends of tip links. *Neuron* 15:1311–21
74. Pickles JO, Comis SD, Osborne MP. 1984. Crosslinks between the stereocilia in the guinea pig organ of Corti, and the possible relation to sensory transduction. *Hear. Res.* 15:103–12
75. Assad JA, Shepherd GMG, Corey DP. 1991. Tip-link integrity and mechanical transduction in a vertebrate hair cell. *Neuron* 7:985–94
76. Mulroy MJ. 1974. Cochlear anatomy of the alligator lizard. *Brain Behav. Evol.* 10:69–87
77. Lim DJ. 1980. Cochlear anatomy related to cochlear micromechanics: a review. *J. Acoust. Soc. Am.* 67:1686–95
78. Turner RG, Muraski AA, Nielsen DW. 1981. Cilium length influences on tonotopic organization. *Science* 213:1519–21
79. Tilney LG, Saunders JC. 1983. Actin filaments, stereocilia and hair cells of the bird cochlea. I. Length, width and distribution of stereocilia of each hair cell are related to the position of the hair cell on the cochlea. *J. Cell Biol.* 96:807–21
80. Köppl C, Authier S. 1995. Quantitative anatomical basis for a model of micromechanical tuning in the Tokay gecko, (*Gekko gecko*). *Hear. Res.* 82:14–25
81. Flock A, Flock B, Murray E. 1977. Studies on the sensory hairs of receptor cells in the inner ear. *Acta Otolaryngol.* 83:85–91

82. Crawford AC, Fettiplace R. 1985. The mechanical properties of ciliary bundles of turtle cochlear hair cells. *J. Physiol.* 364:359–79
83. Howard J, Ashmore JF. 1986. Stiffness of sensory hair bundles in the sacculus of the frog. *Hear. Res.* 23:93–104
84. Pickles JO. 1993. A model for the mechanics of the stereociliar bundle on acousticolateral hair cells. *Hear. Res.* 68: 159–72
85. Weiss TF, Leong R. 1985. A model for signal transmission in an ear having hair cells with free-standing stereocilia. III. Micromechanical stage. *Hear. Res.* 20:157–74
86. Strelioff D, Flock A, Minser KE. 1985. Role of inner and outer hair cells in mechanical frequency selectivity of the cochlea. *Hear. Res.* 18:169–75
87. Wever EG. 1978. *The Reptile Ear: Its Structure and Function*. Princeton, NJ: Princeton Univ. Press
88. Freeman DM, Weiss TF. 1990. Hydrodynamic analysis of a two-dimensional model for micromechanical resonance of free-standing hair bundles. *Hear. Res.* 48: 37–68
89. Frishkopf LS, DeRosier DJ. 1983. Mechanical tuning of free-standing stereociliary bundles and frequency analysis in the alligator lizard cochlea. *Hear. Res.* 12: 393–404
90. Holton T, Hudspeth AJ. 1983. A micromechanical contribution to cochlear tuning and tonotopic organization. *Science* 222:508–10
91. Manley GA, Yates GK, Köppl C. 1988. Auditory peripheral tuning: evidence for a simple resonance phenomenon in the lizard *Tiliqua*. *Hear. Res.* 181–90
92. Authier S, Manley GA. 1995. A model of frequency tuning in the basilar papilla of the Tokay gecko, *Gekko gecko*. *Hear. Res.* 82:1–13
93. Eatock RA, Manley GA, Pawson L. 1981. Auditory nerve fibre activity in the Tokay gecko: implications for cochlear processing. *J. Comp. Physiol.* 142:203–18
94. Ricci AJ, Fettiplace R. 1997. The effects of calcium buffering and cyclic AMP on mechano-electrical transduction in turtle auditory hair cells. *J. Physiol.* 501:111–24
95. Corey DP, Hudspeth AJ. 1983. Analysis of the microphonic potentials of the bullfrog sacculus. *J. Neurosci.* 3:942–61
96. Eatock RA, Corey DP, Hudspeth AJ. 1987. Adaptation of mechanoelectrical transduction in hair cells of the bullfrog's sacculus. *J. Neurosci.* 7:2821–36
97. Ohmori H. 1985. Mechano-electrical transduction currents in isolated vestibular hair cells of the chick. *J. Physiol.* 359:189–217
98. Assad JA, Hacohen N, Corey DP. 1989. Voltage dependence of adaptation and active bundle movements in bullfrog saccular hair cells. *Proc. Natl. Acad. Sci. USA* 86:2918–22
99. Crawford AC, Evans MG, Fettiplace R. 1989. Activation and adaptation of transducer currents in turtle hair cells. *J. Physiol.* 419:405–34
100. Crawford AC, Evans MG, Fettiplace R. 1991. The actions of calcium on the mechano-electrical transducer current of turtle hair cells. *J. Physiol.* 434:369–98
101. Assad JA, Corey DP. 1992. An active motor model for adaptation by vertebrate hair cells. *J. Neurosci.* 12:3291–309
102. Kros CJ, Rüsch A, Richardson GP. 1992. Mechano-electrical transducer currents in hair cells of the cultured neonatal mouse. *Proc. R. Soc. London Ser. B* 249:185–93
103. Art JJ, Fettiplace R. 1984. Efferent desensitization of auditory nerve fibre responses in the cochlea of the turtle *Pseudemys scripta elegans*. *J. Physiol.* 356:507–23
104. Ricci AJ, Wu Y-C, Fettiplace R. 1998. The endogenous calcium buffer and the time course of transducer adaptation in turtle auditory hair cells. *J. Neurosci.* 18: 8261–77
105. Ricci AJ, Fettiplace R. 1998. Calcium permeation of the turtle hair cell's mechanotransducer channel and its relation to the composition of endolymph. *J. Physiol.* 506:159–73
106. Hudspeth AJ, Gillespie PG. 1994. Pulling strings to tune transduction. Adaptation by hair cells. *Neuron* 12:1–9
107. Hasson T, Gillespie PG, Garcia JA, MacDonald RB, Zhao Y, et al. 1997. Unconventional myosins in inner-ear sensory epithelia. *J. Cell Biol.* 137:1287–307
108. Gillespie PG, Hudspeth AJ. 1993. Adenine nucleoside diphosphates block adaptation of mechano-electrical transduction in hair cells. *Proc. Natl. Acad. Sci. USA* 90:2710–14
109. Yamoah EN, Gillespie PG. 1996. Phosphate analogs block adaptation by inhibiting adaptation-motor force production. *Neuron* 17:523–33
110. Tucker T, Fettiplace R. 1995. Confocal imaging of calcium microdomains and calcium extrusion in turtle hair cells. *Neuron* 15:1323–35

111. Yamoah EN, Lumpkin EA, Dumont RA, Smith PJS, Hudpseth AJ, Gillespie PG. 1998. Plasma membrane Ca^{2+}-ATPase extrudes Ca^{2+} from hair cell stereocilia. *J. Neurosci.* 18:610–24
112. Howard J, Hudspeth AJ. 1987. Mechanical relaxation of the hair bundle mediates adaptation in mechanoelectrical transduction by the bullfrog's saccular hair cell. *Proc. Natl. Acad. Sci. USA* 84:3064–68
113. Rüsch A, Thurm U. 1990. Spontaneous and electrically induced movements of ampullary kinocilia and sterovilli. *Hear. Res.* 48:247–64
114. Denk W, Webb WW. 1993. Forward and reverse transduction at the limit of sensitivity studied by correlating electrical and mechanical fluctuations in frog saccular hair cells. *Hear. Res.* 60:89–102
115. Benser ME, Marquis RE, Hudspeth AJ. 1996. Rapid, active hair bundle movements in hair cells from the bullfrog's sacculus. *J. Neurosci.* 16:5629–43
116. Brix J, Manley GA. 1994. Mechanical and electromechanical properties of the stereovillar bundles of isolated and cultured hair cells of the chicken. *Hear. Res.* 76:147–57
117. Manley GA, Gallo L. 1997. Otoacoustic emissions, hair cells and myosin motors. *J. Acoust. Soc. Am.* 102:1049–55
118. Köppl C. 1995. Otoacoustic emissions as an indicator for active cochlear mechanics: a primitive property of vertebrate auditory organs. In *Advances in Hearing Research* ed. GA Manley, GM Klump, C Köppl, H Fastl, H Oeckinghaus, pp. 207-16. Singapore: World Sci.
119. Tanaka K, Smith CA. 1978. Structure of the chicken's inner ear: SEM and TEM study. *Am. J. Anat.* 153:251–72
120. Gummer AW, Smolders JWT, Klinke R. 1987. Basilar membrane motion in the pigeon measured with the Mössbauer technique. *Hear. Res.* 29:63–92
121. Dallos P. 1985. Response characteristics of mammalian cochlear hair cells. *J. Neurosci.* 5:1591–608
122. Russell IJ, Cody AR, Richardson GP. 1986. The responses of inner and outer hair cells in the basal turn of the guinea-pig cochlea and in the mouse cochlea grown in vitro. *Hear. Res.* 22:199–216
123. Kros CJ. 1996. Physiology of mammalian cochlear hair cells. In *Springer Handbook of Auditory Research: The Cochlea*, ed. P Dallos, AN Popper, RR Fay. 8:318–85. New York: Springer-Verlag
124. Kiang NYS, Liberman MC, Sewell WF, Guinan JJ. 1986. Single unit clues to cochlear mechanisms. *Hear. Res.* 22:171–82
125. Rhode WS. 1971. Observations on the vibrations of the basilar membrane in squirrel monkeys using the Mössbauer technique. *J. Acoust. Soc. Am.* 49:1218–31
126. Patuzzi R, Robertson D. 1988. Tuning in the mammalian cochlea. *Physiol. Rev.* 68:1009–82
127. de Boer E. 1983. No sharpening? A challenge for cochlear mechanics. *J. Acoust. Soc. Am.* 73:567–73
128. Neely ST, Kim DO. 1983. An active cochlear model shows sharp tuning and high sensitivity. *Hear. Res.* 9:123–30
129. Brownell WE, Bader CR, Bertrand D, de Ribaupierre Y. 1985. Evoked mechanical responses of isolated cochlear outer hair cells. *Science* 227:194–96
130. Ashmore JF. 1987. A fast motile response in guinea-pig outer hair cells: the cellular basis for the cochlear amplifier. *J. Physiol.* 388:323–47
131. Kalinec F, Holley MC, Iwasa KH, Lim DJ, Kachar BA. 1992. A membrane-based force generation mechanism in auditory sensory cells. *Proc. Natl. Acad. Sci. USA* 89:8671–75
132. Santos-Sacchi J. 1991. Reversible inhibition of voltage-dependent outer hair cell motility and capacitance *J. Neurosci.* 11:3096–110
133. Tunstall MJ, Gale JE, Ashmore JF. 1995. Action of salicylate on membrane capacitance of outer hair cells from the guinea-pig cochlea. *J. Physiol.* 485:739–52
134. Mammano F, Ashmore JF. 1993. Reverse transduction measured in the isolated cochlea by laser Michelson interferometry. *Nature* 365:838–41
135. Gale JE, Ashmore JF. 1997. An intrinsic frequency limit to the cochlear amplifier. *Nature* 389:63–66
136. Housley GD, Ashmore JF. 1992. Ionic currents of outer hair cells isolated from the guinea-pig cochlea. *J. Physiol.* 448:73–98
137. Nakagawa T, Kakehata S, Yamamoto T, Akaike N, Komune S, Uemura T. 1994. Ionic properties of $I_{K,n}$ in outer hair cells of guinea pig cochlea. *Brain Res.* 661:293–97
138. Mammano F, Ashmore JF. 1996. Differential expression of outer hair cell potassium currents in the isolated cochlea of the guinea pig. *J. Physiol.* 496:639–46
139. Nenov AP, Norris C, Bobbin RP. 1997. Outwardly rectifying currents in guinea

pig outer hair cells. *Hear. Res.* 105:146–58
140. Preyer P, Renz S, Hemmert W, Zenner H-P, Gummer AW. 1996. Receptor potential of outer hair cells isolated from base to apex of the adult guinea-pig cochlea: implications for cochlear tuning mechanisms. *Aud. Neurosci.* 2:145–57
141. Santos-Sacchi J. 1992. On the frequency limit and phase of outer hair cell motility: effects of the membrane filter. *J. Neurosci.* 12:1906–16
142. Holley MC, Ashmore JF. 1988. On the mechanism of a high-frequency force generator in outer hair cells isolated from the guinea-pig cochlea. *Proc. R. Soc. London Ser. B* 232:413–29
143. Sewell WF. 1984. The effect of furosemide on the endocochlear potential and auditory nerve fiber tuning curves in cats. *Hear. Res.* 14:305–14
144. Ruggero MA, Rich NC. 1991. Furosemide alters organ of Corti mechanics: evidence for feedback of outer hair cells upon basilar membrane. *J. Neurosci.* 11:1057–67
145. Zakon HH, Wilczynski W. 1988. The physiology of the anuran eighth nerve. In *The Evolution of the Amphibian Auditory System*, ed. B Fritzsch, MJ Ryan, W Wilczynski, TE Hetherington, W Walkowiak, pp. 125-55. New York: Wiley
146. Schermuly L, Klinke R. 1985. Changes of characteristic frequency of pigeon primary afferents with temperature. *J. Comp. Physiol. A* 156:209–11
147. Kros CJ, Crawford AC. 1990. Potassium currents in inner hair cells isolated from the guinea-pig cochlea. *J. Physiol.* 421:263–92
148. Wallner M, Meera P, Toro L. 1996. Determinant for β-subunit regulation in high-conductance voltage-activated and Ca^{2+}-sensitive K^+ channels: an additional transmembrane region at the N-terminus. *Proc. Natl. Acad. Sci. USA* 93:14922–27

Annu. Rev. Physiol. 1999. 61:835–56

ION CHANNELS OF NOCICEPTION

Edwin W. McCleskey
Vollum Institute, Oregon Health Sciences University, Portland, Oregon 97201-3098;
e-mail: mccleske@ohsu.edu

Michael S. Gold
Department of Oral and Craniofacial Biological Sciences, University of Maryland–Baltimore Dental School, Baltimore, Maryland 21201;
e-mail: msg001@dental.umaryland.edu

KEY WORDS: pain, sensory neurons, dorsal root ganglia, Na^+ channels, ligand-gated channels

ABSTRACT

Nociceptors are the first cells in the series of neurons that lead to the sensation of pain. The essential functions of nociceptors—transducing noxious stimuli into depolarizations that trigger action potentials, conducting the action potentials from the peripheral sensory site to the synapse in the central nervous system, and converting the action potentials into neurotransmitter release at the presynaptic terminal—all depend on ion channels. This review discusses recent results in the converging fields of nociception and ion channel biology. It focuses on (*a*) the capsaicin receptor and its possible role in thermosensation, (*b*) ATP-gated channels, (*c*) proton-gated channels, and (*d*) nociceptor-specific Na^+ channels.

INTRODUCTION

In their landmark paper, Melzack & Wall (1) presented two opposing theories on the nature of pain: (*a*) the specificity theory, which proposes that pain is a sensation, like vision or hearing, conveyed via unique anatomical structures; and (*b*) the pattern theory, which proposes that pain results from a pattern of intense activity of neurons that also can encode subtle sensations such as warmth or fine touch. The specificity theory arose from the work of a number of investigators, including Charles Sherrington, who postulated the existence of cells specialized to detect noxious events and who coined the term nociceptor to describe these cells (2). Some 50 years after Sherrington, nociceptors with sensory terminals

0066-4278/99/0315-0835$08.00

in skin were demonstrated unequivocally by Burgess & Perl (3) and Bessou & Perl (4). These papers reported a population of sensory neurons that were silent until stimuli were intense enough to threaten or cause tissue damage. In contrast, sensory neurons that detect warmth or fine touch reach maximal firing frequency at stimulation intensities below this noxious threshold and, therefore, cannot by themselves signal the existence of tissue damage.

The modern pursuit of nociception follows several fronts. One front asks the molecular definition of a nociceptor. Do nociceptors have unique ion channels, neuropeptides, growth factor receptors, or signal transduction cascades, as compared with other types of sensory neurons? Alternatively, nociceptors and low-threshold sensory neurons might differ only in the level of expression of the same kinds of molecules. The difference is crucial to the treatment of pain because molecules unique to nociceptors offer targets for pharmacologically suppressing pain without affecting other sensations. A second front asks about the diversity of nociceptors. Nociceptors in skin differ from those in viscera (5), and nociceptors with unmyelinated axons differ from those with myelin (6). A third, and very active, front is plasticity. In response to continued inflammation or nerve damage, nonnoxious stimuli can become painful (for example, the sensation of a warm shower on badly sunburned skin) (7). Nociceptor plasticity contributes to this hyperalgesia, and the interaction of nerve growth factor and nociceptors is crucial (8, 9).

This review considers whether there are ion channels that are unique to nociceptors. The emphasis is on a small handful of putative nociceptive channels for which there has been considerable recent activity: the capsaicin receptor, heat-activated channels, ATP-gated channels, proton-gated channels, and certain voltage-gated Na^+ channels. Other reviews consider additional channels (10, 11). The trend of this research supports the notion of nociceptor-specific ion channels and, thus, encourages the pursuit of ion channels as targets for analgesic therapy.

THE CAPSAICIN RECEPTOR AND TEMPERATURE SENSATION

Capsaicin is the compound in peppers that makes them taste "hot." Small-diameter sensory neurons selectively die after capsaicin injections in newborn rats (12), and topical application of capsaicin is analgesic because it desensitizes the nociceptive sensory terminal (13). Because of the therapeutic potential, understanding the molecular basis of capsaicin action has been a major goal for pain research. That goal has now been reached, by Caterina et al, who successfully cloned the receptor using a novel expression strategy (14). This landmark paper demonstrates that the receptor is a channel that is gated by noxious heat.

Because a vanilloid moiety is the common feature of capsaicin and resiniferatoxin (a particularly potent ligand of the receptor), the cloned receptor is called VR1, the first vanilloid receptor. The nucleotide sequence of VR1 predicts a protein of 838 amino acids with a molecular weight of 95,000. The predicted topological organization consists of six transmembrane domains with a hydrophobic loop between the fifth and sixth domain. Noticeable sequence homology exists between VR1 and transient receptor potential (TRP) channels, but the significance of this is unclear. Much of the homology is in ankyrin repeats near the amino terminus, so it may only indicate a common mechanism for cellular localization.

When expressed in either frog oocytes or a mammalian cell line, VR1 has the appropriate pharmacological properties: activation by either capsaicin or resiniferatoxin and block by the competitive antagonist, capsazepine, and by the noncompetitive antagonist, ruthenium red. The pore of VR1 is about ten times more permeable to Ca^{2+} than to monovalent cations. Ca^{2+} overload likely accounts for the cell death seen upon chronic exposure to capsaicin.

Much of the interest in the capsaicin receptor arises from the presumption that it has an endogenous physiological stimulus. Two results suggested that noxious heat might be the stimulus: (*a*) In skin-nerve preparations, nociceptors that respond to heat also respond to capsaicin, whereas nociceptors that respond only to mechanical stimuli are insensitive to capsaicin (15); and (*b*) in dissociated sensory neurons, there is an unequivocal overlap between the populations of cells exhibiting heat-evoked current (see below) and those exhibiting capsaicin-evoked current (16). Another theory proposed that acid is the endogenous activator of the capsaicin receptor (17). This would be relevant to pain caused by ischemia, inflammation, and infection—conditions that all drop extracellular pH in the affected tissue. Results with heterologously expressed VR1 partially support both hypotheses. Caterina et al (14) show that temperatures above 40°C, which are noxious when applied to the skin, activate VR1 and that the effect is blocked by ruthenium red. On the other hand, protons do not activate VR1, but they modulate it: The response to a submaximal dose of capsaicin can be greatly enhanced at pH 6.3. Thus, it appears that VR1 may play a central role in thermosensation while also contributing to the nociceptive response to tissue acidity.

A year prior to the cloning of VR1, a heat-sensitive ion channel was discovered on sensory neurons (18). This channel is opened by noxious temperatures (>42°C) and is present on about 50% of small sensory neurons but not large ones. It is absent in sympathetic neurons (19). The channel is modulated by bradykinin (18) and by prostaglandin E_2 (19), two compounds that are released during inflammation. Is this channel the same as VR1? In support of this notion, Kirschstein et al (16) show that heat-evoked currents and capsaicin-evoked currents appear on nearly identical subsets of sensory neurons and that prior capsaicin enhances responses to a heat stimulus. In conflict, Reichling & Levine (19) report that the heat-evoked current is not blocked by ruthenium red or capsazepine, as is VR1. Also, there is a quantitative discrepancy between the reported Ca^{2+} permeability (P) of VR1 (P_{Ca}:P_{Na} = 9.6) (14) and the heat-evoked current (P_{Ca}:P_{Na} = 0.78) (18). Given these conflicts, it is premature to conclude that VR1 is the heat-sensitive ion channel.

Capsaicin evokes several currents that differ in kinetics and pharmacology, including sensitivity to capsazepine (20). Thus, VR1 will likely be one of a variety of related channels. There also appear to be differences between the heat-evoked currents reported by different laboratories. Understanding the molecular variety and the relations between the capsaicin- and heat-evoked currents will likely be the critical step in understanding how we sense warm temperatures. This field will progress rapidly in the next few years.

ATP-GATED ION CHANNELS

The recent molecular characterization of ATP-gated ion channels has resurrected interest in the role of extracellular ATP in pain. The subject traces to the mid-1970s, when Bleehen & Keele (21) proposed that ATP released from damaged cells contributes to pain caused by tissue damage. Two types of experiments suggested the hypothesis. First, ATP applied to blisters causes pain (21). Second, and more interesting, fractions of cell cytosol caused pain when applied to blisters (22). Most fractions had no effect, but the fractions that caused pain were those enriched in adenine nucleotides, the bulk of which is ATP. Despite this provocative start, an unequivocal function for ATP in pain remains to be described. The molecular and cellular work described below finds that an ATP-gated channel that is unique to nociceptors is strategically expressed on sensory endings and presynaptic terminals. This raises the need for further whole animal research to test possible roles for ATP in pain.

Two kinds of molecules must exist for ATP to function as an extracellular mediator. The first is an ATP sensor. In the 1980s, ion channels that are opened by extracellular ATP were discovered and characterized on sensory neurons (23–25). They open in response to micromolar ATP concentrations; because millimolar concentrations exist within cell cytosol, substantial dilution of intracellular contents in extracellular space should still activate the channels. The second necessary molecule must either remove or degrade ATP, thereby keeping extracellular concentrations low unless there is recent, nearby ATP release. This is accomplished by extracellular nucleotidases, which remove phosphate groups from ATP and are expressed in all tissues (26). Ecto-nucleotidases are fast: In brain slices, adenosine appears with a half-time of 200 ms after release of ATP (27). (This provides a lower estimate of the termination of ATP signals because the adenosine arises upon removal of all three phosphates, whereas the removal of one is sufficient to halt activation of ATP-gated channels.) Although a bolus of extracellular ATP can, itself, cause only a transient effect, the subsequent appearance of adenosine has been shown to inhibit synaptic transmission in the spinal cord (28, 29).

The ion channels opened by ATP are called P2X receptors, and the G-protein coupled receptors activated by ATP are called P2Y (30). The first P2X receptor was cloned in 1994 (31, 32), and the P2X family rapidly expanded to seven members in the next few years (33). The third member, P2X3, was cloned from sensory neuron libraries (34, 35). Sensory neurons express mRNA for six of the seven P2X receptors, but in rats P2X3 mRNA is present only in sensory neurons (34, 35). [Humans are different: P2X3 mRNA is present in human spinal cord and heart (36).] The discovery of an ATP-gated channel unique to sensory neurons prompted Burnstock & Wood (37, 38) to recall and expand upon the Bleehen & Keele hypothesis (21).

Cook et al (39) pursued the suggestion that P2X3 receptors were unique to nociceptors using several new tools: antibodies to the P2X3 protein, and preparations of dissociated, fluorescently tagged nociceptors and muscle stretch receptors. The nociceptors were retrogradely labeled tooth pulp afferents; the stretch receptors were muscle afferents projecting to the mesencephalic nucleus of the Vth nerve. ATP-gated currents on nociceptors are typically 10-fold larger than on stretch receptors, and there are clear kinetic and pharmacological differences (Figure 1). Nociceptors have two distinct ATP-evoked currents. One has the appropriate pharmacology and transient kinetics expected of channels made only of P2X3 subunits (P2X3 homomers). The other has the sustained kinetics and pharmacology of channels made of combinations of P2X3 and P2X2 subunits (P2X3/P2X2 heteromers). The single type of current in stretch receptors behaves like P2X5 homomers. Thus, P2X3 receptors underlie both types of ATP-gated current in identified nociceptors and may be unique to nociceptors. Use of the P2X3 antibody demonstrated that the protein is present on nociceptive sensory endings (39). Thus, P2X3 is expressed at high density, and maybe exclusively, on nociceptors and is located at the correct subcellular site for detecting ATP in the periphery.

Vulchanova et al (40) also showed that central terminals of sensory neurons express P2X3 receptors. Activation of presynaptic P2X receptors enhances glutamate release from sensory neurons in culture (41), and ATP enhances neurotransmission at the sensory synapse in spinal cord slices (28). Thus, ATP coreleased with glutamate at sensory presynaptic terminals first enhances transmission and then, upon degradation to adenosine, should suppress transmission (29).

A major difficulty in the field has been the absence of selective antagonists for P2X receptors. Suramin and PPADS block P2X1, P2X2, P2X3, and P2X5

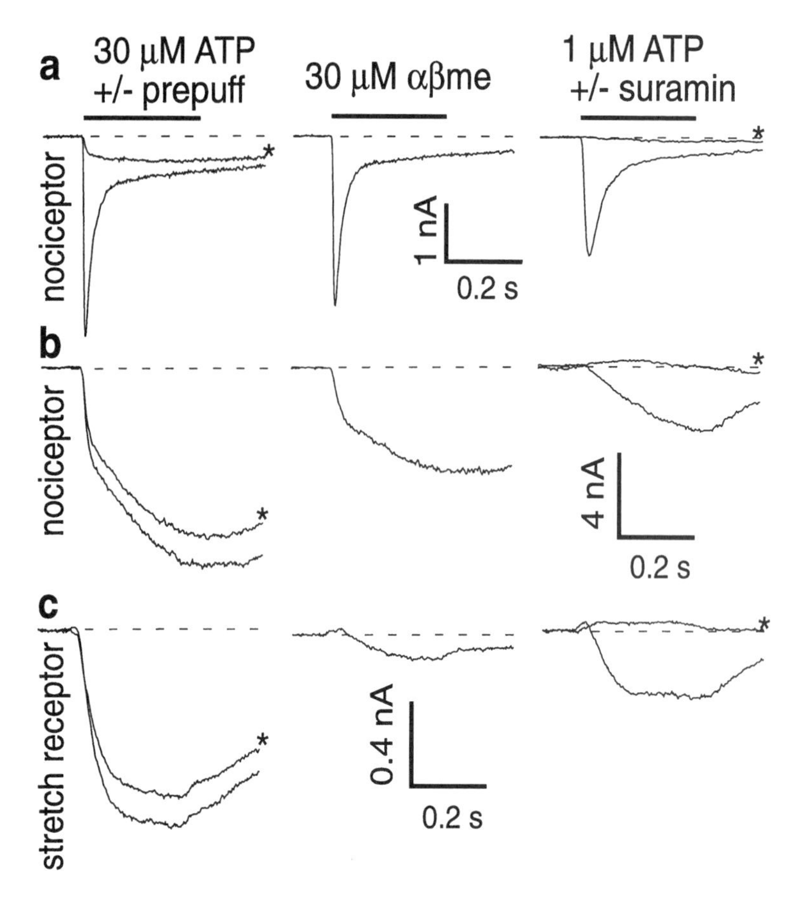

Figure 1 Nociceptors contain P2X3 receptors; stretch receptors do not. (*a*) Recordings from a tooth pulp nociceptor enriched in transient type of ATP-gated current. Current is desensitized by an ATP application 15 s prior to the stimulus (prepuff, *left column*); it is activated by α,β-methylene-ATP (*middle column*); it is blocked by suramin (*right column*). This pharmacology and the rapid desensitization kinetics confirm the channel to be a P2X3 homomer. (*b*) The persistent ATP-gated current in nociceptors is activated by α,β-methylene-ATP and blocked by suramin, confirming it as a P2X2/P2X3 heteromer. (*c*) ATP-gated currents in stretch receptors are all persistent, but not activated by α,β-methylene-ATP, unlike the persistent current in nociceptors. (From Reference 39.)

receptors at micromolar concentrations and the other P2X receptors at substantially higher concentrations (30). However, they are dirty drugs that inhibit a variety of molecules. A more promising antagonist has recently appeared: Trinitrophenyl-ATP (ATP-TNP) selectively inhibits P2X1 and P2X3 receptors and heteromeric channels that contain one of these receptors as a subunit (42). A selective agonist, α,β-methylene-ATP, activates P2X1 and P2X3 receptors (and some heteromeric channels containing these receptors) at far lower concentrations than are needed for the other receptors (30). Distinguishing P2X1 and P2X3 homomeric channels has been difficult because they both desensitize (albeit at noticeably different rates) and have similar pharmacology. Rae et al (43) argue that β,γ-methylene-L-ATP activates P2X1, but not P2X3, channels; this would indicate that the transient ATP-gated current in sensory neurons is entirely due to P2X3 receptors.

Although it is intriguing that a unique molecular machine, the P2X3 receptor, is located at the correct subcellular site (the sensory endings of nociceptors) to allow ATP to be a mediator between tissue damage and nociception, the evidence falls short of proving such a function. The field needs further whole animal research. However, a number of factors make such research challenging and false negatives likely. First, ecto-nucleotidases destroy ATP in the interstitial space in a fraction of a second (27). Therefore, crude injection into tissue should fail to deliver ATP to its site of action. Nucleotidase-resistant analogs of ATP must be used. Second, the homomeric P2X3 channel desensitizes quickly ($<$100 ms) and recovers slowly ($>$20 min) (44). Therefore, any procedure that disrupts the tissue and releases ATP should render P2X3 channels insensitive to ATP for some time thereafter. Third, some P2X receptors are pH sensitive. In particular, the P2X2/P2X3 heteromer that makes the sustained current in nociceptors is greatly enhanced when pH drops below 7.0 (45). Because inflamed tissue has relatively low pH, sustained ATP responses may manifest themselves preferentially in inflamed tissue. Consistent with these observations, perfusion of ATP into a blister causes pain (21) whereas injection of ATP into "normal" skin does not (46).

Despite the difficulties discussed above, there have been recent successes in demonstrating ATP-evoked pain in whole animals. Bland-Ward & Humphrey (47) used a nucleotidase-resistant P2X agonist, α,β-methylene-ATP, to show that activation of P2X receptor in the rat paw induces overt nociceptive behavior. This behavior is blocked by a local anesthetic, indicating that it is caused by nociceptor activation in the periphery. The behavior desensitizes following pretreatment with the agonist whereas other nociceptive stimuli (formalin and bradykinin) remain effective, indicating receptor specificity in ATP-induced nociception. As expected given its sensitivity to nucleotidases, ATP itself had just a modest nociceptive effect and only at very high concentrations. Another study showed that P2X receptor activation enhances nociception induced by formalin and that the enhancement is blocked by suramin (48).

ACID-SENSING ION CHANNELS

Muscle ischemia, inflammation, and local infection all evoke pain and each is accompanied by local acidosis. Whether as a modulator of nociceptors or as their primary drive, acidity plays a role in the nociception (49). In the case of muscle ischemia, human pain increases perfectly in time with decreasing extracellular pH on the surface of the ischemic muscle (50). In skin, the mechanical threshold of all unmyelinated nociceptors diminishes when pH drops, whereas low-threshold mechanosensors are unaffected by pH (51). A subset (38%) of mechano-heat–sensitive, unmyelinated nociceptors actively fire action potentials in response to decreasing pH, exhibiting a clear dose-response relation between firing frequency and pH (51). The sensors proposed for this response are acid-sensing ion channels that were first discovered by Krishtal & Pidoplichko (52, 53). The first acid-sensing ion channel (ASIC1) was recently cloned (54), and as of this writing, three close relatives have been reported (55–57). This family likely will grow further.

The strategy that resulted in the discovery of ASIC1 illustrates a different paradigm from that used to find the capsaicin and P2X receptors. As described above, capsaicin and P2X receptors were the targets of expression cloning strategies designed to find them exclusively. In contrast, ASIC1 was cloned as part of an attempt to fully describe a family of ion channels that seemed unrelated to acid-sensing channels. The family includes the amiloride-sensitive epithelial Na^+ channel, which controls Na^+ reabsorption by the kidney, and degenerins, ion channels in nematodes that cause neuronal cell death when they are constitutively active. The channels in this family all pass Na^+ in preference to other ions, a property shared with acid-sensing channels of sensory neurons (53, 58). This analogy led the Lazdunski group to test whether any of the various novel clones they found were gated by protons when expressed in frog oocytes. This creative approach unmasked ASIC1 and demonstrated its essential properties: It is closed at pH 7.4, it opens when pH drops below 7.0, it is Na^+ selective, and it is expressed in sensory neurons (54). The three related acid-sensing channels are called ASIC2a, ASIC2b, and ASIC3 (in the original papers, these were called MDEG1, MDEG2, and DRASIC) (59).

The predicted membrane topology of ASICs and the related channels indicates a large extracellular loop connecting two transmembrane domains with the amino and carboxyl termini inside the cell (54). This is like the predicted topology of P2X receptors even though there is no sequence homology (59). It is completely unlike the capsaicin receptor, thus disproving a previously popular theory that the capsaicin receptor was the acid-sensing channel.

Like the other members of the extended family of degenerins, each ASIC is sensitive to amiloride and selective for Na^+. They are all blocked by relatively high concentrations (ca 100 μM) of amiloride that are well above the clinically relevant dose for diuresis. Selectivity for Na^+ is an unusual property for ligand-gated cation channels, which generally pass monovalent cations indiscriminately. It is unclear whether the Na^+ selectivity of ASICs is significant or vestigial.

Which ASIC is responsible for the acid-evoked current in sensory neurons? There will not be a single answer because sensory neurons express several such currents that differ in their rates of activation and desensitization (53, 60). Bevan & Yeats (61) showed that a transient proton-activated current activated in sensory neurons below pH 7 was followed by a sustained current seen only when pH dropped further, to pH 6 and below. Although the transient current is Na^+ selective, the sustained current does not distinguish Na^+ and K^+. The simple explanation of this—that the transient, selective current and the sustained, nonselective current pass through different channels—may be wrong. Heterologous coexpression of ASIC3 and ASIC2b generates a current with a transient, selective component and a sustained, nonselective component much like that in native sensory neurons (57). The nonselective component proves that ASIC2b and ASIC3 coassemble because the current is not seen when either is transfected alone. The heteromer generates either (*a*) a sustained, nonselective current that is much larger than the sustained, selective current of ASIC3 or (*b*) a channel that changes its selectivity during a prolonged stimulus.

Pain due to inflammation, infection, or ischemia is not transient, so a persisting current must underlie the response (61, 62). The large, persisting current that is evoked when extracellular pH drops below 6 has been proposed to underlie the pain of these conditions, but this presumes that such low pH is reached. This seems not to be true in muscle and cardiac ischemia. Muscle exercise of an arm held in a tourniquet drops extracellular pH only to 7.0, and pain tracks perfectly with this pH change (50). The most extreme experimental cardiac ischemia (complete cessation of arterial perfusion) causes extracellular pH to drop a full pH unit after about 30 min (63); such complete blockage of perfusion is quickly fatal in vivo, so such large pH changes should never occur in heart. Skin nociceptors that fire action potentials in response to pH changes have activation thresholds as high as pH 6.9, far too high to activate the persistent component of acid-evoked current (51). It seems clear that persistent activation of a population of nociceptors occurs when extracellular pH drops from 7.4 to 7.0. The molecular basis of this is not yet understood, but rapid progress in the field may provide an answer soon.

Na^+ CHANNELS AND PAIN

Although the ionic currents involved in establishing the excitability of nociceptor terminals have yet to be identified, there is evidence that changes in nociceptor excitability reflect modulation and/or changes in the expression of several voltage- and Ca^{2+}-dependent currents. These currents include voltage-dependent K^+ (64, 65), Na^+ (66–69), and Ca^{2+} (70–72) currents, an inwardly rectifying nonselective cationic current (73), and Ca^{2+}-dependent K^+ currents

(74, 75). Rather than discuss the role each of these currents may play in the modulation of nociceptor excitability, we limit our discussion to a family of voltage-gated currents that has been the focus of a large body of research in the last several years: voltage-gated Na^+ currents (VGSCs). We suggest that the cellular processes involved in the modulation of VGSCs are likely to apply to other currents that may also contribute to changes in afferent excitability.

Several factors have contributed to a renaissance in research focused on elucidating the contribution of VGSCs to changes in afferent excitability. First, there is a long-standing appreciation of the critical role played by VGSCs in the generation and conduction of neuronal action potentials. Second, there is a growing body of evidence indicating that modulation of these currents is an endogenous mechanism used to control neuronal excitability (67, 76). Third, evidence from injury in experimental animals (77–80) and humans (81, 82) suggests that therapeutic interventions with compounds known to block Na^+ channels may be effective for the treatment of hyperalgesia and pain. And fourth, molecular biological tools that facilitate the study of VGSCs are now available.

At least three VGSCs have been described in mammalian sensory neurons that are distinguished on the basis of pharmacological and biophysical properties as well as on distribution among sensory neurons (83). Based on data obtained with molecular probes specific for the various cloned VGSCs, the macroscopic Na^+ current evoked from sensory neurons appears to reflect activation of a number of distinct ion channels (84). Nevertheless, these currents are generally divided into two current types based on their sensitivity to tetrodotoxin (TTX). One current is blocked by nanomolar concentrations of TTX (the TTX-sensitive current) while resistant to TTX at concentrations as high as 10 μM (the TTX-resistant current) (85–88). Of note, evidence for a second TTX-resistant Na^+ current recently has been reported (89, 90). Unlike the TTX-sensitive current, which is present in all sensory neurons (67, 85–88), expression of TTX-resistant current is largely restricted to a subpopulation of neurons with nociceptor characteristics (67, 86).

The ratio of the two types of VGSC in a given neuron can have profound effects on excitability (91). The ratio of these currents is not constant and may change in milliseconds with changes in resting membrane potential. Rapid change in the ratio of these two currents reflects, in part, differences in steady-state inactivation properties. TTX-sensitive Na^+ currents are subject to steady-state inactivation at relatively hyperpolarized membrane potentials [$V_{0.5}$ of ~-65 mV (86)], whereas membrane depolarization is required to induce steady-state inactivation of TTX-resistant currents [$V_{0.5}$ of ~-39 mV (86)]. Thus, small changes in resting membrane potential have a large effect on the number of TTX-sensitive channels available for activation and on the ratio of TTX-sensitive to insensitive Na^+ current. Furthermore, because recovery from inactivation occurs more rapidly in TTX-resistant Na^+ currents than in the TTX-sensitive currents present in uninjured neurons, it has been proposed that neurons with a large proportion of TTX-resistant Na^+ currents would be able to fire long trains of action potentials (88). The relative contribution of different VGSCs to action potential generation in afferent terminals is unknown. However, there is a growing body of evidence indicating that in normal tissue, TTX-resistant Na^+ current is critically involved in the process (41, 92, 93) (Figure 2).

Acute Modulation

Changes in nociceptor excitability are typically observed following injury. The most rapidly developing changes in excitability (on the order of seconds to minutes) appear to reflect the action of mediators released at the site of injury. The suggestion that TTX-resistant Na^+ currents contribute to injury-induced increase in nociceptor excitability is supported by several observations. First,

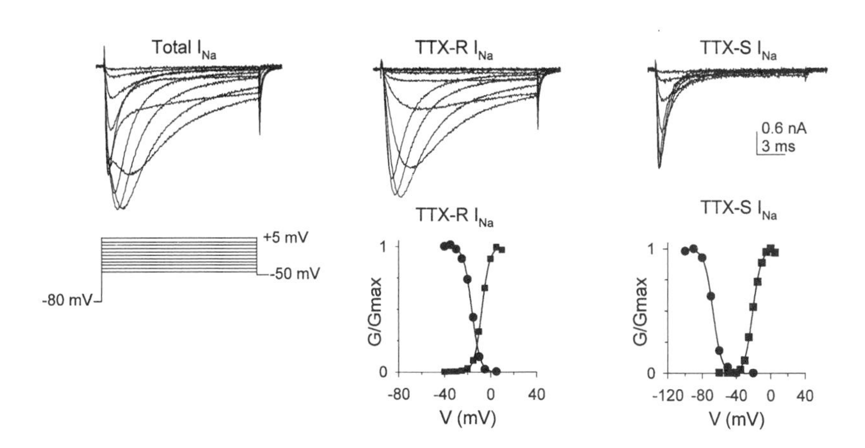

Figure 2 Voltage-gated Na^+ currents (I_{Na}) present in dorsal root ganglion (DRG) neurons are distinguished by sensitivity to tetrodotoxin (TTX) and gating properties. (*Left column*) Voltage-gated Na^+ current evoked from a 25-μm DRG neuron during 20-ms command potentials ranging between −40 mV and +5 mV from a holding potential of −80 mV; the voltage clamp protocol used to evoke the current is shown beneath the current traces. (*Center column*) TTX-resistant (TTX-R) I_{Na} is isolated following bath application of 50 nM TTX; normalized conductance-voltage relationship for activation and steady-state inactivation of TTX-R I_{Na} are plotted beneath the current traces (a 500-ms conditioning pulse was used to generate the steady-state inactivation data). (*Right column*) TTX-sensitive (TTX-S) I_{Na} is isolated as the difference between the current evoked before and after application of TTX (current evoked at −5, 0, and +5 mV has been omitted for clarity); normalized conductance-voltage relationships for activation and steady-state inactivation of TTX-S I_{Na} are plotted beneath the current traces (a 500-ms conditioning pulse was used to generate the steady-state inactivation data). [From Reference 67, copyright (1996) National Academy of Sciences, USA.]

because the distribution of TTX-resistant Na^+ current is restricted to a subpopulation of neurons with nociceptor properties (67), the current is in the right population of afferents. Second, it has been demonstrated (64, 67, 94) that TTX-resistant Na^+ current is selectively modulated by hyperalgesic inflammatory mediators in a manner consistent with a role in sensitization and hyperalgesia. Hyperalgesic inflammatory mediators, including prostaglandin E_2, serotonin, and adenosine, decrease the activation threshold, increase the rates of activation and inactivation, and increase the magnitude of TTX-resistant Na^+ current (67). These changes could contribute to both the decrease in threshold and the increase in the number of action potentials evoked from a sensitized nociceptor. An inflammatory mediator chemically related to prostaglandin E_2 that does not produce hyperalgesia, thromboxane B_2, does not modulate TTX-resistant Na^+ current (67). Third, the time course for the modulation of the current in the cell body parallels that of prostaglandin E_2–induced nociceptor sensitization (67, 95). And fourth, a μ-opioid that blocks hyperalgesic inflammatory mediator-induced hyperalgesia also blocks inflammatory mediator-induced modulation of TTX-resistant Na^+ current (96).

The time course of the inflammatory mediator-induced modulation of TTX-resistant Na^+ current suggests that modulation of the current involves a phosphorylation/dephosphorylation event(s). Consistent with this suggestion, it has been demonstrated that prostaglandin E_2–induced modulation of the current involves activation of cAMP-dependent protein kinase (PKA) (64, but see 94). That is, prostaglandin E_2–induced modulation of TTX-resistant Na^+ current was blocked by PKA inhibitors and occluded following modulation of the current by forskolin and membrane permeable analogs of cAMP (64). Recent evidence suggests that TTX-resistant Na^+ current also is modulated following activation of protein kinase C (MS Gold, unpublished observation).

Although it is possible that inflammatory mediator-induced modulation of TTX-resistant Na^+ current involves the phosphorylation of proteins associated with TTX-resistant Na^+ channels, it has been demonstrated that other VGSCs are modulated subsequent to phosphorylation of the channel protein (97, 98). A channel encoding a TTX-resistant Na^+ current has been cloned from sensory neurons (99, 100). It has yet to be determined whether this channel is directly phosphorylated following activation of PKA or protein kinase C (PKC) in situ. However, the deduced sequence of the cloned channel indicates the presence of several consensus sites for PKA-induced phosphorylation, including two sites that appear to be unique to the Na^+ channel subtype called PN3/SNS (100).

Long-Term Changes in VGSCs

In addition to changes in nociceptor excitability associated with acute injury or inflammatory reactions, researchers have begun looking at changes in nociceptor excitability in response to ongoing, or chronic, injury. Several animal models of chronic injury have been developed to facilitate the identification of underlying mechanisms of injury-induced changes in afferent excitability. Recent evidence suggests that different forms of injury are associated with unique changes in the expression and/or distribution of VGSCs.

Nerve Injury: Complete Transection

Axotomy is one of the more widely studied models of nerve injury, in which an entire peripheral nerve, typically the sciatic nerve, is transected (101). If the nerve is prevented from reinvervating its original target, a neuroma forms. Over several weeks following axotomy, the neuroma becomes a site of hyperexcitability, associated with a low mechanical threshold, prolonged after-discharges, and/or spontaneous activity (102).

Several lines of evidence suggest that changes in the expression and distribution of VGSCs contribute to the increase in afferent excitability observed following axotomy. First, spontaneous activity is exquisitely sensitive to compounds that block VGSCs (80). Second, VGSCs appear to accumulate at the site of the neuroma (103). Third, changes in the expression of VGSCs are observed. These include a decrease in two distinct species of mRNA encoding TTX-resistant Na^+ channels [i.e. PN3/SNS (104) and NaN (90)] and an increase in the expression of mRNA encoding a TTX-sensitive Na^+ current (brain type III). mRNA encoding brain type III channels is detectable in uninjured sensory neurons only during development (105). Consistent with these changes in mRNA levels, axotomy results in a decrease in density of TTX-resistant Na^+ current present in the cell body of neurons giving rise to the injured axons (66, 106). An increase in the density of TTX-sensitive currents also is observed in situ (106). A more detailed analysis of the TTX-sensitive currents present in sensory neurons following axotomy revealed the presence of a Na^+ current that has unique gating properties: The current recovers rapidly from inactivation (66). Thus, the hyperexcitability observed in the presence of axotomy may reflect a shift in the ratio of TTX-resistant to TTX-sensitive Na^+ current, with a low-threshold, rapidly "repriming" TTX-sensitive Na^+ current becoming the dominant VGSC.

Nerve Injury: Partial Transection

Several animal models have been developed to help identify changes in afferent excitability that may be associated with nerve compression and/or partial transection (107–109). The most widely studied of these models was developed by Bennett & Xie (109) and involves the placement of loosely tied ligatures around the sciatic nerve. This injury is generally referred to as the chronic constriction injury (CCI). Animals with CCI display signs of spontaneous pain and hyperalgesia that begins to develop within hours of placing the ligatures and reaches a peak 4–7 days later. These behavioral changes are associated with the development of spontaneous activity in the injured nerve arising, in part, from within the sensory ganglia (110). That spontaneous activity is due, in part, to changes intrinsic to the sensory neuron is suggested by the observation that spontaneous activity is present in a subpopulation of sensory neuron cell bodies isolated from ganglia innervating the injured nerve (111, 112).

In contrast to axotomy, CCI does not appear to be associated with changes in the expression of VGSC mRNA (68). However, CCI-induced changes in the distribution of TTX-resistant Na^+ channels have been reported (68). Using an antibody against PN3, Novakovic et al (68) observed a decrease in PN3-like immunoreactivity in cell bodies of neurons associated with the injured nerve and an increase in immunoreactivity in axons near the site of injury. The decrease in immunoreactivity in the cell bodies was associated with no change either in the density of TTX-resistant current when measured in the cell bodies of injured neurons in vitro or in mRNA levels. CCI-induced changes in the properties of TTX-resistant Na^+ currents also have been reported (113). In a preliminary study, Kral et al (113) observed a hyperpolarizing shift in the voltage dependence of TTX-resistant current measured in the cell body of injured neurons. That Kral et al (113) studied sensory neurons within 8 h of dissociating whereas Novakovic et al (68) performed their experiments 18–24 h after dissociating the neurons may explain why the former group was able to detect a change in the voltage dependence of TTX-resistant current.

Chronic Inflammation

Most injuries to peripheral tissue are associated with inflammation. Stereotypical inflammatory responses involve changes in vascular permeability, the infiltration and activation of immunocompetent cells, and the synthesis and/or release of inflammatory mediators. Several of these processes may be involved in an inflammation-induced increase in nociceptor excitability that develops over minutes and hours following injury (114). Although it is likely that a number of the processes involved in the initiation of nociceptor sensitization are responsible for the maintenance of sensitization in the presence of ongoing or chronic inflammation, a growing body of evidence indicates that chronic inflammation results in sustained changes in nociceptor physiology. For example, neuronal sprouting (115) and changes in gene expression in the presence of chronic inflammation (115–118) are well documented.

To date, there are conflicting reports on the effects of chronic inflammation and changes in the expression of VGSCs. Inflammation resulting from the cutaneous injection of carrageenan is associated with an increase in the expression of mRNA encoding a TTX-resistant Na^+ channel (SNS/PN3) (69).

An increase in the density of TTX-resistant Na^+ current in the cell bodies of sensory neurons innervating the site of inflammation is also observed (69). In contrast, inflammation resulting from the injection of complete Freund's adjuvant appears to have no effect on the level of SNS/PN3 mRNA (119). The basis for the discrepancy between these two studies remains to be determined.

Other Models of Peripheral Nerve Injury

Changes in the excitability of primary afferent nociceptors are observed in response to several other processes in addition to those described above. VGSCs have been implicated in two such processes, and these include diabetes and spinal cord transection. One of the many bodily organs that suffer in the presence of untreated diabetes is the peripheral nervous system. In humans, diabetic neuropathy is often associated with burning pain in the extremities. In an animal model of diabetes, nociceptors become hyperresponsive (120). These changes in peripheral nerves are associated with a decrease in the expression of SNS mRNA (119) and with abnormalities in the properties of Na^+ channels present in axonal nodes of Ranvier (121).

Spinal transection results in bladder hyperreflexia and incontinence. These changes occur as a result of the loss of the normal supraspinal pathway regulating micturition. Work in animal models has revealed that the hyperreflexia is due to changes in the afferents involved in the control of micturition. Bladder afferents become hyperexcitable, displaying a dramatic increase in mechanosensitivity (122). This hyperexcitability is associated with an increase in the density of TTX-sensitive Na^+ currents and a decrease in the density of TTX-resistant Na^+ currents (123).

A Mechanism for Changes in the Expression of VGSCs

Differences in the injury-induced changes in the expression of VGSCs appear to reflect differences in the availability of neurotrophic factors, in particular nerve growth factor (NGF). NGF is involved in regulating the expression of both TTX-resistant Na^+ current and brain type III VGSC in somatic sensory neurons (124–126). An increase in the concentration of NGF is associated with an increase in the expression of TTX-resistant Na^+ current and vice versa (124–126). In contrast, an increase in the concentration of NGF decreases the expression of brain type III currents (126). The peripheral target of innervation appears to be the source of NGF maintaining the density of TTX-resistant and brain type III Na^+ currents in sensory neurons in vivo. When access to this source of NGF is interrupted, as in the case of axotomy, TTX-resistant Na^+ current density decreases whereas that of brain type III increases. Consistent with this suggestion is the observation that providing an artificial source of NGF to axotomized neurons is capable of reversing the axotomy-induced decreases in

SNS mRNA (127) and TTX-resistant Na^+ current (128). Conversely, because the concentration of NGF is increased in inflamed tissue (129), the expression of TTX-resistant currents innervating this tissue should be increased. As noted above, an increase in SNS mRNA and TTX-resistant Na^+ currents is observed following carrageenan-induced inflammation (69).

Although the differential regulation of VGSCs by NGF provides a useful framework with which to understand differences in the changes observed in sensory neurons in response to various injuries, several observations suggest that this framework should be used with caution. First, there is at least one report in which manipulating the concentration of NGF applied to sensory neurons had little effect on the expression of SNS/PN3 mRNA (119). Second, the changes in the expression of SNS/PN3 mRNA and distribution of SNS/PN3 channels observed in the presence of CCI (68) do not fit well within the NGF regulation framework. This is particularly true given that CCI is associated with inflammation at the site of injury (130). And third, the concentration of NGF increases in hypertrophied bladders (131), whereas changes in the expression of TTX-resistant and -sensitive currents in sensory neurons innervating hypertrophied bladders are opposite to those predicted by an NGF-induced regulation of VGSCs.

Ancillary Subunits

Although we limited our discussion of the modulation of VGSCs to mechanisms involving changes in the α-subunit of the channel protein, the properties of VGSCs, like other voltage- and Ca^{2+}-dependent currents, are influenced by the presence of β-subunits. For example, the kinetics of inactivation of brain type III and skeletal muscle channels (SkM1) are increased, and the activation kinetics of brain type IIA channels are increased by the presence of β1-subunits (132). The presence of β1-subunit increases the expression of cardiac Na^+ channels (rH1/SkM2) (133). Although the influence of β-subunits on the VGSCs present in sensory neurons has yet to be investigated in detail, there is evidence that the presence of β-subunits may influence the expression and/or biophysical properties of both TTX-sensitive (132) and TTX-resistant Na^+ currents (100). Thus, changes in the expression of β-subunits in sensory neurons may influence the VGSCs present, consequently altering afferent excitability.

ACKNOWLEDGMENT

Work in our laboratories is supported by grants from NIDA and NINDS.

Literature Cited

1. Melzack R, Wall PD. 1965. Pain mechanisms: a new theory. *Science* 150:971–79
2. Sherrington CS. 1906. *The Integrative Action of the Nervous System*. New York: Scribner
3. Burgess PR, Perl ER. 1967. Myelinated afferent fibers responding specifically to noxious stimulation of the skin. *J. Physiol.* 190:541–62
4. Bessou P, Perl ER. 1969. Response of cutaneous sensory units with unmyelinated fibers to noxious stimuli. *J. Neurophysiol.* 32:1025–43
5. Cervero F, Jänig W. 1992. Visceral nociceptors: a new world order? *Trends Neurosci.* 15:374–78
6. Cooper BY, Vierck CJ Jr, Yeomans DC. 1986. Selective reduction of second pain sensations by systemic morphine in humans. *Pain* 24:93–116
7. Woolf CJ. 1995. An overview of the mechanisms of hyperalgesia. *Pulm. Pharmacol.* 8:161–67
8. Lewin GR, Mendell LM. 1993. Nerve growth factor and nociception. *Trends Neurosci.* 16:353–59
9. McMahon SB. 1996. NGF as a mediator of inflammatory pain. *Philos. Trans. R. Soc. London Ser. B* 351:431–40
10. Wood JN, Docherty R. 1997. Chemical activators of sensory neurons. *Annu. Rev. Physiol.* 59:457–82
11. Nowycky M. 1992. Voltage-gated ion channels in dorsal root ganglion neurons. In *Sensory Neurons: Diversity, Development, and Plasticity*, ed. A Scott, pp. 97–115. New York: Oxford Univ. Press
12. Jancso G, Kiraly E, Jancso-Gabor A. 1977. Pharmacologically induced selective degeneration of chemosensitive primary sensory neurones. *Nature* 270:741–43
13. Szallasi A, Blumberg PM. 1996. Vanilloid receptors: new insights enhance potential as a therapeutic target. *Pain* 68:195–208
14. Caterina MJ, Schumacher MA, Tominaga M, Rosen TA, Levine JD, Julius D. 1997. The capsaicin receptor: a heat-activated ion channel in the pain pathway. *Nature* 389:816–24
15. Szolcsanyi J, Anton F, Reeh PW, Handwerker HO. 1988. Selective excitation by capsaicin of mechano-heat sensitive nociceptors in rat skin. *Brain Res.* 446:262–68
16. Kirschstein T, Busselberg D, Treede RD. 1997. Coexpression of heat-evoked and capsaicin-evoked inward currents in acutely dissociated rat dorsal root ganglion neurons. *Neurosci. Lett.* 231:33–36
17. Bevan S, Geppetti P. 1994. Protons: small stimulants of capsaicin-sensitive sensory nerves. *Trends Neurosci.* 17:509–12
18. Cesare P, McNaughton P. 1996. A novel heat-activated current in nociceptive neurons and its sensitization by bradykinin. *Proc. Natl. Acad. Sci. USA* 93:15435–39
19. Reichling DB, Levine JD. 1997. Heat transduction in rat sensory neurons by calcium-dependent activation of a cation channel. *Proc. Natl. Acad. Sci. USA* 94: 7006–11
20. Liu L, Szallasi A, Simon SA. 1998. A non-pungent resiniferatoxin analogue, phorbol 12-phenylacetate 13 acetate 20-homovanillate, reveals vanilloid receptor subtypes on rat trigeminal ganglion neurons. *Neuroscience* 84:569–81
21. Bleehen T, Keele CA. 1977. Observations on the algogenic actions of adenosine compounds on the human blister base preparation. *Pain* 3:367–77
22. Bleehen T, Hobbiger F, Keele CA. 1976. Identification of algogenic substances in human erythrocytes. *J. Physiol.* 62:131–49
23. Bean BP. 1990. ATP-activated channels in rat and bullfrog sensory neurons: concentration dependence and kinetics. *J. Neurosci.* 10:1–10
24. Jahr CE, Jessell TM. 1983. ATP excites a subpopulation of rat dorsal horn neurones. *Nature* 304:730–33
25. Krishtal OA, Marchenko SM, Obukhov AG. 1988. Cationic channels activated by extracellular ATP in rat sensory neurons. *Neuroscience* 27:995–1000
26. Zimmermann H. 1996. Biochemistry, localization and functional roles of ecto-nucleotidases in the nervous system. *Prog. Neurobiol.* 49:589–618
27. Dunwiddie TV, Diao L, Proctor WR. 1997. Adenine nucleotides undergo rapid, quantitative conversion to adenosine in the extracellular space in rat hippocampus. *J. Neurosci.* 17:7673–82
28. Li J, Perl ER. 1995. ATP modulation of synaptic transmission in the spinal substantia gelatinosa. *J. Neurosci.* 15:3357–65
29. Li J, Perl ER. 1994. Adenosine inhibition of synaptic transmission in the substantia gelatinosa. *J. Neurophysiol.* 72:1611–21
30. North RA, Barnard EA. 1997. Nucleotide receptors. *Curr. Opin. Neurobiol.* 7:346–57

31. Brake AJ, Wagenbach MJ, Julius D. 1994. New structural motif for ligand-gated ion channels defined by an ionotropic ATP receptor. *Nature* 371:519–23
32. Valera S, Hussy N, Evans RJ, Adami N, North RA, et al. 1994. A new class of ligand-gated ion channel defined by P2x receptor for extracellular ATP. *Nature* 371:516–19
33. Collo G, North RA, Kawashima E, Merlo-Pich E, Neidhart S, et al. 1996. Cloning OF P2X5 and P2X6 receptors and the distribution and properties of an extended family of ATP-gated ion channels. *J. Neurosci.* 16:2495–507
34. Chen CC, Akopian AN, Sivilotti L, Colquhoun D, Burnstock G, Wood JN. 1995. A P2X purinoceptor expressed by a subset of sensory neurons. *Nature* 377:428–31
35. Lewis C, Neidhart S, Holy C, North RA, Buell G, Surprenant A. 1995. Coexpression of P2X2 and P2X3 receptor subunits can account for ATP-gated currents in sensory neurons. *Nature* 377:432–35
36. Garcia-Guzman M, Stuhmer W, Soto F. 1997. Molecular characterization and pharmacological properties of the human P2X3 purinoceptor. *Brain Res. Mol. Brain Res.* 47:59–66
37. Burnstock G, Wood JN. 1996. Purinergic receptors: their role in nociception and primary afferent neurotransmission. *Curr. Opin. Neurobiol.* 6:526–32
38. Burnstock G. 1996. A unifying purinergic hypothesis for the initiation of pain. *Lancet* 347:1604–5
39. Cook SP, Vulchanova L, Hargreaves KM, Elde R, McCleskey EW. 1997. Distinct ATP receptors on pain-sensing and stretch-sensing neurons. *Nature* 387:505–8
40. Vulchanova L, Riedl MS, Shuster SJ, Buell G, Surprenant A, et al. 1997. Immunohistochemical study of the P2X2 and P2X3 receptor subunits in rat and monkey sensory neurons and their central terminals. *Neuropharmacology* 36:1229–42
41. Gu JG, MacDermott AB. 1997. Activation of ATP P2X receptors elicits glutamate release from sensory neuron synapses. *Nature* 389:749–53
42. Thomas S, Virginio C, North RA, Surprenant A. 1998. The antagonist trinitrophenyl-ATP reveals co-existence of distinct P2X receptor channels in rat nodose neurones. *J. Physiol.* 509:411–17
43. Rae MG, Rowan EG, Kennedy C. 1998. Pharmacological properties of P2X3-receptors present in neurones of the rat dorsal root ganglia. *Br. J. Pharmacol.* 124:176–80
44. Cook SP, McCleskey EW. 1997. Desensitization, recovery and Ca(2+)-dependent modulation of ATP-gated P2X receptors in nociceptors. *Neuropharmacology* 36:1303–8
45. Stoop R, Surprenant A, North RA. 1997. Different sensitivities to pH of ATP-induced currents at four cloned P2X receptors. *J. Neurophysiol.* 78:1837–40
46. Reeh PW, Kress M. 1998. Boole's algebra and the Gordian knot in peripheral nociception. *Pain Forum* 7:84–86
47. Bland-Ward PA, Humphrey PP. 1997. Acute nociception mediated by hindpaw P2X receptor activation in the rat. *Br. J. Pharmacol.* 122:365–71
48. Sawynok J, Reid A. 1997. Peripheral adenosine 5′-triphosphate enhances nociception in the formalin test via activation of a purinergic p2X receptor. *Eur. J. Pharmacol.* 330:115–21
49. Steen KH, Steen AE, Reeh PW. 1995. A dominant role of acid pH in inflammatory excitation and sensitization of nociceptors in rat skin, in vitro. *J. Neurosci.* 15:3982–89
50. Issberner U, Reeh PW, Steen KH. 1996. Pain due to tissue acidosis: a mechanism for inflammatory and ischemic myalgia? *Neurosci. Lett.* 208:191–94
51. Steen KH, Reeh PW, Anton F, Handwerker HO. 1992. Protons selectively induce lasting excitation and sensitization to mechanical stimulation of nociceptors in rat skin, in vitro. *J. Neurosci.* 12:86–95
52. Krishtal OA, Pidoplichko VI. 1980. A receptor for protons in the nerve cell membrane. *Neuroscience* 5:2325–27
53. Krishtal OA, Pidoplichko VI. 1981. A receptor for protons in the membrane of sensory neurons may participate in nociception. *Neuroscience* 6:2599–601
54. Waldmann R, Champigny G, Bassilana F, Heurteaux C, Lazdunski M. 1997. A proton-gated cation channel involved in acid-sensing. *Nature* 386:173–77
55. Waldmann R, Bassilana F, de Weille J, Champigny G, Heurteaux C, Lazdunski M. 1997. Molecular cloning of a non-inactivating proton-gated Na^+ channel specific for sensory neurons. *J. Biol. Chem.* 272:20975–78
56. Bassilana F, Champigny G, Waldmann R, de Weille JR, Heurteaux C, Lazdunski M. 1997. The acid-sensitive ionic channel subunit ASIC and the mammalian degenerin MDEG form a heteromultimeric H+-gated Na^+ channel with novel properties. *J. Biol. Chem.* 272:28819–22

57. Lingueglia E, de Weille JR, Bassilana F, Heurteaux C, Sakai H, et al. 1997. A modulatory subunit of acid sensing ion channels in brain and dorsal root ganglion cells. *J. Biol. Chem.* 272:29778–83
58. Kovalchuk YN, Krishtal OA, Nowycky MC. 1990. The proton-activated inward current of rat sensory neurons includes a calcium component. *Neurosci. Lett.* 115:237–42
59. Waldmann R, Lazdunski M. 1998. H(+)-gated cation channels: neuronal acid sensors in the NaC/DEG family of ion channels. *Curr. Opin. Neurobiol.* 8:418–24
60. Pidoplichko VI. 1992. Ammonia and proton gated channel populations in trigeminal ganglion neurons. *Gen. Physiol. Biophys.* 11:39–48
61. Bevan S, Yeats J. 1991. Protons activate a cation conductance in a sub-population of rat dorsal root ganglion neurones. *J. Physiol.* 433:145–61
62. Steen KH, Issberner U, Reeh PW. 1995. Pain due to experimental acidosis in human skin: evidence for non-adapting nociceptor excitation. *Neurosci. Lett.* 199: 29–32
63. Cobbe SM, Poole-Wilson PA. 1980. The time of onset and severity of acidosis in myocardial ischaemia. *J. Mol. Cell. Cardiol.* 12:745–60
64. England S, Bevan S, Docherty RJ. 1996. PGE2 modulates the tetrodotoxin-resistant sodium current in neonaatal rat dorsal root ganglion neurons via the cyclic AMP-protein kinase A cascade. *J. Physiol.* 495:429–40
65. Nicol GD, Vasko MR, Evans AR. 1997. Prostaglandins suppress an outward potassium current in embryonic rat sensory neurons. *J. Neurophysiol.* 77:167–76
66. Cummins TR, Waxman SG. 1997. Downregulation of tetrodotoxin-resistant sodium currents and upregulation of a rapidly repriming tetrodotoxin-sensitive sodium current in small spinal sensory neurons after nerve injury. *J. Neurosci.* 17:3503–14
67. Gold MS, Reichling DB, Shuster MJ, Levine JD. 1996. Hyperalgesic agents increase a tetrodotoxin-resistant Na^+ current in nociceptors. *Proc. Natl. Acad. Sci. USA* 93:1108–12
68. Novakovic SD, Tzoumaka E, McGivern JG, Haraguchi M, Sangameswaran L, et al. 1998. Distribution of the tetrodotoxin-resistant sodium channel PN3 in rat sensory neurons in normal and neuropathic conditions. *J. Neurosci.* 18:2174–87
69. Tanaka M, Cummins TR, Ishikawa K, Dib-Hajj SD, Black JA, Waxman SG. 1998. SNS Na^+ channel expression increases in dorsal root ganglion neurons in the carrageenan inflammatory pain model. *NeuroReport* 9:967–72
70. Bean BP. 1989. Neurotransmitter inhibition of neuronal calcium currents by changes in channel voltage dependence. *Nature* 340:153–56
71. McCleskey EW. 1994. Calcium channels: cellular roles and molecular mechanisms. *Curr. Opin. Neurobiol.* 4:304–12
72. Nicol GD, Klingberg DK, Vasko MR. 1992. Prostaglandin E_2 increases calcium conductance and stimulates release of substance P in avian sensory neurons. *J. Neurosci.* 12:1917–27
73. Ingram SL, Williams JT. 1994. Opioid inhibition of Ih via adenylyl cyclase. *Neuron* 13:179–86
74. Weinreich D. 1995. Cellular mechanisms of inflammatory mediators acting on vagal sensory nerve excitability. *Pulm. Pharmacol.* 8:173–79
75. Gold MS, Shuster MJ, Levine JD. 1996. Role of a slow Ca^{2+}-dependent slow afterhyperpolarization in prostaglandin E_2-induced sensitization of cultured rat sensory neurons. *Neurosci. Lett.* 205:161–64
76. Cantrell AR, Smith RD, Goldin AL, Scheuer T, Catterall WA. 1997. Dopaminergic modulation of sodium current in hippocampal neurons via cAMP-dependent phosphorylation of specific sites in the sodium channel alpha subunit. *J. Neurosci.* 17:7330–38
77. Abram SE, Yaksh TL. 1994. Systemic lidocaine blocks nerve injury-induced hyperalgesia and nociceptor-driven spinal sensitization in the rat. *Anesthesiology* 80:383–91
78. Chabal C, Russell LC, Burchiel KJ. 1989. The effect of intravenous lidocaine, tocainide, and mexiletine on spontaneously active fibers originating in rat sciatic neuromas. *Pain* 38:333–38
79. Puig S, Sorkin LS. 1996. Formalin-evoked activity in identified primary afferent fibers: systemic lidocaine suppresses phase-2 activity. *Pain* 64:345–55
80. Devor M, Wall PD, Catalan N. 1992. Systemic lidocaine silences ectopic neuroma and DRG discharge without blocking nerve conduction. *Pain* 48:261–68
81. Chabal C, Jacobson L, Mariano A, Chaney E, Britell CW. 1992. The use of oral mexiletine for the treatment of pain after peripheral nerve injury. *Anesthesiology* 76:513–17

82. Rizzo MA. 1997. Successful treatment of painful traumatic mononeuropathy with carbamazepine: insights into a possible molecular pain mechanism. *J. Neurol. Sci.* 152:103–6
83. Caffrey JM, Eng DL, Black JA, Waxman SG, Kocsis JD. 1992. Three types of sodium channels in adult rat dorsal root ganglion neurons. *Brain Res.* 592:283–97
84. Black JA, Dib-Hajj S, McNabola K, Jeste S, Rizzo MA, et al. 1996. Spinal sensory neurons express multiple sodium channel alpha-subunit mRNAs. *Brain Res. Mol. Brain Res.* 43:117–31
85. Kostyuk PG, Veselovsky NS, Fedulova SA, Tsyndrenko AY. 1981. Ionic currents in the somatic membrane of rat dorsal root ganglion neurons. I. Sodium currents. *Neuroscience* 6:2424–30
86. Ogata N, Tatebayashi H. 1993. Kinetic analysis of two types of Na^+ channels in rat dorsal root ganglia. *J. Physiol.* 466:9–37
87. Roy ML, Narahashi T. 1992. Differential properties of tetrodotoxin-sensitive and tetrodotoxin-resistant sodium channels in rat dorsal root ganglion neurons. *J. Neurosci.* 12:2104–11
88. Elliott AA, Elliott JR. 1993. Characterization of TTX-sensitive and TTX-resistant sodium currents in small cells from adult rat dorsal root ganglia. *J. Physiol.* 463:39–56
89. Rush AM, Elliott JR. 1997. Phenytoin and carbamazepine: differential inhibition of sodium currents in small cells from adult rat dorsal root ganglia. *Neurosci. Lett.* 226:95–98
90. Dib-Hajj SD, Tyrrell L, Black JA, Waxman SG. 1998. NaN, a novel voltage-gated Na channel, is expressed preferentially in peripheral sensory neurons and down-regulated after axotomy. *Proc. Natl. Acad. Sci. USA* 95:8963–68
91. Schild JH, Kunze DL. 1997. Experimental and modeling study of Na^+ current heterogeneity in rat nodose neurons and its impact on neuronal discharge. *J. Neurophysiol.* 78:3198–209
92. Strassman AM, Raymond SA, Burstein R. 1997. Modulation of mechanosensitivity of rat intracranial meningeal afferents by mechanical and chemical stimuli. *Soc. Neurosci. Abstr.* 23:1256
93. Jeftinija S. 1994. The role of tetrodotoxin-resistant sodium channels of small primary afferent fibers. *Brain Res.* 639:125–34
94. Cardenas CG, Del Mar LP, Cooper BY, Scroggs RS. 1997. 5HT4 receptors couple positively to tetrodotoxin-insensitive sodium channels in a subpopulation of capsaicin-sensitive rat sensory neurons. *J. Neurosci.* 17:7181–89
95. Gold MS, Dastmalchi S, Levine JD. 1996. Co-expression of nociceptor properties in dorsal root ganglion neurons from the adult rat in vitro. *Neuroscience* 71:265–75
96. Gold MS, Levine JD. 1996. DAMGO inhibits prostaglandin E_2-induced potentiation of a TTX-resistant Na^+ current in rat sensory neurons in vitro. *Neurosci. Lett.* 212:83–86
97. Frohnwieser B, Chen LQ, Schreibmayer W, Kallen RG. 1997. Modulation of the human cardiac sodium channel alpha-subunit by cAMP-dependent protein kinase and the responsible sequence domain. *J. Physiol.* 498:309–18
98. West JW, Numann R, Murphy BJ, Scheuer T, Catterall WA. 1991. A phosphorylation site in the Na^+ channel required for modulation by protein kinase C. *Science* 254:866–68
99. Akopian AN, Sivilotti L, Wood JN. 1996. A tetrodotoxin-resistant voltage-gated sodium channel expressed by sensory neurons. *Nature* 379:257–62
100. Sangameswaran L, Delgado SG, Fish LM, Koch BD, Jakeman LB, et al. 1996. Structure and function of a novel voltage-gated, tetrodotoxin-resistant sodium channel specfic to sensory neurons. *J. Biol. Chem.* 271:5953–56
101. Wall PD, Gutnick M. 1974. Ongoing activity in peripheral nerves: the physiology and pharmacology of impulses originating from a neuroma. *Exp. Neurol.* 43:580–93
102. Devor M. 1994. The pathophysiology of damaged peripheral nerves. In *Textbook of Pain*, ed. PD Wall, R Melzack, pp. 79–100. New York: Churchill Livingstone. 3rd ed.
103. Devor M, Govrin LR, Angelides K. 1993. Na^+ channel immunolocalization in peripheral mammalian axons and changes following nerve injury and neuroma formation. *J. Neurosci.* 13:1976–92
104. Dib-Hajj S, Black JA, Felts P, Waxman SG. 1996. Down-regulation of transcripts for Na channel alpha-SNS in spinal sensory neurons following axotomy. *Proc. Natl. Acad. Sci. USA* 93:14950–54
105. Waxman SG, Kocsis JD, Black JA. 1994. Type III sodium channel mRNA is expressed in embryonic but not adult spinal sensory neurons, and is reexpressed

following axotomy. *J. Neurophysiol.* 72: 466–70
106. Zhang JM, Donnelly DF, Song XJ, Lamotte RH. 1997. Axotomy increases the excitability of dorsal root ganglion cells with unmyelinated axons. *J. Neurophysiol.* 78:2790–94
107. Mosconi T, Kruger L. 1996. Fixed-diameter polyethylene cuffs applied to the rat sciatic nerve induce a painful neuropathy: ultrastructural morphometric analysis of axonal alterations. *Pain* 64:37–57
108. Seltzer Z, Dubner R, Shir Y. 1990. A novel behavioral model of neuropathic pain disorders produced in rats by partial sciatic nerve injury. *Pain* 43:205–18
109. Bennett GJ, Xie YK. 1988. A peripheral mononeuropathy in rat that produces disorders of pain sensation like those seen in man. *Pain* 33:87–107
110. Kajander KC, Wakisaka S, Bennett GJ. 1992. Spontaneous discharge originates in the dorsal root ganglion at the onset of a painful peripheral neuropathy in the rat. *Neurosci. Lett.* 138:225–28
111. Study RE, Kral MG. 1996. Spontaneous action potential activity in isolated dorsal root ganglion neurons from rats with a painful neuropathy. *Pain* 65:235–42
112. Petersen M, Zhang J, Zhang JM, LaMotte RH. 1996. Abnormal spontaneous activity and responses to norepinephrine in dissociated dorsal root ganglion cells after chronic nerve constriction. *Pain* 67:391–97
113. Kral MG, Xiong Z, Study RE. 1997. Alterations of Na^+ currents in dorsal root ganglion neurons from rats with painful neuropathy. *Soc. Neurosci. Abstr.* 23:1476
114. Levine JD, Basbaum AI, Fields HL. 1993. Peptides and primary afferent nociceptors. *J. Neurosci.* 13:2273–86
115. Leslie TA, Emson PC, Dowd PM, Woolf CJ. 1995. Nerve growth factor contributes to the up-regulation of growth-associated protein 43 and preprotachykinin A messenger RNAs in primary sensory neurons following peripheral inflammation. *Neuroscience* 67:753–61
116. Cho HJ, Kim SY, Park MJ, Kim DS, Kim JK, Chu MY. 1997. Expression of mRNA for brain-derived neurotrophic factor in the dorsal root ganglion following peripheral inflammation. *Brain Res.* 749:358–62
117. Donnerer J, Schuligoi R, Stein C, Amann R. 1993. Upregulation, release and axonal transport of substance P and calcitonin gene-related peptide in adjuvant inflammation and regulatory function of nerve growth factor. *Regul. Pept.* 46:150–54
118. Ji RR, Zhang Q, Law PY, Low HH, Elde R, Hokfelt T. 1995. Expression of mu-, delta-, and kappa-opioid receptor-like immunoreactivities in rat dorsal root ganglia after carrageenan-induced inflammation. *J. Neurosci.* 15:8156–66
119. Okuse K, Chaplan SR, McMahon SB, Luo ZD, Calcutt NA, et al. 1997. Regulation of expression of the sensory neuron-specific sodium channel SNS in inflammatory and neuropathic pain. *Mol. Cell. Neurosci.* 10:196–207
120. Ahlgren SC, White DM, Levine JD. 1992. Increased responsiveness of sensory neurons in the saphenous nerve of the streptozotocin-diabetic rat. *J. Neurophysiol.* 68:2077–85
121. Brismar T. 1993. Abnormal Na-currents in diabetic rat nerve nodal membrane. *Diabet. Med.* 10(Suppl. 2):110–12S
122. de Groat WC, Kawatani M, Hisamitsu T, Cheng CL, Ma CP, et al. 1990. Mechanisms underlying the recovery of urinary bladder function following spinal cord injury. *J. Auton. Nerv. Syst.* 30(Suppl.):S71–77
123. Yoshimura N, de Groat WC. 1997. Plasticity of Na^+ channels in afferent neurones innervating rat urinary bladder following spinal cord injury. *J. Physiol.* 503:269–76
124. Helliwell RJA, Winter J, McIntyre P, Bevan S. 1997. NGF regulates the expression of a tetrodotoxin-resistant sodium channel in cultured sensory neurones. *Soc. Neurosci. Abstr.* 23:911
125. Aguayo LG, White G. 1992. Effects of nerve growth factor on TTX- and capsaicin-sensitivity in adult rat sensory neurons. *Brain Res.* 570:61–67
126. Black JA, Langworthy K, Hinson AW, Dib-Hajj SD, Waxman SG. 1997. NGF has opposing effects on Na^+ channel III and SNS gene expression in spinal sensory neurons. *NeuroReport* 8:2331–35
127. Dib-Hajj SD, Black JA, Cummins TR, Kenney AM, Kocsis JD, Waxman SG. 1998. Rescue of alpha-SNS sodium channel expression in small dorsal root ganglion neurons after axotomy by nerve growth factor in vivo. *J. Neurophysiol.* 79:2668–76
128. Oyelese AA, Rizzo MA, Waxman SG, Kocsis JD. 1997. Differential effects of NGF and BDNF on axotomy-induced changes in GABA(A)-receptor-mediated conductance and sodium currents in cutaneous afferent neurons. *J. Neurophysiol.* 78:31–42
129. Constantinou J, Reynolds ML, Woolf CJ,

Safieh-Garabedian B, Fitzgerald M. 1994. Nerve growth factor levels in developing rat skin: upregulation following skin wounding. *NeuroReport* 5:2281–84

130. Wagner R, Janjigian M, Myers RR. 1998. Anti-inflammatory interleukin-10 therapy in CCI neuropathy decreases thermal hyperalgesia, macrophage recruitment, and endoneurial TNF-alpha expression. *Pain* 74:35–42
131. Steers WD, Kolbeck S, Creedon D, Tuttle JB. 1991. Nerve growth factor in the urinary bladder of the adult regulates neuronal form and function. *J. Clin. Invest.* 88:1709–15
132. Patton DE, Isom LL, Catterall WA, Goldin AL. 1994. The adult rat brain beta 1 subunit modifies activation and inactivation gating of multiple sodium channel alpha subunits. *J. Biol. Chem.* 269:17649–55
133. Qu Y, Isom LL, Westenbroek RE, Rogers JC, Tanada TN, et al. 1995. Modulation of cardiac Na^+ channel expression in *Xenopus* oocytes by beta 1 subunits. *J. Biol. Chem.* 270:25696–701

Annu. Rev. Physiol. 1999. 61:857–71

CONTROVERSIAL ISSUES IN VERTEBRATE OLFACTORY TRANSDUCTION

Geoffrey H. Gold
Monell Chemical Senses Center, 3500 Market St., Philadelphia, Pennsylvania 19104-3308

KEY WORDS: olfaction, cyclic, AMP, IP_3

ABSTRACT

A number of controversial issues in olfactory transduction are discussed including the matter of multiple transduction pathways, with a new experiment proposed. Evidence is reviewed concerning the fact that cyclic AMP is the only pathway mediating olfactory transduction. Two knockout mice have been produced: a knockout for a cyclic nucleotide-gated channel and a G_{olf} knockout. The results obtained with both mice are consistent with cyclic AMP being the only second messenger. The evidence for gaseous second channel messengers is also reviewed. Slow gating kinetics of the cyclic nucleotide-gated channel and the detection of single-odorant molecules are reviewed. A new phenomenon in which odorants can block odorant responses is discussed.

INTRODUCTION

Numerous reviews have been written about the vertebrate olfactory transduction mechanism (1–8). Therefore, the purpose of this review is to focus on issues that, in my opinion, remain controversial.

Anatomy of the Olfactory Epithelium

Before discussing the olfactory transduction mechanism, it is useful to describe the cell types found in the olfactory epithelium and their functions (Figure 1). There are three cell types in the olfactory epithelium: olfactory receptor cells, supporting (or sustentacular) cells, and basal cells (9).

0066-4278/99/0315-0857$08.00

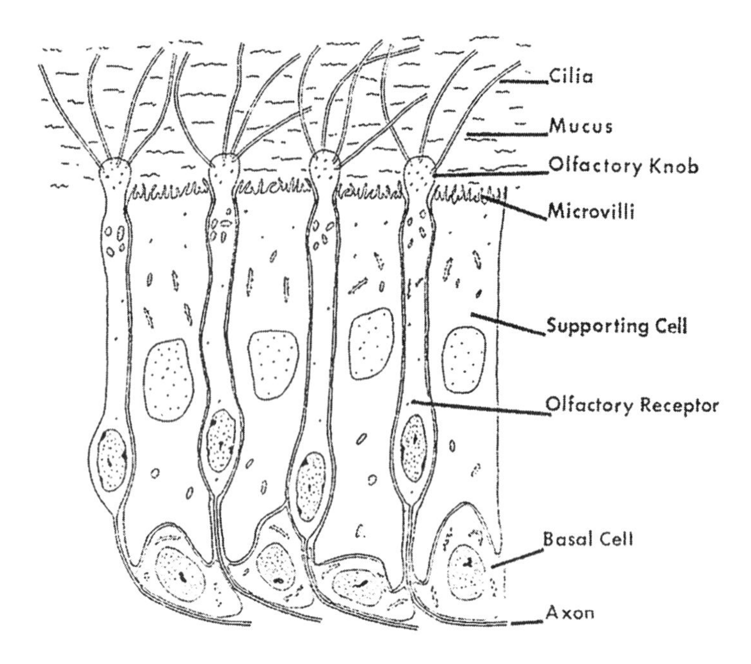

Figure 1 Diagram of the olfactory epithelium showing the cell types found there. (Reprinted with permission from the American Physiological Society from Reference 9.)

The olfactory receptor cells are bipolar neurons, having a single dendrite that extends to the apical surface of the epithelium and a single axon that projects to the olfactory bulb. At the tip of the dendrite, a number of cilia extend into a thin layer of mucus that covers the epithelium. The function of the receptor cells is to transduce odorants into membrane depolarization (10–12). Lowe & Gold (12) have shown that odorant sensitivity and the odorant-evoked inward transduction current are uniformly distributed along the cilia. Thus, all components of the transduction mechanism must be present in the cilia. Lowe & Gold (12) also showed that there is an outward current, probably caused by depolarization of voltage-dependent K^+ channels, in the dendrite and cell body. This creates an apically directed (upward in Figure 1) extracellular current, which is turn creates an extracellular field potential called the electro-olfactogram (EOG) (13). This signal is negative at the apical surface of the epithelium during an odorant response because current flows toward more negative potentials. This is an easily measured signal that can be recorded simply by placing a saline-filled glass microelectrode in contact with the mucus layer. Finally, Lowe & Gold (12) showed that the latency of the transduction current is independent of the region of the cilia that are stimulated: This implies that current is generated at the site of odorant binding.

The supporting cells have two functions. Okano & Takagi (14) and Getchell et al (15) have shown that odorants evoke secretion from the supporting cells into the mucus layer. This secretory transduction mechanism also generates a field potential that is positive on the apical surface of the epithelium. Hence, this signal is termed the positive EOG. Interestingly, the secretory transduction mechanism has an even shorter latency than that of the transduction mechanism in the receptor cells, consistent with the fact that IP_3 is produced more rapidly than cyclic AMP (16). Consequently, odorants that stimulate secretion generate a small positive transient before the larger negative EOG dominates the response. The supporting cells also contain a high concentration of cytochrome P450-like enzymes (17). These enzymes are thought to oxidize volatile odorants, making them less membrane permeable. Because odorants must be hydrophobic to be volatile, they can readily diffuse across cell membranes. Therefore, oxidation of odorants in the supporting cells may prevent odorants from entering the brain. In most animals, the olfactory epithelium lines the base of the skull (called the cribriform plate), which is porous, thus allowing odorants easy access to the brain.

The basal cells divide and differentiate into mature receptor cells throughout the life of an animal. Basal cells have been divided into two classes: horizontal (flat, cytokeratin-expressing) and globose (round, cytokeratin-negative) (18, 19). Olfactory receptor cells have a lifetime of several months, much shorter than other neurons, possibly because they are exposed to a variety of toxic or infective agents. Cell death has been shown to result from apoptosis (20). Calof et al (21) have proposed two models to explain how receptor cell death might trigger the formation of new receptor cells. In one hypothesis, the feedback inhibition model, proliferation of progenitor cells results from interruption of a negative feedback signal that inhibits progenitor cell proliferation. This model is supported by experiments showing that inhibition of progenitor cell differentiation was caused by culturing of progenitor cells in the presence of an excess of differentiated receptor cells (22). According to the second hypothesis, dying or dead olfactory receptor neurons produce a stimulatory signal that promotes progenitor cell division. This model is supported by experiments showing that apoptotic death of olfactory receptor cells precedes maximum cell loss and the peak of progenitor cell proliferation (20).

Multiple Transduction Mechanisms

Numerous reviews of the olfactory transduction mechanism written during the past six years (2–4, 7, 8) state that there are two excitatory transduction mechanisms, one mediated by cyclic AMP for one subset of odorants, and the other by IP_3 for a different subset of odorants. According to the cyclic AMP model, one subset of odorants activates a subset of receptor proteins (23) that couple, via G_{olf} (24), a G_s-like heterotrimeric G protein, to type 3 adenylyl cyclase (25). This causes a rise in cyclic AMP concentration, which activates cyclic nucleotide-gated ionic channels in olfactory cilia (26). The cyclic nucleotide-gated ionic channels also have a high Ca^{2+} permeability (27) due to a single negative charge within the pore region (28), which results in the activation of a Ca^{2+}-dependent Cl^- channel (29, 30). Lowe & Gold (31) have shown that sequential activation of the cyclic nucleotide-gated and Ca^{2+}-dependent Cl^- channels introduces a threshold into the olfactory transduction mechanism.

According to the IP_3 model (8, 32), a different subset of odorants activates a different subset of receptor proteins that couple via a $G\alpha_q/G\alpha_{11}$-like heterotrimeric G protein to phospholipase C (PLC). PLC cleaves the headgroup of the membrane phospholipid phosphotidyl inositol, producing diacylglycerol (which remains in the membrane) and IP_3 (which is water soluble). According to the IP_3 model, there are IP_3-gated Ca^{2+} channels in the ciliary membrane that mediate Ca^{2+}-influx and membrane depolarization.

The origin of the dual second messenger model can be traced to a biochemical study by Sklar et al (33), who reported that certain odorants did not evoke a significant increase in adenylyl cyclase activity. They concluded from this that there must be a different transduction mechanism to detect odorants that failed to evoke significant cyclase activity. However, the fact that a particular biochemical assay does not detect a significant increase in cyclase activity does not necessarily imply that there is no elevation in cyclase activity. In fact, the largest elevations demonstrated by Sklar et al were quite small, e.g. only a 30–65% increase above the basal cyclase activity for the most effective odorants (33). Thus, the fact that many odorants did not evoke a significant increase in cyclase activity is most likely a consequence of the low sensitivity of this assay. This study was followed by biochemical studies by Breer's group (16, 34, 35), who reported that odorants that did not produce cyclic AMP produced IP_3 instead. This, of course, implied that certain odorants (cyclic AMP odorants) are transduced via the cyclic AMP mechanism, and that other odorants (IP_3 odorants) are transduced by the IP_3 mechanism.

However, it is important to note that the starting material for biochemical measurements is quite impure. Cilia are obtained by a "Ca shock" procedure (36), which removes not only a fraction of the cilia, but also microvilli from the supporting cells, which express an odorant-evoked secretory mechanism (14, 15), as well as other components of the apical and basal surfaces of the olfactory epithelium. There is presently no assay to determine what fraction of membranes in a ciliary preparation consists of cilia. Therefore, it cannot be concluded that any odorant-evoked biochemical responses observed in a ciliary preparation originate in olfactory cilia.

Whether IP_3 production originates in the receptor cells could easily be investigated. Sectioning the olfactory nerve causes transient disappearance of mature receptor cells, which are replaced in about a month by the basal cells, which differentiate into mature receptor cells (18). Therefore, if deciliation were performed before regeneration of the receptor cells occurred, biochemical measurements on the membranes produced by deciliation could definitively establish whether PLC activity is present in the receptor cells. For example, if PLC activity disappeared in the absence of receptor cells, this would indicate that IP_3 formation does indeed originate in the receptor cells. However, if IP_3 production persisted in the absence of the receptor cells, this would indicate that IP_3 production occurs in the supporting cells instead. In this context, it is relevant to note that the kinetics of IP_3 production are slightly faster than the kinetics of cyclic AMP formation. This is consistent with a role for IP_3 in the secretory response, because the latency of the secretory response is shorter than that of olfactory transduction. In fact, immunohistochemistry has been done following bulbectomy that abolished immunoreactivity against an antibody to $G\alpha_q/G\alpha_{11}$ (37). However, this study would be more convincing if in situ hybridization had been used instead of antibodies.

Evidence that the Cyclic AMP Cascade Is the Only Excitatory Transduction Mechanism

As noted above, the first suggestion that there might be more than one transduction mechanism for odorants was the biochemical study by Sklar et al (33). This study was carried out on a bullfrog ciliary preparation and the odorants used were dissolved in an aqueous medium. However, there is an alternative interpretation for these data. It is well known from single unit recordings that there are large differences in the number of receptor cells that respond to individual odorants (38). Thus, an alternative interpretation of the Sklar et al data is that those odorants that failed to evoke significant cyclase activity simply stimulated a smaller number of receptor cells.

Lowe et al (39) tested this hypothesis by comparing the magnitudes of the EOG in bullfrog with the magnitude of cyclase stimulation for 35 of the odorants that were tested by Sklar et al (33). As the EOG is an extracellular field potential, its magnitude reflects not only the magnitude of responses in single cells, but also the number of cells that are activated by each odorant. Consequently, if the differences in the magnitude of cyclase stimulation reported by Sklar et al (33) were due to differences in the number of cells that were activated by each odorant, then one would expect a positive correlation between the magnitude of cyclase activity and the magnitude of the EOG for individual odorants. A correlation coefficient of 0.86 was observed between the magnitudes of cyclase activity and the EOG. This argued that differences in the magnitude of the cyclase activity simply reflected differences in the number of cells that responded to each odorant, and hence that adenylyl cyclase activity was the sole excitatory transduction mechanism.

In spite of this study and concerns about the purity of ciliary preparations, the dual second messenger transduction model has gained widespread acceptance, as can be seen in review articles written during the past six years (2–4, 7, 8). Recently, a different approach was taken to addressing the existence of multiple transduction mechanisms. Knockout mice have been bred for both the cyclic nucleotide-gated ionic channel (40) and for G_{olf} (41), the G protein that is thought to couple olfactory receptor proteins to the type 3 adenylyl cyclase.

In the channel knockout mouse, responses to both the cyclic AMP and IP_3 odorants were abolished (40). This argues that all odorants are transduced by activation of cyclic nucleotide-gated channels. Interestingly, the only odorant that evoked a positive EOG, which originates in the supporting cells, was triethylamine, the strongest of the IP_3 odorants (16).

In the G_{olf} knockout mouse (41), a different phenotype was observed. This is because olfactory receptor cells also express G_s at birth, and G_s has 80% amino acid identity to G_{olf} in the mouse (41). Therefore, G_s is likely to substitute for the missing G_{olf}. In newborn mice, the peak amplitudes of the odorant responses in the G_{olf} knockouts were about 25% of the wild-type responses: This was true for both the cyclic AMP and for IP_3 odorants. However, G_s expression declines after birth (42), and by 3 weeks of age the peak amplitudes of the responses in the G_{olf} knockouts were only 2.5% of the wild-type responses for both cyclic AMP and IP_3 odorants. Also, response latency increased as the peak amplitude decreased. This is expected because as the concentration of G protein decreases, the latency should increase since it takes longer for an activated receptor protein to activate the cyclase as G-protein concentration decreases (43). As reponses to cyclic AMP and IP_3 odorants were affected similarly in the G_{olf} knockout mouse, this study also supports the hypothesis that the cyclic AMP transduction mechanism is the sole excitatory transduction mechanism in vertebrate olfactory receptor cells.

Much of the evidence supporting the IP_3 model rests on the assumption that substances such as ruthenium red and neomycin selectively attenuate the IP_3 pathway (44–46). However, Ma & Michel (47) have shown that these compounds also block the cyclic nucleotide-gated channel.

Gaseous Second Messengers

It has been proposed recently that gaseous second messengers, such as NO and CO, produce cyclic GMP and activate cyclic nucleotide-gated channels. This effect is hypothesized to enhance or prolong responses to odorants, because the production of cyclic GMP outlasts that of cyclic AMP (48). Breer & Shepherd (4) specifically proposed that NO produced during high concentrations of odorant would diffuse to adjacent cells to activate soluble guanylyl cyclase in adjacent cells. However, as receptor proteins are expressed in a random spatial manner, this would lead to loss of specificity. Such an effect is incompatible with adaptation, which is well known to desensitize olfactory receptor cells following exposure to odorants (50). Kurahashi & Menini (51) have shown that adaptation in the newt is mediated by calmodulin-mediated desensitization (52) of the cyclic nucleotide-gated channels. This would desensitize the channels to both cyclic AMP and cyclic GMP.

Zufall & Leinders-Zufall (53) have proposed that the CO/cyclic GMP pathway in tiger salamander mediates a long-lasting form of adaptation. However, the production of CO requires the presence of a free heme group, and it has not been shown whether free heme is present in olfactory receptor cells (54). The data on CO have come from experiments on tiger salamander. However, the generality of this phenomenon, particularly to humans, is questionable because it is well known that CO is odorless to humans. If CO could activate cyclic nucleotide-gated channels in humans, then this gas would have to have an odor, because it would activate a large fraction of receptor cells at the same time.

Broillet & Firestein (55) have shown that NO activates the beta subunit of the cyclic nucleotide-gated channel. However, this begs the question of what ionic channel causes a Ca^{2+} influx that would lead to activation of the NO synthase. As the vomeronasal organ is divided into two halves, one which expresses the beta subunit of the cyclic nucleotide-gated ionic channel, and the other which does not express the beta subunit, there would be no possibility of adjacent cells releasing NO that could diffuse to and activate neighboring cells (56).

A good example of pharmacologic differences between tiger salamander and mammals is illustrated by the drug LY-83583, which has been reported to rapidly and reversibly block the cyclic nucleotide-gated channel in tiger salamander (57). However, I tested this drug on EOG responses in rat and found no effect, at the same concentration that completely blocked the channel in salamander (G Gold, personal observation). This is a good example of the pharmacologist's credo which states that the same drug in a different system is a different drug. Thus, one cannot generalize the effects of drugs across species, even for closely related ionic channels, such as the cyclic nucleotide-gated channel.

Finally, the concentrations of NO and CO reached in the olfactory epithelium have not been measured. Thus, it is not known if the NO and CO concentrations reached in the ciliary layer ever reach the levels of NO and CO as were used in these experiments.

Slow Gating Kinetics of the Cyclic Nucleotide-Gated Ion Channels

Zufall et al (58) have reported that dissociation of cyclic AMP from the olfactory cyclic nucleotide-gated ionic channel is slow. A possible motivation for these observations might be to reconcile the very fast kinetics of cyclic AMP formation and disappearance described by Breer's group (16, 34, 35) with the relatively slow time course of odorant responses measured electrophysiologically. However, the biochemical measurements by Breer's group were all done at 37°C, whereas all electrophysiological measurements have been carried out at room temperature. Thus, there is no contradiction between the fast kinetics of the biochemical responses and those of the electrophysiological responses. In addition, the biochemical measurements have also been performed at very low Ca^{2+} concentrations, making them not directly comparable to electrophysiological measurements. This is because the cyclic nucleotide-gated channels exhibit a high Ca^{2+} permeability (27), so there must be a rise in ciliary Ca^{2+} during an odorant response, which has been confirmed by Leinders-Zufall et al (59).

Two approaches have been used to study the kinetics of the olfactory cyclic nucleotide-gated channel. One is the use of flash photolysis of caged cyclic AMP (31) and the other is rapid solution changes applied to excised patches (58). Figure 2 compares the time course of the current evoked by photolysis of caged cyclic AMP with the duration of an odorant response, recorded from a rat receptor cell. It is clear that the gating kinetics of the photolysis response do not limit the speed of transduction.

In contrast, Zufall et al (58) reported slow dissociation of cyclic AMP from the cyclic nucleotide-gated channel in native membrane patches from the tiger salamander and recombinant rat cyclic nucleotide-gated channels. However, their data do not, in my opinion, demonstrate slow dissociation, as will be explained below. First, their calibration for the speed of solution changes was to apply a step of K^+ concentration to an excised patch and to observe the time-course of the current evoked by this step in K^+ concentration. However, K^+ channels exhibit a logarithmic (non-saturating) dependence on K^+ concentration, whereas cyclic nucleotide-gated channels exhibit a saturating dose dependence. Therefore, observing fast kinetics for K^+ removal does not establish how rapidly cyclic AMP concentrations that are superthreshold for activating channels would decline after the channels are exposed to a suprasaturating cyclic AMP concentration. In fact, Zufall et al (57) observed only a slow decay in the cyclic AMP-evoked current when the peak cyclic AMP concentration was 1 mM, well above the half-saturating cyclic AMP (20 μM). This implies that the slow decay was simply a consequence of the time it takes for a suprasaturating cyclic AMP concentration to decay to ineffective levels. Thus, the evidence that

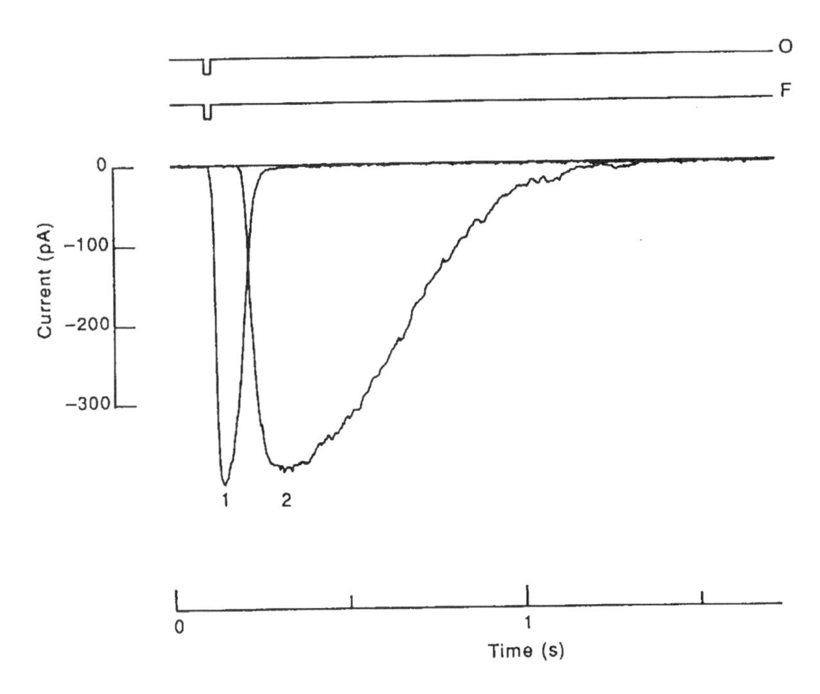

Figure 2 *Trace 1*, response to a 40 msec flash of ultraviolet light. *Trace 2*, response to a 40 msec pulse of odorant from a stimulus micropipette. (Reprinted with permission from *Nature* from Reference 31.)

dissociation of cyclic AMP from the olfactory cyclic nucleotide-gated channel is slow may be weak.

Detection of Single Odorant Molecules

The minimum stimulus that can be detected reliably by a cellular transducer is determined by the magnitude of the stimulus energy relative to thermal energy. Every cellular transducer is in thermal equilibrium with its environment. Consequently, the ability of an olfactory receptor cell to detect single odorant molecules is determined by the binding energy of an odorant molecule relative to thermal energy. Whereas Torre et al (60) state that binding affinities for volatile odorants are in the micromolar range, in fact, the affinity of an olfactory receptor protein for a volatile odorant has never been measured. One cannot infer the affinity of a receptor protein for its ligand from the dose-response curve because, as shown by Lowe & Gold (31), the shape of the dose-response curve is determined by the mechanism of current generation in olfactory receptor cells, not by the affinity of the receptor protein for odorants. Consequently, the quantitative relationship between the dose-response curve and odorant-receptor binding affinity remains unknown.

Rod photoreceptors (61) and certain invertebrate photoreceptors (62–64) can detect single photons of light because the energy contained by a 500 nm photon, the wavelength of maximal absorption for many rod photoreceptors, is many times the mean thermal energy. The activation energy for thermal bleaching of rhodopsin is about 23.2 kcal/mol at 20°C (65) or about 1.6×10^{-12} erg per molecule of rhodopsin. In contrast, the total energy of a 500 nm photon is $hc/\lambda = 4 \times 10^{-12}$ erg, where $h = 6.6 \times 10^{-34}$ Joule · sec (Planck's constant), $c = 3 \times 10^{8}\ m \cdot sec^{-1}$ (the speed of light), and $\lambda = 5 \times 10^{-7}$ m (the wavelength of light) (66). Not all of this energy is absorbed by rhodopsin. Therefore, a single photon contains about $4/1.6 = 2.5$ times the mean thermal energy and provides a significant energy increment to a cell. In addition, visual pigments are stable because of the covalent attachment between the chromophore and the opsin protein. By contrast, the affinities of odorant receptors for volatile odorants have never been measured. Measuring such affinities is problematic because volatile odorants are hydrophobic and are concentrated in membrane preparations.

Boeckh et al (67) argued that the male silk moth, *Bombyx mori*, can detect single molecules of the female pheromone. This determination rests on the assumption that pheromone evaporation rate is proportional to the amount of odorant loaded onto a piece of filter paper. Adam & Delbruck (68) pointed out that this extrapolation may not be valid. Perhaps the most convincing evidence of single molecular detection comes from experiments on dogs (69). Neuhaus & Muller (69) showed that the detection threshold of the dachshund for butyric acid corresponds to an odorant concentration that provides one molecule of butyric acid per 82 receptor cells. This implies that the dachshund can detect single molecules of butyric acid.

In 1995, Menini et al (70) published a paper claiming to estimate the current evoked by a single odorant molecule in certain receptor cells from the tiger salamander. From an analysis of the frequency of failures, i.e. the frequency of repeated stimuli that failed to generate a response, it was concluded that single molecules of cineole evoked currents of 0.3–1.0 pA in some salamander receptor cells. However, the use of this analysis is not valid when applied to olfactory receptor cells because the frequency of failures requires a linear system (71), and it is well known that olfactory transduction is highly non-linear, exhibiting Hill coefficients of 3 or higher (31, 72). This contrasts with the situation in photoreceptors, where the dose-response curve is linear down to zero intensity (73). Lowe & Gold (74) instead argued that fluctuations in the amplitudes of near threshold responses can be explained by fluctuations in the basal cyclic AMP concentration, with respect to the threshold for current generation.

That the fluctuations in response amplitude reported by Menini et al (70) are not likely to reflect fluctuations in the number of odorant-receptor interactions is also supported by a comparison between traces b and c, in Figure 1 of Menini et al, which show responses to 0.5 and 1.0 μM odorant. If the current bumps seen in trace b, were really due to single odorant molecules, then the frequency of bumps should be doubled in trace c. However, the mean current in trace c is much more than double that in trace b, which argues that these bumps are not due to single odorant molecules. The large increase in current, caused by doubling the odorant concentration, is more readily explained by the cAMP concentration exceeding the threshold for current generation (31).

Finally, one other problem with the Menini et al study was that it required a very high odorant concentration (0.5 sec pulse of 10 μM cineole). Based on equation 2.23 of Berg (75),

$$I = 4\pi \text{ Da Co/ln } (2a/b),$$

[where I is total flux, Co is concentration at infinity, and the ellipsoid of revolution $\rightarrow a^2 \gg b^2$ (true cilium)], we estimated that this concentration creates a flux of about 10^8 molecules per second onto the combined surface area of the cilia (76). While it is formally possible that the receptor proteins on this cell have a low affinity for this odorant, a high affinity would be required for each odorant molecule to generate a current of about 0.3–1.0 pA. This is because low affinity implies a short duration of binding between the odorant molecule and the receptor proteins on this cell; a short duration of binding could not generate a large response.

As odorant detection thresholds in humans vary across odorants over many orders of magnitude (77), it cannot be concluded that single molecular detection is a common property of vertebrate olfactory receptor cells. As a result, the demonstration of single molecular detection may not be possible until methods exist for repeatedly recording from a receptor cell expressing a known receptor protein.

Suppression of Odorant Responses by Odorants

In 1994, Kurahashi et al published a paper (78) showing that odorants can have a dual effect on olfactory receptor cells. Not only do odorants evoke an inward current in olfactory receptor cells, but odorants can also suppress this current. Interestingly, the suppressive effect has a shorter latency than the initiation of an inward current.

How can odorants suppress the odorant-evoked current with a shorter latency than that of excitatory transduction? As proposed by Kurahashi et al (78), a simple explanation for this phenomenon would be a blockage of ionic channels by odorants. As volatile odorants are hydrophobic, they are likely to be concentrated in cell membranes, where they could exert an anesthetic-like effect on ionic channels. Recently, Kurahashi and colleagues (79) have shown that odorants block a variety of voltage-dependent Na^+, Ca^{2+}, and K^+ channels in olfactory receptor cells. Thus, it is likely that odorants may also block cyclic nucleotide-gated channels, which would cause suppression of odorant responses. It is important to remember that responsive cells are selected at random from dissociated cells in the recording chamber. This procedure for finding a responsive cell is simply to apply the odorant solution used until one finds a cell that responds to the odorant or odorants used. This procedure also selects for cells that are relatively insensitive to the odorant or odorants used. This provides a simple explanation for suppression: The odorant concentration is initially quite high, immediately after the bolus of odorant is ejected from the stimulus micropipette, and then decays as the bolus of odorant spreads by diffusion. Thus, there is no contradiction between the relatively rapid effect of odorants on suppressing the odorant response and the latency of transduction. Consequently, in many experiments, the long latency of olfactory transduction seen in single-cell recordings may be a direct effect of blockage of the cyclic nucleotide-gated channels by odorants, which are initially present at high concentrations.

Literature Cited

1. Lancet D. 1986. Vertebrate olfactory reception. *Annu. Rev. Neurosci.* 9:329–55
2. Reed RR. 1992. Signalling pathways in odorant detection. *Neuron* 8:205–9
3. Ronnett GV, Snyder SH. 1992. Molecular messengers of olfaction. *Trends Neurosci.* 15:508–13
4. Breer H, Shepherd GM. 1993. Implications of the NO/cGMP system for olfaction. *Trends Neurosci.* 16:5–9
5. Firestein S, Zufall F. 1994. The cyclic nucleotide gated channel of olfactory receptor neurons. *Semin. Cell Biol.* 5:39–46
6. Zufall F, Firestein S, Shepherd GM. 1994. Cyclic nucleotide-gated channels and sensory transduction in olfactory receptor neurons. *Annu. Rev. Biophys. Biomol. Struct.* 23:577–607
7. Ache BW, Zhainazarov A. 1995. Dual second-messenger pathways in olfactory transduction. *Curr. Opin. Neurobiol.* 5: 461–66
8. Restrepo D, Teeter JH, Schild D. 1996. Second messenger signalling in olfactory transduction. *J. Neurobiol.* 30:37–48
9. Moulton DG, Beidler LM. 1967. Structure and function in the peripheral olfactory system. *Physiol. Rev.* 47:1–52
10. Firestein S, Werblin F. 1989. Odor-induced membrane currents in vertebrate-olfactory receptor neurons. *Science* 244:79–82
11. Kurahashi T. 1989. Activation by odorants of cation-selective conductance in the olfactory receptor cell isolated from the newt. *J. Physiol.* 419:177–92
12. Lowe G, Gold GH. 1991. The spatial distributions of odorant sensitivity and odorant induced currents in salamander olfactory receptor cells. *J. Physiol.* 442:147–68
13. Ottoson D. 1956. Comparison of the slow potentials evoked in the frog's nasal mucosa and olfactory bulb by natural stimulation. *Acta Physiol. Scand.* 35:1–86
14. Okano M, Takagi SF. 1974. Secretion and electrogenesis of the supporting cell in the olfactory epithelium. *J. Physiol.* 242:353–70
15. Getchell ML, Zielinski B, DeSimone JA, Getchell TV. 1987. Histological and histochemical studies of the secretory compo-

nents of the salamander olfactory mucosa: effects of isoproterenol and olfactory nerve section. *J. Comp. Physiol.* 160:155–68
16. Breer H, Boekhoff I. 1991. Odorants of the same class activate different second messenger pathways. *Chem. Senses* 16:19–29
17. Lazard D, Zupko K, Poria Y, Nef P, Lazarovits J, et al. 1991. Odorant signal termination by olfactory UDP glucuronosyl transferase. *Nature* 349:790–93
18. Graziadei PPC, Monti Graziadei GA. 1979. Neurogenesis and neuron regeneration in the olfactory system of mammals. I. Morphological aspects of differentiation and structural organization of the olfactory sensory neurons. *J. Neurocytol.* 8:1–18
19. Calof AL, Chikaraishi DM. 1989. Analysis of nuerogenesis in a mammalian neuroepithelium: proliferation and differentiation of an olfactory neuron precursor in vitro. *Neuron* 3:115–27
20. Holcomb JD, Mumm JS, Calof AL. 1995. Apoptosis in the neuronal lineage of the mouse olfactory epithelium: regulation in vivo and in vitro. *Dev. Biol.* 172:307–23
21. Calof AL, Mumm JS, Rim PC, Shou J. 1988. The neuronal stem cell of the olfactory epithelium. *J. Neurobiol.* 36:190–206
22. Mumm JS, Shou J, Calof AL. 1996. Colony-forming progenitors from mouse olfactory epithelium: evidence for feedback regulation of neuron production. *Proc. Natl. Acad. Sci. USA* 93:11167–72
23. Buck L, Axel R. 1991. A novel multigene family may encode odorant receptors: a molecular basis for odor recognition. *Cell* 65:175–87
24. Jones DT, Reed RR. 1989. G_{olf}: an olfactory neuron-specific G protein involved in odorant signal transduction. *Science* 244:790–95
25. Bakalyar HA, Reed RR. 1990. Identification of a specialized adenylyl cyclase that may mediate odorant detection. *Science* 250:1403–6
26. Nakamura T, Gold GH. 1987. A cyclic nucleotide-gated conductance in olfactory receptor cilia. *Nature* 325:442–44
27. Kurahashi T, Kaneko A, Shibuya T. 1990. Ionic mechanisms of the olfactory transduction studied on isolated receptor cells of the newt. *Neurosci. Res. Suppl.* 12:S85–96
28. Eismann E, Muller F, Heinemann SH, Kaupp UB. 1994. A single negative charge within the pore region of a cGMP-gated channel controls rectification, Ca^{2+} blockage, and ionic selectivity. *Proc. Natl. Acad. Sci. USA* 91:1109–13
29. Kleene SJ. 1993. Origin of the chloride current in olfactory transduction. *Neuron* 11:123–32
30. Kurahashi T, Yau KW. 1993. Co-existence of cationic and chloride components in odorant-induced current of vertebrate olfactory receptor cells. *Nature* 363:71–74
31. Lowe G, Gold GH. 1993. Nonlinear amplification by calcium-dependent chloride channels in olfactory receptor cells. *Nature* 366:283–86
32. Berridge MJ. 1993. Inositol triphosphate and calcium signalling. *Nature* 361:315–25
33. Sklar PB, Anholt RRH, Snyder SH. 1986. The odorant-sensitive adenylate cyclase of olfactory receptor cells. Differential stimulation by distinct classes of odorants. *J. Biol. Chem.* 261:15538–43
34. Breer H, Boekhoff I, Tareilus E. 1990. Rapid kinetics of second messenger formation in olfactory transduction. *Nature* 345:65–68
35. Boekhoff I, Tareilus E, Strotmann J, Breer H. 1990. Rapid activation of alternative second messenger pathways in olfactory cilia by different odorants. *EMBO J.* 9:2453–58
36. Anholt RRH. 1995. Preparation of olfactory cilia. In *Experimental Cell Biology of Taste and Olfaction*, ed. AI Spielman, JG Brand. pp. 163–68. Boca Raton, FL: CRC Press
37. Dellacorte C, Restrepo D, Menco BP, Andreini I, Kalinoski DL. 1996. $G\alpha_q/G\alpha_{11}$: immunolocalization in the olfactory epithelium of the rat (*Rattus rattus*) and the channel catfish (*Ictalurus punctatus*). *Neuroscience* 74:261–73
38. Revial MF, Sicard G, Duchamp A, Holley A. 1982. New studies on odour discrimination in the frog's olfactory receptor cells. I. Experimential results. *Chem. Senses* 7:175–90
39. Lowe G, Nakamura T, Gold GH. 1989. Adenylate cyclase mediates olfactory transduction for a wide variety of odorants. *Proc. Natl. Acad. Sci. USA* 86:5641–45
40. Brunet LJ, Gold GH, Ngai J. 1996. General anosmia caused by a targetted disruption of the mouse olfactory cyclic neucleotide-gated cation channel. *Neuron* 17:681–93
41. Belluscio L, Gold GH, Nemes A, Axel R. 1998. Mice deficient in G_{olf} are anosmic. *Neuron* 20:69–81
42. Jones DT. 1990. Distribution of the stimulatory GTP-binding proteins G_s and G_{olf} within olfactory neuroepithelium. *Chem. Senses* 15:333–40
43. Lamb TD, Pugh EN Jr. 1992. A quantitative account of the activation steps

involved in phototransduction in amphibian photoreceptors. *J. Physiol.* 449:719–58
44. Miyamoto T, Restrepo D, Cragoe EJ Jr, Teeter JH. 1992. IP_3- and cAMP-induced responses in isolated olfactory receptor neurons from the channel catfish. *J. Memb. Biol.* 127:173–83
45. Okada Y, Teeter JH, Restrepo D. 1994. Inositol 1,4,5-trisphosphate-gated conductance in isolated rat olfactory neurons. *J. Neurophysiol.* 71:595–602
46. Schild D, Lischka FW, Restrepo D. 1995. $InsP_3$ causes an increase in apical $[Ca^{2+}]_i$ by activating two distinct current components in vertebrate olfactory receptor cells. *J. Neurophysiol.* 73:862–66
47. Ma L, Michel WC. 1998. Drugs affecting phospholipase C–mediated signal transduction block the cyclic nucleotide-gated channel of adult zebrafish. *J. Neurophysiol.* 79:1183–92
48. Breer H, Klemm T, Boekhoff I. 1992. Nitric oxide mediated formation of cyclic GMP in the olfactory system. *Neuroreport* 3:1030–32
49. Deleted in proof
50. Kurahashi T, Shibuya T. 1990. Ca^{2+}-dependent adaptive properties in the solitary olfactory receptor cells of the newt. *Brain Res.* 515:261–68
51. Kurahashi T, Menini A. 1997. Mechanism of odorant adaption in the olfactory receptor cell. *Nature* 385:725–29
52. Liu M, Chen TY, Ahamed B, Yau KW. 1994. Calcium-calmodulin modulation of the olfactory cyclic nucleotide-gated cation channel. *Science* 266:1348–54
53. Zufall F, Leinders-Zufall T. 1997. Identification of a long-lasting form of odor adaptation that depends on the carbon monoxide/cGMP second-messenger system. *J. Neurosci.* 17:2703–12
54. Maines MD, Kappas A. 1974. Cobalt induction of hepatic heme oxygenase; with evidence that cyctochrome P-450 is not essential for this enzyme activity. *Proc. Natl. Acad. Sci. USA* 71:4293–97
55. Broillet MC, Firestein S. 1997. Beta subunits of the olfactory cyclic nucleotide-gated channel form a nitric oxide activated Ca^{2+} channel. *Neuron* 18:951–58
56. Berghard A, Buck LB, Liman ER. 1996. Evidence for distinct signalling mechanisms in two mammalian olfactory sense organs. *Proc. Natl. Acad. Sci. USA* 93: 2365–69
57. Leinders-Zufall T, Zufall F. 1995. Block of cyclic nucleotide-gated channels in salamander olfactory receptor neurons by the guanylyl cyclase inhibitor LY83583. *J. Neurophysiol.* 74:2759–62
58. Zufall F, Hatt H, Firestein S. 1993. Rapid application and removal of second messengers to cyclic nucleotide-gated channels from olfactory epithelium. *Proc. Natl. Acad. Sci. USA* 90:9335–39
59. Leinders-Zufall T, Rand MN, Shepherd GM, Greer CA, Zufall F. 1997. Calcium entry through cyclic nucleotide-gated channels in individual cilia of olfactory receptor cell: spatiotemporal dynamics. *J. Neurosci.* 17:4136–48
60. Torre V, Ashmore JF, Lamb TD, Menini A. 1995. Transduction and adaptation in sensory receptor cells. *J. Neurosci.* 15(12): 7757–68
61. Baylor DA, Lamb TD, Yau K-W. 1979. Responses of retinal rods to single photons. *J. Physiol.* 288:613–34
62. Fuortes MGF, Yeandle S. 1964. Probability of occurrence of discrete potential waves in the eye of *Limulus*. *J. Gen. Physiol.* 47: 443–63
63. Scholes J. 1965. Discontinuity of the excitation in locust visual cells. *Cold Spring Harbor Symp. Quant. Biol.* 40:517–27
64. Srebro R, Behbehani M. 1972. The thermal origin of spontaneous activity in the *Limulus* photoreceptor. *J. Physiol.* 224:349–61
65. Yau KW, Matthews G, Baylor DA. 1979. Thermal activation of the visual transduction mechanism in retinal rods. *Nature* 279:785–86
66. Halliday D, Resnick R. 1986. *Fundamentals of Physics*. New York: Wiley
67. Boeckh J, Kaissling KE, Schneider D. 1965. Insect olfactory receptors. *Cold Spring Harbor Symp. Quant. Biol.* 30:263–80
68. Adam G, Delbruck M. 1968. Reduction of dimensionality in biological diffusion processes. In *Structural Chemistry and Molecular Biology*, ed. A Rich, N Davidson. San Francisco: Freeman
69. Neuhaus W, Muller A. 1954. Das Verhaltnis der Iriechzellenzahl vur Riechschwelle veil Hund. *Naturwissenschaften* 41:237–38
70. Menini A, Picco C, Firestein S. 1995. Quantal-like current fluctuations induced by odorants in olfactory receptor cells. *Nature* 373:435–37
71. Del Castillo J, Katz B. 1954. Quantal components of the end-plate potential. *J. Physiol.* 124:560–73
72. Firestein S, Picco C, Menini A. 1993. The relation between stimulus and response in olfactory receptor cells of the tiger salamander. *J. Physiol.* 468:1–10
73. Baylor DA, Lamb TD, Yau KW. 1979. The membrane current of single rod outer segments. *J. Physiol.* 288:589–611

74. Lowe G, Gold GH. 1995. Olfactory transduction is intrinsically noisy. *Proc. Natl. Acad. Sci. USA* 92:7864–68
75. Berg HC. 1993. *Random Walks in Biology*. Princeton, NJ: Princeton Univ. Press
76. Gold GH, Lowe G. 1995. Single odorant molecules? *Nature* 376:27
77. Devos M, Patte F, Rouault J, Laffort P, Van Gemert LJ. 1990. *Standardized Human Olfactory Thresholds*. New York: IRL Press
78. Kurahashi T, Lowe G, Gold GH. 1994. Suppression of odorant responses by odorants in olfactory receptor cells. *Science* 265:118–20
79. Kawai F, Kurahashi T, Kaneko A. 1997. Nonselective suppression of voltage-gated currents by odorants in the newt olfactory receptor cells. *J. Gen. Physiol.* 109:265–72

Annu. Rev. Physiol. 1999. 61:873–900

CELLULAR MECHANISMS OF TASTE TRANSDUCTION

M. Scott Herness
College of Dentistry, Ohio State University, 305 West 12th Avenue, Columbus, Ohio 43210-1241; e-mail: herness.1@osu.edu

Timothy A. Gilbertson
Pennington Biomedical Research Center, Louisiana State University, 6400 Perkins Road, Baton Rouge, Louisiana 70808-4124; e-mail: tim.gilbertson@tasteful.com

KEY WORDS: gustatory, chemical senses, sensory physiology, receptors, ion channels

ABSTRACT

Taste receptor cells respond to gustatory stimuli using a complex arrangement of receptor molecules, signaling cascades, and ion channels. When stimulated, these cells produce action potentials that result in the release of neurotransmitter onto an afferent nerve fiber that in turn relays the identity and intensity of the gustatory stimuli to the brain. A variety of mechanisms are used in transducing the four primary tastes. Direct interaction of the stimuli with ion channels appears to be of particular importance in transducing stimuli reported as salty or sour, whereas the second messenger systems cyclic AMP and inositol trisphosphate are important in transducing bitter and sweet stimuli. In addition to the four basic tastes, specific mechanisms exist for the amino acid glutamate, which is sometimes termed the fifth primary taste, and for fatty acids, a so-called nonconventional taste stimulus. The emerging picture is that not only do individual taste qualities use more than one mechanism, but multiple pathways are available for individual tastants as well.

INTRODUCTION

The peripheral gustatory system has two distinct roles. During ingestion, it must distinguish the nutritive and beneficial compounds from those that are potentially harmful or toxic. These two functions, one of nutrient detection

0066-4278/99/0315-0873$08.00

and the other of toxin avoidance, place a heavy demand on the gustatory system. Taste receptor cells must be able to detect a wide range of chemicals, everything from simple ions, such as sodium and protons, to very complex compounds, including numerous bitter and sweet molecules (1–3). Thus the major role of taste receptor cells is to recognize these chemical signals and translate this information into the language of the cell, as either changes in membrane potential or intracellular free calcium concentration. These changes alter the release of neurotransmitters onto gustatory afferent nerve fibers, which relay this information to the brain. As might be expected by the diverse chemical compounds that stimulate the gustatory system, the transduction mechanisms found in taste receptor cells are both numerous and varied. The specific signal transduction pathways in taste cells, involving interactions of sapid molecules with ion channels, ionotropic and metabotropic receptors, and intracellular targets, are similar to those found in most other neurons.

Despite the rich array of chemicals to which the taste system responds, there are generally considered to be only four or five basic tastes. These tastes are grouped according to the human descriptors of salty, sour, sweet, and bitter. In addition, the taste of monosodium glutamate (MSG) may represent a taste, termed *umami*, distinct from the other basic tastes (4, 5). Broadly speaking, the appetitive tastes (salty, sweet, and umami) reflect the identification of potential nutrients, whereas the generally aversive bitter, and possibly sour, tastes may reflect the rejection of toxic compounds. It has long been assumed that the most energy-dense nutrient, fat (9 kcal/gm vs 4 kcal/gm for protein and carbohydrate), had virtually no taste component (6, 7). However, recent evidence has identified that fat itself, in the form of free fatty acids, may possess salient gustatory cues (8, 9). Thus progress in recent years has been made in terms of the identification of additional taste stimuli and their mechanisms of action.

Recent work has made it increasingly clear that individual classes of taste stimuli or even individual compounds do not rely on one single transduction mechanism. In addition, overlap may exist among various classes of stimuli on a single transduction pathway. These properties have two effects in the gustatory system. First, they may contribute to the many subtle tastes present in foods containing mixtures of individual chemical components. Second, overlap of transduction pathways may account for the ability of individual taste stimuli to be described as having more than a single taste, such as sodium chloride being described as both salty and sour (10, 11). The following sections focus on the taste transduction mechanisms described for the major classes of gustatory stimuli, with a particular emphasis on work in mammalian species.

FUNCTIONAL ANATOMY OF THE PERIPHERAL TASTE SYSTEM

Location of Taste Receptor Cells

In mammals, taste receptor cells are grouped into morphological units known as *taste buds*. Taste buds are distributed throughout the oral cavity in both lingual and extralingual locations (e.g. 12). In humans, about two-thirds of these taste buds are located on the tongue in three specialized structures: fungiform, foliate, and circumvallate papillae. The remaining third are located on the soft palate and in the epiglottis. Lower mammals have an additional extralingual location: the nasoincisor duct, a specialized structure immediately caudal to the incisor teeth that forms a conduit between the oral and nasal cavities.

Taste buds are remarkably similar in appearance, regardless of their location within the oral cavity. Variously described as onion shaped or bulb-like, taste buds comprise 50–100 individual cells collected together into a spherical structure that is 20–40 μm in diameter and 40–60 μm in length (thus an entire taste bud may be the size of a single motorneuron soma). Individual taste cells are slender and columnar, stretching from the basal lamina to the most apical region, where they sequester into a pore region, about 5–7 microns in diameter. Nerve fibers enter from the base of the taste bud and synapse onto some of the taste cells. Depending on their location within the oral cavity, the nerve fibers entering the bud have origins in facial, glossopharyngeal, or vagus nerves (cranial nerves VII, IX, or X). Branches of the facial nerve, the chorda tympani and greater superficial petrosal nerve, innervate the anterior two-thirds of the tongue and the palate, respectively. The glossopharyngeal nerve innervates the foliate and circumvallate papillae of the posterior tongue, and the superior laryngeal nerve, a branch of the vagus nerve, innervates the epiglottal taste buds. These nerve fibers, which transmit information to the brain, may be classified as intragemmal because they enter the taste bud. Nerve fibers of trigeminal origin (cranial nerve V) may surround taste buds; these perigemmal fibers serve as free nerve endings, to relay thermal, tactile, and common chemical sense information to the brain.

Cell Types

Although taste buds display similarity across locations within the oral cavity, individual taste cells within a taste bud are diverse. Multiple classification schemes have arisen to describe these cells. One of the earliest schemes divided taste cells into two groups: light and dark cells (13). With the application of electron microscopy to taste cells, Murray & Murray (14) applied ultrastructural criteria to taste cells and classified cell types using roman numerals I through IV. Of these, only Types I through III could theoretically be considered taste receptor cells, because they had processes extending into the taste pore; Type IV cells are basal cells and do not contact taste stimuli directly.

Some overlap exists between these classification schemes. Type I cells are also considered dark cells. They are the predominant cell type of the bud, constituting about 55–75% of all the cells (e.g. 14, 15). Their distinctive features include the presence of dense granules in apical cytoplasm that are thought to be secreted into the taste pore, numerous intermediate filaments, abundant rough endoplasmic reticulum, and deeply indented, irregularly shaped nuclei. Type II cells are considered light cells; they are distinguished by electron-lucent cytoplasm and large oval nuclei. Further distinguishing them from Type I cells is the presence of smooth endoplasmic reticulum and scant rough endoplasmic reticulum. Type II cells constitute about 20% of the cells in the bud. Type III cells are unique. Continuing the light-dark axis of categorization, they are sometimes called intermediate cells. Although they are similar to Type II cells, they possess numerous dense-core vesicles, particularly in their basal portion. Their unique feature is their unequivocal synaptic connections to afferent nerve fibers. For some time, only Type III cells were thought to be connected to the afferent nervous system. Type III cells have been reported in rabbits (16), monkeys (16, 17), humans (18), and mice (19). In mouse taste buds, synapses have been observed on both Type I and Type II cells, challenging the uniqueness of the Type III category (20); however, in rabbit, Type III cells are the only cell type that forms synapses (21, 22).

Because taste cells regenerate (23), a recurrent discussion has arisen over whether these cell types arise from separate lineages or represent a continuum of cells in varying stages of differentiation (24, 25). Along this line, researchers explored the application of autoradiography with high-voltage electron microscopy on rat taste cells (15). Mouse taste buds were injected with tritiated thymidine (which is incorporated only into dividing, and hence young, cells) and subsequently observed at varying times after injection. From the resulting images of labeled cells, the researchers concluded that one cell type was undergoing a repeated turnover cycle; thus the taste cell might be viewed as a progression from basal to dark to intermediate to light cells. Others, however, regard light cells as a separate cell line (26, 27). In support of this view, one study suggests that cell types in the rat circumvallate papillae are distinct cell types rather than a continuum (28). Distinctions between true taste receptor cells and supporting cells remain unresolved.

GENERAL STEPS IN TASTE RECEPTOR CELL ACTIVATION

Within the past decade, it has become generally accepted that taste receptor cells respond to taste stimuli with action potentials. Previously, taste cells were thought to be electrically inexcitable. Intracellular recordings of the taste-cell membrane potential had consistently reported graded receptor potentials rather than action potentials in response to taste stimuli, agreeing well with the notion that taste cells are of epithelial origin and thus electrically inexcitable. Hence, these cells were considered passive—that is, they could be understood by simple electrical cable theory as a fixed resistor-capacitor model with potentials spreading electronically. With improved electrophysiological techniques, it became clear that, in electrical terms, taste cells are more like neurons than like epithelial cells. They elicit action potentials through a variety of active currents, many of whose biophysical properties have now been studied in detail.

Membrane Properties of Taste Receptor Cells

To generate an action potential, taste cells would require both a prerequisite repertoire of ion channels, such as voltage-dependent sodium and potassium channels, and a high input resistance, which would allow small ionic currents to have large effects on the membrane potential. Electrical excitability was not observed initially in taste cells. Even though the cells had the requisite set of ion channels, early work inadvertently reduced the input resistance by several orders of magnitude because of the injury of impalement by sharp microelectrodes. Adequate voltage-clamp of the cells was not possible. With patch-clamp recordings, injury became minimal and the input resistance of taste cells was discovered to be quite high. For example, in rat taste cells the input resistance of taste cells can be in the range of 1 to 10 GΩ (29–31). In this range, a receptor current of only a few picoamperes could change the membrane potential by several tens of millivolts. Hence a tastant that elicited a receptor current of only a few picoamperes could be sufficient to reach threshold for eliciting an action potential mediated by voltage-dependent sodium channels.

High-quality voltage-clamp studies of mammalian taste cells have characterized biophysically a variety of voltage-dependent ion channels. In mammals, these currents include voltage-dependent sodium channels (31, 32), outward potassium currents (30), inward potassium currents (33), voltage-dependent calcium currents (29, 34), and chloride currents (35). There are also ionic currents that are not voltage dependent, such as the amiloride-sensitive sodium current (described below). In frog taste cells a sodium-activated potassium current (36) and a unique cyclic nucleotide-suppressible current (37) have been reported. In rat taste cells, a channel has been cloned that is activated by cyclic nucleotides (38).

Voltage-dependent sodium channels are found in most taste cells (31, 32, 39). However, some taste cells have too low a density of voltage-dependent sodium channels to be electrically excitable. The density of sodium channels varies considerably among individual taste cells (31). Population studies of maximal sodium current showed two peaks, one at 250 pA and one at 500 pA. It is unclear what other variables, such as chemical sensitivity or cell age, may correlate with sodium current density. In taste cells, the maximal conductance of sodium currents may be up to 9 nS.

Outward potassium currents are similarly varied. These currents are composed of transient currents (with time constants ranging from 1 to 9 s), delayed rectifier currents, and calcium-activated potassium currents (30). The maximal conductance of potassium currents ($\sim$18 nS) is much higher than of sodium currents. In contrast, inward potassium currents were more homogeneous across cells (33). All tested cells possessed inward-rectifying potassium currents, with a conductance of about 1.5 nS. These currents are thought to contribute to the resting potential of taste cells and may be gated directly by G proteins (40) because GTPβS inhibited these currents, whereas GDPβS, cyclic AMP (cAMP) analogs, or forskolin were ineffective. Presumably a G protein–linked receptor, whose agonist remains to be elucidated, is coupled to these channels. Chloride currents are also diverse. Although their conductance is small ($<$1 nS), chloride currents may also contribute to the resting potential. These currents have both calcium-activated and outward-rectifying components.

Role of Action Potentials in Taste Cell Activity

When action potentials were first observed in taste receptor cells, their physiological basis was not apparent. Many classical justifications for action potentials were not germane to taste cells. For example, propagation over a long distance is unnecessary. Based on the length constant of the taste cell, passive receptor potentials would not be reduced much and could be sufficient for transmitter release. However, action potentials may be a more effective stimulus for transmitter release by activating high-threshold calcium current (29). Thus an action potential would serve as an explicit signal to release transmitter. Another explanation could involve cell-to-cell communication. Taste cells are thought to be electrically coupled via gap junctions, and not all cells are synaptically connected to the afferent nerve. Thus an action potential in one cell could unambiguously excite its neighbor. The excited cell could thus cause transmitter release even though it does not have a synapse (31). These explanations are not mutually exclusive. Action potentials may serve multiple functions.

Taste stimuli may elicit action potentials in taste receptor cells. Action potentials have been recorded extracellularly from taste cells (41–43) and intracellularly in isolated taste cells in response to sweet stimuli (29, 42). A variety of ionic currents likely contribute to the action potential (30). Sodium and calcium currents contribute to the depolarizing phase, whereas potassium currents contribute to the repolarization and afterhyperpolarization phases. Mammalian taste cells have at least two types of action potentials, termed FAST and SLOW (30). SLOW action potentials have a half-duration of 9.6 ms compared to 1.4 ms for FAST action potentials. About 25% of cells eliciting action potentials are classified as SLOW. The two types of action potentials are correlated strongly with potassium-channel density. FAST has large potassium currents, with a mean of 2500 pA, compared to a mean of 370 pA for SLOW cells. Differences in inward currents are not apparent. These differences in potassium currents may be related to cell turnover or cell age. A similar phenomenon, suggesting that the repertoire of ion channels in taste cells is linked developmentally, has been observed in the mudpuppy, in which most immature taste cells lacked inward currents and mature cells had both inward and outward currents (44).

Neurotransmitter Release

The ultimate consequence of an action potential in a taste cell is the release of neurotransmitter onto the afferent nerve. Much effort has been expended toward identifying this neurotransmitter, but a single candidate has failed to emerge; rather, multiple transmitters may operate within the taste bud (see 45 for a recent review). In addition to afferent nerve stimulation, neurotransmitters may also have neuromodulatory roles within the taste bud. Recent developments in this area have focused on GABAergic, serotonergic, and adrenergic systems.

Using an immunocytochemical approach, researchers localized GABA and the GAT-3 GABA transporter to taste receptor cells in rat circumvallate papillae (46). As with other neurotransmitters, only a few taste cells within the bud stained immunopositive for GABA. The GAT-3 transporter was also localized to one or two taste cells within the bud, generally at its margin, whereas the GAT-2 transporter was localized to extragemmal nerve fibers and GAT-1 was not observed. The localization of GABA and its transporters certainly suggests a possible role for GABA in taste cell physiology.

Serotonin immunoreactivity has been observed in taste cells of several amphibian and mammalian species (e.g. 47). These anatomical localizations have been supplemented with physiological observations in both mudpuppy and rat taste receptor cells. In the mudpuppy, a subpopulation of basal cells, rather than taste receptor cells, contains serotonin (48). It was hypothesized that these basal cells release serotonin onto taste cells in a neuromodulatory fashion during taste stimulation. When exogenous serotonin was applied to mudpuppy taste cells, an increased response to potassium chloride with an increased input resistance was observed (49), although the underlying membrane conductance remains unknown. Calcium currents were examined recently. Serotonin enhanced the current in one-third of the tested cells, whereas it inhibited the current in the other cells (50). These observations suggest that a complex system of interaction may occur within the taste bud.

Serotonin also has effects on rat taste cells. For example, exogenous serotonin application inhibited a calcium-activated potassium current by up to 50% (51). This current was both apamin and charybdotoxin sensitive, suggesting that it is composed of both high-conductance and low-conductance calcium-activated potassium channels. About 60% of the tested taste cells were sensitive to serotonin, and pharmacological analysis preliminarily suggested a 5HT1A receptor to be involved. It is unknown if this receptor acts indirectly by inhibiting calcium current or if it acts directly on the calcium-activated potassium channels.

Finally, taste cells appear to be sensitive to adrenergic agents. At least two effects of adrenergic agents on membrane currents have been observed in patch-clamp analysis of rat posterior taste cells. Both norepinephrine and isoproterenol (a β-receptor agonist) reduced outward potassium currents by about one third (52). These inhibitions were prevented by prior exposure to the β-receptor antagonist propranolol. GTPγS and the cAMP analog 8CPT-cAMP mimicked the effect, suggesting an adenoreceptor cascade through β receptors and the cAMP second messenger system. The opposite effect was observed on chloride currents. Isoproterenol enhanced chloride currents, and prior exposure to propranolol prevented this enhancement (53). Calcium was required for this effect, suggesting that the enhancement occurs on calcium-activated chloride currents.

CELLULAR MECHANISMS OF TASTE TRANSDUCTION

Transduction of Salts

Sodium chloride, the prototypical salty stimulus, has been reported to be transduced in a variety of ways in taste cells. The best-described mechanism involves permeation of sodium ions through amiloride-sensitive sodium channels (ASSCs) present on the apical membrane of taste cells. Support for this mechanism has come from a variety of studies, beginning with the work of DeSimone and colleagues, who demonstrated that sodium transport across canine lingual epithelium was inhibited reversibly by the diuretic amiloride (54). Thus it appears that much of sodium transport may be similar to that reported in other transporting epithelia, such as kidney or colon, and that it involves apical sodium entry and extrusion via ouabain-sensitive sodium/potassium transporters (55–57). Confirmation for this mechanism has come from a variety of levels, including afferent nerve recordings (58–60), patch-clamp studies (32, 61, 62), in situ taste bud recording (41, 61), central taste nuclei recording (63, 64), and behavioral studies (11, 65–67).

More recent experiments using modern molecular and electrophysiological approaches have begun to shed more light on the physiology, distribution, and regulation of ASSCs. ASSCs found in taste cells, particularly in mammalian species, are similar to the recently cloned epithelial sodium channels (ENaC) found in a variety of peripheral tissues (see 68). Although they have been studied most extensively in taste buds from the fungiform papillae, ASSCs are apparently distributed throughout the oral cavity. In rats, functional ASSCs have been identified electrophysiologically in fungiform and foliate taste cells (32) and in the soft palate and Geschmacksstreifen (62). This distribution may be linked with innervation by branches of the seventh cranial nerve because functional ASSCs are absent from the vallate papillae (32). Vallate ASSCs have been identified by immunocytochemistry and in situ hybridization (69–71). However, combined with electrophysiological data showing an insensitivity of sodium chloride responses to amiloride (32, 57, 72), these results suggest that these channels are either (*a*) nonfunctional or (*b*) functional (i.e. conductive) but insensitive to amiloride. The distribution of ASSCs appears highly species dependent. Hamsters, for example, have functional ASSCs in each taste bud–containing region of the tongue and palate (62), whereas certain mouse strains may lack these transduction channels altogether (73).

Studies of ASSC physiology in mammals reveal that these channels are permeable to sodium, lithium, and protons but not significantly permeable to potassium. Moreover, like the ENaCs, they are saturable, exhibit sodium self-inhibition (74), have amiloride inhibition constants around 0.1–0.3 μM (32, 41, 43, 62), have a small unitary conductance ($\sim$5 ps) (75), and are regulated by the hormones involved in salt and water balance (61, 76; see below).

Sodium movement through the paracellular pathway may also enable sodium entry into taste cells. The ability of sodium ions to diffuse through the tight junctions in the lingual epithelium may profoundly influence the activity of taste cells. This junctional diffusion, which is anion dependent, may cause local alterations in extracellular sodium concentrations. These changes in extracellular sodium may lead to sodium entry through basolateral ASSCs to depolarize the taste cell directly (70, 77). The presence of basolateral ASSCs, however, is equivocal. In virtually all sodium-transporting epithelia, the epithelial sodium channels are restricted to the apical membranes of the cells (78), yet this may not be the case in taste cells.

A recent report has identified ASSCs in the basolateral membrane of taste cells, though with different permeability properties and amiloride sensitivity (56). Despite this finding, other reports have found no functional ASSCs on the basolateral membrane of lingual epithelia (57) nor any ASSCs with a higher inhibition constant (32, 62). This change in sodium concentration may also alter the membrane potential of the basolateral surface of the taste cell and lead to changes in the net transepithelial potential, which influences the response to sodium salts. Moreover, these changes in transepithelial current caused by the paracellular movement of small ions depends on the anion permeability, although other factors, such as anion channels, may contribute to these sodium salt responses. Whatever the mechanism, the selective anion permeability of the tight junctions likely contributes to the distinct taste of various sodium salts (77, 79).

Although ASSCs clearly are involved in the gustatory response to sodium salts, the overall contribution of amiloride-sensitive pathways to salt taste may be limited in some species and nonexistent in others. For example, certain mouse strains (73) and the mudpuppy (80) respond to sodium chloride but in a manner that does not involve ASSCs. Even in most studies that demonstrate an amiloride-sensitive component to sodium salt responsiveness, amiloride only partially inhibits the sodium response. The presence of amiloride-insensitive sodium transduction mechanisms has been demonstrated at the level of the single cell (32, 74), lingual epithelium (55–57), afferent nerve (58, 59), and brain and behavior (67). Even within species that show marked amiloride sensitivity, regional differences may exist in the gustatory sodium salt transduction mechanisms. This observation is most evident in rats, which have ASSCs in the anterior tongue yet appear to have none in the posterior tongue. These results are consistent with the interpretation that although amiloride-sensitive pathways may contribute to sodium salt taste, an additional, yet unidentified, sodium salt transduction mechanism is a major contributor to salt taste.

Humans may rely more on amiloride-insensitive pathways for detecting salty taste. In recent psychophysical experiments, amiloride inhibited only the sourness component of sodium chloride's taste (10, 11) while not altering the intensity of the compound's saltiness. Although salt-taste transduction has been the object of intense research, we still do not have a complete understanding of the process or how amiloride-sensitive and amiloride-insensitive pathways contribute to it.

Transduction of Acids

The primary stimulus responsible for acid (sour) taste is the proton (81, 82). Consistent with this interpretation, acids have been demonstrated to cause concentration-dependent responses in the gustatory system at a variety of levels. Acidic stimuli elicit action potentials from taste cells in a dose-dependent manner with decreasing pH in afferent nerve recordings, in situ recordings, and in isolated taste cells (42, 83). However, acidic stimuli likely have the broadest effects of all gustatory stimuli in the taste system. Because protons affect virtually every class of ion channel (84) and have significant permeability through the tight junctions in the lingual epithelium, they likely have the capacity to directly affect a variety of cellular targets. Moreover, acidic stimuli alter intracellular pH, which may have a number of effects on potential signal transduction pathways (85, 86). Thus it is not surprising that a number of taste transduction mechanisms have been proposed for acids.

The most complete descriptions of acid-taste transduction mechanisms have come from studies of amphibians, in which acidic stimuli inhibit potassium channels. In the mudpuppy, apically localized potassium channels that are partially open at normal resting potentials (83, 87) are inhibited in a concentration-dependent manner by protons, resulting in a direct membrane depolarization. Moreover, acids also appear to alter the coupling of gap junctions between taste receptor cells (88), which may contribute to acid-taste transduction. Protons have been shown to activate a cation conductance in frogs (89–91), which also leads to the development of a depolarizing receptor potential. However, there is little information about whether these same mechanisms operate in mammalian species. The presence of apically localized potassium channels in mammalian taste buds is uncertain, and although mammalian taste buds may contain gap junctions (92), it is unknown whether acids (protons) affect these taste receptor cells in mammals in the same way.

An acid-taste transduction mechanism described in some detail in mammals involves the same ASSC implicated in the taste of sodium salts. A common feature of ASSCs in all tissues is their significant proton permeability (93). In hamster taste cells, protons have been shown to permeate ASSCs and lead to receptor-cell depolarization at the level of the isolated cell and intact taste bud (43, 61). This observation has been confirmed in acid responses in the nucleus tractus solitarius (94) and in behavioral preference tests showing that amiloride could reduce the aversion that subjects showed to acid tastes (67). This mechanism may be complex, however, because both protons and sodium ions interact at the level of the ASSC. In a species like hamster, which has low salivary sodium levels (~6 mM) (95), protons may effectively permeate these channels to depolarize taste receptor cells. At higher salivary sodium levels, the permeation of protons may be less effective because of competition with sodium ions for the binding site within the channel (43). Consistent with this interpretation, amiloride has little effect on the behavioral effects of acids in preference tests or in conditioned taste-aversion paradigms in rats (96), which have almost 10-fold higher salivary sodium concentrations than do hamsters (95). One implication for the role of ASSCs in acid-taste transduction is that acid responses in N-best (sodium best) chorda tympani fibers might display amiloride sensitivity. Acid responses recorded in hamster chorda tympani are consistent with this interpretation (65). However, acid responses recorded in H-best (acid best) fibers, which are at least as numerous as the N-best fibers, are not inhibited by amiloride (65) and apparently operate via an independent transduction mechanism.

The distinct taste of different acids, independent of proton concentration, suggests that other contributing factors may be involved in the response to these stimuli (82, 97, 98). As in sodium salt transduction, the permeability of paracellular pathways may account for the anion effects in acid stimulation. Thus proton movement through the paracellular pathway also may contribute to acid transduction. Acids also bind to the fixed anionic sites in the tight junctions, thereby modifying their normal selectivity from cationic to anionic (99). Because of the ubiquity of the effects of acids (84), the changes in proton concentration in the local environment around the taste receptor cell would likely affect basolateral ion channel activity, intracellular acidity, or the afferent nerve fiber directly.

Transduction of Bitter Compounds

Compounds as diverse as quinine, urea, denatonium, certain amino acids, and potassium chloride produce bitter taste sensations in humans. Not surprisingly, multiple transduction mechanisms have been proposed to account for such chemical diversity. Leading theories of bitter-taste transduction mechanisms include the involvement of the cAMP and inositol trisphosphate (IP_3) second messenger systems. Ion channels independent of second messengers may also be involved.

A role for cyclic nucleotides in the transduction of bitter-tasting stimuli has been discussed for over two decades. Early studies noted that many bitter substances could modulate the activity of phosphodiesterase by either increasing or decreasing levels of cyclic nucleotides produced from taste tissue extracts. In one study, bitter stimuli, such as quinine, urea, strychnine, nicotine, and magnesium, activated phosphodiesterase in taste tissue extracts (100), whereas in another study, opposite effects were noted for quinine, strychnine, and methylxanthines (101). Renewed interest for the involvement of phosphodiesterase in bitter-taste transduction mechanisms came with the cloning of a taste-specific G protein, termed gustducin, that is highly homologous to transducin (102), a G protein involved in visual transduction. The function of gustducin in taste cells was proposed to act analogously to transducin in the retina—to activate phosphodiesterase. Thus a bitter stimulus, putatively coupled to gustducin by a seven-transmembrane receptor, would lower cyclic nucleotide levels in the cell, and these lowered levels of cyclic nucleotide would subsequently alter membrane potential through a cyclic nucleotide–gated ion channel (see 103 for a recent review on gustducin).

Much experimental evidence has been gathered to support this hypothesis. All components of this signaling cascade have been localized to taste cells, with the exception of the bitter receptor, which has remained elusive. These components include gustducin (102), transducin (104), two cAMP-type phosphodiesterases (105), and cyclic nucleotide–gated ion channels (37, 38). Functional data have emerged using a trypsin-digest assay composed of bovine membrane preparation from either taste or non-taste tissue reconstituted with transducin (104). Bitter tastants, such as denatonium and quinine, have been demonstrated to activate transducin as evidenced by protein fragments corresponding to either activated or nonactivated transducin (104, 106). Because gustducin is specific for taste cells, researchers expected that gustducin-null mice would be impaired in their ability to discriminate bitter tastants. Surprisingly, when gustducin knockout mice were assayed for their taste sensitivity, significant behavioral and electrophysiological impairment was observed in relation to both bitter and sweet stimuli (107). The reasons for this observation are not yet clear. Adding another layer of complexity is the recent cloning of a cyclic nucleotide–gated ion channel from rat taste tissue (38) that appears to operate in a fashion opposite to the channel reported in frog taste cells. The channel in rat taste cells opens to elevated levels of cyclic nucleotide rather than to lowered levels of cyclic nucleotide. This channel is more sensitive to cGMP than to cAMP, but its physiological role is not yet known.

Initial observations suggesting a role for IP_3 and intracellular calcium in bitter-taste transduction came from fura-2 calcium imaging on rat circumvallate taste cells using the intensely bitter stimulus denatonium (108). Subsequently, many of the signaling components of the IP_3 system were localized to circumvallate taste cells (109). Localization of IP_3 receptors was implied with binding of tritiated IP_3, and mass levels of IP_3 were elevated within 15–30 seconds after denatonium stimulation in taste tissue but not in non-taste tissue when stimulated with either sucrose or quinine. The generation of IP_3 in response to bitter-taste stimulation was measured on a more physiological time course using a quench-flow apparatus (110). Two strains of mice, both responding to denatonium but differing in their ability to taste sucrose octacetate (SOA; another bitter compound), were tested. Denatonium produced IP_3 in both strains of mice, with maximal production at 75–100 ms, but as expected, SOA was effective only in SOA tasters. IP_3 production was potentiated by GTP and inhibited by pertussis toxin, suggesting involvement of a G protein (111).

Studies with fluorescent imaging of intracellular calcium levels have further associated bitter stimuli with IP_3. In mudpuppy taste cells, stimulation with denatonium increased intracellular calcium levels. This increase was inhibited by an inhibitor of phospholipase C, the enzyme that produces IP_3 (112), and thapsigargin treatment suggested that calcium elevations were independent of outward calcium. Calcium elevations were unaffected by inhibition of phosphodiesterase or adenylate cyclase, or by application of membrane-permeant cyclic nucleotide analogs. These findings suggest that denatonium operates via IP_3-mediated elevations of calcium from intracellular stores. This increase in intracellular calcium was not observed in guinea pig fungiform taste cells (113), which are known to be much less responsive to bitter stimuli. In response to denatonium, a calcium increase was observed, but it required extracellular calcium, unlike either rat circumvallate or mudpuppy taste cells.

In patch-clamp analysis, quinine was demonstrated to block potassium channels in rat taste cells at extremely low concentrations; the threshold of inhibition was 10^{-7} M (34). The biophysical properties of this inhibition, such as shifts in normalized conductance and inactivation curves, along with the time course of the inhibited currents, suggested that multiple mechanisms may be operative. Higher concentrations of quinine, about one log step, inhibited sodium currents, and a biphasic effect was noted on calcium currents that were enhanced at 10^{-5} M but inhibited at 10^{-4} M. Quinine altered the waveform of the action potential, and in some cells quinine produced a highly unusual action potential, lasting up to several seconds. In frog taste cells, electrophysiological studies suggested that a unique cation conductance was activated by quinine (114), but active chloride secretion in response to quinine stimulation in frog taste cells has also been suggested (115).

The somewhat surprising conclusion emerging from these studies is that individual bitter tastants may not fall into a single transduction category. Quinine, for example, was an effective stimulus in the trypsin-digest experiment, implicating a gustducin/cAMP pathway. However, quinine was also effective in IP_3 production and in the inhibition of potassium currents at quite low concentrations. Similarly denatonium appears capable of altering the intracellular concentrations of both cAMP and IP_3. Thus more than one mechanism may be responsible for a particular tastant.

Transduction of Natural and Artificial Sweeteners

The chemical nature of compounds called sweet is diverse. Naturally occurring compounds, such as carbohydrates and certain amino acids, and artificially created compounds, such as saccharins and cyclamates, produce sensations reported as sweet in humans. In animal models, the emerging picture is that many natural sweeteners may use the cAMP second messenger system, whereas many artificial sweeteners and amino acids may use the IP_3 second messenger system.

Many lines of evidence suggest that cAMP is involved in taste cell function and that at least one of the roles of cAMP is in the transduction of sweet stimuli. For example, multiple lines of indirect evidence have suggested that a membrane-bound receptor, such as would be needed for activation of G_s and adenylate cyclase, is involved in sensing sweet stimuli. This evidence includes the observations that sweet stimuli such as carbohydrates are membrane impermeant and unlikely to pass through tight junctions, that certain proteolytic enzymes can specifically impair sweet sensations, and that a protein extract from the plant *Gymnemia sylvestre* can specifically block sweet responses. This receptor has thus far eluded cloning, although orphan receptors with unknown function are candidates (116, 117). The G proteins G_s and G_i, which are associated with the regulation of adenylate cyclase, were identified in taste cells in the process of cloning the taste-specific G protein gustducin (102, 105). Several biochemical assays have demonstrated that cAMP levels are elevated after incubation with sweet stimuli. In intact taste buds of the rat circumvallate, sucrose levels above 100 mM caused enhanced cAMP levels, which were blocked by xanthine, whereas the artificial sweeteners saccharin and SC-45647 had no effect on cAMP levels (118). These same artificial sweeteners have been observed to increase IP_3 (119). It is interesting to note that sodium saccharin actually inhibits adenylate cyclase activity in non-taste cells (120) such as adipocyte and astrocyte membrane fractions. These experiments suggest that taste cells possess the transductive utensils for cAMP production and that cAMP production in response to sweet stimuli occurs.

Electrophysiological experiments suggest that elevation of cAMP alters the membrane conductance of cells by closing a resting potassium conductance. Injection of cAMP into frog taste cells caused depolarization in one subset of cells (121) that could be blocked with protein kinase inhibitor (PKI), a specific inhibitor of protein kinase A (122). In mouse taste cells, cAMP injection also depolarized the cell with an increased membrane resistance (123). In both frog and mouse taste cells, injection of cGMP elicited stronger depolarization than did cAMP (121, 123). In rat circumvallate taste cells, outward potassium currents were inhibited by cAMP and by membrane-permeant cAMP analogs. These inhibitions were blocked by PKI. Forskolin, a commonly used pharmacological activator of adenylate cyclase, had direct effects on potassium currents in taste cells, independent of adenylate cyclase activation, suggesting the cautious interpretation of forskolin use in taste cells. Saccharin decreased outward potassium currents in rat fungiform taste cells (29).

Hamster fungiform taste cells are particularly sensitive to sweet stimuli, and a strong correlation between these stimuli and cAMP has been observed (42). Taste buds responding with action potentials to sweeteners also responded to exogenously applied cAMP analogs, whereas those not responding to sweeteners did not respond to cAMP analogs. A distinction between artificial sweeteners and cAMP was not found, as both sucrose and the artificial sweeteners saccharin and NC01 were correlated with cAMP. Subsequent work (124) demonstrated that sweeteners and cyclic nucleotides reduced a potassium current and that this current was open at rest and therefore would result in a depolarization of the cell membrane potential.

Calcium elevations through IP_3 may also participate in sweet-taste transduction. In rats, a subset of taste cells responded to the artificial sweeteners saccharin and SC-45647 with an increase in production of IP_3 and cytosolic calcium from intracellular stores. These sweeteners did not elevate cAMP levels. In contrast, sucrose increased cAMP, and calcium elevations depended on the uptake of calcium from extracellular media. These observations suggest the possibility of dual signaling in which different ligands activate separate transduction cascades in the same sweet-responsive cell. This scheme would imply the coexistence of two receptor types. Nutritive sweeteners would activate one receptor type through elevated cAMP, membrane depolarization, and calcium influx through voltage-dependent calcium channels. Artificial sweeteners, acting through a separate receptor, would elevate IP_3 and subsequently elevate intracellular calcium from intracellular stores. Studies in gerbil taste cells support this proposal of dichotomous mechanisms (125, 126). In these cells, the sweet stimuli sucrose and saccharin decreased outward potassium currents via elevations of cAMP and then were thought to activate a calcium influx through voltage-dependent calcium channels. The amino acids phenylalanine and tryptophan enhanced outward potassium currents through a mechanism involving IP_3, causing elevations of calcium from intracellular stores.

Although data appear to support a correlation between sweetener type and two different second messenger systems, many discrepancies remain. For example, saccharin may be capable of activating both cAMP and IP_3, and these may be variable among species and possibly also taste bud location. Additionally, the reduction of a potassium current by cAMP is only one possible link to ion channels of the cell membrane. Cyclic nucleotide–gated channels may represent another mechanism for changes of cyclic nucleotide levels, with elevated levels either opening (38) or closing (37) these channels. Here, the overlap of sweet-taste and bitter-taste transduction mechanisms within an individual taste cell may help resolve the apparent conflicts of these data.

Transduction of Amino Acids

The transduction of amino acids has been well studied in two arenas: the catfish model, which is particularly sensitive to amino acids, and the study of glutamate, which elicits umami, a unique sensation in humans.

The taste system of the catfish has been examined using a variety of techniques (see 127–129 for reviews). In brief, catfish are exquisitely sensitive to amino acids, in the nanomolar range, and appear to have three major classes of amino acid receptors. The L-alanine receptor triggers a G protein–dependent increase in the production of second messengers IP_3 and cAMP, though with differing time courses. Conversely, receptors for L-arginine do not increase second messengers but appear to activate a cation channel that is gated directly by the amino acid (130). Individual taste receptor cells of the catfish may preferentially express receptors to either L-arginine or L-alanine (131). The third receptor, for L-proline, may also activate ion channels directly.

In mammals, amino acids are often categorized into traditional qualities of sweet and bitter (e.g. many L-amino acids are often reported as sweet, whereas D-isomers taste bitter); however, the situation for one amino acid, L-glutamate, is unique. Recent attention in the study of amino acid–taste transduction has been devoted to delineating the types of glutamate receptors expressed in taste cells. Evidence exists for both ionotropic and metabotropic glutamate receptors in mammalian taste cells.

After incorporating mouse taste epithelial membrane fraction into phospholipid bilayers, researchers observed glutamate to increase bilayer conductance (129). The absence of metabolic components in this preparation would suggest the involvement of ionotropic receptors, although this would not exclude a role for metabotropic receptors in intact cells. Later work by the same group (132), using simultaneous calcium imaging and voltage-sensitive dye in mouse taste buds, suggested that both receptor types may be operative. Three stimuli were employed: L-glutamate, NMDA (an ionotropic agonist), and L-AP4 (a metabotropic agonist). NMDA increased intracellular calcium and membrane depolarization, whereas L-AP4 decreased intracellular calcium. L-glutamate, in contrast, either increased or decreased calcium in different cells. The researchers suggested that ionotropic receptors were responsible for excitatory glutamate responses as this would require an increase in intracellular calcium.

There is also evidence for both receptor types in rat posterior taste cells, including the metabotropic glutamate receptor mGluR4 (133). Using RT-PCR, researchers detected several ionotropic receptors in lingual tissue that either contained or was devoid of taste buds. The receptor mGluR4 was detected only in tissue that had taste buds, and in situ hybridization further localized this receptor specifically to taste buds. Another study by this group used patch-clamp recordings to examine the electrophysiological responses of rat posterior taste cells to glutamate (134). Most cells responded to exogenously applied glutamate with an outward current and reduced membrane conductance that were probably caused by the closure of a cation channel. This effect was mimicked by L-AP4 (an agonist of mGluR4). A small minority of cells responded with a transient inward current opening a nonselective cation channel. The researchers concluded that two types of channels, one closed by glutamate and one opened by glutamate, are present in rat taste cells.

Transduction of Fatty Acids, a Nonconventional Taste Stimulus

Although the taste system is crucial for nutrient detection, researchers have long assumed that it played no role in the detection of dietary fat, the most energy dense of all nutrients. Rather it was assumed that fat's only salient feature was its texture (6, 7), which was mediated through the trigeminal system.

However, fat ingested in the form of triglycerides may be broken down into mono- and diglycerides and free fatty acids via lingual lipase (135, 136), and these lipophilic molecules may be transported in the aqueous environment of the oral cavity by the von Ebner's gland proteins (137, 138). Thus the taste system may use several potential molecules to signal the presence of fat. Recent experiments have shown that free fatty acids directly affect taste-receptor-cell activity through an extracellular inhibition of delayed-rectifying potassium channels ($EC_{50} \sim 1\ \mu M$) (8), apparently of the Shaker Kv1.5 subtype (139). These channels, which are also found in the heart and display similar sensitivities (140), are sensitive to only the *cis*-polyunsaturated, or essential, fatty acids, again implicating the taste system in the detection of needed nutrients.

Fatty acids may also be taken up into taste cells by diffusion or may be transported intracellularly by the activity of fatty acid transporters in taste cells (141). Activity of fatty acid transporters apparently results in a rise in intracellular calcium in these cells (142), which would be predicted to result in an increase in neurotransmitter release. Some evidence indicates that the impurities in fat may contribute to their recognition by the gustatory system (143), although no mechanism has been described for this phenomenon. The reader is referred elsewhere for a review on the transduction of fat and its implications (9).

OTHER CONSIDERATIONS

Specificity of Taste Receptor Cells

Although the mechanisms of chemosensory transduction have been the object of extensive research, little information is currently available about the chemical specificity of individual taste receptor cells. Few studies have been aimed directly at examining this question in peripheral taste receptor cells. In contrast, the specificity of both afferent nerve fibers and central gustatory neurons has been well established (see 144). One might predict, though, that taste information is more broadly tuned at each successive stage because of progressive convergence from the periphery to the central nervous system. There is convergence of receptor cells onto afferent fibers (22, 145, 146), afferent fibers onto neurons in the nucleus of the solitary tract (NST) (147), and NST neurons onto neurons in the parabrachial nucleus (148–150).

Although evidence of taste cell specificity is lacking, multiply chemically sensitive taste buds clearly exist. In situ taste bud recordings have shown that action potentials may be generated in response to sodium salts, artificial sweeteners, and acids in a single taste bud (41–43). Furthermore, some evidence suggests that broadly tuned taste responses begin at the peripheral receptors; that is, even the peripheral taste receptor cells may respond to more than a single class of taste stimuli. Early microelectrode recording in rats (151), mice (81) and frogs (152) are consistent with the general interpretation that individual taste receptor cells may be multiply chemically sensitive. However, since these early experiments, little research has been conducted using more advanced electrophysiological methods. Recent preliminary reports using patch-clamp recording on isolated cells have demonstrated that subsets of mammalian taste receptor cells exhibit specificity whereas others are responsive to three (or more) classes of stimuli (153, 154). Studies of stimuli cross-adaptation in humans are consistent with there being multiple sensitivity at the receptor-cell level (155, 156).

Overlap in mechanisms of taste transduction may lead to taste cells that exhibit multiple sensitivity. As discussed above, the finding that protons (acid taste) and sodium salts (salt taste) permeate the same ASSCs in hamsters (43, 61, 67) implies that there is at least partial overlap between these two taste stimuli in single cells. A recent report supports broad tuning in rat taste receptor cells (157). The finding that fatty acids inhibit delayed-rectifying potassium channels in approximately 95% of taste receptor cells (8) suggests that there will be overlap between the response to fats (i.e. fatty acids) and those of other stimuli (9). The ability of fats to alter both the taste reactivity and hedonics of other tastes is well established (158, 159) and may represent the ability of individual cells to respond to more than a single stimulus class. Closer exploration of this issue will require careful electrophysiological, biochemical, and molecular approaches and the identification of specific receptors.

Plasticity of Peripheral Taste System: Studies in Sodium Chloride Transduction

The peripheral taste system, specifically in its ability to detect sapid molecules, generally has been depicted as a passive transducer of chemical signals and as being relatively insensitive to underlying nutritional and physiological changes in the organism. Recent studies have begun to challenge this concept of the peripheral gustatory system. Specifically, the amiloride-sensitive pathways involved in the transduction of sodium salts, and apparently acids, have been shown to display a certain degree of plasticity. As such, these pathways might be an appropriate model for understanding the ability of the taste system to respond to extrinsic cues. The regulation of amiloride-sensitive sodium transport by a number of factors has been well documented in a variety of transporting epithelia including the kidney, lung, and colon. These factors include sodium ions, mineralocorticoid hormones, and a number of peptide hormones involved in salt and water balance (68). Because of the similarity between the ENaC in these tissues and the ASSC in taste buds, it might be predicted that the salt-taste transducing pathways, which are responsible for the detection of salts prior to ingestion, also fall under many of the same regulatory controls.

The cloning of the ENaC in colon and lung (160–162) has lent support to the theory that ASSCs in mammalian taste cells are similar to those found in these areas. This finding has facilitated the use of molecular and biochemical techniques to identify expression of ASSCs in taste tissue. As mentioned above, probes against the α subunit of the ASSC labels rat taste receptor cells in the vallate papillae, which shows that both mRNA and the protein for this channel are present (69–71, 163). However, electrophysiological evidence for this channel is lacking. Neither patch-clamp recording on isolated rat vallate taste receptor cells (32) nor glossopharyngeal nerve recording (72) are consistent with the presence of functional ASSCs in the vallate papillae. ASSC protein precedes the functional expression of these channels during development (71, 164). Thus there may be dormant ASSCs—apically, basolaterally, or in submembrane vesicles—that may be awaiting a physiological signal to become active. Such expression and regulation of ENaC function in transporting epithelia comes under the control of a number of hormones that play a role in salt and water balance. Like transporting epithelia that contain ENaC, taste tissue is also responsive to a number of hormones. Increases in amiloride-sensitive sodium transport caused by application of aldosterone (165, 166) and arginine-vasopressin (61, 167) have been demonstrated at the cellular, lingual epithelial, and afferent nerve levels and are consistent with the action of these hormones elsewhere.

Preliminary studies have also revealed that atrial natriuretic peptide and oxytocin, which lead to decreases in sodium transport, cause a net reduction in ASSC activity in rat taste tissue (76). Thus the humoral signals that control salt and water balance in the body also alter the activity of the amiloride-sensitive salt-taste transduction pathways in predictable ways. However, because there are other undefined salt-taste transduction mechanisms, it is not clear whether these hormones exert analogous effects on the amiloride-insensitive salt-taste transduction pathways.

Regulation of the salt transducing pathways in taste tissue is not limited to the aforementioned humoral signals. Sodium ions themselves also influence the activity of ASSCs in isolated taste buds and lingual tissue. Sodium ions act at ENaCs to decrease sodium permeability in a concentration-dependent fashion (168). Several theories have been proposed to explain this behavior, including (*a*) feedback inhibition owing to an increase in intracellular sodium (169–171), (*b*) self-inhibition caused by extracellular sodium ions (172) binding to a sulfhdryl reagent-sensitive site to decrease sodium permeability, and (*c*) saturation of the binding sites for sodium ions within the channel pore (84).

Gilbertson & Zhang (74) have demonstrated that the sodium-dependent saturation of ASSCs in rat taste tissue is, at least in part, the result of the self-inhibition phenomenon. Saturation of sodium transport at both the cellular and epithelial levels is apparent in electrophysiological studies as a permeability decrease of ASSCs with increasing extracellular (or mucosal) sodium concentrations. This saturation, which occurs within 10–15 s, may be ameliorated by *p*-hydroxymercuribenzoate, a sulfhydryl compound that acts at cysteine residues in the channel (173). This inhibition by sodium ions is found only in those taste cells that contain ASSCs, suggesting that it is a property of only these channels and not necessarily all sodium salt transduction pathways. In rats, self-inhibition is most evident at approximately 70 mM sodium chloride, because of the balance between the increases in driving force for sodium and in self-inhibition with increasing extracellular sodium. This concentration is close to the sodium concentrations that are found in rat saliva (95). Thus self-inhibition may be important in the taste cell adaptation to sodium, which follows a similar time course (41, 174, 175), the conservation of cellular resources during chronic sodium exposure, or the gustatory response to water (74).

The elucidation of the mechanisms underlying the regulation of the ASSCs provides a unique insight into the flexibility of the peripheral taste system to respond to systemic changes in the organism and presents a new picture of the peripheral gustatory receptor cells as a responsive and flexible system that can do more than just relay signals passively.

SUMMARY/PERSPECTIVE

Significant strides continue to be made in our understanding of the function of peripheral taste receptor cells and, in particular, the mechanisms of taste transduction. In recent years, this progress has been accelerated by the application of molecular biological and electrophysiological techniques that have helped to explain the cellular mechanisms underlying much of the early physiological and behavioral data.

Despite this progress, there remain more transduction pathways to be elucidated. Several other issues will require attention in the near future in order to gain a better picture of how the peripheral gustatory system operates. The issues of coding at the receptor cell are not well understood and are only now beginning to be addressed. Little is currently known about the specificity of individual taste receptor cells or taste buds, and this issue will be important for understanding numerous processes in the response to gustatory stimuli. Furthermore, the model of taste cell plasticity that is apparent in the salt-taste transduction pathways has changed the thinking of researchers about the role of taste receptor cells from passive chemical transducers to responsive participants in the nutritional homeostasis of the organism. It will be of interest to determine if other chemoreceptive mechanisms (e.g. sweet, amino acid, and fat taste) are similarly regulated by nutritional status. These areas of investigation will be important for understanding not only how taste receptors detect sapid molecules but also how these cells contribute to the broader area of ingestive behavior.

ACKNOWLEDGMENTS

The authors wish to acknowledge the support of their laboratories from the following grants: NIH NIDCD 02507, NIH NIDCD 00353, and a Novartis Research Award (TAG); NIH NIDCD 00401 and NSF IBN 9724062 (MSH).

Literature Cited

1. Gilbertson TA, Kinnamon SC. 1996. Making sense of chemicals. *Chem. Biol.* 3:233–37
2. Spielman AI, Huque T, Whitney G, Brand JG. 1992. The diversity of bitter taste signal transduction mechanisms. In *Sensory Transduction*, ed. DP Corey, SD Roper, pp. 307–24. New York: Rockefeller Univ. Press
3. Schiffman SS, Gatlin CA. 1993. Sweeteners: state of knowledge review. *Neurosci. Biobehav. Rev.* 17:313–45
4. Schiffman SS, Gill JM. 1987. Psychophysical and neurophysiological taste responses to glutamate and purinergic compounds. In *Umami: A Basic Taste*, ed. Y Kawamura, MR Kare, pp. 271–88. New York: Dekker
5. Yamaguchi S. 1991. Basic properties of umami and effects on humans. *Physiol. Behav.* 49:833–41
6. Drewnowski A. 1997. Taste preferences and food intake. *Annu. Rev. Nutr.* 17:237–53
7. Mela DJ, Marshall RJ. 1991. Sensory properties and perceptions of fats. In *Dietary Fats: Determinants of Preference, Selection and Consumption*. ed. DJ Mela, pp. 43–57. New York: Elsevier
8. Gilbertson TA, Fontenot DT, Liu L, Zhang H, Monroe WT. 1997. Fatty acid modulation of K^+ channels in taste receptor cells: gustatory cues for dietary fat. *Am. J. Physiol.* 272:C1203–10
9. Gilbertson TA. 1998. Gustatory mechanisms for the detection of fat. *Curr. Opin. Neurobiol.* 8:447–52
10. Ossebaard CA, Smith DV. 1995. Effect of amiloride on the taste of NaCl, Na-gluconate and KCl in humans: implications for Na^+ receptor mechanisms. *Chem. Senses* 20:37–46
11. Ossebaard CA, Polet IA, Smith DV. 1997. Amiloride effects on taste quality: comparison of single and multiple response category procedures. *Chem. Senses* 22:267–75
12. Miller IJ. 1995. Anatomy of the peripheral taste system. In *Handbook of Olfaction and Gustation*, ed. RL Doty, pp. 521–57. New York: Dekker
13. Kolmer W. 1927. Geschmacksorgan. In *Handbuch der Mikroskopischen Anatomie des Menschen, Haut und Sinnesorgane*, ed. Anonymous, 3:154–91. Berlin: Springer
14. Murray RG, Murray A. 1970. The anatomy and ultrastructure of taste endings. In *Taste and Smell in Vertebrates*, ed. GEW Wolstenholme, J Knight, pp. 3–30. London: Churchill
15. Delay R, Kinnamon JC, Roper SD. 1986. Ultrastructure of mouse vallate taste buds. II. Cell types and cell lineage. *J. Comp. Neurol.* 253:242–52
16. Murray RG. 1973. The ultrastructure of taste buds. In *The Ultrastructure of Sensory Organs*, ed. I Friedemann, pp. 1–81. Amsterdam: North Holland
17. Farbman AI. 1985. Structure of taste buds in foliate papillae of the rhesus monkey, *Macaca mulatta*. *Am. J. Anat.* 172:41–56
18. Paran N, Mattern CFT, Henkin R. 1975. Ultrastructure of the taste bud of the human fungiform papilla. *Cell Tissue Res.* 161:1–10
19. Takeda M, Suzuki Y, Shishido Y. 1985.

Effects of colchicine on the ultrastructure of mouse taste buds. *Cell Tissue Res.* 242:409–16
20. Kinnamon JC, Taylor BJ, Delay RJ, Roper SD. 1985. Ultrastructure of mouse vallate taste buds. I. Taste cells and their associated synapses. *J. Comp. Neurol.* 235:48–60
21. Murray RG. 1986. The mammalian taste bud type 3 cell: a critical analysis. *J. Ultrastruct. Mol. Struct.* 95:175–88
22. Royer SM, Kinnamon JC. 1991. HVEM serial-section analysis of rabbit foliate taste buds. 1. Type-III cells and their synapses. *J. Comp. Neurol.* 306:49–72
23. Beidler LM, Smallmen RL. Renewal of cells within taste buds. *J. Cell Biol.* 27: 263–72
24. Farbman AI. 1965. Fine structure of the taste buds. *J. Ultrastruct. Res.* 12:328–50
25. Kinnamon JC. 1987. Organization and innervation of taste buds. In *Neurobiology of Taste and Smell*, ed. TE Finger, WL Silver, pp. 277–97. New York: Wiley
26. Farbman AI. 1980. Renewal of taste bud cells in rat circumvallate papillae. *Cell Tissue Kinet.* 13:349–57
27. Murray RG, Murray A. 1971. Relations and possible significance of taste bud cells. *Contrib. Sens. Physiol.* 5:47–95
28. Pumplin DW, Yu CS, Smith DV. 1997. Light and dark cells of rat vallate taste buds are morphologically distinct cell types. *J. Comp. Neurol.* 378:389–410
29. Béhé P, DeSimone JA, Avenet P, Lindemann B. 1990. Membrane currents in taste cells of the rat fungiform papilla. Evidence for two types of Ca currents and inhibition of K currents by saccharin. *J. Gen. Physiol.* 96:1061–84
30. Chen YS, Sun XD, Herness MS. 1996. Characteristics of action potentials and their underlying outward currents in rat taste receptor cells. *J. Neurophysiol.* 75: 820–31
31. Herness MS, Sun XD. 1995. Voltage-dependent sodium currents recorded from dissociated rat taste cells. *J. Membr. Biol.* 146:73–84
32. Doolin RE, Gilbertson TA. 1996. Distribution and characterization of functional amiloride-sensitive sodium channels in rat tongue. *J. Gen. Physiol.* 107:545–54
33. Sun XD, Herness MS. 1996. Characterization of inwardly rectifying potassium currents from dissociated rat taste receptor cells. *Am. J. Physiol.* 271:C1221–32
34. Chen Y, Herness MS. 1997. Electrophysiological actions of quinine on voltage-dependent currents in dissociated rat taste cells. *Pflugers Arch.* 434:215–26
35. Sun XD, Herness MS. 1995. Characterization of chloride currents recorded from dissociated rat taste cells. *Soc. Neurosci. Abstr.* 21:1656 (Abstr.)
36. Miyamoto T, Fujiyama R, Okada Y, Sato T. 1996. Properties of Na^+-dependent K^+ conductance in the apical membrane of frog taste cells. *Brain Res.* 715:79–85
37. Kolesnikov SS, Margolskee RF. 1995. A cyclic-nucleotide-suppressible conductance activated by transducin in taste cells. *Nature* 376:85–88
38. Misaka T, Kusakabe Y, Emori Y, Gonoi T, Arai S, Abe K. 1997. Taste buds have a cyclic nucleotide-activated channel, CNGgust. *J. Biol. Chem.* 272:22623–29
39. Akabas MH, Dodd J, Al-Awqati Q. 1990. Identification of electrophysiologically distinct subpopulations of rat taste cells. *J. Membr. Biol.* 114:71–78
40. Herness MS, Sun XD, Chen Y. 1996. Inhibition of inwardly rectifying potassium currents by G-protein activation in rat taste receptor cells. *Soc. Neurosci. Abstr.* 22:1826 (Abstr.)
41. Avenet P, Lindemann B. 1991. Noninvasive recording of receptor cell action potentials and sustained currents from single taste buds maintained in the tongue: the response to mucosal NaCl and amiloride. *J. Membr. Biol.* 124:33–41
42. Cummings TA, Powell J, Kinnamon SC. 1993. Sweet taste transduction in hamster taste cells: evidence for the role of cyclic nucleotides. *J. Neurophysiol.* 70:2326–36
43. Gilbertson TA, Avenet P, Kinnamon SC, Roper SD. 1992. Proton currents through amiloride-sensitive Na channels in hamster taste cells: role in acid transduction. *J. Gen. Physiol.* 100:803–24
44. Mackay-Sim A, Delay RJ, Roper SD, Kinnamon SC. 1996. Development of voltage-dependent currents in taste receptor cells. *J. Comp. Neurol.* 365:278–88
45. Nagai T, Kim DJ, Delay RJ, Roper SD. 1996. Neuromodulation of transduction and signal processing in the end organs of taste. *Chem. Senses* 21:353–65
46. Obata H, Shimada K, Sakai N, Saito N. 1997. GABAergic neurotransmission in rat taste buds: immunocytochemical study for GABA and GABA transporter subtypes. *Mol. Brain Res.* 49:29–36
47. Kim DJ, Roper SD. 1995. Localization of serotonin in taste buds: A comparative study in four vertebrates. *J. Comp. Neurol.* 353:364–70
48. Delay RJ, Taylor R, Roper SD. 1993. Merkel-like basal cells in *Necturus* taste buds contain serotonin. *J. Comp. Neurol.* 335:606–13

49. Ewald DA, Roper SD. 1994. Bidirectional synaptic transmission in *Necturus* taste buds. *J. Neurosci.* 14:3791–804
50. Delay RJ, Kinnamon SC, Roper SD. 1997. Serotonin modulates voltage-dependent calcium current in *Necturus* taste cells. *J. Neurophysiol.* 77:2515–24
51. Herness MS, Chen YS. 1997. Serotonin inhibits calcium-activated K^+ current in rat taste receptor cells. *NeuroReport* 8:3257–61
52. Sun XD, Herness MS. 1996. Cascade of adrenoceptor, G-protein, and cAMP inhibits outward potassium currents in rat taste receptor cells. *Soc. Neurosci. Abstr.* 22:1826 (Abstr.)
53. Herness MS. 1997. The cAMP cascade affects sodium and chloride currents in rat taste receptor cells. *Soc. Neurosci. Abstr.* 23:1037 (Abstr.)
54. DeSimone JA, Heck GL, DeSimone SK. 1981. Active ion transport in dog tongue: a possible role in taste. *Science* 214:1039–41
55. Heck GL, Mierson S, DeSimone JA. 1984. Salt taste transduction occurs through an amiloride-sensitive sodium transport pathway. *Science* 223:403–5
56. Mierson S, Olson MM, Tietz AE. 1996. A basolateral amiloride-sensitive Na^+-transport pathway in rat tongue epithelium. *J. Neurophysiol.* 76:1297–309
57. Gilbertson TA, Zhang H. 1998. Characterization of sodium transport in gustatory epithelia from the hamster and rat. *Chem. Senses* 23:283–93
58. Brand JG, Teeter JH, Silver WH. 1985. Inhibition by amiloride of chorda tympani responses evoked by monovalent salts. *Brain Res.* 334:207–14
59. DeSimone JA, Ferrell F. 1985. Analysis of amiloride inhibition of chorda tympani taste response of rat to NaCl. *Am. J. Physiol.* 249:R52–61
60. Heck GL, Persuad KC, DeSimone JA. 1989. Direct measurement of translingual epithelial NaCl and KCl currents during the chorda tympani taste response. *Biophys. J.* 55:843–57
61. Gilbertson TA, Roper SD, Kinnamon SC. 1993. Proton currents through amiloride-sensitive Na^+ channels in isolated hamster taste cells: enhancement by vasopressin and cAMP. *Neuron* 10:931–42
62. Gilbertson TA, Fontenot DT. 1998. Distribution of amiloride-sensitive sodium channels in the oral cavity of the hamster. *Chem. Senses.* 23:495–99
63. Scott TR, Giza BK. 1990. Coding channels in the taste system of the rat. *Science* 249:1585–87
64. Giza BK, Scott TR. 1991. The effect of amiloride on taste-evoked activity in the nucleus tractus solitarius of the rat. *Brain Res.* 550:247–56
65. Hettinger TP, Frank ME. 1990. Specificity of amiloride inhibition of hamster taste responses. *Brain Res.* 513:24–34
66. Tennison AM. 1992. Amiloride reduces intensity responses of human fungiform papillae. *Physiol. Behav.* 51:1061–68
67. Gilbertson DM, Gilbertson TA. 1994. Amiloride reduces the aversiveness of acids in preference tests. *Physiol. Behav.* 56:649–54
68. Garty H, Palmer LG. 1997. Epithelial sodium channels: function, structure and regulation. *Physiol. Rev.* 77:359–96
69. Li XJ, Blackshaw S, Snyder SH. 1994. Expression and localization of amiloride-sensitive sodium channels indicate a role for non–taste cells in taste perception. *Proc. Natl. Acad. Sci. USA* 91:1814–18
70. Simon SA, Holland VF, Benos DJ, Zamphigi GA. 1993. Transcellular and paracellular pathways in lingual epithelia and their influence in taste transduction. *Microsc. Res. Tech.* 26:196–208
71. Stewart RE, Lasiter PS, Benos DJ, Hill DL. 1995. Immunohistochemical correlates of peripheral gustatory sensitivity to sodium and amiloride. *Acta Anat.* 153:310–19
72. Formaker BK, Hill DL. 1991. Lack of amiloride sensitivity in SHR and WKY glossopharyngeal taste responses to NaCl. *Physiol. Behav.* 50:765–69
73. Tonosaki K, Funakoshi M. 1989. Amiloride does not block taste transduction in the mouse (SlC:ICR). *Comp. Biochem. Physiol. A* 94:659–61
74. Gilbertson TA, Zhang H. 1998. Self-inhibition in amiloride-sensitive sodium channels in taste receptor cells. *J. Gen. Physiol.* 111:667–77
75. Avenet P. 1992. Role of amiloride-sensitive Na^+ channels in taste. In *Sensory Transduction*, ed. DP Corey, SD Roper, pp. 271–79. New York: Rockefeller Univ. Press
76. Gilbertson TA. 1997. Hormonal regulation of salt taste transduction at the level of the receptor cell. Presented at 10th Int. Congr. Endocrinol., San Francisco (Abstr.)
77. Ye Q, Heck GL, DeSimone JA. 1991. The anion paradox in sodium taste reception: resolution by voltage-clamp studies. *Science* 254:724–26
78. Lewis SA, Wills NK. 1983. Apical membrane permeability and kinetic properties

of the sodium pump in rabbit urinary bladder. *J. Physiol.* 341:169–84
79. Elliot EJ, Simon SA. 1990. The anion in salt taste. A possible role for paracellular pathways. *Brain Res.* 535:9–17
80. McPheeters M, Roper SD. 1985. Amiloride does not block taste transduction in the mudpuppy, *Necturus maculosus*. *Chem. Senses* 10:341–52
81. Tonosaki K, Funakoshi M. 1984. Intracellular taste cell responses of mouse. *Comp. Biochem. Physiol. A* 78:651–56
82. Settle R, Meehan K, Williams GR, Doty RL, Sisley AC. 1986. Chemosensory properties of sour tastants. *Physiol. Behav.* 36:619–23
83. Kinnamon SC, Dionne VE, Beam KG. 1988. Apical localization of K channels in taste cells provides the basis for sour taste transduction. *Proc. Natl. Acad. Sci. USA* 85:7023–27
84. Hille B. 1992. *Ionic Channels of Excitable Membranes*. Sunderland, MA: Sinauer. 607 pp.
85. Thomas RC. 1984. Experimental displacement of intracellular pH and the mechanism of its subsequent recovery. *J. Physiol.* 354:3P–22P
86. Lyall V, Biber TU. 1994. Potential-induced changes in intracellular pH. *Am. J. Physiol.* 266:F685–96
87. Cummings TA, Kinnamon SC. 1992. Apical K^+ channels in *Necturus* taste cells: modulation by intracellular factors and taste stimuli. *J. Gen. Physiol.* 99:591–613
88. Bigiani A, Roper SD. 1994. Reduction of electrical coupling between *Necturus* taste receptor cells: a possible role in acid taste. *Neurosci. Lett.* 176:212–16
89. Okada Y, Miyamoto T, Sato T. 1987. Cation dependence of frog gustatory neural responses to acid stimuli. *Comp. Biochem. Physiol. A* 88:487–90
90. Okada Y, Miyamoto T, Sato T. 1994. Activation of a cation conductance by acetic acid in taste cells isolated from the bullfrog. *J. Exp. Biol.* 187:19–32
91. Miyamoto T, Okada Y, Sato T. 1988. Ionic basis of receptor potential of frog taste cells induced by acid stimuli. *J. Physiol.* 405:699–711
92. Akisaka T, Oda M. 1978. Taste buds in the vallate papillae of the rat studied with freeze-fracture preparation. *Arch. Histol. Jpn.* 41:87–98
93. Palmer LG. 1987. Ion selectivity of epithelial Na channels. *J. Membr. Biol.* 96:97–106
94. Smith DV, Liu H, Vogt M. 1996. Responses of gustatory cells in the nucleus of the solitary tract of the hamster after NaCl or amiloride adaptation. *J. Neurophysiol.* 76:47–58
95. Rehnberg BG, Hettinger TP, Frank ME. 1992. Salivary ions and neural taste responses in the hamster. *Chem. Senses* 17:179–90
96. Harris DE, Gilbertson DM, Monroe WT, Kinnamon SC, Gilbertson TA. 1994. Contribution of amiloride-sensitive pathways to acid transduction in rats. *Chem. Senses* 19:431–32 (Abstr.)
97. Beidler LM. 1967. Anion influences of taste receptor response. In *Olfaction and Taste II*, ed. T Hayashi, pp. 509–35. New York: Pergamon
98. Ganzevles PGJ, Kroeze JHA. 1987. Effects of adaptation and cross-adaptation to common ions on sourness intensity. *Physiol. Behav.* 40:641–46
99. Simon SA, Garvin JL. 1985. Salt and acid studies on canine lingual epithelium. *Am. J. Physiol.* 249:C398–408
100. Price S. 1973. Phosphodiesterase in tongue epithelium: activation by bitter taste stimuli. *Nature* 241:54–55
101. Kurihara K. 1972. Inhibition of cyclic 3′,5′-nucleotide phosphodiesterase in bovine taste papillae by bitter taste stimuli. *FEBS Lett.* 27:279–81
102. McLaughlin S, McKinnon PJ, Margolskee RF. 1992. Gustducin is a taste-cell-specific G protein closely related to the transducins. *Nature* 357:563–69
103. Spielman AI. 1998. Gustducin and its role in taste. *J. Dent. Res.* 77:539–44
104. Ruiz-Avila L, McLaughlin SK, Wildman D, McKinnon PJ, Robichon A, Spickofsky N, Margolskee RF. 1995. Coupling of bitter receptor to phosphodiesterase through transducin in taste receptor cells. *Nature* 376:80–85
105. McLaughlin SK, McKinnon PJ, Spickofsky N, Danho W, Margolskee RF. 1994. Molecular cloning of G proteins and phosphodiesterases from rat taste cells. *Physiol. Behav.* 56:1157–64
106. Ming D, Ruiz-Avila L, Margolskee RF. 1998. Characterization of solubilization of bitter-responsive receptors that couple to gustducin. *Proc. Natl. Acad. Sci. USA* 95:8933–38
107. Wong GT, Gannon KS, Margolskee RF. 1996. Transduction of bitter and sweet taste by gustducin. *Nature* 381:796–800
108. Akabas MH. 1988. A bitter substance induces a rise in intracellular calcium in a subpopulation of rat taste cells. *Science* 242:1047–49
109. Hwang PM, Verma A, Bredt DS, Snyder SH. 1990. Localization of phosphatidylinositol signaling components in rat taste

cells: role in bitter taste transduction. *Proc. Natl. Acad. Sci. USA* 87:7395–99

110. Spielman AI, Huque T, Nagai H, Whitney G, Brand JG. 1994. Generation of inositol phosphates in bitter taste transduction. *Physiol. Behav.* 56:1149–55
111. Spielman AI, Nagai H, Sunavala G, Dasso M, Breer H, et al. 1996. Rapid kinetics of second messenger production in bitter taste. *Am. J. Physiol.* 270:C926–31
112. Ogura T, Mackay-Sim A, Kinnamon SC. 1997. Bitter taste transduction of denatonium in the mudpuppy *Necturus maculosus*. *J. Neurosci.* 17:3580–87
113. Orola CN, Yamashita T, Harada N, Amano H, Ohtani M, Kumazawa T. 1992. Intracellular free calcium concentrations in single taste receptor cells in guinea pig. *Acta Otolaryngol.* 112:120–27
114. Tsunenari T, Hayashi Y, Orita M, Kurahashi T, Kaneko A, Mori T. 1996. A quinine-activated cationic conductance in vertebrate taste receptor cells. *J. Gen. Physiol.* 108:515–23
115. Okada Y. 1988. Ionic mechanisms of generation of receptor potential in response to quinine in frog taste cell. *Brain Res.* 450:295–307
116. Abe K, Kusakabe Y, Tanemura K, Emori Y, Arai S. 1993. Multiple genes for G protein–coupled receptors and their expression in lingual epithelia. *FEBS Lett.* 316:253–56
117. Kusakabe Y, Abe K, Tanemura K, Emori Y, Arai S. 1996. GUST27 and closely related G-protein-coupled receptors are localized in taste buds together with Gi-protein α-subunit. *Chem. Senses* 21:335–40
118. Striem B, Naim M, Lindemann B. 1991. Generation of cyclic AMP in taste buds of the rat circumvallate papilla in response to sucrose. *Cell. Physiol. Biochem.* 1:46–54
119. Bernhardt SJ, Naim M, Zehavi U, Lindemann B. 1996. Changes in IP_3 and cytosolic Ca^{2+} in response to sugars and non-sugar sweeteners in transduction of sweet taste in the rat. *J. Physiol.* 490:325–36
120. Dib K, Wrisez F, Jamali AE, Lambert B, Correze C. 1997. Sodium saccharin inhibits adenylyl cyclase activity in non-taste cells. *Cell. Signal.* 9:431–38
121. Okada Y, Miyamoto T, Sato T. 1987. Depolarization induced by injection of cyclic nucleotides into frog taste cell. *Biochim. Biophys. Acta* 904:187–90
122. Avenet P, Hofmann F, Lindemann B. 1988. Transduction in taste receptor cells requires cAMP dependent protein kinase. *Nature* 331:351–54
123. Tonosaki K, Funakoshi M. 1988. Cyclic nucleotides may mediate taste transduction. *Nature* 331:354–56
124. Cummings TA, Daniels C, Kinnamon SC. 1996. Sweet taste transduction in hamster: sweeteners and cyclic nucleotides depolarize taste cells by reducing a K^+ current. *J. Neurophysiol.* 75:1256–63
125. Uchida Y, Sato T. 1997. Intracellular calcium increase in gerbil taste cell by amino acid sweeteners. *Chem. Senses* 22:83–91
126. Uchida Y, Sato T. 1997. Changes in outward K+ currents in response to two types of sweeteners in sweet taste transduction of gerbil taste cells. *Chem. Senses* 22: 163–69
127. Brand JG, Teeter JH, Kumazawa T, Huque T, Bayley DL. 1991. Transduction mechanisms for the taste of amino acids. *Physiol. Behav.* 49:899–904
128. Caprio J, Brand JG, Teeter JH, Valentincic T, Kalinoski DL, et al. 1993. The taste system of the channel catfish: from biophysics to behavior. *Trends Neurosci.* 16:192–97
129. Teeter JH, Kumazawa T, Brand JG, Kalinoski DL, Honda E, Smutzer G. 1992. Amino acid receptor channels in taste cells. In *Sensory Transduction. Society of General Physiologists, 45th Annu. Symp.*, ed. DP Corey, SD Roper, pp. 291–306. New York: Rockefeller Univ. Press
130. Teeter JH, Brand JG, Kumazawa T. 1990. A stimulus-activated conductance in isolated taste epithelial membranes. *Biophys. J.* 58:253–59
131. Finger TE, Bryant BP, Kalinoski DL, Teeter JH, Böttger B, et al. 1996. Differential localization of putative amino acid receptors in taste buds of the channel catfish, *Ictalurus punctatus*. *J. Comp. Neurol.* 373:129–38
132. Hayashi Y, Zviman MM, Brand JG, Teeter JH, Restrepo D. 1996. Measurement of membrane potential and $[Ca^{2+}]_i$ in cell ensembles: application to the study of glutamate taste in mice. *Biophys. J.* 71: 1057–70
133. Chaudhari N, Yang H, Lamp C, Delay E, Cartford C, et al. 1996. The taste of monosodium glutamate: membrane receptors in taste buds. *J. Neurosci.* 16: 3817–26
134. Bigiani A, Delay RJ, Chaudhari N, Kinnamon SC, Roper SD. 1997. Responses to glutamate in rat taste cells. *J. Neurophysiol.* 77:3048–59
135. Hamosh M, Burns WA. 1977. Lipolytic activity of human lingual glands (Ebner). *Lab. Invest.* 37:603–8

136. Field RB, Spielman AI, Hand AR. 1989. Purification of lingual amylase from serous glands of rat tongue and characterization of rat lingual amylase and lingual lipase. *J. Dent. Res.* 68:139–45
137. Kock K, Bläker M, Schmale H. 1992. Postnatal development of von Ebner's glands: accumulation of a protein of the lipocalin superfamily in taste papillae of rat tongue. *Cell Tissue Res.* 267:313–20
138. Kock K, Ahlers C, Schmale H. 1994. Structural organization of the genes for rat von Ebner's gland proteins 1 and 2 reveals their close relationship to lipocalins. *Eur. J. Biochem.* 221:905–16
139. Liu L, Kim I, Hu S, Wang S, Zhang H, Gilbertson TA. 1998. Identification of a Shaker Kv1.5-like K^+ channel in taste cells: the primary target for fatty acid inhibition. *Chem. Senses* (Abstr.). In press
140. Honoré E, Barhanin J, Attali B, Lesage F, Lazdunski M. 1994. External blockade of the major cardiac delayed-rectifier K^+ channel (Kv1.5) by polyunsaturated fatty acids. *Proc. Natl. Acad. Sci. USA* 91: 1937–44
141. Fukuwatari T, Kawada T, Tsuruta M, Hiraoka T, Iwanaga T, et al. 1997. Expression of the putative membrane fatty acid transporter (FAT) in taste buds of the circumvallate papillae in rats. *FEBS Lett.* 414:461–64
142. Fushiki T, Kawada T, Fukuwatari T. 1997. From the viewpoint of food and nutrition: Why is fat delicious? *Chem. Senses* 22:332 (Abstr.)
143. Ramirez I. 1992. Chemoreception for fat: Do rats sense triglycerides directly? *Appetite* 18:193–206
144. Smith DV, Frank ME. 1993. Sensory coding by peripheral taste fibers. In *Mechanisms of Taste Transduction*, ed. SA Simon, SD Roper, pp. 295–338. Boca Raton, FL: CRC
145. Kinnamon JC, Sherman TA, Roper SD. 1988. Ultrastructure of mouse vallate taste buds. III. Patterns of synaptic connectivity. *J. Comp. Neurol.* 270:1–10
146. Roper SD. 1992. The microphysiology of peripheral taste organs. *J. Neurosci.* 12: 1127–34
147. Sweazey RD, Smith DV. 1987. Convergence onto hamster medullary taste neurons. *Brain Res.* 408:173–84
148. Smith DV, Travers JB. 1979. A metric for the breadth of tuning of gustatory neurons. *Chem. Senses Flav.* 4:215–29
149. Travers JB, Smith DV. 1979. Gustatory sensitivities in neurons of the hamster nucleus tractus solitarius. *Sens. Process.* 3: 1–26
150. Van Buskirk RL, Smith DV. 1981. Taste sensitivity of hamster parabrachial pontine neurons. *J. Gen. Physiol.* 45:144–71
151. Ozeki M, Sato M. 1972. Responses of gustatory cells in the tongue of rat to stimuli representing four taste qualities. *Comp. Biochem. Physiol. A* 41:391–407
152. Sato T. 1972. Multiple sensitivity of single taste cells of the frog tongue to four basic stimuli. *J. Cell Physiol.* 80:207–18
153. Daniels C, Kinnamon SC. 1995. Specificity of hamster fungiform taste cells. *Chem. Senses* 20:687 (Abstr.)
154. Monroe WT, Smith DV, Gilbertson TA. 1996. The MU chamber: a new method to record electrophysiological responses of taste receptor cells to gustatory stimuli. *Chem. Senses* 21:644–45 (Abstr.)
155. Smith DV, McBurney DH. 1969. Gustatory cross-adaptation: Does a single mechanism code the salty taste? *J. Exp. Psychol.* 80:101–5
156. Smith DV, van der Klaauw NJ. 1995. The perception of saltiness is eliminated by NaCl adaptation: implications for gustatory transduction and coding. *Chem. Senses* 20:545–57
157. Sato T, Beidler LM. 1997. Broad tuning of rat taste cells for the four basic taste stimuli. *Chem. Senses* 22:287–93
158. Bacon AW, Miles JS, Schiffman SS. 1994. Effects of race on perception of fat alone and in combination with sugar. *Physiol. Behav.* 55:603–6
159. Johnson SL, McPhee L, Birch LL. 1991. Conditioned preferences: Young children prefer flavors associated with high dietary fat. *Physiol. Behav.* 50:1245–51
160. Canessa CM, Schild L, Buell G, Thorens B, Gautschi I, et al. 1994. Amiloride-sensitive epithelial Na^+ channel is made of three homologous subunits. *Nature* 367:463–67
161. Voilley N, Lingueglia E, Champigny G, Mattei MG, Waldmann R, et al. 1994. The lung amiloride-sensitive Na^+ channel: biophysical properties, pharmacology, ontogenesis, and molecular cloning. *Proc. Natl. Acad. Sci. USA* 91:247–51
162. Lingueglia E, Renard S, Waldmann R, Voilley N, Champigny G, et al. 1994. Different homologous subunits of the amiloride-sensitive Na^+ channel are differentially regulated by aldosterone. *J. Biol. Chem.* 269:13736–39
163. Li XJ, Xu RH, Guggino WB, Snyder SH. 1995. Alternatively spliced forms of the alpha subunit of the epithelial sodium

channel: distinct sites for amiloride binding and channel pore. *Mol. Pharmacol.* 47:1133–40
164. Stewart RE, Hill DL. 1993. The developing gustatory system: functional, morphological and behavioral perspectives. *Mechanisms of Taste Transduction*, ed. SA Simon, SD Roper, pp. 127–58. Boca Raton, FL: CRC
165. Herness MS. 1992. Aldosterone increases the amiloride-sensitivity of the rat gustatory neural response to NaCl. *Comp. Biochem. Physiol. A* 103:269–73
166. Okada Y, Miyamoto T, Sato T. 1990. Aldosterone increases gustatory neural response to NaCl in frog. *Comp. Biochem. Physiol. A* 97:535–36
167. Okada Y, Miyamoto T, Sato T. 1991. Vasopressin increases frog gustatory neural responses elicited by NaCl and HCl. *Comp. Biochem. Physiol. A* 100:693–96
168. Lindemann B. 1984. Fluctuation analysis of sodium channels in epithelia. *Annu. Rev. Physiol.* 46:497–515
169. Ling BN, Eaton DC. 1989. Effects of luminal Na^+ on single Na^+ channels in A6 cells, a regulatory role for protein kinase C. *Am. J. Physiol.* 256:F1094–103
170. Komwatana P, Dinudom A, Young JA, Cook DI. 1996. Control of the amiloride-sensitive Na^+ current in salivary duct cells by extracellular sodium. *J. Membr. Biol.* 150:133–41
171. Komwatana PA, Dinudom A, Young JA, Cook DI. 1996. Cytosolic Na^+ controls an epithelial Na^+ channel via the G_o guanine nucleotide-binding regulatory protein. *Proc. Natl. Acad. Sci. USA* 93:8107–11
172. Fuchs W, Larsen EH, Lindemann B. 1977. Current-voltage curve of sodium channels and concentration dependence of sodium permeability on frog skin. *J. Physiol.* 267:137–66
173. Luger A, Turnheim K. 1981. Modification of cation permeability of rabbit descending colon by sulphydryl reagents. *J. Physiol.* 317:49–66
174. Matsuo R, Yamamoto T. 1992. Effects of inorganic constituents of saliva on taste responses of the rat chorda tympani nerve. *Brain Res.* 583:71–80
175. Nakamura K, Norgren R. 1991. Gustatory responses of neurons in the nucleus of the solitary tract of behaving rats. *J. Neurophysiol.* 66:1232–48

SUBJECT INDEX

A

B

C

D

E

H

I

M

N

Q

R

S

U

V

Y

Z

CUMULATIVE INDEXES

CONTRIBUTING AUTHORS, VOLUMES 57–61

CHAPTER TITLES, VOLUMES 57–61

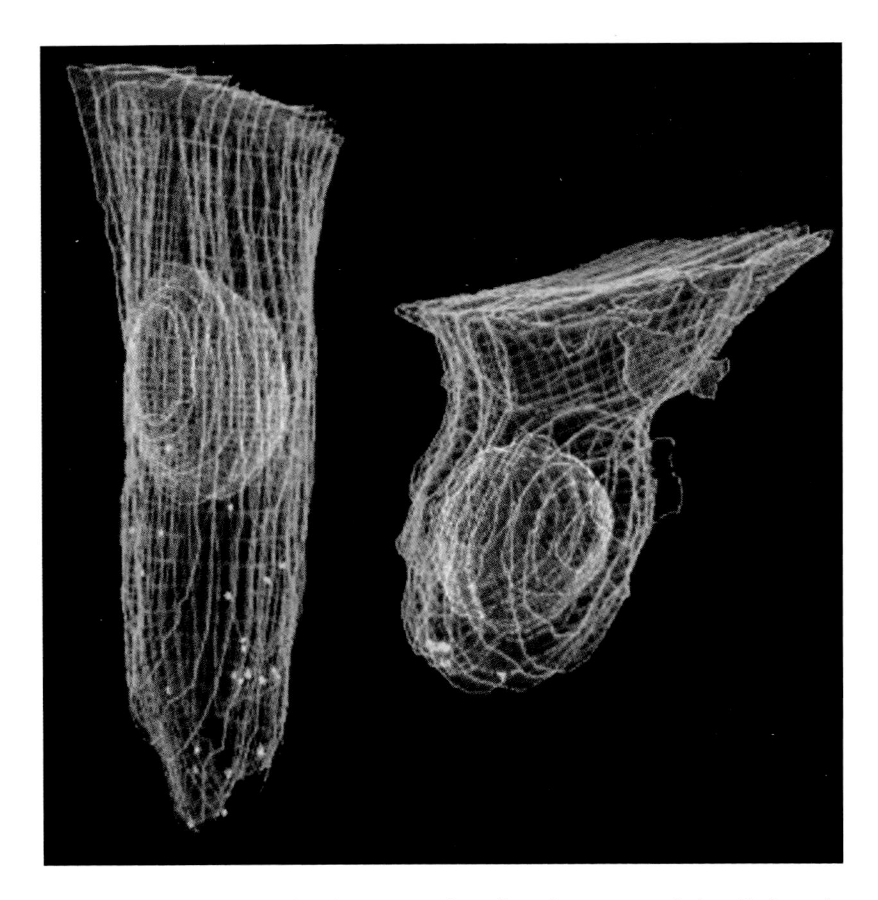

Figure 3 A three-dimensional reconstruction of mechanosensory hair cells from the cochlea of a chick, derived from serial electron micrographs. Presynaptic dense bodies found at sites of transmitter release are shown in *yellow*. tall (inner) hair cells (*left*) contact the majority of afferent neurites and have more numerous release sites and voltage-gated calcium channels than do short (outer) hair cells (*right*) (59). The nuclei (*brown*) are approximately 4 μm in diameter. Image provided by RL Michaels, Univ. Colorado Health Sciences Center.